# THE PRINCIPLES OF
## *General Biology*

By MARY S. GARDINER, Ph.D.

*Professor of Biology, Bryn Mawr College*

NEW YORK · THE MACMILLAN COMPANY

COPYRIGHT, 1952, BY THE MACMILLAN COMPANY

All rights reserved—no part of this book may be reproduced in any form without permission in writing from the publisher, except by a reviewer who wishes to quote brief passages in connection with a review written for inclusion in magazine or newspaper.

PRINTED IN THE UNITED STATES OF AMERICA

*First Printing*

"Of all human ambitions an open mind, eagerly expectant of new discoveries and ready to remold convictions in the lights of added knowledge and dispelled ignorance and misapprehensions, is the noblest, the rarest and the most difficult to achieve."

JAMES HARVEY ROBINSON,<br>
*The Humanizing of Knowledge.*

# FOREWORD

This book is the product of teaching biology to college students for more than twenty years. It is written with the intention of presenting the principles that underlie biological thought and method, and a general picture of the subject, not only to those students who intend to specialize in natural science but also to those who, seeking a liberal education, want to know something about biology as a field of learning and its contribution to man's understanding of the world of which he is a part. The book is designed to supplement the information acquired by the student in the class room and laboratory in a full year course, not primarily as a text to be followed day by day.

Since biology is so dependent upon the concepts and techniques of physics and chemistry, the first section of the book is devoted largely to a presentation of some of these as a background for the study of elementary biology, although of course inadequate for advanced work. I have given some space, too, to a consideration of the ecological relationships of organisms, believing that a biologist, to be more than a mere laboratory scientist, must have some comprehension of biological systems as wholes, of organism and environment and the constant interplay between them. Natural history, although fallen into disrepute with the rapid advancement of precise technical methods in biology, has an appeal for many people and a distinct place in the education of biologists. Renewed attention and a modern approach to it will, I believe, both arouse a more general interest in biological science and make better professional biologists. For as the specialist concentrates more and more on one particular area of investigation, he tends to lose sight of the whole panorama of the living world and the place of his particular object of investigation in it. If, however, he has acquired an appreciation of the relation of natural phenomena to each other, he has a better chance of preserving a broad outlook upon his subject, while achieving deeper and deeper insight into it.

The comparative method has been so fruitful in the development of biology as a science that, in the second section of the book, I have treated the organization of living things comparatively. Plants and animals at the lower levels of structural organization have been discussed together, and so has the differentiation of cells in the Metazoa and the Metaphyta. This presentation may seem dubious to those accustomed to think of botany and zoology as real distinctions of biological science, but it is an approach that I am convinced is desirable in an introduction to biology. Such a presentation emphasizes the unity of living things and the evolutionary development of modern species, the most fundamental concept in biology. In this section I have of necessity dealt to some extent with the functional aspects of organisms, since form can never be detached from function nor function from

# FOREWORD

form. The third section contains a more general consideration of the operation and evolution of biological systems. I have included also, in various parts of the book, facts and ideas that have proved particularly interesting, puzzling or stimulating to the students with whom I have come in contact, assuming that their experiences are common to others beginning the study of biology.

Throughout the book I have avoided categorical statements, synopses and outlines, of value only to the person who makes them, leaving the student to draw his own conclusions from the facts and theories presented. This generation of college students seems both to desire and to deserve material that challenges the intellect and offers opportunity for independent judgments. Biology is not an easy subject, for in their very nature biological systems are complex and variable. They do not lend themselves to definitions that are simple and clear-cut, and few, if any, general laws can be applied to them. To oversimplify the subject by drawing sharp lines of distinction and making generalizations that must be qualified in the light of extended information, however convenient and attractive such generalizations may be to the elementary student, is neither to present it to him fairly nor to help him to learn the way by which he, as a scientist, must work. Learning in science should be an exercise of reason, not of memory, as indeed I believe it should be in all disciplines. But the scientist especially should recognize early in his education the danger of misleading implications and the necessity of evaluating dicta by careful analysis of the evidence before accepting them as facts. He must test and confirm the accuracy of his conclusions as well as of his observations; likewise, he must be ready to modify or change them if new evidence makes it necessary. Educationally I believe it better to let a student make his own judgments, showing him where they are fallacious, than to encourage or allow him to accept uncritically those made by others.

Believing that any concept can best be appreciated and understood by knowing how it has been reached, I have tried everywhere to show how present biological fact and theory have been derived. To follow through the development of an idea is not only a help in grasping it but a fascinating process to anyone interested in the progress of human thought and human civilization. It is for these reasons that I have, for example, traced the emergence of the vitamin and hormone concepts, the theory of enzymes and the doctrine of organic evolution. And, by seeing how others have set up hypotheses that have been verified, modified or discarded, the student not yet in a position to apply it himself gains some understanding of the "scientific method". The recognition, too, that there have been periods of doubt, confusion and controversy in the development of scientific principles now taken for granted may help him in his personal philosophy to accept the present confusion of ideas—scientific, political, sociological—and even to look forward to their clarification.

The written word can never bring to the biologist the thing that is most important to him—the living organism; it can only supplement what he learns by direct observation in the laboratory and the field. But if this book has answered some of the questions that come into the mind of any observant and curious

## FOREWORD

person as he looks upon the plants and animals that live with him on this earth, and especially if it provokes him to ask more and to seek the answers himself, it will have fulfilled its purpose. Many people have helped in its preparation, but I am indebted most of all to those who made its conception and formulation possible and to whom it might most appropriately be dedicated, my teachers, and my students who, more often than they may have guessed, have been my teachers. I particularly want to express my thanks to some of the individuals who have helped me in the preparation of the illustrations and the text, Brannan and Dorothy Reath, Rosemary Gilmartin Smolker, Elenore Schewe and Virginia Berry, and to my colleagues on the Faculty of Bryn Mawr College who have critically read parts of the manuscript, L. Joe Berry, Jane Oppenheimer, William E. Norris Jr. (now at Southwest Texas Teacher's College) and June Zimmermann (now at Pennsylvania College for Women) of the Department of Biology, Lincoln Dryden of the Department of Geology and Marshall Gates (now at the University of Rochester and Assistant Editor of the *Journal of the American Chemical Society*) of the Department of Chemistry.

# DEFINITIONS OF SCIENTIFIC TERMS

**Calorie**  The quantity of heat necessary to change the temperature of one gram of water from 3.5° C to 4.5° C (small calorie). The large calorie (C) is equivalent to 1000 small calories.

**Centigrade**  Unit of temperature defined as 1/100 the difference between the temperature of melting ice and that of water boiling under standard atmospheric pressure.

**Fahrenheit**  Unit of temperature defined as 1/180 the difference between the temperature of melting ice and that of water boiling under standard atmospheric pressure.

**Conversion Factors**  To convert degrees Fahrenheit to degrees Centigrade:

$$(F - 32)\frac{5}{9} C$$

To convert degrees Centigrade to degrees Fahrenheit:

$$\frac{9}{5}(C) + 32 F$$

**Dyne**  The force which will produce an acceleration of one centimeter per second per second in a gram mass.

**Erg**  A unit of work expressing the work performed by a force of one dyne acting through a distance of one centimeter.

**Ampere**  The electric current which, when passed through a solution of silver nitrate under certain conditions, deposits silver at the rate of 0.00111800 gram per second.

**Coulomb**  The quantity of electrostatic units transferred by one ampere in one second.

**Ohm**  The resistance offered to an unvarying current by a column of mercury at 0° C, 14.4521 grams in mass, of constant cross-sectional area and 106.300 centimeters in length. It is that resistance through which a difference of potential of one volt will produce a current of one ampere.

**Joule**  The work expended per second by a current of one International ampere flowing through one International ohm.

**Watt**  One joule of work done in one second.

**Volt**  The electrical potential which, when steadily applied to a conductor whose resistance is one International ohm, will cause a current of one International ampere to flow.

**Anode**  The positive pole of an electric circuit.

# DEFINITIONS OF SCIENTIFIC TERMS

**Cathode**  The negative pole of an electric circuit.

**Mole**  A gram mass numerically equal to the molecular weight of a compound.

**Equivalent**  The weight in grams of a substance displacing or otherwise reacting with 1.008 grams of hydrogen.

**Normal solution**  Contains one gram molecular weight (mole) of the dissolved substance divided by the hydrogen equivalent of the substance (that is, one gram equivalent) per liter of solution.

**Molal solution**  Contains one mole per 1000 grams of solvent.

**Molar solution**  Contains one mole of the solute in one liter of solution.

**Percent solution of a solid by volume**  Dissolve desired percent weight (in grams) of solute in enough solvent to bring to 100% volume (in ml).
*Example:* To make a 20% solution of NaCl in water, add enough water to 20 grams NaCl to bring volume of solution to 100 ml.

**Percent solution of a solid by weight**  Dissolve desired percent weight (in grams) of a solute in amount of solvent equal to difference between percent weight and 100.
*Example:* To make a 20% solution of NaCl in water, dissolve 20 gms. NaCl in 80 ml. water.

**Percent solution of a liquid by volume**  Bring desired percent volume of solute to 100% with solvent.

**Surface of a sphere**  $4\pi r^2 = 12.57\ r^2$; $r =$ radius.

**Volume of a sphere**  $\frac{4}{3}\pi r^3 = 4.189\ r^3$; $r =$ radius.

**Volume of a cylinder**  $\pi r^2 h$; $h =$ height; $r =$ radius.

**Volume of a cube**  $l.w.h$; $l =$ length; $w =$ width; $h =$ height.

## Units of Length (Metric and U. S. Equivalents)

| | | |
|---|---|---|
| 1 Ångstrom (Å) | 0.0001 micron ($1 \times 10^{-7}$ millimeter) | |
| 1 millimicron (mµ) | 0.001 micron ($1 \times 10^{-6}$ millimeter) | |
| 1 micron (µ) | 0.001 millimeter ($1 \times 10^{-3}$ millimeter) | |
| 1 millimeter (mm) | | 0.0393700 inches |
| 1 centimeter (cm) | 10 millimeters | |
| 1 meter (m) | 100 centimeters (1000 millimeters) | 3.28083 feet |
| 1 kilometer (km) | 1000 meters | 0.621372 mile |

## Units of Mass (Metric and U. S. Equivalents)

| | | |
|---|---|---|
| 1 microgram (µg) | 0.001 milligram | |
| 1 milligram (mg) | | 0.015432356 grain |
| | | 0.03527396 ounce avoirdupois |
| 1 gram (g) | 1000 milligrams | 0.05643833 dram avoirdupois |
| | | 2.2046223 pounds avoirdupois |
| 1 kilogram (kg) | | 2.6792285 pounds troy |

## Units of Liquid Measure (Metric and U. S. Equivalents)

| | | |
|---|---|---|
| 1 microliter (µl) | 0.001 milliliter (0.000001 liter) | |
| 1 milliliter (ml) | (1.000027 cubic centimeter) | 0.0338147 ounce |
| 1 liter (l) | 1000 milliliters | 1.056710 liquid qts. |

# CONTENTS

### SECTION ONE
## The Organization of the Natural World

| | | |
|---|---|---:|
| CHAPTER 1. | The Development of Modern Biology | 3 |
| CHAPTER 2. | Matter and Energy | 8 |
| CHAPTER 3. | Atoms, Ions and Molecules | 16 |
| CHAPTER 4. | Atomic Combinations and Chemical Reactions | 22 |
| CHAPTER 5. | Carbon and Its Compounds | 33 |
| CHAPTER 6. | Water and Solutions | 43 |
| CHAPTER 7. | Protoplasm and the Cell | 54 |

### SECTION TWO
## The Organization of Biological Systems

| | | |
|---|---|---:|
| CHAPTER 8. | Biological Systems: The Organism and Its Environment | 75 |
| CHAPTER 9. | The Classification of Biological Systems and the Divisions of Biological Science | 98 |
| CHAPTER 10. | Systems below the Level of Tissue Organization: Unicellular (Acellular) Systems and Cell Aggregates | 116 |
| CHAPTER 11. | Multicellular Systems—Metazoa and Metaphyta of Simple Organization | 141 |
| CHAPTER 12. | The Vascular Plants | 166 |
| CHAPTER 13. | The Tube-within-a-Tube Plan of Metazoan Organization | 204 |
| CHAPTER 14. | The Arthropods | 220 |
| CHAPTER 15. | The Chordata | 257 |
| CHAPTER 16. | Integrating Tissues of the Vertebrate Body | 326 |

### SECTION THREE
## The Operation of Biological Systems

| | | |
|---|---|---:|
| CHAPTER 17. | Nutrition: The Utilization of Food | 393 |
| CHAPTER 18. | Autotrophic Nutrition | 408 |
| CHAPTER 19. | Heterotrophic Nutrition: Feeding Mechanisms and Digestion | 424 |
| CHAPTER 20. | The Dietary Requirements of Heterotrophs | 436 |
| CHAPTER 21. | Metabolism and Its Regulation | 455 |
| CHAPTER 22. | Growth and Regeneration; Fission, Budding and Parthenogenesis | 476 |
| CHAPTER 23. | Gametic Reproduction | 490 |

## CONTENTS

CHAPTER 24. The Inheritance of the Individual     533
CHAPTER 25. The Development of the Individual     560

SECTION FOUR

### The Evolution of Biological Systems

CHAPTER 26. The Doctrine of Organic Evolution     595
INDEX     631

# SECTION ONE

## THE ORGANIZATION OF THE NATURAL WORLD

# CHAPTER 1

# THE DEVELOPMENT OF MODERN BIOLOGY

## The beginnings of biology

Biology began as the study of man and then of the animals or plants useful or dangerous to him. Early biology was closely bound up with medicine, the province of the magicians, the sorcerers and the priests. Man learned about his own anatomy from his early efforts to cure his ills or injuries by surgery; he learned about the anatomy of wild and domestic animals from slaughtering them for food and for religious rites, and he learned something of pharmacology, or the use of drugs, from the effects which the plants and herbs that he ate produced upon him in health and in disease. He knew little physiology beyond the fact that stoppage of the heart beat and of breathing coincided with death, and he concluded therefore that the heart was the seat of life, and the breath the spirit that left the body when that life ceased.

Much of what was learned was kept as closely guarded secrets by the priests and medicine men until the time of the Greeks, when medicine became the province of a special group and natural science could flourish as an independent field of inquiry open to all who wished to pursue it. Later, in its turn, biology became detached from the other natural sciences and from philosophy, which had included all branches of learning, and began its development to a great extent independent of them. This opened the descriptive phase of biology, when vast amounts of information were collected about the habits and forms of plants and animals, their development and their relationships. In this period the great collections were made and natural history museums, zoos and botanical gardens were started. Animals and plants were dissected and their gross and minute anatomy studied. Comparative anatomy and embryology flourished, and the systematic classification of animals and plants into groups with structural and developmental similarities was made.

## Early experiments proving the relationship between biological and physical and chemical processes

The functioning of living organisms was thought to be unique and mysterious, peculiar to them and independent of the laws governing the physical world. Gradually as the sciences of physics and chemistry developed and as the processes by which living things maintain themselves, grow and reproduce were revealed, it became evident that these processes were not unique, but were essentially the same as those which the chemist and the physicist could cause to occur in their laboratories. The first recognition of this similarity was expressed by the Swiss Paracelsus (1493–1541), who argued that bodily processes were simply a series of chemical reactions, and the first demonstration was made by a young English experimental scientist, John Mayow (1640–1679), who in 1668 proved by a series of experiments that burning and breathing, or respiration, are identical phenomena. He floated a lighted candle and a mouse in containers of water, each covered with a bell jar so that no air could enter or leave. He saw that as the candle burned and the mouse breathed the level of the water rose in the container and that after a time the candle went out and the mouse collapsed and died. He thus showed that something was taken from the air by the burning candle and the breathing mouse that was essential to both. That this substance was the same he proved

[ 3 ]

by demonstrating that a candle would not burn in a chamber in which a mouse had been kept until it died, when it had, in his words, "exhausted the vital particles (Fig. 1.1). He did not know what this substance was and called it the "igneo-aereus spirit" a century before Lavoisier, the great French chemist, identified oxygen as a constituent of the air, and showed that its combination with other elements is the process of their burning or combustion.

Mayow's experiment proved that an animal is dependent upon this component of the air for its very existence; a little earlier, Jan Baptist van Helmont (1577–1644), a Swiss doctor and experimental scientist, who, like Paracelsus believed that all the changes going on within the organism could be explained as chemical reactions, had shown that plants derive the material of which their bodies are made from the air. Van Helmont planted a willow shoot, weighing five pounds, in a pot containing exactly 200 pounds of dried earth, carefully covered so that none could blow away nor any dust fall upon it (Fig. 1.2). For five years he watered the pot with rain water and watched its growth. At the end of the five years he again weighed the willow and the earth in the pot. The willow now weighed 169 pounds, and the earth but two ounces less than its original 200 pounds. The air surrounding the plant and the water given to the soil were the only possible sources of its new material. He did not know either what it was that came from the air, nor how the plant made use of it, but his experiment was a clear-cut demonstration of the transformation by the plant of materials of one kind into another, contrary to the prevailing belief that plants drew their substance as such from the earth.

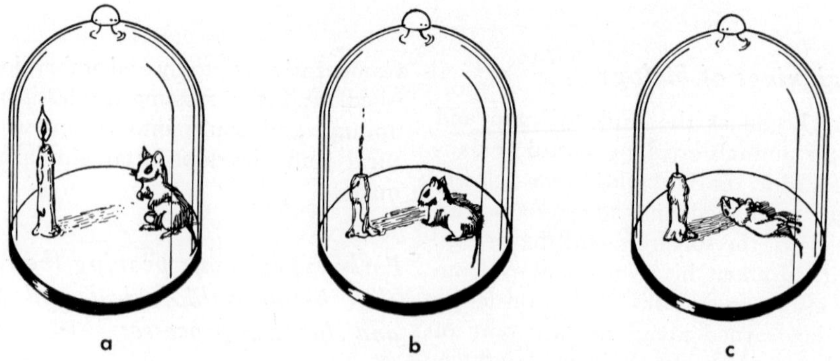

Later an English clergyman, Stephen Hales (1677–1761), confirmed van Helmont's results and carried on experiments of his own devised to show that the flow of water and sap in plants, and the flow of blood in animals, was not caused by any "vital force," but followed the established laws of physics for the flow of water in tubes. He demonstrated blood pressure by inserting tubes held vertically in the arteries of horses, measuring the height to which the blood rose and calculating the force necessary to raise it to such a height against gravity. He also designed experiments to measure the rate of ascent of water in the stems of plants, root pressure or the force

FIGURE 1.1 Diagrammatic representation of Mayow's experiment with a lighted candle and a mouse.

"If a small animal and a lighted candle be shut up in the same vessel, the entrance into which of air from without is prevented, you will see in a short time the candle go out; nor will the animal long survive its funeral torch. Indeed I have found by observation that an animal shut up in a flask together with a candle will continue to breath for not much longer than half the time that it otherwise would, that is, without the candle." (John Mayow, *Tractatus quinque*, 1668.)

determining the upward flow of sap, and he calculated the relationship between the amount of water taken in by the roots and that given off by the leaves. He showed that these phenomena could be reproduced in non-living systems.

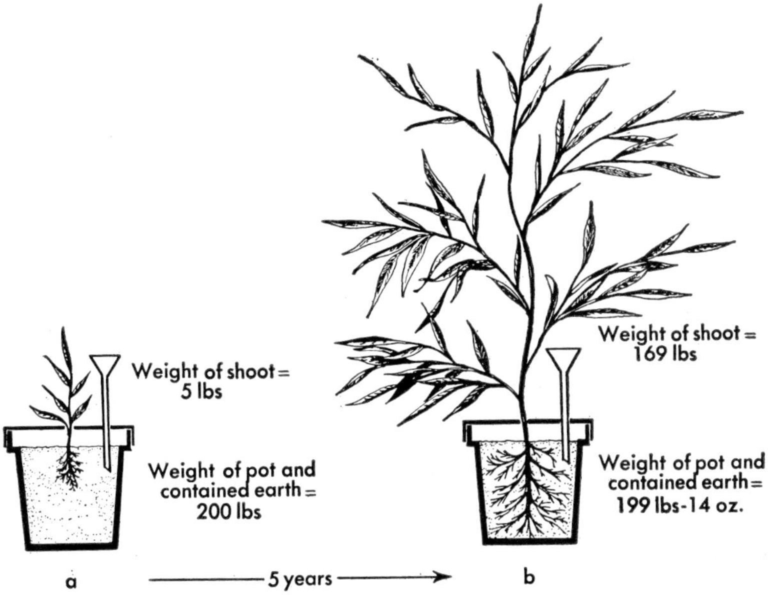

neither created nor destroyed, although capable of transformation from one kind into another. This law, and that of the conservation of matter, Newton's conception that the quantity or mass of a body remains constant through all motion, had been ac-

FIGURE 1.2  Diagram of van Helmont's willow shoot experiment.

Experiments such as these removed the so-called "vital processes" from the realm of the mysterious and occult and taught that the phenomena that go on in the animal and plant body were capable of interpretation in the same terms as those occurring in the physical world. They made evident that the new physics of Isaac Newton (1642–1727) and the new chemistry of Robert Boyle (1627–1691) and Joseph Black (1729–1799) could be applied to the living world as well as to the non-living and opened the way for the development of physiology, the analysis and interpretation of the functioning of living organisms.

Antoine Lavoisier (1743–1794) strengthened this conception of the identity between the reactions that take place in the animate and the inanimate world by showing that the animal body conforms to the law of the conservation of energy, or the First Law of Thermodynamics, which states that the total amount of energy of a system is constant,

cepted by the natural scientists as governing the material world they were investigating. Lavoisier extended this to the world of living things by a carefully planned and carefully executed experiment. He put a lighted candle and a guinea pig in air-tight containers, each surrounded by ice, and by determining the amount of ice melted, measured the heat evolved by the candle as long as it burned and by the guinea pig as long as it breathed. He calculated that the amount of heat produced in each case was proportional to the amount of oxygen lost from the air in the container and so established a relationship between the energy available for combustion, essentially the combination with oxygen, or oxidation, and that evolved as heat by a living and a non-living system.

Later, in 1892, Max Rubner, a German scientist, performed experiments that confirmed Lavoisier's and established the fundamental law of animal thermodynamics, or the heat-energy relationship. The energy values of certain kinds of food had previously been determined by others working in the same laboratory with him. Known quantities of meats and fats and sugars had been completely burned, and the heat produced in their oxidation measured. Rubner devised an apparatus called a calorimeter in which a dog could be kept at rest, fasting during the period of the experiment, or fed weighed amounts of food whose energy values were known, and the heat produced by the animal over a given period of time measured. He calculated the amount of heat that should be produced if the dog oxidized completely in his body the food that was fed him, and compared these figures with the values obtained by actual measurements of the dog's heat production. Table I gives a summary of his results.

TABLE I

| Dog | Condition | Calculated heat production in calories | Heat loss determined calorimetrically | Days |
|---|---|---|---|---|
| 1. | Fasting | 259.3 | 260.1 | 5 |
| 2. | Fasting | 545.6 | 528.3 | 2 |
| 3. | Fed with meat | 329.9 | 339.9 | 1 |
| 4. | Fed with fat | 302.0 | 299.1 | 5 |
| 5. | Meat and fat | 332.1 | 330.0 | 12 |
| 6. | Meat and fat | 311.6 | 331.0 | 8 |
| 7. | Meat | 375.0 | 379.5 | 6 |
| 8. | Meat | 683.0 | 681.3 | 7 |

The average difference between the calculated and the observed results is only 1.01%, well within the limits of the possible errors of such an experiment. Rubner therefore concluded that energy is neither created nor destroyed in the animal body, that the total energy produced in the animal is exactly equal to the energy of the materials burned and that conservation of energy is as true within the animal body as elsewhere in nature. The animal body might therefore be compared to a machine in which the food represents the fuel whose combustion releases energy, in these experiments measured as heat, but capable of transformation into other kinds.

Such experiments as Lavoisier's and Rubner's, which have been confirmed again and again in other animals, proved that the animal body obeys the most fundamental law of the physical, or non-living world, but they throw no light on the changes that go on in the body in the transformation of food into energy. Until a little over a century ago, it was generally believed that the compounds and the products of living things were found in them alone, and could only be made by them, and these materials had a special significance and a mysterious quality as products of "vital activity". In 1828, Friedrich Wöhler, a German chemist, succeeded in making one of these products, urea, out of inorganic raw materials in his laboratory. Urea is a substance constantly being formed in some animals' bodies and until Wöhler's time produced only there. His accomplishment showed not only the essential similarity between products made in vivo, or within the organism, and those that could be made in vitro, or by man outside it, but also the possibility of laboratory synthesis of all such compounds. This possibility has not yet been wholly realized, although many natural products such as oils, some of the vitamins and amino acids, have been synthesized in vitro, often on a large scale. The recent (1947) laboratory synthesis of Penicillin G, a substance destructive to certain bacteria and hitherto known only as a product of one kind of mould, is another illustration of the reproduction in vitro of a process ordinarily taking place only in a living organism.

## The nature of biological systems

It does not necessarily follow that the steps in the natural synthesis are the same as those by which a laboratory product is made, but the similarity in their chemical, physical and biological properties makes the end product indistinguishable. There is no longer any reason to believe that the workings or products of organisms are mysterious to the extent that they are beyond the possibility of interpretation under the established laws which govern phenomena in the physical world, or of reduplication in vitro. Modern biology is based upon the conception that the changes and reactions that go on inside the plant or animal are in no fundamental way different from those which go on outside it, although they may be retarded, accelerated or directed by conditions within it. It is this control and regulation by the organism which distinguishes a living, or organic, system from one which is not alive, and which makes the problems of the biologist at once so challenging and so complex. The living organism is far more than a machine. For one thing, it can never be considered apart from its environment. Living is a continual adjustment and exchange between the organism and its external surroundings, and the conditions of living may be altered or stopped by a change, sometimes very small as reckoned by the chemist or the physicist, in the environment or in the organism's relation to it. Relatively slight differences in temperature, in light and shade, in the pressure or mineral content of water determine what kinds of animals and plants may inhabit certain localities, or whether they can exist there at all, and there are often remarkably sharp lines of demarcation between the zones favoring the growth of one kind of organism and destructive to another.

## The aims of modern biology

The organism and its environment represent a biological system, and biological systems are extremely complex in themselves, as well as in their order and their regulation. It is this order and regulation that the biologist attempts to interpret and to control. To do so, he must make use of the facts and techniques of chemistry and physics, as well as his own, for living matter as far as we now know differs in its structure from non-living only in the arrangement and relations of its component atoms and molecules and in its functioning apparently only in the orderliness, direction and precision of their operation. Biology deals with every aspect of the living organism; it deals with its gross and minute structure, with its relationships to other organisms and to its environment, with its growth, development and reproduction, with all phases of its activity from the general pattern of its behavior down to the reactions of the ultimate parts into which it can be analyzed, and with its past, present and possible future. Modern biology is an experimental science, no longer a descriptive one. Its data are quantitative, its measurements exact. Its problems are intricate and confusing, but as each one is solved, man comes closer to an understanding of the forces that control him and the world in which he lives, and closer therefore to his own control of them.

Modern biology deals with the mass, or matter, of living things in terms of their constituent atoms and molecules, and with their functioning in terms of energy transformations within and outside them. The biologist must first turn to the organization of the physical world before attempting to understand and to explain the organization of the biological. He must have comprehension of the meaning of the words, matter and energy, and a knowledge of the nature of atoms and of molecules and the ways in which they behave, to have any understanding of the ways in which a biological system may be organized and may maintain itself. His first task is therefore to learn something of the physical world in which he lives, and the manifestations of energy constantly appearing in it.

# CHAPTER 2 — MATTER AND ENERGY

## The properties of matter

The early natural scientists and the physicists had recognized that matter might exist as a solid, a liquid or a gas and had defined some of its properties. It was continuous; it occupied space; it showed inertia, or the property of remaining at rest or in motion unless acted upon by some external force. This latter principle was first expressed by Leonardo da Vinci (1452–1519) in his statement "nothing perceptible by the senses is able to move itself," and later demonstrated experimentally by Galileo (1562–1642). The physics of Newton had led to the conception of the conservation of matter, accepting its transformation from one state to another but denying its destruction. Thus when water is heated it changes from a liquid to a gas, steam, of equivalent mass, or when a solid object is burned the elements of which it is composed are not destroyed but converted to gases, water and ash.

## The concept of the atomic structure of matter

Modern science has resolved matter, or mass, into smaller and smaller units, elements, atoms, electrons and other elementary particles, uncharged, or carrying positive or negative charges, and has reached a point in theory where mass and energy are not only inseparable but identical. The steps in this analysis, the experimental evidence and the reasoning that have led to this final concept constitute one of the most fascinating chapters in the history of the development of science, and one of the most important to an understanding of the age in which we live.

An English scientist, John Dalton (1766–1844), first gave expression to the idea that the constituents of matter are themselves reducible into smaller units, or atoms. He arrived at this concept from studying the properties of gases, which he said were best explained by a theory of atoms, and later he applied this idea to all chemical compounds, showing that they could be understood as combinations of atoms with definite and individual weights and characteristics. He thus expressed not only the atomic conception of matter, but also that of atomic weight and of combining power, or valence. Taking hydrogen, the lightest of the elements, as having an atomic weight of 1, he was able to assign relative atomic weights to the other twenty elements known to him and his contemporaries. As chemists and mineralogists studied the composition of the earth and its surrounding atmosphere, more and more elements were identified and their properties established, until the total number now known is 96, the last two of which (Americium, 95, and Curium, 96) were identified in 1945 as a result of the work on the development of atomic energy.*

The Russian chemist, Dimitro Mendeleef (1834–1907), in studying the properties of the elements, saw that if they were arranged in a series of ascending atomic weights each eighth element had somewhat similar properties, and that they could all be put into a table or chart, with these similar elements placed in vertical columns. Two other scientists, John Alexander Newlands (1838–1898) in England and Julius Lothar Meyer (1830–1895) in Germany, working quite independently of each other and of Mendeleef, had the same insight into the relationship between the elements, and the Periodic Table that hangs in every chemistry class-

---

* The recent (1950) discovery of two more elements as the result of atomic fission now brings this number to 98.

room is the result of their recognition of this regular and periodic recurrence of atomic similarities, essentially a relationship between atomic configuration and valence (Fig. 2.1). The Periodic Law that the table expresses turned the attention of scientists again to the old idea of a common basis of matter, an idea which has waited until now for definite and experimental proof.

### The nature of atoms

Dalton's theory of the atomic structure of matter could not be put to experimental test by general chemical methods, for the size of the postulated atom must be so minute that even a small quantity of any substance would contain vast numbers of them. As an illustration of their order of magnitude, suppose that one were to fill a tumbler with water, a fluid composed of hydrogen and oxygen atoms united in groups, or molecules, of one oxygen and two hydrogen atoms, and suppose that each such molecule could be marked so that it could be readily recognized. Then suppose that one were to throw this tumbler of water anywhere on earth and leave it for a few million years until all water on the earth and in its atmosphere had become thoroughly mixed. If the mixing were perfect and if it were possible to conclude the experiment after such a period of time, calculations show that a tumblerful of water drawn from any tap would then contain 2000 of the original water molecules. This means that there are 2000 times more water molecules in a tumblerful than there are tumblersful of water in all the oceans, seas, lakes, rivers and streams on the earth and in all the clouds enclosing the earth.

*The size of atoms; their organization as systems of positive and negative charges:* The extremely small size of atoms and molecules puts them beyond the range of human vision, even with the most powerful of present optical aids, so that information about them must be gained by calculation and deduction rather than by direct observation. In spite of the great technical difficulties, it has nevertheless been possible to test Dalton's postulate experimentally, and during the past half century to obtain weights of individual atoms and so to compare them and, since the discovery of radioactive substances, to observe the effects of individual atoms rather than of multitudes of them. These methods have led to an understanding of the atom as a system of charged particles, or simply electrical charges. The center of this system is called the nucleus, which is positively charged; moving in orbits around the nucleus are negative charges, or electrons. An electron is a unit of electricity whose mass, dimensions and charge have in recent years been at least approximately determined. First recognized in 1897 as one of the fundamental elementary particles by the English physicist, Sir J. J. Thomson (1856–1940), the electron has since been found to have a mass equivalent to 1/1846 of a hydrogen atom; a radius (diameter) of the order of magnitude of $1 \times 10^{-12}$ centimeters; a negative charge equal to $-1.602 \times 10^{-12}$ coulombs*; and in the hydrogen atom at least, a speed of movement which averages $2.18 \times 10^8$ centimeters per second. While it is convenient to think of and to represent electrons as circulating in orbits around the nucleus of an atom, in reality their paths are not definite ones and they move more or less at random in all planes, but mostly toward and away from the nucleus, and with such speed that they effectively occupy space around it, at least to the extent that they block the entrance of other electrons into a definite, although minute, area.

The atoms of the different elements differ in the number of net positive charges on the nucleus, in the number and kind of elementary particles of which the nucleus is made up, and in the number of extra-nuclear electrons. Hydrogen, which Dalton took for his unit of comparison of atomic weights and which occupies the first place in the Periodic Table, has a single positive charge on its nucleus with one negative charge moving around it (Fig. 2.2a). The nucleus of hydrogen is called a proton and as it carries a

---

* A coulomb, named for the French physicist C. A. de Coulomb (1736–1806), is the unit of quantity of electricity, defined as the quantity transferred by one ampere in one second.

| SERIES | I | II | III | IV | V |
|---|---|---|---|---|---|
| 1 | HYDROGEN<br>1 H<br>1.0080 | | | | |
| 2 | LITHIUM<br>Li 3<br>6.940 | BERYLLIUM<br>4 Be<br>9.02 | BORON<br>5 B<br>10.82 | CARBON<br>6 C<br>12.010 | NITROGEN<br>7 N<br>14.008 |
| 3 | SODIUM<br>Na 11<br>22.997 | MAGNESIUM<br>12 Mg<br>24.32 | ALUMINUM<br>13 Al<br>26.97 | SILICON<br>14 Si<br>28.06 | PHOSPHORUS<br>15 P<br>30.98 |
| 4 | POTASSIUM<br>K 19<br>39.096 | CALCIUM<br>Ca 20<br>40.08 | SCANDIUM<br>Sc 21<br>45.10 | TITANIUM<br>Ti 22<br>47.90 | VANADIUM<br>V 23<br>50.95 |
|   | COPPER<br>29 Cu<br>63.57 | ZINC<br>30 Zn<br>65.38 | GALLIUM<br>31 Ga<br>69.72 | GERMANIUM<br>32 Ge<br>72.60 | ARSENIC<br>33 As<br>74.91 |
| 5 | RUBIDIUM<br>Rb 37<br>85.48 | STRONTIUM<br>Sr 38<br>87.63 | YTTRIUM<br>Y 39<br>88.92 | ZIRCONIUM<br>Zr 40<br>91.22 | COLUMBIUM<br>Cb 41<br>92.91 |
|   | SILVER<br>47 Ag<br>107.880 | CADMIUM<br>48 Cd<br>112.41 | INDIUM<br>49 In<br>114.76 | TIN<br>50 Sn<br>118.70 | ANTIMONY<br>51 Sb<br>121.76 |
| 6 | CESIUM<br>Cs 55<br>132.91 | BARIUM<br>Ba 56<br>137.36 | LANTHANUM<br>La 57<br>138.92 | HAFNIUM<br>Hf 72<br>178.6 | TANTALUM<br>Ta 73<br>180.88 |
|   | GOLD<br>79 Au<br>197.2 | MERCURY<br>80 Hg<br>200.61 | THALLIUM<br>81 Tl<br>204.39 | LEAD<br>82 Pb<br>207.21 | BISMUTH<br>83 Bi<br>209.00 |
| 7 | FRANCIUM<br>Fa 87<br>223. | RADIUM<br>Ra 88<br>226.05 | ACTINIUM<br>Ac 89<br>227.05 | KEY TO CHART | |
| 6 | Rare<br>Earths 58-71 | CERIUM<br>Ce 58<br>140.13 | PRASEODYMIUM<br>Pr 59<br>140.92 | NEODYMIUM<br>Nd 60<br>144.27 | (ILLINIUM)<br>Il 61<br>147. |
| 7 | Radioactive<br>Rare<br>Earths 90- | THORIUM<br>Th 90<br>232.12 | PROTACTINIUM<br>Pa 91<br>231. | URANIUM<br>U 92<br>238.07 | NEPTUNIUM<br>Np 93<br>237. |

*(continued columns for Series 6 and 7 rare earths:)*

| | | |
|---|---|---|
| SAMARIUM<br>Sm 62<br>150.43 | EUROPIUM<br>Eu 63<br>152.0 | |
| PLUTONIUM<br>Pu 94<br>239. | AMERICIUM<br>Am 95<br>241. | |

Periodic Arrangement — THE

FIGURE 2.1 The Periodic Table. (Courtesy of the Standard Science

# ATOMS Weights and Numbers

**VI** | **VII** | **VIII**

| | | HELIUM |
|---|---|---|
| | | 2 He 4.003 |

| OXYGEN | FLUORINE | NEON |
|---|---|---|
| 8 O 16.00000 | 9 F 19.00 | 10 Ne 20.183 |

| SULPHUR | CHLORINE | ARGON |
|---|---|---|
| 16 S 32.06 | 17 Cl 35.457 | 18 A 39.944 |

**Moseley's Method of Determination of Atomic Numbers**
A. Cathode Ray Stream (high speed electrons).
B. Concave cathode of X-Ray tube.
C. Anode of X-Ray tube.
D. Target or anode face made of element whose atomic number is to be determined.
E. X-Ray stream.
F. Slit.
H. Crystal of rock salt for diffracting the X-Rays.
K. Photographic film for receiving the X-Ray spectrum.
L. Series of X-Ray spectra.

| CHROMIUM | MANGANESE | | IRON | COBALT | NICKEL |
|---|---|---|---|---|---|
| Cr 24 52.01 | Mn 25 54.93 | | 26 Fe 55.85 | 27 Co 58.94 | 28 Ni 58.69 |

| SELENIUM | BROMINE | KRYPTON |
|---|---|---|
| 34 Se 78.96 | 35 Br 79.916 | 36 Kr 83.7 |

**The BOHR THEORY of the Atom** assumes a central nucleus containing electrons (−particles) and an excess of protons (+particles). Outside the nucleus revolve planetary electrons equal in number to the excess of protons.
The number of planetary electrons is the atomic number. The outer orbit of electrons determines the chemical behavior of the atom. This theory is used in explanations of valence and of spectra.

| MOLYBDENUM | TECHNETIUM | | RUTHENIUM | RHODIUM | PALLADIUM |
|---|---|---|---|---|---|
| Mo 42 95.95 | Tc 43 99. | | 44 Ru 101.7 | 45 Rh 102.91 | 46 Pd 106.7 |

| TELLURIUM | IODINE | XENON |
|---|---|---|
| 52 Te 127.61 | 53 I 126.92 | 54 Xe 131.3 |

MENDELEEFF (1834-1907), famous Russian chemist, was founder of the Periodic Chart. He arranged the 63 known elements of his day in order of increasing atomic weight in horizontal periods, or series, and in vertical groups very nearly as they appear in this chart. The few corrections are due to Moseley's determination of atomic numbers of elements by their X-Ray spectra. Mendeleeff's genius led to the discovery of many new elements whose properties, in many instances, were already known to scientists because they had been studied as blanks in his first Periodic Chart.

| TUNGSTEN | RHENIUM | | OSMIUM | IRIDIUM | PLATINUM |
|---|---|---|---|---|---|
| W 74 183.92 | Re 75 186.31 | | 76 Os 190.2 | 77 Ir 193.1 | 78 Pt 195.23 |

| POLONIUM | ASTATINE | RADON |
|---|---|---|
| 84 Po 210. | 85 At 211. | 86 Rn 222. |

COPYRIGHT 1947
**Standard Science Supply Company**
Stansi Scientific Products
Chicago 22, Illinois

IN NON POLAR (co-valent compounds) the electrons are not transferred but are shared by several atoms. Diagram of Methane CH4 inner electrons of carbon are not shown.

COMBINATION OF ATOMS TO FORM POLAR (Electrolyte forming or electrovalent compounds). Electrons are lost from the outer ring of the metals leaving these atoms positively charged. These electrons enter the outer shell of the non metal to form a stable octet ring. The non metal becomes negatively charged. Diagram illustrates Lithium Fluoride.

| GADOLINIUM | TERBIUM | DYSPROSIUM | HOLMIUM | ERBIUM | THULIUM | YTTERBIUM | LUTECIUM |
|---|---|---|---|---|---|---|---|
| Gd 64 156.9 | Tb 65 159.2 | Dy 66 162.46 | Ho 67 164.94 | Er 68 167.2 | Tm 69 169.4 | Yb 70 173.04 | Lu 71 174.99 |

| CURIUM | | | | | | | |
|---|---|---|---|---|---|---|---|
| Cm 96 242. | Scientists anticipate that this space and the spaces which follow will in time be filled by radioactive rare earth elements yet to be created or discovered. | | | | | | |

Supply Company, Chicago.)

single positive charge compensated by the single negative electron, the atom itself is neutral. The gas helium, which occupies the next place in the Periodic Table, has a nucleus composed of two protons and two uncharged particles, or neutrons, and so carries two positive charges; two negative charges each move in individual orbits around the nucleus of the atom (Fig. 2.2c). Similarly, the other elements of the Periodic Table have been found to be made up of different numbers of protons and neutrons with a related number of negative charges grouped around them. The nucleus of the sodium atom, for example, has a net positive charge of 11, with 11 extra-nuclear electrons in orbits around it; chlorine has 17 positive charges on its nucleus and 17 negative charges associated with it.

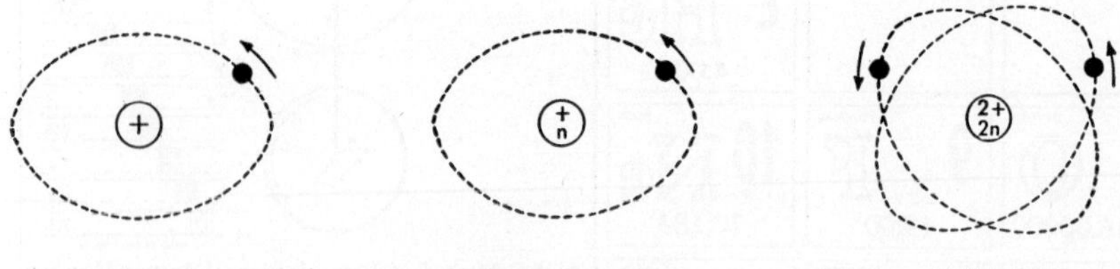

The ultimate structure of the atomic nucleus is still an unsolved problem. Even the composition of the hydrogen nucleus, presumably the simplest in the whole system of elements, is still unknown. Recent studies have shown, too, that not all hydrogen atoms are alike. There are at least two kinds which differ from each other in the mass of their nuclei, one having twice the mass of the other. The atom of deuterium, or heavy hydrogen, has one positive charge on its nucleus and one extra-nuclear electron, but it has twice the mass, for its nucleus is made up of one positively charged proton and one uncharged neutron (Fig. 2.2b). It occupies the same place in the Periodic Table as ordinary hydrogen since it has the same chemical properties, and it and hydrogen are said to be isotopes (Greek, iso = equal + topos = place), that is, occupying the same position in relation to the other elements. Isotopes of virtually all the other elements have also either been discovered in nature or prepared artificially; some of these have been the most useful of tools in biological investigation, for, since they can be distinguished from other atoms, they can act as markers for the molecules that contain them and so be used to trace their course and the fate of substances taken in and used by the living organism in its metabolic activities.

***The elementary particles of matter:*** Matter can then be resolved not only into atoms, but into the particles of which atoms are composed. Table II presents the elementary particles, so far as they are at present known, and some of their characteristics. Of these the proton, neutron and electron are particularly significant in the chemical properties and relations of atoms, for the meson, positron and neutrino are known only through the behavior and effects of disintegration of atomic nuclei.

This understanding of atomic structure has led to a radical change in the understanding of the structure of matter. First, it is not continuous. The electrical particles may be closely packed in the nucleus, but still discrete, and the surrounding electrons may be separated from them by varying dis-

FIGURE 2.2 Diagram of atomic configurations.

a. Configuration of the hydrogen atom, with a nucleus carrying a single positive charge around which a single electron moves in an elliptical orbit.

b. Configuration of the deuterium atom, an isotope of hydrogen, with a nucleus composed of a proton and a neutron, with a single electron moving around it.

c. Configuration of the helium atom, with a nucleus composed of two protons and two neutrons, with two electrons moving around it in elliptical orbits in different planes.

tances, all extremely small to be sure, but still distances and space. Secondly, there is a common basis for all matter in the proton and neutron and beyond that in the elementary particles of which the proton is composed. That is, as we know it now, all matter, living or non-living, consists of atoms bound together in various groupings to form elements or compounds, and all atoms consist of protons bound together with other elementary particles in numbers specific for the different elements with corresponding numbers of electrons circulating around them. Thus Dalton's system of atomic weights has become converted to one of atomic numbers, in which the number represents not the mass of the atom relative to hydrogen but the net number of positive charges on its nucleus relative to the single positive charge on the nucleus of hydrogen. Thirdly, matter represents an energy system; as such it possesses energy, manifests energy and can never be considered apart from energy. Essentially it is energy.

## The concept of energy

Energy is defined as the capacity to do work. If one lifts a pound weight a height of one foot, one does a certain amount of work against gravity; if one lifts two pounds through the same distance, one does twice as much work. That is to say, the work done varies with the resistance to be overcome and the distance through which it is overcome. This represents mechanical energy, but all other kinds of energy are ultimately also measured in terms of the work done. The unit of work and the common unit of energy are therefore one and the same thing, the erg. In absolute units, the erg is the amount of work necessary to overcome the resistance of a dyne, the unit of force, over a centimeter; in relative units, it is the amount of work necessary to raise 1/981 of a gram vertically through one centimeter in the latitude of Paris, where the standard values for measurements of all sorts were first set up in 1801.

## Manifestations of energy

There are different kinds of energy, different sources from which work can be obtained. Light is a form of energy; its unit is the photon. Heat is a form of energy and its unit is the calorie. There is electrical energy, chemical energy and radiant energy; there is the energy of matter and there is mechan-

TABLE II
ELEMENTARY PARTICLES

| Particle | Approximate Mass (in units of physicists' weight scale where oxygen = 16) | Charge | |
|---|---|---|---|
| Proton | 1.00758 | Positive +e | |
| Electron | 0.000548 | Negative −e | Beta particle |
| Neutron | 1.00897 | None o | |
| Meson | 0.1 | Positive or negative +e or −e | Heavy electron |
| Positron | 0.0000548 | Positive +e | Short lived, positive electron |
| Neutrino | 0.0005 | None o | Existence suspected but not yet experimentally proved. |

ical energy. The forms of energy which can most easily be recognized are those which are employed in doing mechanical work and which can therefore be directly estimated in terms of the work done. The English physicist, Lord Kelvin (1824–1907), made the fundamental distinction between "available energy" which can be turned to mechanical effect and "diffuse energy" which is useless for that purpose. A bent wire possesses energy, for it is capable of doing work when it straightens; a charge of gunpowder possesses energy, for it is capable of doing work when it explodes; a lump of coal possesses energy, for it is capable of doing work when it burns. The energy of the bent wire, of the gunpowder and of the coal is potential energy, or the energy which a system has acquired by virtue of work having been done upon it. It becomes kinetic energy or the energy of motion when the wire is released, the gunpowder fired or the coal ignited. The efficiency of an energy system is measured by the extent to which its potential energy can be converted to available kinetic energy and not dissipated as diffuse kinetic energy, into which, according to the Second Law of Thermodynamics, all the available energy in the world is slowly but steadily being degraded.

**The energy of atoms and molecules; diffusion and Brownian movement**

Atoms and molecules possess enormous amounts of energy. If the energy possessed by the molecules in a tumblerful of water could be released and controlled, the calculated amount would be enough to drive a liner like the *Queen Mary* from New York to her home port and back again. The combined efforts of physicists all over the world in the past twenty years have resulted in unleashing the energy bound in some atoms with effects which have not yet been fully determined. Because of their kinetic energy, atoms and molecules under ordinary conditions are in constant and random motion, the extent of their movements depending upon the cohesive forces, or forces of attraction, which hold them together and the medium through which they must move. Thus in a solid, the cohesive forces are relatively great, and though its particles must, in the kinetic nature of matter, be in motion, they have little freedom of movement and what there is is not evident. The particles of a gas or liquid, on the other hand, are less

○ Water molecule   ▲ Molecule from crystal

FIGURE 2.3  Diagram of diffusion. As the crystal in the bottom of the beaker dissolves, its particles move freely among the water particles which are also in incessant random motion. The dissolved particles, at first more numerous in the immediate vicinity of the crystal, gradually become equally distributed throughout the liquid.

strongly attracted to each other, and their movement, if it cannot be directly seen, can at least be measured. If, for instance, two different gases or two different liquids are brought together in a container, their particles, in their incessant random movements, will gradually become evenly distributed, making a homogeneous mixture. The time which it takes for complete mixing is a measure of the kinetic energy of the particles and their freedom of movement. This phenomenon is known as diffusion, and it is one which is incessantly going on in living bodies as well as in the physical world (Fig. 2.3). Moreover, it is one that is constantly being put to practical use in our daily lives. Every time one puts a lump of sugar into a cup of tea or coffee, or salt upon one's food, or stands aside from an open bottle of ammonia or similar strong-smelling substance in order to let the fumes escape, one is applying the principle of diffusion, although relying on temperature changes, air currents and other local conditions to accelerate its very slow progress.

The kinetic energy of the invisible atoms and combinations of atoms or molecules may be translated to larger ones, microscopically or macroscopically visible. This was first observed by an English botanist, Robert Brown (1773–1858), in 1828, when he was making microscopic studies of pollen grains. He saw that the tiny pollen grains of the moss Lycopodium were in rapid, oscillatory movement and at first thought that they were alive and that this movement was a phenomenon peculiar to living things. Later he found that the same kind of movement could be seen in liquids that had never, as far as he knew, been any part of a living system, and recognized that it was a physical, rather than exclusively a biological one. This kind of movement has been called after him, "Brownian movement," and it is due to the bombardment of the larger particles, whose mass is too great to permit movement through their own kinetic energy, by the smaller, rapidly moving ones. Hit first in one place, then in another, the particles are displaced first in one direction then in another, so that they vibrate rapidly in all planes (Fig. 2.4).

This kind of movement can be seen in any system where there are small enough particles of matter, and where there is no great resistance to their displacement. It can be seen in fluids and in gases, but not in solid or in viscous media. John Tyndall (1820–1893) explained the dancing of tiny dust particles of the air visible in a beam of light on the same principle. The molecules of the gases in the air are in rapid and random movement because of the energy they possess; frequently they collide with the larger dust particles and so move them first in one direction, then in another. "Brownian movement" is an expression of the kinetic nature of matter, its constant and spontaneous motion because of its own kinetic energy. The movement can be accelerated by adding energy, such as heat or mechanical energy, to the system. Thus the diffusion of sugar through a cup of tea can be speeded up by stirring, or by shaking the cup, and it is more rapid if the tea is hot rather than cold.

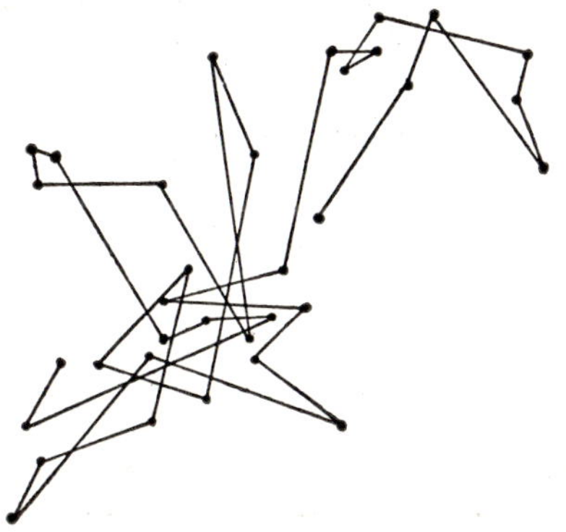

FIGURE 2.4 The course of a particle in Brownian movement. The lines between the dots represent the distance and direction of the movement in each vibration. (After Perrin, from Mavor, *General Biology*, 3rd edition. Copyright 1947 by The Macmillan Company.)

Similarly diffusion is more rapid in a gas or air than in a liquid, more rapid in water and watery liquids than in thick ones, yet more rapid in a thick liquid than in a substance like gelatine.

It is impossible in the light of the knowledge we have today of the physical world, to separate matter from energy; in considering the organization of matter, and its operation, one must inevitably consider its energy and its energy relationships. In the physical world, every change from one state to another is a manifestation of energy; in the biological world, every organism is a complicated energy system and all its reactions are expressions of energy relationships of the atoms and molecules in it and in its environment.

# CHAPTER 3

# ATOMS, IONS AND MOLECULES

## The matter of biological systems

The biologist is concerned primarily with those configurations of atoms and atomic groupings that are found in living organisms; he distinguishes between the living, or organic, and the non-living, or inorganic, in the world around him. He recognizes that this division, like most other biological classifications, is an arbitrary one and finds it difficult to establish a satisfactory set of criteria to distinguish absolutely between the living and the non-living. This was far easier when his ignorance was greater, when he could attribute a vital force or a vital power to things he called alive, or when he supposed them alone capable of assimilation, growth and reproduction. The more that is known about the parts that make up the bodies of plants and animals, the more that is known about the way these parts react and interact with one another, either in the organism or when isolated from it, the harder it becomes to define absolutely the terms alive, or living, and non-living.

## Protoplasm as the material basis of life

The phenomena of life are, as far as we now know, invariably associated with a particular substance called protoplasm, which has definite and specific characteristics. Physically, protoplasm is grayish, translucent and viscous, its consistency varying with different internal and external conditions from a fluid to a fairly firm jelly. It is never found in masses of indefinite size as other substances may be, like water, oil, air and minerals, but always in small, usually microscopic, units called cells. Chemically, it is a complex mixture of many different combinations of elements. Analyses of the protoplasm of different kinds of organisms show that about 34 elements may enter into its composition, 16 at least of which seem to be common to all protoplasm. Biologically, protoplasm and its products form the mass, or structure, of all living things, and it differs from every other kind of matter known in its capacity to metabolize (Greek, meta = between + bole = change), to carry on those chemical changes by which energy is provided for the activities of the cell; by which material is assimilated; by which such assimilated materials and even the protoplasm itself are broken down into their respective constituents; and by which new products and new protoplasm are made. The sum total of these chemical changes is known as metabolism, and living organisms alone can bring them about. A machine cannot metabolize; an internal combustion engine can only oxidize the fuel fed it and so release its energy to do work; it cannot repair the damage to itself through the wear and tear of its own operation, nor can it make more of its own substance. A living organism can, provided that its environment gives it the necessary materials and takes away end products or by-products of its activity which are harmful or destructive to it. Protoplasm is the material, or as Thomas Huxley (1825–1895) defined it the "physical", basis of life, its operation, or metabolism, the condition of life.

When protoplasm is subjected to chemical analysis, it yields the following elements in the proportions expressed by the average percentage by weight.

| Element | Chemical symbol | Percentage by weight (average) |
|---|---|---|
| Oxygen | O | 76 |
| Hydrogen | H | 10 |
| Nitrogen | N | 2.5 |
| Carbon | C | 10.5 |
| Sulphur | S | 0.2 |

| | | |
|---|---|---|
| Phosphorus | P | 0.3 |
| Potassium | K | 0.3 |
| Iron | Fe | 0.01 |
| Magnesium | Mg | 0.02 |
| Calcium | Ca | 0.02 |
| Sodium | Na | 0.04 |
| Chlorine | Cl | 0.1 |
| Copper | Cu | Trace |
| Cobalt | Co | " |
| Zinc | Zn | " |
| Manganese | Mn | " |

Other elements such as lithium (Li), strontium (Sr), rubidium (Rb), nickel (Ni), tin (Sn), gold (Au), and mercury (Hg), may enter into the composition of the protoplasm of groups of animals or plants. Where the soil is especially rich in certain minerals, the plants growing there may incorporate them or the elements of which they are composed, and they may finally find their way into the tissues or hard parts of animals that feed upon the plants. In some parts of the world, gold is particularly abundant in the soil, and the hoofs, horns and hair of the deer living on the vegetation in these regions show relatively large accumulations of it. Agricultural studies in recent years have made evident the importance of the presence in the soil of even minute amounts of some of the elements in promoting the growth of plants and so indirectly of animals, although not necessarily entering into their composition. The leanness and poor quality of the cattle in some areas of the United States are partly at least the result of a deficiency of boron in the soil; if small amounts of boron are spread on the fields the pasturage improves and the cattle thrive. The question of the elements that are necessary for the best growth and development of plants and animals, and the role that they play in that growth and development, is one of great practical value and many theoretical implications.

## Chemical elements and compounds; chemical equations

The biologist is especially concerned with the properties of those elements which are found in protoplasm and which contribute to its activities, as well as with the properties of the substances which these elements combine to form. Atoms unite in different ways into groups, some relatively simple, some very complex. These groupings may consist of two or more, sometimes many, atoms of the same or different elements held together in unions that may be easy or difficult to break. An elementary substance is one which contains atoms of only one kind, like pure metallic silver or copper or gold; a compound is one which is composed of atoms of two or more kinds, like water and salt and sugar. The chemist makes use of a kind of shorthand to indicate the number of atoms of each element that are held together in a complex, indicating the element by its chemical symbol and the number of its atoms by a digit below and to the right of the symbol. Ordinary table salt, for example, is written as NaCl, which shows that one atom of sodium, for which the Greek word was natrium, is bound with one atom of chlorine to make a substance different from either, or sodium chloride. Similarly the formula for water is $H_2O$, which means that 2 atoms of hydrogen are bound to one of oxygen in each molecule, or ultimate particle, of water. To show the reaction that takes place in the formation of elementary substances or compounds, or in their transformation or disintegration, the chemist writes an equation, representing on the left side the reacting substances, or reagents, and on the right the end product or products. The union of sodium and chlorine to make salt can be quickly, if incompletely, represented in this way: $Na + Cl \rightarrow NaCl$, and that of hydrogen and oxygen to form water as $2H + O \rightarrow H_2O$. The figure before the symbol for hydrogen means that 2 atoms are involved in the formation of one molecule of water, while only one of oxygen takes part, and the equation is said to be balanced since the number of each kind of reacting atom is equal to the number of those represented in the end product. This is, however, only part of the story of a chemical reaction; this kind of shorthand does not tell the conditions under which it occurs, the way in which the atoms are held, or bonded, together, nor the energy exchanges, nor other factors that may influence it, but it offers a quick and convenient way of presenting what may be a long and complicated process and to this extent is useful and in common practice. An equation also states the proportional amounts of the reagents necessary for a complete reaction, and therefore indirectly the actual quantities required, since the relative weights of the atoms are known. The equation Na + Cl → NaCl shows that one unit of sodium will combine with one unit of chlorine to form one unit of sodium chloride; 2H + O → H$_2$O shows that 2 units of hydrogen will combine with one unit of oxygen to form one unit of water. The atomic weight of sodium is 23, that of chlorine is 35.5, and according to the equation, 23 units of sodium combine with 35.5 units of chlorine to make 58.5 units of sodium chloride; and, since the atomic weight of hydrogen is 1.008 and that of oxygen is 16, 2.016 units of hydrogen should combine with 16 of oxygen to form 18.016 units of water. This should be true whatever the units are—grams, ounces, pounds or any other measure of weight or its equivalent. And such a quantitative relationship has been verified over and over again for these and many other reactions; it is established as the law of constant or definite proportions.

In making such quantitative determinations, the terms "gram atom" and "gram molecule" or "mole" are frequently used. A gram atom of an element is its atomic weight expressed in grams; a gram molecule, or mole, is the molecular weight of a compound expressed in grams, and like the gram atom, is its weight relative to the atomic weight of oxygen, with an assigned weight of 16. The sample equations given above definitely state then that, in the first case, not only will one atom of sodium unite with one of chlorine to form one unit of sodium chloride, but also that 23 grams of sodium will unite with 35.5 grams of chlorine to form 58.5 grams of salt; and, in the second case, 2 atoms of hydrogen will unite with one of oxygen to form one molecule of water, and also that 2.016 grams of hydrogen will unite with 16 grams of oxygen to form 18.016 grams of water.

### The concept of valence

Dalton's theory of atoms had included a theory of their valence or combining power.
Certain atoms tend to combine with several others at a time, some with only one other, and the number with which they will simultaneously unite is characteristic, with some exceptions, of the atoms of specific elements. Some atoms are more reactive than others, that is, they will form combinations more readily, while others are less active, and some inert. The new knowledge of the structure of the atom has brought new understanding of the forces that unite and hold them together and an explanation of their groupings in the Periodic Table.

### Atomic combinations; the stability and reactivity of atoms

Atoms unite into molecules either by sharing or by transferring electrons. The electrons which circulate about the nucleus of an atom do not all move in orbits of the same size, that is to say, they occupy areas at different distances from the nucleus (Fig. 2.1). They are said to occupy different energy levels which it is convenient to represent diagrammatically as concentric rings around the central nucleus, although actually the extra-nuclear electrons move in more or less elliptical orbits lying in all planes relative to the nucleus. The electrons nearest the nucleus are in the first energy level, those next removed in the second, and so on. The most stable arrangement seems to be that in which there are 8 electrons in the outer orbit or energy level. This is the configuration of the so-called inert or noble gases, which are unique among the elements in that they have relatively few of the properties by which elements are chemically distinguishable and no tendency to form molecular combinations. Table III shows the atomic structure of the inert gases, with the number of electrons on each energy level.

Each of these differs in the number of net positive charges on the nucleus and in the number of extra-nuclear electrons; each is alike, with the exception of helium, in having 8 electrons in the outer energy level. All are chemically stable.

At the other end of the scale are the radioactive elements, characterized by high atomic numbers, electrons on many energy levels and such instability in their config-

TABLE III

| Element | Atomic number | Energy levels of electrons | | | | | |
|---------|---------------|---|---|---|---|---|---|
| | | 1 | 2 | 3 | 4 | 5 | 6 |
| Helium  | 2  | 2 |   |    |    |    |   |
| Neon    | 10 | 2 | 8 |    |    |    |   |
| Argon   | 18 | 2 | 8 | 8  |    |    |   |
| Krypton | 36 | 2 | 8 | 18 | 8  |    |   |
| Xenon   | 54 | 2 | 8 | 18 | 18 | 8  |   |
| Radon   | 88 | 2 | 8 | 18 | 32 | 18 | 8 |

uration that they are constantly losing alpha particles, or helium nuclei, and beta particles, or electrons, and thus disintegrating to form simpler and stabler systems. This disintegration is spontaneous and is accompanied by the release of energy; it proceeds step by step and is not affected by temperature and the other conditions that influence chemical reactions. All the radium in the universe, as far as we know, is continuously disintegrating and its disintegration is following a definite path toward the element lead, along a course that can be represented as:

$$\underset{88}{\underset{\text{Radium}}{226}} \xrightarrow{He^{++}}_{\alpha} \underset{86}{\underset{\text{Radon}}{222}} \xrightarrow{He^{++}}_{\alpha} \underset{84}{\underset{\text{Polonium}}{218}} \xrightarrow{He^{++}}_{\alpha} \underset{82}{\underset{\text{Lead}}{214}} \xrightarrow{-e}_{\beta}$$

$$\underset{83}{\underset{\text{Bismuth}}{214}} \xrightarrow{-e}_{\beta} \underset{84}{\underset{\text{Polonium}}{214}} \xrightarrow{He^{++}}_{\alpha} \underset{82}{\underset{\text{Lead}}{210}} \xrightarrow{-e}_{\beta} \underset{83}{\underset{\text{Bismuth}}{210}} \xrightarrow{-e}_{\beta}$$

$$\underset{84}{\underset{\text{Polonium}}{210}} \xrightarrow{He^{++}}_{\alpha} \underset{82}{\underset{\text{Lead}}{206}}$$

where the numbers above each element represent its atomic weight, those below its atomic number and the arrows the loss of an alpha or a beta particle. The loss of an alpha particle, or helium nucleus, from radium thus gives rise to the element radon, of less mass and lower atomic number, and the loss of an alpha particle from radon gives rise to an isotope of the element polonium, of greater mass than its other isotopes occurring later in the series, but with the same atomic number.

The radioactive elements have great biological importance, for they, and atoms secondarily made radioactive by them, can be used as tracers. Molecules containing radioactive atoms are "tagged" and their course and ultimate fate in the organism can be followed. By this means it has been possible to trace the course of some of the syntheses carried on by biological systems, as well as the steps in the disintegration of some complex molecules taken in by the organism as food and the distribution of the products of this disintegration in the body.

## The metals

Another group of elements, which are similar to each other in their chemical properties, and which the chemist calls metals, have few electrons in the outer energy level, and these are but loosely held in the system and tend to be easily lost. Magnesium, for example, which is a constant constituent of protoplasm, has an atomic number of 12 (Fig. 3.1$b$). That is, there are 12 positive charges on the nucleus and 12 extra-nuclear electrons, 2 in the first energy level, 8 in the second and 2 in the third. The outer two are relatively loosely attracted by the positive charges on the nucleus and tend to detach themselves from the system. They are called the valence electrons, and since there are two of them in this case, magnesium is said to have a valence of 2. Similarly, potassium, another biologically important metal, has an atomic number of 19, with a net positive charge of 19 on its nucleus, 2 planetary electrons on the first energy level, 8 on the second and 8 on the third, with a single one in the outer shell. Potassium tends to part with this outer electron readily, and is said to have a valence of 1. When magnesium loses its two outer electrons, it becomes a system with only 10 electrons circulating around the nucleus, which still has a positive charge of 12, but one in which the outer shell now has 8 electrons. It carries therefore 2 positive charges, and is called an ion, and written $Mg^{++}$ to indicate the extra, or uncompensated, charges of its nucleus. Structurally it now resembles the neon atom, but differs from it in being a charged, rather than a neutral, particle (Fig. 3.1$a$, $c$). Similarly, when potassium loses its outer electron, it becomes an ion, $K^+$, with one positive charge, but a stable system with 8 electrons forming its outer shell.

## The non-metals

A fourth group of elements, the non-metals, also resemble each other in their chemical properties and in the structure of their atoms, in that they lack but a few was based upon atomic weight rather than atomic structure, in which there lies also an explanation for the periodic recurrence of elements with somewhat similar properties when they are arranged in order of ascending atomic weight, and so of their position

Neon atom (Ne)
a

Magnesium atom (Mg) ⟶ 2 electrons + Magnesium ion (Mg++)
b                                                    c

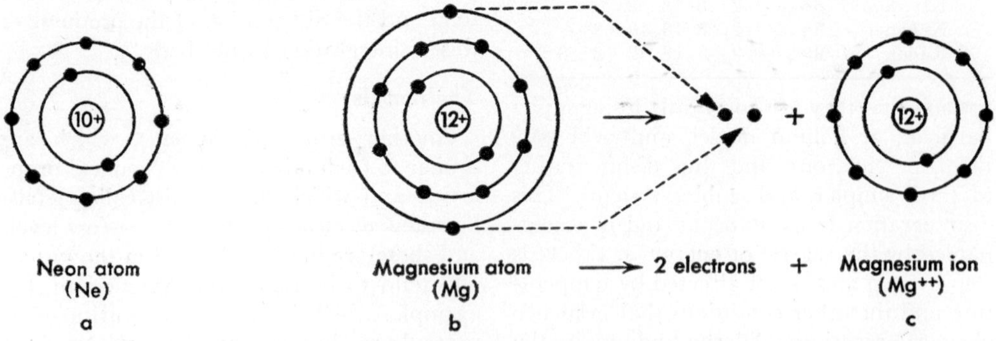

FIGURE 3.1 Diagram of atomic configurations. The neon atom (a) has a nucleus carrying 10 positive charges, with 10 electrons circulating around it. The magnesium atom (b) has a nucleus carrying 12 positive charges with 12 electrons circulating around it. The magnesium ion (c) has a nucleus carrying 12 positive charges, but, owing to the loss of 2 electrons, only 10 negative charges circulating in orbits around it; it is therefore not a neutral but a positively charged particle, Mg++.

electrons in their outer energy level to complete a group of 8. These elements tend to receive rather than give up electrons, and when they add the number requisite for stability, they become negatively charged ions. Oxygen, for instance, with an atomic number of 8, has 2 electrons on the first energy level and 6 on the second. It may take on, or capture, 2 electrons to complete the outer octet. Then it has the same structure as neon, but 2 extra negative charges, and is the rarely occurring oxygen ion, $O^{--}$. Chlorine, one of the most widely distributed of the elements, has 17 electrons circulating around the nucleus. Two of these are on the first energy level, 8 on the second and 7 on the third. It has therefore but one gap to fill in its energy system to complete an outer shell of 8, and it tends to take on 1 electron and to become an ion, $Cl^-$, with a single negative charge (Fig. 3.2).

Valence is then an expression of the number of electrons that an atom will lose or receive, and since it can only lose them to, or receive them from, other atoms, it is an expression of its combining power. Dalton defined it in this way, but his explanation in Mendeleef's Periodic Table. Those with the same number of valence electrons fall into the groups of the Periodic Table (Fig. 2.1); the elements in Group I all have one electron in the outer energy level, those in Group II, two, and so on through the remaining groups. It is therefore predictable that all those in one group will show the same kind of chemical activity and form the same kinds of compounds, and that as one proceeds across the groups, the elements will show progressive differences in their reactivity. In Group I are the active metals like sodium and potassium; Groups II and III contain progressively less active ones; Group IV the elements which have four electrons in the outer energy level, like carbon and silicon, and so in a way stand midway between the inert gases with 8 and the active non-metals with 7; from Group V on, the series passes from the less active non-metals to the most active ones like chlorine.

## Ions and ionization

Ionization is also an expression of the capacity of an atom to lose or gain electrons, and is a property which atoms in compounds as well as free atoms may possess. The word "ion" is the present participle of the Greek verb meaning "to go"; it was first applied to these derivatives of certain atoms by the English scientist, Michael Faraday (1791–

chlorine as an ion, $Cl^-$, have quite different characteristics. The gas is, for example, greenish-yellow in color and has a strong irritating taste and smell, while the ion is colorless. And chemically, atomic or molecular chlorine combines with all metals, with

| Oxygen atom (O) | Oxygen ion ($O^{--}$) | Chlorine atom (Cl) | Chlorine ion ($Cl^-$) |
| --- | --- | --- | --- |
| a | b | c | d |

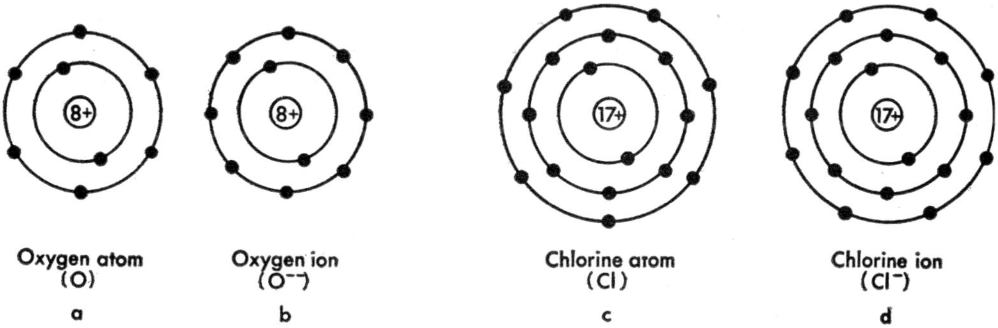

FIGURE 3.2 Diagram of atomic configurations. The oxygen atom (a) has a nucleus with 8 positive charges around which 8 electrons circulate in 2 energy levels. By the addition of 2 electrons to its "incomplete" outer shell of 6, the oxygen atom may be converted to the rarely occurring oxygen ion, $O^{--}$ (b). The chlorine atom (c) has a nucleus with 17 positive charges, around which 17 electrons circulate in 3 energy levels. The addition of 1 electron to those in the outer energy level converts the chlorine atom into a chlorine ion, $Cl^-$ (d).

1867), because as charged particles they move in an electric field and hence are "going." Positively charged ions will move toward the negative pole, or cathode, of an electric circuit and are therefore known as cations, and negatively charged ions will move to the positive pole, or anode, and are therefore called anions. Ions with a single charge, positive or negative, are called univalent; those with two charges bivalent and so on. Sodium and chlorine ions are thus both univalent, the sodium ion ($Na^+$) a univalent cation and the chlorine ion ($Cl^-$) a univalent anion, while magnesium forms a bivalent cation ($Mg^{++}$) and oxygen a bivalent anion ($O^{--}$), although the oxygen ion is rarely found as such in nature, for it is usually combined with hydrogen as a complex ion, the hydroxide ion $OH^-$.

An atom of an element and its ion differ not only in their electrical properties, since the atom is a neutral particle, the ion a charged one, but also in other physical characteristics and in their chemical properties. Chlorine, for example, as a gas where it exists as a diatomic molecule, $Cl_2$, and

some with the release of considerable amounts of energy, while the ion, if it reacts with them at all, does so to much less extent; biologically, chlorine as a gas is suffocating and poisonous even in relatively small quantities, while the ion is very generally present in protoplasm and the fluids surrounding it and plays an important role in protoplasmic reactions.

Indeed, many of the substances in living organisms are in the form of ions, so that it is important to keep in mind the distinction between an element in its atomic or molecular and in its ionic form. Most of the reactions that go on within organisms are between ions, and would not go on unless ions were present. It is because of them that cells have the capacity to conduct electricity and they may be to a considerable extent responsible for the other electrical properties of cells, such as the differences in potential between localized areas and the production of electrical energy. Their distribution and arrangement in the cell also undoubtedly have much to do with the structural organization and energy transformations of protoplasm.

**CHAPTER 4**

# ATOMIC COMBINATIONS AND CHEMICAL REACTIONS

## Atomic unions

The union of atoms takes place either by the transfer of electrons from one atom to another, or by the sharing of electrons by two or more atoms. These unions take place more frequently by sharing than by transfer of electrons between atoms. For example, in the union of two hydrogen atoms to form a molecule of hydrogen, $H_2$, each hydrogen atom contributes its electron to form a more stable pair held by electrical attraction to the two protons. Two oxygen atoms may unite in the same fashion to form a molecule of $O_2$, each atom contributing two electrons to fill the gap in the outer energy level of the other. Or the gap in the shell of the oxygen atom may be filled with the electrons of two hydrogen atoms, forming water, $H_2O$. In this union, the oxygen atom acquires an outer shell of 8 electrons and each hydrogen atom a stable pair. Unions such as these are called non-ionic, or covalent, since they do not dissociate readily, that is, they do not separate into their component ions (Fig. 4.1).

The atoms of the metals and non-metals, which tend to give up and to receive electrons respectively, form compounds by the transfer of electrons. Magnesium and chlorine, for example, form a compound called magnesium chloride, $MgCl_2$, in which one atom of magnesium is linked to two of chlorine. Magnesium, a metal with a valence of 2, tends to lose the two electrons in its outer energy level; chlorine, a non-metal with a valence of 1, tends to take on one to complete its outer octet, so that when the two elements are brought together, each chlorine atom takes one of the loosely held magnesium electrons, and the three atoms, one of magnesium and two of chlorine, form a fairly stable atomic system (Fig. 4.2). Similarly, in its combination with sodium, to form the salt of the sea, of the table, and of tissue fluids, the chlorine atom accepts the single electron in the outer energy level of the sodium atom and the nuclei of the two atoms are held together by their combined extra-nuclear electrons to form a stable configuration (Fig. 4.3).

In losing its electrons, the atom of magnesium becomes an ion with 2 positive charges; the sodium atom, in losing its single electron, likewise becomes an ion but one with a single positive charge. In gaining an electron from either source, the chlorine atom becomes an ion with one negative charge. Compounds formed by the transfer of electrons are therefore ionic, since under appropriate conditions they tend to dissociate into their component ions, and consequently differ in their chemical and biological properties from the non-ionic or covalent compounds formed when two or more atoms share electrons.

## Chemical reactions; types of reactions

All chemical reactions, whether occurring in the living organism or not, fall into three types or categories: union and disunion; partner exchange or double decomposition; and oxidation-reduction.

### Union and disunion

The simplest kind of union is that in which two atoms combine to form a molecule, as in the combination of two hydrogen atoms to form the diatomic molecule, $H_2$, or of one hydrogen and one chlorine atom to form the compound HCl, or hydrochloric acid. But several atoms may also combine to form a single molecule, and molecules may

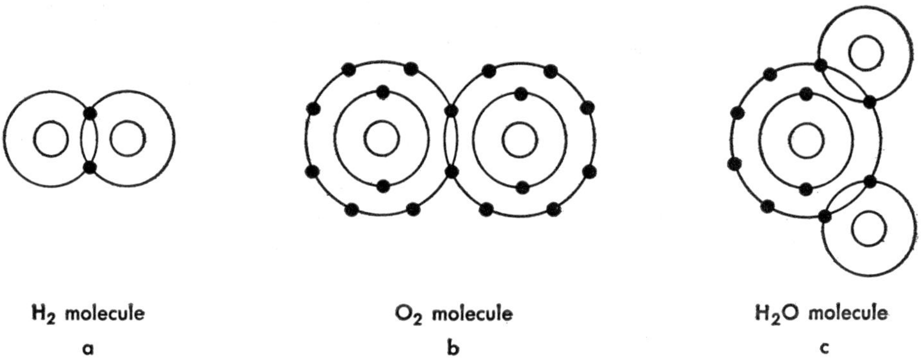

| H₂ molecule | O₂ molecule | H₂O molecule |
|:---:|:---:|:---:|
| a | b | c |

FIGURE 4.1  Diagram of atomic union by sharing of electrons.

a. Two hydrogen atoms combine by sharing electrons into one molecule of hydrogen ($H_2$).

b. Two oxygen atoms combine by sharing electrons into one molecule of oxygen ($O_2$).

c. Two hydrogen atoms and one oxygen atom share their electrons to form one molecule of water ($H_2O$).

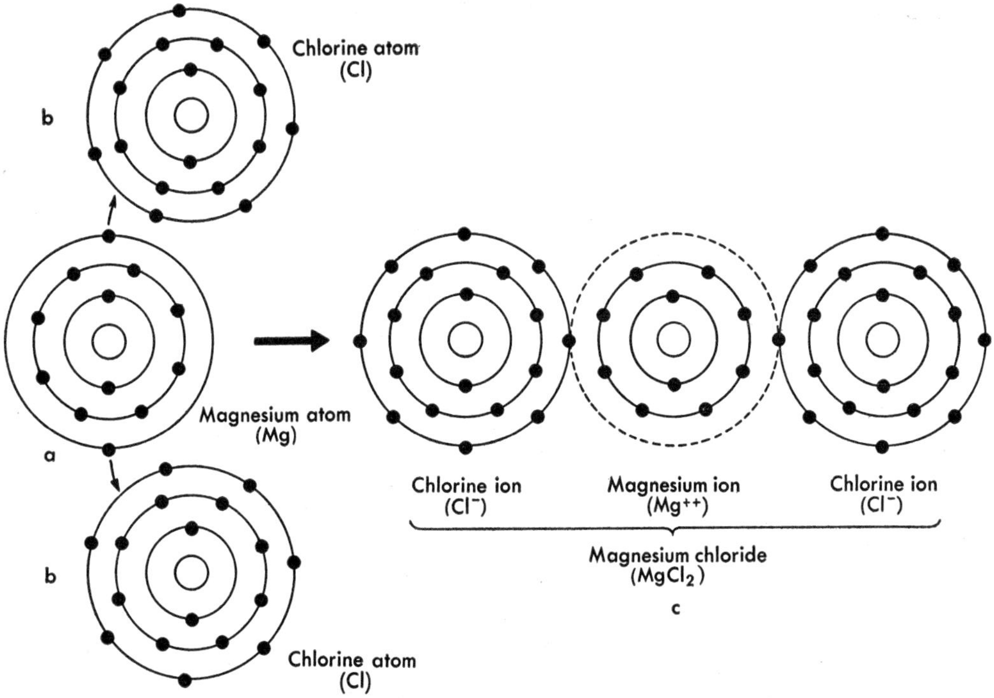

FIGURE 4.2  Diagram of atomic union through transfer of electrons. The two electrons in the outer orbit of the magnesium atom (a) are transferred to chlorine atoms (b-b), each filling the gap in the outer energy level of a chlorine atom, and forming a stable system, magnesium chloride ($MgCl_2$) (c).

unite to form larger aggregates including hundreds and even thousands of atoms, sometimes in very stable union in parts of the molecules and in less stable union in others. These larger aggregates, as well as the simpler molecules, may break up into their component parts which are then free to enter into another reaction. Many of these union and disunion reactions do not involve the loss or gain of electrons. The hydrolysis of substances, which is constantly going on in living organisms, is an illustration of this kind of reaction, which as its name implies takes place by the addition of the elements of water to atoms or to molecules. The disintegration of ordinary sugar into two molecules of simpler sugars occurs in this way, and may be expressed by the equation:

$$C_{12}H_{22}O_{11} + H_2O \rightarrow C_6H_{12}O_6 + C_6H_{12}O_6$$
$$\text{cane sugar} \quad \text{water} \quad \text{glucose} \quad \text{fructose}$$

in which the end result has been the separation of the complex of twelve carbon atoms characteristic of cane sugar into two molecules of six carbon atoms, to each of which one atom of hydrogen from the molecule of water has been added and to one of which the oxygen atom has become attached. The reverse reaction is also one which commonly occurs in biological systems, in which glucose and fructose are combined into cane sugar by the loss of hydrogen and oxygen from their molecules and the combination of these elements into water.

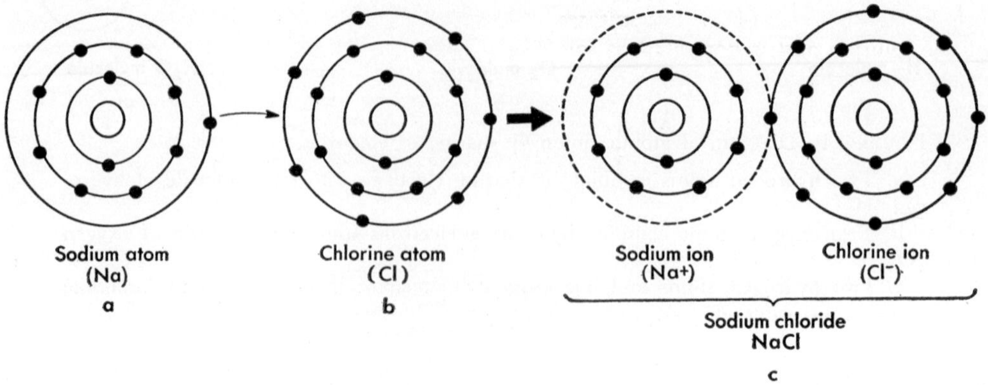

FIGURE 4.3 Diagram of atomic union through transfer of electrons. A sodium atom (a) loses the single electron in its outer energy level to a chlorine atom (b), filling the gap in its outer energy level and forming the stable system, sodium chloride (NaCl) (c).

**Partner exchange (double decomposition)**

This kind of reaction is characteristic of ionic compounds, when the ions of two complexes are exchanged without any transfer of electrons from one group of atoms to another. A simple illustration of such an exchange is the reaction that occurs when sodium chloride, NaCl, and silver nitrate, $AgNO_3$, are brought together. If these two compounds are mixed in a dry state, no reaction takes place, but if they are dissolved in water, each compound dissociates into its positive and negative ions, which move freely in the water, and the positive silver and sodium ions may exchange negative ions, forming sodium nitrate and silver chloride. The reaction might be written in this way:

$$NaCl + AgNO_3 \rightarrow AgCl + NaNO_3$$

but it would be written more completely as an ionic equation, the brackets indicating the partners that exchange:

$$Na^+ + \overbrace{Cl^- + Ag^+} + NO_3^- \leftrightarrows Na^+ + NO_3^- + Ag^+ + Cl^-$$

The double arrows between the two sides of the equation show that the reaction may proceed in either direction, that is, that sodium chloride and silver nitrate may also be formed by the ionization and partner exchange of the newly formed sodium nitrate and silver chloride molecules. But one of the end products of this reaction, silver chloride, does not dissolve readily in water, so that as it is formed it separates, or precipitates, out of the solution and is deposited in solid, or crystalline, form in the vessel containing the reagents. This means that the silver and chlorine ions are being removed from the solution as fast as they come together and form the new compound, leaving the sodium and nitrate ions to unite with decreasing competition from other positive and negative ions and to form crystalline sodium nitrate when the water evaporates.

In this reaction, the silver nitrate molecule dissociates into a simple ion, $Ag^+$ and a compound ion, $NO_3^-$, the nitrate ion. That is, nitrogen and oxygen in the triatomic molecule, $AgNO_3$, tend to stay together and act as a unit. A relatively stable grouping of two or more atoms like this is known as a radical. Some radicals are large and contain many atoms, some are ionic and some are not, but all show this firm bond between their atoms, and the unified action of the whole complex.

The shifting and exchange of ions are constantly going on in solutions of ionic compounds, and since most substances in the living organism are in solution, this kind of reaction plays a very large part in biological processes. Experiments using isotopes, or radioactive compounds, as tracers have shown that the animal body is in a continual state of flux, with atoms that entered it as part of its food incorporated at one time perhaps in its muscles, at another in its fat reserves, at another in its tissue fluids. The condition within the living organism is dynamic, never static, with a perpetual exchange of atoms and of the smaller radicals going on between the molecules that compose it. These exchanges do not necessarily result in the formation of new compounds; they may simply be transfers of similar atoms or radicals between two substances.

## Oxidation-reduction

This type of reaction does not, as its name implies, refer exclusively to reactions in which oxygen is involved. It takes its name, however, from the behavior of oxygen, which, since it has two gaps to fill in its outer energy level to achieve stability, gains electrons in all its combinations with other atoms or molecules, which consequently lose them. In this transfer, the oxygen atom becomes reduced to a negative ion and the contributing atom or atoms become oxidized to a positive ion, or positive ions.

Perhaps the simplest illustration of this kind of reaction comes not from biology but from metallurgy and one of its practical applications. Iron, for example, rarely exists in nature as the pure metal, but as its oxide, a reddish compound which gives the yellow color to sand and to the clay and soil of some regions. In order to obtain the pure metal from iron oxide, or ore, the oxygen must be removed from it. This is done commercially by heating the ore with coke, a form of carbon, which at high temperatures will take the oxygen away from its combination with iron, thereby reducing the ore to the pure metal. The removal of oxygen from its combination with any substance therefore represents the reduction of that substance, just as its combination with oxygen represents its oxidation, and by a broader application of these terms, any reaction in which there is a loss or surrender of electrons by an atom or molecule is called an oxidation and any in which there is a gain or acceptance of electrons by an atom or molecule is called a reduction, whether or not oxygen is actually involved directly in the process. Oxidation then means the de-electronation of an atom or group of atoms and reduction the electronation of an atom or group of atoms.

In general the substance whose atoms gain electrons is known as an oxidizing agent; the substance whose atoms lose electrons as a reducing agent. Oxygen and the non-metals as a rule act as oxidizing agents, while hydrogen and the metals act as reducing agents. When compounds act as oxidizing agents, the positive metallic elements of the compound lose electrons, and when they act as reducing agents the non-metal in the compound gains electrons. It is apparent therefore that there exists a gradation in a series of oxidizing agents, in terms of the readiness with which they receive electrons, and also of reducing agents, in terms of the readiness with which they lose electrons. In an oxidation-reduction reaction in a biological system, a series of transfers of electrons between a number of compounds may take place before their final surrender to the oxygen atom itself, each transfer representing an energy exchange of different value and the whole series resulting ultimately in the reduction of the oxygen atom and the oxidation of the substance contributing the electrons.

Most organisms live in a medium in which there is free oxygen, either as gaseous oxygen in the air, or dissolved in the water or fluids surrounding them, and the end result of the oxidation-reduction reactions going on within them is the oxidation of the carbon atom to carbon dioxide, $CO_2$. In the slow process of the burning, or combustion, of the carbon compounds which they utilize as food, energy is released to initiate other chemical reactions, and to be manifested as heat, movement and all the other phenomena that are associated with life. While the majority of organisms can exist only if free oxygen, $O_2$, is available to them, some can adjust to a medium in which it is reduced or absent, deriving their energy by oxidation-reduction reactions which do not involve it directly, and shifting from one kind of chemical mechanism to the other as the conditions of their environments change, while other organisms, even in the presence of free oxygen, do not make use of it directly, and to others it is even destructive. Organisms of this kind are found principally among plants of simple structural organization, the bacteria and yeasts.

## *Conditions determining and influencing reactions*

Although chemical reactions are taking place all the time outside the bodies of living organisms as well as within them, there are certain conditions which govern their occurrence, their rate and their extent. These conditions are more closely regulated within the organism than outside it, for protoplasm operates within very narrow physical limits, but they are, as the reactions themselves are, fundamentally the same.

The conditions that determine whether or not a reaction will take place are the reactivity of the elements involved, their proximity to each other and the energy available, whether derived from the atoms themselves, that is, chemical energy, or from some source external to them, such as light, heat or electricity. The conditions that affect the rate of a reaction are the quantity of the reagents present, that is, their concentration, temperature, and the presence of other substances, called catalysts, a diverse group of compounds which in general accelerate reactions although they themselves do not contribute to the end products. The extent to which a reaction proceeds depends upon chemical equilibrium within the system, but once the conditions of its occurrence have been satisfied, a reaction will take place, and nothing will stop it, until it has gone to completion or reached equilibrium, but the alteration of those conditions. Chemical reactions are as inevitable as the tides and the winds and the rains, given the conditions that initiate them. A comprehension of this inevitability, and of the kinds of reactions that may occur, gives some basis for an understanding of physiological processes and the behavior of biological systems.

### Reactivity of elements

Modern knowledge of the structure of atoms gives the clue to their reactivity, which rests upon their stability or instability as electronic systems, not in terms of their charges but in the relations of the surrounding electrons to the center or nucleus of the atom. The inert gases are not reactive, because they are stable electronic systems; the radioactive elements are so unstable that their atomic structure is constantly changing as they lose alpha or beta particles; the metals and non-metals lie between these two extremes, having in the one case electrons to lose, and in the other electrons to gain, to reach a satisfactory degree of stability. Reactions must therefore occur between atoms which have electrons to lose and those which have electrons to gain, but cannot occur between those which can only lose or only gain them.

The position of the elements in the Periodic Table permits one to predict their reactivity and their other chemical properties, since it depends upon their valence, i.e., the number of electrons in the outer energy level. Therefore, the chemist need learn the properties of relatively few of the elements, and can deduce those of the remaining 98 from a study of Mendeleef's chart. This has been made use of in many ways by chemists and biologists, especially perhaps in the development of drugs and other medicinal compounds. Arsenic compounds, for example, are poisonous and destructive to microorganisms, the spirochetes, which when present in the blood and tissues cause disease in man. But arsenic and its compounds are also often toxic to the patient, so it is desirable to have a drug with similar properties, also destructive to the invading parasite, but without harmful effects to the host. It would be logical to assume that other elements in the same group as arsenic would have similar properties, and by testing compounds of these other elements, bismuth was found an adequate substitute for arsenic and bismuth compounds less toxic to humans are now used as alternates to arsenic compounds in the treatment of venereal diseases caused by spirochetes.

### Proximity of elements

It is obvious that reactions can only occur if the reagents are brought together so that there is a chance for their atoms, in their random movements, to meet. Atomic or molecular unions take place when atoms, or molecules, collide or at least come so close to each other that there is opportunity for their electron systems to be joined. The reaction that occurs, if three or more substances are mixed, depends upon the competition between them for the sharing or transfer of their electrons. The more reactive a substance is, the more eagerly, so to speak, will it accept or surrender or share its electrons, so that its compounds will predominate in the end products, but if all the reagents are equally reactive, the final combinations are simply a matter of chance, depending upon the random movement and fortuitous collisions of the particles in the mixture.

### Available energy

All reactions are chemical changes, and all chemical changes are transfers of energy. Some are accompanied by the release of energy, some require energy to initiate them. The source of this energy may be stored within the atom itself, that is, as chemical energy, or it may be the energy of light, of heat, of electricity or of some other kind. Some reactions take place with the release of such large amounts of energy that an explosion results. If hydrogen and oxygen as gases are mixed in the proper proportions, their union into water is accompanied by the release of energy of explosive force. But any chemical reaction can be made to occur so that all, or nearly all, of the liberated energy is in the form of heat and so can be measured and the energy exchange in different reactions compared. When the energy release of the hydrogen-oxygen combination into water is so measured, it is found that 116,800 calories are set free per each 4.032 grams of hydrogen reacting. Similarly, when carbon is oxidized to carbon dioxide, $CO_2$—a process that is continually going on in the living organism where carbon and its compounds form a great part of the structural material and all of the solid food—94,400 calories are liberated for every gram molecule, thus every 12 grams, of carbon so burnt or consumed. Chemical changes such as these, where energy is set free which can be measured as heat, are called exothermic reactions. It follows from the Law of the Conservation of Energy that to undo such a combination, once it has taken place, an equivalent amount of energy in some form or another must be supplied. Thus water may be decomposed into the elements of which it is made only by exposure to high temperatures, that is, by the application of energy in the form of heat or by the application of electrical energy. Water undergoes some dissociation into its component ions, hydrogen ions ($H^+$) and hydroxyl ions ($OH^-$)* when an electric current is passed

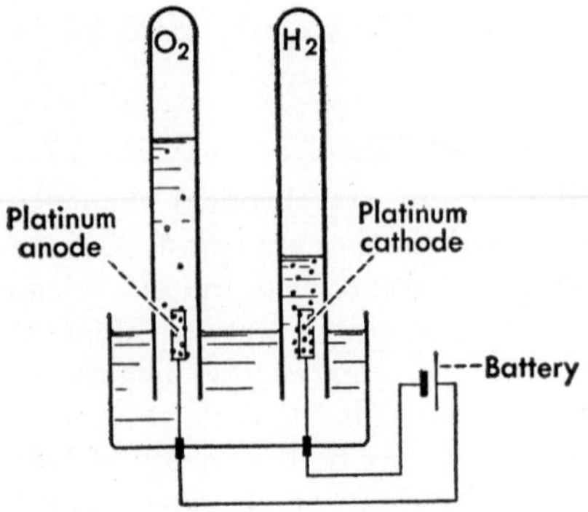

FIGURE 4.4 Diagram of the electrolytic dissociation of water. (After Krauskopf.)

through it. The hydrogen ions migrate to the negative pole of the electric circuit, there gain an electron and unite in pairs, bubbling off the electrode as molecular hydrogen (Fig. 4.4). The hydroxyl ions migrate to the positive pole and each gives up its extra electron. This results in an unstable molecular configuration, the uncharged hydroxyl radical OH without the additional electron which gave it stability as an ion; the radicals unite in pairs, forming one molecule of water and one atom of oxygen. The dissociation of the water then continues, and the oxygen atoms so released unite in pairs and bubble off the positive electrode as molecular oxygen. The amount of energy that must be supplied as electric current to release 4.032 grams of hydrogen is equivalent to 116,800 calories. This kind of reaction, since it requires rather than releases energy, is called an endothermic reaction, and the amount of energy necessary to break up a compound is a measure of that stored within it as potential energy. The energy and chemical relationships in the formation and decomposition of water may be represented by the following equations:

The steps in this reaction are shown in the following series of equations:

(1) $H_2O \leftrightarrows H^+ + OH^-$
(2) $H^+ + -e \to H$
    $H + H \to H_2$
(3) $OH^- -e \to OH$
    $OH + OH \to H_2O + O$
    $O + O \to O_2$

Not only is the heat given out or absorbed in a reaction a measure of the potential energy stored in the complex of atoms but also one of the reactivities of the complex. The greater the energy exchange, the greater the stability of the system. Water and carbon dioxide are both substances with stable molecular configurations; their formation releases and their decomposition requires relatively large amounts of energy. Hydrogen peroxide, $H_2O_2$, on the other hand, is unstable under ordinary circumstances and unless absolutely pure decomposes readily to water with the loss of one oxygen atom from each molecule of peroxide and the evolution of some heat. This reaction

$$2H_2O_2 \to H_2O + O_2$$

is really one of auto-oxidation-reduction, or as it is more generally called, auto-oxidation, in which the peroxide acts simultaneously as an oxidizing and a reducing agent, for half the oxygen atoms in it are oxidized to the elementary substance by the loss of two electrons and half are reduced by gaining them. When hydrogen peroxide is formed in the bodies of plants and animals, its decomposition is accelerated by certain catalysts formed also in the body. The decomposition of hydrogen peroxide is an exothermic reaction and the relatively small amount of heat evolved shows that an equally small amount of energy was necessary to bring about the combination of two hydrogen and two oxygen atoms into the molecule of peroxide, so that it may easily be disrupted.

Chemical energy, the energy stored in the atom as potential energy, and as far as its utilization by man goes, almost entirely locked in it, is the source of the energy

I. $2H_2 + O_2 \to 2H_2O + \text{Energy} = 116{,}800$ calories (exothermic)

II. $2H_2O + \text{Energy} = 116{,}800$ calories $\to 2H_2 + O_2$ (endothermic)

which activates some atoms and initiates some reactions. What releases this energy and what is its magnitude are still unknown, but its effect is evident in those reactions that occur spontaneously. But most reactions require some source of energy external to the reagents themselves to initiate them; this is called the energy of activation, and it may be any of the known forms of energy. Most exothermic reactions, once they are started, produce enough energy as they proceed to carry them through to their completion, just as the fire, started in one lump of coal with a relatively small expenditure of energy, progresses from lump to lump until the whole pile is consumed, or the explosion, initiated at one end of a trail of dynamite, supplies the energy for successive explosions along the trail.

The source of all the energy on earth is ultimately the sun, and it is the sun which is constantly supplying the energy for the most fundamental reaction that there is. This reaction, the synthesis by green plants of certain compounds of carbon, is going on every day, and were it not, life as we know it now would cease to be. For the synthesis is one that not only provides the energy-producing foods upon which plants and animals are dependent for the initiation and continuance of their metabolic processes, but also the basic materials for the synthesis of protoplasm itself.

### Concentration of reagents

Since reactions between atoms or molecules depend upon their chance meeting, the more that there are present in any medium at any one time, the greater are the chances of collisions between them. The more crowded the room, the more apt one is to jostle one's neighbors, but the less also is the freedom of movement and the opportunity to meet everyone in it. This analogy applies to reacting substances, and for most reactions there is an optimum concentration, where the number of particles present provides opportunity enough for them to mix and to meet but is not great enough to retard or prevent their free movement. Up to this optimum concentration, in general the rate of reactions—that is, the time that it takes to come to completion or to equilibrium—increases with concentration.

In living organisms, most substances are present in low concentrations, as dilute solutions, and the range of concentration lies between narrow limits. The maintenance of this physiological range within the organism, that is, the maintenance of the range at which it functions most effectively or indeed functions at all, is one of the most amazing and the most delicately adjusted of the manifestations of the activity of protoplasm.

### Temperature

Since heat is a form of energy, it is clear that it not only may initiate reactions but also influence the rate at which they proceed. Temperature is, in fact, only a concept of the velocity of atomic and molecular motion, and a temperature scale the expression of that velocity in relative terms indicated by points on the scale. The point at which the motion of molecules and of the atoms within them is at a minimum is known as the absolute zero, and at this point their effective motion, as far as the possibility of their combination or disintegration goes, is at an end. Rise in temperature is an indication of increase in movement of the molecules of a gas, a liquid or a solid and an increase in the rate of oscillation of their constituent atoms. In most cases this leads to an increase in the possibilities of their rearrangement. An absolute temperature scale, with the end point of effective molecular motion at zero, was derived mathematically by Lord Kelvin from evidence of the behavior of gases under different experimental conditions. Three points on Lord Kelvin's scale, or the Å scale—the boiling point of water, the freezing point of water and absolute zero—have the following relations to the same points on the ordinary Centigrade and Fahrenheit scales shown in Figure 4.5.

In general, reactions go twice as fast for every ten-degree rise in temperature; that is, a reaction that would take an hour to go to completion at 20°C will be completed in half an hour at 30°C. Again, the temperature adjustment of the reactions of the living organism is delicate and falls within narrow limits, not because of the reaction itself but because protoplasm undergoes destructive physical changes at temperatures above or below its physiological range. This range falls between 0°C, or slightly below,

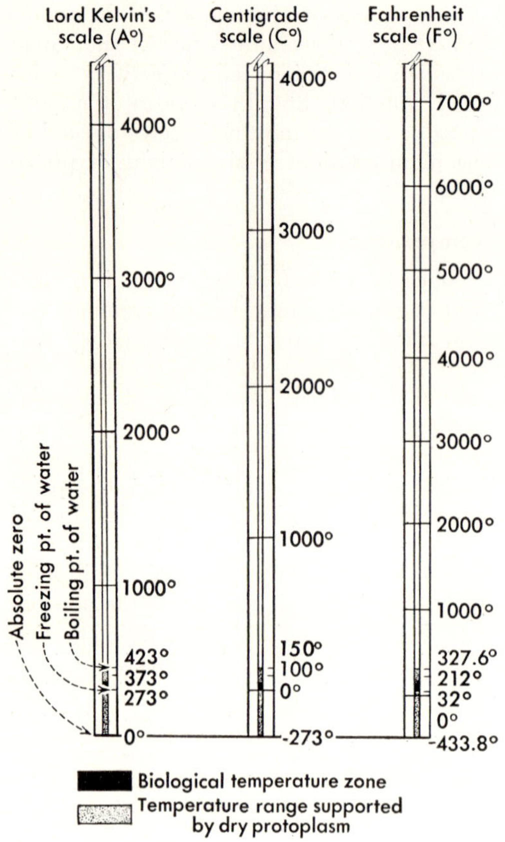

FIGURE 4.5 The three temperature scales, showing the relative positions of absolute zero, the freezing point of water and the boiling point of water on each. The biological temperature zone is shown in solid black; the range of temperature tolerated by dry protoplasm is stippled. (After Bělehrádek.)

and 41°–42°C, although some organisms have been known to resist higher and lower temperatures for periods of varying duration. Certain bacteria and the seeds of some plants, as well as some animals which can undergo and withstand dehydration, have survived and again become active after exposures, sometimes prolonged, to temperatures above and below these limits. In those circumstances, however, the organism is in a state of suspended activity, and the generalization is still true that within the limits set by the properties of living matter—and these limits are very close and on the cold end of the scale in relation to astronomical and physical temperatures—biological reactions follow, as one would expect them to do, the temperature laws of chemical reactions in general.

**Catalysts**

Catalysts are substances which are not included in the end product of a reaction but whose presence accelerates its rate. Many different kinds of substances catalyze different reactions. Water, for example, catalyzes, among many other reactions, the oxidation of iron. Although in contact with air, which contains oxygen, iron when perfectly dry combines very slowly with it. Wet iron on the other hand oxidizes rapidly, a reaction which can easily be detected by the presence of rust, the common name for iron oxide, on nails or other iron objects exposed to rain or dew. Biological catalysts are called enzymes, the word being derived from two Greek ones meaning "in leaven" (en = in + zyme = leaven), since the first recognized instance of a biological catalyst at work was the effect of a yeast extract upon sugar. The suffix *ase* on a word usually indicates that it acts as an enzyme in biological reactions; thus the enzyme first extracted from yeast cells is called zymase, oxidase is the general term for the class of substances that catalyze oxidation-reduction reactions, carbohydrase for the class that accelerates the disintegration of the carbon compounds known as carbohydrates, and so on. As a general rule, enzymes, like other catalysts, do not bring about reactions that would not otherwise occur, but they increase enormously the rate at which they proceed. The way that they cooperate in biological reactions, as the way other catalysts may cooperate in those that occur in the non-living world, is not as yet clearly understood, and different ones may work in different ways. In a reaction that proceeds by a series of steps, the catalyst may combine temporarily with an intermediate compound, and so make it more reactive, or it may serve as a surface upon which reactive ions are held, or adsorbed, so presenting a relatively wide area of them to other ions. It may provide energy in some way, and in oxidation-reduction reactions, may act as a temporary recipient of electrons which will ultimately be passed on to the oxygen atom.

Some catalysts, inside the organism as outside it, act not as accelerators but as inhibitors of reactions. This is perhaps particularly important in biological systems, for metabolism is a delicately balanced set of reactions whose adjustment both in rate and in degree is set for the maintenance of a certain level or range. If this adjustment is upset even to a slight extent, the result may be dangerous, even fatal, to the organism.

### Chemical equilibrium

Reactions may go through to completion, that is, until all the atoms or molecules present have made their appropriate combinations, or they may proceed until equilibrium is reached, a point at which the end product is breaking down into its components as fast as it is formed from them. The reaction between sodium chloride and silver nitrate illustrates the first kind of reaction,

$$NaCl + AgNO_3 \rightarrow AgCl + NaNO_3$$

where the silver chloride, being insoluble in water, precipitates out as soon as it is formed. Ultimately, depending on the rate of the reaction, practically all the silver and chloride ions will be removed from the solution, leaving only sodium and nitrate ions and a few silver and chloride ions, but so few that their effect is negligible for any further reaction. There has then been an almost total shift or exchange of ions between the two substances originally brought together.

The second condition is illustrated by the behavior of carbon dioxide, a product that is constantly being formed in living organisms, when it is dissolved in water, where the two substances unite molecule for molecule to form carbonic acid, $H_2CO_3$.

$$CO_2 + H_2O \rightarrow H_2CO_3$$

This equation does not completely express what is taking place, because carbonic acid is unstable and tends to decompose into its component carbon dioxide and water. When the $CO_2$ is first added to the water, the combination of the two molecules into one of carbonic acid begins at once; after a certain amount of the compound has been formed, however, it begins to break down and to return carbon dioxide and water molecules to the solution. The reaction then is really a double, or reversible one, and can best be shown by placing double arrows between the reagents on the left and the end product on the right of the equation to indicate that both processes are going on simultaneously.

$$CO_2 + H_2O \leftrightarrows H_2CO_3$$

At some time a stage will be reached when just as many carbon dioxide and water molecules are combining together to form carbonic acid as there are molecules of carbonic acid breaking down into carbon dioxide and water. The reaction then, as far as the accumulation of any end products goes, is at a standstill, and this point, when the reaction on the left of the arrows is proceeding at the same rate as that on the right, represents chemical equilibrium. The two reactions are balancing each other; as far as any change in the quantities of the end products produced is concerned, they cancel each other out.

Some substances reach equilibrium in their reactions sooner than others, and in every case the point at which equilibrium is reached changes with changed conditions. Among other things, temperature and a greater concentration of one or the other reagent will shift the point of equilibrium so that more or less of the new compound will be formed before it begins to break up again.

### Carbon fixation by biological systems

Of all chemical reactions the most fundamental is that performed only by green plants and some few bacteria—the union of the carbon dioxide of the air with water to make glucose, a sugar with the molecular formula $C_6H_{12}O_6$. This is a highly endothermic reaction; as it takes place in green plants, the sun furnishes the energy and chlorophyll, the pigment that gives them their distinctive color, acts as a catalyst. This is the only way in which solar energy is trapped and converted into potential energy. The bacteria which lack chlorophyll make use of chemical energy, instead of light, to bring about a similar reaction. This synthesis has never yet been reproduced in vitro, nor have years of research made clear the steps by which it is carried out, although van Helmont's experiments nearly three hundred years ago showed that plants were factories for the manufacture of the substances of life. The willow shoot he planted increased its mass some forty times from material in the air about its leaves and water around its roots. It has been proved, however, that the chlorophyll in the leaves of plants, and the pigments of some bacteria, can absorb certain rays of the visible light of the sun, and that the cells of the plant can use this energy to bring about the combination of the elements of two inorganic compounds, water and carbon dioxide, into an organic one. It is in consequence of this synthesis, carried on through the ages since the earth became habitable by living organisms, that there are the deposits of coal and oil in the surface of the earth that are so valuable to man's existence and economy, and that carbon, one of the most important of the elements biologically, is kept in circulation and not lost after its oxidation in the plant and animal body.

The calculated amount of energy required for the formation of 1 mole of glucose is in the neighborhood of 673,000 calories, which means that this amount of radiant kinetic energy is stored as potential energy in the glucose molecule, if none has been lost in the process of synthesis, and should be released when the molecule is decomposed. When glucose is burned in a calorimeter, the end products are carbon dioxide and water, and heat to the amount of 673,000 calories for every mole of glucose burned. The decomposition of glucose is therefore an exothermic reaction, and is one that goes on continually in plants and animals, providing them with some of the energy that they need for metabolism, growth and their other manifestations of life. The energy exchange represented by these two reactions

$$\text{Endothermic } 6CO_2 + 6H_2O + \underbrace{\text{Energy} \equiv 673{,}000 \text{ cals.}}_{\text{(absorbed from sunlight by chlorophyll of green plants)}} \to C_6H_{12}O_6 + 6O_2$$

$$\text{Exothermic } C_6H_{12}O_6 + 6O_2 \to 6CO_2 + 6H_2O + \text{Energy} \equiv 673{,}000 \text{ cals.}$$

is constantly going on all over the earth and must have been going on for a long time on the geological time scale. If solar energy ever becomes unavailable, life as we know it now with all its multiplicity of diversified forms will cease as soon as the potential energy already stored is used up.

Since the synthesis of glucose by the green plant is dependent upon light, it is known as photosynthesis. Some bacteria, as well as green plants, can photosynthesize and some can also make carbon compounds independent of light by chemosynthesis, using chemical rather than solar energy to bring about the disintegration and recombination of atoms and molecules. The synthesis of organic compounds in this way is also constantly going on, although not on as grand a scale as photosynthesis, for the chemosynthesizing bacteria are not as numerous nor as widely distributed as are green plants. But in these two ways, by photosynthesis and by chemosynthesis, carbon present in the air as carbon dioxide and undoubtedly present as such in the first atmosphere that surrounded the earth in its cooling off, is made into compounds that not only provide energy for the maintenance of life but are also the foundations of its material basis.

CHAPTER 5 — CARBON AND ITS COMPOUNDS

*Properties of the carbon atom*

Carbon occupies a peculiar position among the other elements both chemically and biologically. It forms a great number of compounds, so many indeed that a branch of chemistry, organic chemistry, is devoted entirely to their study. Nearly half a million organic compounds have already been analyzed and characterized, some of which are made exclusively by living organisms and many of which contribute to the structure of plants and animals or are used in their metabolism, for all of them contain a store of potential energy which can be set free in their exothermic reactions and used to do a large share of the work perpetually going on in biological systems.

**Valence and combining power**

The atomic number of carbon is 6 and 4 of its electrons lie in its outer energy level; it therefore has no special tendency to lose or to gain electrons and forms its compounds by sharing rather than by exchanging them. Knowing its structure, its valence and its position in the Periodic Table, one could then predict that it would combine with hydrogen and chlorine in the ratio of 1:4, and with oxygen in the ratio of 1:2, but that it would not combine directly with sodium, magnesium and similar elements. $CH_4$ is methane, or marsh gas; $CCl_4$ is a liquid, carbon tetrachloride, which dissolves fats and so is frequently used as a cleaning fluid; $CO_2$ is the gas, carbon dioxide, formed as one of the final products of the complete combustion of carbon compounds. In these substances, the atoms are held together in molecules by the electrons they share; such a bond is a relatively strong one, and is known as a covalent bond. In this kind of arrangement the atoms of the combining substances achieve a high degree of electronic stability. In the compound methane, for example, the four gaps in the outer shell of the carbon atom are filled by the electrons of the 4 hydrogen atoms so that the carbon atom has the stability of the neon atom, and each hydrogen atom achieves the structure of helium, for one of the four outer electrons of the carbon atom becomes incorporated in its electron system. The union of 2 hydrogen atoms into a molecule of hydrogen is the same kind of covalent bonding, and molecules of this kind are themselves stable and do not dissociate into ions. Such a combination unites more readily with other substances than one in which the carbon atoms are united by a single bond and their remaining valences satisfied by univalent atoms.

**Carbon chains and rings**

Carbon atoms, united to each other by single or double bonds, form the basis or backbone of the very large molecules found in, and produced by, living organisms. A chain of 6 forms the framework of the molecule of the sugar glucose, for this reason called a hexose, from the Greek "hexos," or six, and a ring of 6 the framework for a molecule of benzene.

Ring of 6

—C—C—C—C—C—C—
Chain of 6

In the chain of 6, the terminal carbon atoms have but one valence satisfied; the other four have 2. In the ring configuration, all six carbon atoms have still two valences to fill to bring the number of electrons in the outer energy level to 8. These unsatisfied valences may be filled with univalent atoms, like hydrogen, or by bivalent atoms, like oxygen, forming a double bond, or the carbon atoms themselves may be united by double bonds. Or a radical, perhaps another ring or a chain, may be attached so that large and complicated atomic groupings may be built up.

Because of the many possibilities in arrangement of their constituent atoms, carbon compounds are frequently represented by their "structural" as well as their molecular formulae, since in this way the relations of the carbon atoms to each other, and the positions of the other atoms or radicals attached to them can be shown. The structural formula for glucose, for example, is

$$
\begin{array}{c}
\text{H} \quad \text{OH} \\
\diagdown \diagup \\
\text{C} \\
| \\
\text{H---C---OH} \\
| \\
\text{HO---C---H} \qquad \text{O} \\
| \\
\text{H---C---OH} \\
| \\
\text{H---C---} \\
| \\
\text{CH}_2\text{OH}
\end{array}
$$

which shows that the six carbon atoms are joined in a chain bent into a ring by the bonding of one oxygen atom with one terminal carbon atom and with the subterminal carbon atom at the opposite end, and that the remaining valences of the carbon atoms are satisfied by hydrogen atoms and hydroxyl radicals (Fig. 5.1$b$). The structural formula for benzene, $C_6H_6$, is

$$
\begin{array}{c}
\text{H} \\
| \\
\text{C} \\
\diagup \diagdown \\
\text{H---C} \qquad \text{C---H} \\
|| \qquad || \\
\text{H---C} \qquad \text{C---H} \\
\diagdown \diagup \\
\text{C} \\
| \\
\text{H}
\end{array}
$$

which shows the ring configuration and the position of the hydrogen atoms in relation to the carbon atoms.

## Structural formulae of carbon compounds

Structural formulae, which are derived by a series of complicated chemical processes, also make it possible to distinguish between two compounds which have the same number of carbon atoms and the same number and kind of other atoms attached to them. For instance, glucose and fructose, the two sugars most frequently found in nature, are both hexoses with 6 carbon atoms, 12 hydrogen atoms and 6 oxygen atoms. Both therefore have the same molecular formula, $C_6H_{12}O_6$. Determinations of the structure of their molecules show, however, that the hydrogen and oxygen atoms are arranged differently in respect to the carbon atoms, and their structural formulae make this clear.

$$
\begin{array}{cc}
\begin{array}{c}
\text{H} \quad \text{OH} \\
\diagdown \diagup \\
\text{C} \\
| \\
\text{H---C---OH} \\
| \\
\text{HO---C---H} \qquad \text{O} \\
| \\
\text{H---C---OH} \\
| \\
\text{H---C---} \\
| \\
\text{CH}_2\text{OH} \\
\text{Glucose}
\end{array}
&
\begin{array}{c}
\text{CH}_2\text{OH} \\
| \\
\text{C---} \\
| \\
\text{HO---C---H} \\
| \\
\text{H---C---OH} \qquad \text{O} \\
| \\
\text{H---C---OH} \\
| \\
\text{H}_2\text{C---} \\
\text{Fructose}
\end{array}
\end{array}
$$

### Isomers

Although having the same atoms in the same proportions, these two sugars have different characteristics and chemical properties, as would be expected from the different groupings of their atoms. Such compounds, with the same molecular, but different structural, formulae are known as isomers, that is, having equal or similar parts. Many such isomers are found in nature, differing enough in their chemical properties to have different biological effects.

### Biosynthesis of carbon compounds

The carbon compounds made by living organisms are divided into three great groups, the carbohydrates, the fats and the proteins, distinct in their physical as well as in their chemical properties but all alike biologically in at least the one respect that they are sources of energy for the organism. Carbohydrates and proteins contribute to its structure as well, but even these structural compounds may be burned by the organism to obtain the necessary energy for its metabolism if it cannot obtain a sufficient supply from its environment.

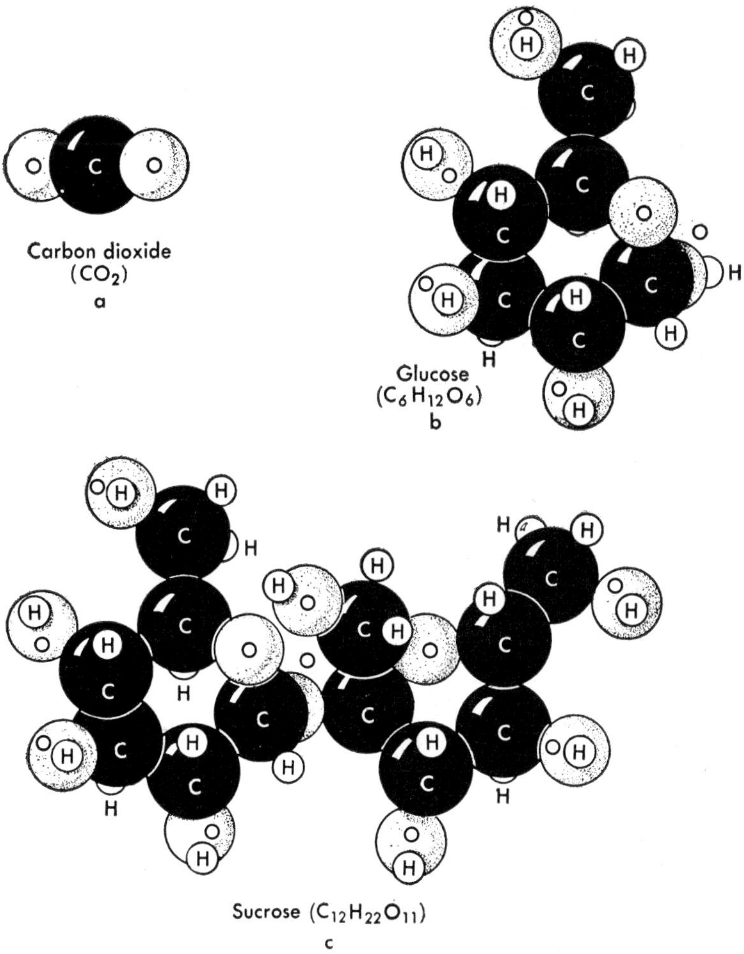

oxygen atom per molecule. The common carbohydrates are starches and sugars, and the simplest of these are hexoses like glucose and fructose, which have a framework of 6 carbon atoms in a chain. In the larger molecules, two or more such chains are united into a longer one of 12, 18, 24 or more carbon atoms. When such a combination is made, two of the terminal carbon atoms of the two hexoses join through an oxygen atom, releasing as they do so one oxygen and two hydrogen atoms which unite to form a molecule of water. This reaction is one of union and disunion. Each

FIGURE 5.1 Models showing the arrangement of atoms in (a) a molecule of carbon dioxide, (b) a molecule of glucose and (c) a molecule of cane sugar. Carbon atoms are represented by black spheres, oxygen atoms by stippled ones and hydrogen atoms by clear ones.

### Carbohydrates

All of the carbohydrates contain carbon, hydrogen and oxygen, and many of them contain these elements in the ratio of one carbon atom to two hydrogen atoms to one

molecule of the sugar made by the sugar cane plant, for example, which refined is ordinary table sugar, is composed of one molecule of fructose and one of glucose joined in this way, so that its molecular formula is $C_{12}H_{22}O_{11}$ (Fig. 5.1c). The combination is represented by the following equation:

$$C_6H_{12}O_6 + C_6H_{12}O_6 \rightarrow C_{12}H_{22}O_{11} + H_2O$$

The hexoses, which are the building blocks for the larger molecules, are called monosaccharides; cane sugar, made of two such building blocks, is a disaccharide and the higher sugars and starches, made of many, are polysaccharides. A molecule of starch formed in the plant or animal body and composed of many hexose molecules linked together end to end may be relatively enormous compared, for example, to a molecule of carbon dioxide (Fig. 5.1a).

**Fats**

Fats are compounds with certain distinct and well-known physical properties. Some of them are solid at ordinary temperatures, some of them are liquid and none of them will dissolve in or mix with water. The first analyses of fat yielded carbon, hydrogen and oxygen, but in proportions different from those of the carbohydrate molecule. As chemical knowledge of this class of compounds has progressed, it has been found that other elements may be included in their molecules and that even the simpler ones show great diversity of structure and composition. The term fat has now become generally restricted to one category of substances, the true fats and oils in the general class of lipoids, or lipids, a word derived from the Greek word lipos, meaning fat. This more general term includes the true fats, compounds with a common structural pattern but great variety in the radicals that compose them, as well as all related substances found and formed in the living organism, but excludes the mineral oils, such as petroleum and its derivatives.

The common pattern of the structure of true fats is a molecule of glycerol, to which are attached fatty acid chains. Glycerol, or glycerine, is made up of a string of 3 carbon atoms to which hydrogen atoms and hydroxyl radicals are attached (Fig. 5.2). Its structural formula is:

$$\begin{array}{c} H \\ | \\ H-C-OH \\ | \\ H-C-OH \\ | \\ H-C-OH \\ | \\ H \end{array}$$

Fatty acids, like carbohydrates, have a backbone of carbon atoms joined in a chain, with one of the terminal carbons bound with one hydrogen and two oxygen atoms in the configuration $\begin{array}{c} C-OH \\ \| \\ O \end{array}$. This configuration is called the carboxyl group, or carboxyl radical, and its presence in any compound gives it the properties of an acid. There is a multitude of different kinds of fatty acids, for they may vary not only in the number of carbon atoms of which they are composed, but also in the union of these carbon atoms, whether by single or by double bonds, and in the number and relation of the hydrogen and oxygen atoms whose electrons they share. Chains with 3 up to 30 carbon atoms are known, and the number may go even higher, but palmitic acid, with a chain of 16 ($C_{15}H_{31}COOH$), and stearic ($C_{17}H_{35}COOH$), with a chain of 18, are the ones most frequently found in the fats of living organisms.

The general formula for true fats then is

$$\begin{array}{c} H \\ | \\ H-C-OOC-R \\ | \\ H-C-OOC-R \\ | \\ H-C-OOC-R \\ | \\ H \end{array}$$

where R stands for the fatty acid chain, joined to the molecule of glycerol by its carboxyl group. Every possible kind of combination of three fatty acids may be represented in this grouping, so that there is a huge, almost infinite, number of different kinds of fat.

Waxes are also included among the lipids

and are built on the same general pattern as the fats, except that the molecule to which the fatty acids are attached is not glycerol but a related carbon compound. Included also are some very complex substances called compound lipids, in which a lipid molecule is attached to one of a different class of compounds, as well as their derivatives, or products of partial disintegration, and those of the fats and waxes.

Lipids do not include the mineral oils, which are not directly of plant or animal origin, but they do include substances of such different qualities and diverse origin as cottonseed, linseed, olive, castor, whale and cod-liver oil, butter, lard and margarine, spermaceti, tallow, bayberry and beeswax, and lecithin, the fat of egg yolk, found also in all cells and probably a structural component of protoplasm, as well as of Vitamin D, and other substances of great biological importance (see pages 450–451).

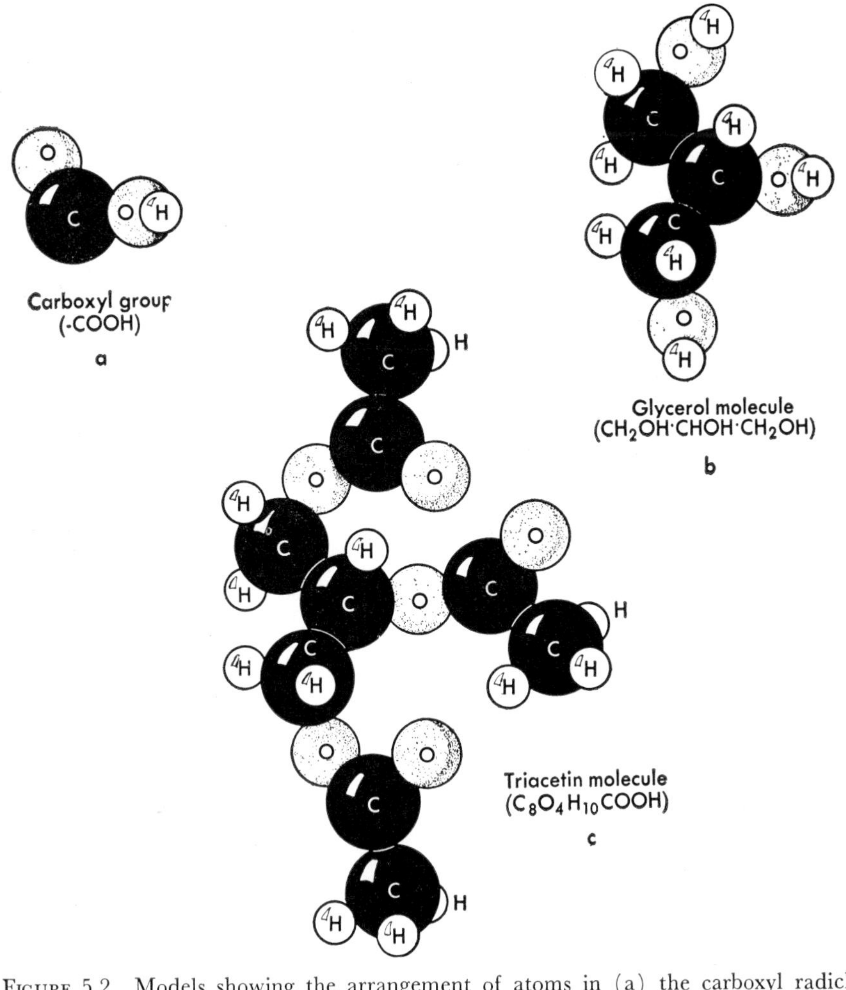

FIGURE 5.2  Models showing the arrangement of atoms in (a) the carboxyl radicle, (b) a molecule of glycerol and (c) a molecule of a simple fat, triacetin. Triacetin, consisting of three molecules of acetic acid ($CH_3COOH$) linked to one of glycerol, is not made by biological systems but can be synthesized in vitro.

Carboxyl group (-COOH)
a

Glycerol molecule ($CH_2OH \cdot CHOH \cdot CH_2OH$)
b

Triacetin molecule ($C_8O_4H_{10}COOH$)
c

### Proteins

Larger and more complicated in the arrangement of their constituent atoms are the molecules of the proteins. The word "protein" means that which is of first or prime importance, and the proteins are in every sense of first or prime importance biologically. They are found only in protoplasm and its products; nowhere in the universe has the presence of protein been detected or suspected except in relation to a living

*Amino acids as building blocks of proteins:* The building blocks of protein molecules are amino acids, which always contain a carboxyl group, –COOH, and an amino group, –$NH_2$, attached to the carbon atom before the carboxyl group (Fig. 5.3a). One

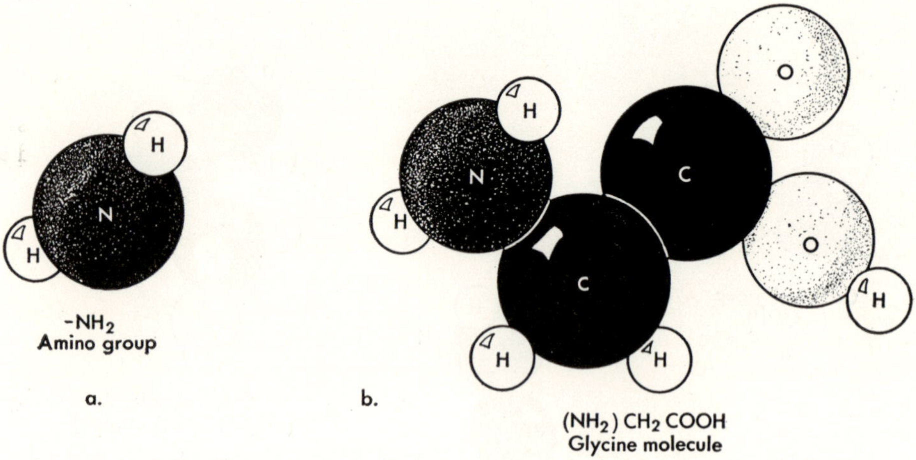

FIGURE 5.3 Models showing the arrangement of atoms in (a) the amino group ($NH_2$), characteristic of proteins, and (b) in a molecule of glycine ($NH_2CH_2COOH$), derived from acetic acid ($CH_3COOH$) by the substitution of an amino radicle for one of the hydrogen atoms in the $CH_3$ group.

thing. Where life does not exist or has not existed, protein does not exist; the whole series of phenomena which make up life are associated with and dependent upon the particular associations and arrangements of atoms which make up the molecules of the different kinds of protein. These molecules form the basis of protoplasm.

Proteins differ in their composition from fats and carbohydrates essentially in the presence of nitrogen in their molecules as well as the carbon, hydrogen and oxygen common to all three. Some proteins contain sulphur and phosphorus as well, but all contain nitrogen. Like the higher sugars and the starches and the fats and oils, proteins are built up from simpler molecules, or building blocks. And like the more complex lipids, the final molecule may be relatively enormous, hundreds, even thousands of atoms included in it. Protein molecules are known which have a mass 35,000 times greater than that of a molecule of hydrogen; there may be some with masses millions of times greater.

of the simplest of the amino acids is alanine, with the structural formula:

$$\begin{array}{c} \text{H} \quad \text{H} \\ | \quad\;\; | \\ \text{H—C—C—COOH} \\ | \quad\;\; | \\ \text{H} \quad NH_2 \end{array}$$

As a group they may be represented by the general structural formula:

$$\begin{array}{c} \text{H} \\ | \\ \text{R—C—COOH} \\ | \\ \text{N} \\ | \\ H_2 \end{array}$$

where R stands for a wide variety of carbon compounds—chains and chains linked to chains, rings and rings linked to chains and rings, with every kind of atom or configuration of atoms replacing, or substituted for, the hydrogen atom bound to the carbons in the ordinary carbohydrate or fatty acid molecule. For example, thyroxin, an amino acid that can be extracted from the thyroid gland and which is responsible for the biological potency of its secretion, has the more elaborate structure of two rings of carbon atoms, in which iodine is substituted for the hydrogen attached to two of those in each ring and the two rings linked to the first carbon atom in a chain of three:

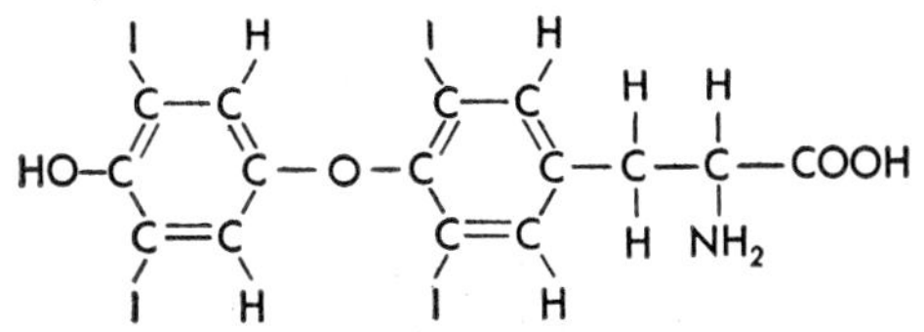

$$HO-\underset{\underset{H}{|}}{\overset{\overset{H}{|}}{\underset{C=C}{\overset{C-C}{\diagdown}}}}\!\!\!\!\!\!\!\!\!\!\!\!\!\!\!\!\!\!C-O-\underset{\underset{H}{|}}{\overset{\overset{H}{|}}{\underset{C=C}{\overset{C-C}{\diagdown}}}}\!\!\!\!\!\!\!\!\!\!\!\!\!\!\!\!\!\!C-\underset{H}{\overset{H}{C}}-\underset{NH_2}{\overset{H}{C}}-COOH$$

About forty different amino acids of natural origin have been identified and their structure determined; some of these have been made artificially in the laboratory. Only twenty-three of them, however, are definitely known to be building blocks of protein, but these twenty-three may be joined in so many different combinations that the number of possible protein molecules is enormous and almost defies the imagination. The number and complexity of the possible protein molecules has indeed so far defied the skill of the chemist, for relatively few of them have been completely

uniform and presumably static protein substance like silk or hair is exposed to such a stream of particles, or of radiation, the "solid" regions of the molecule deflect its components from their straight course, and so an image or a photograph can be obtained from which the pattern of the atoms in the molecule can sometimes be deduced. Both fibroin, the protein of silk, and keratin, the protein of hair, nails, horns, and baleen, or whalebone, among many other things, are fibrous in character. Studies of the structure of silk have shown that this is because it is made of long chain-molecules collected together into bundles, or micelles, far beyond the range of vision even with the highest powers of the microscope. The chain-molecules are made of amino acids, perhaps several hundred of them linked together end to end in such a way that the central axis, or backbone, of the molecule is not a straight, but a zigzag line, which lies roughly parallel to the long axis of the fibre. In fibroin, most of the amino acids in the chain molecules are glycine and alanine, to which radicals, as side chains, are attached. The backbone of the molecular chain of fibroin appears to be like this:

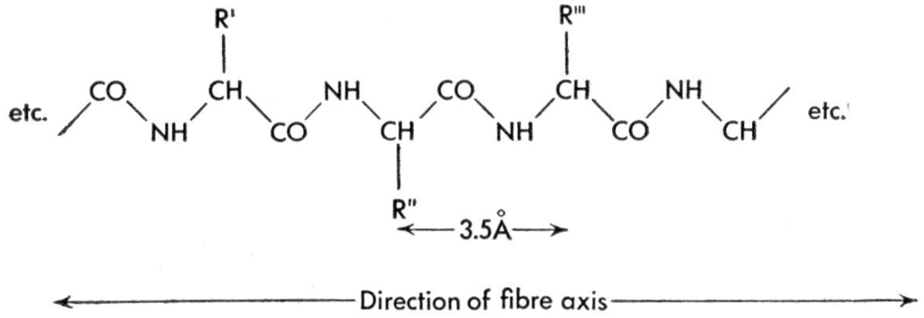

FIGURE 5.4 Diagram showing the "backbone" of the molecular chain of silk fibroin. (After Astbury.)

analyzed and none has been reproduced in vitro.

**Structure of protein molecules:** Both radioactive elements and X-rays have been useful in determinations of the structure of protein molecules. Experimentally, a stream of electrons from a radioactive substance, or a beam of the electromagnetic radiations known as X-rays, can be made to pass through protein substances. When a solid,

with the residue, or what remains of the molecule of glycine or alanine after it has lost some atoms in making combinations into the larger molecule, occupying a measurable extent along the axis of the fibre. This distance is measured in Ångstrom units, first used by the Swedish physicist A. H. Ångstrom (1814–1874) in measuring the wave lengths of light. One Ångstrom unit is equal to one hundred millionth of a centimeter, i.e., $1\text{Å} = 1 \times 10^{-8}$ cm. With different circumstances, the angles between the residues may be smaller, for the chain is capable of extension or of contraction by folding; it represents a kind of molecular spring. The length of each residue in the fibroin chain when fully extended is about 3½ Ångstrom units, or approximately $3½ \times 10^{-8}$ centimeters (0.0000000035 cm.).

In keratin, and probably in many other proteins, several such chain-molecules are linked together by their side chains, so that each molecule in the micelle has more or less the pattern of a grid. The framework of such a complex molecule, containing many amino acid residues, is like this:

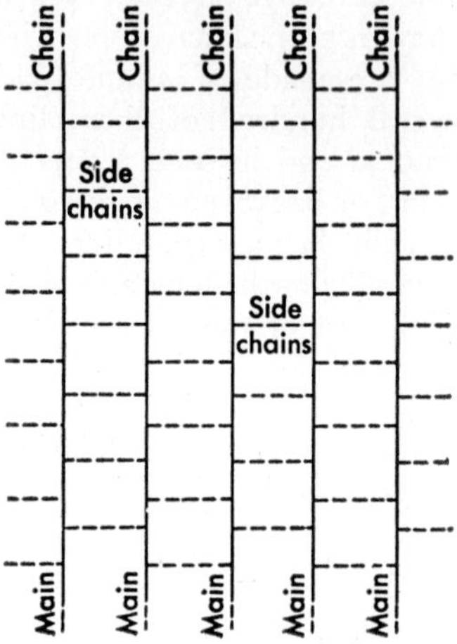

FIGURE 5.5 Diagram showing the framework of a keratin molecule with the main chains held together by side chains, actually of different lengths rather than similar ones as represented in the diagram. The ordinary, or contracted, form of the molecule can be visualized by visualizing the main chains, at right angles to the side chains, regularly folded in such a way that the troughs and crests are parallel to the side chains. (After Astbury.)

It, too, is capable of extension and compression, and presumably is folded in such a way that the troughs and the crests of the folds are parallel to the side chains. This folding probably represents a compromise between the intramolecular stresses and strains, for the side chains are of different lengths and so also are the amino acid residues forming the main molecular chain. Fifteen different amino acids have been isolated from the keratin of hair, and the long chains along the main axis of its molecules parallel to the main axis of the micelle and of the fibre, must therefore be made of units of unequal length.

It is in this folding, and the capacity to unfold, of the protein molecules that a reasonable explanation for the elasticity of fibrous proteins can be found. If the folded condition is that of their equilibrium, they can only be straightened out by the application of force. All protoplasm possesses a certain degree of elasticity; this property is developed to its maximum in certain specialized cells, the muscle cells of organisms. X-ray photographs of muscle show a similar fibrous structure of its proteins; these protein molecules can be deformed by electrical and mechanical force but they can resume their natural shape, the arrangement of equilibrium, by controlled interactions with ions and smaller molecules. This kind of deformation and readjustment goes on in the contraction and subsequent relaxation of muscle cells.

The size of protein molecules has been estimated in various ways, and some of the larger compound, or conjugated, ones have been photographed by means of the electron microscope, which by magnetic focussing of a beam of electrons, can magnify objects from 20,000 to 100,000 times. The viruses, causing diseases in both plants and animals such as the tobacco mosaic diseases, human influenza, poliomyelitis and the common cold, are compound proteins called nucleoproteins, for each virus particle is made up of a large protein molecule linked to another almost equally complex one of a nucleic acid. Electron microscope photographs show that different viruses differ in size and in shape, although the larger ones at least may be aggregates of virus particles rather than single ones. The tobacco mosaic virus, for example, has been shown by this means to be an infinitesimal rod, with a transverse diameter of about 15 millimicra and a length of about 330 millimicra, or about 0.0000015 cm. and 0.000033 cm. respectively. Other viruses are smaller and spherical with diameters of 8–12 millimicra. They are therefore invisible with even the highest magnifications of the ordinary microscope, and most of them are able to pass through the spaces of an ordinary filter which will hold back even the smallest of the bacteria.

***Physical properties of protein molecules:*** The physical properties of the proteins are largely the consequences of the great size of their molecules. These diffuse slowly, and because of this they can be separated by physical means from smaller and more mobile molecules. The chemical properties of the proteins are determined by the amino acids that compose them. They differ in the readiness with which they can be denatured, that is, in which a change may take place in the molecule, but all of them show a considerable degree of instability. Because the molecule is so large, and because there are so many free ends of the radicals that terminate its main or its side chains, a protein can make a number of chemical combinations simultaneously, and similarly can release a number of different ions from different parts of the molecule. The protein molecule then becomes an ion itself, but if it has set free, as it may do, cations from one end and anions from the other, it is negatively charged at one end and positively charged at the other, and so is bipolar, not as a water molecule is because of asymmetry in its electrons, but because of its size and the number and kinds of ions it can release (Fig. 5.6).

Proteins in solution can be precipitated out by heat as well as by chemical agents, and some can be coagulated, or the whole mass of the solution solidified, by similar means. Egg white, for example, contains proteins, principally albumen; its change, when heated, from a translucent, viscous fluid to an opaque white solid is an everyday phenomenon. When milk sours its protein, casein, is coagulated by the acids produced by bacteria in it and precipitates out of the solution leaving the watery whey. A similar physical change can be brought about by the addition of a mineral acid, like hydrochloric or sulphuric, to milk.

***Biological properties of protein molecules:*** Biologically, protein molecules are the basic ones of protoplasmic organization. As organized groups within cells they carry on, and to a great extent must direct, the orderly and regular sequence of changes that go on in a protoplasmic system which result in its destruction, its repair and its

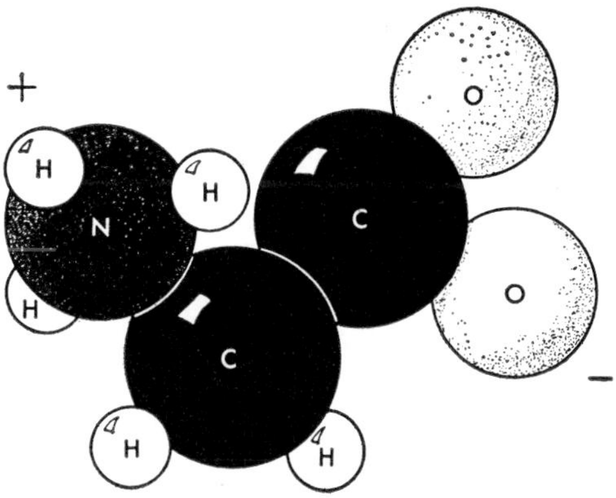

FIGURE 5.6 Model of a di-polar glycine ion. When glycine is dissolved in water, it changes from an uncharged molecule to a charged one. This change may take place through the shift in position of a hydrogen atom from the carboxyl group to the amino group, one end of the molecule thus becoming positively charged, the other negatively charged. (After Amberson and Smith.)

renewal. Most remarkable of all is the capacity of some of them to reproduce themselves as individual units, a capacity definitely established for such nucleoproteins as viruses, bacteriophages (bacteria-destroying agents in cells and body fluids) and genes, the bearers of the hereditary material which is passed on from cell generation to cell generation and which determines the course through which characteristics will develop (see Chapter 25). The genes are known to be made of, or at least to contain, nucleoprotein, and they can duplicate themselves again and again and again and again, provided that the raw products and the energy necessary for so complex a synthesis are available.

The self-duplicating capacity of these protein molecules has raised again the old question of what is alive and what is not, what criteria shall be used to differentiate between what is living and what is non-living in the natural world. In 1935 an American chemist, W. M. Stanley (1904–    ), was able to extract and crystallize a protein from tobacco plants infected with the mosaic disease, which, when introduced in healthy plants, spread rapidly through their leaves and produced the typical morbid effects of mosaic disease. Although quiescent in their crystalline state, the virus molecules multiplied rapidly when in contact with the tissues of the plant. Is a crystalline protein in a bottle alive, or does it come alive only in a living environment, and if so, what is the change that comes over it? If it is not alive, is the capacity to reproduce themselves without their own destruction a property that should be attributed to living things alone or is it shared by objects in the physical world?

Behind such philosophical speculation lies the fundamental fact that the phenomena of life are always associated with protoplasm. The gene duplicates itself and exerts its effects only within the cell, the virus and the bacteriophage multiply only within the organism. None of them has been known, nor has any yet been caused, to reproduce itself except in protoplasm, nor has the presence of any been detected except through the effects it has produced upon a biological system.

***Biosynthesis of proteins:*** Plants are ultimately the source of all protein, as they are of all carbohydrate and indeed of almost all the energy available to all living things. That animals can make their own lipids and their own specific kind of fat from carbohydrate is evident every time one looks at a cow or a sheep or a horse grazing and remembers the amount and the kind of fat stored up in its muscles or beneath its skin. A similar kind of metamorphosis is going on in the human body when beef or mutton fat, or the fats and oils derived from plants, are converted into human fat. This transformation involves the disintegration of carbohydrate or fat molecules that were eaten and the rearrangement of the carbon, hydrogen and oxygen atoms in them into molecules of the fat typical of that particular animal, an elaborate and complicated series of energy changes. But the animal cannot perform the initial synthesis of carbon dioxide into glucose, although it can, and incessantly does, bring about its decomposition and liberation of its potential energy. Neither can an animal bring about the union of the amino group, $NH_2$, with a carbohydrate radical, the essential step in the formation of an amino acid. Plants, however, can make this synthesis, and so provide a starting point for the synthesis of proteins. Animals can build up the specific kinds of protein of their bodies from simpler molecules, just as they can build up carbohydrates and fat, but they are dependent upon plants for their supply of these simpler molecules, just as they are dependent upon them for their carbohydrate building blocks. And plants, in turn, are ultimately dependent upon the sun for the energy for carbohydrate synthesis; if man knew how this was done, and what other sources of energy might be used, he would have even greater control over the conditions of his existence than he now has.

# CHAPTER 6

# WATER AND SOLUTIONS

Proteins form the structural basis of living matter, but in solution rather than in solid form; solid proteins like hair, horns, claws and nails, are structures accessory to organisms and are relatively, though not entirely, static. Proteins dissolved in water together with simple and complex carbohydrates and some inorganic compounds are dynamic; they are protoplasm, and as such metabolize and live.

Water represents a large proportion of the mass of living things, for protoplasm itself has a high water content, and in the bodies of plants and animals composed of many cells, fluids circulate around and between the individual cells as tissue fluids, and may also, as blood and lymph in animals and sap in plants, be carried throughout the organism in special channels. Every cell lives in an aqueous environment, and the exchange of materials, from this environment to the cell for its metabolism and from the cell to the environment as products of its metabolism, takes place while they are in solution in water. Water is therefore vital to active cells; and the properties of water as a dissolving agent, and those of aqueous solutions, in general, are of the greatest importance biologically.

## *The properties of water*

The solvent properties of water are related to its molecular structure. Each molecule of ordinary water consists of two hydrogen atoms and one oxygen atom which have shared electrons. In this sharing the greatest number of electrons are near the oxygen nucleus, so that there is an accumulation of negative charges there, and the molecule is therefore electrically asymmetrical (Fig. 6.1a). It is said to be polarized, by analogy with magnets which have positive and negative poles, and it and similar compounds with asymmetrical or "bent" molecules are called polar compounds. Such electrical asymmetry tends to make the molecules clump together, negative poles attracting positive poles, and liquid water shows such molecular groupings, being made up actually not of isolated molecules but of groups of two or three or more. It is said to be polymerized, that is, its compound molecules are of many parts, and properly its molecular formula should be written $(H_2O)_2$, $(H_2O)_3$ and so on. Each molecule in the complex is complete, however, and bound to its neighbors by electrical forces that are intermolecular, rather than intramolecular as in the formation of new compounds.

Water at ordinary temperatures is a liquid, and its molecules and their polymers move of their own kinetic energy at random, in all planes and in all directions. If it is exposed to air, some of them are constantly leaving its surface and mingling with the molecules of oxygen, nitrogen, carbon dioxide and other atmospheric gases, and simultaneously, molecules of these gases are entering the surface layer of the water. As the water molecules leave the liquid, its volume becomes less and less and it gradually evaporates, that is, is converted to a gaseous state or vapor. This conversion can be hastened by increasing the kinetic energy of the water molecules; if energy as heat is added to liquid water, their movement is accelerated and the whole mass changed into water vapor or steam. In this state, the energy of the system can be, and in thousands of ways is, converted to mechanical energy and made to do useful work.

If, on the other hand, energy is removed

[43]

from liquid water, and the movement of its molecules slowed down, as can be done by cooling, liquid water is converted to its solid state, or ice. The hexagonal star pattern of all ice crystals, manifold as its variations may be, is an expression of the polarized enough to be visible. Solids are distinguished from each other as amorphous and crystalline, depending on whether or not their particles are irregularly arranged or whether they form a definite pattern. Rubber is an amorphous solid; it owes its elasticity to the

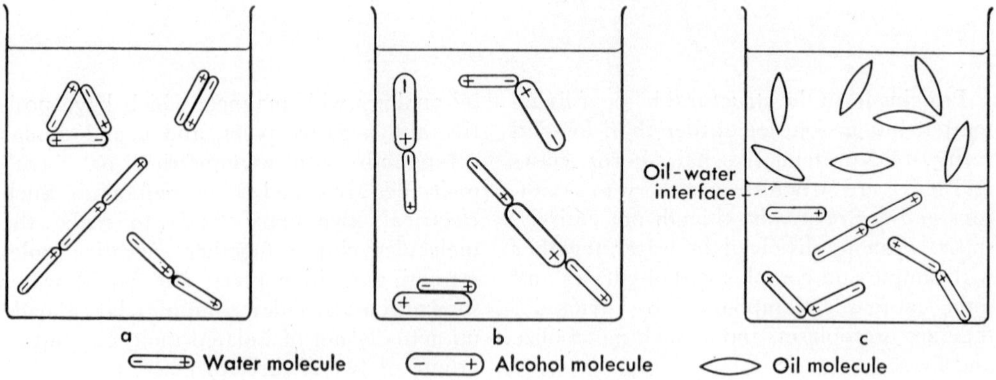

FIGURE 6.1 Diagrams showing the relations of polar and non-polar molecules to each other. (After Krauskopf.)

a. Aggregation of di-polar water molecules, held together in groups of two or three through electrostatic attraction of their oppositely charged poles.

b. Oppositely charged poles of di-polar water and di-polar alcohol molecules attract each other, and alcohol and water mix readily together.

c. There are no electrostatic forces of attraction between di-polar water molecules and non-polar oil molecules. The two liquids therefore do not mix when brought together, but separate into two layers with oil, whose specific gravity is lower than that of water, forming the upper layer.

state of the water molecules. As their movement slows, and at very low temperatures finally virtually ceases, the clumps of molecules remain closer and closer together, but always under the force of attraction of their opposite poles, so that the points of the star represent similarly charged poles of the molecular clumps which repel each other and so form a radiating rather than a compact solid.

## The properties of solids

All solids are physically distinguished from gases and liquids in that the attractive forces between the particles of which they are composed are stronger, so strong that the particles are no longer free to move about. Brownian movement therefore cannot be seen in a solid, for although its particles are in motion, their displacement is not great fact that its large molecules have no definite orientation, as have the protein molecules in the micelles of silk or hair, and spring back into their normal but irregular positions after stretching or compression. Salt is a crystalline solid, and X-ray studies of salt crystals have shown that they consist of alternate sodium ($Na^+$) and chlorine ($Cl^-$) ions, placed at definite distances from each other and, within limits, moving within the spaces of the lattice they compose (Fig. 6.2). The crystals of other ionic compounds are similarly formed of alternate positive and negative ions; the crystals of non-ionic, or covalent, compounds are formed of molecules, rather than ions but also in definite spatial relationships to each other. Many other solids which do not show an obvious crystalline structure have been found on X-ray analysis to have a regular molecular pattern, and similarly, under cer-

# WATER AND SOLUTIONS [45]

tain conditions, drops of fluid may be shown to have a crystalline structure, and hence are called "liquid crystals."

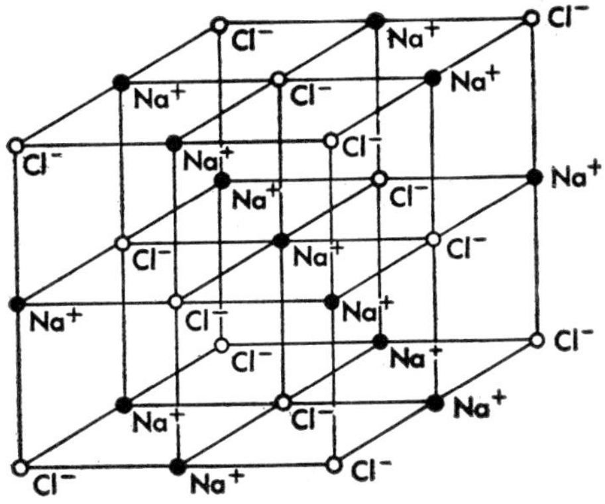

FIGURE 6.2 Diagram of a crystal of sodium chloride (NaCl), showing the arrangement of sodium ($Na^+$) and chlorine ($Cl^-$) ions in the crystal lattice. (After Cheronis, Parsons and Renneberg.)

## Dissolution of solids in water

The dissolving of a solid, like its breaking or its splitting, requires some force sufficient to offset the forces of attraction, or cohesion, which cause its molecules to stay close together and so maintain a solid state. When a substance, or solute, dissolves in water, as the solvent, this force is the electrical one between the poles of the water molecule and the ions of opposite charge of ionic compounds, or the opposite poles of polarized molecules of covalent compounds. When a crystal of sodium chloride is dropped into a vessel of water, the water molecules cluster around its surface, their negative poles attracted to the positive sodium ions ($Na^+$) and their positive poles to the negative chlorine ions ($Cl^-$) (Fig. 6.3). When enough water molecules have gathered around an ion to overcome the forces which bind it to the others in the crystal, their combined kinetic energies will make it break away and the ion surrounded by water molecules, or hydrated, will move around among the other water molecules. As the surface layer of ions is removed, the next will be exposed to the attractive forces of the water molecules, and gradually the crystal will be disintegrated and its ions evenly and equally distributed among the water molecules. The crystal is then said to be dissolved and the system in the vessel will be a solution of sodium chloride in water. Its properties will be neither those of pure water nor crystalline salt, but essentially those of the ions it contains.

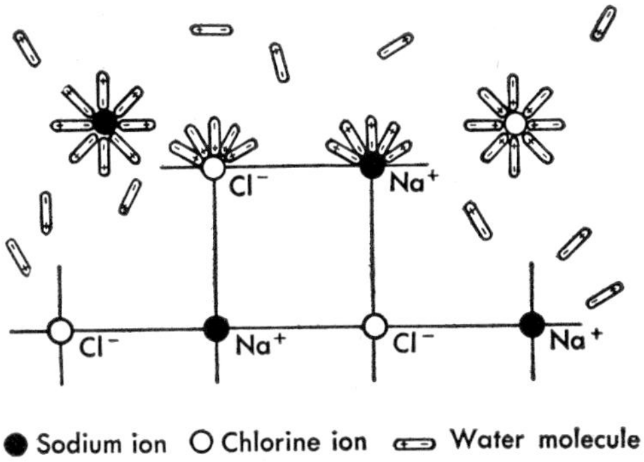

● Sodium ion ○ Chlorine ion ⊂⊃ Water molecule

FIGURE 6.3 Diagram of the dissolution of a crystal of sodium chloride in water. (After Krauskopf.) When a crystal of sodium chloride is dropped into water, the positive poles of the water molecules are attracted by the negatively charged chlorine ions in the crystal, and the negative poles by the positively charged sodium ions. When a sufficient number of water molecules have become attached to an ion in the crystal, their kinetic energy is sufficient to draw it away from the others, exposing those further within the lattice to the attractive forces of other water molecules. The figure shows a sodium ion and a chlorine ion that have become detached in this way and are moving among the rest of the water molecules as hydrated ions.

The same kind of thing happens with covalent, or non-ionic, compounds, if their molecules are asymmetrical, or polar. Sugars are such compounds because of their terminal $C = O$ group, and their hydroxyl groups
|
H
(OH), and readily dissolve in water. The units of sugar crystals are molecules instead of ions, but there is the same kind of attraction between the opposite poles of the sugar and water molecules as there is between the ions of the salt crystal and the water molecules. When a crystal of sugar is put into water, the sugar molecules will be gradually drawn apart, the crystal will break up and

the molecular mixture will have the properties of a sugar solution.

## Differences in solubilities of solids

Not all substances are equally soluble in water and some are insoluble. Among those that are soluble, there is a definite limit to the amount that will go into solution at any given temperature. At 20°C, for example, 100 grams (100 ml.) of water will dissolve 26.4 grams of sodium chloride, and no more. This is the saturation point of the solution at this temperature, and it represents a state of equilibrium between the solvent and the solute. The saturation points of different compounds in water differ; for any given solid compound the saturation point is raised, in general, with increase in temperature, and lowered with its decrease. A saturated solution of sodium chloride at 30°C then contains more of the solute than one at 20°C, but if the solution is cooled, the excess of salt above its solubility at that particular temperature will crystallize out of solution. Moreover, the presence of certain ions affects the solubility of some substances so that the extent to which they dissolve in water is conditioned by the presence or absence of other substances in the solution.

## Behavior of polar and non-polar compounds in relation to water

The whole question of solubility is much more intricate than such simple illustrations suggest. Its answer must lie in the electronic structure of matter, but there are many other factors than those just cited which influence or contribute to the solubility or insolubility of substances in each other. In general it is the rule that the more strongly polarized a compound is, the more readily will it dissolve in water; non-polar compounds are but slightly soluble or insoluble.

Alcohol, as a polar compound, will mix with water in any proportions; oils and fats, which are non-polar, will not (Fig. 6.1a, b). If oil and water are mixed, no matter how finely the oil may be divided, it will be present in the mixture as tiny discrete droplets which gradually join together, and since oil is lighter than water, gather on its surface. The water molecules tend to stay together in a homogeneous mass, and so do those of the oil, possibly because molecules with similar kinds of electrical fields tend to cluster together; the oil molecules, with nearly symmetrical electrical fields, gather together, and the water molecules, with highly asymmetrical electrical fields, draw away from them.

There is a surface between the layer of oil and the water below it, for the two kinds of molecules tend to repel rather than attract each other. If, however, some substance is introduced which has affinity both for the oil and for the water molecules, the oil droplets can be kept from running together and the oil will remain in the water in a finely divided state. This is essentially what soaps do, for soaps are compounds of sodium or potassium with fatty acids, the metal replacing the hydrogen in the carboxyl group, so that one end of the molecule has the formula, —COONa or —COOK. This end dissociates, and as an ionized part of the molecule has an affinity for water; the other end is a fatty acid chain, and therefore mixes freely with the molecules of oil (Fig. 6.4). The oil droplets are therefore surrounded by a layer, or film, of soap molecules, which prevents their coalescing if and when they come into contact with each other, and which also holds them to the water since there is electrostatic attraction between the ionized soap and the polar water molecules.

This principle is put to practical use in the employment of soaps for washing purposes; the organism makes use of it in its digestion of fats, for as the fatty acids are released from their combination with glycerol by hydrolysis, they combine with the sodium and potassium ions present in cells, or in digestive tracts, to form soaps, whose action serves to keep the fat in a finely divided state so that it offers a larger surface area for the action of lipases, the enzymes that catalyze the disintegration of fat, than if it remained in one large mass.

Oils and other fluid lipids will, on the other hand, mix directly without the intervention of soap or any other molecule with some other non-polar compounds, so that solutions in oil may be obtained. The fats and oils in the living organism may be reservoirs of dissolved substances; the colors of some flowers are due to pigments dissolved in oil droplets in their petals, and one large group of vitamins is distinguished from the other on the basis of its solubility in fats rather than water.

***Solubility of gases in water:*** Water will dissolve gases as well as solids, and the laws governing the solubility of gases in water and other liquids are somewhat different from those which govern the solubility of solids. The molecules of a gas have more freedom in their movement than those of a solid or a liquid and hence diffuse more readily, provided that the gas is not confined. If it is so confined, it is put under pressure; a force is set up opposing its free movement, the amount of pressure depending upon the volume of the gas, that is, the number of its molecules present in relation to the volume, or dimensions, of the container. When a gas is brought into contact with water, the molecules of both intermingle at the surface, or the interface, between the two substances. Gas molecules enter the liquid, and water molecules leave it and enter the gas until equilibrium is established. The number of gas molecules entering the liquid depends upon the pressure to which they are subjected and the temperature.

The two most important gases biologically are oxygen and carbon dioxide, both of which are present in air, and both of which are but slightly soluble in water. When carbon dioxide enters water it combines with it, molecule for molecule, to form a new compound called carbonic acid,

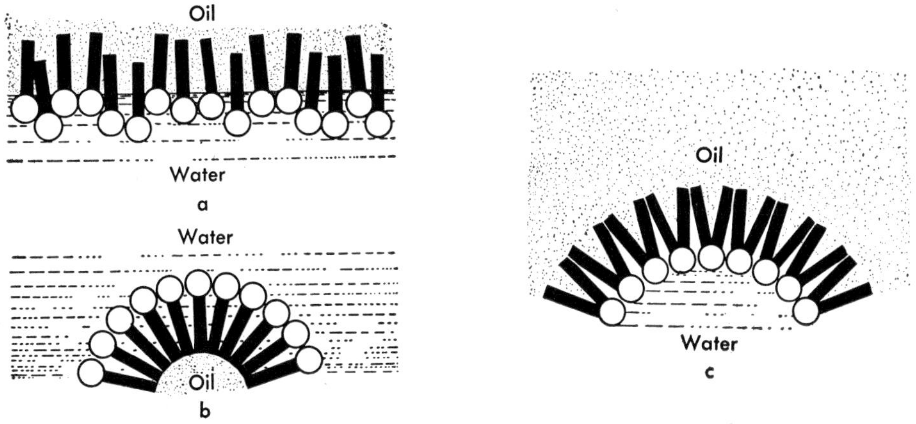

FIGURE 6.4 Diagrams showing the orientation of polar fat and soap molecules at the surfaces of oil and water. The fat molecules are indicated by open circles, representing the –COOH group, attached to black rods representing the long carbon chains terminating in a –CH$_3$ group. (After Seifriz.)

a. Orientation of stearic acid molecules at an oil-water interface. The carboxyl (–COOH) groups of the molecules unite with water, leaving the main chain protruding into the oil.

b. Orientation of sodium stearate molecules at an oil-water interface. In the sodium stearate molecule, one atom of sodium replaces the hydrogen atom in each carboxyl group, and the molecule is both polar and asymmetrical, the –COONa group being larger than any other combination of atoms in the carbon chain. The –COONa groups are oriented in water, the carbon chains to which they are attached in oil, but because of their asymmetry the molecules do not lie in a straight line but in an arc. An emulsion of oil in water results, coalescence of the oil droplets being prevented by the surrounding layer of soap molecules.

c. Orientation of calcium stearate molecules at an oil-water interface. In the calcium stearate molecule, one atom of calcium replaces a hydrogen atom in each of the carboxyl groups of two stearic acid molecules. The two carbon chains are therefore longer than their combined –COOCa–OOC– groups which are oriented in the water, and the soap layer curves with its carbon chains on the outer curvature of the arc, its combined carboxyl groups on the inner. This forms a water-in-oil emulsion, the water droplets being separated from the oil and from each other by the surrounding film of soap.

$H_2CO_3$. This is an unstable atomic configuration and the point of chemical equilibrium is soon reached when the reverse reaction, returning carbon dioxide and water to the system, goes on as fast as the one in which carbonic acid is formed from them. The reaction is thus expressed as a reversible one:

$$H_2O + CO_2 \leftrightarrows H_2CO_3$$

## Electrolytes

When ionic compounds are dissolved in water, positive and negative ions, with charges depending upon the valence of their atoms, are set free. One of the properties which a solution containing ions has is the capacity to conduct an electric current, and compounds that on solution release ions are therefore called electrolytes. The extent to which such a compound dissociates, or ionizes, in solution is a measure of its conductivity and so of its strength or weakness as an electrolyte. When sodium chloride is dissolved in water, practically all the particles are in the form of ions; in other words, it is fully ionized.

$$NaCl \rightarrow Na^+ + Cl^-$$

The sodium and chlorine ions are free to move around with and among the water molecules, and if the electrodes from a battery are put into the solution, the cations ($Na^+$) will move toward the negative electrode, or cathode, and the anions ($Cl^-$) will move toward the positive electrode, or anode (Fig. 6.5). They thus complete the electric circuit and current will flow continuously through the solution as long as there are sodium and chlorine ions present. Sodium chloride is a strong electrolyte, since the majority of its dissolved particles are ions. Carbonic acid, on the other hand, is a weak electrolyte, for although a covalent and not an ionic compound, it does dissociate to a slight extent, releasing a small number of positively charged hydrogen ions ($H^+$)* and negatively charged bicarbonate radicals or ions, $HCO_3^-$.

$$H_2CO_3 \leftrightarrows H^+ + HCO_3^-$$

Some other compounds are non-electrolytes, for they do not release ions on solution, and therefore have not the capacity to conduct an electric current. Sugar is an illustration of a non-electrolyte, for its particles are in solution not as ions but as neutral molecules. But many of the compounds found in living organisms are electrolytes, and strong electrolytes as well, and their behavior in and effect upon biological systems can only be interpreted through a knowledge of their electrochemical properties.

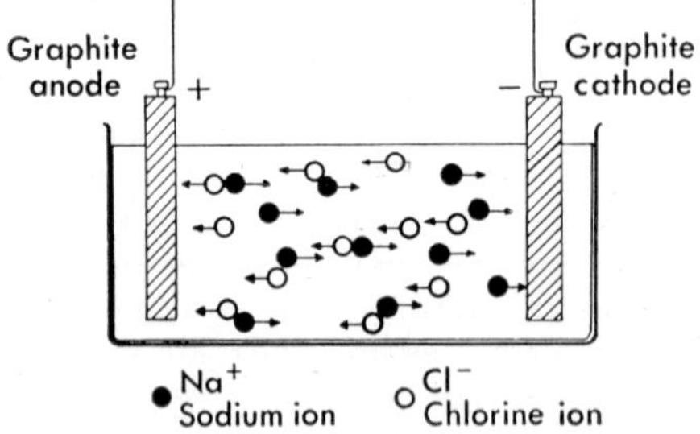

### Acids, bases and salts

Electrolytes, whether weak or strong, are of three main types: acids, bases and salts. For elementary and general working purposes, acids may be defined as those compounds which on dissociation release hydro-

---

* Recent studies have shown that the hydrogen ion, actually a proton, tends always to be bound to a molecule of water as a hydronium ion $H_3O^+$. This alliance with water, or hydration, is common to all ions, the negative ions attracting the positive pole of the water molecule and the positive ions the negative pole, and seems to have a stabilizing effect upon the ion. Cations show an especial tendency to attract or attach water molecules in numbers equal to the charge on the cation; sometimes the forces within a hydrated ion are so strong that the ions retain a layer of water molecules, the water of hydration, even when they are assembled in crystalline form. The term 'hydrogen ion" has, however, been in use for so long and is so common in biological literature that it and its symbol $H^+$ have been retained throughout this book. Students who pass beyond the elementary stage in the study of biological systems will recognize that some of the properties of the so-called hydrogen ion are related to its hydrated state.

FIGURE 6.5 Diagram showing the dissociation of sodium chloride when dissolved in water, and the migration of sodium and chlorine ions in an electric field. (After Krauskopf.)

gen ions, H⁺, biologically the most important of the ions; bases, or alkalies, as those compounds which release hydroxyl ions, OH⁻; and salts as those compounds which are formed by the union of an acid or a base, with water as the by-product of the reaction. In modern chemistry, however, acids and bases are defined in terms of the electronic conditions within the complex of atoms of which they are composed, one set of conditions conferring acidic properties upon such a complex and another conferring basic properties.

Acids, bases and salts have distinct chemical and physical properties, which are essentially the properties of their ions. The greater the dissociation of the electrolyte, the greater is the expression of these properties. It is the presence of hydrogen ions that gives acids their sour taste, and the greater the dissociation, the sourer the taste. The hydroxyl ion gives alkalies their bitter taste and their slippery feeling, because of its ability to dissolve the surface layer of the skin. The presence of hydrogen ions, themselves colorless, may cause a change in the color of other substances; this property is a useful one in detecting the presence, and the relative concentrations, of hydrogen ions. Litmus will turn red, for example, in the presence of hydrogen ions and blue in the presence of hydroxyl ions. Such substances are called indicators, for their color indicates the presence of a strong or a weak acid or base and they are frequently used to test the alkaline or acid properties of solutions. The pigments of some flowers act as indicators, and the color of the flower may shift from blue to pink, or from pink to blue, depending upon the conditions of acidity or alkalinity in the soil.

### *Properties of acid and basic solutions*

Water, whose molecule contains both hydrogen and hydroxyl ions, dissociates to a very slight extent; in pure water only one molecule in every 500,000,000 ionizes as

$$H_2O \text{ (or HOH)} \leftrightarrows H^+ + OH^-$$

setting free equal, though minute, numbers of hydrogen and hydroxyl ions. Acid or basic solutions are therefore the consequence of the ions of the dissolved substances, not of the water itself. If an acid, like the weak electrolyte carbonic acid, $H_2CO_3$, or the strong electrolyte, hydrochloric acid, HCl, is added to the water, the number of hydrogen ions is increased and this increase suppresses the dissociation of the water. The equilibrium is shifted to the left and the number of hydroxyl ions in the solution is consequently reduced. The ratio of hydrogen to hydroxyl ions becomes greater than it was in pure water, where they were present in equal, though very small, numbers. The solution now has the properties of an acid, its strength depending upon the amount of the acid electrolyte added and the extent of its dissociation, that is, the quantity of hydrogen ions that it contributes to unit volume of the solution.

In the same way, if a base like sodium hydroxide, NaOH, which dissociates into Na⁺ and OH⁻, or potassium hydroxide, which dissociates into K⁺ and OH⁻, is added, the dissociation of water is suppressed and the reaction is shifted to the left, but the ratio of hydrogen to hydroxyl ions becomes less. The solution, because of the presence of hydroxyl ions in excess of hydrogen ions, takes on the properties of an alkaline or basic one, the degree of alkalinity again depending upon the number of hydrogen ions present in relation to hydroxyl ions.

*pH:* The acidity or alkalinity of a solution is therefore an expression of the relative proportions of hydrogen and hydroxyl ions in it, or more briefly of the concentration of hydrogen ions, since their number must always be relative to that of the hydroxyl ions. Biologists customarily express the concentration of hydrogen ions, and so indirectly of hydroxyl ions, according to a scale proposed in 1909 by a Danish scientist, Søren Peter Lauritz Sørensen. This scale, which is known as the pH scale, runs from 0 to 14, with the point of neutrality, where the concentrations of hydrogen and hydroxyl ions in a solution are equal, at 7. By delicate measurements of the conductivity of the purest water possible, or its ability to transfer electricity, the concentration of hydrogen ions in it has been found to be 0.0000001 gram per liter. This value can also be expressed as a fraction, 1/10,000,000 gram, or as a negative power of 10, as $1 \times 10^{-7}$ gram, but however it is expressed, it represents the amount of hydrogen present in its ionic state in terms of weight, that is, of gram atoms, or more accurately, gram ions, in 1000 ml. of water. These are all rather cumbersome ways of expressing small quantities and as the biologist must frequently refer to the conditions of acidity or alkalinity within organisms or outside them, a briefer method is desirable. On Sørensen's scale, the negative exponent is replaced by a positive number which, as he originally defined it, is the logarithm of the reciprocal of the number expressing the concentration, in this case, $\log \dfrac{1}{1 \times 10^{-7}}$.

It might also be replaced by the negative logarithm of the number itself, and pH is usually defined in this way, as the negative logarithm of the number expressing the concentration of gram ions of hydrogen per liter of solution. Because pH represents a negative logarithm, or the logarithm of the reciprocal of the concentration, lower pH values indicate higher concentrations of hydrogen ions. If, for example, an acid is added to pure water so that the concentration of hydrogen becomes 0.000001, or $1 \times 10^{-6}$, gram ion per liter, the pH of the solution would be 6. And if, on the other hand, a base were added to pure water so that the hydrogen ion concentration were decreased to 0.00000001, or $1 \times 10^{-8}$, gram ion per liter, and that of the hydroxyl ions proportionately increased, the solution would have a pH of 8. Each full interval on the scale thus represents a tenfold difference in the ratio of hydrogen ions to the total volume of the solution, and also to the hydroxyl ions. At 0, the ratio of hydrogen ions to volume is 1:1 and at 14 it is 1:100 million million and therefore so small that the concentration is negligible.

Intermediate values between the whole numbers can be equally well expressed on the scale. For example, the concentration of hydrogen ions in one of the most complex of biological solutions, human blood, is on the average close to $0.4 \times 10^{-7}$. The negative logarithm of this number (0.00000004) and the logarithm of its reciprocal, $\frac{1}{4} \times 10^{-7}$, is 7.39 and the pH of human blood is therefore 7.39, a figure which makes readily apparent to one familiar with the pH scale that it is a slightly alkaline solution.

*Relation of pH to conditions in protoplasm:* All the reactions of protoplasm take place within a narrow range of pH on both sides of neutrality. Beyond the limits on both the acid and the alkaline side, protoplasm undergoes changes from which it cannot recover. But acids are constantly being produced by cells in consequence of some of the chemical reactions going on in them, which if accumulated would prove fatal. Hydrogen ions may be removed from solutions by two kinds of chemical reactions, both of which are continually going on in biological systems, so that, in spite of the formation of acids and bases in them, or the introduction of such electrolytes into them, their pH remains remarkably constant.

## Neutralization of acids

Acids and bases can combine to form salts which upon dissociation release neither hydrogen nor hydroxyl ions and therefore do not affect the pH of a solution, although since they may be strong or weak electrolytes they do affect its electrochemical equilibrium. The reaction that takes place between hydrochloric acid (HCl) and sodium hydroxide (NaOH) when they are mixed in the proper proportions in solution illustrates the way in which salts in general are formed. Both HCl and NaOH are electrolytes and their ions in solution undergo partner exchange or double decomposition, the sodium and chlorine ions joining to form sodium chloride, the hydrogen and hydroxyl ions to form water, as expressed in the equation:

$$H^+ + Cl^- + Na^+ + OH^- \rightarrow Na^+ + Cl^- + HOH\ (H_2O)$$

Na+ and Cl− appear on both sides of the equation in equal concentration, so that the actual change has been the union of the hydrogen ions from hydrochloric acid with the hydroxyl ions from sodium hydroxide to form water, which is neither acid nor alkaline, but neutral. The acid is thus said to be neutralized by the base; essentially the neutralization of an acid by a base is the combination of their respective hydrogen and hydroxyl ions to form water, and the union of their other ions to form a salt, which may remain ionized in the solution without altering the pH, or, depending upon conditions of equilibrium, precipitate out and so be removed entirely. Salt is the general name for compounds formed in this way; its popular use for NaCl specifically is because this is the one most commonly found.

**Buffers**

Another way in which hydrogen ions may be removed from solutions is by their union with substances, in living organisms present in cells or in the fluids surrounding them, called "buffers." These substances were first called "tampons" or sponges by French scientists to convey the idea that they mop up or soak up hydrogen ions as a sponge soaks up liquids. Tampon is the word also used for railway buffer, the contrivance at the end of a track into which trains may bump without damage since it yields to the shock of the impact, and when the word was translated into German it was translated in this sense as "Puffer," which in its turn became translated into English as "buffer." The original French word, or an English one closer to its meaning in the sense it was originally used, would be preferable to "buffer" as descriptive of the effect of these substances upon acid solutions. Buffers are usually salts of weak acids and strong bases, that is, combinations between active metals, like sodium and potassium, and acids like carbonic and phosphoric, which are weak electrolytes, such as, for example, sodium bicarbonate, $NaHCO_3$, and potassium bicarbonate, $KHCO_3$, the sodium and potassium salts of carbonic acid. Since carbonic acid is being steadily formed in living organisms, and since potassium and sodium are two of the elements consistently found in protoplasm, these salts are of common biological occurrence and frequently act as buffers. When an acid stronger than carbonic is present, either as a product of protoplasmic activity or introduced in some way into the organism, the cation of the salt unites by double decomposition with the anion of the acid, the other two ions uniting into the weakly dissociated carbonic acid. For example, hydrochloric acid is produced by some cells in the human body and in the bodies of other animals. Hydrochloric acid is a strong electrolyte, and its dissociation markedly increases the hydrogen ion concentration, that is, lowers, the pH, of the solution containing it. In the organism the following reaction takes place:

$$H^+ + Cl^- + Na^+ + HCO_3^- \rightarrow Na^+ + Cl^- + H_2CO_3$$

The bicarbonate here acts as a buffer, and by contributing its cation and taking up the hydrogen ion to form an acid which ionizes only slightly, removes the excess hydrogen ions of the strong acid which, if left in solution, would lower the pH below the limits within which protoplasm can operate.

The constancy of pH of sea water, which all over the world is about 8.1, is due largely to the buffering action of the bicarbonates in it; so, too, is the pH of protoplasm and body fluids, although there, in addition to inorganic buffers, there are certain organic ones. Proteins, for instance, may act as very efficient buffering systems and their presence in cells helps to maintain the constancy of pH within them.

*Crystalline and colloidal solutions*

In addition to their distinctions as electrolytic or non-electrolytic, acidic, basic or neutral solutions, solutions may also be classified, according to the size of the molecules dissolved in the solvent, as crystalline or colloidal. If a crystalline solution is viewed either by transmitted or reflected light, it is clear and transparent; the ions or molecules in it are so small that they do not deflect or refract the rays of light and so it appears optically homogeneous. When a colloidal solution is so studied, it appears cules or colloidal particles are separate from each other, and constitute the disperse phase of the system, in which water is the continuous phase; under other conditions, the colloidal particles may draw nearer together and come in contact with each other, form-

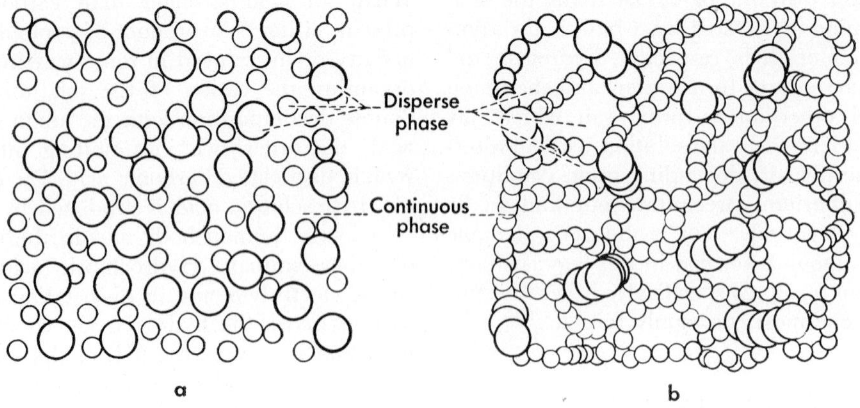

FIGURE 6.6 Diagram showing the reversal of phase in a colloidal system. (After Gerard.)

   a. Sol state. The colloidal particles, represented as circles of different diameters, are separated from each other, as the discontinuous phase, by water, as the continuous phase. Such a solution has the physical properties of a liquid.
   b. Gel state. The colloidal particles adhere together in strands, as the continuous phase, separating isolated areas of water from each other. Such a solution has the physical properties of a soft and spongy solid, holding its shape and not flowing freely.

translucent, even sometimes opaque, by transmitted light, and like a galaxy of stars by reflected light. The particles within it, though of sub-microscopic dimensions and capable of Brownian movement, are large enough to refract the light, and they appear as bright, rapidly moving points of light against a dark background. These particles may be aggregates or polymers of inorganic substances, as in colloidal gold solutions; the large organic molecules of the proteins, polysaccharides and lipids, are all of dimensions to make colloidal solutions.

Colloidal solutions are viscous; that is, there are forces within them opposing their free flow; they vary in consistency from that of a syrup to a soft jelly. Some of them are sticky, and it is from this property that their name is derived, for the Greek word for glue is kollos. Under certain conditions, the mole- ing the continuous phase of the system, while the water, held in the interstices of the molecular groups, forms the disperse phase (Fig. 6.6). In the first condition, when the colloidal particles form the disperse phase, the solution is a sol; in the second it is a gel. The change from sol to gel, and the reverse from gel to sol, can be brought about by energy changes inside and outside the system; chemical changes that alter the salt balance, pressure changes, temperature and electrical changes, all bring about the transition from one state to another. There is no sharp limit between them, and except at the extremes of fluidity or gelation, a colloidal solution might better be described in the relative terms of more or less sol-like or gel-like, than in absolute ones.

Protoplasm is a colloidal system, for protoplasm is a solution in water of huge though still ultramicroscopic molecules, proteins, compound proteins, lipids and polysaccharides, together with a great variety of inorganic and other organic solutes. It is, like other colloids, a complex, delicately balanced system whose balance can be shifted by energy changes within or outside it, but it is unlike all other colloids in that it can metabolize, grow and reproduce itself, manifesting within the narrow limits in which it can exist all those diverse phenomena which together are called life.

# CHAPTER 7 PROTOPLASM AND THE CELL

## Protoplasm as an organized system

Protoplasm is a highly complex colloidal system, but it is more than that; it is also a highly organized one, and very likely in its kind and degree of organization lies the secret of its capacity to do work and to control and direct the series of reactions that result in its growth and multiplication and other manifestations of life. The water in a quiet pool does no appreciable work, nor does the air on a still day, for the molecules of water and of the atmospheric gases are in random movement, moving this way and that in all directions, but if they become organized so that the majority of them move in one direction, they can do effective work. Water, running downhill or over a fall under the influence of gravity, or churned into currents by the propellers of a ship, does work which can be converted into useful mechanical work; the quiet atmosphere, if put in motion by incoming air currents, or mechanically by a fan or the propellers of an airplane, can likewise do work. Under these circumstances, the molecules of water or of gas are organized and their movement directed. One might carry the analogy of protoplasmic organization further, and point out that nothing is accomplished by a disorganized society, whose members pursue different objectives and follow individual and independent lines of action. It is only when they become organized, and all move toward one goal with a common plan, that results, good or bad, are achieved. Similarly, when protoplasm becomes disorganized it also becomes incapable of achieving its ends, metabolism, growth, reproduction.

## The unit of protoplasmic organization, the cell. First observations

The unit of protoplasmic organization is the cell. The word cell is not a very happy one in this connection, but it has significance in the history of biology, for it was given by Robert Hooke (1635–1703), one of the first scientists to make use of a newly developed biological tool, the microscope, to the tiny divisions that he saw in thin slices of cork. The cork slice, through his microscope, looked as if made up of many small compartments, arranged in rows, and reminded him of the tiers of monks' cells in English monasteries. He therefore called each compartment a cell, and the name has survived, although it does not accurately convey the picture of a protoplasmic unit. What Hooke actually saw in the cork was the non-living wall which had once surrounded the living protoplasm, but not the protoplasm itself. Some of his other microscopic studies, which carried him over a wide range of objects—needle points, razors' edges, materials like taffeta and watered silk, the crystals of snow and ice, such biological objects as the feathers of ducks and peacocks, the scales of fish, some sponges and seaweeds, the stings of nettles and the hairy kidney bean brought to him as a curiosity by a sea captain from the East Indies, blue mold and the wings, eyes and feet of flies—brought him closer to a sight of living cells, but not yet close enough to see the living substance. All of these observations, and some conclusions from them, such as an explanation of the ability of flies to walk on glass and ceilings, and the connection between putrefaction and the presence of mold, are set down in his *Micrographia*, published in London in 1665. In this he also states a principle important not only for microscopists but for students in all branches of learning—that one must proceed from the simple to the complex; "we must learn to make letters before we can write sentences."

There were many others beside Hooke in the seventeenth century who in different countries and in different ways were making use of the microscope to study parts of the natural world hitherto invisible to them, for this was the period of the development of the microscope and the age of individual scientific endeavor. This new tool opened up a whole new world which awakened the interest and piqued the curiosity of laymen as well as professional scientists. Indeed, the seventeenth century was one of spiritual and intellectual uplift in general, for it produced such men as Spinoza and Milton, Christopher Wren and Vermeer, Newton, Galileo, Kepler, Descartes, Francis Bacon and Harvey, and among the microscopists, Malpighi, Leeuwenhoek, Swammerdam and Grew. The careful and complete observations of these latter men, as they peered through their simple optical instruments and studied in detail the finer structures of living things, make the background of our knowledge of the anatomy of animals and plants and of the cell as a unit in them.

Marcello Malpighi (1628–1694) was an Italian doctor whose life was punctuated by the writing of letters and the publication of beautifully illustrated discourses and monographs describing the objects that he had seen through the lenses of the microscope. Among these were the lungs, brains, tongues, livers and kidneys of animals, the capillaries or tiny vessels connecting arteries and veins in animals with closed circulatory systems, stages in the development of the chick, and most complete of all the anatomy and life history of the silkworm, brought into Europe from China in the hope of competing for the silk trade of the civilized world. Besides full verbal descriptions and beautifully executed and beautifully accurate illustrations, Malpighi included in his monograph on the silkworm, published in 1669, accounts of experiments he performed to determine the function of the tracheae, long, slender tubes that run through the bodies of these and most other insects carrying air to the inner tissues and cells. By painting the larvae with oil, and covering none, some or all of the external openings of these tubes, called spiracles, through which the air enters and leaves, he showed that there was a progressive diminution in the well-being of the caterpillar as more and more of the spiracles were blocked off and less air, and hence less oxygen, brought to its cells.

Antony van Leeuwenhoek (1632–1723) was born in Delft, where he lived the greater part of his life as a prosperous business man and public servant, grinding lenses and studying all manner of things through them and communicating his observations through a steady stream of letters sent to the Royal Society of London. He published no papers and he wrote no books but in these letters are recorded some of the most detailed and accurate microscopic observations of a wide range of objects, from the non-living as well as from the living world. He studied water—fresh water, salt water, snow water—vinegar in which he first of any man saw tiny worms, the vinegar eels; and pepper water, which he made with the idea of finding out what made pepper hot to the taste; he studied the micro-organisms that he found in these waters and he made accurate measurements of them, for he was among other things a qualified surveyor and interested in linear relationships; he studied the parts of mussels and oysters, and first saw the beat of the fine, hair-like threads, the cilia, which cover the gills; he studied the bile of cows, lambs, sheep, rabbits, fowls and other animals and was the first to see some of the small parasites that infest these animals; he studied his own saliva and the scrapings from his teeth and saw bacteria for the first time. He saw, too, blood cells suspended within liquid plasma; and spermatozoa, the male germ cells, in the fluid discharged from the reproductive organs. There was little with which he came in contact in his life that he did not put beneath his lenses and write about to be read and marvelled at in the meetings of the Royal Society. As the information that he gathered was spread abroad and popularized, many people came to his house in Delft to see and to buy his lenses, and to be shown wonders through his microscope. Among his visitors were the reigning monarchs of England, the Emperor of Germany and the Czar, Peter the Great, who was shown the circulation in the tail of an eel and was greatly astonished by it. Leeuwenhoek's skill lay not only in making his lenses, which he ground himself, but in preparing objects for study; his fame as a microscopist rests upon this skill as well as his enormous natural curiosity, which led him to examine everything he saw with the utmost care and to report his observations in the greatest detail, almost with naiveté, omitting nothing, not even the most personal of his findings.

Jan Swammerdam (1637–1680) was also a Dutchman, having been born in Amsterdam but going as a young man to Leyden where he studied medicine and spent the greater part of his life. He made beautiful studies of insects by dissection, at which he had extraordinary skill, and by microscopic observation he traced the development of the frog and saw for the first time some of the minute structures of ferns, and he also carried on experiments which threw some light on the processes of respiration and muscular contraction. His *Biblia Naturae*, published in Leyden in 1737–38, over a half a century after his death, contains the manuscripts and drawings that escaped destruction by fire, for he had periods of great depression and mental cloudiness and during his life burnt much of his own work. The *Biblia* has been called "the finest collection of microscopical observations ever produced by one worker."

Nehemiah Grew (1641–1712) was an English physician who devoted his spare time to the study of plants, both macroscopically and microscopically, seeking always to find resemblances between them and animals, since they "came at first out of the same Hand are therefore contrivances of the same Wisdom." His great work, *The Anatomy of Plants*, was published in London in 1682, and contains descriptions and beautiful plates of the parts as well as the cellular structure of plants. He speaks of the cells as bladders, and notes that in the younger parts they are juicy, and here he comes closer than Hooke to their true nature.

## The cell theory

Observations such as these of the classical microscopists and those of their successors on individual cells and cells as parts of organisms, both plant and animal and large and small, led to the development of cytology (Greek, kytos = a hollow receptacle + logos = discourse), a branch of biology which deals particularly with the cell, and to one of the greatest and for a time most useful of biological generalizations, the Cell Theory. Although by no means original with them, this concept was first brought to general attention in 1838–39 by two German scholars, the botanist M. J. Schleiden and the zoologist Theodor Schwann, and is usually associated with their names although certainly not to be attributed to them alone. It was a natural outcome of the many observations that had been made during the early part of the nineteenth and the preceding centuries, and very briefly, it states that all organisms are composed of cells or of a single cell, and further that all cells, and hence all organisms, arise from the division of pre-existing cells. This theory was to biology, at that stage of its development, what Dalton's atomic theory was to chemistry.

## Methods of studying cells

As the wonders of the natural world as revealed by the microscope had claimed the attention of the earlier scientists, so now cells as individuals or as parts of individuals became the objects of particular interest and special study. The architecture of the cell has been studied in many ways, none of which alone has proved satisfactory but which taken all together can be put into a composite picture which probably represents pretty closely that biological system which still remains, no matter how much further it may be resolved into its component parts, the structural and functional unit of living things.

***Means of preserving cells:*** The limitations of studying living cells, even with continued development and perfection of the microscope, became apparent soon after the observations of the classical microscopists. Although the innermost cells of organisms could be studied by removing the tissues from the body and tearing them apart with needles or otherwise separating them into their individual cells, they soon underwent physiological changes and putrefaction. Alcohol had been known since the seventeenth century as a preserving agent and had been generally used to prevent the decomposition of bodies by the action of bacteria and of their own enzymes, a process of self-disintegration known as autolysis (Greek, autos = self + lysis = loosening). More or less by accident, formaldehyde was found to be even better in its preservation of cells, when in 1893 a German scientist, F. Blum, began to dissect a mouse which had died of anthrax, and wishing to keep it overnight put it in a solution of formaldehyde which was known to have antiseptic properties. The next morning he found the mouse as hard as if it had been preserved in alcohol, and even more details in its cells visible. The shapes and general characteristics of cells had been seen, but biologists were concerned with finding out much more about their intimate structure, and this observation of Blum's led to his own experimentation, and to that of many other men, with many chemicals and mixtures of chemicals as preserving or "fixing" agents, which either precipitate or coagulate or are precipitated on the cell contents and so render more of it visible than in the living, or dying, cell. This development of methods of fixation was accompanied by a development in the technique of using stains or dyes so that the different areas and structures in the cell were colored and so made even more readily distinguishable, and in the technique of sectioning or cutting slices of the preserved material thin enough for microscopic study. Although sections of living and of fixed material had been cut with very sharp knives or razors, these left much to be desired in the way of thinness and of uniformity. In 1870, Wilhelm His (1831–1904), a Swiss anatomist, invented an instrument called a microtome, which can cut uniform and very thin slices, as thin as 1 micron (1 micron = 0.001 mm.), of tissues that can be taken from any part of an animal or plant, properly fixed and embedded in a block of some firm material like paraffin wax, to hold them during cutting. The principle of the microtome is like that of the meat slicer in butcher shops, very likely developed from His' biological invention; a sharp knife is brought in contact at set distances with the material to be cut and sections are made which can be spread upon small glass plates, called slides, appropriately stained, and mounted and studied under very high magnifications. By these means, much important and valuable information about cellular architecture has been gained, but these methods, useful and fruitful as they have been and still are, have distinct limitations; they do not present the cell as an active biological system, which is actually the only way in which it exists; in precipitating or coagulating the cell contents they very likely alter its geography and give false impressions of the size and spatial relationships of its parts, and they give little or no information about the chemical or physical properties of the structures they reveal.

***The study of living cells:*** In order to overcome these difficulties, biologists have again turned to the living cell and by methods of micromanipulation, microchemistry, ultra microscopy and the differential absorption of ultraviolet light, and electrical studies are adding more and more to the static picture gained from the fixed and stained cell in the early part of the century. There still remains the difficulty of dealing with cells in the innermost parts of organisms, a difficulty which has to a certain extent been overcome by the development of the methods of tissue culture, first devised by an American, Ross Harrison (1870–    ), for the study of growing nerves. By these methods, small pieces of tissue from any part of the body can be cut out and put into a sterile nutrient fluid, in which they will survive for long periods of time, and in some cases at least reproduce for many cell generations (Fig. 7.1). From such a culture made in a drop of nutrient medium hanging (Fig. 17.2). These accumulated materials may then be tested chemically by micromethods, or with even more rapid and longer centrifugation, cells may be broken up into separate parts containing materials of different specific gravity, and thus the

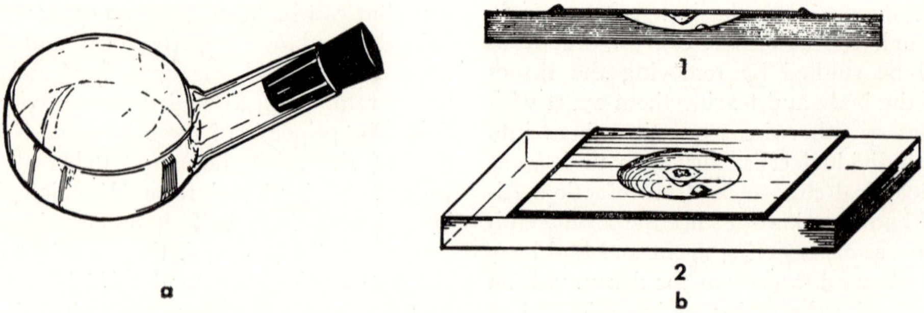

FIGURE 7.1 Techniques of tissue culture.

    a. Flask technique. A Carrel flask, designed by Alexis Carrel (1873–1944), in which a fragment of tissue can be placed in a sterile medium, which is both nutrient and supporting.

    b. Hanging drop technique. The piece of tissue is placed in a drop of sterile culture medium on a cover slip, which is then inverted over a depression slide and sealed down. A drop of water may be placed in the bottom of the depression as a precaution against loss of water by evaporation from the medium.

    1. Preparation seen from the side.
    2. Preparation seen from above.

over a hollow depression on a slide, cells will migrate or grow out, and as they are usually extended and flattened against the glass, they are relatively thin and can be studied microscopically (Fig. 7.2).

The micromanipulator makes it possible to operate upon cells in various ways, either by tearing them, cutting pieces from them, injecting substances like indicators or dyes into them or removing parts of their contents from them. Fine glass needles can also by this means be inserted into the cell, and the differences in viscosity and elasticity of different areas in it tested as well as the effect of displacement of its parts. Mass displacement of microscopically visible particles can also be brought about by centrifugation, for, while the contents of the cell are ordinarily not affected by the gravitational pull, very rapid rotation will produce a force many times that of gravity which will separate the substances of different specific gravities into layers within the cell role that they play in the cell as a whole indirectly determined through the effects produced by their displacement or their absence. Microchemical methods include also studies of the cell contents by their differential solubilities in water or other solvents, and studies of their inorganic content by the method of microincineration, in which individual cells or sections are put in an oven at very high temperature so that all the organic material is burned away leaving only the inorganic ash as a sort of skeleton of the living cell. Since this is deposited in situ, it gives a faithful picture of the distribution of inorganic matter which in some cases can be further identified as specific chemical elements.

The basis of all microscopy is the ability of different substances to refract light to different degrees, that is, to bring about the bending of light rays, or their deflection from a straight course, through angles of different magnitudes. The extent of this deflection is known as the refractive index of the substance, and it is only by the differences in their refractive indices that two unstained objects become distinguishable from each other, in ordinary light. One of the great difficulties in studying living cells is

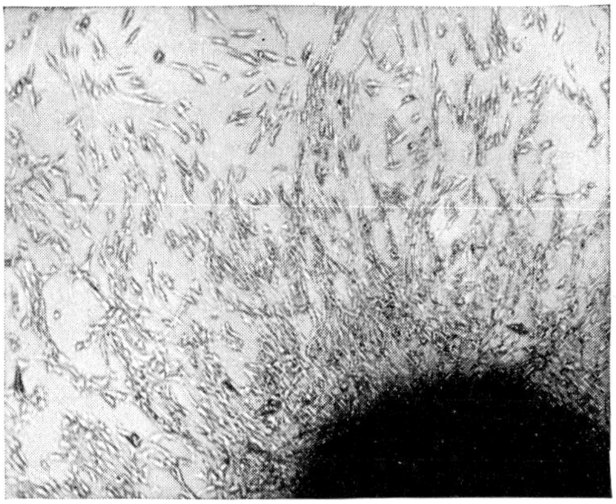

FIGURE 7.2 Fibroblasts growing out from an explant of 1-day old mouse tissue. × 60. (Courtesy of Dr. Warren H. Lewis.)

that many of their components have the same, or very nearly the same, refractive index and therefore cannot be resolved into separate images. While the magnifying power of the modern microscope is practically unlimited, its resolving powers have set a limit to its complete effectiveness as an optical tool. Phase microscopy, now in the course of development, may solve this difficulty, for the lenses of phase microscopes are so constructed that besides magnifying an object they combine some of the light rays passing through it and refracted by it, putting some "in step" or in phase and others "out of step" or out of phase, and so by reinforcing some and interfering with others afford greater contrast between objects. The capacity of different parts of the cell to absorb ultraviolet light or to rotate a beam of polarized light to different extents provides another means of distinguishing between them and learning something of their chemical constitution and physical properties, and the use of both these methods has furnished many significant data. Finally, the electrical conditions of the living cell can be studied by measuring the current in it and the difference of potential between different regions of it, and by observing and interpreting the effects of an electric current applied to it.

## The concept of the cell as a structural and functional unit of biological systems

From all of these methods, biologists have arrived at a morphological, or structural, concept of the cell in terms of the bodies visible in it and to a certain extent at least of their physical and chemical properties. They have arrived simultaneously at a physiological concept of it as a functioning protoplasmic unit from studying and interpreting its behavior in its natural environment or in ones in which it has been placed experimentally. While neither of these concepts tells the whole story, for there is still much about cells hidden from the eye and not yet deduced by the mind, and while there is no complete agreement about some of the finer points either of their structure or their function, there are certain features generally accepted as common to all cells and therefore presumably fundamental to them.

### The common characters of cells

No two cells are exactly alike; cells of different kinds differ in shape and in size, in the degree of their metabolic activity, in the amount of material stored within them and the functions they perform if they are part of an organism composed of many cells (Figs. 11.1, 11.2). Within every active cell, however, is a body, usually spherical or oval, but sometimes irregular in shape, called the nucleus; the protoplasm outside the nucleus is called the cytoplasm to distinguish it from that which is inside it, the nucleoplasm, and in the cytoplasm lie numerous microscopically visible bodies; a surface layer of the cytoplasm can be distinguished through the absence of formed bodies so that this region appears homogeneous, clear or hyaline, while the inner cytoplasm is optically heterogeneous, or granular (Fig. 7.3). Although none of these has an independent existence outside of the cell of which it is a part, for the cell is both structurally and functionally a unit, for purposes of description it is convenient to take each up separately.

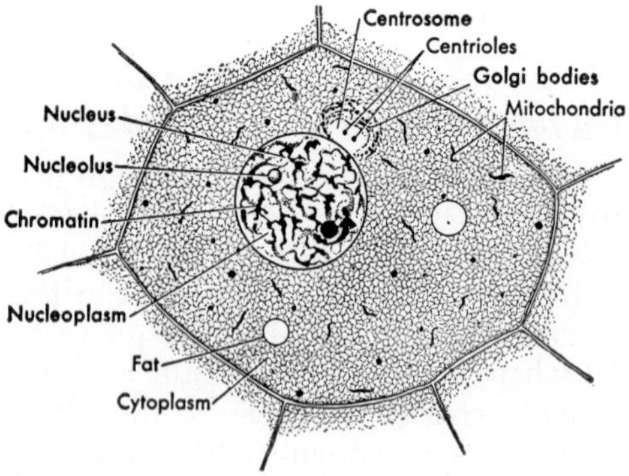

FIGURE 7.3  Diagram of a generalized cell.
(From Huettner, *Fundamentals of Comparative Embryology of the Vertebrates*, revised edition. Copyright 1949 by The Macmillan Company.)

## Nucleus

In the fixed and stained preparations of cells studied by the microscopists of the late nineteenth century, some of the contents of the nucleus were found to have an especial affinity for dyes and to take up certain stains very readily. At times this stainable material within the nucleus collected in small distinct bodies to which, because they stained so deeply and so sharply, were given the name chromosomes, or the staining bodies, by the German biologist, Otto Waldeyer (1863–1921). At other times this material seemed to be distributed in a sort of meshwork throughout the nucleus, so that the term "body" was no longer applicable, and chromatin was used as a general term for this substance in all its phases. In addition to the chromatin, many cells were found to have further differentiation of the nuclear material in the form of one or more small, spherical bodies, also deeply staining but distinguishable from the chromosomes. These bodies were called nucleoli, or little nuclei, and though not invariably present are commonly found in active cells.

The nucleus of the living cell, except during the time of division, appears optically homogeneous except for the nucleolus or nucleoli, which if present can be seen because of their relatively high refractive indices. But if a microdissection needle is put into a cell and moved around, it encounters obstacles, regions in the nucleoplasm which are more rigid than the general fluid medium, even if such a difference is not detectable by the eye. These obstacles probably represent the chromosomes, present as such in all phases of the cell's activity although microscopically invisible except during division, when even in the living cell they can be seen and can be moved around by a microdissection needle.

Chemical and ultraviolet light absorption studies of nuclei have shown that the chromatin contains protein and a complicated organic substance called nucleic acid, which like protein is a general name for a class of compounds and may be of several kinds. Some of the proteins of the chromosomes at least are nucleoproteins, and like the nucleoproteins of viruses, capable of self-duplication. They are constantly reduplicating themselves, for every time the nucleus divides the chromosomes divide and yet persist as constant elements through cell generation after cell generation. Ultraviolet light absorption studies have shown too that the nucleolus, whose function in the cell has long been debated, contains a kind of nucleic acid which may be used in the synthesis of the nucleoproteins of the chromosomes.

That the nucleus is essential to the continued life and activity of the cell has been proved many times. It appears to control the organization and the activity of the cell but in ways which are not yet entirely clear. Microchemical methods have proved the presence in the nucleus of enzymes which catalyze reactions going on in the cytoplasm as well as in the nucleus itself and it may exercise its control by synthesizing these enzymes and discharging them into the cytoplasm at appropriate times. So that, besides containing the chromosomes, which modern genetic research has shown to be the bearers of the material handed on from generation to generation that determines the course of development, the nucleus is also all-important to the cell in the initiation and regulation of its activities.

## Cytoplasm

The extent of the cytoplasm varies with different kinds of cells, depending upon their activities and functions and the amount of reserve or waste material stored in them. Seen either by transmitted or reflected light, most cytoplasm looks granular, but beyond the range of visibility are the molecules of protein, lipid, lipo-protein and carbohydrate floating in a watery solution that forms the ground cytoplasm. The presence of such proteins, the structure proteins, has been demonstrated by an American biologist, R. R. Bensley (1867– ), and his colleagues by methods which involve the progressive dissolving out of other compounds in the cell by a series of reagents, leaving finally a sort of framework of protein molecules. The tiny visible granules are in constant Brownian movement in the living cell, and interspersed among them are larger particles some of which are more or less static while others participate directly in the cell's metabolism. In this latter category are the mitochondria and the Golgi substance.

*Mitochondria:* The mitochondria are small granules, rods or filaments, depending upon the type of cell and upon conditions within it. Half a century ago, a German biologist, Richard Altmann (1852–1902), in studying fixed and stained cells, saw these granules and called them bioblasts (Greek, bios = life + blastos = germ), since he thought them the elements in the cell upon which its life depended. Many other microscopists saw, and had seen, bodies which stained and behaved similarly, but which were in the form of rods and filaments as well as granules. Most of these workers invented their own names for them so that there are about fifty synonyms for these bodies which all evidence shows to be fundamentally the same although having different forms in different circumstances; the name, mitochondria (Greek, mitos = thread + chondros = grits), and given to them in 1897, is the one now generally accepted.

Studies of mitochondria by chemical and physical methods show that they are composed of lipid and of protein and that they have a higher specific gravity than the cytoplasmic granules, for when cells are centrifuged they are thrown to the centrifugal pole. They are visible in the living cell, for they have a higher refractive index than the ground cytoplasm and also they can be stained in vivo by certain non-toxic dyes; in some cells they are evenly distributed throughout the cytoplasm, never in the nucleus, in others they may be collected in one area, or their position may shift with changing conditions in the cell; they have been reported travelling back and forth between the nucleus and cell surface in tissue culture cells.

They are very sensitive to conditions within the cell and are the first elements to react to its injury. If cells under observation are pinched or compressed beyond their margin of safety, filamentous mitochondria will break up into granules; in some diseases or other pathological conditions, they show alterations in their constitution or their arrangement. In scurvy, for example, the filaments break up and gather together in clumps; in cyanide poisoning they keep their shape but lose their motility.

They appear to be gelated colloidal systems within the protoplasmic sol; outside of it they have no existence, and within it their function is still not clear. Yet they have been demonstrated in every kind of active cell that has been studied, both plant and animal, and certainly within the cell they must provide, because of their size and shape and number, a relatively enormous surface area to which ions or other molecules may be temporarily attached and so exposed or transported about within the cell for its varied chemical reactions.

*Golgi substance:* Another cellular element was demonstrated in 1898 by an Italian physician, Camillo Golgi (1844–1926), in some of the cells in the brain of the barn owl, and so was called after him Golgi substance or Golgi body. Golgi first described it as a network, or mass of twisted threads, lying near the nucleus. It has since been described in a variety of different forms in different kinds of cells after special chemical treatments, but it has never satisfactorily been seen in living cells. Partly because of this, and partly because of the special and often elaborate methods needed to demonstrate it in fixed cells and its inconstancy in form and in distribution even with these methods, its acceptance as a constant cellular element has been extremely controversial. In the light of present knowledge, it cannot be included in the same category of cytoplasmic inclusions as the mitochondria, and should most probably be considered only as an evidence of certain activities going on within the cell, a product rather than an agent of its metabolism.

*Other cytoplasmic inclusions:* The other visible components of the cytoplasm, also products of its metabolism, are of two principal kinds: solid inclusions and fluid inclusions, or vacuoles. The solid inclusions may be in the form of granules or of crystals. The granules may be of starch, a water-insoluble polysaccharide, or of protein; the latter, since some of the proteins are colored compounds, may provide pigment granules. The crystals may be those of organic or inorganic compounds, produced perhaps in excess of the solubility relations within the cell and so precipitated out, or they may be ones of substances entirely insoluble in the cytoplasmic fluid. In some cases at least, they are of materials produced in the cell as waste products which would be toxic if accumulated in solution; in crystalline form they can be retained in the cell in an inactive condition if they cannot otherwise be eliminated.

The fluid inclusions, or vacuoles, are diverse in their contents and their size. Water is constantly being made in cells as a by-product of the exothermic reaction in which carbohydrate is oxidized to carbon dioxide and water, yet the viscosity of protoplasm varies only within relatively narrow limits. Some of this water at least is collected into minute droplets or vacuoles generally distributed throughout the cytoplasm but not incorporated in it, and often, perhaps invariably, containing dissolved substances; other water may enter it from its environment and be similarly collected into vacuoles. Oil or fat synthesized in the cell beyond its immediate energy needs may be stored in fat drops or oil vacuoles, often too with substances dissolved in them.

Many cells are particularly active in the synthesis of specific products, and these may be temporarily stored in granules or in vacuoles, until they are needed for the use of the cell or the organism of which it is a part. The gland cells of the digestive tracts of animals, for instance, synthesize the enzymes which bring about the digestion of food and store them in inactive form in their cytoplasm until they are discharged; the egg cells of most animals contain large amounts of yolk, protein or fat, which has been synthesized by the cell in the course of its growth and will be used to provide energy for the changes it will undergo in its development as an embryo; and the cells of many plants contain large reserves of carbohydrate, such as the starch in the tubers of potatoes or the insoluble sugars in the seeds of peas and corn, or of protein such as that in the outer layers of the coats surrounding the corn or wheat seed, or of oil as in the seeds of nuts, olives and some grains.

Some of these products may be discharged from the cell, periodically or as fast as they are formed; those which represent reserves may be broken down by cellular enzymes and used as sources of energy or as building blocks for other compounds in accordance with the requirements of the cell or of the organism as a whole. The amount of them accumulated in any cell is to a certain extent a measure of its synthetic activity, although other cells may be equally active yet not retain their products, discharging them in solution as soon as they are formed.

### The cell surface

All cells have a surface layer of greater or lesser extent which is optically clear and non-granular, whatever may be its submicroscopic constitution. In some cells this area is so distinct and extensive that it forms a definite region of ectoplasm, distinguishable by its hyaline appearance and comparative gelation from the granular and more fluid endoplasm which it encloses.

While apparently most of the chemical reactions of the cell—the energy transformations, the syntheses and the disintegration of substances—go on in the endoplasm, the surface layer is the final arbiter of its activity, for it is the region where the adjustment between cell and environment is maintained. The properties of this surface enable protoplasm to exist in varied surroundings; its absence from virus particles may be the explanation of the restricted environment in which they can reproduce themselves.

*The plasma membrane:* Protoplasm differs from all other colloidal systems in that it is never directly in contact with its surroundings, but always separated from them by a membrane, inside of which lies the ectoplasm and outside of which may be additional protective or supporting structures. This membrane, the plasma membrane, is invisible and its presence has been determined by inference rather than by direct observation. When a cell, freed from any of the superficial layers that may enclose it, is pressed by a microdissection needle, its surface is dented as one might dent the surface of a bladder filled with water by pressing it with one's finger; it requires some force to puncture the surface layer with a needle, but when this is done, the fluid endoplasm flows out through the hole, rounds up and immediately forms another membrane around itself, or else it becomes disorganized and disintegrates. The membrane therefore seems to be an integral part of the protoplasmic system, and as important to the life of the cell as the nucleus.

The membrane has certain very important properties from which its presence around the cell can also be deduced. Primarily, while it permits the free diffusion of certain molecules, it prevents that of others, and so acts as a semi-permeable membrane, allowing some kinds of ions and molecules to enter and leave the cell but barring the passage of others. It also has elastic properties and can be stretched or compressed within limits, yet return to its original form after the removal of the force which has brought about its deformation; electrical measurements show that it has high electrical resistance, and measurements and calculations of the surface tension of cells show that it is usually low in potential energy.

The presence of the plasma membrane affects the cell in various ways. Since it is a semi-permeable one, special conditions for the phenomenon of diffusion are set up; the tendency for the diffusion of ions and molecules remains the same but the impermeability of the membrane to some makes these virtually non-diffusible, at least as far as their passage into and out of cells is concerned. These special conditions obtain in every living biological system, for protoplasm is everywhere separated from its environment by a semi-permeable membrane. This is probably the nature of the membrane surrounding the nucleus and that of the membranes surrounding every vacuole and fluid inclusion in the cell. The solid inclusions may well be similarly surrounded but since there is no exchange of molecules between them and the cytoplasm, or at most a very small one, the effect of such a membrane is here negligible.

*Semi-permeable membranes and osmosis:* Protoplasm is a fluid, a complex solution, and it invariably exists in fluid environments, which are also solutions of various degrees of complexity, for all active cells, whether individuals or part of a many-celled organism, are bathed by liquids, either the tissue fluids or the salt or fresh water of oceans, lakes, streams and other natural habitats. Everywhere in the natural world, when two solutions are brought together in which there is free diffusion of the solvent but restrictions to the diffusion of the solute, a condition is set up known as osmosis, from a Greek word, osmos, meaning impulse. This condition obtains in all biological systems by virtue of the semi-permeable nature of the plasma membrane and also certain other factors that exist within the cells, so that osmosis and osmotic relationships are of the utmost importance to them.

The plasma membrane is apparently always freely permeable to water, and since protoplasm as well as its natural environments are aqueous solutions there is free exchange of water molecules back and forth across the cell surface. This exchange occurs because of the rapid movements of the water molecules which at all ordinary temperatures are in incessant thermal motion. In the course of these movements, some of the molecules come in contact with both surfaces of the plasma membrane and since it offers no obstruction to them, no matter in what direction they strike it, they behave as if it were not there. The general direction of their movement is like that of any freely diffusing substance, from the region of greater concentration to that of less, along a concentration gradient. In any system in which there is a limitation or restriction to the diffusion of the solute, there are ions and molecules that are also in movement yet cannot move along the natural concentration gradients. Within the cell, these particles may also strike against the plasma membrane, but if it is impermeable to them, they bounce back, as a ball bounces back when it is thrown against a wall. The pressure of these particles, returned to the solution which they would tend to leave if the conditions allowed them to do so, is known as the osmotic pressure of the solution and as such is a definite and measurable property of all solutions.*

OSMOTIC RELATIONS OF CELLS: The effect that osmotic relationships have upon the cell can best be illustrated by hypothetical examples, since the colloidal solution, protoplasm, is extremely complex in its components and also variable in its osmotic behavior. Suppose that one were to immerse a cell in pure water, where there were nothing but water molecules, and therefore a far greater concentration outside than inside the plasma membrane. The water molecules will pass freely back and forth into and out from the cell, but many more will enter it than will leave it in the same period of time, because the chances of their coming in contact with the outer surface of the membrane are far greater than those of their hitting the inner surface, where there are not only fewer of them but where much larger molecules of proteins, polysaccharides and lipids, as well as other non-diffusible substances get in their way (Fig. 7.4). Water will therefore enter the cell at a faster rate than it leaves it, and the cell will swell. Theoretically, this unequal exchange will go on until equilibrium is reached, the moment when just as many water molecules are entering the cell as are leaving it; practically, this point could never be reached, for the plasma membrane, though elastic, is not indefinitely extensible, and the cell would burst while equilibrium was still a long way off.

Suppose one establishes another set of conditions, one for instance in which there are diffusible and non-diffusible substances on both sides of the membrane. This would be the case if one immersed cells in solutions of cane sugar and the effect would depend upon the concentration of cane sugar used, that is, upon the concentration of non-diffusible solute to diffusible solvent. Again the water diffuses freely along its concentration gradient and leaves and enters the cell at unequal rates. Whether it enters the cell faster than it leaves or leaves it faster than it enters depends upon its concentration inside it and outside it, that is, upon the number of its molecules that can pass across the same area of the membrane in each direction in the same period of time. Since the number of molecules that can strike and pass any area of the membrane depends also upon the concentration of the non-diffusible molecules that bounce back from the membrane when they strike it, and also impede the movement of the water molecules toward it, whether the addition of water to the cell contents or its loss from it is the end result of osmosis depends upon the relative osmotic pressures of the two solutions. If the cell is put into a solution of cane sugar of such a concentration that initially twice as many water molecules collide with the same

* Osmotic pressure and osmosis are complicated physico-chemical phenomena for which no one theory yet proposed provides a complete or wholly satisfactory explanation. The bombardment theory outlined here, proposed by the Dutch physical chemist Jacobus van't Hoff (1852-1911), has been presented as offering the best introduction to these phenomena for an elementary student of biology and a foundation upon which the necessary revisions and additions may later be laid.

area of the membrane from the outside as from the inside, then they will start to enter the cell twice as fast as they leave. But as more enter the cell than leave it, the effect is the gradual dilution of the cell contents and the equally gradual concentration of the surrounding solution, until the two concentrations become equal. Two solutions reach osmotic equilibrium when the exchange of solvent molecules between them is equal in rate.

If on the other hand, a cell is put into a solution of greater osmotic pressure than that of its protoplasm, water passes out through the plasma membrane faster than it passes in. This would happen if a cell were put into a solution of cane sugar in which the concentration of sugar was such, for example, that half as many water molecules impinged upon the same area of the membrane's outer surface as upon the inner in the same period of time. Then initially twice as many would leave the cell than would enter it, and it would shrink, but as its contents gradually became more concentrated the difference in the rate of exchange would become less and less and would finally be equal, and the two solutions would be in osmotic equilibrium.

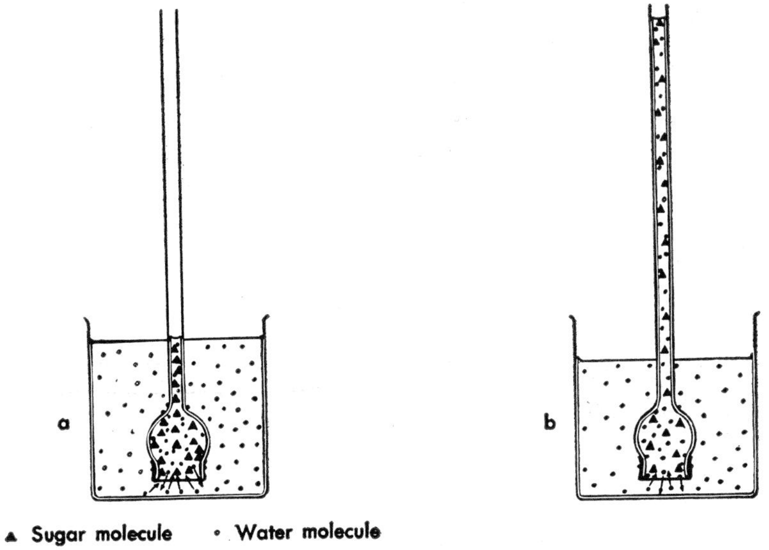

▲ Sugar molecule    • Water molecule

FIGURE 7.4 Diagram illustrating the principle of osmosis. A tube whose expanded open end is covered with a semi-permeable membrane is partly filled with sugar solution and immersed in a beaker of water. The arrows show the direction of movement of the water molecules which pass freely across the membrane, while the sugar molecules cannot. In a, more water molecules are shown moving into the tube than leaving it, and the water in the tube therefore rises and the solution becomes more dilute. In b, the water is shown as having risen to a considerable height and osmotic equilibrium reached, with the same number of water molecules passing across the membrane in both directions. The cell is a far more complicated osmotic system than this, but the principle of exchange of diffusible molecules is the same.

EXPERIMENTAL DETERMINATION OF OSMOTIC RELATIONS: The exchange of diffusible particles across the plasma membrane is constantly going on; it becomes evident only when this takes place at an unequal rate. The inequality depends upon the concentrations of these particles on the two sides of the membrane, and hence upon the concentrations of the non-diffusible particles, since, when these are present, they replace some of the diffusible particles and in a sense block their movements. The osmotic pressure of any solution is related to the concentration of non-diffusible particles in it and hence the osmotic relations of any

[ 66 ] THE ORGANIZATION OF THE NATURAL WORLD

two solutions depend upon their respective osmotic pressures. A solution which is in osmotic equilibrium with the cell contents, when the exchange of water molecules across the membrane is equal, is said to be isotonic to it (Greek, isos = equal + tonos = meas-

living condition, by immersing it in solutions of different concentrations of cane sugar, proteins or other non-diffusible substances. The red blood cells of vertebrates lend themselves readily to this kind of experiment and have been very frequently used,

FIGURE 7.5 Osmotic relations in living cells.

   a. Hemolysis of red blood cells.

   1. The effect of a hypotonic solution upon a mammalian red blood corpuscle. In a, the corpuscle is shown in its natural form, a flattened disc; figures b-e show its gradual enlargement to a spherical form as water molecules from the surrounding medium enter it faster than they leave it.

   2. The effect of a hypertonic solution (1% NaCl) upon the corpuscle. Water diffuses out of the corpuscle faster than it diffuses into it, causing it to shrink and its membrane to collapse irregularly (crenation).

   b. Plasmolysis in a plant cell. If a plant cell is immersed in a medium hypertonic to its cell sap, water leaves the vacuole faster than it enters it, and the protoplast collapses and draws away from the cellulose walls surrounding it, which are not affected by such water loss. (From Hylander and Stanley, *College Botany*. Copyright 1949 by The Macmillan Company.)

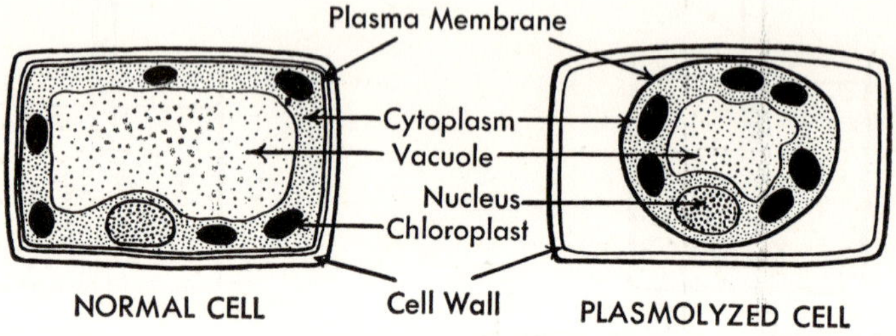

ure); one of greater osmotic pressure, when water leaves the cell faster than it enters it, is said to be hypertonic to it (Greek, hyper = above); and one of lower osmotic pressure, when water enters the cell faster than it leaves, is said to be hypotonic to it (Greek, hypo = under).

These relations can be experimentally determined for any cell that can be isolated and maintained for a period of time in a

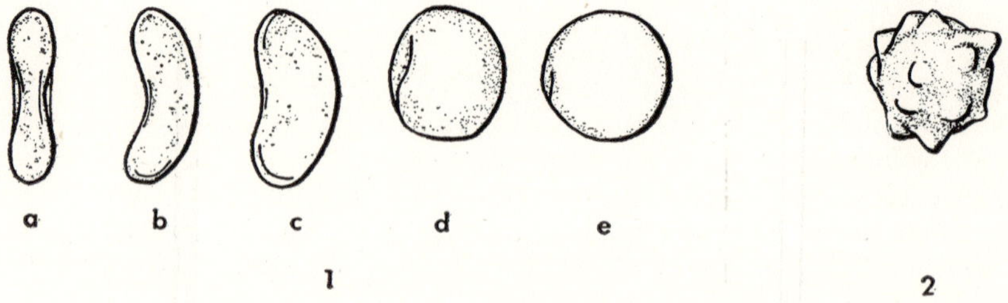

for they can be obtained in large numbers and are easily handled and observed through a microscope (Fig. 7.5). If any cell is in an isotonic medium, there is no change in its size, for water is leaving it as fast as it is entering and the exchange has no effect upon its volume or the concentration of its contents. If it is put in a hypertonic medium, it shrinks, for its volume decreases as it loses water; if the osmotic pressure of the surrounding solution is considerably greater than that of the cell contents, this water loss will continue beyond the limits in which it can maintain itself, and it will undergo a kind of disintegration known as cytolysis, but if the difference in osmotic pressure between the two solutions is relatively small, equilibrium will be reached before this disintegration occurs and the only obvious effect will be its decrease in size. If on the other hand, a cell is put into a hypotonic solution, water molecules enter it faster than they leave; if the difference is slight, the cell slowly swells and stays enlarged after equilibrium is reached; if the difference is great, it swells rapidly and undergoes cytolysis by bursting.

FACTORS INFLUENCING OSMOSIS IN CELLS: Another property of the plasma membrane, its elasticity, has an effect upon the osmotic relationships of the cell. The membrane will stretch as the cell contents increase, but after a certain degree of distention, tends to collapse again, unless it is stretched rapidly past its limit of expansion. When a cell is in a hypotonic medium, this elasticity sustained by additional cell membranes or other supporting structures sets up a pressure in the cell counter to that of the osmotic pressure of the surrounding solution so that it exerts a force against the entrance of water molecules. This force may be great enough to retard the entrance of some of the water molecules, and so to bring about an equalization in the rate of their passage from one side of the plasma membrane to the other. Its effect is then to cancel out that of the difference in the osmotic pressures of the two solutions and to bring about osmotic equilibrium even while a diffusion gradient persists. This is not a true equilibrium, but a "steady state," when the exchange of solute particles is balanced not because of their equality in concentration but because of a condition opposing their difference in the rate of passage across the membrane.

The osmotic relations of cells are never so simple as in the foregoing illustrations, for cells and their surrounding fluids are extremely complex solutions. The large colloidal particles of protoplasm, its electrolytes with electrostatic attraction between ions of opposite charge, its shifting conditions of metabolic activity all make it a complicated and unstable osmotic system, and tissue fluids, pond and sea water are themselves by no means simple solutions of one or two substances. The cell itself, by doing work, can concentrate certain of the substances which enter it, thereby permitting their diffusion into it beyond the point of theoretical osmotic equilibrium. Moreover, the plasma membrane has been shown to be both variable and selective in its permeability, allowing the passage of substances at one time but not at another and permitting the entrance of some substances into the cell but not their exit from it, and vice versa. Some ions appear to enter more slowly than others, if they enter at all, although on the physical grounds of charge and mass it would seem that they would diffuse with equal readiness. There are still many open questions about osmotic phenomena in biological systems; the use of radioactive ions, whose actual penetration, as well as the rate at which they enter the cell, can be determined, should soon provide some of the answers.

The nature of the membrane, as well as its action, is also not yet clearly understood. It acts as a semi-permeable membrane only in the living cell; when the cell dies for any reason it becomes freely permeable, and when it is destroyed in any way, the cell dies. At present, because it is in general permeable to lipid-soluble substances and because it can be destroyed by lipid solvents, it is thought to be lipid itself, perhaps with protein attached (Fig. 7.6). It is probable that the surface layer of the cell is made up of a layer of lipid one or two molecules thick, with a single layer of protein molecules adsorbed on both surfaces, the whole complex forming a thin film enclosing the cell, a film whose integrity is essential to its life, and whose nature controls its water balance and the loss of substances from it as well as their penetration into it. Among other things, the distention, or turgor, of cells is a consequence of their osmotic relationships, for it is related to their water content. Most tissues are fairly firm, not flaccid, and this firmness is due to the water content of their individual cells, for if water is withdrawn, they become limp. This is most evident in plants, where wilting is a direct consequence of water loss from the cells of the stems and leaves whose turgor usually keeps them erect or extended. Osmosis, too, is related to the root pressure which Stephen Hales recognized and measured over two hundred years ago, for the root hairs, the delicate processes extending into the soil from the smallest roots of a plant, are exchanging water molecules with the drops of moisture around the particles of earth, and are receiving them and others more rapidly than they are giving them up (Fig. 7.7).

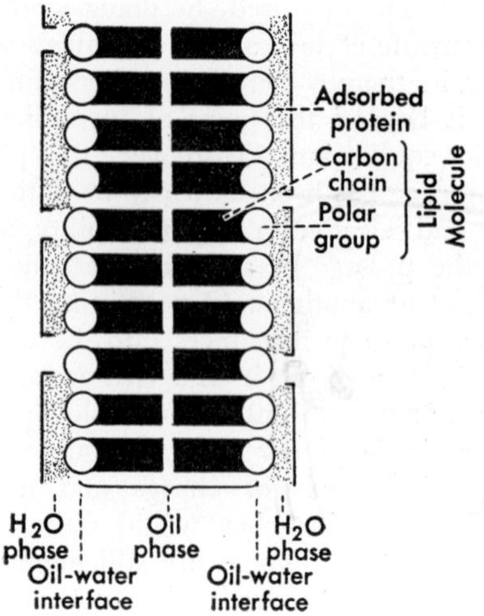

**Differences between cells; size differences**

Most cells are microscopic, but some, like the eggs of birds and fish, are not only macroscopic but of considerable size. In such eggs, however, the actual mass of cytoplasm is small, for nearly all of the volume of the cell is filled with yolk, nutrient material which has been synthesized during the growth of the cell and stored up for use during its development into a new individual. In the hen's egg, for example, the so-called yolk as distinct from the white represents the egg cell proper; this "yolk" is in reality but a thin envelope of cytoplasm, in which lie the nucleus and the other cytoplasmic inclusions, enclosing a mass of reserve protein and lipid, and surrounded by additional nutrient in the egg white and by the protective coverings, the shell and its membranes. This same arrangement is true of heavily-yolked fish and amphibian eggs, and of the cells of fat or adipose tissue, where the central part of the system is filled with inactive, stored material and the protoplasm is pushed back against the wall of the cell. But the majority of active animal cells show a considerable degree of uniformity in size; the difference in volume between the liver of a mouse and the liver of an elephant lies not in the size but in the number of cells that compose it. There is a limit to the amount of cytoplasm that a nucleus can control and that a surface can accommodate and regulate, so that for physiological reasons there is an upper limit to the volume that cells may reach and still remain efficient biological systems.

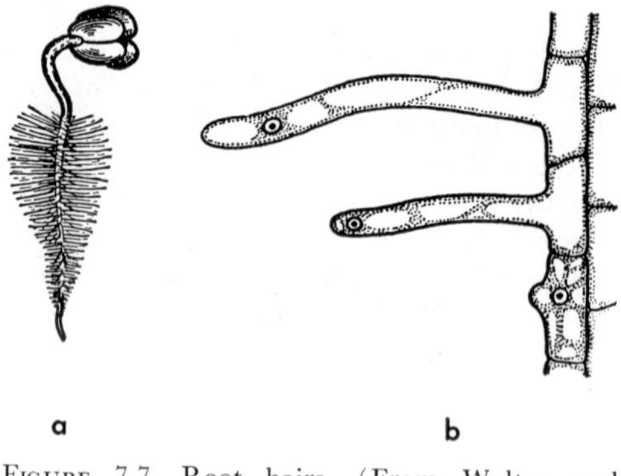

FIGURE 7.6 Diagram showing the theoretical structure of the plasma membrane. The lipid molecules, represented as black rods with open circles at one end, are oriented so that their polar groups are in the oil-water interfaces (compare Figure 6.4); a layer of protein molecules is adsorbed on both these interfaces. (After Danielli.)

FIGURE 7.7 Root hairs. (From Walter and Sayles, *Biology of the Vertebrates*. (Copyright 1949 by The Macmillan Company.)

a. A seedling showing the bushy outgrowths of root hairs along its root.
b. A section through the root, showing the epidermal cells and their root hairs as protoplasmic extensions.

## PROTOPLASM AND THE CELL

*Distinctions between plant and animal cells:* In plant cells the protoplasm also occupies a relatively small space, for the central part of the cell is filled with a large vacuole, an aqueous solution of many different substances formed during its growth by the flowing together of smaller vacuoles and separated from the cytoplasm by a semipermeable membrane, the tonoplast or vacuolar membrane (Fig. 7.8). Only in the young and growing regions of the plant do the cytoplasm and nucleus form the main mass of the cell as a whole. Plant cells are distinguished from animal cells by two other characteristics besides the central vacuole—by the presence of an outer supporting wall of cellulose, and of a particular kind of cytoplasmic inclusion known as a plastid. Cellulose is a carbohydrate whose molecules have a lattice arrangement like the ions in a crystal of sodium chloride and which is made by the cell and deposited around it, outside the plasma and other cell membranes, during the course of its growth. The cellulose wall may be of different thickness in different cells, and it may become im-

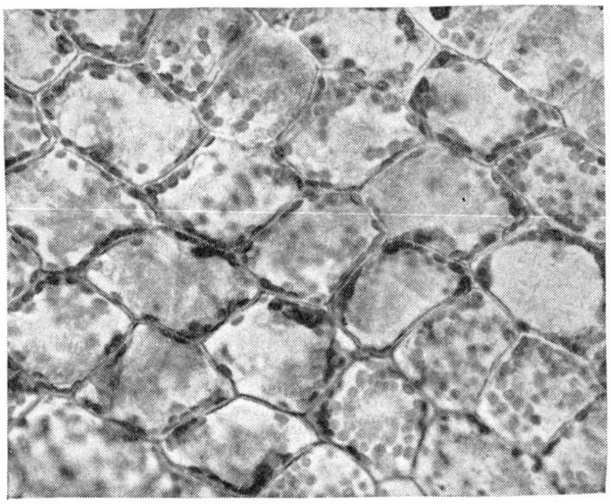

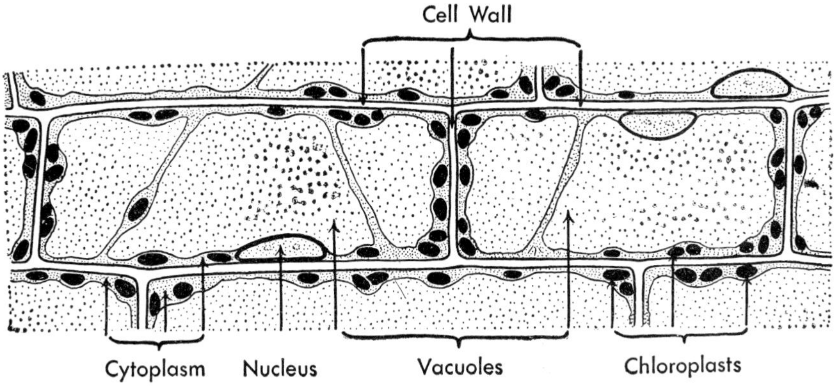

FIGURE 7.8  Plant cells.

    a. Cells from a leaf of the pond weed, Vallisneria. × 500. (Microphotograph by C. F. Reather from Moment, *General Biology for Colleges*. Copyright 1942 by the D. Appleton-Century Company.)

    b. Cells from a leaf of the pond weed, Anacharis, showing details of structure. (From Hylander and Stanley, *College Botany*. Copyright 1949 by The Macmillan Company.)

pregnated with other substances during the ageing of the cell; by lignin, a substance whose chemical constitution is unknown, in the woody tissues; by cutin, a waxy substance which acts like a waterproof coat, in the superficial cells; by suberin, chemically something like cutin, in the cork cells; by chitin, a substance found also in the outer coverings of insects, in some of the simpler plants, and by tannins and mucilages. The plastids are small bodies of various shapes and sizes, most probably derived from some of the mitochondria in the young cell. They may be colorless, when they are known as leucoplasts, or they may contain pigments when they are called chromoplasts. Those which contain among other pigments the green one, chlorophyll, are known as chloroplasts and their presence in the leaves and other exposed regions of the plant is essential to its photosynthesis (Fig. 7.9). Other chromoplasts may contain different kinds of yellow pigments, the flavones or xanthones, and the red, blue and violet anthocyanins of the cell sap; these pigments, and the pH of the medium in which they are dissolved, are responsible for the colors and color variations of the flowers and other parts of plants.

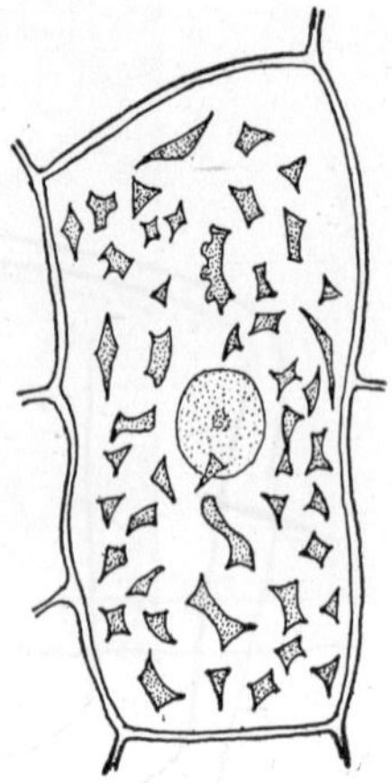

***Differences in shape:*** The shapes of all cells are to some extent determined by the conditions of internal and external pressure to which they are subjected. Under equal conditions of pressure inside and outside it, a cell would be spherical, for that is the form in which the greatest volume of a fluid mass can be enclosed by the smallest area of surface. But this ideal condition is not reached by any cell, for the accumulation of products inside it and in the many-celled organism, the contact of its neighbors or of more rigid structures around it, distort it in one way or another. It is most closely approximated in the eggs of some marine animals, like starfish and sea urchins, which contain a relatively small amount of yolk fairly evenly distributed throughout the cytoplasm and which, since they are shed into the water, are subjected to equal pressure all over their surfaces. Free cells which contain a large amount of reserve

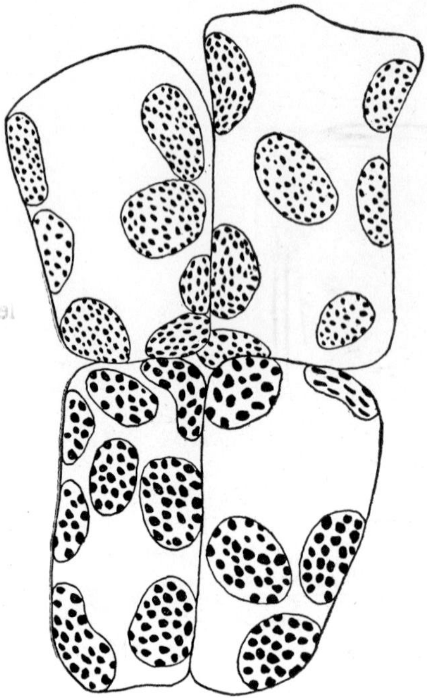

FIGURE 7.9 Plant plastids. (From Smith, Gilbert, Evans, Duggar, Bryan and Allen, *A Textbook of General Botany*. Copyright 1942 by The Macmillan Company.)

a. Chloroplasts from the leaf of Colocasia, an Egyptian plant like a water lily. (After Heitz.)
b. Chromoplasts in the cell of a nasturtium flower.

material are either ovoid or elliptical, but cells which are packed together in tissues become faceted (Figs. 7.8a, 11.1a). The possible shapes and sizes of cells in aggregates have been studied in various ways—by making models with soap bubbles and soap films for instance, and also by mathematical calculations of the possible geometric forms. They do appear to conform to the law of minimal surfaces, and the most common form of soft-walled cells in plant and animal tissues is that of a 12- or 14-sided polygon.

But in certain cells the shape is intrinsic and as much a part of their distinguishing characteristics as their other structural and functional differentiations. Most unicellular organisms, for example, have constant and specific shapes; the processes which extend from the central cytoplasmic mass of the nerve cell and the long, spindle shape of the smooth muscle cell are as much a part of their constitutions as the ability to conduct a nervous impulse or to contract spontaneously or on stimulation. As the function of a cell in an organism is determined by its own constitution as well as by its position in the body, so its shape is the result of conditions within it as well as outside it.

*Protoplasmic movement:* The motile cells in organisms, such as the leucocytes that move about in the body fluids and tissue spaces of most animals, are constantly changing shape, as are the single-celled animals, like amoebae and the multinucleate protoplasmic masses, the slime molds (Fig. 7.10). These movements are accompanied by local changes in the sol-gel relationships of the cytoplasm, and by streaming of the more fluid regions. In such cells there is no constancy of shape, nor of position of the internal structures which are carried along in the direction of the main currents. Such streaming probably occurs to a lesser extent in all cells; it is most evident in motile animal and in plant cells where the cytoplasm around the central vacuole can be seen to be in constant motion, circling now this way and now that around the periphery of the cell, and carrying along with its current the plastids, mitochondria and other visible granules, the smallest of which are in

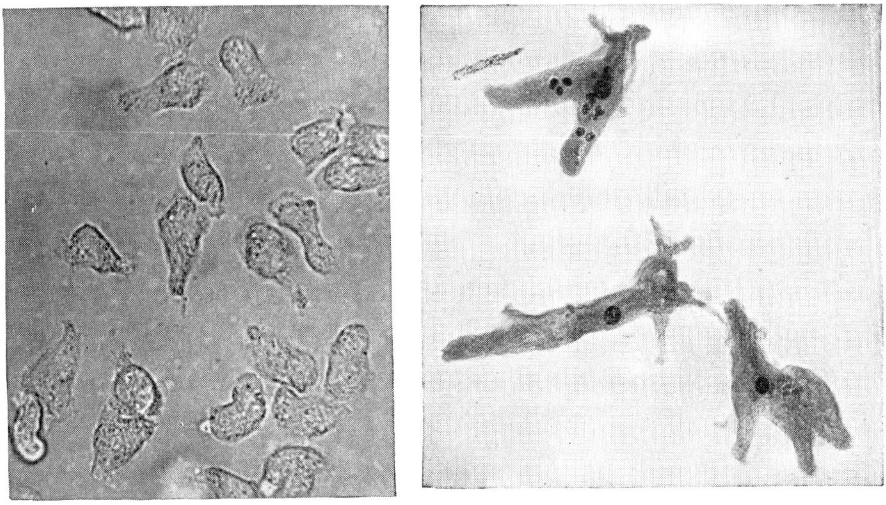

FIGURE 7.10 Amoeboid movement.

    a. Leucocytes (neutrophils) of human blood in tissue culture. × 1100. (Microphotograph by courtesy of Dr. Warren H. Lewis.)

    b. Amoeba proteus. (Photograph by courtesy of the General Biological Supply House, Inc., Chicago.)

Brownian movement. The streaming, around and around the vacuole, is called cyclosis; it is a phenomenon of protoplasm which has been extensively studied, but though many theories to explain it have been proposed, none as yet is wholly satisfactory.

**The cell as a physico-chemical system**

The living cell is thus a complex, organized and integrated system, functionally indivisible although showing regions of differentiation that can be recognized as units in its general organization. Physically, it is a colloidal solution, bounded at every surface by a semi-permeable membrane, and showing the characteristics of an electrical system; in the sizes and shapes which it may assume, it follows in general the mathematical law for the minimal surfaces of fluids. Chemically, it is a colloidal solution of large and intricate molecules and of electrolytes, and a system in which reactions of all types are constantly going on, energy exchanges which result in the formation and the degradation and disintegration of compounds, the storing of potential energy and the release of kinetic energy. Biologically, it is the unit of protoplasm, the substance of all living things, and the smallest unit which exhibits all the phenomena of life. Its kinetic energy is manifested as movement, heat, and in a few cases as light, as electrical energy and as chemical energy for all those reactions which are included in the general word metabolism, by means of which special substances and even new protoplasm are synthesized so that the cell increases its own mass and ultimately uses some of its kinetic energy for the elaborate series of nuclear and cytoplasmic changes that lead to its division and reproduction. As a physico-chemical system, protoplasm and the cell evade none of the established laws of the natural world; as a biological system, they go beyond them.

SECTION TWO

THE ORGANIZATION OF
BIOLOGICAL SYSTEMS

# CHAPTER 8

# THE ORGANISM AND ITS ENVIRONMENT

## The earliest living things and the continuity of life on earth

No living thing is independent of its physical surroundings nor is any part of the physical world independent of the life it supports. Organism and environment together, between which there is a constant exchange of energy and of material substances, constitute the systems whose operations and mutual relationships are the concern of the biologist. No one knows when or how protoplasm first became organized, or when or how life began on this planet, but the history of plants and animals, sketched in their remains found as fossils in different levels of the earth's crust, represents a sequence of life presumably unbroken since the Proterozoic and Archeozoic Eras of the geological time-scale, some 1,200,000,000 years ago (Figs. 8.2, 8.3).

It is most likely that the first organisms to meet the conditions of life on this planet were ones of simple organization, either animal-like and capable of subsisting upon mineral salts and organic compounds already formed, such as other complex atomic configurations and protoplasm itself, solely by physical processes independent of biological ones, or else were plant-like and capable of constructing carbohydrate from atmospheric $CO_2$ by photosynthesis or some other chemical mechanism. The most convincing evidence for the belief, for which there can be no actual proof, that the first animals to appear were marine ones is the striking similarity in ionic composition between the body fluids of modern animals and sea water. This is shown in Table IV, in which the relative concentrations of the more common ions of sea water and the body fluids of a few representative animals are given; in this table, the concentration of the sodium ion is taken as 100 and that of the others expressed as percentages of it. Presumably the fluids of the first animals were identical with the water in which they lived, while in the millions of years that life has existed on this planet, these fluids have become modified and, for reasons concerned with relative motility and capacity for passing across membranes, the proportions of the ions in them altered and, in some animals at least, other components added.

TABLE IV

Relative Ionic Compositions of the Bloods and Tissue Fluids of Animals. (Macallum, 1926)

| | Na | K | Ca | Mg | Cl | SO$_4$ |
|---|---|---|---|---|---|---|
| Sea Water | 100 | 3.61 | 3.91 | 12.10 | 180.90 | 20.90 |
| Jellyfish (Aurelia) | 100 | 5.18 | 4.13 | 11.40 | 185.50 | 13.18 |
| Lobster | 100 | 3.75 | 4.85 | 1.72 | 171.20 | 6.67 |
| Dogfish | 100 | 4.61 | 2.71 | 2.46 | 165.70 | |
| Frog | 100[a] | 11.80 | 3.17 | 0.79 | 135.60 | |
| Dog | 100 | 6.62 | 2.80 | 0.758 | 139.50 | |
| Man (serum) | 100 | 6.75 | 3.10 | 0.695 | 128.80 | |

[a] The high value for the potassium ion is attributed to the injury of red blood cells and the consequent release of potassium ions from them.

Whether the multiplicity of different kinds of living things that inhabit the earth today, and that we know from the geologic record to have inhabited it in past Eras, had a single common ancestor in the Proterozoic seas, or several, is only a matter of speculation. But we do know that in the course of the earth's history various types of organisms have appeared, flourished, persisted or disappeared, and that the measure of their success has been the extent to which they have been able to meet the conditions of existence on this planet, to adapt themselves to its changing conditions, and to reproduce their kind (Fig. 8.4). Through such adapta-

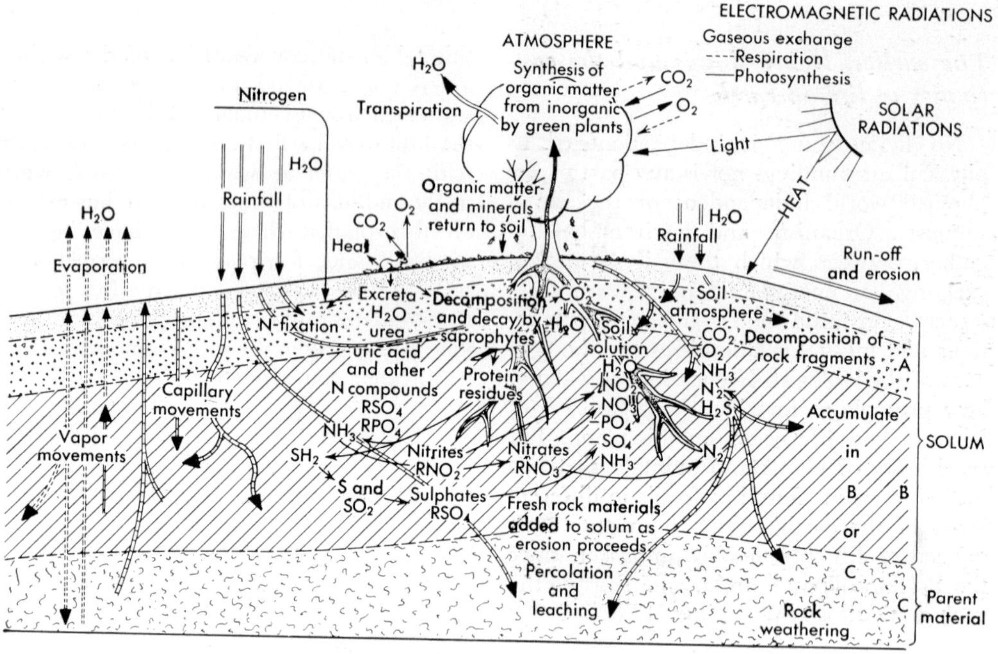

*Factors determining the conditions of existence*

The conditions of existence under which an organism must live, grow and reproduce are both general ones, common to all parts

FIGURE 8.1 Diagram showing the relations between terrestrial organisms and the environment. (After Kellogg.)

tion and reproduction, which has been going on since life first began upon the planet, the population of the world to-day includes some one and one-half million different kinds of living things, inhabiting its waters, its surface, its soil and the atmosphere above it from the polar ice-caps to the equator. Some of these have bodies made of millions of cells, others of comparatively few or even of but a single cell. Fundamental similarities between all of them in organization and in operation indicate a common ancestry; fundamental differences indicate that they have met the conditions of existence in a variety of ways and that the paths that they have followed in their development have been different and often widely divergent ones.

of this planet, and local ones, characteristic of particular areas of it; in both cases, they are determined by physical and biological factors. The physical factors include energy in its various forms; the distribution of the elements and their compounds, and the configuration and nature of the earth's surface. The biological factors are those resulting from the previous, or the contemporaneous, existence of other organisms upon the earth.

### Physical factors: energy

The ultimate source of all the energy impinging upon the earth and its inhabitants is the sun, only a part of whose radiation is directly appreciated by man as light and heat. Over 200 years ago Isaac Newton showed that if a transparent prism were placed in a beam of sunlight, this white light was resolved into seven colors, the violet, indigo, blue, green, yellow, orange and red of the familiar visible spectrum. Each of these colors is now known to have a different energy value or, on the wave theory of light, to represent a different range of wave-length. But the spectrum of light represents only a small part of all the solar energy to which the earth and its biological systems are exposed, energy which may likewise be resolved into components of different energy values, or wave-lengths, as the electromagnetic spectrum. The range of this spectrum, and the order of magnitude of its wave-lengths, are shown in Table V.

**Distribution of the elements and their compounds:** The chemical elements, as elementary substances or as compounds, are present in the atmosphere that surrounds the earth, in solution in the waters of its oceans, rivers, lakes, streams and smaller bodies of water, and in its solid surface. The distribution of these elements, particularly the distribution and the combinations of those that are requisite to the composition and operation of protoplasm, is one of the most important factors in determining whether an area of its surface is capable of supporting life at all, and if so, what forms of life can exist there. In some regions, all of those requisite to biological systems may be abundant in forms directly available to living organisms; in others some or all of them may be deficient, or combined in ways that make them less readily obtainable, imposing conditions that demand special adjustments from organisms if they are to exist there.

The atmosphere is a mixture of gases, with an average composition, at sea level, of:

| | |
|---|---|
| Oxygen | 20.65% |
| Nitrogen | 77.11% |
| Carbon dioxide | 0.03% |
| Water vapor | 1.40% |
| Other gases | 1.00% |
| (helium, neon, argon, etc.) | |

The relative proportions of these gases are remarkably constant, at least at the levels of the atmosphere close to the earth, although in local areas other gases may be added from natural sources, such as volcanoes and mineral springs and, in the upper regions of the atmospheric envelope, the proportions of oxygen and carbon dioxide in relation to the other gases are less. The atmosphere has mass and exerts a pressure upon the earth's surface equal, at sea level, to that of a column of mercury 760 mm. in height; above sea level, its pressure is less than this and below it, greater.

At the surface of all natural bodies of water where air and water meet, water molecules are constantly leaving the aqueous surface and diffusing through the atmosphere as water vapor, and molecules of the atmospheric gases are entering the water and diffusing through it. The gaseous content of any body of water depends upon the partial pressure of each gas, or the fraction of the total atmospheric pressure that each one represents; upon its solubility; and upon the salinity and the temperature of the water. Neither oxygen nor nitrogen is very soluble in water; carbon dioxide is not only

FIGURE 8.2 A fossil plant. Spermatophyte leaf from the Miocene beds, Florissant, Colorado. (Photograph by courtesy of Dr. Horace Richards.)

more soluble, but also combines with water to form carbonic acid, which in turn may combine with dissolved salts to form carbonates. The amount of free carbonic acid near the surface of an ocean or a pond may be equivalent to the amount of carbon dioxide in the air with which it is in contact, but the amount of oxygen and nitrogen in the same volume of water is much less than that of air. And the higher the temperature and greater the degree of salinity of the water, the lower its oxygen and nitrogen content. Fresh water at 30°C, for example, when fully saturated with oxygen, contains about half as much of the gas as it does at 0°C, and a 3% solution of NaCl, in equilibrium with the atmosphere, about 4/5 as much oxygen as a corresponding volume of fresh water.

The primary, or parent, material of the earth's crust is rock, solid mineral matter which is, in most regions, a mixture of at least two, and usually more, different minerals. In the course of the earth's history, this parent rock has been exposed to physical and mechanical conditions that have brought about its weathering, or gradual disintegration, so that it has become covered to a greater or less extent by a loose surface layer, the soil, made up of the fine mineral particles to which have been added, since life has existed, products of organic activity, decomposition and decay. The layers of the earth's surface accessible to man, and whose composition is therefore known to him, may be divided into three major horizons, designated as A, B and C, of which the C horizon includes essentially unaltered parent material and the A and B horizons, the soil, and each of which may be further

## TABLE V
### Electromagnetic Spectrum

| Name | Wave-length (order of magnitude) |
|---|---|
| Radio waves | $2 \times 10^6$ cm. (2,000,000 cm.) |
| Short electric waves | $4 \times 10^3$ cm. (4,000 cm.) |
| Infrared (heat) [Spectrum of Sunlight] | $3.5 \times 10^{-2}$ cm. (0.35 cm.) |
| Visible light [Spectrum of Sunlight] | $7 \times 10^{-5}$ cm. (0.00007 cm.) |
| Ultraviolet [Spectrum of Sunlight] | $4 \times 10^{-5}$ cm. (0.00004 cm.) |
| Extreme ultra-violet | $1.2 \times 10^{-6}$ cm. (0.0000012 cm.) |
| X rays | $5 \times 10^{-7}$ cm. (0.0000005 cm.) |
| Gamma rays | $1.2 \times 10^{-9}$ cm. (0.0000000012 cm.) |
| | $5 \times 10^{-11}$ cm. (0.00000000005 cm.) |
| Cosmic rays | $1 \times 10^{-12}$ cm. (0.000000000001 cm.) |
| | $1 \times 10^{-13}$ cm. (0.0000000000001 cm.) |

divided into a number of minor horizons, as $A_0$, $A_1$, and so on, the whole constituting a "soil profile" that is unique for each different kind of landscape (Fig. 8.5).

The mineral composition of the C horizon determines the general character of the inorganic components of the soil above it, and the nature and variety of inorganic compounds available to organisms inhabiting any particular locality, except insofar as the native character of a soil may be altered by the transportation of surface layers from one region to another by natural agents such as wind and flowing waters or, deliberately, by man.

*Configuration and nature of the earth's crust:* The configuration of the earth's crust, no more uniform than its composition, likewise presents different conditions and offers varied environments to living things. Its mountains, hills and valleys, its plains and water-filled depressions, with differences in light, temperature, pressure and available inorganic and organic supplies, all demand adjustments of different kinds from living

a

b

FIGURE 8.3 Fossil animals.

a. The wing of an extinct, fossilized insect (Stylotermes Washingtoniensis) from the Miocene beds near Spokane, Washington. (Photograph by courtesy of the U.S. Department of Agriculture, Bureau of Entomology and Plant Quarantine.)

b. Phacops rana, a trilobite, from the Devonian beds near Silica, Ohio. (Photograph by D. F. Reath.)

Trilobites, the first arthropods whose remains have been preserved, were cosmopolitan in their distribution and their remains have been found all over the world. They are called trilobites because of the longitudinal furrows, clearly visible in the extended specimen in this figure, that delimit a median lobe, the axis, from two lateral lobes, the pleura. They have a number of characters in common with the wood lice that are widely distributed today, including the ability to roll up in a ball like Armadillidium, the pill bug.

# Progression of Life-forms on Earth According to the Geological Time Scale.

*(The succession of geological and biological events can best be understood by reading from the bottom upwards.)*

FIGURE 8.4 The succession of life-forms upon the earth. (Photograph of a mural in Park Hall, Bryn Mawr College, by Mildred Burrage.) *Caption continued on facing page.*

| Geologic Eras | Periods and Epochs | Estimated Duration | Major geological and biological events (in North America). |
|---|---|---|---|
| **CENOZOIC** (Greek kainos = recent + zoe = life) | Recent (post-glacial) | 2 million years | Rise of human civilization. Human mentality dominates the organic world. |
| | Pleistocene Epoch (Greek, pleistos = most + kainos) | | Continued deformation of earth's surface and elevation of mountains. Periodic glaciation in northern hemisphere. Many of the large mammals become extinct. Herbaceous angiosperms more specialized and widespread. First record of Man. |
| | Pliocene Epoch (Greek, pleion = more + kainos) | 53 million years | Climate becomes generally cooler. Migrations of land animals across land bridges between North America and Eurasia continue. |
| | Miocene Epoch (Greek, meion = less + kainos) | | Great deformations of the earth's surface and elevation of mountains. Intercontinental migrations of land animals across Bering land bridge. Mammals attain greatest diversity of type and widest distribution. Herbaceous angiosperms appear. |
| | Oligocene Epoch (Greek, oligos = small + kainos) | | Climate becomes drier; drying up of swamps favors spread of meadow vegetation and evolution of grasses. Grazing types of mammals evolve, and many browsing types become extinct. Higher mammals arise; great apes appear in Eurasia. Extensive meadowlands favor specialization and spread of birds and insects. |
| | Eocene Epoch (Greek, eos = dawn + kainos) | | Moist, temperate, uniform climate. Rise of angiosperms, bony fishes and toothless birds. Rise of precursors of modern mammals. Gastropods and pelecypods dominant among invertebrates. Large foraminifera (nummilites) abundant in shallow seas. |
| | Paleocene Epoch (Greek, palaios = ancient + kainos) | | Deformation of the earth's surface with formation of mountains. Archaic mammals, small and unspecialized, dominate the land. |
| **MESOZOIC** (Greek, mesos = middle + zoe) | Cretaceous Period (Latin, creta = chalk) | 55 million years | Last extensive submergence of North America, followed by retreat of seas from inland areas. Formation of Rocky Mountains in North America and Andes in South America. General fall in temperature in early part of period, with restoration of mild climate later. Deciduous trees appear, making vast hardwood forests. Marsupials and insectivores arise. Modern types of aquatic and terrestrial invertebrates are well-established. Period terminates with the "Great Dying"; the huge reptiles (dinosaurs, flying and large aquatic reptiles) and ammonites become extinct. Surviving reptiles become more specialized; first appearance of snakes. |
| | Jurassic Period | 28 million years | Climate in general more humid and cooler, but desert conditions prevail in southwest of North America. Herbaceous and tree ferns, cycads, conifers and gingkos widely distributed in the forests. First appearance of angiosperms? Rise of giant dinosaurs and flying reptiles; first reptile-like birds. Primitive mammals appear. The ammonites reach their climax. |
| | Triassic Period | 23 million years | Climate becomes drier. Cycads dominate forests; conifers abundant. Reptiles widespread on land and in the seas and streams; small dinosaurs dominate land. Period of rapid evolution of cephalopods; ammonites dominant among aquatic invertebrates. Modern types of echinoderms and crustacea develop. |
| **PALEOZOIC** (Greek, palaios = ancient + zoe) | Permian Period | 33 million years | Continued elevation of continent, with mountain formation and limitation of the seas. Extensive glaciation in southern hemisphere. Climate with local extremes of cold and dryness. Period of many extinctions and rapid evolution and specialization of surviving forms. Vegetation of coal swamps declines, and a new land flora becomes established (modern ferns, cycads and conifers). Rapid evolution of reptiles and of insects, with establishment of some modern insect species (Mayflies, dragonflies, cockroaches). Rise and specialization of cephalopods (ammonites). |
| | Carboniferous — Pennsylvanian Period / Mississippian Period | 74 million years | Submergence of western and central North America, with later emergence of most of the continent. Deformation of earth's crust and mountain formation. Climate mild and moist, and uniform over large areas. "Coal vegetation," rapidly growing, spore-bearing plants with soft wood, develops rapidly. Rise of echinoderms and foraminifera. Rapid development of insect types (several hundred species), scorpions, centipedes, spiders, gastropods. Amphibians become more widespread and diverse. |
| | Devonian Period | 37 million years | Submergence of southeastern and northwestern parts of continent, with probably 40% of its present land mass under water, followed by gradual and complete emergence. Deformation of the earth's crust, and mountain formation, in the eastern area, with extensive lava flows there. Climate uniform and mild. Land flora becomes established—first woody plants (ferns and seed (tree) ferns with soft wood). First tetrapods (small amphibia) appear. Fishes evolve rapidly; rise of sharks and lung fishes. Emergence of terrestrial, air-breathing invertebrates (spiders and wingless insects). Climax of brachiopods. Corals widespread. |
| | Silurian Period | 22 million years | Slow submergence of most of eastern part of continent, followed by nearly complete emergence. Climate uniform and mild, becoming increasingly less humid. Primitive fishes appear. First terrestrial plants appear? Many kinds of invertebrates; first air-breathers (scorpions and millepedes). |
| | Ordovician Period | 79 million years | Second and most extensive submergence of continent, with 2 periods of emergence. Local lava flows. Climate probably uniform and mild. Marine thallophytes flourish. First corals appear. First traces of insects and of fishes. |
| | Cambrian Period | 69 million years | Gradual submergence of most of the continent except for mountainous eastern, western and southwestern borderlands, followed by recession of the waters from the interior, leaving it again exposed. Climate probably warm and uniform. All the main phyla of invertebrates represented by marine types. Sponges, brachiopods, arthropods abundant. Marine thallophytes. |
| | Period without representative rocks and fossils, giving no evidence of geological conditions or biological events. | | |
| **PROTEROZOIC and ARCHEOZOIC** (Greek, proteros, former; arche, beginning) | Pre-Cambrian Period | 1300 million years | Vast lava flows over all the earth's crust. Climate probably uniformly warm and humid, with periodic rainfall and continuous cloud banks, and at least two periods of glaciation. Calcareous algae flourished in warm, shallow seas; probably also marine annelids. Other living things have left no definitive traces, but local deposits of carbon (as scattered particles, hydrocarbons or coal) indicate fixation of atmospheric carbon by undefined biological systems. |

things. That such systems have succeeded in meeting these conditions and adapting themselves to them in one way or another is evidenced by the fact that there is no known part of the world that does not support life of some kind.

The soil that covers almost all of the parent rock, except for the limited regions where it is exposed, is a complex system whose texture, structure, water, gaseous and organic content are of direct importance to the inhabitants of any locality. The texture of the soil is determined by the size of its mineral particles; on this basis, soils may be distinguished as gravels, in which the average size of the particles is relatively large, and, in descending order of particle size, sands, silts and clays. In fine clay soils the particles are of colloidal dimensions and, with sufficient water, such soils have the properties of colloidal systems. The structure of the soil is determined by the arrange-

FIGURE 8.5 Soil profiles (Photographs by courtesy of the Soil Conservation Service, U.S. Department of Agriculture.)

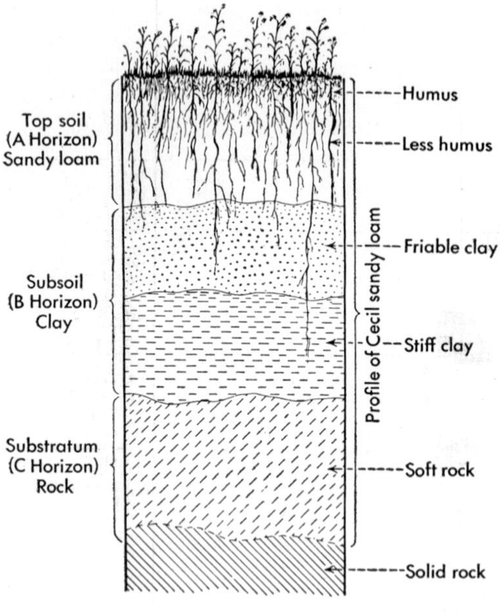

a. A cut in the ground in Spartanburg County, South Carolina, showing the different horizons of the soil profile.

b. Diagram of the soil profile in the same area. The A horizon consists of sandy loam, a mixture of clay and fine gravel; the uppermost layer of this horizon consists of organic plant debris recently fallen to the ground (litter); the next, of litter of the previous year in the course of decomposition (duff); and the next, of older and more completely decomposed litter (leaf mold). Below these superficial layers, the organic material is mixed with the mineral particles of the soil as humus, forming a layer of topsoil over the subsoil of the B horizon and the rock of the C horizon. In a forest, the total animal population in soil and litter is estimated at some 10,000 animals per square foot, including protozoa, nematodes, earthworms, insects, mites, and burrowing vertebrates such as gophers, moles, rats and mice. The plant population of bacteria, algae, fungi and the roots and underground parts of plants is even more numerous. The excreta from this soil population contribute to the composition of the soil atmosphere and soil solution.

ment of its inorganic components, which may be loosely or closely packed together, providing a porous soil or a compact one.

The soil, like bodies of water, is in contact with the atmosphere which penetrates between its particles as "soil atmosphere." Coarse, porous soils, with relatively large spaces between their particles, facilitate the diffusion of gases and in them the composition of the soil atmosphere is essentially the same as that above the ground. In fine-textured, compact soils, on the other hand, diffusion is impeded and the relative proportions of the gases in their atmospheres may be shifted in one direction or another.

Soil atmosphere, like aerial atmosphere, has also a fluctuating content of water vapor, depending upon the amount of water present in the soil. Water reaches the soil principally through the rain that falls upon it, but to some extent also from springs and through seepage from streams, rivers and other bodies of water. Some of this water, as gravitational water, drains away under the influence of gravity and contributes to the water table, a region of the ground at variable distances below the surface which is fully saturated with water; some, as capillary water, is held in films around the individual soil particles or in the interstices between them; some, as hygroscopic water, is bound so firmly to the soil particles that it can only be removed as vapor; and some, as vapor, contributes to the composition of the soil atmosphere. Fine-textured soils, such as silts and clays, tend to hold the water as capillary or hygroscopic water more than coarse-textured sands and gravels, where the gravitational water moves freely and there are fewer particles to provide surface areas for films, or interstitial areas for the retention of water droplets.

The soluble components of the soil are dissolved in the soil water, actually a complex solution of atmospheric gases, minerals and organic compounds. Many of these solutes are electrolytes, and the ions present in the soil solution, or adsorbed on the surface of the soil particles, have much to do with establishing the character of a soil, and making any given locality a favorable one for the existence of many kinds of plants and animals, or one that can support some but not others.

## Biological factors

It is not only to the physical aspects of the earth that living things must be adjusted in order to survive, but to its biological aspects as well, for conditions in different regions are influenced, often to a great extent, by the organisms that inhabit them. Part of the energy to which living things are exposed results from the transformations of energy that take place within biological systems, manifested as heat, electrical energy, motion and sometimes as light. The gaseous content of different environments is affected by their inhabitants; this is particularly evident in aquatic ones, where the oxygen content may fall below the level determined by existing physical conditions, especially in stagnant waters where there is an accumulation of carbon dioxide and other gases resulting from the metabolic activities of organisms, or may rise to a point of supersaturation in localities where there are many actively photosynthesizing plants. The biological conditioning of an environment may also be expressed in the competition between its inhabitants for the materials with which it supplies them, or in the provision of food, one kind of organism being able to maintain itself only upon substances that others can make and dependent, therefore, upon their presence for existence. Or it may be that products eliminated from the bodies of organisms, either as end-products or as by-products of their chemical reactions, make the area inhabitable, or uninhabitable, for others. There is, moreover, in every favorable environment where many kinds of organisms live together, competition between them for space and for mates as well as for the necessities of their individual existence.

## *Types of environment*

The earth provides three principal types of environment—aquatic, terrestrial and aerial—in each of which the physical conditions are different (Figs. 8.6, 8.7). The seas, with their relatively high content of

FIGURE 8.6 Aquatic and terrestrial environments. (Photographs by courtesy of the Soil Conservation Service, U.S. Department of Agriculture.)

a. A fresh-water pond. The water plants, with their roots anchored in the mud at the bottom, provide cover for water fowl and small animals; the floating duckweed (Lemna) that covers much of the surface of the pond is a favorite food of ducks. The quiet water of such a pond is a favorable location for many small aquatic animals (protozoa, rotifers, nematodes, annelids, crustacea and mollusks) and for unicellular and colonial algae that can live and reproduce there in great numbers.

b. A wooded area, clear of underbrush, that offers cover and food for animals such as deer, rodents and birds of all kinds, as well as for terrestrial insects.

FIGURE 8.7 A rock tide pool. (Photograph by courtesy of the American Museum of Natural History, New York.)

Inhabitants of the littoral zone of the sea, such as starfish, sea urchins and sea anemones (foreground); marine algae like Laminaria (left foreground) and Fucus (center); and barnacles, mussels and snails (top half) are alternately exposed directly to the air, and often to the sun, and covered by sea water.

dissolved mineral salts, and bodies of fresh water, with their relatively low one, represent the two extremes of aquatic environments, between which all gradations are found in estuaries, mineral springs, bogs and marshes.

All aquatic environments offer an organism buoyancy, thus reducing the effects upon it of gravity, or the force of attraction between the earth and objects upon it; some stability in temperature and in fluctuations of pressure, for water is a poor conductor of heat and offers resistance to movement or displacement; opportunity for the solution and diffusion, or more rapid removal, of substances eliminated from the body; an abundance of water; and through its currents and surface movements, passive transportation from place to place. Below the surface of the water, organisms are subjected to increasingly greater constant pressures, as their distance below the surface increases, representing the combination of atmospheric pressure at that level and the mass of the water above them, and to differences in the absolute amount, as well as the relative proportions, of the atmospheric gases.

Terrestrial environments are, as a rule, more variable and more exacting than aquatic ones. They may be on the shores of seas or of bodies of fresh water, in valleys or plains, on the slopes or crests of mountains, and in different levels of the soil and atmosphere. All terrestrial organisms, whether living on the surface of the earth or below or above it, are exposed to the dangers of desiccation, or water loss, by evaporation from the surfaces of their bodies; of the effects of gravity; of the pressure of moving masses of air in winds or gales; and of fluctuations in temperature that may extend above and below the range that protoplasm can tolerate. These are dangers from which the more stable conditions in water to some extent protect aquatic organisms. Terrestrial ones have, on the other hand, the advantage of a more favorable gaseous environment and greater constancy in atmospheric pressure, for it is only at considerable distances above and below the earth's surface that the pressure and composition of the atmosphere become altered to an extent that demands particular biological adjustment.

Such are, in general, the conditions to which the earth's plant and animal population, its flora and its fauna, have had to adapt. They have met these conditions in various ways, some of them attaining greater independence of their physical surroundings than others but all of them retaining, directly or indirectly, dependence upon the physical world for certain things without which life, at least in our present understanding of it, could not have arisen nor could it continue. Chief among these are the light and heat of solar radiation, water, oxygen, carbon dioxide and the chemical compounds, collectively known as nutrients, that provide the elements necessary for the synthesis of protoplasm and its products.

## Light and life

The energy of certain wave-lengths of light is used directly by green plants for the synthesis of carbohydrate, from which they build up the organic compounds included in their protoplasm and its products. This represents a transformation of kinetic into potential energy, and is the only effective way in which solar energy is trapped and made available to all living things. For it is by the oxidation of the products of photosynthesis, directly by the plants that make them and indirectly by the animals that feed upon the plants, that organisms derive the energy for their manifestations of vital activity, or life. Without light, carbon fixation on the grand scale in which it has been, and still is being, carried on by photosynthesizing plants would be impossible, and the reconstitution of carbohydrate from carbon dioxide by all but chemosynthesizing organisms would cease. If green plants had never appeared upon this planet and the mechanism of photosynthesis never evolved, animal life would have been vastly more limited and the evolution of animal types greatly restricted. Even those animals and plants that live in semi, or in total, darkness depend for their survival upon those that live in the light and put to advantage that part of the sun's radiant energy that can be appreciated as light.

Although only photosynthesizing plants are directly dependent upon light for their very survival, most organisms, and possibly all of them, are sensitive to it, responding in one way or another to its different intensities and wave lengths. Some of these responses are readily apparent, others are more subtle and less easily detected. Most animals have regions of special photosensitivity, ranging from localized areas of modified protoplasm and groups of cells with such modified protoplasm to elaborate photoreceptor organs, or eyes, which enable them not only to appreciate light and color but also to obtain images of objects around them. Plants have never developed such organs, but their sensitivity to light, apart from their photosynthetic activity, is apparent in the modifications of their growth that result from alterations in the intensity, duration, direction and wave-length of light to which they are exposed. Plants grown in darkness are etiolated (French, étoiler = to blanch), showing, in addition to the pale color of their tissues, various other abnormalities of growth such as greatly elongated stems, deficient development of supporting tissues and decreased root systems. Plants that grow in the temperate zones of the earth are accustomed to alternating periods of light and darkness, and observation and experiment have shown that the formation of flowers and of fruits is greatly influenced by the length of the day, a response on the part of the plant that is known as photoperiodism. Plants and animals also respond to the direction of light by turning toward it or away from it, responses that are known as phototropisms (Greek, tropein = to turn). In plants, phototropisms depend upon alterations in the usual growth patterns of the cells in the part of the plant giving the response. The leaves of a green plant, for example, show positive phototropism in bending toward the light if it reaches them only from one side; this bending is the result of the enlargement and elongation of the cells of the petiole (the stalk attaching the leaf to the stem) located on the side away from the light.

## Heat and life

The range of temperature that protoplasm and protoplasmic systems can tolerate is a limited one, in the lower regions of the absolute temperature scale (Fig. 4.5). The limits of this range are set partly by the complexity of the molecules that contribute to protoplasmic structure and partly by the complexity and the physical properties of the colloidal system called protoplasm. In the inorganic, and presumably also in the organic, world, atomic combinations and molecular groupings tend to become more complex as the temperature falls. At the high temperatures that may be supposed to exist in the sun, for example, calculated at about 40,000,000°C, matter is believed to be represented by free atoms, electrons and free particles of atomic nuclei. At lower temperatures, where their movement is slower, atoms may combine into molecules whose complexity increases with diminishing thermal energy. Presumably life did not begin on earth until its temperature had reached a level that made possible combinations of atoms into large and complicated molecules of protein, carbohydrate and lipid, and were the temperature to rise above this level, disintegration of these molecules would be expected. But temperatures much lower than those postulated for the disruption of complex molecules also bring about the disorganization of protoplasm through changes in its physical state and sol-gel relationships. These changes are related to the water content of the system, for those whose free water is reduced below the level characteristic of their active metabolic state can stand the effects of temperatures both above and below those that otherwise destroy them. For example, the spores of bacteria, the seeds of plants, the eggs and even the body tissues of some animals—all systems with a low content of free water and in a state of suspended activity—can withstand prolonged exposure to zero or subzero temperatures. At such temperatures, free water passes from its liquid to its solid phase, and the formation of ice crystals within cells may injure them mechanically, if the comparatively slow reduction of their water content, by the conversion of water from a fluid to a solid, does not cause other effects also destructive to the organization and operation of the protoplasmic system. In the geologic record there is abundant evidence that the periods of glaciation, when great parts taken various forms; some organisms, for example, become inactive during periods of unfavorable temperature, remaining in a condition of suspended activity, or dormancy, at some stage of their life cycle, until conditions again become propitious or pos-

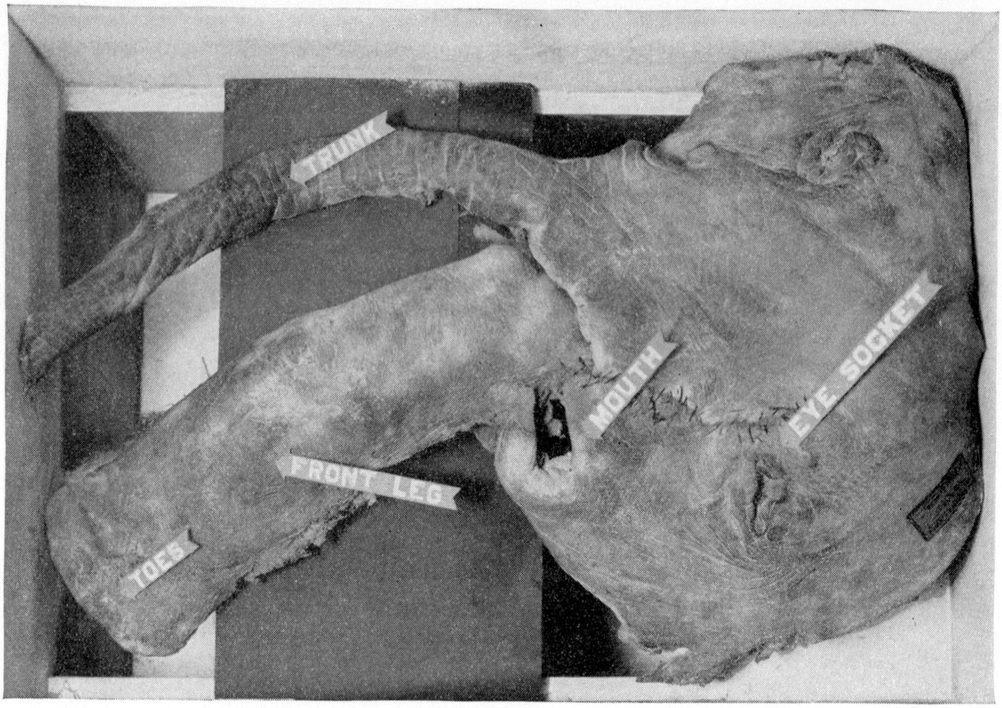

FIGURE 8.8 Well-preserved baby woolly mammoth, dug out of frozen earth in Alaska in 1949. (Photograph by courtesy of the American Museum of Natural History, New York.) Mammoths, whose fossil remains have been found in the Pleistocene deposits of Alaska and Siberia, were elephant-like mammals, resembling the modern Indian elephant.

of the earth's surface were ice-bound, were also periods of extinction for many previously existing life-forms (Fig. 8.8).

But all living things in the world to-day are subject to fluctuations in temperature, not only within the narrow range that protoplasm can tolerate, but both above and below it and, as the great majority of them are poikilothermic (Greek, poikilos = variegated + therme = heat), their internal temperature varying with that of their external surroundings, their survival has depended upon their capacity to make adjustments for the extremes of temperature to which they may be exposed. These adjustments have sible for their activity; some migrate, going deeper into the depths of the water or the ground, or travelling great distances over the surface of the earth to keep themselves in climates where they can continue their activity and still survive; some have coverings that are poor conductors of heat and so are to some extent insulated from the effects of external temperature change, protected by these coverings from loss of the heat released within their bodies by exothermic reactions when the external temperature is lower than that of their bodies, and from gain of heat by them when the external temperature is higher. Only two classes of living things, the birds and the mammals, a mere handful among all those that populate the earth, have mechanisms for maintaining a relatively constant internal temperature, independent of the external one. Such animals are homoiothermic (Greek, homoio = similar + therme = heat), and are often referred to as "warm-blooded," for the temperature range in birds is approximately 104–108°F, and in mammals from approximately 98°F (man) to 104°F (rabbit).

## Water and life

Water is essential to all living things. Not only does it constitute a large proportion of protoplasm, but also because of its solvent properties it is the medium in which substances in solution, or in suspension, are moved from place to place within the bodies of organisms, for their juices, tissue and body fluids are all aqueous solutions of considerable complexity. Moreover, most, if not all, of the reactions that take place in biological systems can do so only if the reagents are dissolved in water. Many of these reactions are hydrolytic ones, in which water is directly involved, and though some of these may yield water as an end product that is directly available to the body in which it is produced, with a very few exceptions organisms require an additional supply from an outside source, which they obtain by diffusion of water across the membranes of such cells as are exposed to it. For aquatic species, a plentiful water supply is no problem, but for most terrestrial ones this is not the case, and their adaptation to life on land and their survival there have depended upon the development either of structures that can maintain constant contact with water or of mechanisms for the conservation of the water they imbibe at intervals or take in with their food.

It is not only the availability of water that is of importance to biological systems but also the regulation of the water content of their bodies, cells and internal fluids. All cells, whether independent organisms or members of a multicellular system, exist in a fluid environment with which they must maintain osmotic equilibrium, or a steady state, if they are to prosper or even to survive. Nearly three-quarters of a century ago a great French physiologist, Claude Bernard (1813–1878), pointed out, in particular reference to animals, that the multicellular organism actually exists in two environments, the external one of the physical world and the internal one of the fluid medium that surrounds and bathes its cells and tissues. "Constancy of the internal environment is the condition of a free and independent life," he wrote in "Leçons sur les phénomènes de la vie communs aux animaux et végétaux" (1878), and the mechanisms that allow a biological system to carry on an existence not immediately governed by conditions in the external world are those that maintain such constancy.

With the exception of a few marine species whose body fluids are isotonic, or nearly so, to sea water, an osmotic gradient exists between the organism and the medium in which it lives. Those plants and animals that first left the sea and entered streams and lakes met the danger of destruction from an overabundance of water, literally death by flooding of their bodies, for protoplasm is hypertonic to fresh water and the rate at which water enters cells exposed to that of lakes or ponds or rivers is greater than that at which it leaves them. Existence in habitats of this kind would therefore be impossible without some protection from the consequences of such an intake of water, for between the extremes of collapse from water loss and bursting from its gain there are degrees of dilution of the cell's contents that are unfavorable to its operation if not entirely disastrous to it. Organisms adapted to life in fresh water have become so by virtue of the development of devices for ridding their bodies of excess water and of protecting them from its entrance at a rate more rapid than they can control. This is achieved by structures or organs for filtering off and eliminating the surplus water, to which may be added unnecessary or undesirable solutes accumulated in the body, and by waterproof coverings over all but limited areas of the surface. Life on land presents different conditions and different hazards, and for terrestrial organisms the great danger is dehydration by the evaporation of water from their exposed surfaces. Waterproof coverings, as well as mechanisms for conserving adequate amounts of the water they do obtain, have also proved valuable to them.

*Atmosphere and life*

Of all the atmospheric gases only oxygen and carbon dioxide are of general biological importance, although some of the more simply constructed plants can combine the free nitrogen of the air with carbohydrate and so make organic compounds that they and others can use in their synthesis of protein. Most organisms are aerobes (Greek, aeros = air + bios = life), dependent upon atmospheric oxygen for the completion of their oxidative reactions. But there are some which, as anaerobes, can do without free oxygen, deriving their necessary energy from intermolecular shifts of atoms, usually in oxygen-containing compounds, with the resulting degradation of these compounds to a state where they, or their components, have less potential energy. Carbon dioxide, an end-product of aerobic oxidations and also of most of the anaerobic mechanisms, must be eliminated from the cells in which it is made and from their immediate environment, for its accumulation results, among other things, in a lowering of pH below the level optimal for them. The gaseous interchange of biological systems—the intake of oxygen from the environment, its utilization either directly or indirectly for oxidation-reduction reactions, and the discharge of carbon dioxide to the environment—is called respiration, or more specifically, aerobic respiration, to distinguish it from the energy-releasing mechanisms in which free oxygen is not involved, often called anaerobic respiration. Some few bacteria, of which the tetanus bacillus is the most familiar example, are exclusively anaerobic in their respiration, obligatory anaerobes since free oxygen is toxic to them; others, facultative anaerobes, can make use of free oxygen if it is present but in its deficiency or absence can shift from an aerobic to an anaerobic mechanism. And some of the tissues of higher plants and of animals can exist for limited periods in the absence of free oxygen by making use of anaerobic mechanisms, although they are dependent ultimately for their survival upon the molecular oxygen of the atmosphere, either in the air or dissolved in the water of their surroundings.

While in some of the smaller and more simply organized biological systems oxygen may diffuse in and carbon dioxide may diffuse out all over the surface of their bodies, this is not possible for those with impermeable, protective coverings nor adequate for those of large size, for diffusion is a slow process. While other conditions may have made such protective coverings desirable, or even imperative, the respiratory needs of the organism have required the retention of areas exposed to the environment for the gaseous interchange of the body as a whole, or its external respiration; increase in bodily size has required some means of conveying the oxygen absorbed through these exposed areas to other regions of the body, and equally for the transport of carbon dioxide from them to the place of external respiration. This gaseous interchange between cells remote from the external environment and the fluids that bathe them is known as internal respiration.

Carbon dioxide is one of the compounds used by plants in their synthesis of carbohydrate and is constantly being removed from the atmosphere by them for this purpose. They also return a certain amount of it as a result of their respiratory processes, and they likewise restore to the atmosphere oxygen, released as a by-product of their carbohydrate synthesis in amounts far in excess of their own respiratory needs. Plants are therefore most important factors in the biological conditioning of the natural environment, not only for their transformation of solar energy but also for their removal of a potentially toxic gas and return of an almost universally essential one.

Although nitrogen is for most biological systems an inert gas, since it enters into no chemical reactions in them, its presence in such volume in the atmosphere and its solubility in water and aqueous solutions are of considerable importance to them, particularly to those that are naturally subject to sudden changes in atmospheric pressure, or that in special circumstances may become so. With increase of pressure, more nitrogen as well as more carbon dioxide and oxygen are dissolved in the body fluids; when the pressure is suddenly reduced, the nitrogen, not held in any chemical combination, bubbles off as free gas and the tissues become super-saturated with it. This effect of atmospheric nitrogen has been of considerable importance to man especially in his exploitation of the earth's resources underground and his investigations of the depths of the sea and its floor, for the presence of gas bubbles in his muscles and joints causes the acute pains and cramps called "bends," and the blocking of a small blood vessel in a vital part of his body, such as his brain or his lungs, by one trapped there may cause serious disability or death. Such effects in miners and divers are prevented by bringing them up to the surface in a series of stages through decompression chambers, so that the adjustment of the nitrogen content of their body fluids to atmospheric pressure at ground level is a gradual and a harmless one. But this problem took on a new aspect during the recent war, when the risks of the effects of too rapid decompression were often balanced against those of remaining underwater in a damaged submarine or near an underground mine. A number of English physiologists and human volunteers experimented with different mixtures of gases to determine the effects upon the human system of an atmosphere with reduced nitrogen content but additional amounts of other gases naturally present, such as helium and argon, in efforts to devise an atmosphere in which sudden changes to different pressure levels could be made with safety. If such an atmosphere, in which the oxygen and carbon dioxide content is kept within the range

FIGURE 8.9 Herbivorous and carnivorous heterotrophes. (Photographs by courtesy of the Soil Conservation Service, U.S. Department of Agriculture.)

    a. Herbivores. Grasshoppers feeding on a corn plant.
    b. Carnivore. A coyote eating a jack rabbit.

of physiological safety and the inert gases have either a low solubility in the liquids of the body or a slow rate of evolution from them when their partial pressures are reduced, could be provided to those who in peace or war are obliged to change rapidly from one level of atmospheric pressure to another, the attendant dangers and even the discomforts could be minimized, if not entirely eliminated, and man would have an even greater area of the earth to range than he has now.

## Nutrients and life

All living things are dependent upon their surroundings for food, from which they derive the materials necessary for their growth and reproduction and for their energy requirements. Some of them can make use directly of inorganic compounds and by photosynthesis or chemosynthesis, processes discussed more fully in Chapter 19, can convert them to the organic compounds that they need. Such organisms are called auto-

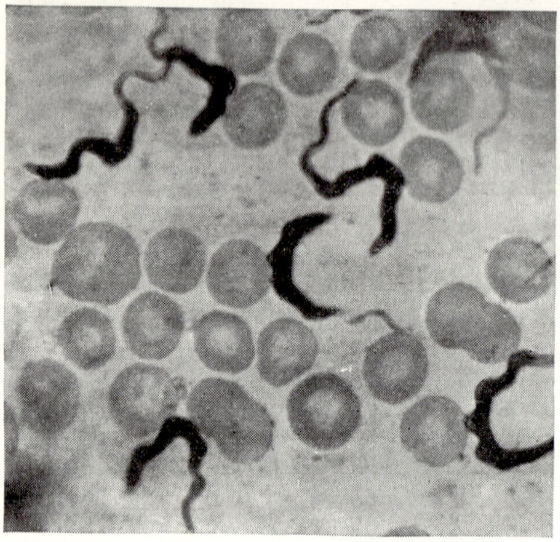

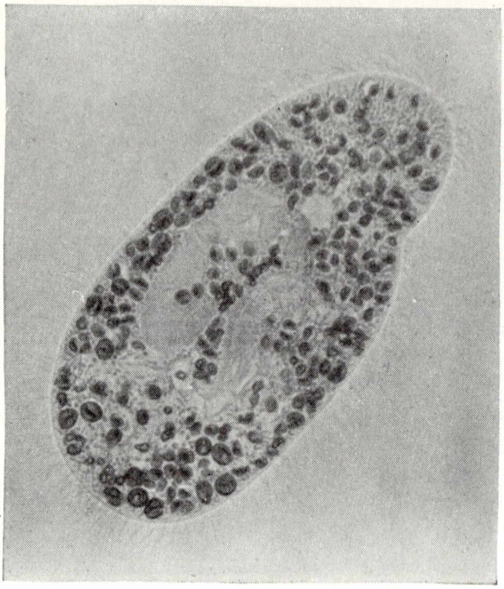

FIGURE 8.10  Animal Associations.

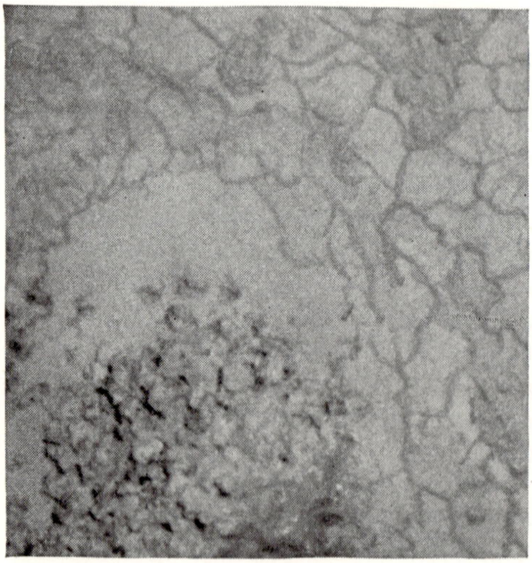

a. Parasitic protozoan (Trypanosoma gambiense) in the human blood stream. These parasites, transmitted from human host to human host through the bite of the tsetse fly (Glossina), are the agents causing African sleeping sickness. (Photograph by courtesy of the Army Institute of Pathology.)

b. A saprophytic slime mold, spreading over the surface of raw Quaker oats. (Photograph by D. F. Reath.)

c. Symbiotic algae (Chlorella) living in the cytoplasm of a protozoan (Paramoecium bursaria). (Photograph of living animal, taken by phase contrast microscopy, by Dr. O. Richards, Research Laboratory, American Optical Company. From *Cold Spring Harbor Symposia on Quantitative Biology*, vol. XI, with permission of the Biological Laboratory.)

trophes (Greek, autos = self + trophos = feeder), since they are independent of others for their food supply, and to that extent nutritionally self-sufficient. Those that cannot carry on such syntheses are called heterotrophes (Greek, hetero = other), living in or on the bodies of other organisms and feeding off their living tissues; or they may have become saprophytes (Greek, sapros = rotten + phyton = plant), living on dead organisms or the products of live ones and bringing about their decomposi-

FIGURE 8.11 Animal Associations.

A commensal association between a spider crab (Libinia) and a colonial hydroid attached to its shell. (Photograph by courtesy of the American Museum of Natural History, New York.)

since they are wholly dependent upon organic compounds and so upon other biological systems for their food. Heterotrophes vary widely in the nature and degree of complexity of the compounds they require, some being able to carry on a greater range of syntheses than others and so to use simpler compounds as sources of food; others are dependent for their subsistence upon the components of complex proteins, carbohydrates and lipids already synthesized. They vary also in the sources from which they obtain their food, and in the ways that they obtain it. They may be free-living, feeding on vegetation or the bodies of animals that they capture and kill (Fig. 8.9); or they may have adopted a parasitic mode of life (Greek, para = beside + sitos = table),

tion by putrefaction and decay; or they may be symbionts (Greek, sun = with + bios = life), or commensals (Latin, cum = with + mensa = table) (Figs. 8.10, 8.11). Symbionts are organisms that live in close association with each other, in a kind of partnership from which each member derives some advantage; commensals are those that share the same food, one finding adequate nutrition in what is left or rejected by the other. These relations of parasitism, saprophytism, symbiosis and commensalism are ones of closer dependence than those between any free-living biological systems, for which the organisms exhibiting them have become particularly modified, in some cases to such an extent that existence for one is impossible without the other.

## The unity and diversity of biological systems

The various structural and functional adaptations to the different conditions of existence shown by biological systems are the basis for distinctions between them, as fundamental similarities in their construction and operation are the basis for the concept of unity in life and in life forms, one of the general principles of biological science. That man has long recognized such distinctions is evident from the earliest records that he has left of paintings and written descriptions of the other inhabitants of his world. How these differences have originated has long been a puzzle and a matter of speculation to him, for in the history of scientific and philosophical thought are evidences of his many attempts to explain them. The doctrine of organic evolution, or the development of new biological types from previously existing ones, has appeared in a variety of forms in the history of human thought, for it seems to have appealed to some minds in nearly every generation as the most rational explanation of the diversity, and the relationships, between the many kinds of living things known to them. The development of this doctrine is outlined in Chapter 26; in its modern interpretation, the modifications of common anatomical structure and physiological operation evident in existing types are expressions of the close relation between organism and environment, the result of interactions between them determined by the nature of the organism and the general and particular conditions of the environment in which it finds itself.

The general course of evolution has been toward specialization of generalized struc-

a

b

tures and chemical and physical processes. Through specialization, a system, or a unit in a system, gains precision and efficiency in the performance of a particular operation or set of operations, but becomes increasingly dependent upon others for those things it can no longer effectively do for itself. Cells have become specialized, or differentiated, to perform particular functions in the multicellular body and such specialized cells collected into the tissues and organs that constitute its various parts; bodies have become specialized for particular kinds of biological and physical operations and for existence in particular kinds of environments. Parts that are similar in development and structure, but different in function, are said to be homologous; those that are developmentally and structurally different but functionally similar, analogous. For example, the forelimbs of four-footed vertebrate animals, or tetrapods (Greek, tetra = four + pous = foot), are homologous, for they are all constructed on the same general plan, with the same pattern of bones and muscles, blood vessels and nerves that enabled the first animals that possessed them to crawl or walk upon the ground. But this plan has become modified in most of their modern descendants, most strikingly in those that have returned to an aquatic existence as the flippers of seals and whales, or taken to the air as the wings of birds, or to climbing among the treetops as in the grasping arms of primates. The wings of birds and of insects, the only groups of animals that have adopted the air as their principal environment, are, on the other hand, analogous organs, for they are entirely different in their construction and development although they serve the same purpose in keeping the bodies of which they are a part above

FIGURE 8.12 Responses in plants. (From Hylander and Stanley, *College Botany*. Copyright 1949 by The Macmillan Company.)

a. Geotropism, or response to gravity. Normal response to the gravitational pull is shown in the left-hand figure; when the potted seedling is rotated so that it is parallel to the ground (middle figure), it responds to the gravitational pull by downward bending of the root tip and upward bending of the stem.

b. Thigmotropism, or response to contact. The coiling of the tendrils of a plant like the cucumber is a growth response to contact with a support.

c. Phototropism, or response to light. When one side of the plant is exposed to light of greater intensity than the other, the leaves become oriented so that their greatest area is exposed to the light rays.

d. Turgor changes. The leaves of a sensitive plant curl when the plant is jarred or touched.

the ground and in propelling them through the air.

Although specialization and differentiation have often led to greater complexity in biological systems, the course of evolution is not always a progressive one from the simple to the complex. A number of existing species give evidence of retrogressive evolution, a reduction of structural and functional complexity and in some cases a return from special to more generalized conditions. Illustrations of this are the loss of limbs by snakes, descended from tetrapod ancestors, of chlorophyll and so of the capacity for photosynthesis of certain saprophytic and parasitic plants like the Indian pipe and the dodder, and of various structures and mechanisms associated with an independent existence by parasites of all kinds.

The greatest divergence betwen biological systems is that between plants and animals, whose course of evolution has been radically different, due primarily to the fundamental difference in the way they obtain their food. With a very few exceptions, all plants are exclusively autotrophic, a mode of nutrition that may have been the primary one, through which the first forms of life could exist wholly on material supplied by their inorganic environment, although the complexity of the process suggests that it has been derived from some simpler nutritional mechanism. The evolution of plants has been influenced particularly by the necessity of maintaining access to adequate supplies of carbon dioxide and of water, and in the photosynthesizing ones, of light. Their production of carbohydrate, even in those growing most rapidly, is usually far in excess of their immediate nutritional needs; some of this excess has been diverted to the construction of supporting walls for their soft cells and of mechanical tissues to give some rigidity to the bodies of those of large size and many cells. All plant cells are distinct from animal cells in being enclosed by a wall of cellulose, and all plant bodies of any considerable size from animal bodies in being supported by woody tissues in which the cellulose walls of some cells are strengthened by another and more rigid compound called lignin. The architectural plan of plants is quite different from that of most animals, for the exposure of a maximum surface area to light and air is to their advantage and they are, in general, constructed on the plan of a central axis from which lateral branches originate at approximately constant angles, making a more or less symmetrical whole. By the development of a root system, extending sometimes far down into the ground, terrestrial plants have achieved a means of keeping contact with water, for which they have especial need in their process of photosynthesis. Roots entail anchorage as well as provide access to water and, though the reproductive cells of some may be motile, no multicellular terrestrial plant is able to move independently from place to place as animals can do. Even those that live in the water, without roots or with roots that never touch the bottom, move only with the currents or surface movements of the body of water they inhabit and are incapable of directing their course or saving themselves from destruction if carried to an unfavorable locale.

All animals are heterotrophes and their evolution has been influenced particularly by the necessity of obtaining the organic substances they require as food and of escaping from destruction themselves as food for others. This has put a premium on the development of means of locomotion for foraging, for pursuit or for escape, and of mechanisms for locating and obtaining food and retaining it, once it is obtained, until its assimilation by the body is completed. Effective locomotion depends not only upon localized movements of different parts of the body, but also upon coordination between those parts. Movement in animals has become possible through the development of special contractile cells, the muscle cells, with physical properties and chemical mechanisms that allow them to shorten and to thicken and then to return to their original shape. Coordination in movement has become possible primarily through the development of special cells, the nerve cells, capable of receiving, conducting and transmitting messages from one part of the body to another, and from the external world to various parts of the body. Such cellular differentiation has permitted the development in animals of regions or organs of special sensitivity—to light, to gravity, to pressure and waves of pressure, to dissolved substances—that give them awareness of things at a distance as well as in their immediate surroundings, and enable them to prepare for, as well as to adjust to, changing conditions. Plants have never developed such organs, although in their growth they give definite and specific responses to gravity, pressure and the location of water as well as to light and, by changes in the water content of localized groups of cells, react to various internal and external conditions (Fig. 8.12). The seed capsule of the jewel weed, for example, virtually explodes when it is touched, expelling the enclosed seeds with considerable force and scattering them some distance from the parent plant; the dry pods of peas and beans crack open when the seeds within them are ripe. These responses are hydration movements, caused either by imbibition of water by the walls of dead cells or the loss of water from them. Plants also respond by turgor movements, which, like the responses of an animal, may be repeated again and again. The leaves of a number of plants, for example, curl or droop when they are touched or jarred, and after an interval, expand again; some flowers, like morning glories, regularly close about noon and do not open again until the next morning; some, like tobacco, close about dusk, and others, like four o'clocks, open only toward the end of the day; and the leaves of some grasses roll up when the water content of the soil becomes low, and become flat again when more water is available. Turgor movements such as these are due to adjustments of the water content of living cells, by virtue of which they undergo partial collapse, or become maximally distended. These responses are as rapid and as adaptive as those of animals, although the mechanisms underlying them are wholly different.

The bodies of animals are considerably more varied in architectural pattern than those of plants, and show greater diversity of form. With no excess of carbohydrate, they have made use of protein substances or of deposits of inorganic salts for external protection and internal support. In general their tendency has been to retain a minimal surface area, making their bodies more compact than those of plants. Those that have been most successful in their adaptation to varied environments are constructed on a metameric plan (Greek, meta = after or succeeding + meros = part), in which the body is primitively a series of segments joined together in linear order. This serial repetition of parts has the advantage of offering some degree of functional independence to each and so of minimizing the effects to the body as a whole of loss of any of them or of injury to them, and also of giving flexibility to a body of any considerable length. It has proved itself to be a plan allowing of modification in many ways, for a great variety of animal types are recognized as descendants of segmented ancestors.

# CHAPTER 9

# THE CLASSIFICATION OF BIOLOGICAL SYSTEMS AND THE DIVISIONS OF BIOLOGICAL SCIENCE

## The need for classification

The task of the biologist today would be an almost impossible one were there not some orderly arrangement of his material, some kind of systematic cataloguing of the thousands of different kinds of biological systems with which he deals. The necessity of such an arrangement was recognized by the earliest students of natural history and, from the time of Aristotle (384–322 B.C.) through succeeding centuries, there exist records of systems of classification, some alphabetical, some based on the uses to which animals and plants can be put in service to man, and some on structural differences between them. They are all to greater or less extent arbitrary and artificial ones, and biological records also show dissatisfaction with them and continued efforts by man to find natural divisions into which living things obviously fall.

## The Linnaean system of classification

The division of biological science that deals with classification is known as systematics or taxonomy (Greek, taxis = arrangement + nomos = law). It has been recognized as a specialized branch of biology for over 200 years, since a Swedish doctor and botanist, Karl Linnaeus (1707–1778), with a passion for classification and a genius for minute and accurate observation and for detaching the important from the trivial, set standards for describing and naming plants and animals and criteria by which relationships and affinities between different types could be estimated. His method of classification and the system he devised for the comparatively limited number of organisms that were known to him are the foundations upon which the modern systematic grouping of biological systems has been built, which gives to every biologist in every specialized branch of the science and in every country in the world a common name for every living thing and a universal catalogue of them.

While Linnaeus recognized that the greater part of his system was an artificial one, he considered the species as a distinct, separate and natural division of living things. He believed that a pair of every different kind, or species, of animal or plant known to him had been divinely created and that all existing animals and plants were lineal descendants of these progenitors. All members of a species then had a common ancestry and their type was fixed and unchangeable; this concept was later expanded to define the members of a species as individuals not only with a common ancestry but also incapable, as a rule, of mating with others outside their own kind, a distinction between species and other divisions in the classificatory system that still remains a useful, if not wholly an exact, one.

Starting with the species as a fixed and established life-form, Linnaeus then assembled groups of species, according to similarities in certain of their physical characters, into a larger category, the genus; similar genera were included in orders, and similar orders, in classes. In 1732, he was chosen by the University of Upsala, where he had been a student, to make an expedition into Lapland as a collector of northern plants; he added Norway and Sweden to his travels and later visited France, Germany, Holland and England, collecting and studying specimens. The outcome of these travels and studies was the great *Systema Natura,* first published in Holland in 1735. In this he described every known animal and plant completely and exactly, yet succinctly, and designated each by a double name, that of its genus and that of its species. It had already been established that certain parts of the flowers of plants are concerned with the formation of what were then called the "elements" that were brought together in their reproduction, the stamens with the pollen and the styles with the "female elements." Linnaeus made his distinctions between the classes and orders of plants on the basis of these generative parts, including in his class Monandria those with one stamen, in the Diandria, those with two, and so on, while those with one style he put in the order Monogynia, those with two in the Digynia, and so on up the numerical scale. Less interested in animals than he was in plants, and apparently almost repelled by the coldblooded ones, Linnaeus gave them less attention and was less successful with them; this was perhaps also due to the fact that they did not lend themselves to the method of distinction between classes and orders that had worked so well with plants. He divided the animal kingdom into six classes: Mammalia, Aves, Amphibia (which included reptiles as well as those animals recognized as amphibia in any system), Pisces, Insecta, including all the arthropods, and Vermes, including everything else. Man was placed among the mammals, and in doing this Linnaeus was bold, for he gave human beings a place among animals and did not set them apart as special objects in the world of living things.

## The modern system of classification

Linnaeus' technique of description and principle of "binomial nomenclature" have been standards of taxonomic procedure since the days of *Systema Natura,* but naturally as biological knowledge has increased his original scheme has undergone expansion and radical revision. The general principles he used still persist and the taxonomist today applies them as he identifies each new specimen and assigns it to its proper pigeonhole in the catalogue of biological systems.

The modern taxonomist has, however, a much larger range of characteristics upon which to make his judgments than Linnaeus had, and he obtains his data not only from his own observations but also from those of other specialists in the different fields of biological science—from physiologists and biochemists, from geneticists and embryologists. The modern scheme of classification is thus less one-sided than Linnaeus' in that it takes into account many more than one set of physical characters. Distinctions between systems are based upon resemblances and differences in their habits, their anatomical structure as adults, their embryological development and certain genetic and physiological features. New categories have been added to his system, such as phylum, family and, in some cases, tribe and variety, and sub-divisions of its categories have been made, such as sub-classes, sub-orders and so forth. Latin and Greek roots or words are still most generally used for the names of phyla, classes, orders and other categories, for Latin and Greek remain the languages all scholars have in common, and such names are thus universally descriptive of the most characteristic features of the members of a particular category. For example, bivalve mollusks like clams, oysters and mussels are in the class Pelecypoda, from the Greek words pelekys, meaning hatchet, and pous, meaning foot, descriptive of the bladelike foot which projects from their shells when they plough through the sand, and the worms are in the phylum Annelida, from the Latin word anellus, a ring, descriptive of the succession of ring-like segments which make up their bodies. Sometimes a genus or a species is called by the name of the biologist who first identified it, and in many cases the name, or the initial, of the original describer and namer of a species is attached to its name, thus establishing his priority in its identification. Thus Rosa alba Linn. means the white rose that Linnaeus first described and catalogued as a distinct and definite type among roses, and it means just that one thing to anyone anywhere who is familiar with the taxonomic system, no matter what his language of ordinary speech or the special field in which he is working. The name of the genus is by custom always written with a capital letter, that of the species usually with a small one.

It sometimes happens that as the result of experiment or analysis new light is thrown upon the characteristics of an organism, in consequence of which its position may be shifted from one to another of the smaller sub-divisions in the general scheme, for classification is not a "fait accompli" or taxonomy a static field of biology. Sometimes, too, taxonomists do not agree upon the place to which an organism should be assigned, so that it may have two or more names or positions, yet it is always identifiable through the description, according to Linnaean technique, of its salient and distinguishing characters.

In the modern scheme, biological systems are divided into two great Kingdoms, the Kingdom Planta and the Kingdom Animalia. Within the plant kingdom there are four main divisions or phyla, within which are the subdivisions of classes, orders, families, genera, species and finally varieties. The animal kingdom is similarly divided into a number of phyla and these into classes and the other smaller categories. To illustrate the system in general, one might take the classification of two such well-known species as an apple and a fly. A Golden Delicious apple could be classified in this way:

### Kingdom : Planta

PHYLUM:

Spermatophyta (seed-bearing plants and so distinct from those which do not reproduce by means of seeds).

SUB-PHYLUM:

Angiosperma (plants with enclosed seeds and so distinct from those whose seeds are "naked").

CLASS:

Dicotyledonae (plants which have two embryonic leaves, or cotyledons, and so distinct from those with one or many).

ORDER:

Rosales (plants whose flowers have separate petals, including among others, roses, pears, plums).

FAMILY:

Rosacea: (plants whose flowers have five petals).

GENUS:

Pyrus (Latin for pear).

SPECIES:

malus (Latin for apple).

VARIETY:

Golden Delicious.

And a housefly is classified this way:

### Kingdom : Animalia

PHYLUM:

Arthropoda (animals with segmented bodies and paired jointed appendages or legs attached to all or some segments).

CLASS:

Insecta (arthropods whose bodies are divided into head, thorax and abdomen, with one pair of antennae, only three pairs of legs and usually two pairs of wings).

ORDER:

Diptera (insects with only one pair of fully developed wings).

FAMILY:

Muscidae (from muscus, the Latin word for fly).

GENUS:

Musca.

SPECIES:

domestica.

Pyrus malus and Musca domestica, whatever their local names may be, mean but one particular kind of plant and one particular kind of animal in the universal language of scientists, and each occupies a particular place in relation to other plants and to other animals in the scheme of classification. A condensation of these schemes is given on pages 105–114, a skeleton outline only of the great and comprehensive system that has developed from the work of Linnaeus and of many generations of biologists after him. Figure 9.1 shows the relative sizes, according to the number of species included in them, of the different major divisions in the two Kingdoms.

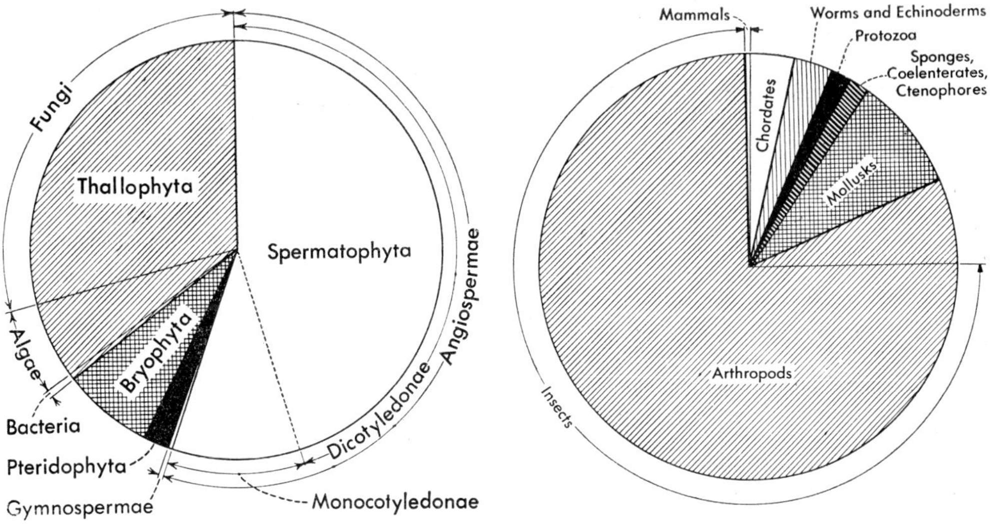

FIGURE 9.1 Diagrams showing the relative numbers of identified species of plants and animals. The subdivisions of the major groups are indicated around the periphery of the circle.

## The main divisions of biological science

### Anatomy and physiology as methods of biological investigation

Man has followed various lines of attack in his attempts to understand the nature of the living world and to interpret the organization and operation of living things, their relations to each other and to the world in which they live. His first recorded approach was a descriptive and an anatomical one (Greek, anatomein = to cut up), study of the external characters of organisms and, by dissection, or taking them apart, study of their internal construction and organization, in the search to discover what are the various parts that make the functional whole, and, as corollaries, how these parts develop in the growing individual and how they are reproduced in successive generations. His interest in the functioning of these parts led him to attempt, by experimentation, to find out how they operate, how they are coordinated into a harmoniously working whole, to what physical laws they are subject and which, if any, of these they evade or transcend. This approach, which follows naturally upon a knowledge of general form and detailed structure, is the physiological (Greek, physis = nature + logos = discourse) and experimental one. A biological experiment consists in altering the conditions in which a biological process takes place, and analyzing the effects upon it of such altered and carefully controlled conditions in relation to those in which it naturally proceeds; wherever it is possible to do so, the experimental biologist expresses the results of such analyses in exact, quantitative terms. Man has used both the anatomical and the physiological approach in his study of plants and animals, but because their numbers are so great and the apparent differences between them so marked, the biologist is almost perforce limited to the study of one or the other of the great divisions of living things, and because of the special techniques demanded, to one or the other of the principal lines of investigation. Botany (Greek, botane = herb or plant) and Zoology (Greek, zoion = animal + logos = discourse) have therefore come to be recognized as the two main divisions of biological science, anatomy and physiology as its two primary methods.

**Botany and zoology as areas of investigation; the development of botany**

In the early days of man's history botanical information accumulated faster than zoological, partly because the practical value of plants for agricultural and medicinal purposes gave impetus to their collection, description and cultivation, partly because, except in the most enlightened periods of his civilization, dissection of the bodies of animals and particularly of the human body, at once the most interesting and most precious to man, was discouraged if not actually proscribed by law. The earliest botanical information is collected in the treatises of the Greeks Theophrastus (380–328 B.C.) and Dioscorides, living probably during the first century A.D.; in the Herbals of the sixteenth century, great compendia of existing knowledge, in which fact was often confused with fiction; and in the writings of the systematists contemporary with Linnaeus, and preceding and succeeding him.

*The development of zoology:* Similar collections of zoological information have also been made throughout the centuries. Aristotle compiled the current classical and pre-classical information about the organization and operation of animals, contributing also many observations of his own that were both penetrating and accurate. The great animal anatomist of classical times was Galen (b. 131), a Greek living in Rome, whose writings record dissections of fish, turtles, swine, dogs, horses, elephants and Barbary apes; possibly, too, he was able to make some dissections of humans, although most of his conceptions of human anatomy were drawn largely from his studies of apes and other mammals. He made many additions to the knowledge of animal structure and functioning, for he concerned himself with the purposes of the organs he exposed and examined as well as with their parts and position in relation to others in the body. He was especially successful in his studies of the nervous system, performing experiments to determine the effects of cutting or destruction of certain parts and so finding out the role that the nerves play as well as their distribution in the body. Galen's influence, and that of the Greek culture he represented, was even greater and more far-reaching in later centuries than in his own, for the respect for his knowledge and achievements was so immense that all his statements were for a long time accepted as incontrovertible, and the limitations and errors of his observations, and his misrepresentations of them, persisted and influenced scientific thought fully as much as his accurate ones.

Not until the sixteenth century was anatomical study and teaching in the great European universities, and the accepted method of reading from Galen's texts by the professor while a demonstrator displayed the parts under discussion, abandoned in favor of first-hand dissection by the students themselves. This was initiated by Andreas Vesalius (1514–1564), a Belgian who, having studied medicine at Louvain, was at the age of twenty-two appointed professor at the University of Padua. Vesalius made his own dissections himself and taught his students to make theirs. Although it was not difficult at that time to obtain human material for autopsy on one legal pretext or another, it was still not easy to get it for purely scientific purposes, but the practice of body-snatching, adopted by medical students of all centuries, also produced a fair number of cadavers. Dissection was not limited to the medical schools; Leonardo da Vinci is known to have dissected at least thirty human bodies, and his representations of them are testimony of his exact anatomical knowledge (Fig. 9.2).

In his dissections of the human body Vesalius, with the intellectual integrity of all good scholars, could not reconcile the evidence of his own eyes with statements in the texts of Galen, so he rejected them and started anatomy on new paths unfettered by preconceived notions. Altogether, while he confirmed many of Galen's observations, he corrected some 200 of his errors about the structure of the human body, and by comparing its parts with those of dogs and other animals, laid the foundations for studies in comparative anatomy through whose pursuit man has arrived at some understanding

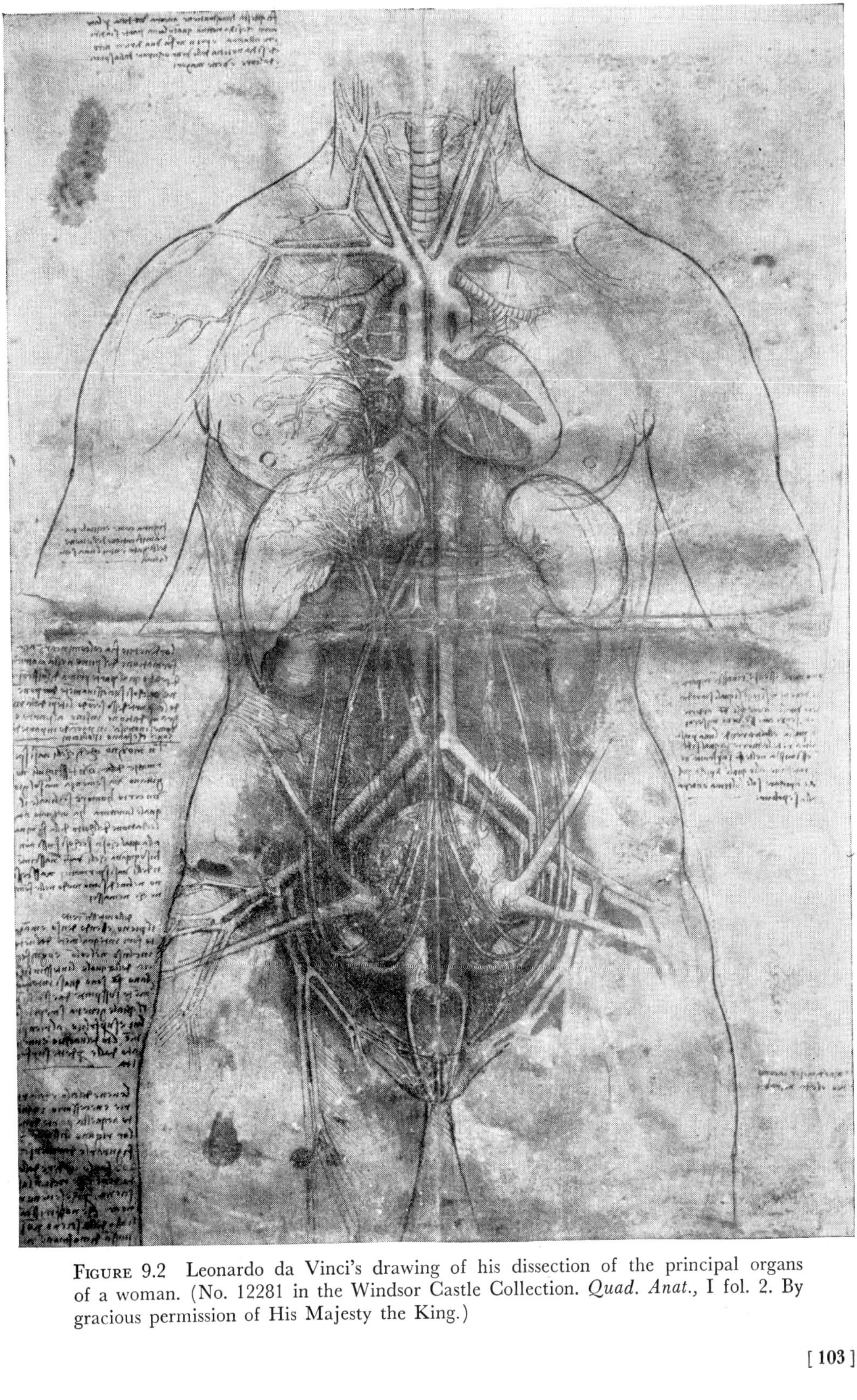

FIGURE 9.2  Leonardo da Vinci's drawing of his dissection of the principal organs of a woman. (No. 12281 in the Windsor Castle Collection. *Quad. Anat.*, I fol. 2. By gracious permission of His Majesty the King.)

of the structural relationships between animals of different species. Vesalius' *De humani corporis fabrica,* published in 1543, the same year as Copernicus' great astronomical contribution, *De revolutionibus orbium celestium,* is the first human anatomy ever written. But by "fabrica" Vesalius meant more than the mere fabric of the human body; the word should be translated as "machinery" or "works," implying, as these words do, the operation of a mechanism and the work that it does as well as its material parts. He thought, in the modern way, of the body as a totality in which, though one part or set of parts may be selected for particular study, none has meaning apart from the whole. The illustrations of the *Fabrica,* beautifully drawn from actual specimens principally by a pupil of Titian's under Vesalius' close supervision, show this as much as the text implies it. The muscles, for example, are represented beneath a skin made transparent so as to reveal the parts beneath it, in the positions in which they are found in the living body, and very often flexed as if that body were performing some action. In addition to the descriptions and figures of the construction of the human body, Vesalius expounded theories about its operation, and included directions for dissection as well as methods for physiological experimentation, for he not only repeated many of Galen's experiments but planned and performed a considerable number of his own.

But Vesalius' influence extended even farther than his written work, for he was an inspired and inspiring teacher and among his pupils and his pupils' pupils who carried on his tradition are some of the greatest names in the history of biology and medicine. Foremost among these are Bartolomeo Eustachi (1520–1574), who worked in Rome and was the first to study anatomical variations in individuals rather than in species; Gabriele Fallopio (1523–1562), who succeeded his professor in the chair at Padua and made new contributions to the study of the reproductive organs and of the ear and throat; Volcher Coiter (1543–1576), a Dutchman who was a pupil of Fallopio's; and Hieronymo Fabrizzi (1537–1619), known also as Fabricius of Aquapendente from the Tuscan village where he was born, who also was a pupil of Fallopio's and, like him and Vesalius, a professor at the University of Padua. Coiter turned his attention to comparative anatomy, especially that of the skeleton, examining and comparing those of almost all kinds of vertebrates, and also followed through the embryology of the chick by opening incubated eggs on successive days to watch the progress of their development. But it was Fabricius who raised embryology to an independent status among the biological sciences by his studies, his lectures and his writings on the comparative embryology of many mammals, the dogfish, the viper and birds of different kinds.

### The derivation of biological terminology

Much of the biological terminology, especially anatomical terminology, in use today is due to the classical scientists and their sixteenth century successors, who used both Greek and Latin words to describe the different parts and organs of the body. For instance, the main vessels that carry blood through the neck to the head in man and other vertebrate animals are called the carotid arteries, from the Greek word caroun, meaning to stupefy, for Galen had found that pressure upon them caused a man to become drowsy; the Greek words hepar, meaning liver, cephale, meaning head, nephros, meaning kidney, and the Latin ones, cauda, meaning tail, dextra, meaning right, and sinister, meaning left, are found in his writings and are still used in scientific terminology, as hepatic, in reference to the liver, cephalic and caudal in reference to the head and tail respectively, nephric in reference to the kidney and so on. Similarly, the Greek words phloos, meaning bark, rhiza, root and kaulos, stem, used by Theophrastus, have been carried down in botanical terminology in such words as phloem, rhizoid and cauline. The meaning of many biological terms is clear only through a knowledge of their derivation from such Greek and Latin roots, with which the beginning student would do well to familiarize himself, for learning biological names will then become an exercise of reason and not a feat of memory alone.

## The subdivisions of biological science

The revelation, during the seventeenth century, of the finer details of anatomical structure, beyond the limits of vision without the magnification provided by such an instrument as the microscope, as well as of a world of life invisible to the unaided human eye, increased the range of biological investigation enormously. And as knowledge of form and structure has increased, inquiry into functional processes has been correspondingly stimulated and the laws and techniques of the other natural sciences employed more and more in the search for solutions of physiological problems. Biologists, while recognizing always, as a basic principle of their science, unity in life-forms and life-processes, have become increasingly restricted to specialized study and investigation in limited areas in each of the great fields and methods of biological science. Thus within the fields of botany and zoology the individual biologist may confine himself to the systematic study of plants or animals, and their classification by various criteria, or taxonomy; to the study of their relationships to their immediate environment, or ecology (Greek, oikos = house or habitat); to the study of their organization, or anatomy, including both their gross anatomy and that of their finer parts, microscopic anatomy or histology (Greek, histos = web or tissue); to the study of the cell itself, or cytology; to the study of their individual development, or embryology; to the study of their reproduction and transmission of developmental potentialities from one generation to another, or genetics (Greek, genesis = origin or descent); or to some aspect of the great field of physiological investigation, which in particular makes use of the methods of chemistry, physics and mathematics in the analysis and interpretation of the operation of the plant and animal organism as a whole and of its several parts. But no one of these areas of specialization is sharply delimited from another and there is much overlapping between them, just as there is between the divisions into which natural science falls and within which it has progressed, for along with the biochemist and the biophysicist one finds the cytophysiologist and the chemical embryologist.

Although modern biologists may, and indeed of necessity must, limit themselves in some such way in their actual investigations, in their thinking they break down these distinctions and aim, as the best of the natural scientists in past centuries have done, to find general principles equally applicable to all biological systems. The modern trend in biology, as in the other natural sciences, is toward the unification and correlation of data derived by various means from various sources, and so to their analysis and interpretation. This is manifesting itself, among other ways, in the establishment of great research endowments and research institutions, where specialists in the different branches of biology, physics and chemistry work together, pooling their knowledge and their skills toward the common solution of a biological problem. The Nutrition Foundations, the Institutes for Biophysics and for Cancer Research that are scattered all over this and other countries are only a few illustrations of this kind of cooperation in scientific investigation today; there are many other kinds of biological problems under unified attack by groups of specialized scientists not necessarily under one roof but working in different ways toward the same end in research laboratories of colleges and universities all over the world.

## PRINCIPAL GROUPS OF BIOLOGICAL SYSTEMS ACCORDING TO TAXONOMIC SYSTEM

*(Groups entirely extinct are marked by an asterisk)*

### Kingdom : Planta

PHYLUM:
Thallophyta (Greek, thallus = shoot + phyton = plant).
Unicellular or multicellular plants without roots, stems or leaves.
SUB-PHYLUM:
Algae (Latin, alga = seaweed).

Photosynthesizing thallophytes, with chlorophyll. With a few exceptions, aquatic or living in moist habitats.

CLASS:

Cyanophyceae (Greek, cyanos = dark blue + phykos = seaweed).
Unicellular or filamentous blue-green algae.
Examples: Gleocapsa (Fig. 10.6); Nostoc.

CLASS:

Chlorophyceae (Greek, chloros = yellow-green + phykos).
Unicellular, filamentous, plate-like or spherical green algae.
Examples: Pleurococcus (Fig. 10.7); Spirogyra (Fig. 10.15); Volvox (Fig. 10.14).

CLASS:

Bacillariophyceae (Latin, bacillum = small staff + phykos). Diatoms.
Unicellular; filamentous; or irregular clusters of chlorophyll-containing cells. The cell wall is impregnated with silicon and is composed of two overlapping parts.
Examples: Pinnularia; Surirella.

CLASS:

Phaeophyceae (Greek, phaios = dun-colored + phykos).
Multicellular brown algae. Marine.
Examples: Laminaria (kelp); Fucus (rockweed).

CLASS:

Rhodophyceae (Greek, rhodon = rose + phykos).
Multicellular red algae. Largely marine.
Example: Chondrus (Irish moss).

SUB-PHYLUM:

Fungi (Latin, fungus = mushroom).
Chemosynthesizing, parasitic or saprophytic thallophytes, without chlorophyll.

CLASS:

Schizomycetes (Greek, schizein = to split + mykes = fungus).
Microscopic, unicellular fungi; the bacteria.
Examples: Bacillus cereus (Fig. 10.8).

CLASS:

Myxomycetes (Greek, myxos = slime + mykes).
Multinucleate fungi, often forming large protoplasmic masses; slime molds.

CLASS:

Phycomycetes (Greek, phykos = seaweed + mykes).
Filamentous fungi, whose mycelium, without cross-walls, is multinucleate.
Example: Rhizopus (black bread mold) (Fig. 10.16a).

CLASS:

Ascomycetes (Greek, askus = sac + mykes).
Unicellular or filamentous fungi in which the spores are enclosed in a sac, or ascus.
Examples: Saccharomyces (yeast) (Fig. 10.11); Neurospora (pink bread mold) (Fig. 24.12).

CLASS:

Basidiomycetes (Latin, dim. of Greek basis = base + mykes).
Filamentous fungi whose spores are produced from club-shaped cells called basidia at the tips of fertile hyphae only.
Example: Agaricus campestris (field mushroom).

CLASS:

Lichenes (Greek, leichein = to lick).
Composite thallophytes composed of an alga and a fungus (usually an ascomycete) in symbiotic relationship.
Example: (Fig. 10.17).

PHYLUM:

Bryophyta (Greek, bryon = moss + phyton = plant).
Multicellular, terrestrial, photosynthesizing plants, without differentiation into stems, leaves and roots. Metagenetic, a sexual generation (gametophyte) with specialized reproductive organs (archegonia ♀ and antheridia ♂) alternating with an asexual generation (sporophyte), parasitic upon the gametophyte and producing spores.

CLASS:

Hepaticae (Greek, hepar = liver).
Plants with a prostrate habit of growth, the body either a lobed thallus, several cells in thickness, or a creeping axis with leaf-like extensions.
Example: Riccia (Fig. 11.19); Porella (Fig. 11.20).

CLASS:

Musci (Latin, muscus = moss).
The gametophyte consists of an erect central axis, with radiating plates of cells containing chloroplasts superficially resembling leaves.
Example: Polytrichum (Fig. 11.22).

PHYLUM:

Pteridophyta (Greek, pteris = fern + phyton = plant).
Multicellular, photosynthesizing plants, both terrestrial and aquatic in habit. Metagenetic, the sporophyte a plant often growing to considerable size with stem, leaves and rootlets, and cells specialized for the transport of water and its solutes; the gametophyte is a small, inconspicuous plant.

CLASS:

\* Psilophytineae (Greek, psilos = bare + phyton = plant).
Extinct terrestrial ferns which flourished in the Paleozoic Era and have left many fossil traces in Devonian strata.

CLASS:

Filicineae (Latin, filix = fern).
Leafy plants, with leaves elevated on petioles arising from underground stem, or rhizome.
Example: Osmunda (Fig. 12.1a).

CLASS:

Equisetineae (Latin, equus = horse + seta = bristle).
Rush-like plants, with jointed and mostly hollow stems.
Example: Equisetum (Fig. 12.1b), the only extant genus.

CLASS:

Lycopodineae (Greek, lykos = wolf + pous = foot).
Small, evergreen plants of creeping habit, the ground pines and club mosses.
Examples: Selaginella (Fig. 12.1d); Lycopodium (Fig. 12.1c).

PHYLUM:

Spermatophyta (Greek, sperma = seed + phyton = plant).
Seed-bearing plants, terrestrial or aquatic in habit. Metagenetic, the sporophyte a tree, shrub or herb with stems, leaves and roots and highly differentiated tissues and the gametophyte very much reduced in size and wholly dependent upon the sporophyte. Photosynthetic, with a few exceptions.

CLASS:

Gymnospermae (Greek, gymnos = naked + sperma = seed).
Trees and shrubs with flowers usually unisexual and always without perianth. Seeds borne on the surface of the sporophylls.
Examples: Pinus (Fig. 12.2); Sequoia.

CLASS:

Angiospermae (Greek, aggeion = receptacle + sperma = seed).
Trees, shrubs and herbs with unisexual or bisexual flowers, the sporophylls surrounded by modified leaves as petals and sepals, the whole structure forming the flower. Seeds enclosed by one or more sporophylls. Prostrate, creeping or erect habit of growth.

SUB-CLASS:

Dicotyledonae (Greek, dis = two + kotyledon = cup-shaped hollow).
Embryo with two seed leaves. Mature plant with leaves usually netted-veined and open vascular bundles in stem, with cambium, arranged in a ring. Flowers various.
Example: Cornus canadensis (Fig. 12.3c).

SUB-CLASS:

Monocotyledonae (Greek, monos = one + kotyledon).
Embryo with one seed leaf. Mature plant with leaves parallel-veined and closed vascular bundles, without cambium, scattered through stem.
Example: Zea mays (Fig. 12.3b).

**Kingdom : Animalia**

SUB-KINGDOM:

Protozoa (Greek, protos = first + zoion = animal).
Unicellular (acellular) animals.

PHYLUM:

Protozoa.
Body consists of a single cell, usually microscopic; solitary individuals, colonies or cell aggregates, without specialization of function.

SUB-PHYLUM:

Plasmodroma (Greek, plasma = something molded + dromos = running).
Organelles for locomotion are pseudopodia, flagella or none.

CLASS:

Rhizopoda (Greek, rhiza = root + pous = foot).
Locomotion by pseudopodia.
Examples: Amoeba (Fig. 10.1a); Arcella (Fig. 10.1b); Difflugia (Fig. 10.1c); Entamoeba (Fig. 10.1d); Rhabdammina (Fig. 10.2a); Reophax (Fig. 10.2b); Nummulites (Fig. 10.2c).

CLASS:
  Mastigophora (Greek, mastix = whip + phorein = to bear).
  Locomotion by flagella (one or several at some stage in life cycle).
  Examples: Euglena (Fig. 10.5a); Hematococcus (Fig. 10.5b); Chlamydomonas (Fig. 10.5c); Mastigamoeba (Fig. 10.5d).
CLASS:
  Sporozoa (Greek, spora = seed + zoion = animal).
  All internal parasites; no locomotor organelles.
  Example: Plasmodium; Gregarina.
SUB-PHYLUM:
  Ciliophora (Latin, cilium = hair + Greek, phorein = to bear).
CLASS:
  Ciliata.
  Locomotion by cilia; nuclear apparatus distinct as micro- and macro-nuclei.
  Examples: Paramoecium (Fig. 10.4a); Didinium (Fig. 10.3b); Vorticella (Fig. 10.3d); Coleps (Fig. 10.3a).
CLASS:
  Suctoria (Latin, suctum = sucking).
  Cilia in young animals; mature ones attached by stalk and with sucker-like tentacles. Free-living, or parasitic.
  Example: Paracineta.
SUB-KINGDOM:
  Metazoa (Greek, meta = beyond + zoion = animal).
  Body composed of many cells, arranged in layers or tissues.
BRANCH A:
  Mesozoa (Greek, mesos = middle + zoion).
PHYLUM:
  Mesozoa.
  Cellular animals with a solid, two-layered construction.
  The outer layer is somatic, the inner reproductive.
  Endoparasitic.
  Example: Microcyema.
BRANCH B:
  Parazoa (Greek, para = beside + zoion).
PHYLUM:
  Porifera (Latin, porus = pore + ferre = to bear).
  The sponges.
  Animals with two layers of cells, and only incipient tissue formation. Body permeated by pores, canals and chambers into which water flows. One or more water exits or oscula. Internal skeleton composed of spicules or fibres.
CLASS:
  Calcarea (Greek, chalix = lime). The calcareous sponges.
  Spicules composed of lime, and are one-, three- or four-rayed. Body bristly.
  Example: Sycon (Fig. 11.6).
CLASS:
  Hexactinellida (Greek, hexa = six + aktis = ray). The glass sponges.
  Spicules 6-rayed, siliceous and in definite arrangement, often intermeshed.
  Examples: Euplectella (Venus' flower basket); Hyalonema (Fig. 11.7).
CLASS:
  Demospongiae (Latin, demo = populace + Greek, spongia = sponge).
  Spicules siliceous or horny or both or none; not 6-rayed.
  Example: Spongia.
BRANCH C:
  Eumetazoa (Greek, eu = good, true + meta = beyond + zoion).
  Animals with definite form and symmetry; well-developed tissues and organs. A digestive tube (enteron) opening by a mouth and lined with an epithelium of endodermal origin.
PHYLUM:
  Coelenterata (Greek, koilos = hollow + enteron = intestine).
  Animals with radial or biradial symmetry arranged around an oral-aboral axis. Two cell-layers, separated by a gelatinous mesogleoa (which often contains cells). Individuals either sessile, cylindrical polyps—often colonial—or free-swimming bell-shaped medusae. Tentacles around the mouth; sac-like digestive system, opening only by mouth; no anus. Often show alternation of polypoid with medusoid generation. Possess sting organs (nematocysts).
CLASS:
  Hydrozoa (Greek, hydor = water + zoion). The hydroids and hydromedusae.
  Coelenterates with radial symmetry. Polymorphic, with alternation of polypoid and medusoid forms; or exclusively polypoid or exclusively medusoid. The medusoid forms possess a velum.

Examples: Obelia (Fig. 11.8); Hydra (Fig. 11.9); Physalia (Fig. 11.13).
CLASS:
Scyphozoa (Greek, skyphos = cup + zoion). The jellyfish or true medusae.
Medusae without velum; 4-part radial symmetry. A great deal of mesogleoa. True polypoid generation lacking.
Examples: Aurelia; Cassiopeia.
CLASS:
Anthozoa (Greek, anthos = flower + zoion). Corals and sea anemones.
Exclusively polypoid and attached. Biradial symmetry imposed by elongation of the stomodaeum. Enteron divided by vertical septa. Often secrete calcareous or horny exoskeleton (corals). Cellular mesogleoa.
Example: Metridium.
PHYLUM:
Ctenophora (Greek, ktenos = comb + phoros = to bear). Comb-jellies.
Biradial symmetry; digestive system opening only by mouth, with pharynx, stomach and branched lateral canals; no anus. 8 external rows of ciliated comb-plates.
CLASS:
Tentaculata (Latin, tentare = to handle or feel).
With tentacles.
Examples: Cestum Veneris (Fig. 11.14b); Pleurobrachia (Fig. 11.14a).
CLASS:
Nuda (Latin, nudus = bare, naked).
Without tentacles.
Example: Beroë.
PHYLUM:
Platyhelminthes (Greek, platys = flat + helmins = worm). Flatworms.
Bilateral symmetry; three germ layers; body usually flattened dorso-ventrally. Digestive system lacking anus; usually branched. Acoelomate (no coelome), the space between digestive tract and body-wall being filled with parenchyma. Excretion by means of "flame-cells" connected to ducts.
CLASS:
Turbellaria (Latin, turbellae = bustle, stir). Free-living flatworms.
Flatworms with ciliated epidermis and mucous glands. Usually pigmented, often brilliantly. Ventral mouth; no suckers or organs of attachment.

Examples: Euplanaria (Fig. 11.15a); Stylochus (Fig. 11.15b).
CLASS:
Trematoda (Greek, trematos = hole + eidos = form). Flukes.
Ecto- and endo-parasitic. Body covered with cuticle resistant to digestion. Mouth usually anterior; two main branches to digestive tract. Oral and ventral suckers for attachment to host. One group (Monogenetic) has direct development, inhabiting only one host; the other (Digenetic) has indirect development, characterized by a series of stages which must live in specific organs of at least two specific hosts.
Example: Fasciola hepatica.
CLASS:
Cestoidea (Greek, kestos = girdle). Tapeworms.
All endoparasitic. Body covered with thick cuticle. No digestive tract in adults. Body differentiated into a scolex, bearing suckers and often hooks, followed by a series of pseudo-segments (proglottids) each sexually complete. The proglottids are shed to the exterior (through the feces, etc.).
Examples: Taenia solium (pork tapeworm); Diphyllobothrium latum (fish tapeworm).
PHYLUM:
Nemertinea (Greek, Nemertes = name of a Nereid in mythology). Nemertine worms.
Bilateral symmetry; three germ layers. Body slender, soft and highly contractile; unsegmented. Eversible proboscis in sheath above digestive tract. Digestive tract straight with posterior anus. Acoelomate.
Example: Micrura.
PHYLUM:
Endoprocta (Greek, endos = within + proktos = anus).
Pseudocoelomate (space between digestive tract and body wall not a true coelome); bilateral symmetry; three germ layers. Colonial, with each branched colony composed of many individuals each enclosed in a theca (zoecium). Intestine looped, bringing anus near mouth. Mouth and anus enclosed in a circlet of ciliated tentacles.
Examples: Pedicellina; Loxosoma.
PHYLUM:
Trochelminthes (Greek, trochos = wheel + helmins = worm).

Bilateral symmetry; three germ layers; pseudocoelomate. Intestine straight with posterior anus.

CLASS:

Rotifera (Latin, rota = wheel + ferre = to bear). "Wheel animalcules."
Nearly cylindrical, microscopic forms with ciliated disc anteriorly and forked foot posteriorly.
Examples: Asplanchna (Fig. 13.2b); Hydatina (Fig. 13.2a).

CLASS:

Gastrotricha (Greek, gaster = stomach, belly + trichinos = hair).
Microscopic forms with flat, ciliated, ventral surface and arched, spiny dorsal surface. Elongate and flexible.
Example: Chaetonotus.

CLASS:

Kinorhyncha (Greek, kinetos = moving + rhynchos = snout).
Minute marine worms with body composed of 13 or 14 rings (not true segments). Two rings form head, which is encircled by spines and has short, retractile proboscis containing the mouth.
Example: Echinoderes.

PHYLUM:

Nemathelminthes (Greek, nematos = thread + helmins = worms).
Bilateral symmetry; pseudocoelomate; unsegmented; bodies usually long and slender.

CLASS:

Nematoda (Greek, nematos = thread + eidos). Roundworms.
Worms with slender, cylindrical, unsegmented body, covered with cuticle. No proboscis. Longitudinal muscle fibers only, in body wall, resulting in whip-like movements of body.
Examples: Filaria (Fig. 16.14); Rhabditis (Fig. 13.3).

CLASS:

Nematomorpha (Greek, nematos + morphe = form). Horsehair worms.
Extremely long and slender unsegmented worms; cylindrical body; blunt anterior end, swollen coiled posterior end. Body wall covered by thin cuticle bearing small papillae. Digestive tract lacks mouth and anus in adults.
Example: Gordius.

CLASS:

Acanthocephala (Greek, akantha = thorn + kephale = head). Spiny-headed worms.
Parasitic in intestines of vertebrates. Anterior, cylindrical proboscis bearing rows of recurved spines; proboscis retractile and sheathed. Body elongated, flattened and rough. No digestive tract.
Example: Acanthocephalus.

PHYLUM:

Bryozoa (Ectoprocta: Greek, ektos = outside + proktos = anus). Moss animals.
Colonial animals with gelatinous, calcareous or chitinous encasement. Circular or crescent-shaped structure (lophophore) bearing ciliated retractile tentacles. Intestine looped, bringing anus near mouth. Mouth within lophophore; anus outside. True coelome.
Examples: Bugula; Plumatella.

PHYLUM:

Phoronidae (Greek, Phoronis, surname of Greek river goddess, Io).
Worm-like animals with anterior spiral or horse-shoe shaped lophophore, bearing two rows of ciliated tentacles. Housed in self-secreted tube. True coelome. U-shaped digestive tract with mouth inside and anus outside lophophore.
Example: Phoronis.

PHYLUM:

Brachiopoda (Latin, brachium = arm + Greek, pous = foot). Lamp shells.
Marine animals with external bivalve shell, superficially similar to mollusks. Ventral shell larger than dorsal with a beak. Fleshy peduncle for attachment to substratum. Lophophore bearing tentacles around mouth. Well-developed coelome.
Examples: Magellania; Lingula (Fig. 26.12).

PHYLUM:

Mollusca (Latin, mollis = soft). The mollusks.
Body covered by thin dorsal fold, the mantle, which generally secretes a calcareous shell of one or more pieces. Anterior head region generally developed; ventral foot, highly muscular, used in burrowing, crawling or swimming. Mouth generally possesses radula, bearing rows of small chitinous teeth. Coelome restricted to cavities of nephridia (excretory organs), gonads and pericardium.

CLASS:
Amphineura (Greek, amphi = both + neuron = nerve).
Body elongate; shell of eight plates, or none at all. Head reduced. Two longitudinal nerve cords.
Example: Chiton.

CLASS:
Scaphopoda (Greek, skapho = boat + pous = foot). Tooth shells.
Slender, tubular shell, slightly curved; open at both ends. Conical foot. Delicate tentacles around mouth.
Examples: Dentalium; Siphonodentalium.

CLASS:
Gastropoda (Greek, gaster = stomach, belly + pous = foot). Snails, slugs, etc.
Visceral mass generally coiled, asymmetrically, within a spiralled shell. Head distinct, with one or two pairs of tentacles and one pair of eyes. Large foot.
Examples: Littorina; Helix; Cyclostrema; Limax.

CLASS:
Pelecypoda (Greek, pelekys = hatchet + pous = foot). Bivalved mollusks.
Shell with two hinged lateral halves; large adductor muscles to close shell. Mantle with right and left lobes, margins forming siphons which direct water flow in and out of the mantle cavity. No head; no radula. Labial palps around mouth. Large ventral foot between valves when moving.
Examples: Ostrea; Venus; Pecten; Mytilus.

CLASS:
Cephalopoda (Greek, kephale = head + pous). Squids, octopuses, nautili.
Forms with large arms or tentacles around mouth opposite visceral mass. Mouth bears hard jaws and radula. Well-developed, conspicuous eyes. Shell external (nautili), internal (squid) or lacking.
Examples: Nautilus; Loligo (squid); Octopus.

PHYLUM:
Sipunculoidea (Greek, siphon = tube + eidos = form).
Unsegmented worm-like animals with an eversible proboscis. Spacious coelome. Looped intestine with dorsal, anterior anus. Crown of retractile tentacles.
Examples: Phascolosma; Sipunculus.

PHYLUM:
Priapuloidea (Greek, priapus = phallus + eidos = form).
Unsegmented worm-like animals with eversible proboscis bearing small spines; no tentacles. Spacious coelome. Straight digestive tract with posterior anus.
Example: Priapulus.

PHYLUM:
Echiuroidea (Greek, echis = adder + oura = tail + eidos).
Unsegmented worm-like animals with no eversible proboscis. No tentacles. Spacious coelome. Straight digestive tract with posterior anus.
Example: Urechis.

PHYLUM:
Annelida (Latin, anellus = a ring). Segmented worms.
Segmented worms with elongated bodies; paired bristles (setae); thin, non-chitinous cuticle. Straight, tubular digestive tract. Spacious coelome; well-developed, closed circulatory system. External segmentation reflected internally by segmental pattern of circulatory, nervous and excretory systems.

CLASS:
Archiannelida (Greek, archi = beginning + Latin, anellus).
Small, with segmentation usually internal. No appendages (parapodia) or setae.
Examples: Polygordius; Dinophilus.

CLASS:
Polychaeta (Greek, polys = many + chaite = hair). Tube-worms, sand-worms.
External and internal segmentation; numerous somites (segments). Lateral parapodia with many setae. Head region generally bearing tentacles.
Examples: Nereis (Neanthes) (Fig. 13.7); Aphrodite.

CLASS:
Oligochaeta (Greek, oligos = small + chaite). Earthworms, etc.
Conspicuous segmentation; no parapodia; setae few per somite.
Examples: Lumbricus (Fig. 13.12); Tubifex.

CLASS:
Hirudinea (Latin, hirudo = leech). Leeches.
Body usually flattened dorso-ventrally. Large posterior sucker; often smaller anterior sucker.

No tentacles, parapodia or setae. Segmentation sub-divided externally by many annuli.
Examples: Placobdella; Hirudo.

PHYLUM:

Arthropoda (Greek, arthron = joint + pous). Segmented animals with chitinous exoskeleton. Jointed appendages, primitively one pair per somite. Appendages may be variously modified as feeding, sensory, swimming or locomotor organs. Straight digestive tract. Open circulatory system. Well-developed segmented nervous system.

CLASS:

Onychophora (Greek, onycho = claw + phorein = to bear).
Elongated, cylindrical, unsegmented, except insofar as series of paired appendages and nephridia are concerned. One pair of short antennae; one pair of oral papillae. Show relations to Annelida.
Example: Peripatus (Fig. 14.28).

CLASS:

*Trilobita (Greek, tri = three + lobos = lobe).
Extinct group which possessed biramous appendages; segmented body marked by two lengthwise furrows into three lobes. Head and abdomen distinct.
Example: Phacops (Fig. 8.3b).

CLASS:

Arachnida (Greek, arachne = spider). Spiders, scorpions, mites, king-crabs, etc.
Body usually sub-divided into cephalothorax and abdomen. No antennae or jaws. Paired anterior chelicerae, bearing claws; two pairs of pedipalps and four pairs of legs. Abdomen without appendages.
Examples: Limulus (Xiphosura) (Fig. 14.29); Centrurus (Fig. 14.27a); Dermacentor (Fig. 14.27c); Miranda (Argiope) (Fig. 14.27b).

CLASS:

Myriopoda (Greek, myrias = a myriad + pous). Centipedes, millipedes, etc.
Terrestrial forms respiring by means of tracheae. Body elongated and divided into head (with a pair each of antennae, mandibles, and maxillae) and trunk regions; trunk divided into many segments, each bearing one (Chilopoda) or two (Diplopoda) pairs of appendages.
Examples: Scolopendra; Julus; Spirobolus.

CLASS:

Crustacea (Latin, crusta = hard surface, shell). Shrimps, water-fleas, lobsters, etc.
Body divisible into three main regions—head, thorax and abdomen. Head composed of five or six segments, with two pairs of antennae, one pair of mandibles (jaws) and two pairs of maxillae. Respiration by gills (nearly all aquatic). Appendages variously modified, generally biramous.
Examples: Artemia; Cancer (Fig. 14.4a); Cambarus (Fig. 14.1); Uca (Fig. 14.4b).

CLASS:

Insecta (Latin, insecare = to cut in—because bodies look almost divided).
Arthropods with distinct head (five or six segments), thorax (three segments) and abdomen (typically eleven segments). One pair antennae. Mouth parts modified for chewing, piercing-sucking, lapping, etc. Thorax with three pairs of legs and usually two pairs of wings (may be variously modified or absent altogether).
Examples: Libellula (Fig. 14.14b); Melanoplus; Tenodera (Fig. 14.6e); Tabanus (Fig. 14.13); Malacosoma (Fig. 14.26); Papilio (Fig. 14.6f); Telea (Fig. 14.6a); Pediculus (Fig. 14.6d); Solenius (Fig. 14.14c); Polistes (Fig. 14.14a).

PHYLUM:

Echinodermata (Greek, echinos = hedge-hog + derma = skin). Star-fish, brittle stars, sea-cucumbers, etc.
Secondary radial symmetry, usually with five radii around an oral-aboral axis. No segmentation. Calcareous body wall composed of series of plates bearing spines and pedicellariae. Coelome includes water-vascular system with tube feet extending in rows along each radius.

SUB-PHYLUM:

Pelmatozoa (Greek, pelma = sole + zoion). Stalked echinoderms.
Body box-like and composed of many calcareous plates; slender arms with food grooves. Stalk from aboral surface for attaching to substratum.

CLASS:

*Cystoidea (Greek, kystis = bladder + eidos = form).

CLASS:

*Blastoidea (Greek, blastos = sprout + eidos).

CLASS:
Crinoidea (Greek, krinoeides = like a lily) Sea-lilies.
Cup-shaped body; branched arms; tube feet without suckers. No spines or pedicellariae. Stalk from aboral surface for attachment.
Example: Antedon.

SUB-PHYLUM:
Eleutherozoa (Greek, eleutherios = free + zoion).
No stalk from aboral surface.

CLASS:
Asteroidea (Greek, aster = star + eidos). Star-fishes.
Body star-shaped and pentagonal. Short spines and pedicellariae. Open ambulacral groove, with tube feet with suckers. Arms not usually sharply set off from disc.
Examples: Asterias; Solaster.

CLASS:
Ophiuroidea (Greek, ophio = serpent + oura = tail + eidos). Brittle stars.
Five slender jointed and flexible arms, sharply set off from central disc. Tube feet suckerless and sensory. No pedicellariae. Sac-like stomach without anus.
Examples: Ophiopholis (Fig. 26.9); Gorgonocephalus.

CLASS:
Echinoidea (Greek, echinos = hedge-hog + eidos). Sea-urchins, sand-dollars, etc.
Body hemispherical or disc-shaped. No arms. Many movable spines and pedicellariae. Tube feet with suckers.
Examples: Strongylocentrotus; Echinarachnius.

CLASS:
Holothuroidea (Greek, holothuria = a type of polyp + eidos). Sea-cucumbers.
Body elongated or worm-like. No arms, spines or pedicellariae. Plates may be present as minute scattered elements. Usually with tube feet. Mouth surrounded by retractile tentacles.
Examples: Thyone; Leptosynapta.

PHYLUM:
Chaetognatha (Greek, chaite = hair + gnathos = jaw). "Arrow worms."
Bilateral symmetry. Elongated body with lateral fins. Straight digestive tract with ventral anus. Coelome consisting of three cavities.
Example: Sagitta.

PHYLUM:
Chordata (Latin, chorda = cord). Sea-squirts, lancelets, tongue-worms and vertebrates.
Bilateral symmetry, three-cell layers, segmented. Complete digestive tract and well-developed coelome. Dorsal tubular nervous system; notochord; gill slits in pharynx.

SUB-PHYLUM:
Hemichordata (Greek, hemi- = half + chorda). Tongue-worms.
Soft-bodied, worm-like animals with many paired gill slits; short notochord, dorsal and ventral nervous tissue.

CLASS:
Enteropneusta (Greek, entero = intestine + pneustosa = breathing).
Burrowing worm-like animals with body divided into proboscis (containing short notochord), collar and trunk.
Examples: Dolichoglossus (Fig. 15.2); Saccoglossus.

CLASS:
Pterobranchia (Greek, ptero = feather + branchia = gill).
Small, colonial forms, secreting an encasement. U-shaped digestive tract. Only one pair of gill slits or none at all.
Examples: Cephalodiscus; Rhabdopleura.

SUB-PHYLUM:
Tunicata (Latin, tunicare = to clothe with a tunic). Sea-squirts.
Animals secreting tunicin as covering for body. Sessile or free-living, solitary or colonial. U-shaped digestive tract; water enters through incurrent siphon and leaves through excurrent siphon from atrium.

CLASS:
Larvacea (Latin, larva = ghost).
Free-swimming forms with tails.
Example: Appendicularia.

CLASS:
Ascidiacea (Greek, askidion = wineskin, bag). Sessile forms, often colonial; larva has all chordate characteristics but undergoes drastic metamorphosis in which most of these are lost.
Examples: Molgula; Botryllus.

CLASS:
Thaleacea (Greek, thaleia = luxuriant).
Barrel-shaped tunicates with several rings of

circular muscles. Incurrent and excurrent siphons at opposite ends of body.
Examples: Salpa; Doliolum.

SUB-PHYLUM:

Cephalochordata (Greek, kephale = head + Latin, chorda).
Fish-like animals, generally small; elongated body, laterally compressed and pointed at both ends. No distinct head. Obvious metamerism externally and internally. Long, low, dorsal fin and short ventral fin. Large number of gill slits.
Example: Amphioxus (Fig. 15.4).

SUB-PHYLUM:

Craniata. (Greek, kranion = skull).
Chordates with enlarged portion of dorsal nervous system, the brain, with which various sense organs are associated; brain enclosed in cartilaginous or bony cranium. Skeleton internal; main axial support a series of segmentally arranged vertebrae enclosing spinal cord. Internal skeleton also serves to support various organs and appendages when the latter are present. Highly developed muscular system to move skeletal elements. Digestive tract with anterior mouth and posterior anus; two digestive glands associated with intestine (liver and pancreas). Closed circulatory system, consisting of heart, muscular arteries, capillaries and veins; lymphatic system well-developed. Respiration by gills or lungs, with progressive separation of blood going to respiratory organs and that going to rest of body. Excretory organs originally segmented, draining products from coelome and blood; in higher forms they are non-segmented and drain products only from blood. Sexes almost always separate; close association of urinary and reproductive ducts.

CLASS:

*Ostracodermi (Greek, ostrakon = shell + derma = skin).
Jawless; covered with bony scales, often fused to form head-shield. No true appendages.
Example: Cephalaspis.

CLASS:

Cyclostomata (Greek, kyklos = circle + stoma = mouth). Lampreys and hag-fishes.
Jawless; without scales or bony plates. Sucking mouth with rasping teeth. 6–14 gill slits in adult. No fins.
Examples: Petromyzon; Myxine.

SUPER-CLASS:

Pisces.
With lateral fins.

CLASS:

*Placodermi (Greek, plax = flat plate + derma = skin).
With jaws; one or two pairs of lateral fins. Armor of bony scales; cartilaginous skeleton, with some ossification.
Example: Acanthodii.

CLASS:

Chondrichthyes (Greek, chondros = cartilage + ichthys = fish).
The cartilaginous fishes.
Shark-like fish with cartilaginous endoskeleton. Jaws and two pairs of lateral fins (pectoral and pelvic). Covered with small scales homologous to teeth. Claspers in males.
Examples: Squalus (Fig. 15.5); Dasyatis (Fig. 15.34a); Chimaera.

CLASS:

Osteichthyes (Greek, osteon = bone + ichthys). Bony fishes.
Partly or completely ossified skeleton; jaws. Gill slits covered by operculum. Pectoral and pelvic fins. Body covered with rhomboid, cycloid or ctenoid scales. Air-bladder (outgrowth from digestive tract) which serves as hydrostatic organ or as lung in some forms (lung-fish). No claspers.
Examples: Amia; Lepidosteus; Micropterus (Fig. 15.5); Stizostedion; Anguilla; Lung-fish.

SUPER-CLASS:

Tetrapoda (Greek, tetra = four + pous).
With paired fore- and hind-limbs.

CLASS:

Amphibia (Greek, amphi = of both kinds + bios = life). Frogs, salamanders, etc.
Aquatic or terrestrial tetrapods, usually naked. Appendages modified as limbs. Lungs as respiratory organs; may also have gills. Two occipital condyles (points for articulation of skull and vertebral column).

ORDER:

*Labyrinthodontia (Greek, labyrinthos = labyrinth + odon = tooth).
The first tetrapods. Armored and with simple vertebrae.

ORDER:

*Lepospondyli (Greek, lepos = husk, rind + spondylos = vertebra).

Extinct amphibians.

ORDER:

Urodela (Greek, oura = tail + delos = visible). Salamanders and newts.
Naked, tailed amphibia. Often with external gills.
Examples: Ambystoma (Fig. 15.6); Salamandra.

ORDER:

Anura (Latin, an = not + Greek, oura = tail). Frogs and toads.
Naked tailless amphibians, without external gills.
Examples: Rana (Fig. 15.6b); Hyla.

ORDER:

Apoda (Latin, an = not + Greek, pous). Blind-worms, caecilians.
Worm-like amphibians, without limbs.
Example: Typhlonectes.

CLASS:

Reptilia (Latin, repere = to creep). Snakes, lizards, turtles, etc.
Tetrapods breathing by lungs only; may be naked, but generally have scales or bony plates as exoskeleton. Cold-blooded. One occipital condyle.

SUB-CLASS:

Anapsida (Latin, an = not + Greek, apsis = arch).
Skull completely roofed over.

ORDER:

Chelonia (Greek, chelone = tortoise). Turtles.
Anapsids enclosed in armor composed of horny and bony elements; broad and stout; jaws without teeth, but usually with horny beak.

The Sub-Classes Synapsida, Parapsida and Euryapsida are extinct.

SUB-CLASS:

Diapsida (Greek, dis = two + apis = arch). Skull with two vacuities.

ORDER:

Rhynchocephalia (Greek, rhynchos = snout + kephale = head).
Lizard-like animals with long tails; persistent pineal eye.
Example: Sphenodon.

ORDER:

Crocodilia (Greek, krokodilos = lizard, crocodile).
Large reptiles living in water or partly on land. Bony plates beneath horny thickenings of skin. Secondary palate separating nasal passage from front of mouth.
Examples: Alligator (Fig. 15.7a); Crocodilus.

ORDER:

Squamata (Latin, squamata = scaly). Lizards and snakes.
Reptiles with horny thickenings of skin forming "scales"; long tails. Skull has secondarily lost one or both vacuities.

SUB-ORDER:

Lacertilia (Latin, lacertus = lizard). Lizards. With limbs; one temporal vacuity in skull.
Examples: Anolis; Heloderma (Fig. 15.7b).

SUB-ORDER:

Ophidia (Greek, ophis = snake). Snakes. Without limbs; no temporal vacuities.
Examples: Python; Naja; Thamnophis; Crotalus (Fig. 15.17).

CLASS:

Aves (Latin, avis = bird).
Tetrapods with feathers (modified reptilian scales). Forelimbs modified to form wings. One occipital condyle. Warm-blooded.

SUB-CLASS:

Archaeornithes (Latin, archae = old + Greek, ornis = bird).
Extinct birds, with long tail bordered by feathers. Metacarpals unfused. Teeth present.
Example: Archaeornis (Fig. 26.6).

SUB-CLASS:

Neornithes (Greek, neos = new + ornis = bird).
Tail-feathers arranged in fanlike manner around short tail stump. Fused metacarpals. Teeth lost in all extant forms. Warm-blooded.
Examples: Bonasa; Corvus (Fig. 15.8a).

CLASS:

Mammalia (Latin, mamma = breast). The mammals.
Tetrapods covered with hair or naked. With muscular diaphragm. Young nourished by milk secreted by mammary glands. Skull with zygomatic arch below eye-orbit; two occipital condyles; secondary palate separating nasal passage from front of mouth. Warm-blooded.
Examples: Lepus (Fig. 15.9); Rattus; Erethizion; Dasypus (Fig. 25.22); Phoca (Fig. 15.9).

# CHAPTER 10

# SYSTEMS BELOW THE LEVEL OF TISSUE ORGANIZATION: UNICELLULAR (ACELLULAR) SYSTEMS AND CELL AGGREGATES

## Distinctions between plant and animal systems

Superficially, plants and animals appear to be very different in their organization and in their biological behavior, so that the division of the living world into the two great Kingdoms, Planta and Animalia, seems to be a natural and a valid one. The divergence between members of the two Kingdoms is readily apparent, at least in those at the higher levels of organization, in the characters of their differentiated cells, the nature of their cell walls, their architectural patterns, degrees of motility, modes of nutrition and of reproduction, and capacity for regeneration and for continuous growth. Typically, the plant cell contains a large central vacuole, filled with cell sap; the animal cell does not. The plant cell is surrounded by a supporting wall of cellulose, or cellulose and lignin, compounds that are not generally formed by the animal cell. The general pattern of plant growth is to provide a large surface area, that of animal growth to maintain a minimal one. Plants have no special contractile cells as animals have, nor those to conduct a nervous impulse, and the fluid that bathes their tissues is not like the blood and lymph of animals, and it travels through less well-defined channels, which have no contractile walls and hence can exert no propulsive force upon it. As a rule, plants are stationary, anchored in the soil by their roots or rootlets, and spreading their leaves to the sun and air, while the majority of animals are motile, swimming in the water, crawling or walking upon the ground, or flying in the air. Plants, with a few exceptions, are autotrophic, animals heterotrophic. The life cycle of plants shows an alternation of generations, one individual producing spores that germinate into individuals of the next generation which produce specialized reproductive cells called gametes (Greek, gamein = to marry) that unite, and the cell resulting from this union divides to become a spore-producing individual of the next generation; no animal produces spores like those of plants, and each generation arising from gametic union produces, in its turn, gametes which give rise to the individuals of the next generation. Plants are capable of regeneration, or restoration of parts lost by accident, a capacity which is very limited in animals, and some plants continue to grow and to live for hundreds of years, while the growth of an animal ceases after it has reached a size characteristic of the species to which it belongs, and its life span is limited.

But these distinctions, marked as they may be among the more specialized members of each Kingdom, are not rigid ones and they break down in a number of cases. Some plants, for example, are independently motile, and some animals are sessile (Latin, sedere = to sit), or attached throughout the greater part, or all, of their lives; the growth of some plants is restricted and their life spans limited to a single season; the investing coats of some animals, the tunicates, are made largely of cellulose, or of a substance chemically closely allied to cellulose, while the cell walls of some plants, certain of the fungi, contain chitin, a material that is very commonly found in the external coverings of animal bodies. Such exceptions as these illustrate the danger of generalization, the application of data found true for one type of organism, or group of related types, to all others, a kind of reasoning against which the biologist, particularly, should be on guard. For living things, although exposed to the same conditions upon the Earth and with a common need for many of the things offered by the environment they share, meet these conditions and utilize these materials in different ways.

## Types of organization in biological systems

In both Kingdoms there are marked differences of organization, or in the body plans of their members. The individual body may consist of a single cell; of an aggregate of cells forming a structural unit but with each cell retaining its functional independence; or of a mass of cells in which there is division of labor between different ones especially adapted for the performance of a particular kind of activity in the body and usually assembled into layers or masses, the tissues, which may be primarily protective, conducting, supporting or secretory and, in animals, contractile. It is among the single-celled organisms that the distinction between plants and animals is most difficult to make, for while some have clearly the general attributes of animals and are therefore properly classed as Protozoa (Greek, protos = first + zoion = animal) and others those of plants and so called Protophyta (Greek, protos = first + phyton = plant), there are others which seem to share the characteristics of both and to occupy a sort of middle ground. The term Protista (Greek, protistos = the very first) is sometimes used for these borderline organisms, a word proposed in 1866 by the German zoologist, Ernst Haeckel, for all unicellular organisms and cell aggregates in order to avoid the dilemma of assigning them definitive positions in either the animal or the plant kingdom.

## Unicellular (acellular) systems

While among the animals the phylum Protozoa includes only the unicellular animals and certain colonial forms in which there is a more or less permanent association of an indefinite number of functionally independent individuals, the unicellular plants are included by the botanists in the division Thallophyta (Greek, thallus = green shoot + phyton = plant), those plants which have no differentiated tissues, nor roots, stems or leaves, and in which the body is often a thallus, an irregular mass of cells showing some degree of mutual dependence. The thallophytes are further distinguished as Algae, those that contain chlorophyll and often other pigments as well, and Fungi, or those without chlorophyll and so incapable of photosynthesizing organic compounds from inorganic ones. All of the unicellular plants are included in the thallophytes, but not all the thallophytes are unicellular.

## Protozoa: general characters

Among the Protozoa the individual is a single cell, with all the components of a typical cell—plasma membrane, cytoplasm and its inclusions, nucleus and its contents —and additional localized structural differentiations or organelles (Latin, organella = little organ), related primarily to their protection, locomotion, nutrition and water regulation and characteristic of the different species within the phylum. Often the cell is surrounded by a wall, which may be a thin, investing sheath or pellicle or a comparatively thick and heavy case. The Protozoa are very numerous and very widely distributed. At least 15,000 species have been identified; they are found on land and in water, both fresh and salt, foul and unpolluted, and in and on the bodies of other animals and of plants. Because of their small size, their existence was not recognized until the discovery of the microscope brought them within the range of human vision; Leeuwenhoek describes many of these "animalcules" in rain water and the other fluids that he examined. Also because of their small size and because the entire body is represented by but one cell, they and the Protophyta have been considered the simplest organisms, and the ones from which all others have been derived. But to consider them the simplest is probably erroneous, for the incorporation of all phases of vital activity within a single protoplasmic unit represents a high degree of organization and local specialization of that unit, an elaboration rather than a simplification of living matter. For this reason the term acellular rather than unicellular has been proposed for them as indicative of the fact that all the manifestations of life, which in many-celled organisms are delegated to different tissues and organs of the body, in them are carried out without the division of that body into cellular units.

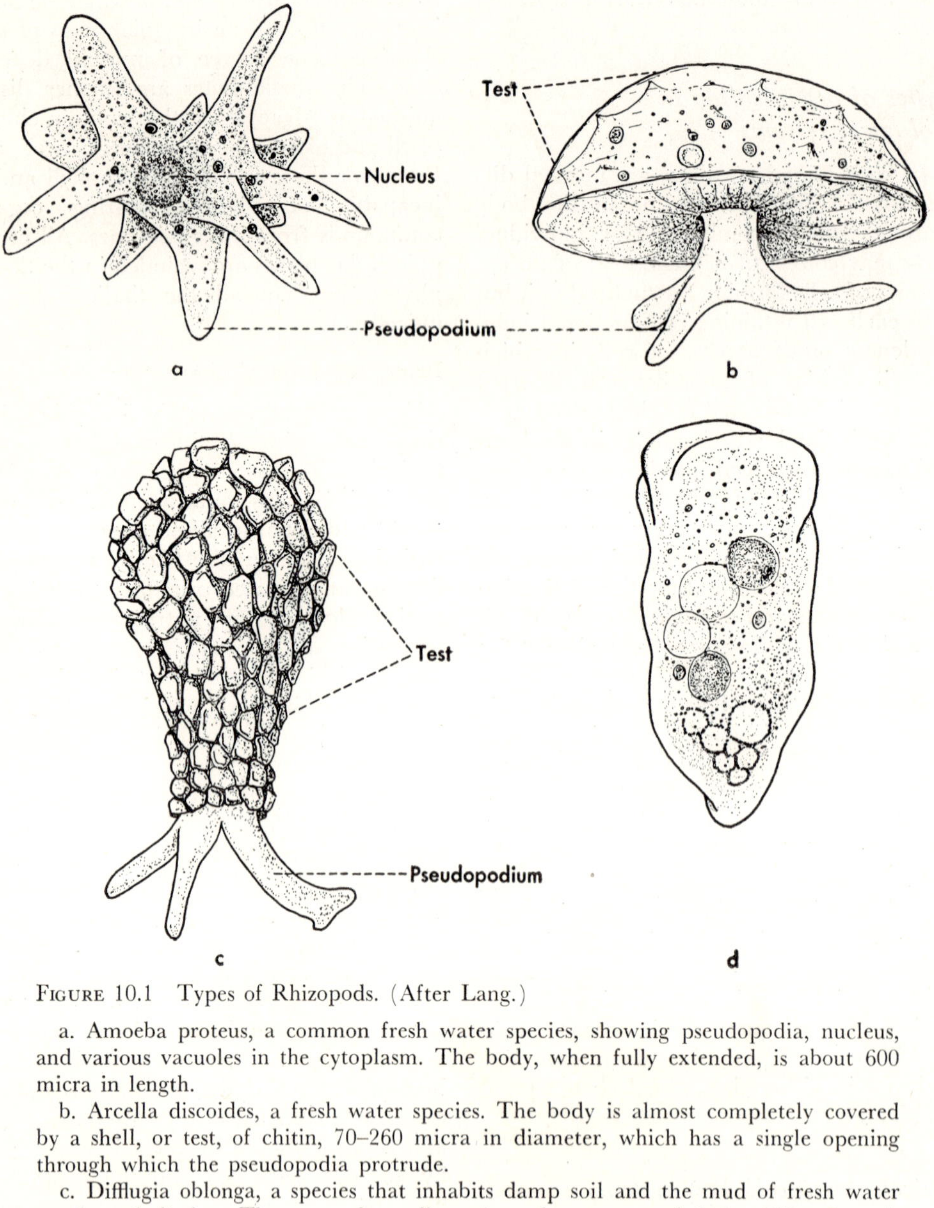

FIGURE 10.1  Types of Rhizopods. (After Lang.)

a. Amoeba proteus, a common fresh water species, showing pseudopodia, nucleus, and various vacuoles in the cytoplasm. The body, when fully extended, is about 600 micra in length.

b. Arcella discoides, a fresh water species. The body is almost completely covered by a shell, or test, of chitin, 70–260 micra in diameter, which has a single opening through which the pseudopodia protrude.

c. Difflugia oblonga, a species that inhabits damp soil and the mud of fresh water ponds and ditches. The test, whose dimensions do not exceed 240 × 580 micra, is made of sand grains, diatom shells and other foreign bodies held together by a mucous secretion.

d. Entamoeba histolytica (20–30 micra in diameter), a species parasitic in the digestive tract of man and other animals.

**Rhizopoda:** While many of these organisms differ from each other in size, shape, organelles and habits of life so that they seem to fall naturally into different categories—the classes, orders, genera and other subdivisions of the systematic biologists—in a number of (Fig. 10.1b) where most of the body is enclosed in a shell through whose single aperture the pseudopodia protrude. The organization of the cell body of the rhizopods is relatively simple; the cell contains a nucleus and in the surrounding cytoplasm, usually

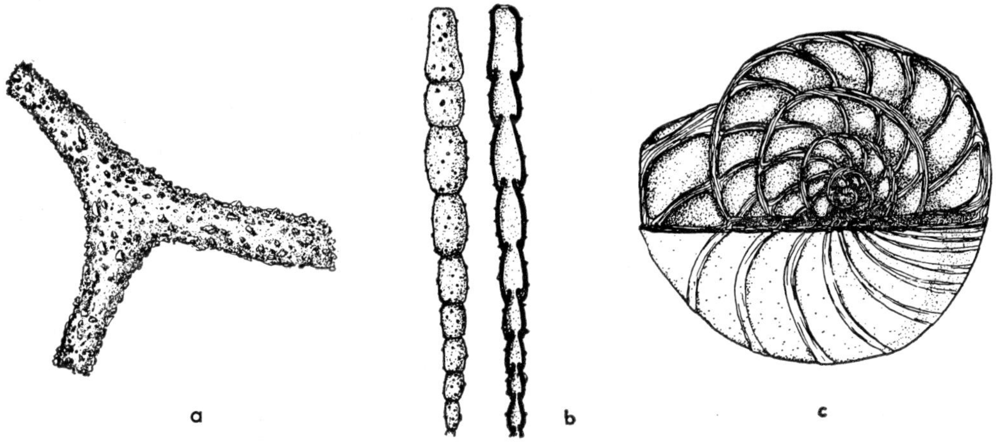

FIGURE 10.2  Types of Foraminifera.

    a. Rhabdammina abyssorum, a fossil and recent Foraminiferan, whose shell is composed of a single chamber, with a central body and radiating arms, representing material collected around the pseudopodia of the animal inside it. (After Kudo.)

    b. Reophax nodulosa, a fossil and recent Foraminiferan, whose shell is composed of several chambers in linear order. As the animal grows, it moves out of the old shell and secretes a new and larger one. (After Lang.)

    c. Nummilites Cummingii, an extinct Foraminiferan, and one of the largest known. Its shell, which may be as much as 19 cm. in diameter, is composed of many chambers arranged as a flat spiral. The blocks of which the Egyptian Pyramids were built are of nummilitic limestone, made by the accumulation and packing together of thousands of these shells. (After Lang.)

cases such distinctions are hard to make and there is a good deal of overlapping not only between the different classes of Protozoa but also between the Protozoa and the Protophyta. Among the Protozoa there are some forms, the Rhizopoda (Greek, rhiza = root + podion = small foot), in which locomotion and food capture is effected by means of protoplasmic projections, the pseudopodia (Greek, pseudo = false + podion), which in the different species range from delicate slender threads to blunt, thick cytoplasmic processes. They may be formed, retracted and re-formed at any point on the surface of the animal as in the different species of Amoeba (Fig. 10.1a, d), or they may arise from only one area as in Arcella clearly defined as ecto- and endoplasm, are granules, crystals and vacuoles of different kinds. The rhizopods maintain themselves as animals, enclosing other micro-organisms between pseudopodia and incorporating them with a surrounding film of water in their cytoplasm as gastric vacuoles in which their chemical disintegration, or digestion, takes place and from which the end products of digestion ultimately diffuse into the surrounding endoplasm. In the fresh water species one vacuole is distinct from all the others; this is the contractile vacuole which periodically enlarges and bursts, discharging its watery contents to the medium outside the animal through a temporary rupture of the plasma membrane. This mechanism re-

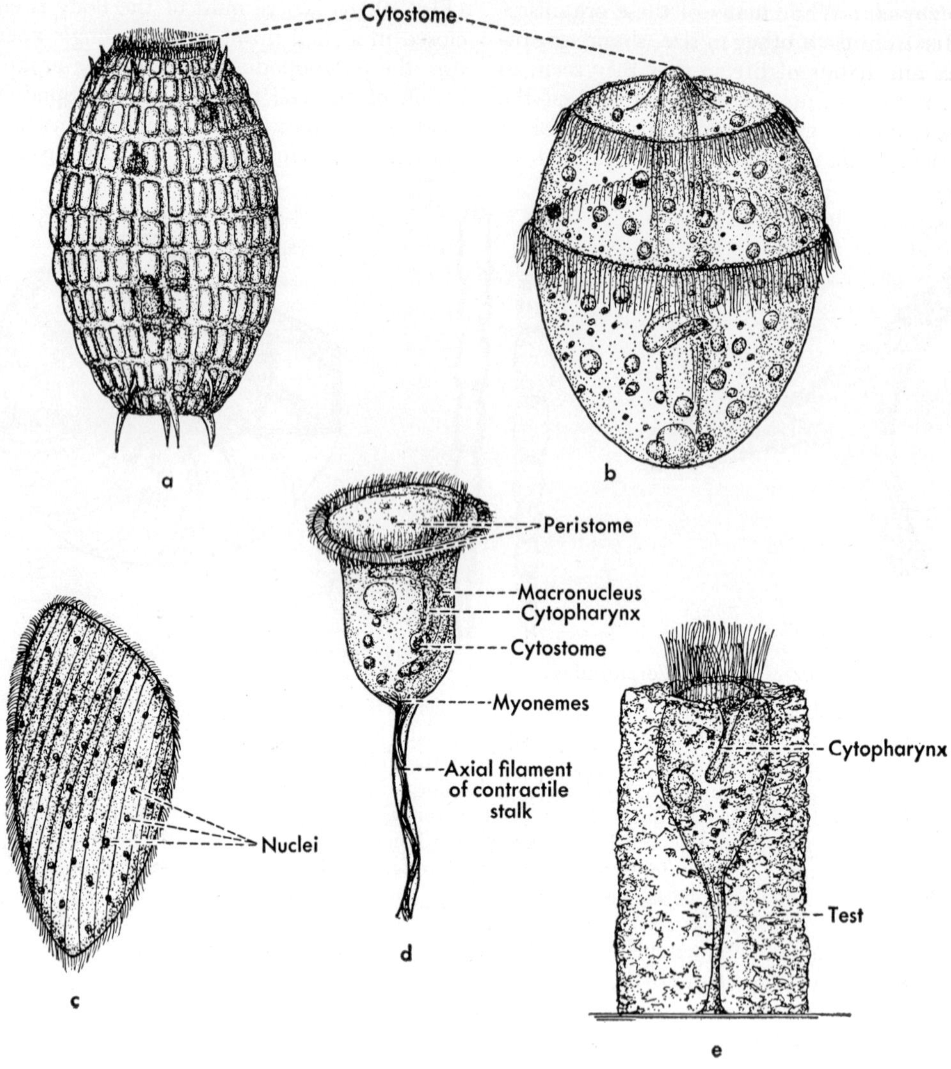

FIGURE 10.3  Types of Ciliates.

a. Coleps octospinus (80–110 micra in length), inhabiting marshy water. (After Kudo.)

b. Didinium nasutum (80–200 micra in length), inhabiting fresh water. (After Blochman.)

c. Opalina (400–500 micra in length), a genus of ciliates that live in the intestines of frogs and toads, with two to hundreds of nuclei in the single protoplasmic mass. (After Hyman.)

d. Vorticella (500 × 100 micra, or smaller), a genus of fresh water ciliates. The body is highly contractile; the myonemes converge at the base of the bell-shaped cell to form the axial filament of the stalk that by contraction can draw the bell down toward the base to which it is attached. (After Hyman.)

e. Tintinnidium semiciliatum (40–60 micra in length), whose chitinous test is attached to plants growing in fresh water. (After Saville Kent.)

lieves the cell of the excess water which, because of its osmotic relations with its environment, is constantly entering and maintains the water content of the protoplasm at an approximately constant level.

What structural elaboration the Rhizopoda have undergone seems to have been in the direction of the construction of complicated and often beautiful skeletons, such as are found in the Foraminifera (Latin, foramen = opening + fer = bearing), where the living cell forms around itself a shell, in some species with a single chamber, in others with many (Fig. 10.2). In the marine species the shell is made of a combination of mineral salts extracted and condensed from the sea water, of which the greatest proportion is calcium carbonate, while silica, magnesium sulphate and other minerals are present in lesser amounts. The skeletons of these tiny animals sifting slowly down from the surface to the bottom of the sea when their life span is completed and gradually washing toward shore form the main part of many of the cliffs and other land formations that border on the sea and its arms. The stones of which the Egyptian Pyramids are made, for example, contain fossil Foraminifera of macroscopic dimensions which probably lived in the waters of the Mediterranean about 50 million years ago.

The Rhizopoda represent but one class of the Protozoa of which there are in all five; of these the Mastigophora and the Ciliata best illustrate the diversity of cellular types. Simple as their structural organization may be, the rhizopods are generally regarded as less primitive than the flagellates; on the other hand, the ciliates show the highest degree of specialization of the cytosome, or cell body (Greek, kytos = hollow receptacle or cell + soma = body).

**Ciliata:** The Ciliata (Latin, cilium = eyelash) are Protozoa in which locomotion is effected by the beating or oar-like action of fine protoplasmic processes, the cilia, which are either uniformly distributed over the surface of the cell or localized in particular regions (Fig. 10.3). Their bodies are constant in shape, with a distinction between the anterior, or forward, end and the posterior, or hinder, end. Ectoplasm and endoplasm are clearly delimited, and the surface of the ectoplasm may be further differentiated as a cuticle or pellicle encasing the cell. This may be in part responsible for the relative rigidity of their bodies and their constancy in shape. The principal differentiations of the cytosome have been in the direction of food-capturing devices; canalicular systems related to the contractile vacuole; mechanisms for offense and defense; and in the development of cytoplasmic fibrils, the myonemes (Greek, mus = muscle + nema = thread), where the contractility of the protoplasm is at a maximum, and the neurofibrillae (Greek, neuron = nerve + Latin, fibrilla = a little fibre) where conductivity is at a maximum. While the myonemes may be seen in the living cell under proper optical conditions as delicate striations, the neurofibrillae are visible only after special treatment. The devices for food capture have followed two main lines of development in relation to the two principal ways in which the ciliates obtain their food, either actively hunting prey as large as or larger than themselves or else constantly feeding on the micro-organisms that are swept into their bodies in the water currents set up by the steady beating of their cilia. In the first type, the cytostome (Greek, kytos = cell + stoma = opening), or mouth, lies at the anterior end of the body either flush with the surface of the cell as in Coleps (Fig. 10.3a), or mounted on an elevation or proboscis as in Didinium (Fig. 10.3b). In the second, or current-producing types, a part of the surface, the peristome (Greek, peri = around + stoma = opening), is modified for producing ciliary currents; this may be depressed to form an oral groove as in Paramoecium (Fig. 10.4a) or elevated as a disk as in Vorticella (Fig. 10.3d). The cilia of the peristome are particularly strong and have a powerful beat, sweeping a continuous current of water containing small animals and plants along it and into the cytopharynx, a funnel-like depression at its base which leads into the endoplasm through the cytostome. The cytopharynx and the cytostome in ciliates like these usually lie in about the midregion of the cell; the water and food particles are swirled into the endoplasm as gastric vacuoles, which move in a circular course through the cytosome while digestion is in progress.

Contractile vacuoles are found in all the members of this class; in some species there

These are the trichocysts (Greek, tricho- = hair + kystos = cyst); upon mechanical or chemical stimulation they shoot out through the pellicle as slender threads. The manner of their discharge is not clear nor is there a common explanation of the role that they play. In Dileptus they appear to be useful in

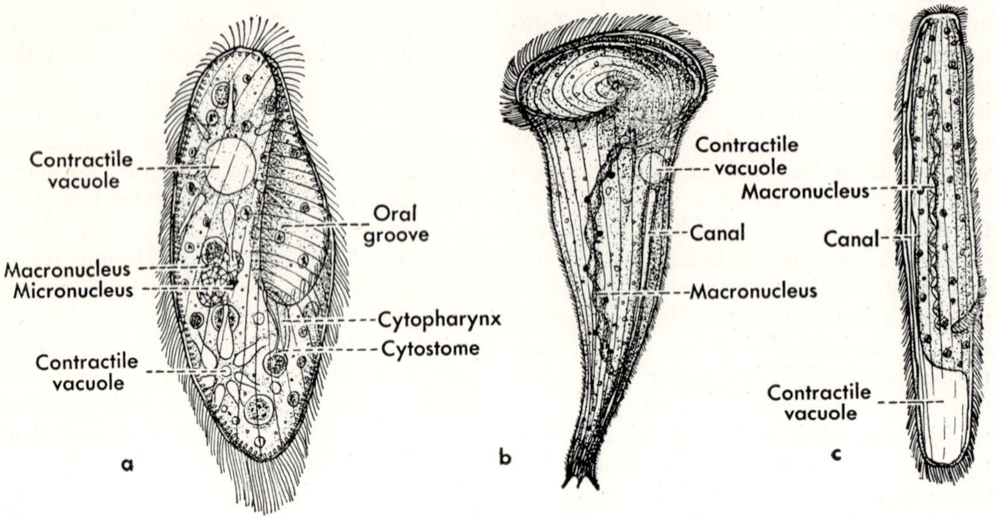

FIGURE 10.4  Types of Ciliates.

    a. Paramoecium caudatum (200–260 micra in length, one of the most common of fresh water ciliates. (After Lang.)

    b. Stentor polymorphus (1–2 mm. long when extended), a fresh water ciliate. (After Lang.)

    c. Spirostomum ambiguum (1–3 mm. in length), a fresh water ciliate. (After Kudo.)

is but a single one, in others two or many, but whatever the number, they always arise in definite regions in the cell. In Paramoecium and some others the water flows into the vacuole through several channels, or canals, in the cytosome (Fig. 10.4a); in Stentor (Fig. 10.4b) and Spirostomum (Fig. 10.4c) there is one long canal leading to the vacuole. These systems of canals and vacuoles represent local modifications in the cytoplasm, and, as in the rhizopods, are a mechanism by which water balance is maintained between the animal and its environment. In many members of this class tiny rods are found beneath the surface layer, in some evenly distributed over the surface of the body, in others limited to special areas.

capturing prey and there is some evidence that a substance is secreted from them that is poisonous, or toxic, to other animals. In Paramoecium they may be used to ward off enemies, for when a didinium attacks a paramoecium, upon which it customarily feeds, the victim will emit a cloud of trichocysts so dense that the attacker may be pushed away. Possibly their primary function is by local discharge to anchor the ciliate temporarily while it is feeding on bacteria. The ability to secrete a substance called tectin, a combination of protein and carbohydrate and chemically allied to mucus and slime, is widespread among the Protozoa; some put it to advantage by making capsules of it around their bodies to which sand grains and other foreign particles adhere to make a kind of shell, as the rhizopod Difflugia (Fig. 10.1c), and it is possible that the trichocysts of the ciliates represent another adaptation of this common capacity, an adaptation that reaches its highest degree of specialization when used for offense and defense.

In nearly all of the ciliates the nuclear apparatus is separated into two bodies, the macronucleus (Greek, macros = large) and the micronucleus (Greek, micros = small), or the somatic and generative nuclei respectively. This division of nuclear components and apparently also division of nuclear function is peculiar to the ciliates and is found in no other group of organisms. The existing evidence shows that the inheritable or genic material is transmitted from generation to generation through the divisions of the micronucleus; whether any is handed on through the macronuclear material or through the cytoplasm is still problematical.

There are no shelled members of the Ciliata as there are of the Rhizopoda although in some, the Tintinnidae, the body is enclosed in a transparent, vase-like case (Fig. 10.3e) and in others, like Coleps (Fig. 10.3a), there are plates of hard material below the surface of the ectoplasm which make a kind of armor. All of them are aquatic, inhabiting salt and fresh water and the body fluids of other animals; most of them are free-swimming individuals although there are some, like Vorticella, which may be attached during the greater part of their life cycle and others, like the Tintinnidae, which are permanently so.

*Flagellata:* While the ciliates represent the most diversified and the most elaborately organized of the Protozoa, the flagellates are the most generalized and the most primitive. The names Flagellata (Latin, flagellum = whip) and Mastigophora (Greek, mastix = scourge + phoros = bearing) are used synonomously for this class, having been proposed by different people at different times as descriptive of the distinguishing characteristic of these animals—the presence of one or more delicate protoplasmic filaments extending from the anterior end of the cell (Fig. 10.5). Movement of the animals is brought about by the lashing of these filaments. Flagellates are found in waters of all kinds and some also in the body fluids of multicellular animals; their bodies are definite in shape, spherical, ovoid or elongated, with a distinct anterior end, which may be pointed or rounded, and marked by a furrow or groove in the cytoplasm which in some members acts as a cytopharynx. The flagellum or flagella lie within this groove; in some species the free ends are directed anteriorly, in some posteriorly. Within the cytosome are found a nucleus and various organelles—in some, food vacuoles and in the fresh water forms, contractile vacuoles. Most of the flagellates also have chromoplasts in their cytosomes, of varying shapes and containing pigments of different kinds. In some the pigment is exclusively chlorophyll, and many of them together contribute to the green scum so often seen on ponds and pools. In others there may be red, brown or yellow pigments as well, masking the green color of the chlorophyll. In some, too, there is a small red spot, the eyespot, at the anterior end, a cup of the pigment hematochrome, which protects a photosensitive region of the cytosome beneath it and thus enables the organism to respond to localized light stimuli. In some, such as Hematococcus (Fig. 10.5b), hematochrome is distributed diffusely in the cytosome so that the whole minute organism is red; large numbers of them give a definitely red color to their surroundings. These are the organisms responsible for the "red snow" of the Arctic, the "red rain" reported in puddles after a shower, and the red streaks that sometimes appear in the sea.

The presence of chloroplasts in some of these flagellates makes it difficult to define them as animals or plants, for the ability to derive material for maintenance and growth from inorganic substances by photosynthesis is generally attributed to plants alone. In the genus Euglena (Fig. 10.5a), for example, which includes about fifty species, there are some species which are green, some red and some colorless. Though provided with a cytopharynx, there is no evidence that any of them take in solid food, nor is there unequivocal evidence that any of them can

[ 124 ]   THE ORGANIZATION OF BIOLOGICAL SYSTEMS

subsist as true plants, growing in an environment that offers only light and inorganic materials. Though the chlorophyll-containing ones can make their own carbohydrate in the light, they appear to require an organic source of nitrogen for their protein

for as biological systems these organisms meet the demands of existence, regardless of the category into which for convenience they are put, in the way that is most effective and efficient for them under any particular set of environmental conditions.

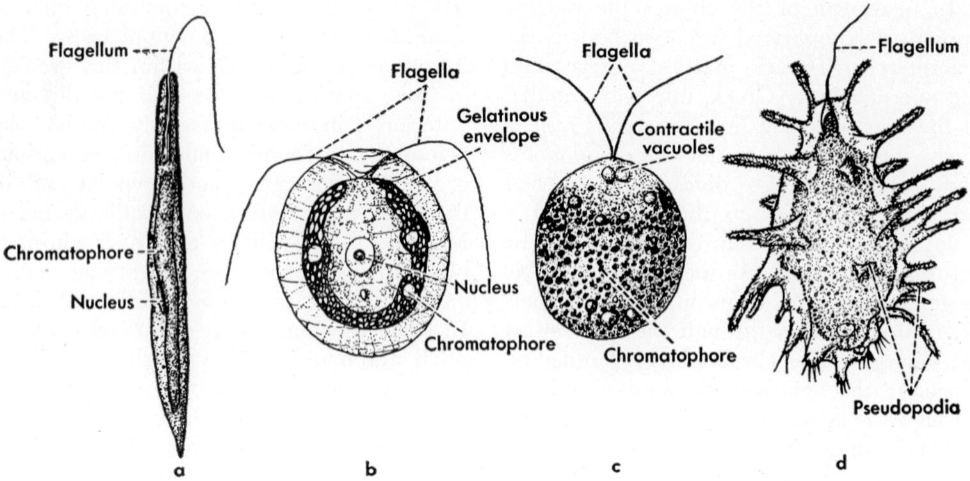

FIGURE 10.5  Types of Flagellata.

    a. Euglena elongata (60–70 micra in length), inhabiting fresh water. (After Lang.)
    b. Hematococcus pluvialis (8–50 micra in diameter), inhabiting fresh water. (After Kudo.)
    c. Chlamydomonas (15–30 micra in diameter), inhabiting fresh water. (After Hyman.)
    d. Mastigamoeba aspera (150–200 micra in length), living in the ooze at the bottom of fresh water ponds. Mastigamoeba may at times lose its flagellum and become amoeboid in its locomotion.

synthesis; although this may be a simple compound compared to those that most animals require, it must be some linkage of amino acids. They cannot, as most plants can, utilize the nitrogen of nitrites ($-NO_2$) or of nitrates ($-NO_3$) for this synthesis. The fact that the chlorophyll-containing species can live in the dark without making use of their photosynthesizing mechanism and after using up their stored starch indicates that they are able to subsist, as most animals do, on complex organic compounds. It has long been debated whether systems like Hematococcus, Euglena and the equally ambiguous Chlamydomonas (Fig. 10.5c) should be called plants or animals. This seems a question which there seems little value now either in raising or in debating,

Not only do the flagellates combine the attributes of plants and animals but some also share certain characteristics with the rhizopods. While the cytosome of most of them is surrounded by a pellicle or cuticle, and the more plant-like members of the class have a cellulose wall, there are some few without even a pellicle, or else with a very thin one, whose bodies do not show the characteristic constancy of form so that they seem both amoeboid and flagellate. Indeed, in these transitional forms a true distinction between the classes is hardly possible, for some organisms now classified as rhizopods may become flagellate under certain conditions, and some now classified as flagellates may at times lose their flagella and become amoeboid (Fig. 10.5d).

## Unicellular thallophytes: algae

Both the algae and the fungi include unicellular species, as well as cell aggregates and colonial forms. On the basis of the pigment or pigments that they synthesize and are contained in their chloroplastids or dissolved in their cell sap, the algae are distinguished as green, blue-green, brown and red. Included in this sub-division of the Thallophyta is also a group of unicellular plants, the diatoms, that make up the class Bacillariophyceae.

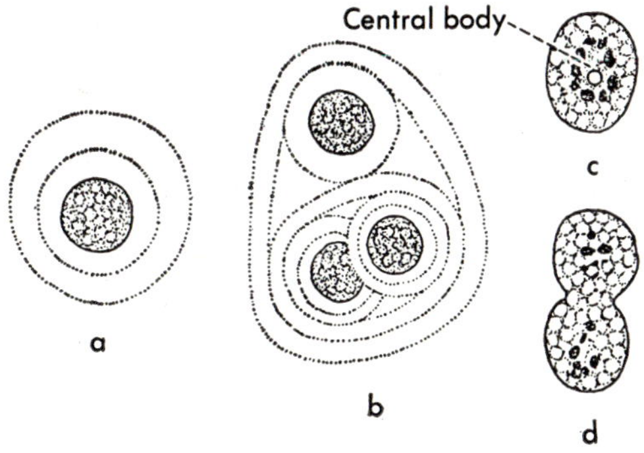

FIGURE 10.6 Gleocapsa, one of the blue-green algae. (From Smith, Gilbert, Evans, Duggar, Bryan and Allen, *A Textbook of General Botany.* Copyright 1942 by The Macmillan Company.)

*Blue-green algae:* The organization of the protoplast, the living or protoplasmic part of the cell in distinction to the non-living parts such as the cellulose wall and the central vacuole which, though structurally part of the cell, are not metabolically active in it, is simplest in the blue-green algae. Only two vaguely defined areas can be seen in these cells, a clear region which has been called the "central body" and the darker surrounding area (Fig. 10.6). The central body most probably represents the nucleus, since it has been shown to contain nucleoprotein, and the peripheral area the cytoplasm, but their characteristics are too ill-defined to make their identification easy. At least four pigments have been found to be present in these organisms; chlorophyll, carotin and xanthophyll are found as tiny grains or granules in the cytoplasm, and a blue pigment, phycocyanin, is dissolved in the cytoplasmic water, giving the plants their characteristic color.

*Green algae:* Most of the algae are aquatic, living in pools and puddles of stagnant water, as well as in fresh-running streams and in larger bodies of water, ponds, lakes and various parts of the oceans. Perhaps the most familiar exception is the green alga Pleurococcus which when present in large numbers contributes to the green streaks and smears so commonly seen on the weather side of trees. If one scrapes off a little of this green incrustation and examines it under a microscope, it is seen to consist of hundreds of small cells sometimes temporarily adhering together but actually free and independent of each other (Fig. 10.7). Each cell is roughly spherical with a centrally placed nucleus and a dense chloroplast filling most of the rest of the space within the enveloping cellulose wall. The protoplast is simple in organization and shows few local differentiations.

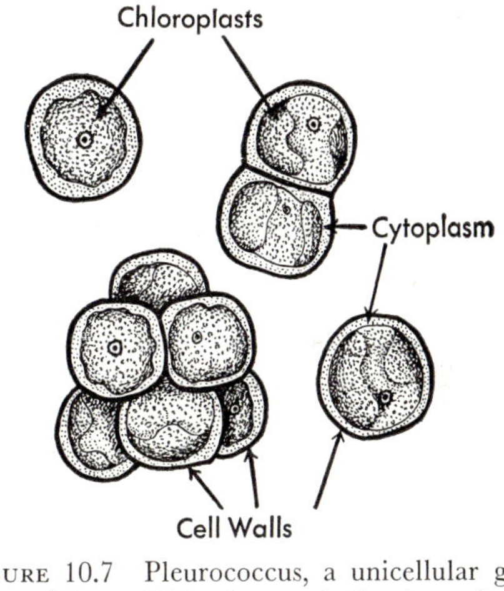

FIGURE 10.7 Pleurococcus, a unicellular green alga. (From Hylander and Stanley, *College Botany.* Copyright 1949 by The Macmillan Company.)

Although most of the algae are free-living, there are some which habitually live in the cytoplasm of animal cells. Chlorella is a very simply organized green alga which lives in water and also as a symbiont in the cytosome of Paramoecium bursaria (Fig. 8.10c) and also within some of the cells of Hydra viridis, a multicellular animal. Its presence in these animals gives both of them a green color, but in each case the alga and the animal are functionally independent of each other but mutually beneficial; the tiny plant receives protection and transportation from its animal associate, as well as a continual supply of carbon dioxide, and the animal has the benefit of the immediate removal of much of its carbon dioxide and a continual supply of oxygen from its photosynthesizing occupant.

**Desmids and diatoms:** The desmids (Greek, desmos = band or chain) are also unicellular green algae. There are hundreds of species of desmids and they are very widespread; their most distinguishing characteristics are the constriction of the single cell into two similar halves, called semi-cells, and the presence of other materials, most frequently iron, in the outer layer of the cellulose wall. The greatest variety and beauty are shown in the sculpturing of these walls, which are lobed, indented or otherwise variously and intricately patterned. Somewhat similar to the desmids are the diatoms (Greek, diatomos = cut through), which make up the class Bacillarophyceae. They also have beautiful and elaborate shells made of two parts, but in the diatoms these are of silica without any cellulose framework, so that they are hard and glassy; the two halves or valves fit closely together, one overlapping the other as a cover fits over a dish. The organization of the cell inside of the shell is simple; the chromoplasts are yellow-brown in color and contain chlorophyll as well as xanthophyll and carotene and some other as yet unidentified pigments. Thousands of species of diatoms have been described; at certain times of the year they may be present in enormous numbers in the sea and in bodies of fresh water. They produce an oily substance as a result of photosynthesis, and the presence of an oily scum or oily streaks in water is sometimes an indication of their presence. They provide one of the most important sources of food for aquatic animals, especially fish, for they represent a large share of the plankton (Greek, planktos = wandering),

the collective name for all the small and weakly-swimming organisms in the surface layers of bodies of water. Certain marine animals feed almost entirely upon diatoms and the important vitamins of cod liver and other fish oils are derived directly or indirectly from them. They too are responsible for fossil deposits, the diatomaceous earth, used commercially for the filtration of liquids in sugar refineries especially, for the insulation of boilers and smelting furnaces and for abrasives of various kinds. One of the largest of these deposits is in California, where about 12 square miles are covered with a layer of diatoms alone about 1400 feet in thickness, and another layer, about 3000 feet thick, of diatoms mixed with sand and gravel.

## Fungi

The fungi also include unicellular forms as well as those whose bodies are made up of numbers of cells. Bacteria and yeasts are usually included among these unicellular species, although the position of bacteria is regarded by many botanical systematists as a debatable one. In general, the subdivision of the Fungi is considered to include six classes, represented by the bacteria, the slime molds, the algal-fungi, the sac fungi, the club fungi and the lichens.

**Bacteria; general characters:** Bacteria were first seen by Leeuwenhoek in the microscopic preparations that he made of saliva and the scrapings of his teeth; his descriptions of his observations make it clear that he saw some of the larger types. But most bacteria are so small, not exceeding 1 micron (0.001 mm.) in diameter, that ordinary optical methods, even at high magnifications, reveal little of their internal structure. Electron microscopy and ultraviolet absorption methods have been more successful in revealing the shapes and some, at least, of the structural details of these micro-organisms. In shape, they are of three general types—spheres, rods and spirals. The spherical bacteria are known in general as cocci (Greek, kokkos = grain), the rod-like forms as bacilli (Latin, bacillum = little stick), and the spiral ones as spirilla (Latin, spirillum = little coil) (Fig. 10.8). Though many are colorless, some contain pigments of various colors—reds, yellows and purples especially, either in the protoplasm or in its enveloping sheath. Like the blue-green algae, bacteria appear to be at a very low level of structural organization, each a minute mass of protoplasm that contains granules and vacuoles of carbohydrate, protein and fat, and a nucleus that can, however, only be made evident by special methods. Outside the plasma membrane is a thin wall that is rigid, yet elastic, which upon chemical analysis has been found to be of cellulose, or of a substance closely related to it, or else of chitin, a nitrogen-containing compound regularly found in the external skeletons of insects and found also in various parts of other animals. This wall is surrounded by a slime layer, of varying thicknesses in different types of bacteria and under different conditions in those of the same type. When this slime layer is thick and firm enough to have a form, it is known as a capsule, and the formation of such a capsule may occur under various environmental conditions. Bacteria may likewise, under certain conditions, form endospores; in the formation of an endospore, all or part of the protoplast seems to concentrate into a mass and the wall to thicken around this mass. Usually there is but one such condensation, but occasionally there are two. In this condition, the bacterium is in an inactive state, and after a period of such quiescence or dormancy, it may emerge again as an active organism.

The most marked signs of activity are the rapid multiplication of the micro-organisms and their movement from place to place. Under favorable conditions of temperature and nutrition, each individual may divide every twenty minutes; even if division occurs only once an hour, it has been calculated that, starting with a single, isolated organism, there would be 17,000,000 of its descendants at the end of 24 hours. Motility is common among bacteria and their movement may be either a creeping one, a result of waves of contraction that spread along the organism, or an active swimming one caused by the lashing of flagella which have been revealed in many forms by electron microscopy. Most cocci are non-flagellate, but the majority of bacilli and spirilla are flagellate, either with a single flagellum at one or at both ends, or with a tuft of them at one end, or with a general distribution

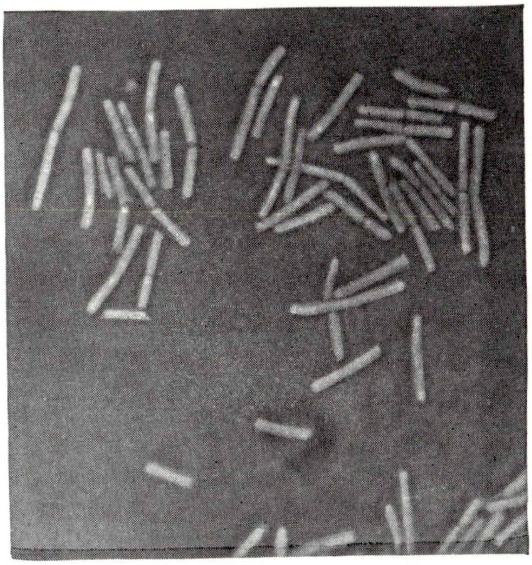

FIGURE 10.8 Bacillus cereus ($\times 1300$), an aerobic bacillus very widely distributed in the soil. (Photograph of living organisms taken by phase contrast microscopy by Dr. O. Richards, Research Laboratory, American Optical Company, from *Cold Spring Harbor Symposia on Quantitative Biology*, volume XI, with permission of the Biological Laboratory.)

of them over the surface of the body. The rate of movement of flagellate bacteria varies greatly; the spirillum of Asiatic cholera has been seen to move for a short time at a rate as fast as 7 inches, or 80,000 times its own length, in an hour.

RELATION TO OXYGEN: Bacteria are the most widely distributed of organisms, for they can withstand, or adapt themselves to, environmental conditions outside the tolerance range of most biological systems. Although certain conditions are optimal for the members of different species, in general they can exist at temperatures both above and below those that bring about destructive changes in the majority of organisms, and they can endure water loss and oxygen deficiency beyond ordinary limits. Some of them, as obligatory anaerobes, can live only in the absence of molecular oxygen; others can exist, by anaerobic respiration, in body tissues, in deep waters and in poorly-drained soils, all environments where the concentration of molecular oxygen is very low.

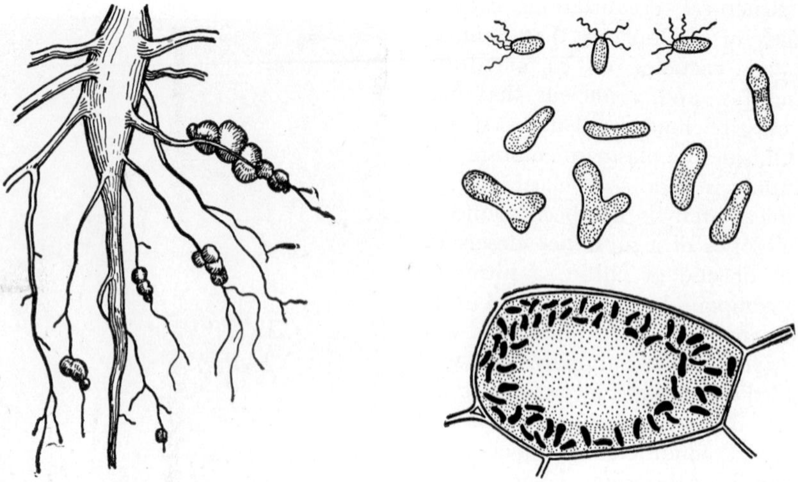

roots of the host plant (Fig. 10.9). Such a relationship is one of mutual benefit to the two kinds of organisms, for the bacteria are offered protection and subsistence by their host and they in their turn supply the host with nitrogenous compounds that may serve

FIGURE 10.9 Nitrogen-fixing bacteria live in nodules on the roots of such plants as clover, alfalfa, lupins and beans. The cells that form the nodules are filled with bacteria, shown in the right hand figure. (From Hylander and Stanley, *College Botany*. Copyright 1949 by The Macmillan Company.)

RELATION TO NITROGEN: Although they are not alone among biological systems in their ability to get along without molecular oxygen, they are almost unique in their relation to nitrogen, for with the exception of Nostoc and some other blue-green algae, they are the only organisms known that can combine the free nitrogen of the air with carbohydrate to form organic compounds that can be made use of by other plants in their synthesis of protein. Two genera of bacteria—Clostridium, a bacillus, and Azotobacter, a coccus—that can "fix" free nitrogen live free in the soil; it has been estimated that 15–40 pounds of nitrogen per acre can be combined with carbohydrate by these bacteria in a year's time. Another genus, Rhizobium, lives a symbiotic existence with other plants such as clover, alfalfa, peas, beans and other legumes, penetrating into the tissues of the roots of these plants and carrying on their synthetic activities there, multiplying to form masses that accumulate in rounded enlargements or nodules on the

as material from which its proteins can be synthesized.

The results of the activity of these symbiotic bacteria is, however, usually far in excess of the host's needs or capacity to use, so that much of the nitrogen-carbohydrate compound is returned to the soil and what is not lost by leaching out can be made use of by other plants or by animals that can avail themselves of it in their synthetic processes. The combined activities of these three genera of bacteria thus restore to usefulness in biological economy an element that is essential to the existence of all biological systems, since it is a component of protoplasm itself. It is in fact the only significant way in which free nitrogen is made available to them, for although during electrical storms some undergoes oxidation into inorganic compounds that can be used by some plants in their syntheses of organic material, this represents only a very small amount of the total nitrogen of the atmosphere.

Two other genera of soil bacteria, Nitrosomonas and Nitrosococcus, can oxidize ammonia and ammonium compounds, which are constantly being produced as a result of the metabolic activities of animals particularly and also in consequence of the disintegration or decay of the bodies of dead convert to nitrates ($-NO_3$), compounds which in solution in the soil water can be assimilated by green plants and used by them in protein synthesis.

The reduction of nitrates to nitrites and to ammonia can be brought about by many

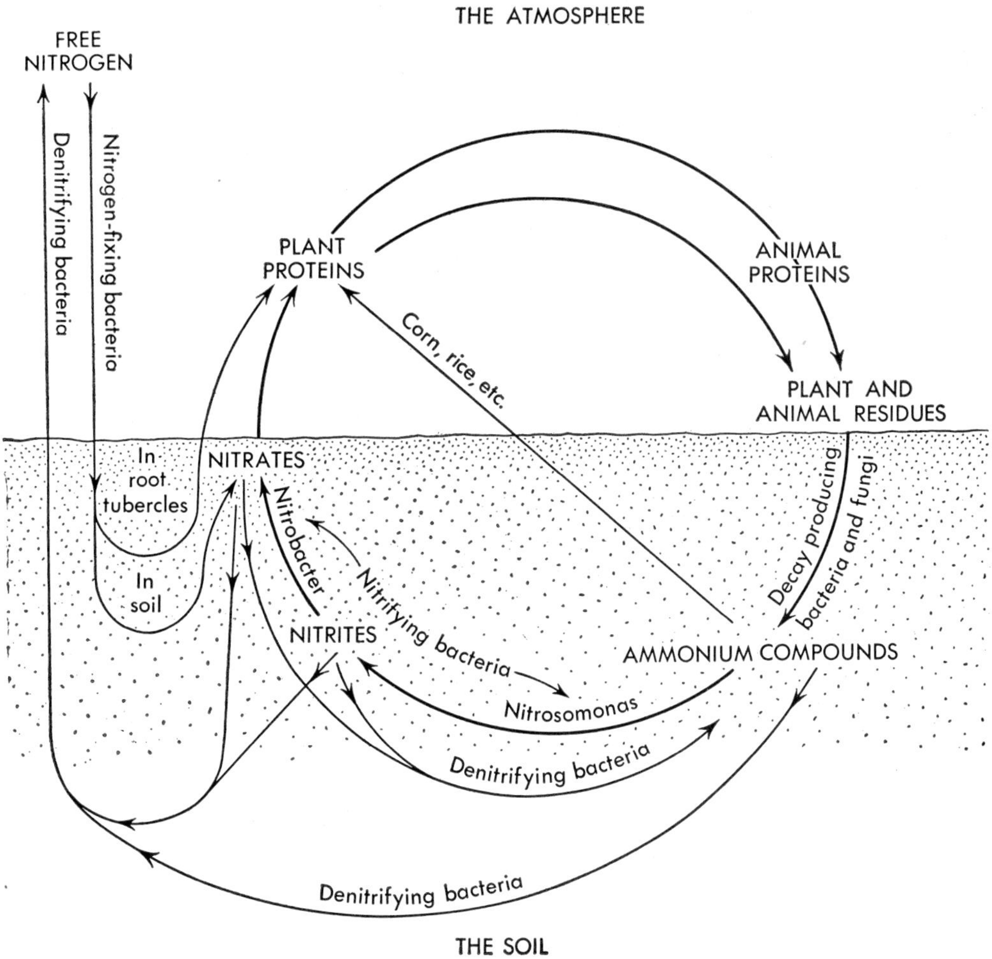

FIGURE 10.10  Diagram illustrating the Nitrogen Cycle. (From Smith, Gilbert, Evans, Duggar, Bryan and Allen, *A Textbook of General Botany*. Copyright 1942 by The Macmillan Company.) The ordinary course of the cycle is shown by heavy lines; light lines indicate deviations from this course.

animals and plants. This reaction results in the production of nitrites ($-NO_2$), compounds which in themselves are useless, indeed toxic, to most plants. But they furnish the substrate from which another group of bacteria, Nitrobacter, can by a process of anaerobic respiration derive energy and also plants as well as by certain soil bacteria. Of these latter, Bacteria denitrificans especially can further reduce nitrites to molecular nitrogen, thus returning it to the atmosphere in a form unavailable to other organisms, except of course those few that can "fix" free nitrogen. The activity of this group of bacteria is particularly favored by an excess of nitrogen compounds in the soil and by oxygen deficiency, and does not take place to any great extent in well-aerated soils.

Two small groups of bacteria have a somewhat similar relation to iron and to sulphur, for they can use inorganic compounds of these elements as sources of energy, converting them to ones of lower energy value. The presence and activity of these bacteria can often be detected by the rusty or sulphur-yellow color of these degraded compounds which may be abundant in their vicinity. The energy so derived is used by these organisms for the synthesis of substances that are used as food, and they thus obtain their nutriment by a process of chemosynthesis rather than of photosynthesis as green plants do.

Certain kinds of bacteria obtain their food from the products of other plants and animals or from the bodies of those that are dead, bringing about their decomposition, while others derive theirs from those that are alive, living within their tissues or on the surfaces of their bodies. The former are known as saprophytes (Greek, sapros = rotten + phyton = plant) and the latter as parasites (Greek, para = beside + sitos = food). Many kinds of saprophytic bacteria cooperate in the disintegration of the bodies of dead animals and plants, bringing about their decay or putrefaction and thus removing them from the earth and returning the elements of which they are formed to the general environment. The activity of bacteria of this kind is put to practical use by man in sewage disposal plants, where bacterial action is encouraged to remove the accumulation of animal waste. Ammonia and ammonium compounds are some of the products of this kind of disintegration of plant and animal protein, compounds which furnish the substrate for the operation of bacteria like Nitrosococcus and Nitrosomonas, which bring about their nitrification or conversion to nitrites.

The combined operations of these saprophytic bacteria and of certain of those inhabiting the soil thus result in the restoration of nitrogen, either free in the atmosphere or bound in inorganic or in organic compounds in the bodies of plants and animals, making it available to organisms that can reconstruct from it new compounds that form the substance of their own bodies or that are essential to their functioning. These combined operations make up what is known as the nitrogen cycle, that can be charted as shown in Figure 10.10.

*Louis Pasteur as a bacteriologist:* Although it was Leeuwenhoek in the seventeenth century who first saw bacteria as individual organisms, it was the great French chemist and biologist, Louis Pasteur (1822–1895), who identified certain of them with specific activities and made the initial experiments that led to the development of bacteriology as a branch of biological inquiry. Pasteur began his scientific studies with investigations of isomeric organic acids, from which he went on to the study of sugars and their decomposition into isomeric alcohols and acids, or fermentation. In 1857 he reported that there is in sour milk a substance that causes the formation of lactic acid which he had been able to transfer to sweet milk and so to bring about its souring. His studies were of great practical interest to the wine makers and distillers of France and when those in the vicinity of Lille, at whose university Pasteur had been professor of chemistry, were plagued with the souring of their wines, they called him in to help them find the cause. He showed that considerable quantities of lactic acid as well as of alcohol were being formed in the vats; furthermore he was able to show that the presence of lactic acid was invariably associated with that of minute, rod-shaped bodies along with that of the yeast cells which the brewers used to bring about the fermentation of their wines. By isolating these bodies and the yeast cells and introducing them into separate sugar solutions, he showed that alcohol only was produced when yeast alone was in the medium, and that lactic acid only was produced when the little rods alone were present. It was thus made evident that different organisms or their products, then called ferments, may bring about different changes in the same medium in which they may be caused to live or in which they may live naturally; moreover it was apparent from these experiments that the rod-like organisms flourished and multiplied very rapidly in the sugar solutions, for after a short time the medium contained many more than had been originally introduced.

This particular bit of evidence had far-reaching consequences, for it led to the experiments by which Pasteur finally proved the fallacy of the concept of spontaneous generation of micro-organisms; also to those of a contemporary German doctor, Robert Koch (1843–1910), who succeeded in isolating and culturing anthrax bacilli and in producing the disease in animals inoculated with the cultural micro-organisms and so established a causal relationship between the presence of a micro-organism in the tissues of an animal and the specific symptoms of a disease; and to the operative technique of the English surgeon, Joseph Lister (1827–1912), who recognized the value of excluding micro-organisms from open sores and wounds and so initiated the methods of aseptic surgery and of antisepsis in general.

SPONTANEOUS GENERATION (ABIOGENESIS): The concept of spontaneous generation, or abiogenesis, appears in the writings of Aristotle and has been held to greater or less extent by some scientists in almost every succeeding period. It was a "philosophical necessity" to the speculative biologists who could not otherwise account for the sudden appearance of organisms in water and other media that had not previously supported life, and even the more critical biologists found it hard to believe that the myriads of tiny organisms that they saw through the lenses of their microscopes, and that seemed to increase in number almost before their eyes, had not suddenly and miraculously arisen as such from the materials of their environment or descended from the skies in the rains. In the seventeenth century a Florentine, Francesco Redi (1626–1698), although himself believing in the spontaneous generation of intestinal worms and of gall flies, proved by experiment that the "worms" in rotting meat arose from eggs laid by flies that crawled across it, not from the process of putrefaction itself nor from its products.

Redi had seen flies hovering over meat that later became "wormy" and thus came to the belief that there was a causal connection between the flies and the "worms," actually their larvae or maggots. But in *Observations of the Generation of Insects* he writes, "Belief unconfirmed by experiment is vain"; so he planned experiments to test his belief. He took eight large, wide-mouthed flasks and put a dead snake into one, a slice of veal into another and some dead fish into two others and sealed them carefully. He then filled the other four flasks in the same way but did not seal them. Although the meat in the sealed flasks underwent putrefaction, no maggots appeared on it, while they were plentiful in the unsealed flasks which flies had entered freely. "Thus," he writes, "the flesh of dead animals cannot engender worms unless the eggs of the living be deposited therein."

But while this might be true for maggots and worms, Redi's evidence still failed to convince scientists that other kinds of organisms might not be spontaneously generated, especially those that appeared in infusions of hay and of meat in such multitudes that the originally clear liquids turned cloudy and opaque in a few days' time. In the eighteenth century the question of abiogenesis again came to the front of scientific thought, for about the middle of that century an English Catholic priest, John Needham, conducted experiments similar to Redi's but with rather more refined technique. Needham aimed to exclude from his experimental material not only flies and their larvae but also all microscopic organisms. He made infusions of meat and of hay and put them in tightly sealed glass flasks. But when he opened the flasks and examined their contents under the microscope, he saw a swarming mass of minute organisms. How else could they have arisen in the air-tight vessels except by spontaneous generation from the medium in the flasks? A contemporary Italian scientist, Lazzaro Spallanzani (1729–1799), argued that in their early stages these organisms might be so small as to be outside the range of visibility, so that the problem became one of excluding from such infusions micro-organisms that were not detectable even with the microscope. He attempted to do this by boiling the medium and so driving the air from it, and finally found that no micro-organisms appeared in an infusion in a sealed flask that had been boiled for 30–45 minutes—that is, none appeared as long as the flask remained sealed. Even this evidence did not settle the question entirely, for those most convinced of abiogenesis, at least for certain kinds of living organisms under certain conditions, held that by heating the air in the flasks Spallanzani had destroyed something within it that was necessary to life and had not proved that organisms could not be spontaneously generated in air that still retained its vital principles. The German zoologist, Theodor Schwann, however, repeated Spallanzani's experiments in the years 1836–1837 with the same positive results, showing moreover that the air in the flasks that had been heated was adequate for the respiratory needs of animals and so capable of supporting life.

Pasteur's experiments nearly a century later drew him into the controversy, for those with the soured wines especially had shown that yeast cells were the cause, not the result of alcoholic fermentation, and that the rod-like organisms were the cause, not the result of lactic acid fermentation. The concept of spontaneous generation in fermenting liquids was prevailing just then among French scientists, its especial protagonist Félix Archimède Pouchet (1800–1872), a chemist primarily but also something of a biologist. Pasteur's experiments to prove the concept false were long and painstaking and led him into bitter scientific controversy with Pouchet and to a defense of his views and an open demonstration of his experiments supporting them before a meeting of the Académie des Sciences. In substantiating the doctrine of biogenesis, or the origin of new individuals only from pre-existing ones, Pasteur sealed infusions of various kinds, known to be "putrescible liquids," in glass flasks and boiled them for varying periods of time until even after months of standing no organisms could be discovered in them. Then he showed that if such sterile fluids were exposed to an inflow of dusty air, micro-organisms soon appeared in them and multiplied rapidly; if on the other hand, the flasks were opened in the clear, still air of the mountains rather than in the dusty streets and drafty cellars of Paris, they might escape contamination. In this way he demonstrated that living forms would not appear in infusions, boiled long enough to destroy any that might initially have been present, unless they were introduced from the air. Still the objection was raised that exposure to heat in a sealed flask so altered the air in it that spontaneous generation of living forms became impossible, but that it would take place if the air had not been so vitiated. As a final answer to this, Pasteur devised a flask with a long neck that he bent down into the form of an S so that air could pass in and out of the flask but any dust particles that it carried would settle through the force of gravity in a curve of the S. In such flasks putrescible liquids made sterile by boiling remained so as long as the fluid in them was not allowed to enter the S-shaped neck and to come into contact with any dust that might be there; under these conditions no living organisms appeared in the medium, although the air with which it was in contact could no longer be said to be vitiated. Although these experiments did not definitely exclude the possibility of spontaneous generation as such, they did show conclusively the failure of life to originate in media that had been exposed to temperatures destructive to protoplasmic systems and to which the entrance of those from other sources had been prevented. The principle of Pasteur's experiments is applied to-day not only in the process of sterilization of milk that bears his name but also in sterile procedures of all kinds.

THE GERM THEORY OF DISEASE: The relation between morbid symptoms in the host, called disease, and the presence of bacteria living as parasites within its tissues was definitely established by Koch, who succeeded in isolating and culturing the bacillus responsible for the disease called anthrax in cattle, earlier identified in the blood of animals suffering from the disease by a French physician, Casimir Joseph Davaine (1812–1882), and in following the history of the micro-organism in the body of the diseased animal and its transmission to that of another. First using animal blood as a culture medium and later gelatine, Koch was able to obtain cultures that contained no organisms but anthrax bacilli, and by introducing such pure cultures into healthy animals to cause them to develop the symptoms of anthrax. He saw that the bacilli multiplied rapidly in the blood of the infected animal, and that after the animal died they formed tiny spores that were resistant to dehydration, to heat and to cold and that might be carried from place to place in the dust of the air, or by other means, and so ultimately find a point of entrance into the body of another animal where conditions were again favorable for their rapid multiplication and movement from place to place. He identified as well the micro-organisms that cause cholera and tuberculosis, establishing the causal relationship between the presence of these bacteria and the specific symptoms of each of the two diseases. Koch's technique of culturing bacteria on solidified gelatine is the basis for the procedures used in bacteriological laboratories all over the world to-day where agar-agar, a gelatinous substance extracted from certain of the marine algae, is a standard culture medium.

From these investigations of Pasteur's and Koch's primarily arose the germ theory of disease, which related certain diseases to the presence of parasitic micro-organisms which produce, as a result of their increase in numbers and of their activities within the bodies of their hosts, specific conditions symptomatic of specific diseases. Such diseases could no longer be said to be the consequence of morbid humors within the individual through which micro-organisms were brought into being.

**Yeasts:** Yeasts are indisputably unicellular fungi, included in the class of Ascomycetes (Greek, askos = bladder or sac + mycetes = fungi), so-called because their special reproductive cells, or spores, are contained within a small sac. In some species of yeast, the cell is but little larger than the largest of the bacteria, that is, about 0.1 mm. at its greatest dimension, but most of them are many times larger and show a higher degree of differentiation. Although a nucleus cannot readily be seen in the living cell, it can be demonstrated by special staining methods so

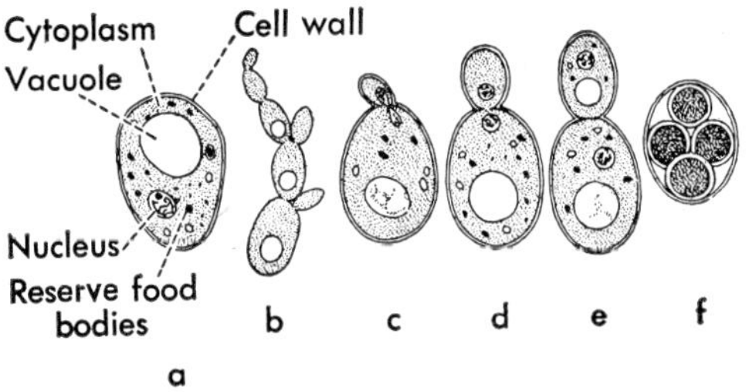

FIGURE 10.11 Yeast. (From Smith, Gilbert, Evans, Duggar, Bryan and Allen, *A Textbook of General Botany*. Copyright 1942 by The Macmillan Company.)

a. Mature yeast cell.
b. Colony formed by repeated cell division.
c–e. Stages in cell division (from stained preparations).
f. Ascospores.

that a general distinction between nucleus and cytoplasm can be made. The cytoplasm is, however, usually restricted to a film just within the inner layer of the double cellulose wall, for one of the most conspicuous features of the actively metabolizing yeast cell is a large vacuole, usually surrounded by oil droplets, which occupies most of the center of the cell (Fig. 10.11). In the presence of an adequate supply of sugar but a limited supply of oxygen, yeast cells can carry on anaerobic respiration which results in the conversion of the sugar into the partial decomposition products of alcohol and carbon dioxide, expressed by the chemical equation, $C_6H_{12}O_6 \rightarrow 2\ C_2H_5OH + 2\ CO_2 +$ Energy $= 25{,}000$ calories. Long before any attempt was made to understand the mechanism by which this conversion is brought about, man put it to practical advantage in the brewing of wines and beers and the leavening of bread, using yeast to bring about the fermentation of the sugars of grapes, malt and hops and so the production of alcohol from them, and in bread-making, to produce the gas that makes the dough rise. Yeasts that are used in wine-making are mostly strains of wild yeasts, carried into the vats in the waxy covering or "bloom" on the skins of the grapes that are crushed to yield the sugar, but those that are used in brewing and in baking are cultivated ones that have been selected and maintained as pure cultures by brewers for years. Like bacteria, yeasts multiply rapidly in a favorable medium which, as Pasteur found, must contain a source of nitrogen as well as sugar; often their multiplication is so rapid that the cells do not immediately separate from each other but remain together in temporary chains or clusters.

**Multinucleate organisms:** While in most of the Protozoa and Protophyta the individual is a single cell with a single nucleus, there are some which are multinucleate—that is, which contain two or more nuclei in a common protoplasmic mass. Individuals of this kind are found in all classes of Protozoa (Fig. 10.3c) and among the Thallophytes as well. The green alga Valonia, living in tropical and semi-tropical seas, has a protoplast with many nuclei, and among the Fungi, the slime molds at one stage of their life cycle are macroscopic protoplasmic masses, sometimes with an area of a square inch or more, containing hundreds of nuclei (Fig. 8.7b). Organisms such as this are said to be syncytial (Greek, sun = with + kytos = cell) or coenocytic (Greek, koinos = common + kytos = cell); the body is a single protoplasmic mass, with a common surface area and without internal divisions, in which each nucleus directs and controls the activity of a more or less restricted region of the cytoplasm. The German biologist, Richard Hertwig (1850–1937), was the first to give expression to the assumption that the influence of the nucleus can extend to only a limited amount of cytoplasm, and that there exists a nuclear-cytoplasmic ratio (Kernplasmarelazion), a determining factor in the size of uninucleate cells. In these multicellular individuals, the conditions of the nuclear-cytoplasmic ratio have been met by the inclusion of many nuclei in a large protoplasmic mass.

## Cell aggregates

Individuals whose bodies are made up of a number of cells in permanent association with varying degrees of interdependence are found among both the Protozoa and the Thallophyta. Among the Protozoa, such cell aggregates are found particularly in the classes of the Ciliata and Flagellata. The marine ciliate Cothurnia (Fig. 10.12a) is composed of two elongated cells in a delicate case of tectin fastened to some object by a short stalk. Epistylis (Fig. 10.12b) is a colony of numerous bell-shaped individuals or zooids, each one at the end of a branch of the stiff central stalk. In Zoothamnium (Fig. 10.12c), also a colony of bell-shaped zooids, there is a differentiation in size between the macrozooids and the microzooids which occupy fixed positions in the aggregate and follow a different pattern of behavior in its reproduction.

There are also some aggregates of flagellate cells. Anthophysis (Fig. 10.13b), for example, is an aggregate of an indefinite number of spherical cells at the ends of short stalks, while the zooids of Rhipidodendron emerge from the ends of gelatinous tubes; in neither is there any apparent difference between the individual members, and all of them feed as animals upon organic matter. There are also colonial as well as solitary individuals among the Choanoflagellata (Greek, choane = funnel + Latin, flagellum = whip), a group of flagellates characterized by the presence of a rim or collar of protoplasm that rises from the anterior end of the ovoid cell and partially encloses the single flagellum. The collar acts as a food-catching device, for micro-organisms of various kinds adhere to its surface and are passed along it down into the cytosome. Monosiga is a solitary choanoflagellate; Codosiga (Fig. 10.13a) is a colonial one, an aggregate of similar cells. In at least one genus, Proterospongia (Fig. 10.13c), there is a distinction between two types of cells in the aggregate. In these individuals, collared zooids are embedded on the surface of an irregular gelatinous mass while in the interior there are amoeboid individuals derived from surface members that have migrated down and lost their flagella. This type of aggregate is quite different from the branching or fan-like colonies of Codosiga, Anthophysis or Zoothamnium; it suggests a connection between these systems, at the aggregate level of organization, and the sponges, which are generally regarded as multicellular animals but whose body plan represents but a slightly higher degree of cellular organization and interdependence than that of an aggregate of cells.

In both the blue-green and the green algae there are colonial forms, in which a number of cells are combined in spherical or disc-like masses of gelatinous material, or

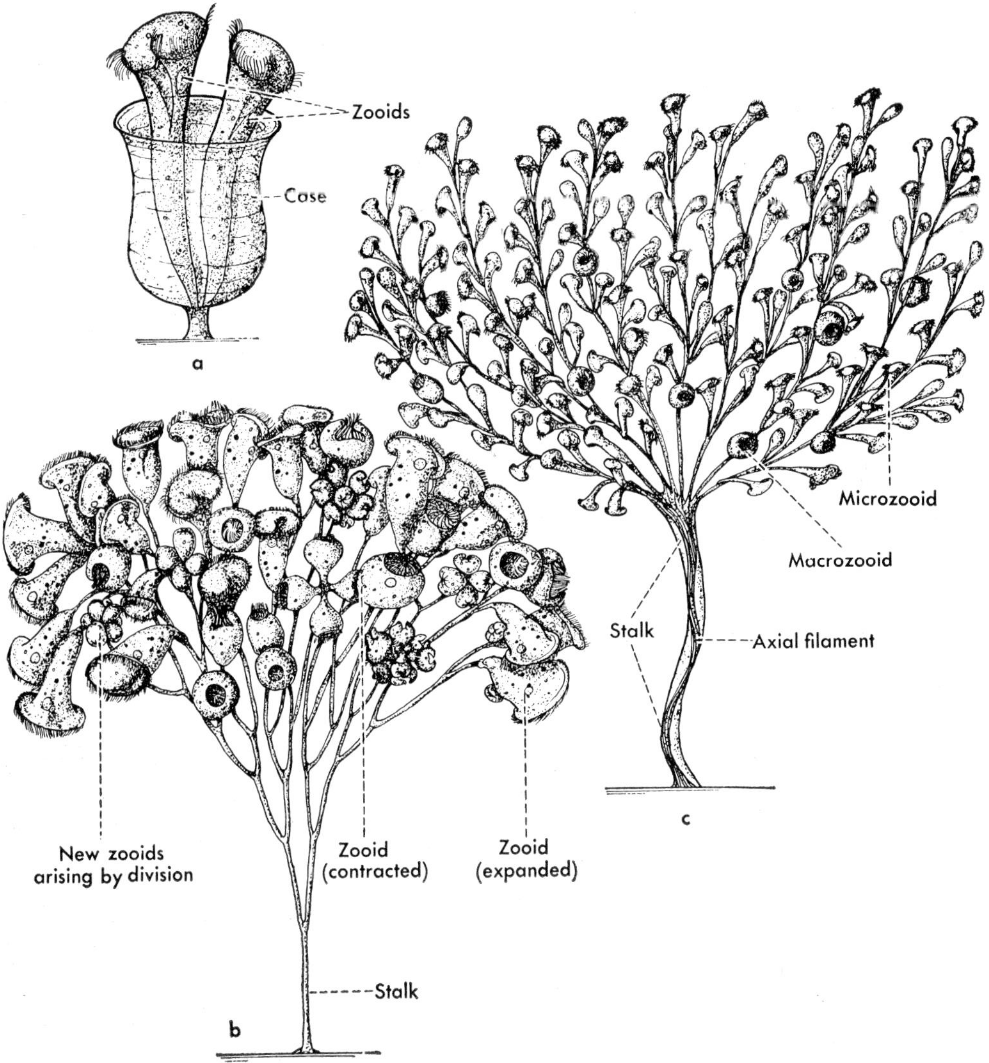

FIGURE 10.12 Colonial Ciliates. (After Saville Kent.)

    a. Cothurnia patula. The case is 50–80 micra in height.

    b. Epistylis, a fresh water colonial aggregate. The entire colony may reach a height of 3 mm., the zooids a length of 90–100 micra.

    c. Zoothamnium arbuscula. The colony may reach a height of 6 mm., the zooids a length of 4–6 micra.

joined together end to end to form chains or filaments, which may branch and which often reach considerable lengths. One genus of green algae, Gonium, includes a species in which four cells are embedded in a flat plate of jelly and another in which the jelly individual is a tiny hollow ball of thousands of flagellate cells. The gelatinous secretion around each cell holds them together in the surface layer and the microscopic sphere revolves slowly through the surface layers of fresh water ponds and pools. In Volvox,

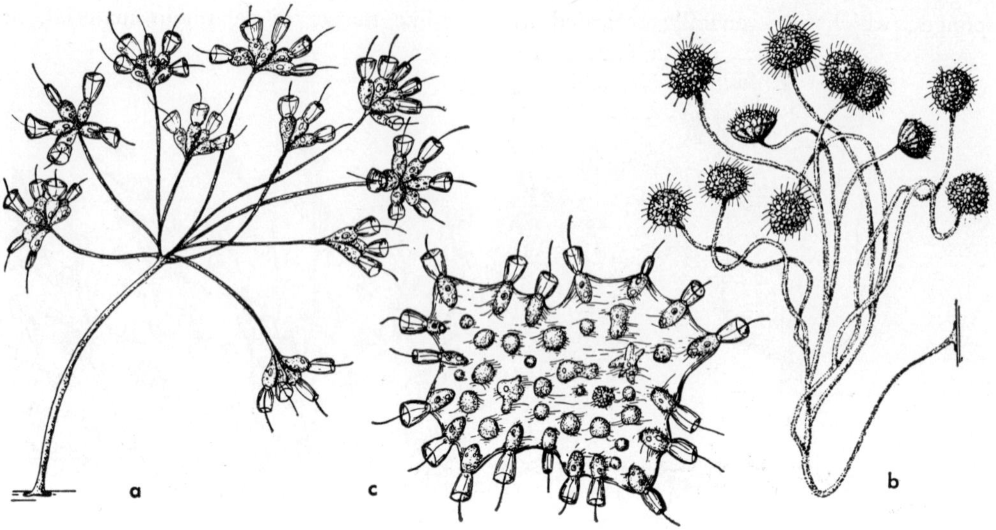

FIGURE 10.13  Colonial Flagellates. (After Saville Kent.)
  a. Codosiga alloides, a fresh water form.
  b. Anthophysis vegetans, a fresh water form.
  c. Proterospongia, a fresh water form.

mass contains 16 similar cells; in both species, each cell is a small, pear-shaped one, with a nucleus, a chloroplast, an eyespot and two flagella which project from the surface of the jelly and through whose lashing the organisms move from place to place. Each cell carries on its own photosynthesis and its own metabolism apparently independently of the others, and is capable of reproducing a new individual like that of which it was itself a part. Pandorina is another genus of similar organization, with 16 flagellate cells closely packed in a flat jelly mass that moves and acts as a unit. In Eudorina, 32 cells are embedded near the surface of a jelly sphere and in Pleodorina as many as 128. In Pleodorina, there is loss of reproductive capacity in some of the cells, so that while all may photosynthesize and metabolize independently, only certain ones are capable of division and so of perpetuating their kind. In Volvox (Fig. 10.14), the only a few of the cells can reproduce; these enlarge, drop from the surface into the fluid within the center of the sphere and from them new individuals like the parent are produced, composed of many cells initially indistinguishable from one another. A difference becomes apparent only when some few enlarge and drop into the center, where they cease to photosynthesize and prepare for, or immediately start upon, the rapid divisions that eventually lead by one road or another to a new generation of individuals.

Spirogyra is one of the green algae in which the cells are united end to end to form an unbranched filament. It derives its name from the flat, ribbon-like chloroplast that is spirally wound within the cylindrical cell (Fig. 10.15). The different species of Spirogyra, some with cells containing but a single chloroplast and others with cells containing two or more, are very common in fresh water ponds and pools, making up a good part of the green scum that often covers them. In Spirogyra, all the cells of the filament are alike, but in Oedigonium, another filamentous green alga, one of the terminal cells in the series is modified as a "hold-fast" by which the filament is at-

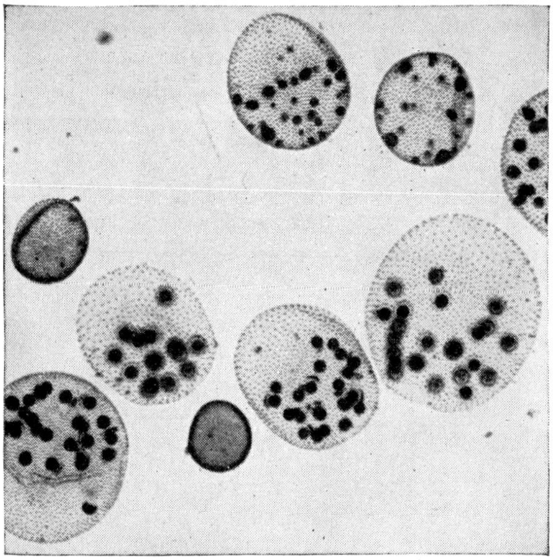

FIGURE 10.14 Colonies of Volvox. The large reproductive cells may be seen through the translucent wall of the colony. (Photograph by courtesy of the General Biological Supply House, Inc., Chicago.)

tached to another plant, a rock, a stick or some other object in the water, and only certain cells are capable of reproducing a new filament. Among the blue-green algae, the most familiar filamentous aggregates are Oscillatoria, so called because of the oscillating movements that the thallus may sometimes show, and Nostoc, a genus that lives in damp soil as well as in water.

In other aggregate forms of green algae, the thallus is in the form of a plate of cells, sometimes of considerable breadth and one or two cells in thickness. One of the most familiar of these along the Atlantic seacoast is Ulva, the sea lettuce, that is very common in the tidal zone. It is an attached form, fastened to rocks or other objects in the water by an irregularly shaped hold-fast, its broad, curled blade rising free in the water. The blade is made of two layers of cells, each cell with a single chloroplast.

Both the red and the brown algae contain species in which the thallus is filamentous and those in which it is flat and fleshy. The pigment that gives the red algae their characteristic color is called phycoerythrin; its presence masks the green of the chlorophyll that is also present. Most of the red algae are marine, although there are some few species that inhabit fresh water. In some of the filamentous forms the thallus is branched, in some species so much so that it has a feathery appearance. In some, the Corallines, the much-branched thallus is heavily impregnated with calcium salts; these live in the warmer waters and frequently, along with the animals that abound there, contribute to the formation of reefs and atolls. Some of the red algae have blade-like thalli, a broad expanse of cells that lie side by side as well as end to end.

The pigment in the brown algae is known as fucoxanthin; it too masks the chlorophyll that is also present. Like the red algae, most of the brown are marine and may have the form either of branched filaments or of flat

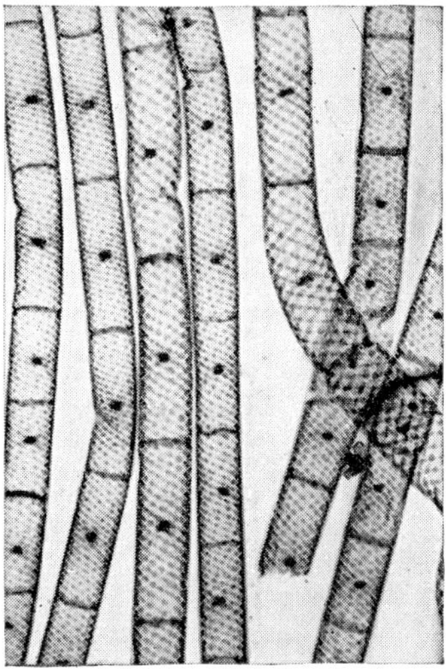

FIGURE 10.15 Spirogyra. (Photograph by courtesy of the General Biological Supply House, Inc., Chicago.)

plates or blades. They include the kelps, of which the most common along the northern part of the coast of North America is Laminaria, a genus in which the highest degree of cellular differentiation is reached of any of the algae. The thallus of Laminaria consists of a branched hold-fast, superficially resembling the roots of a higher plant, by which it is attached to an object in the water and from which there rises a cylindrical "stem" which expands into a flattened blade (Fig. 23.28). A thallus may be six feet or more in length, and may live for several years; each autumn the blade is shed from the stem, or axis, and a new one grown again by the multiplication of cells at the upper end of the axis. Within the axis and the blade the central cells are elongated and do not contain chromoplasts; these may act as conducting cells, conveying materials from one part of the thallus to another as do some of the highly specialized cells in the higher plants.

In the multicellular fungi, the thallus is filamentous, often branching; these are the organisms commonly known as molds, mushrooms, toadstools, mildews, rusts and smuts, which, primarily on the basis of the way in which the reproductive cells are formed, are classified as Phycomycetes (Greek, phykos = seaweed + mycetes = fungi) or algal fungi; Ascomycetes, or sac fungi; and Basidiomycetes (Greek, diminutive of basis = base), or club fungi. The bodies of such fungi consist of strands or threads, often matted together in a thick, felted mass. The individual thallus is known as a mycelium (Greek, mykes = slimy), which may form an extensive mass of branched or unbranched threads, as do molds like Rhizopus, the common black bread mold, or which may be packed together in a compact, fleshy mass as they are in the mushrooms, toadstools and puffballs (Fig. 10.16). The thallus in its early development is usually a multinucleate mass of protoplasm, enclosed within a wall made of cellulose and chitin; in some species cross walls or septa appear later, dividing the mass into a series of multinucleate cells arranged in linear series, but in others the thread remains permanently syncytial. There is little distinction evident between the different parts of the mycelium, although in the vegetative portion that penetrates into the dead or living organic material upon which the fungus feeds there may be

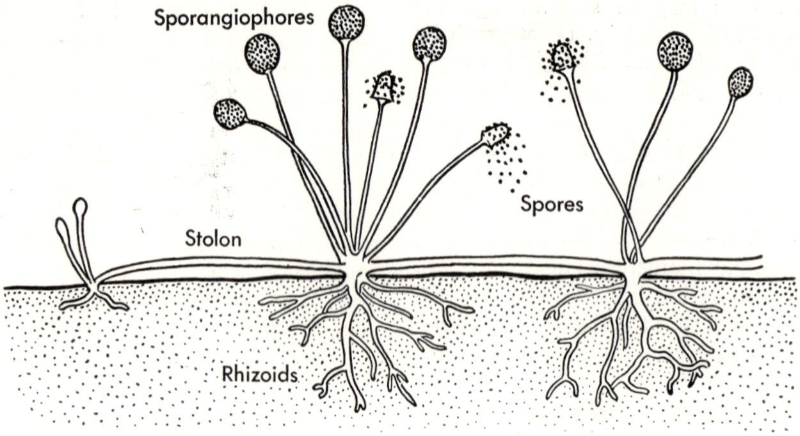

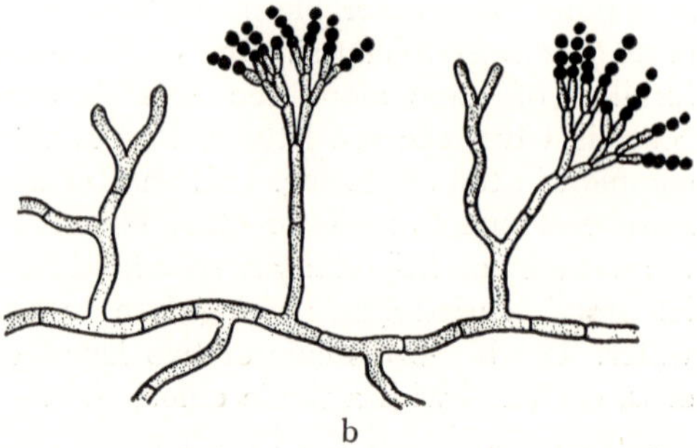

FIGURE 10.16 Filamentous Fungi. (From Hylander and Stanley, *College Botany*. Copyright 1949 by The Macmillan Company.)

a. Mycelium of the black bread mold, Rhizopus, showing spores formed in capsules at the tips of the sporangiophores.

b. Mycelium of Penicillium, showing the conidia (spores) successively constricted off the tips of the upright hyphae.

a great accumulation of vacuoles, reserves of oil, protein and starch. The starch is stored in the form of glycogen as it is in animal cells rather than of that of any of the polysaccharides compounded by green plants. With growth, a part of the mycelium extends up into the air, forming the familiar fuzzy and fluffy masses of the common molds or the buttons and caps of mushrooms and similar fungi; it is from this part of the mycelium that the reproductive cells, or spores, are formed. At the time of spore formation, there is usually a flowing of vacuoles from the vegetative part of the thallus in to its aerial part, in which at other times they are comparatively sparse, and also the formation of pigments, within the spores, so that the growth as a whole may appear black, blue-green, or brilliantly colored in shades of yellow or red.

## Inter-relationships of fungi and algae

Like the unicellular fungi, the filamentous ones are very general in their distribution and like them, too, contribute to the decomposition of organic material, either the products of plants or of animals or their dead bodies, returning their components to the environment. Many flourish in soils rich in humus, decomposing the organic material within it, and in various organic liquids, bringing about fermentative changes in them. Others live on the bodies of other plants and of animals. Empusa musca, for example, grows specifically upon the bodies of flies; if a spore happens to reach a fly's body and find a favorable spot for its germination and the penetration of its protoplast into the tissues of the insect, a flourishing mycelium may soon develop and spread through the body of the fly, draining its tissues of their sustenance and ultimately killing it. The water mold, Saprolegnia, infects fish and is a common cause of the disease and death of aquarium fish. Some molds, too, infect human beings and there are many that infect plants, often with serious consequences to the economy of nations. It was the destruction of the potato crop in Ireland by the phycomycete, Phytopthora infestans, that was directly the cause of the great Irish famine in 1845, which resulted in the starvation of thousands of the Irish people and the emigration of thousands more to other countries. There are many known species of basidiomycetes that live upon almost every kind of seed plant and upon some of the ferns; these are the rust or smut fungi whose presence can be detected by the reddish or black streaks or spots that appear on infected plants. Those that infect grain and cereal plants especially, like Puccinia graminis, the wheat rust, Ustilago zeae, the corn smut, and the different species of Tilletia, the "stinking smuts" of wheat, may bring about very serious economic consequences in the reduction or total destruction of important food crops, and the study of their life cycles and most effective control is a problem that constantly concerns biologists.

## Antagonistic relations between fungi; antibiotics

The antagonistic effects of the fungi upon each other is another one of the many problems under active investigation by biologists to-day, for a number of molds have already been found to produce substances that have destructive effects upon other organisms, particularly upon micro-organisms. Since these substances are produced by biological systems and are destructive to other biological systems, they are known as antibiotics and their isolation and identification increases the number of bacteriacidal agents, until recently only of chemical origin, with which man has been combatting the deleterious effects of micro-organisms since the time of Joseph Lister. In 1897 a Frenchman, E. Duchesne, reported that some species of the ascomycete Penicillium retard or suppress the growth of certain bacteria present in the same medium. Some thirty years later an English physician, Alexander Fleming (1881–    ), in culturing bacteria of the staphylococcus group (so-called because in their growth they form masses or clusters that look like bunches of grapes, from the Greek word staphyle meaning bunch of grapes) observed the disintegration and apparent dissolution of those that were in the immediate vicinity of a mold that had infected his culture medium. He isolated the mold, which was grown in pure cultures and identified as Penicillium notatum. Its antibiotic effects were tested on a variety of species of bacteria and found to be marked on certain ones of the coccus type. Later a substance was extracted from cultures of the mold that was called penicillin and that has been widely used clinically to combat certain infections in man and other animals.

Not all strains of Penicillium are equally potent in producing penicillin, nor is the same strain under some conditions of growth; other species of Penicillium have been found also to produce antibacterial substances such as citrinin, penicillic acid, which is also antagonistic to the growth of yeasts, and clavacin. Other molds have likewise been found to form such substances, and so have yeasts and bacteria themselves, among which are gramcidin, streptomycin and polymycin. Some of these organisms produce at least two antibiotic substances; others only one, as far as present determinations go. And some of the naturally occurring antibiotics have been crystallized and their chemical structures determined, the first step toward the syntheses of them in the chemical laboratory. Indeed, one of them known as Penicillin G has already been synthesized in very small quantities by a team of scientists at the Rockefeller Institute in New York; the synthesis of another, chloromycetin, was reported in the spring of 1949 by another group of scientists in Detroit.

### Algal-fungal associations; the lichens

The lichens constitute another group of the fungi, the class Lichenes, although what is called a lichen is not a single plant but two, an alga and a fungus living in a symbiotic, rather than an antagonistic, relationship (Fig. 10.17). In most lichens, the fungus belongs to a group of the ascomycetes, and the alga is either a unicellular green one, like Pleurococcus, or one of the blue-green group. But each association of the two plants grows in a typical way and reproduces its own kind with all its typical characteristics. In some of them, the walls of the fungus contain pigment, so that the whole growth has a characteristic color; litmus, that is used sometimes to test for the acidity or alkalinity of substances, is extracted from species of Rocella and Lecanora, and so is orcein, a dye that is frequently used for the staining of microscopic preparations of biological material. Lichens are very widely distributed throughout the world, growing in tropical and polar regions as well as in the temperate zones; they frequently form encrustations on rocks, growing where there appears to be neither anchorage nor water. Gradually they may bring about the disintegration of the rock and in so doing contribute to the formation of the soil.

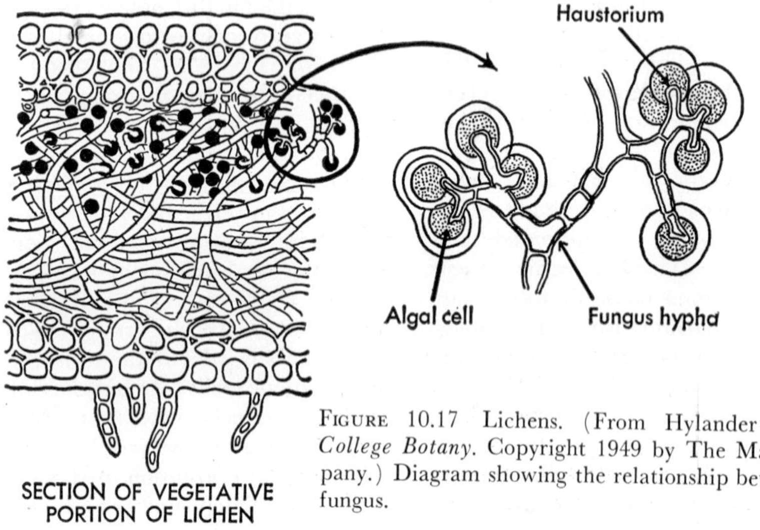

FIGURE 10.17 Lichens. (From Hylander and Stanley, *College Botany*. Copyright 1949 by The Macmillan Company.) Diagram showing the relationship between alga and fungus.

# CHAPTER 11

# MULTICELLULAR SYSTEMS—METAZOA AND METAPHYTA OF SIMPLE ORGANIZATION

## *Differentiation of cells in tissues*

The bodies of multicellular organisms are composed of many hundreds, thousands and even millions of cells, most of which are differentiated to such a degree that they are capable of performing only one set of functions in the body, thus showing the "division of labor" pointed out by a Belgian comparative anatomist, Henri Milne-Edwards (1800–1885) toward the end of the last century. Cells which perform similar functions in the body are collectively spoken of as tissues; in biological systems at the upper levels of evolutionary development, tissues of several kinds may be included in the various organs or organ systems through which particular sets of operations in the total activity of the complex body are carried out.

### Differentiation in animal cells

In the multicellular animals these tissues may be broadly classified as epithelial, muscular, connective and reproductive. Epithelium is primarily any tissue that covers any surface inside or outside the body, and it may further be modified for protection, for secretion, for absorption or for the reception of stimuli, such as light, temperature, chemical substances and pressure changes (Fig. 11.1*a*). Muscular tissue is made up of cells that under certain conditions shorten and thicken, thus changing their shapes and so altering that of the body as a whole, or a part of it, or else exerting a pull upon a part to which they were attached and so bringing about its movement (Fig. 11.1*b, c*). The cells of nervous tissue are specialists in the reception of stimuli and the transmission of the disturbance, or impulse, so initiated (Fig. 11.1*d*). Connective tissue may be either supportive or vascular, depending upon the nature of the matrix (Latin, matrix = womb) that surrounds the cells. Mesenchyme (Greek, mesos = middle + Latin, enchyma = type of tissue) is the most primitive and least specialized of the connective tissues; its cells, which have migrated from more compact masses of mesoderm, lie in a gelatinous matrix of mucus, one of the many kinds of protein derived from animal cells, of consistencies that range from sols to firm gels (Fig. 11.1*e*). In other types of connective tissue, the intercellular substance contains protein fibres secreted by the cells; these types are distinguished as fibrous, elastic, reticular (Latin, reticulum = little net) and areolar (Latin, diminutive of area = space), depending upon the type of fibre that predominates in the matrix and the compactness and looseness of their arrangement (Fig. 11.1 *f*). Cartilage and bone are supportive connective tissues in which the organic fibrous matrix is impregnated with inorganic compounds, principally the phosphates and carbonates of calcium (Fig. 11.1*g, h*). Bone is the firmest and the hardest of the connective tissues, with a high percentage of inorganic material; cartilage, which is found in some animals together with bone, in others as the only rigid tissue, has less inorganic material and is compressible and to a certain extent elastic. In vascular connective tissue the matrix is fluid so that the cells are suspended in a liquid medium. Such tissues can be set in motion by propulsive forces of different kinds and caused to flow around and among the other tissues of the body. The bloods of animals, lymph and other body fluids are tissues of this kind. Reproductive tissues are those that give rise to the generative or germ cells. Although such cells have the potentiality of producing, either singly or in combination

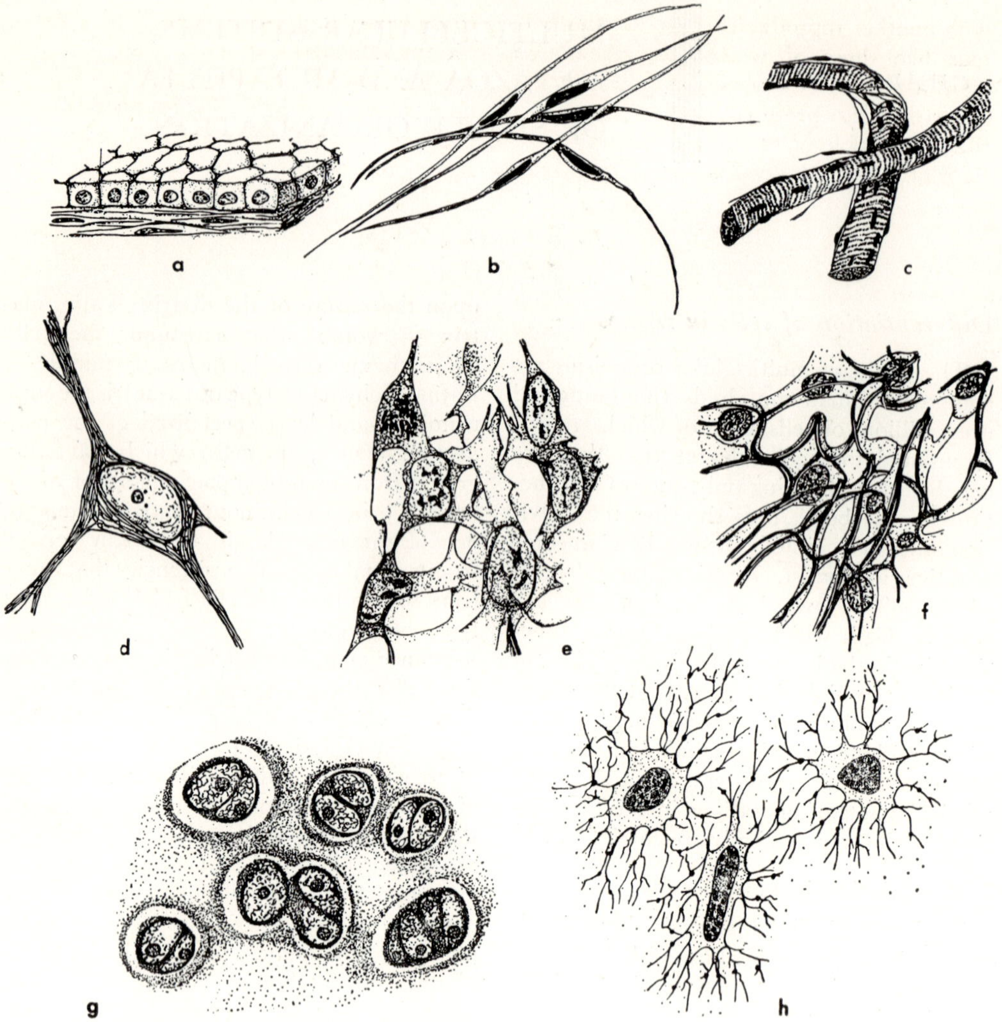

FIGURE 11.1   Types of animal tissues.

a. Cuboidal epithelium. (After Maximow and Bloom.)

b. Smooth muscle cells from the wall of a cat's stomach. (After Maximow and Bloom.)

c. Striated muscle fibres from man. The upper fibre is crushed and shows the sheath, or sarcolemma. (After Maximow and Bloom.)

d. Nerve cell from the cortex of a rabbit's brain. (After Heidenhain.)

e. Mesenchyme cells from the head of a 9–10 day rabbit embryo. The cell at the upper left is in division. (After Maximow and Bloom.)

f. Reticular connective tissue from the lymph gland of a cat. The fibres in the matrix are shown in dense black. (After Heidenhain.)

g. Hyaline cartilage from a calf. (After Maximow and Bloom, after Krause.)

h. Bone cells from a membrane bone of a white mouse. (After Maximow and Bloom.)

with another reproductive cell, new individuals like those of which they themselves were a part, they are not totipotent in the sense that the protozoan cell is totipotent, that is, capable of carrying on all the functions of a living individual organism. While those below the ground and those above it; the fundamental tissues are those that make up the bulk of its body and the vascular ones those through which materials are transported from place to place within the body. The basic type of tissue, from which

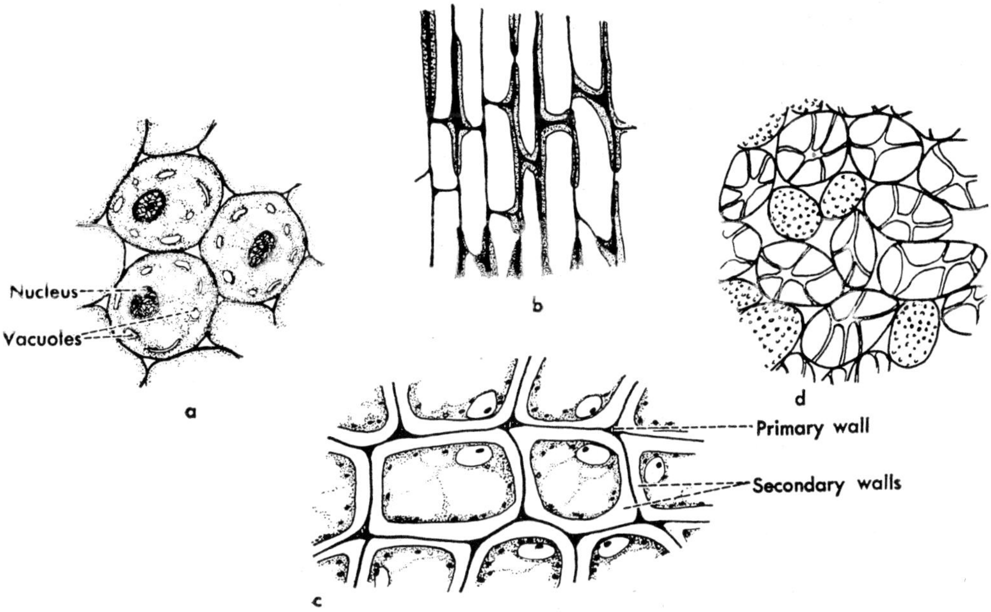

FIGURE 11.2  Types of plant tissues.

    a. Parenchyma cells from the cortex of the coast jointweed. (After Sharp.)
    b. Collenchyma cells from the stem of the potato. (After Eames and MacDaniels.)
    c. Cells of pine wood, showing the primary wall of pectin and cellulose that becomes the middle lamella, and the secondary walls laid down by adjacent cells. (After Mottier.)
    d. Stone cells from the fruit of the pear. (After Eames and MacDaniels.)

retaining the capacity to divide and to direct the organization of the new cells arising from them into new individuals, germ cells are not generalized ones in the multicellular body but ones specialized for the particular purpose of reproduction and as such most carefully protected and nurtured by the other tissues.

**Differentiation in plant cells**

In multicellular plants the differentiated cells form three great tissue systems, the epidermal (Greek, epi = upon + derma = skin), the fundamental and the vascular. The epidermal system includes those tissues that cover the surfaces of the plant, both all others are thought to be derived, is known as parenchyma (Greek, para = beside + enchyma); parenchyma cells have thin walls and are various in their shapes but usually isodiametric (Greek, isos = equal + dia = through + metron = measure), that is, approximately equal in all three of their dimensions (Fig. 11.2a). They are cells that are usually capable of division and of carrying on chemical syntheses. Those that contain chloroplasts and thus photosynthesize are known as chlorenchyma; a region of actively dividing parenchyma cells is known as meristem (Greek, meristos = divisible). Collenchyma cells (Greek, kollos = glue + enchyma) are somewhat more differentiated, though still capable of division; they are usually elongated or cylindrical cells whose walls are thickened by deposits of cellulose situated most frequently among their smaller arcs or "corners," and they serve as a kind of supporting tissue, especially in young plants before the development of their heavier and permanent supporting framework (Fig. 11.2b). Sclerenchyma cells (Greek, skleros = hard + enchyma) are ones in which the walls have become thick and rigid through the addition of cellulose and the deposition of lignin in the spaces between its micelles. The walls of plant cells, whether thin or thick, are the result of the activity of their living protoplasts and are made of substances that are end- or by-products of the chemical reactions that go on in them. The first material to be deposited outside the plasma membrane is pectin, the name given to a class of compound carbohydrates of varied composition, which with water become viscous colloidal solutions. Cellulose, a carbohydrate whose molecules are long chains of carbon atoms and, like the long chain molecules of proteins, held together in bundles or micelles, is next deposited; these substances together make up the primary wall of the cell, which is elastic, extensible and freely permeable. The primary walls may be thickened by the addition of more layers of cellulose and the accumulation within them of lignins, pectins, waxes, tannins, mucilages and other substances whose chemical composition is not yet well known. All of these substances are mixtures of related compounds and all have different properties and impart different characters to the cell wall; lignin particularly stiffens and strengthens it, making it less liable to compression so that lignified tissues have considerable mechanical strength. The additional layers are laid down between the primary wall and the plasma membrane so that the initial deposits of pectin and cellulose become further and further removed from the protoplast; these first walls of adjacent cells become the middle lamella of the common wall between them. In many cases the walls are not of uniform thickness but have places, often numerous ones, where they are thin or may disappear entirely; these places become the pits, which may be simple, pore-like openings, or bordered ones, with extensions of the thickened wall overhanging their margins.

In mature sclerenchyma cells there is no living protoplast and the walls have become so thickened that the central area is reduced to a very small space. Stone cells, found in the seeds and fruits of many plants, are sclerenchyma cells that are usually isodiametric but sometimes irregular in shape (Fig. 11.2d); sclerenchyma fibres, on the other hand, are long, slender cells with tapering ends and often are found in groups within the stems and roots of plants, associated particularly with the vascular tissues. In the vascular tissues there are two general regions, the phloem (Greek, phloios = bark) and the xylem (Greek, xylon = wood), in both of which there is a variety of cells some of which reach the highest degree of differentiation of any plant cells. The phloem includes some living cells with active protoplasts as well as some fibrous dead cells; most of the cells within the xylem are dead cells with walls that have become lignified in characteristic patterns, but it includes also some cells of parenchymatous type that function in the condensation of excess food materials and in their storage.

In distinction to the Protozoa and Protophyta, the multicellular animals and plants are known as Metazoa and Metaphyta, both of which include biological systems of simple, as well as complex, organization. Particularly in the pattern of their growth, some of the Metazoa at the lower levels of evolutionary development resemble Metaphyta, and because of this were confused with plants by early students of natural history. Although their identification as animal systems is now without question, they represent a degree of structural differentiation and adaptation comparable to that of the simpler plants. For this reason they are considered together in this chapter, while the other Metazoa and Metaphyta are considered separately, for with increased differentiation of their parts and increased specialization in the operation of those parts, the divergence between these two categories of

# METAZOA AND METAPHYTA OF SIMPLE ORGANIZATION [145]

biological systems becomes so marked that any possible evolutionary relationships between them are obscured.

## Metazoa of simple organization
### Porifera

The most simply organized of the Metazoa are the sponges, which make up the phylum Porifera (Latin, porus = pore + ferre = to bear). Sponges are all sessile, aquatic animals and, except for one family of widely-distributed fresh water inhabitants, all are marine. Also, with the exception of a few members which are consistently vase-shaped, they show little regularity in shape or in size. Their habit of growth is like that of plants, for they branch, often irregularly, and continue this spreading growth as long as they are alive. Some of those that live in tropical or semi-tropical waters reach such an enormous size that their height may be one or two meters and their dry weight a ton or more (Fig. 11.3). The tissues of all sponges consist essentially of epithelia and mesenchyme; there are no nervous or sensory cells, no organs or systems of organs, and the various activities of their bodies are carried on by cells which, though collected into definite layers, act more or less independently of each other.

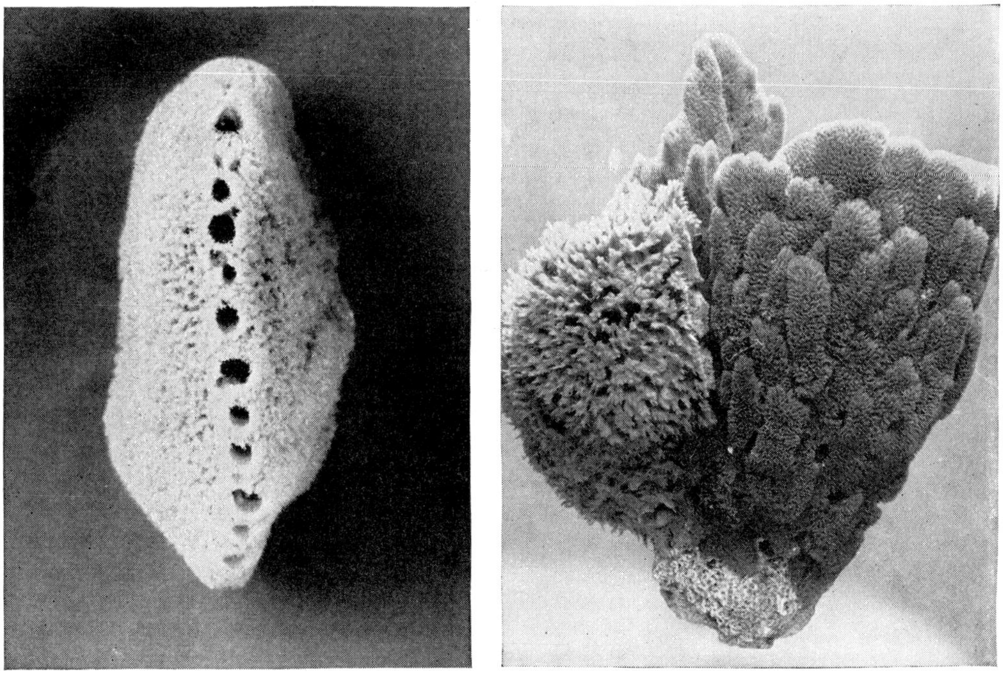

FIGURE 11.3 Sponges. (Photographs by courtesy of the U.S. Fish and Wildlife Service.)
 a. Reef sponge from the Bahama Islands.
 b. Grasswool and sheepswool sponges attached to a common base.

*The body plan of sponges:* In the most primitive sponges, the outer epithelium consists of flattened cells which form a continuous layer, except where it is interrupted at intervals by porocytes (Latin, porus = pore + Greek, kytos = cell), taller cells through whose cytoplasm a tube or channel passes, connecting the inner spaces of the sponges with the water around it (Fig. 11.4). The external openings of these cells are the pores through which a stream of water passes to the interior; under certain conditions, such as foulness or contamination of the water, the pores of some sponges will close through the contraction of cells surrounding them, the myocytes, which respond directly to the stimulus. The inner epithelium consists of collared cells, or choanocytes, embedded some distance from each other in a gelatinous matrix, each resembling a choanoflagellate with all its organelles, including, in the fresh water species, a contractile vacuole. The steady, but not always synchronous, beat of the flagella of these cells keeps a current of water carrying

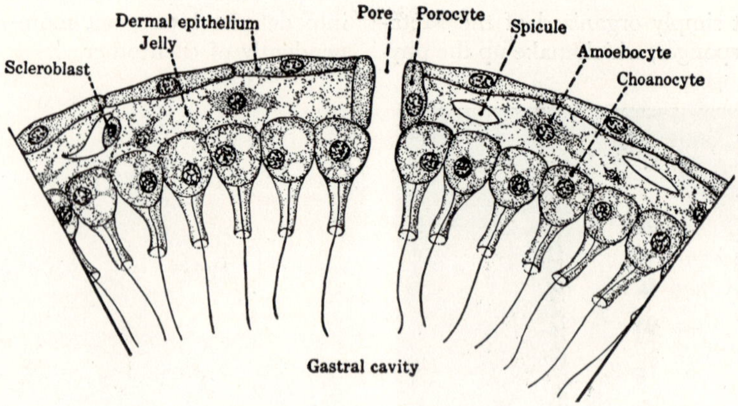

FIGURE 11.4  Diagram showing the structure of the body of a simple sponge. (From Hegner, *College Zoology*. Copyright 1942 by The Macmillan Company.)

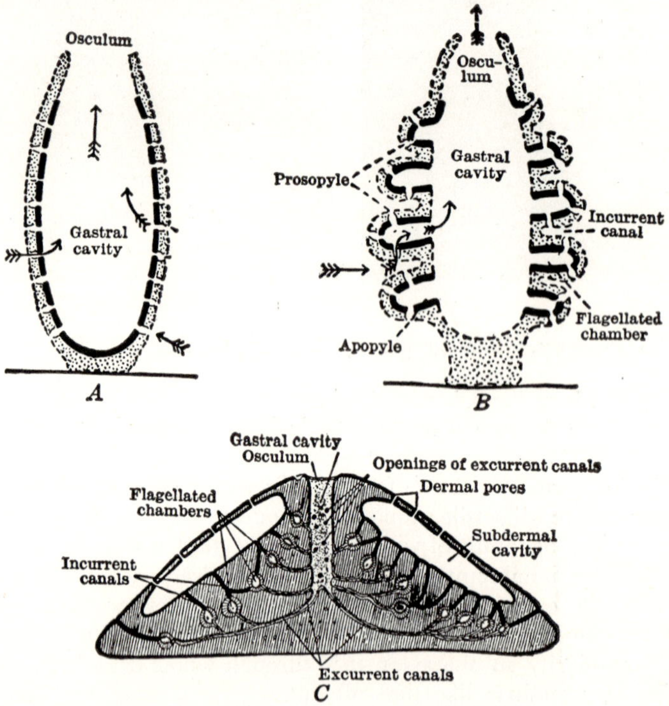

FIGURE 11.5  Diagrams showing the canal system of sponges. The thick black lines in A and B represent the gastral layer; the dotted area the dermal layer. The arrows indicate the direction of the current of water. (From Hegner, *College Zoology*, 5th edition. Copyright 1942 by The Macmillan Company. A and B from Minchin; C from Parker and Haswell.)

food particles and dissolved oxygen passing through the porocytes and past the cells of the inner layer; the water is swept out of the sponge's body through openings, the oscula (Latin, osculum = little mouth) at the upper end of the sponge. This method of feeding is the reverse of that of all other metazoa, where food is taken in by a single aperture, the mouth. In the most highly organized sponges, the choanocytes are restricted to local areas, the flagellate chambers, which communicate with the central cavity in the interior of the body by a system of canals, often elaborate and tortuous in their course (Fig. 11.5). The canals and chambers offer a haven and protected habitation to many other animals, and different kinds of fish, shrimps and mollusks are often found living in them.

*Histology:* In all sponges, between the inner and outer epithelia is a kind of filling and supporting tissue, perhaps properly to be called mesenchyme, for it consists of cells that have migrated there from the other layers and secreted a fairly stiff mucus, the mesogloea (Greek, mesos = middle + gloia = glue). Some of these cells are amoebocytes, wandering cells that move about in the intercellular substance and incorporate foreign particles of various kinds in vacuoles in their cytoplasm. Some of them are reproductive cells from which the generative cells are produced, and some of them are skeletogenous cells, with the special function of secreting rods or spicules of silica or of calcium salts, or fibres of spongin, a protein allied to that found in the fibres of some connective tissues and in the cartilage, bone, horns, hoofs and teeth of animals far higher in the evolutionary scale. The main distinction between the different categories of sponges is in the type of supporting framework, or internal skeleton, that these cells produce, for in some the spicules are exclusively calcareous, in others exclusively siliceous and of elaborate design, and in others either spongin alone or spongin in combination with simple siliceous spicules (Fig. 11.6).

The formation of the skeleton represents the expenditure of large amounts of energy on the part of the sponge as a whole and of its individual skeletogenous cells as well as remarkable cooperation between them. The only source of the mineral elements for the spicules is the water in which the sponge lives; this has been experimentally shown in

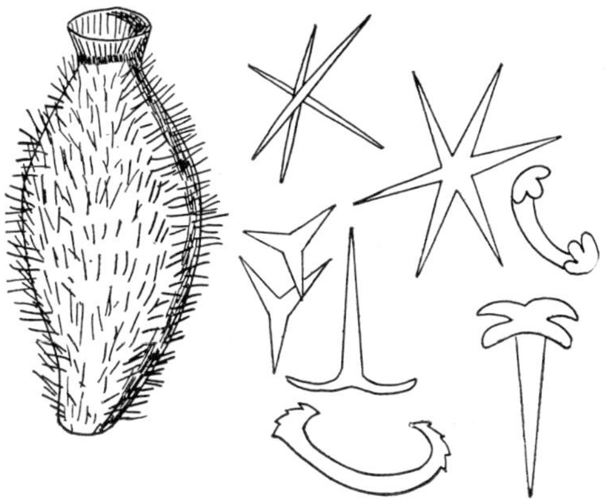

FIGURE 11.6 Calcareous sponges.

a. Sycon, a calcareous sponge of relatively simple organization. Sycon is a genus of solitary sponges, reaching a maximum size of about $12 \times 3$ mm., and common in the Atlantic Ocean at depths up to 60 fathoms. (Drawn from life.)

b. Types of spicules from calcareous sponges.

the case of calcium, for if calcareous sponges are made to grow in calcium-free sea water, no skeleton is constructed, and the body collapses and degenerates. Even in calcium-rich water, enormous amounts must pass through the body for the cells to extract and to concentrate enough to build a skeleton. And the glass sponges, whose skeleton is wholly siliceous, require an even greater current, since the concentration of silicon in sea water is only about 0.0015 per cent. It has been estimated that in order to obtain enough to make 1 ounce of skeleton a glass sponge must sweep one ton of sea water through its pores and canals (Fig. 11.7).

In laying down a single skeletal rod, two cells cooperate as "founder" and "thickener." The process has been most completely followed in the calcareous sponges where the tiny rod first appears as a sliver of organic material in a vacuole in the cytoplasm of the founder cell; calcium salts are then deposited on the surface of this organic core, so that the spicule grows in length. As it grows it is extruded from the cytoplasm of the founder cell, which still remains applied to it, depositing calcium salts as it moves along the surface of the gradually

FIGURE 11.7 Hyalonema, the glass sponge. (Photograph by courtesy of the American Museum of Natural History, New York.)

lengthening rod. The thickener cell follows along behind the founder, adding its inorganic material until the spicule has reached its definitive size, when both cells wander off into the mesogloea, leaving the spicule behind them. In the three-rayed, six-rayed and other elaborately patterned spicules, as many pairs of cells, representing founders and thickeners, are concerned as there are straight, monaxon (Greek, monos = single + axon = axis) spicules in the finished product.

*Habits:* While the organization of the bodies of sponges and their mechanisms for feeding are wholly unlike those of other animals, they rely, as other animals do, entirely on organic sources for their nutrients, feeding upon a variety of small animals and plants and detritus from them. Their food is swept into their bodies in the current of water drawn in by the beating of the flagella of the choanocytes. Since they do not move about nor have they any devices to capture food at long range, they are dependent upon the population of their immediate neighborhood for food and are consequently most numerous in waters where there are many animals and plants and an abundant potential food supply. In the case of the calcareous and siliceous sponges available calcium and silicon are also conditioning factors of the environment for them, and such sponges are exclusively marine.

*Systematic position and capacity for regeneration:* The body plan of the Porifera, if they can be said to have one, naturally leads to speculation about their position in the animal kingdom. Are they truly Metazoa or simply cell aggregates of high grade? (Fig. 10.13c) This question could be answered by determining the degree of mutual independence or dependence of the constituent cells of the sponge body, and it has been answered by experiments. By squeezing sponges through very fine-meshed cloth it is possible to break them up into groups of a few cells each, or even into individual cells, and, by watching closely the fate of these isolated cells or cell groups kept in favorable environmental conditions, to see whether this disintegration results in the total destruction of the body; or whether a single cell of any one type can divide and its descendants organize themselves into a typical sponge body; or whether only groups of cells that contain representatives of the different types found in the adult sponge are capable of this. It has been found that isolated amoebocytes, if not too far apart,

# METAZOA AND METAPHYTA OF SIMPLE ORGANIZATION [149]

will move together and form a clump called a reunion mass from which the different types of cells are reorganized and a typical sponge developed. Such regenerates cannot arise from reunion masses of choanocytes alone nor from isolated amoebocytes.

cells into tissues and, in some groups, the assembling of such tissues into organs. Animals constructed on such a plan are represented by the members of the phylum Coelenterata (Greek, koilos = hollow + enteron = intestine), the Ctenophora (Greek, ktenos

FIGURE 11.8 Types of coelenterates. (Photographs by courtesy of the American Museum of Natural History, New York.)

a. Model of a colonial hydroid, showing the common axis of the colony, and two types of zooids.

b. Model of a jellyfish, illustrating the medusoid type. The mouth is situated at the end of the tubular manubrium extending below the concavity of the bell.

## Body plans of other Metazoa

*The simple sac plan:* The bodies of other multicellular animals fall into two master plans, that of a hollow sac whose single opening serves both for the intake of food and for the elimination of its undigested residue, and that of a tube-within-a-tube. Those that are constructed on the hollow sac plan are for the most part ones of simple organization although their bodies show symmetry, a distinct differentiation of their = comb + phoros = bearing) and the Platyhelminthes (Greek, platus = broad + helmis = worm).

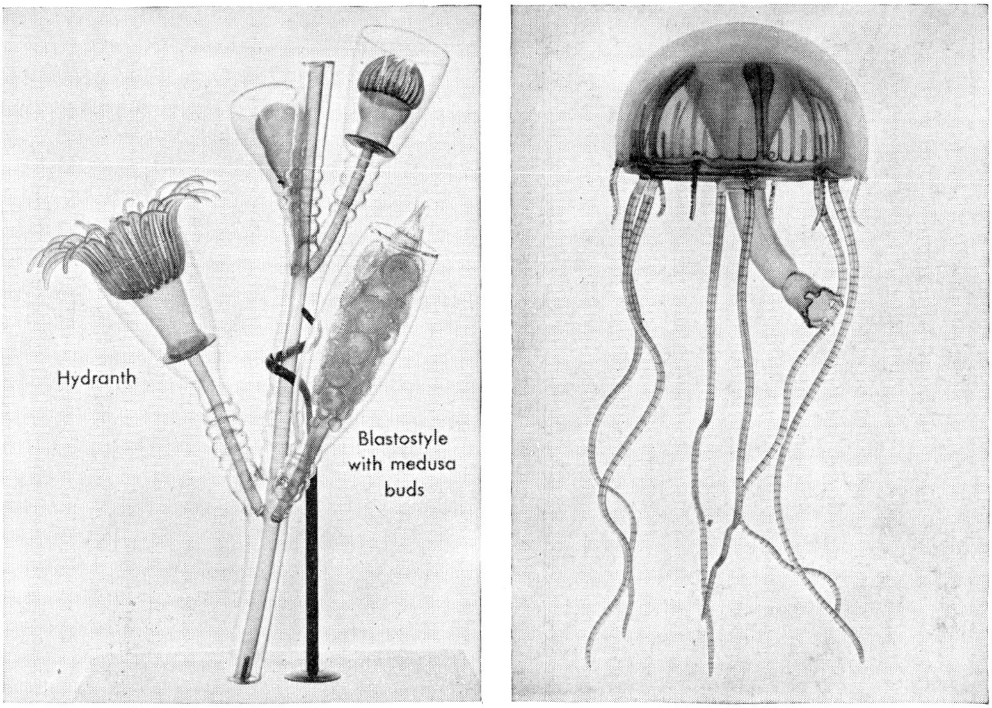

COELENTERATES: The coelenterates are all aquatic animals, most of them living in salt water where they are represented by the familiar jellyfish and anemones, the corals and colonial species that are often found growing as feathery masses on the piles of docks or wharves, on rocks and on the shells of other animals, particularly the mollusk shells inhabited by hermit crabs. Coelenterate individuals whose bodies are cylindrical with a single central cavity are known as polyps (Greek, polypous = many footed), and those whose bodies are disc or bell-shaped, with a system of internal canals, as they are capable of expanding and contracting, their bodies have definite proportions and symmetry. They spend the greater part of their lives attached to some object in the water, fastened there by a secretion from the cells at the basal, or closed, ends of their

a

b

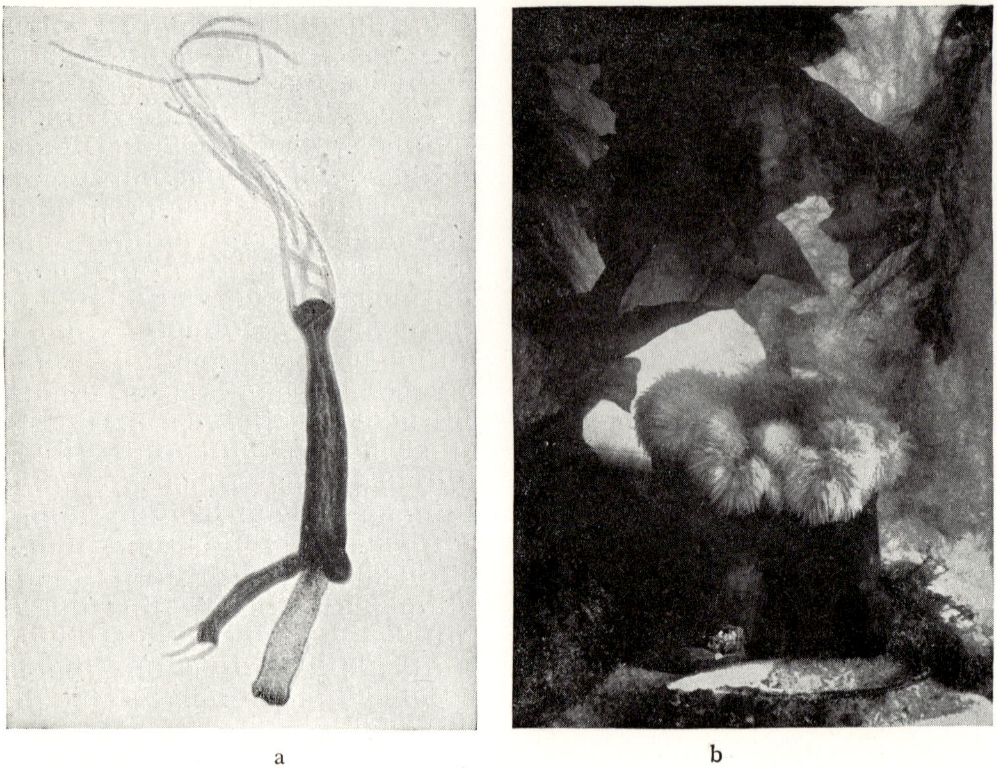

FIGURE 11.9  Types of coelenterates (polyps).
   a. Hydra with bud. (Photograph by courtesy of the General Biological Supply House, Inc., Chicago.)
   b. Sea anemone. (Photograph by courtesy of the American Museum of Natural History, New York.)

medusae, presumably because their many dangling and often writhing tentacles reminded those who first saw them of the snakes on the head of the Gorgon, Medusa (Fig. 11.8).

*The polyp type: Hydra:* The structurally simplest representatives of isolated polyps are the various species of the genus Hydra found in bodies of fresh water all over the world (Fig. 11.9). They are all small animals, for the main part of their bodies is not more than 15 mm. in length, and, although bodies but they can detach themselves and move about by gliding along an object in mucus secreted by the basal cells, or by looping movements. The basal cells also secrete a gas which, when held as bubbles inside them, gives the animal buoyancy and allows it to rise to the surface and be carried passively about by the currents that it may encounter.

At its free end the body is drawn out into a small elevation, the hypostome (Greek, hypo = under + stoma = mouth), in the center of which the mouth lies. Surrounding

# METAZOA AND METAPHYTA OF SIMPLE ORGANIZATION

the mouth are extensions of the body called tentacles which, like the body itself, are capable of extension and contraction so that they can be used for grasping food and pushing it into the mouth. The main body of the

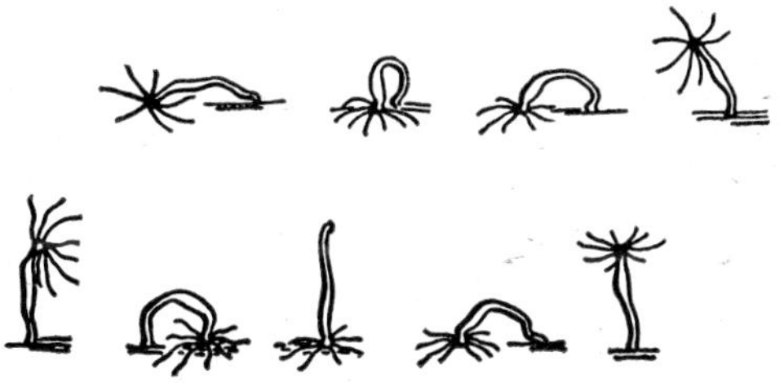

FIGURE 11.10 Locomotion in Hydra by looping movements. (After Trembley, from Walter and Sayles, *Biology of the Vertebrates.* Copyright 1949 by The Macmillan Company.)

hydra is cylindrical and so radially symmetrical, that is, when cut along any of its radii, it is divided into two halves that are mirror images of each other, but the number of tentacles reduces the axes of symmetry of the animal as a whole to the planes of the radii bisecting any two of them and to those of the interradii between them. A hydra with eight tentacles can therefore be cut into two similar halves along only eight radii, not along all those theoretically possible in a cylinder or a sphere (Fig. 11.11). Radial symmetry such as this, which is not complete but limited to the planes of certain radii, is characteristic of animals which spend the greater part of their lives attached to some object; to a sessile animal there are some obvious advantages in being equally sensitive, equally contractile and equally responsive on all of its surfaces.

*Histology:* The wall of the sac is made of two layers of epithelium, an outer ectoderm and an inner endoderm which lines the central cavity and the hollow tentacles around the mouth. Between the ectoderm and the endoderm is a thin film of mesogloea. The ectoderm consists of a single

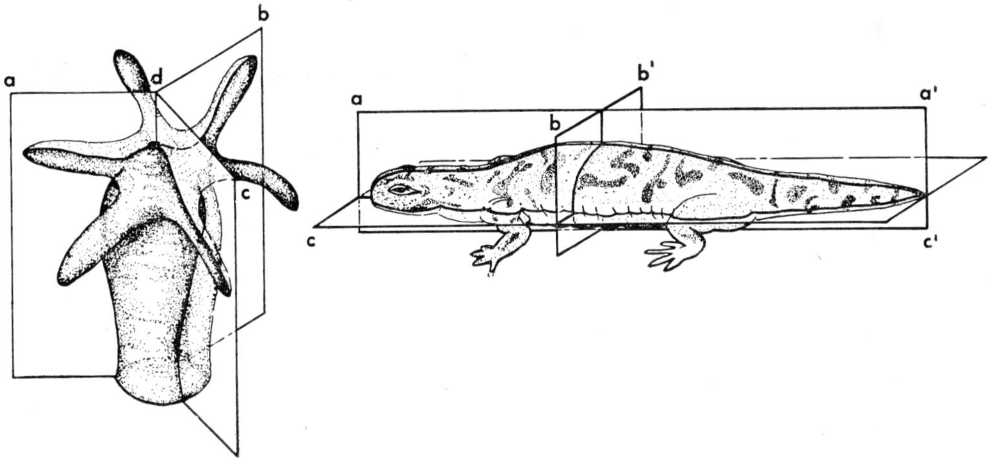

FIGURE 11.11 Diagrams illustrating the planes of symmetry of radial and bilaterally symmetrical animals.

a. Complete sections continued along the planes a-d, b-d, or c-d of a radially symmetrical animal like Hydra will divide the body into two equal and similar halves.

b. Section along the plane a-a' only will divide a bilaterally symmetrical animal like a salamander into two similar halves, actually mirror images of each other. Sections along b-b' and c-c' will divide it into two dissimilar parts, an anterior and a posterior part, and a dorsal and a ventral part, respectively. Sections along the plane a-a' are longitudinal sections; along the plane b-b', tranverse, or cross, sections; and those along the plane c-c', frontal sections. Only a median longitudinal section, through the midline of the animal, will give two equal and similar halves of its body and of those organs that are strictly bilateral, or paired, in their arrangement.

[152] THE ORGANIZATION OF BIOLOGICAL SYSTEMS

layer of cells whose inner ends are extended into slender, contractile processes directed along the length of the body. The cells of the inner epithelium, or endoderm, are similar in shape and also have muscle processes which are, however, directed around the circumference of the body, or at right angles to those of the ectoderm cells (Fig. 11.12). Both ectoderm and endoderm therefore are said to be made up of epithelio-muscular cells, since they combine the properties of epithelial and muscular tissues, and it is due to the coordinated action of these cells that the stretching and shortening of the body takes place. Certain of the ectoderm cells are further differentiated as sensory cells for the reception of stimuli of various kinds. These are distributed generally over the surface of the animal's body in such a way as to form a kind of network, whose meshes are finest at the free, or hypostome, end where the nerve cells are most numerous. The ectoderm cells at the base are modified primarily as secretory cells, for they produce the mucus which fastens the animal, when it is stationary, or through which it moves when it is motile, and the gas which causes it to float up in the water.

Various modifications are found among the endodermal cells, which, while having the characteristics of epithelio-muscular cells, are the ones primarily concerned with the digestion and absorption of the food taken in through the mouth into the central cavity or coelenteron. Some of them discharge enzymes into this cavity to start the decomposition of the food, which consists wholly or in great part of small animals. Some of them complete the digestion of the food intracellularly by extending pseudopodia into the central cavity and incorporating a bit of the partially decomposed food as a gastric vacuole. Others are permanently flagellate, or can form flagella, and so help to keep the fluid in motion, although the movements of the animal's body are probably the primary cause of the circulation of the contents of the coelenteron. The final

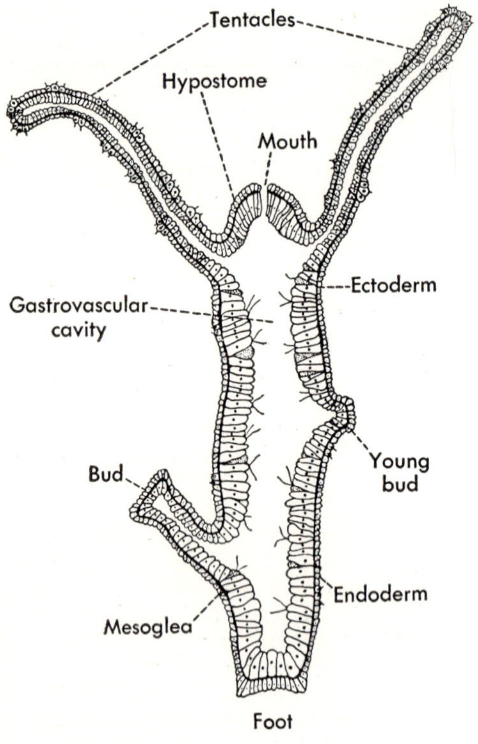

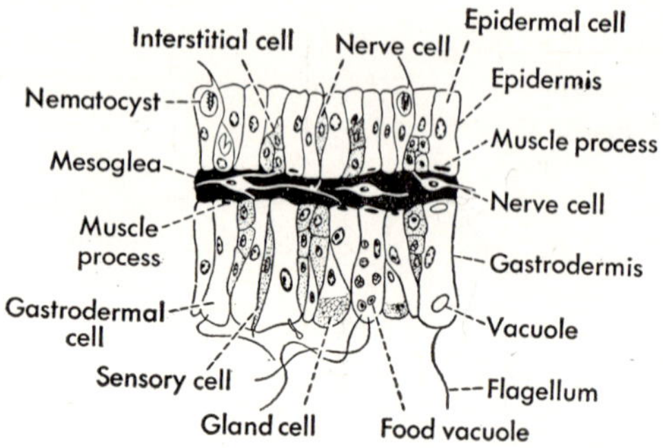

FIGURE 11.12 Histology of Hydra. (From Mavor, *General Biology*, 3rd edition. Copyright 1947 by The Macmillan Company.)

a. Longitudinal section of Hydra, showing the cellular structure.

b. Section of a portion of the body wall at higher magnification showing the different types of cells of which it is composed.

products of digestion diffuse from cell to cell, and any undigested residue is expelled from the coelenteron through the mouth opening.

A highly specialized kind of cell, the cnidoblast (Greek, knide = nettle + blastos = germ) is found among the ectoderm cells; these are particularly numerous in the tentacles. A cnidoblast is a cell which develops within a vacuole in its cytoplasm a small capsule, the nematocyst (Greek, nema = thread + kystus = bladder) which can be shot out of the cell under appropriate stimulation (Fig. 11.13b). The capsules have either barbed or unbarbed threads coiled within them which are everted when the nematocyst is discharged. Seventeen different types of nematocysts have been recognized among all the coelenterates, although in many cases the differences are but slight ones in the character of the thread. Some nematocysts secrete a substance toxic to other animals and so poison them; others mechanically impede the progress of enemies or of prey by coiling around their bodies or their limbs. Certain kinds of mechanical and chemical stimulation to the cnidocil, a fine protoplasmic projection from the outer margin of the cnidoblast, leads to the discharge of the nematocyst; the cnidoblast is generally thought to be an "independent effector" like the myocytes around the pores of some sponges, that is, both to receive the stimulus and to make the response to it. The mechanism that causes some stimuli to be effective and others not is still to be determined, although observation and experiment both show that there is discrimination between them. The presence of ciliates in the surrounding water will, for example, usually cause a vigorous discharge of nematocysts from Hydra, which on the other hand give no response to the presence of Kerona, a ciliate that frequently lives on the surfaces of their bodies, and touches and bends the cnidocils as it moves along, nor does stroking the surface of the coelenterate with a glass rod bring about a reaction. Even more remarkable, Mesostoma, a flatworm that feeds upon Hydra, will digest all the body except the nematocysts, which it preserves in its own tissues as weapons of attack and defense where they are lodged intact until a stimulus to the worm brings about their discharge.

The spent cnidoblasts are constantly replaced during the hydra's life by new ones differentiated from groups of cells which lie at the bases of the epithelial cells. These are undifferentiated cells, capable of replacing other parts of the body as well as the cnidoblasts and also of giving rise to the reproductive cells. Because of their position in the insterstices of the epithelium, they have been called interstitial cells; possibly they have sufficient similarity to the undifferentiated or "formative" cells of sponges and other animals to justify their designation as mesenchymal cells.

While the body of Hydra is essentially two-layered, in other coelenterates both cells and fibres are found in the mesogloea and their bodies therefore consist of three strata if not definitely three layers of cells. The polyp type may further be modified by the development of endodermal septa that project into the coelenteron and so divide it wholly or partly into separate chambers, the condition, for example, in the sea anemones and the corals, where there is also a greater specialization of the different regions of the body.

*The medusoid type:* In the medusoid individuals, represented by the many kinds of marine jellyfish as well as fresh water medusae, the body is either disc or bell-shaped, with the mouth on the lower surface or in the concavity of the bell, and the coelenteron is not a single central cavity but a system of endodermal canals originating in a relatively small space above the mouth and uniting in a circular canal around the margin of the disc or the bell (Fig. 11.8). Variations in complexity of the canal system and the development of structures for the reception of special kinds of stimuli are characteristic of the different kinds of medusae. An organ of special sense, among animals in general, is a structure, often complex in character, for the reception of one particular kind of stimulus and in many cases is the only region of the body sensitive to that particular kind of stimulation. The

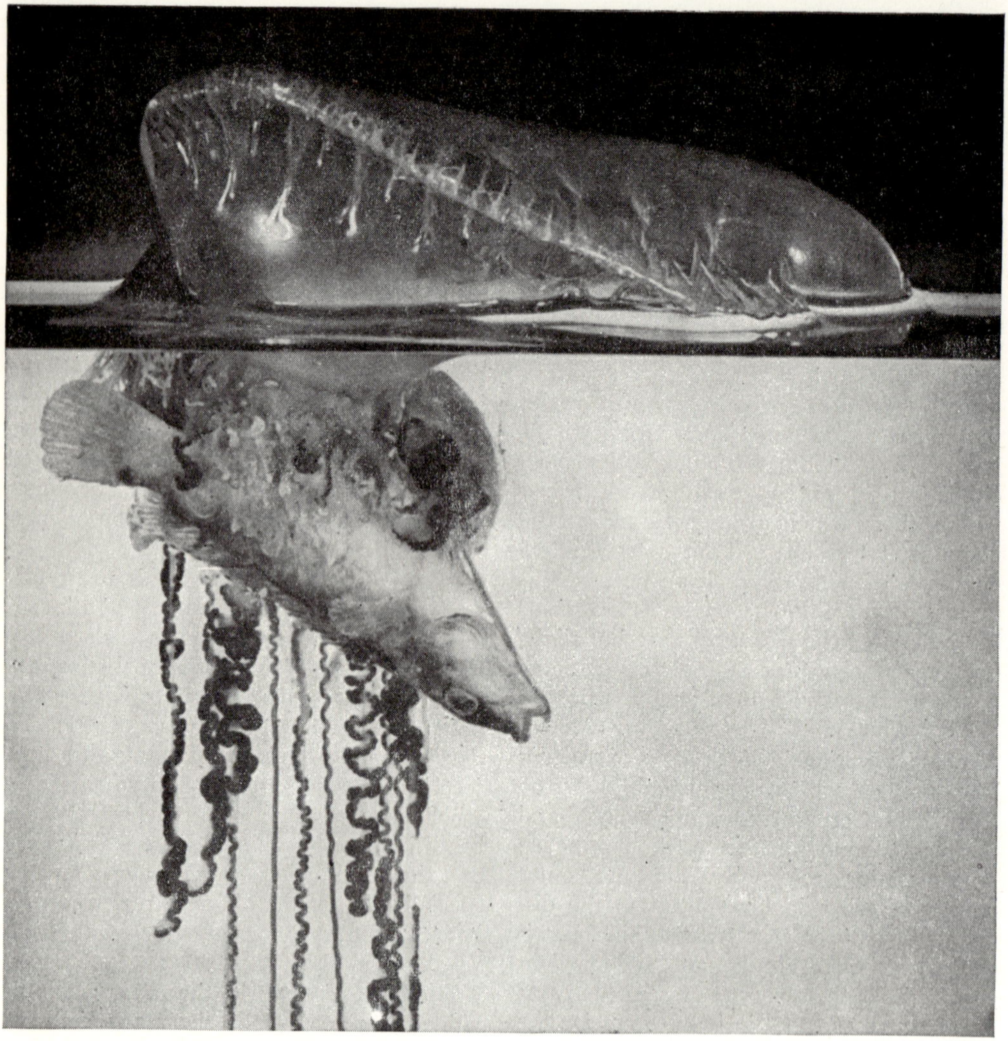

a

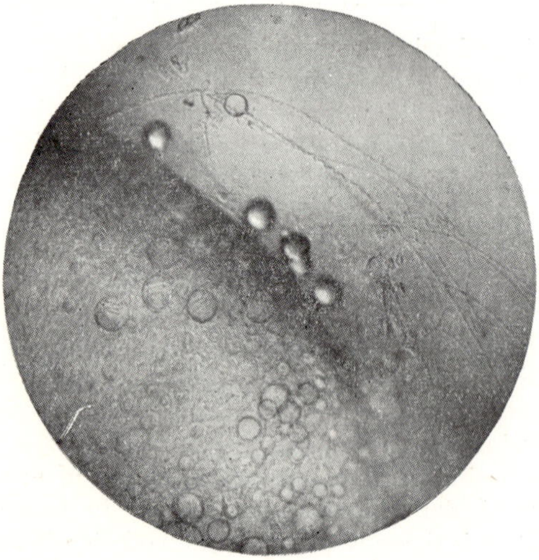

FIGURE 11.13 Physalia, the Portuguese Man-of-War. (Photographs by Douglas P. Wilson, reproduced by kind permission of the author and publisher from *They Live in the Sea* by Douglas P. Wilson, Collins, London.)

a. Physalia eating a fish that it has captured and killed. The translucent, gas-filled float drifts along the surface of the water. Chains of differentiated zooids hang from it down into the water. Some of these pendant strings are wrapped around the fish, whose digestion has already been begun by the gastrozooids, the feeding individuals of the polymorphic colony.

b. Portion of a tentacle showing undischarged nematocysts. Some discharged nematocysts can also be seen still within the tentacle; others are free in the water outside.

regions of special sense in the coelenterates are ocelli (Latin, ocellus = little eye) and statocysts (Greek, statos = standing + kystos = bladder); in many there are also collections of sensory cells forming patches of neuro-epithelium, localized areas for general sensation. The positions of the ocelli on the body of a coelenterate are marked by spots of red, brown or black pigment, usually on the tentacles near the point of their attachment to the bell or on the margin of the bell itself. In the marine jellyfishes, the ocelli lie on club-shaped organs called rhopalia (Greek, rhopalion = club) typical of certain species.

The statocysts are little pits or sacs lined by cells called lithocytes (Greek, lithos = stone), each of which contains a small round mass called a statolith that moves freely within the cell; the mass has a center of organic material surrounded by calcium carbonate. Below the lithocytes are sensory cells whose processes extend under them and whose delicate sensory hairs come in contact with the statoliths. The statocysts are usually situated around the margin of the bell and although their function has been in doubt, recent experiments confirm the belief that they act as organs of equilibration and enable the animal to orient itself in respect to gravity. An intact animal ordinarily maintains itself in a horizontal position, and if experimentally tilted, the muscle processes of the cells on the margin that is higher contract more strongly than those on the lower side, and contract continuously rather than rhythmically, and by so doing bring the two sides of the body level again. This "righting reaction" does not take place if the statocysts have been removed from the side of the body that is raised; the displacement of the statoliths presumably stimulates the sensory hairs of the nerve cells and the impulse so aroused is transmitted to the muscle processes that bring about the appropriate response.

*Colonial coelenterates:* There are many colonial members of the coelenterates, where, as in the protozoan colonies, a number of relatively independent zooids are united to a common stalk or base, in some species in linear order, in others branching like a tree from a central axis. Each zooid in the colonial coelenterate is, however, a multicellular unit, and in many there are two or more kinds of zooids in the colony, different in appearance and in the part that they play in the life of the colony as a whole. The simplest colonies are those which are di- or trimorphic (Greek, di = two; tri = three + morphe = form) with only two or three types of zooids, the hydranths or feeding zooids with tentacles and mouths; the blastostyles or reproductive zooids with no tentacles nor mouths, maintained by the hydranths and producing reproductive cells from which a new generation develops; and in many cases a free-swimming medusoid generation detached from the parent colony (Fig. 11.8). Some colonies are polymorphic (Greek, poly = many + morphe = form). One of the most commonly known of these is Physalia, the Portuguese Man-of-War, in which some of the zooids act as stomachs ingesting the food for the entire colony and secreting the enzymes that bring about its digestion, while others, whose bodies are structurally little more than long tentacles, capture the food and still others produce the generative cells (Fig. 11.13). These three are the polypoid members of the colony; the medusoid members are modified as floats, their bodies filled with gas which keeps the whole collection near the surface of the water, as swimming bells which propel it slowly along, or as protective shields over the feeding and reproducing members. The coelenteron is common to all the individuals in a colony, and the nutrient fluid in it slowly passes from the feeding members to all the others.

While many of the coelenterates are soft-bodied, with no supporting material except the mesogloea, a number of them have an internal support, or endoskeleton, developed by the mesenchyme, or else are enclosed in cups of firm or rigid material as an external or exoskeleton, developed through secretions from the ectoderm cells. Either kind of skeleton may be of inorganic or organic material, or a combination of both. Mesogloea itself is composed largely of water and inorganic salts with but a small organic content. Although on analysis it yields nitrogen, the organic material is not a protein but a carbohydrate, a hexose called glucoseamine in which an amino group replaces one of the hydroxyl radicles.

$$\begin{array}{c} \text{H H OH H H} \\ |\ |\ \ |\ \ \ |\ \ | \\ -\text{C}-\text{C}-\text{C}-\ \ -\text{C}-\text{C}-\text{CH}_2\text{OH} \\ |\ \ |\ \ \ |\ \ \ |\ \ | \\ \text{O N H O O} \\ \text{H H}_2\ \ \ \ \ \ \text{H} \end{array}$$

The internal skeletons of some of the coelenterates are made of spicules of calcium carbonate embedded in the matrix of mesogloea; in some the spicules may be so closely packed that they form a solid and continuous mass. In others, like the sea fans and feathers, the internal skeleton is of gorgonin, an organic compound similar to keratin, the protein of horn, but chemically not identical with it. Most of the hydroid colonies are surrounded by a perisarc (Greek, peri = about + sarx = flesh), a transparent and delicate covering of chitin, a carbohydrate compound of acetic acid and glucoseamine secreted by the ectoderm cells. The massive external skeletons of some, like the stony corals, are wholly inorganic, made of one of the crystalline forms of calcium carbonate called aragonite; their manner of formation has not yet been clearly determined.

Because their skeletons have been preserved as fossils with the record of the earth's history, modern coelenterates are known to have a long ancestry, dating back to Paleozoic times about three hundred million years ago. The growth of the skeleton-forming colonies, too, over long periods of time has led and is leading to new geographical formations, the reefs and atolls of the warmer seas. Although corals have probably been mainly responsible for their formation, other coelenterates like sea pens, sea fans and sea feathers as well as sponges and the coralline algae have also contributed to them.

*Capacity for regeneration:* While both individual and colonial members of the coelenterates show elaboration and modification of the simple sac of Hydra's body, their basic architectural plan remains that of two epithelial layers separated by mesogloea or by a mesenchyme of greater or less complexity. As with sponges, questions naturally arise as to the extent to which, in the simple members at least, the cells are specialized and to what extent, if at all, they have lost the totipotency of an independent cell. Some of the earliest experiments to answer these questions were performed on hydras by Abraham Trembley and in the years succeeding his experiments, coelenterates have furnished a great deal of the experimental material used in the study of the complex problem of regeneration and regulation of growth in animals. Trembley showed the high regenerative powers of Hydra by cutting the animals into small pieces either transversely or longitudinally and finding that such pieces grew into whole new animals, complete in every way. Later experiments on Hydra and on other coelenterates have confirmed their capacity for regeneration, and have shown that it is related to the presence of the interstitial or formative cells, which by division and differentiation can grow into new parts. It has also been shown that under ordinary circumstances, the hypostome, mouth and tentacles of a polyp will develop from the upper, or apical, surface of a fragment, while the lower portions of the body develop from the basal surface. This is true also of segments of the stalks of colonial forms, indicating that there is some internal difference, not morphologically evident, between the cells at an upper level in the organism and those below them, imposing a polarity upon the body as a whole.

*Polarity:* The term polarity is one borrowed from physics; as it is used in biology it means that there is a difference between one region of an organism, or of an individual cell, and another; this difference may be expressed in various ways. Various explanations have been offered for the polarity of organisms, which the regeneration of fragments of coelenterates and other organisms clearly show, but none of them alone is completely satisfactory. On the other hand, experimental evidence is clear that the inherent or innate polarity of a tissue, an organ and even of whole organisms may be altered, suppressed or reversed by the use of chemical agents which are depressants of cellular activity like narcotics and anaesthetics; by reducing the oxygen supply to the apical end and increasing that to the basal; characterized by the presence of eight meridional bands (Fig. 11.14), beneath each of which lies a canal of the endodermal system and on the surface of which are plates of stiff cilia, the combs from which the phylum derives its name. They are all marine,

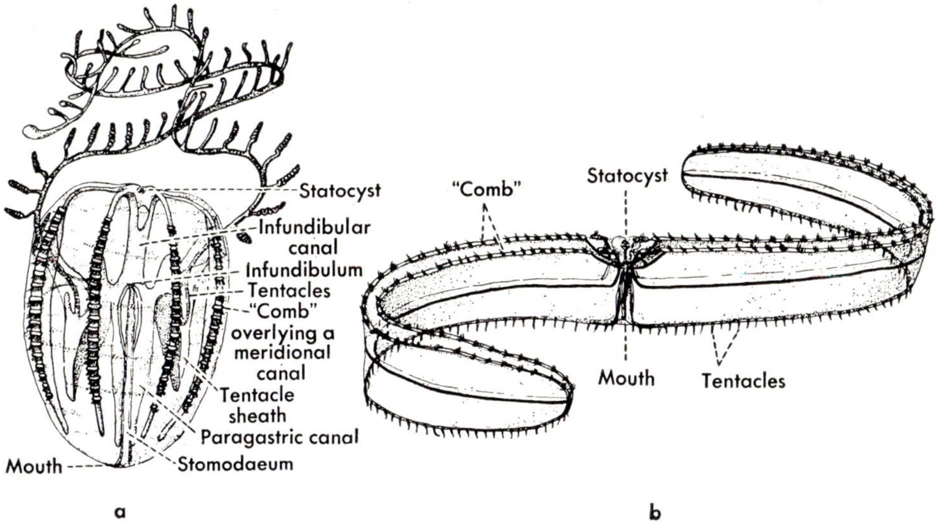

FIGURE 11.14 Ctenophores. (After Mayer.)

a. Pleurobrachia, the sea walnut, a genus found in the Pacific, Atlantic and Antarctic Oceans. The body, egg-shaped or almost spherical in form, measures 17–20 mm. from oral to aboral pole, and 14–18 mm. across at its greatest diameter. Four of the eight meridional canals are shown; the other four lie opposite these.

b. Cestum Veneris, abundant in the Mediterranean and tropical waters of the Atlantic and Pacific Oceans. The body is flat and thin, compressed in the oral-aboral axis and greatly extended laterally, measuring about 80 mm. in height and 800–1500 mm. in width.

and by the application of an electric current.

CTENOPHORA: The organization of the body in the ctenophores, or comb jellies, is similar to that in the coelenterates, although ctenophores are considered higher in the evolutionary scale since there is in them a greater definition of the parts of the central cavity for special purposes in relation to food intake, digestion and absorption and a greater differentiation of their cells, particularly in the development of typical muscle cells or fibres from the mesenchyme and a consequent separation of epithelial tissue from muscular. They have no nematocysts and a single sense organ, a dome-shaped statocyst at the aboral pole, or that which is opposite the mouth opening. All ctenophores are usually ovoid like the "sea walnuts" common along the Atlantic coast, although some few, like Cestum Veneris (Venus' Girdle) found in the surface waters of the Mediterranean, have long flattened bodies that may reach a meter and a half in length (Fig. 11.14).

PLATYHELMINTHES: In the Platyhelminthes, or flatworms, the architectural plan of a simple sac is modified by the presence of a definite layer of cells between the superficial ectoderm and the endoderm of the often greatly branched digestive tract (Fig. 11.15). The derivation of this middle layer is wholly unlike that of the mesenchyme of the sponges, coelenterates and ctenophores, which is made up of cells that have migrated into this middle region from the endoderm and the ectoderm. The cells of the middle layer of flatworms are derived for the most part from two strands of cells that appear early in embryonic development and give rise to a third primary tissue, the mesoderm

The free-living and commensal members of the phylum alone show the typical characters of the group, for the parasitic species show the degeneration of the structures associated with locomotion, feeding and the reception of stimuli from the outside world

FIGURE 11.15 Flatworms. (Drawn from life.)

a. Euplanaria, a triclad turbellarian in which the digestive tract has one anterior and two posterior arms, all branching extensively (compare Figure 11.17). These flatworms inhabit fresh water, and reach a length of 15–20 mm.

b. Stylochus, a polyclad turbellarian, in which the digestive tract branches extensively through the body. These flatworms inhabit salt water and attain a body length of about 40 mm. Their bodies are yellowish-brown and crossed irregularly by lighter lines and stripes.

(Greek, meso = between + derma = skin). The development of such a third layer has had great effect upon the evolution of animal types, for it offered greater possibilities for the development of new structures and the consequent modification of body plans.

*General characters:* The flatworms are all soft-bodied animals without supporting structures of any kind. Many of them are free-living, inhabiting fresh, salt and brackish water and damp places on land all over the world; some, too, live as parasites in the bodies of other animals, including man, or in association with them as commensals.

and with other conditions of an independent existence that is characteristic of parasites in general.

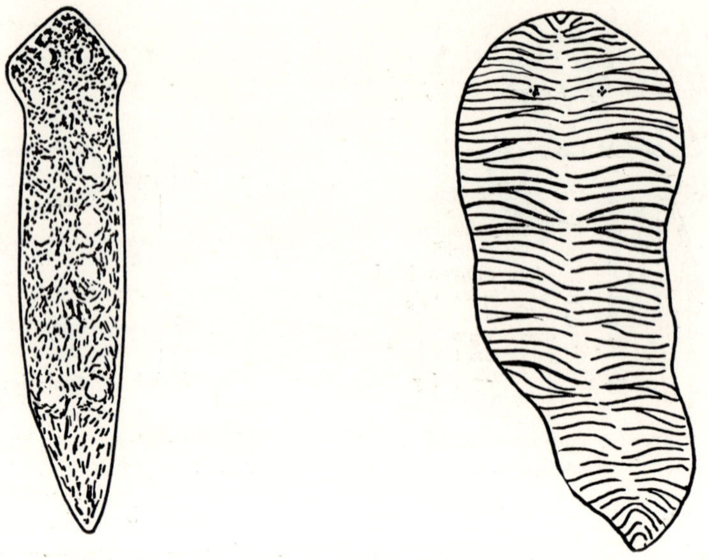

The typical flatworm is a bilaterally symmetrical animal; that is, there is only one plane through which the animal can be cut to give two similar halves. Such symmetry is characteristic of animals that move actively about and is associated with a distinction between the anterior and posterior ends of the body; with the development of organs in pairs, one member of each pair on either side of the body; and with the localization of sensory structures in the anterior end and the development of a head. Moreover, in bilaterally symmetrical animals, a distinction can be made between the surfaces of the body as the front, or ventral, upon which the mouth usually lies; the back, or dorsal, opposite to it; and the right and left sides or lateral surfaces (Fig. 11.11*b*).

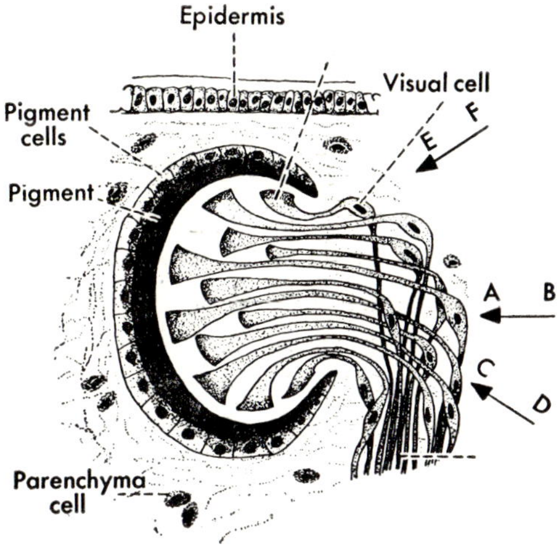

FIGURE 11.16 Eye of a flatworm (Planaria gonocephala). (After Hesse-Doflein.)

Rays of light entering the eye in the direction of the arrow A–B stimulate the terminations of all the visual cells; those entering in the direction of the arrows C–D and E–F stimulate only some of them.

*Organs and organ systems:* Although the bodies of the free-living flatworms show no real differentiation into a head, the anterior end is distinguished by the presence of pairs of organs of special sense, the eyes, on the dorsal surface which overlie two masses of nerve cells called the anterior ganglia (Greek, ganglion = tumor or swelling), and the ciliated pits of the lateral surfaces which appear to respond primarily to chemical stimuli. The eyes of a flatworm like the common Euplanaria or Dorotocephala (Fig. 11.16) are cups of cells derived from the ectoderm, that have sunk below the surface and are covered by transparent ectoderm. The wall of each cup is made of cells filled with dark pigment granules which absorb the energy of light, preventing its further passage or its reflection; consequently only those rays that strike the body at the opening of the cup are effective as light stimuli.

The interior of the cup is filled with specialized nerve cells with delicate processes, the fibrillae, in contact with the pigmented base of the cup and a thicker process, the fibre, which terminates in contact with one of the ganglia. In addition to these sensory organs and the ciliated pits, which are also made of a number of specialized cells, there are individual sensory cells on the surface of the body, usually most thickly distributed in the anterior region, some of which respond to changes in the rate of the flow of water past the surface, and others to chemical differences in it. Except for these superficial cells, the nerve cells of flatworms are sunk below the surface as a network, at least two strands of which are thicker, with more cells and smaller spaces between them than elsewhere, so that they are visible as chains or cords running along the sides of the body from the ganglia toward the posterior end.

The mesoderm makes up a large part of their bodies, forming a kind of parenchyma, although it is more than a packing tissue. The cells are irregular in shape with a good deal of intercellular substance between them and some of them at least are migratory (Fig. 11.17). They are cells active in the general metabolism of the body, transporting food material from the site of digestion in the endodermal sac to the tissues and structures some distance from it, taking up unwanted by-products of metabolism, and carrying them to the cells which eliminate them from the body; and in their own cytoplasm elaborating a substance that eventually appears as slime discharged from the surface of the animal or as short, stiff rods, the rhabdites (Greek, rhabdos = rod) that are lodged in the ectoderm cells and on appropriate stimulation discharged from them to the surrounding water, where they liquefy. In all but the marine flatworms, a system of canals in the mesenchyme serves as a water regulating mechanism, and to some extent at least as an excretory one in removing metabolic waste. It consists of two main canals, which are usually clearly evident along the sides of the animal's body and which open to the exterior through one, two or several pores (Fig. 11.18). Internally they branch into finer and finer tubes and the

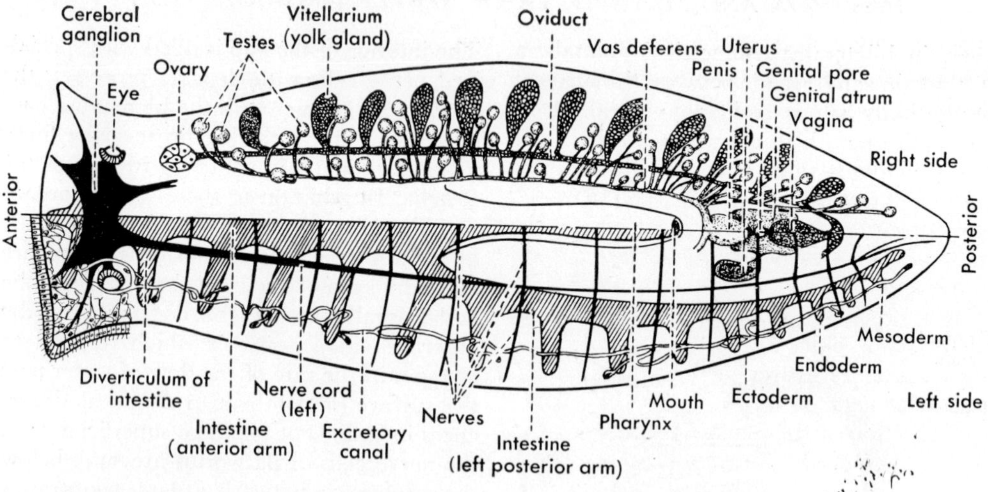

FIGURE 11.17 Diagram of the internal anatomy of a free-living triclad. The reproductive organs only are shown on the right side of the animal (upper half in the diagram); the other organs are shown on the left side (lower half of the diagram). In a small area of the left anterior region, the ectoderm is shown as a covering layer of compact, ciliated cells and the parenchyma (mesoderm) as loosely arranged, stellate cells with large intercellular spaces. The endoderm of the enteron is indicated by cross-hatching. (After Lankester.)

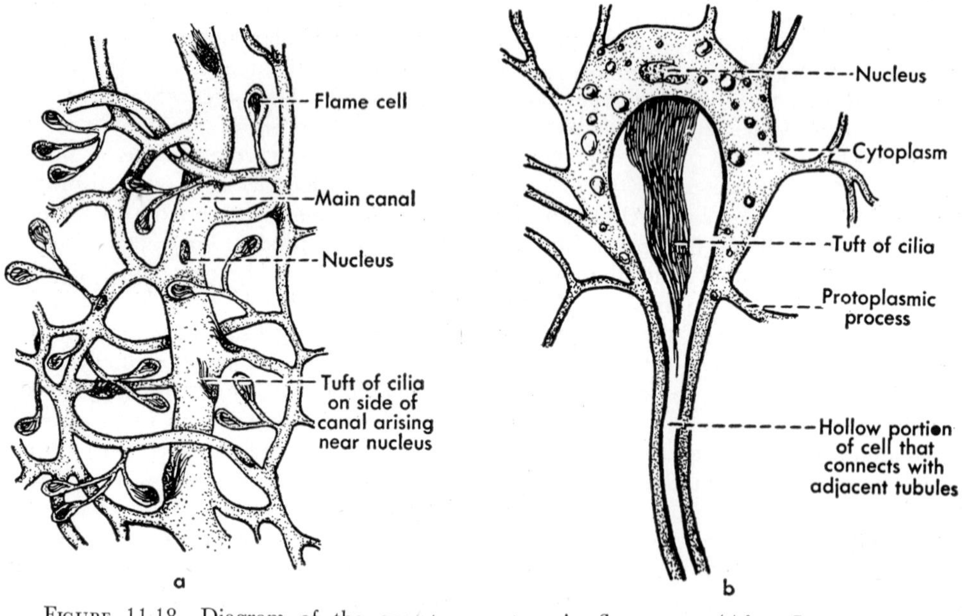

FIGURE 11.18 Diagram of the excretory system in flatworms. (After Lankester.)
  a. Part of the system of canals, terminating in flame bulbs.
  b. A single flame cell.

finest branches end in flame bulbs. These are small cells, or clusters of cells, whose processes extend between the neighboring mesenchymal cells; the surface that is in contact with the tube is slightly indented and from it originates a tuft of cilia which are constantly in motion. The cells of the walls of the tube discharge, or excrete, excess water and dissolved metabolic waste into the lumen, or cavity of the tube, while the cilia of the flame bulbs by their constant flickering maintain a hydrostatic pressure insuring the movement of fluid along the canal in the direction of the openings or pores.

The mesoderm also gives rise to the reproductive cells and to most of the often complicated system of organs in which these cells are matured, stored and ultimately passed outside of the animal. And in addition to such highly specialized cells as those of the reproductive and excretory systems, and of the muscles extending around and across the body, this middle layer also contains embryonic cells which can give rise to new parts.

*Capacity for regeneration:* Like the coelenterates, the flatworms have furnished much of the material for experimental studies on regeneration and polarity in the animal body. They can be operated on with a good deal of precision and the effect upon the organism as a whole of the removal of some of its parts and its capacity to replace them can be determined. If, for example, the ganglia are removed, the animal makes no response to the ordinary stimuli of its environment and remains quiescent, but if the anterior end of such an operated animal is stimulated artificially by poking with a needle, it will move readily, showing that coordinated movement is mediated by the nerve net, while the ganglia act as relay stations for the stimuli received from the special sensory areas, passing them on to the nerve net which evokes the appropriate response. When the body is cut into segments, the embryonic cells in the parenchyma migrate to the cut surfaces and there multiply and differentiate into the characteristic tissues and organs of the missing parts. Similarly, when an entire animal is starved, its body shrinks in size and loses most of its organ systems by the progressive utilization of them as sources of energy for its minimal needs, but will grow again to normal proportions and replace its lost systems, when fed, through the multiplication of these formative cells and the localization and differentiation of their descendants.

The presence of such an extensive middle layer has made possible, or demanded, the development of the flatworm body in more elaborate and complicated ways than could be achieved by a system like that of the coelenterate body, or would be necessary to it. In none of them, however, has differentiation proceeded in the direction of skeleton formation, although the bodies of the parasites that live in the digestive tracts of other animals are covered by a thick cuticle that resists the action of its host's digestive juices. Because of the absence of hard parts, little of the history of the Platyhelminthes has been preserved in fossil remains and nothing is known of the ancestral type of those inhabiting the world to-day. All the modern free-living flatworms are comparatively small, the largest not more than about six inches in length, although the bodies of some of the parasitic ones, the cestodes or tapeworms, may reach a length of several feet in a chain of detachable segments united by nerve cords and excretory canals.

## Metaphyta of simple organization: Bryophytes

The most simply organized of the multicellular plants are the liverworts and mosses, both of which are included in the division Bryophyta (Greek, bryon = moss + phyton = plant) in which there are some 22,500 species. Within this division, the 8,500 species of liverworts make up the class Hepaticae, and the mosses, with some 14,000 species, the class Musci. The bryophytes are for the most part terrestrial plants and are very general in their distribution, living, like the lichens, in all parts of the globe and often on rocks or other surfaces that appear to offer neither opportunity for anchorage nor materials for subsistence except those that can be derived from the air. The bryophytes are all photosynthesizing plants, their bodies made up largely of chlorenchyma cells. The body of a bryophyte is essentially a thallus, for no moss nor liverwort has the differentiated leaves, stems and roots of the higher plants, but they are distinct from the algae, particularly in the construction of their reproductive organs, and so form a separate division of plants.

## Hepaticae

In most of the Hepaticae the conspicuous part of the thallus is a flat plate of irregular outline; in the shape of these lobed plates is the origin of the class's name, for they resemble more or less an animal liver and so, according to the old doctrine of signatures described by Paracelsus, which attributes the specific therapeutic properties of plants to their resemblance in shape to different parts of the body, were believed to be especially effective in curing ailments related to that organ. The plate is usually several cells in thickness; in the genus Riccia, which grows on the surface of ponds and pools, the upper margin of the thallus is covered by an epidermis only one cell in thickness, interrupted at intervals by small pores. Beneath the epidermis strands of cells, arranged end to end, extend downward, forming vertical columns which enclose air chambers or spaces, some of the uppermost of which are in direct communication with the atmosphere through the pores in the upper epidermis and so provide access to air for all the tissues of the plant (Fig. 11.19). The lower margin of the thallus is covered by a continuous epidermis. From some of these epidermal cells slender protoplasmic strands extend as rhizoids (Greek, rhiza = root + eidos = like) which reach down into the water, the mud or the soil on which the plant is living; from others grow filaments of cells, called scales. Toward the middle of the thallus the cells are more compactly arranged and, like those of the lower epidermis, do not contain chloroplasts. The photosynthetic processes of the entire thallus are carried on by the chlorenchyma cells of the upper epidermis and of the walls of the air

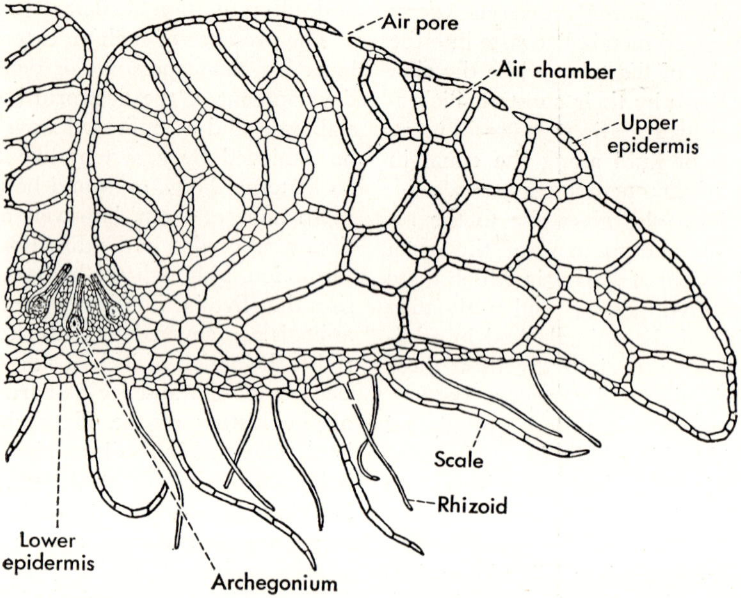

FIGURE 11.19 Portion of a cross section of a thallus of a liverwort, Riccia, showing the air pores and air chambers and also, in the midregion, the female sex organs, or archegonia. (From Smith, Gilbert, Evans, Duggar, Bryan and Allen, *A Textbook of General Botany*. Copyright 1942 by The Macmillan Company.)

chambers through which there is free diffusion of gases and water vapor.

In some of the liverworts, the body consists of an erect axis from which extend lateral plates of cells that externally at least resemble leaves (Fig. 11.20), but internally

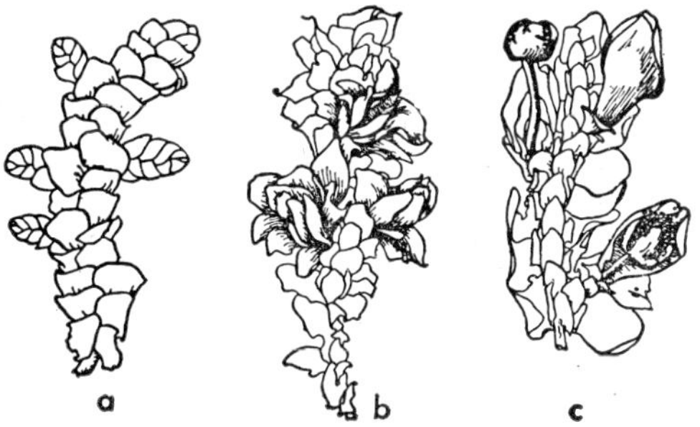

FIGURE 11.20 Porella, a foliate liverwort. (From Smith, Gilbert, Evans, Duggar, Bryan and Allen, *A Textbook of General Botany*. Copyright 1942 by The Macmillan Company.)

a. Male plant.
b. Female plant.
c. Female plant with spore-bearing plants of the next generation attached to it.

are without the differentiation of cells characteristic of the true leaf. These foliate or leafy species are often mistaken for certain of the true mosses whose habit of growth is similar.

## Mosses

The moss plant is, however, distinct from the liverwort in its origin from a protonema (Greek, protos = first + nema = thread), an alga-like filament of cells that develops from a single reproductive cell, or spore (Fig. 11.21). The moss protonema spreads over the surface of damp or dry soil, of a rock or a tree, often covering a considerable area before it begins to send up erect shoots from different points along its length. These shoots are slender columns of several rows of cells from the superficial ones of which flat plates, often but a single cell in thickness, grow out laterally as the "leaves." The erect shoots are not more than a few inches high in modern mosses but fossilized specimens show that those that flourished in the Carboniferous Age 250 million years ago grew very much taller. Rhizoids may also develop from the protonema, pushing down below the surface on which the plant is growing. In many mosses the protonema dies after the growth of a few erect shoots, and each shoot, with its rhizoids, may become an independent plant, growing and branching and often covering a large area. Except for the rhizoids, the cells of the vegetative thallus are chlorenchyma cells, although in some species those in the center of the axis may be elongated ones with comparatively thick walls and serve the plant for support and storage rather than for photosynthesis (Fig. 11.22). Some moss plants grow from year to year by the development of an extension of the axis with new "leaves" at the tip of the old one; the basal part of the plant then loses its leaves and ultimately dies, providing a substrate upon which saprophytic bacteria can live and decompose. This is especially true of the sphagnum, or bog, mosses, whose dead lower layers, which are added to year after year, become closely packed together and make part of the sub-

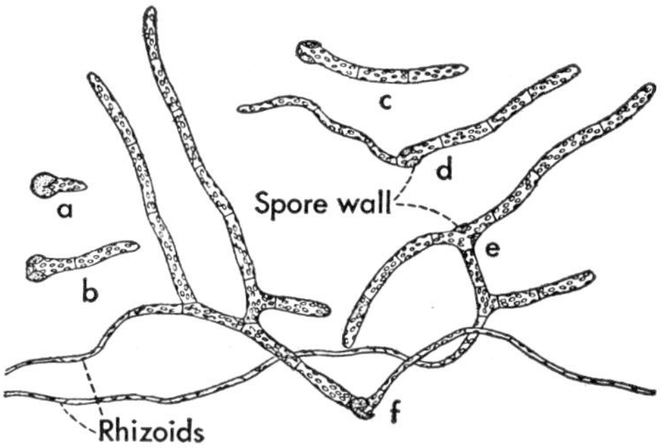

FIGURE 11.21 Growth of a moss plant. (From Smith, Gilbert, Evans, Duggar, Bryan and Allen, *A Textbook of General Botany*. Copyright 1942 by The Macmillan Company.)

a. Germination of the moss spore. b–f. Successive stages in the growth of a protonema.

stance of peat that is used in many countries as fuel and that, in the course of ages, may become converted to coal. Like sponges, mosses furnish a haven for many kinds of small animals whose dead remains, together with those of the moss itself, provide a wealth of organic material for saprophytic micro-organisms, and since diffusion of air from the surrounding atmosphere becomes more and more limited as the surface mass of this material becomes thicker and thicker, the respiration of anaerobes is correspondingly favored and nitrifying bacteria may flourish there. And like the lichens, the bryophytes that grow upon rocks contribute to their fragmentation, especially to that of rocks containing limestone or other minerals soluble in weak acids. The carbon dioxide given off by bryophytes and lichens alike as one of the end products of the oxidative reactions that go on within them combines with water to form carbonic acid, which is a solvent for such minerals, so that very gradually the rock is dissolved, rather than worn, away.

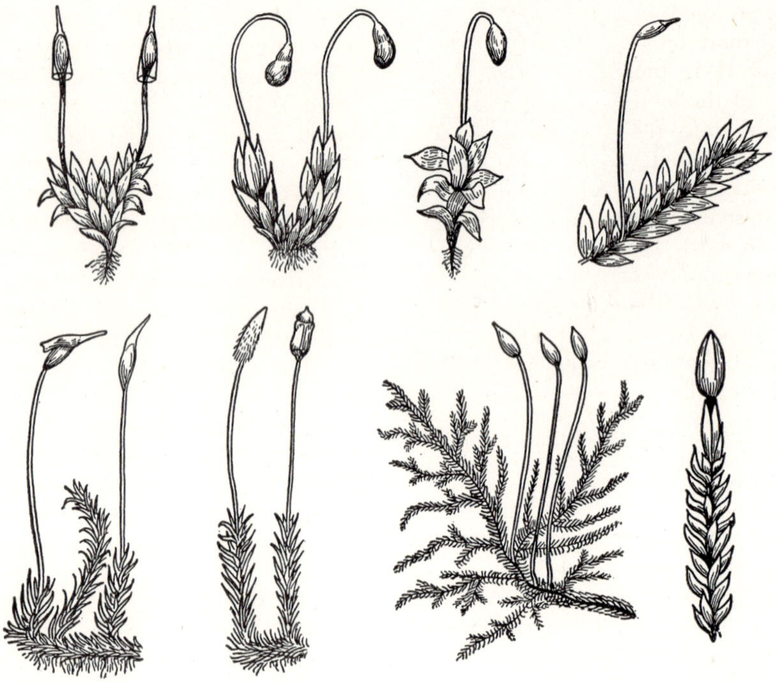

*Capacity for regeneration:* The bryophytes show great capacity for regeneration, a property common to most plants, even those at the highest levels of evolutionary development. Almost any fragment of a bryophyte will grow into a complete new plant, given the proper environmental conditions. Indeed, the growth of such fragments, occurring frequently in nature, is a common means of their propagation. The development of several moss plants from a single protonema is also a common occurrence, so that although both liverworts and mosses have developed, in the course of their evolution, specialized reproductive cells and specialized structures in which these cells are produced, they are not wholly dependent upon them for the multiplication of individuals, or the increase in population of a species.

FIGURE 11.22  Representative Mosses. (From Hylander and Stanley, *College Botany.* Copyright 1949 by The Macmillan Company.) Upper row, from left to right: Encalypta, Funaria, Mnium, Fissidens. Lower row, from left to right: Dicranum, Polytrichum, Hylocomium, Andraea.

## Ecological and evolutionary relationships

Although these biological systems have left little trace of their developmental histories in the earth's crust, for their soft bodies have disintegrated and have not been preserved as fossils, their modern representatives may be taken as illustrations of evolutionary progress, showing the different lines of development that animals and plants have followed. They also show the diversity of types and the degree of specialization of structure and of function that have been attained, in different ways, in organisms of more or less the same degree of complexity. It is therefore instructive, as illustrative of the biological principle of the fundamental unity of living things, to consider them together, not as animals and plants, or metazoa and metaphyta, but as biological systems meeting the conditions of existence on earth in ways that have been possible to them and that have proved satisfactory for their perpetuation and establishment as species.

Of these systems, the flatworms have attained structurally the highest degree of evolutionary development, with their specialized and concentrated nerve and muscle cells, their canalicular system for water regulation and for excretion, and their localized and permanent reproductive organs. All sponges, coelenterates, ctenophores and bryophytes, however, show division of labor between the different cells and the different parts of their bodies. The bryophytes alone, with the exception of a few species of free-living flatworms inhabiting moist soil, have become emancipated from the necessity of a wholly aqueous environment and as terrestrial systems have become fully adapted to life on land. While the liverworts require damp and moist habitats for their most active development and growth, they can, through mechanisms evolved during their long period of existence upon earth, withstand prolonged droughts and maintain themselves as biological systems, although in a state of suspended activity. Some species, for example, form subterranean tubers, which survive when the rest of the plant has perished through desiccation; others can protect themselves by rolling up the thallus, thus reducing the surface exposed to the dry air and conserving the water stored in their cells and cell walls. Many mosses can live and flourish under conditions of extreme aridity by means of adaptive mechanisms for the retention and conduction of water achieved in the course of evolutionary development. By virtue of such mechanisms, the bryophytes have attained a degree of independence of existence beyond that of the algae and of the metazoa of comparable organization. Although they are still dependent upon water for their physiological processes and for the transmission of their reproductive cells, they are free from the necessity of a water supply continuously accessible to all surface areas, and have successfully accomplished the transition from water to land, with all the physiological adjustments involved, while still retaining their structural simplicity.

CHAPTER 12 | THE VASCULAR PLANTS

*The distinguishing characters of vascular plants; types of vascular plants*

The multicellular plants of more complex organization with roots, stems and leaves, all structures that are more or less specialized for particular purposes in their bodies, and with localized tissues devoted primarily to the movement of water and its dissolved solutes, are grouped by the systematists into two divisions, Pteridophyta (Greek, pteris = fern) and Spermatophyta (Greek, sperma = seed). The division Pteridophyta contains 9,000 or more species of ferns as well as the plants commonly known as club mosses, or ground pines, and the horsetail or scouring rushes, of which only one genus, Equisitum, exists to-day (Fig. 12.1). The division Spermatophyta includes some 200,000 known living species of trees, shrubs, grasses, grains and the flowering and edible plants of gardens as well as the wild flowers and weeds of uncultivated areas (Figs. 12.2, 12.3). Spermatophytes are distinguished from all other plants by the fact that they produce seeds, a feature to which may be attributed much of their success in survival and in population, for with the exception of the thallophytes, they are the largest group of plants and those most widely distributed. They and the pteridophytes have existed through many ages of the earth's history;

a

FIGURE 12.1 Representative Pteridophytes.

a. Cinnamon fern (Osmunda cinnamomea), showing sterile (vegetative) and fertile (spore-bearing) leaves. (Photograph by D. F. Reath.)

FIGURE 12.1 Representative Pteridophytes (*continued*).

b. Horsetail or scouring rush (Equisetum arvense), showing the sterile shoots with whorls of needle-shaped leaves, and the fertile shoots with cone-like strobili. (Photograph by C. J. Hylander, from Hylander and Stanley, *College Botany*. Copyright 1949 by The Macmillan Company.)

FIGURE 12.1 Representative Pteridophytes (*continued*).

c. Club moss (left) and ground pine (right), two species of Lycopodium, showing spreading vegetative leaves and fertile leaves packed into cone-like strobili. (Photograph by C. J. Hylander, from Hylander and Stanley, *College Botany*. Copyright 1949 by The Macmillan Company.)

FIGURE 12.1 Representative Pteridophytes (*continued*).

d. Resurrection plant, a species of Selaginella. (New York Botanical Garden, from Hylander and Stanley, *College Botany*. Copyright 1949 by The Macmillan Company.)

the earliest fossil specimens yet found, from the strata of the Paleozoic Age, show that they were growing 100 million to 250 million years ago. Indeed, the most primitive of the modern spermatophytes, the Cycads, have an unbroken history since early Mesozoic times, about 130 million years ago.

A seed is a unit that contains an embryo plant in which the primordia of future structures are already established and which is embedded in nutrient and protective tissues derived from the generations immediately preceding it (Fig. 12.4). Seeds become detached from the parent plant and may be scattered some distance from it, or by one means or another they may be carried away and ultimately develop into a new individual in a region far removed from that of the plant that produced them. Some can remain dormant or in a condition of arrested development for long periods of time, months or even years, and yet quickly start to germinate and grow into a new individual in a favorable environment. The division of the Spermatophyta is subdivided on the basis of certain seed characters into Gymnospermae (Greek, gymnos = naked + sperma = seed) and Angiospermae (Greek, aggeion = receptacle), the distinction being made according to the number and the derivation of the layers that surround the embryo as seed coats. In both subdivisions, some of the leaves are modified as reproductive ones or sporophylls (Greek, spora = seed + phyllon = leaf); these alone bear the reproductive organs and the reproductive cells of the vegetative plant. In most of the gymnosperms, the reproductive organs are produced on the surface of the sporophylls which are packed together in cones or strobili (Latin, strobilus = fir cone); in the angiosperms, they are produced within those at the center of the flower, itself a cluster of modified leaves, concentrically arranged and often brightly colored; those that surround the sporophylls are called

FIGURE 12.2 Representative Gymnosperms.

a. Eastern White Pine (Pinus strobus). (Photograph by courtesy of the U.S. Forestry Service.)

b. Cycad (Cycas). (Photograph by C. J. Hylander, from Hylander and Stanley, *College Botany*. Copyright 1949 by The Macmillan Company.)

a

b

FIGURE 12.3  Representative Angiosperms.

a. American Elm (Ulmus americana). (Photograph by courtesy of the U.S. Forestry Service.)

b. Corn (Zea mays). (Photograph by courtesy of the Soil Conservation Service, U.S. Department of Agriculture.)

c. Bunchberry (Cornus canadensis), a plant of creeping habit, shown here growing near lichen-covered rocks. (Photograph by Mary Dameral.)

petals and form the corolla. Many of the gymnosperms are therefore commonly known as conifers and the angiosperms as flowering plants. Modern gymnosperms are represented by only some 700 living species which include the Cycads, restricted to the tropics, as well as the common conifers of temperate zones, but fossilized or petrified remains show that three orders flourished on the earth in Paleozoic times 250 million years ago and perished long before the advent of man. The far more numerous angiosperms fall into two classes on the basis of the number of cotyledons (Greek, kotyledon = cup-shaped hollow), the embryonic leaves of the plant within the seed; the embryos of plants like the grasses, grains and lilies have one such leaf and are therefore classed as Monocotyledonae, while those of the majority of other flowering plants have two and make up the class Dicotyledonae.

The conspicuous, or vegetative, body of a pteridophyte or a spermatophyte consists of three main regions or parts, the roots, the stems and the leaves, each of which contributes in some particular way to the functioning of the system as a whole. The three tissue systems, epidermal, fundamental and

c

vascular, are continuous throughout the entire plant body but in each of its part show modifications in type and in arrangement peculiar to them. The pattern of the tissues in any one region also varies in the members of the two divisions and in those of the subdivisions of the spermatophytes.

*Roots and root systems*

Roots are ordinarily that part of a plant that is below the ground, penetrating into the soil and so anchoring its aerial parts, and, even more important to the life of the plant, establishing contact with the soil solution. The roots not only absorb this soil solution, principally from that present as "capillary water," but also conduct it, through their specialized vascular tissues (Latin, vasculum = small vessel), from its point of entry to the more remote parts of the plant. But not all roots are underground, nor are all the underground parts of a plant roots, nor do all plants have roots (Fig. 12.5). Many epiphytic plants (Greek, epi = upon + phyton = plant), like the orchids and ferns that rest on trees or other objects and derive their water and minerals from the

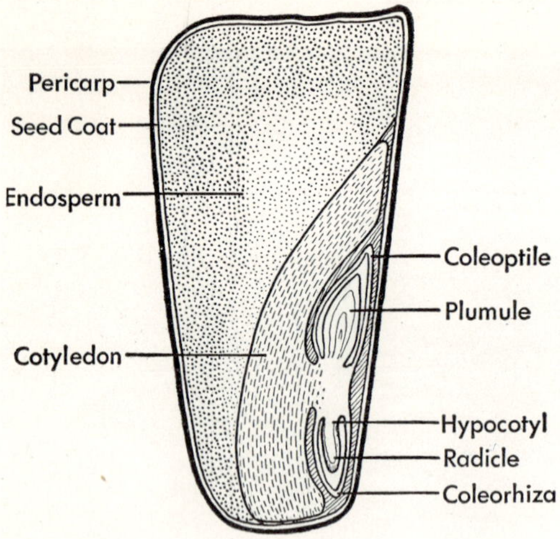

FIGURE 12.4 Seeds. (From Hylander and Stanley, *College Botany*. Copyright 1949 by The Macmillan Company.)

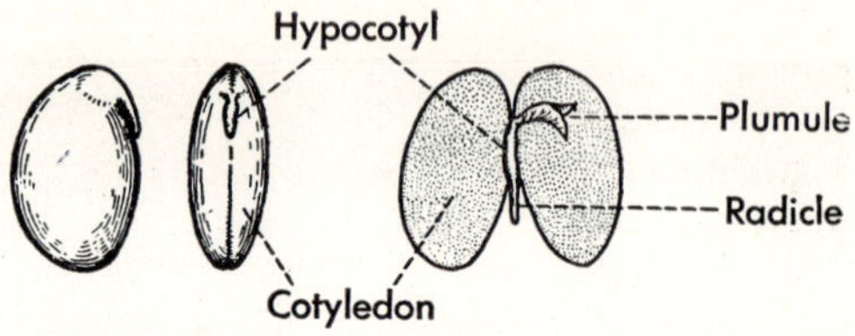

a. Corn seed, typical of the seed structure of Monocotyledons. (Adapted from G. M. Smith.)

b. Bean seed, typical of the seed structure of many Dicotyledons.

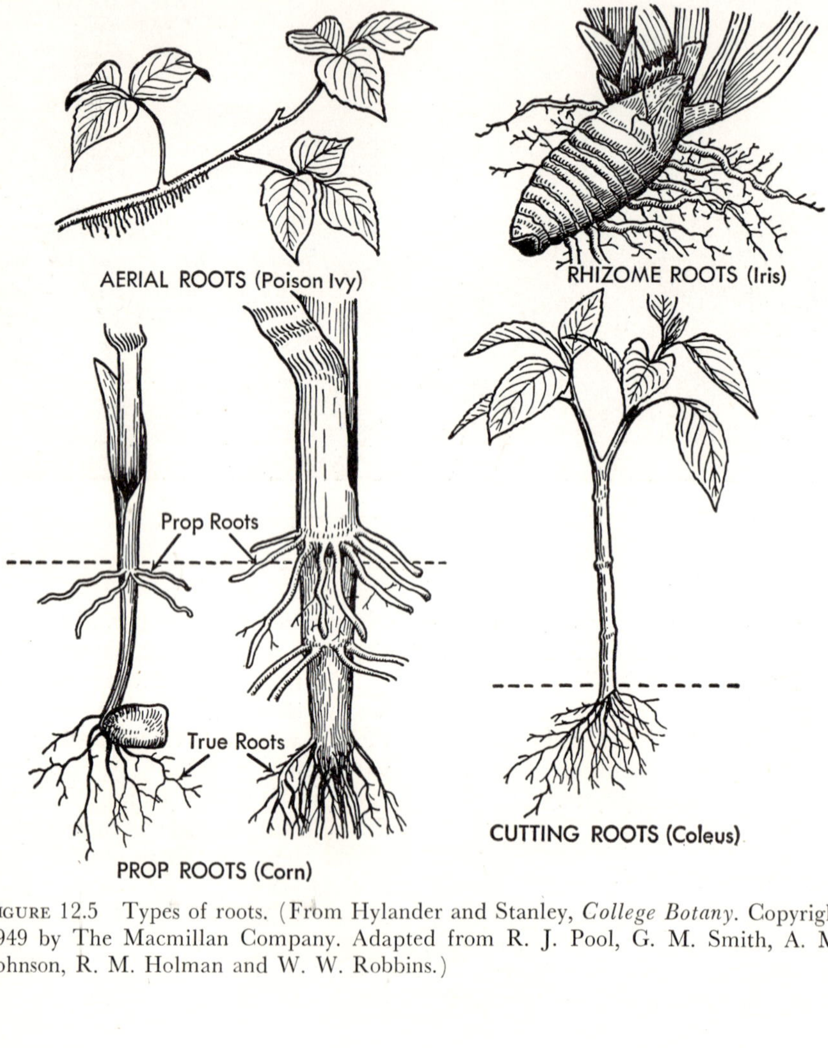

FIGURE 12.5 Types of roots. (From Hylander and Stanley, *College Botany*. Copyright 1949 by The Macmillan Company. Adapted from R. J. Pool, G. M. Smith, A. M. Johnson, R. M. Holman and W. W. Robbins.)

rain as it falls, rather than from that which has penetrated the soil, have aerial roots, exposed to the upper atmosphere instead of that in the soil. In the ferns, and among the spermatophytes, in some grasses, in sorrel, goldenrod and Solomon's Seal for example, the root dies early in the life of the developing plant and the main stem grows underground as a rootstalk or rhizome developing rootlets or rhizoids along its length. Since rootlets do not ordinarily arise from stems, those growing from one that is underground are called adventitious, or ones that appear out of their accustomed places. Adventitious roots may arise from various parts of a plant; such are the prop roots that regularly grow from the base of the stem in corn and other cereals and penetrate into the ground; the aerial climbing roots of vines like ivy, poison ivy and the climbing hydrangea that also develop along the stem and, penetrating into the cracks and crevices of a support or clinging to its surface, hold up the main body of the plant; the roots that arise in the notches of the leaves of the stonecrop Bryophyllum; and those that develop from the basal ends of cut stems of plants like carnations, roses and willows when they are put into water or moist soil. Some few plants, like Tillandsia, the "Spanish moss" that is actually a spermatophyte belonging to the pineapple family, have neither roots nor rhizomes and live an epiphytic existence absorbing what water and minerals they need through the general surface of their bodies.

**Growth and differentiation of root tissues**

But the majority of spermatophytes have roots or root systems that penetrate into the ground; typically the primary root develops from the radicle, a differentiated region of the embryo contained within the seed (Fig. 12.4). As the young spermatophyte root breaks through the seed coats and grows into the soil, four histologically different areas are evident in it. These are, from the tip inward, the root cap, the zone of multiplication, the zone of enlargement and the zone of maturation (Fig. 12.6). The root cap is one of the distinguishing features of roots; it develops in all of them whether growing in soil, water or air, and in no other part of the plant. It is composed of sclerenchyma cells with thickened walls and empty centers which form a protective sheath and provide mechanical support for the soft tissues of the root tip. In plants rooted in soil the outer cells of the root cap are worn away, as the root tip grows, and pushes among the particles of earth; the inner cells undergo progressive disintegration and decay and the slimy mass that results facilitates the movement of the root through the soil at least by reducing frictional resistance to it. But a root cap always remains, for the sloughed off and disintegrated cells are replaced by new ones from the embryonic cells beneath them.

Within the root cap the cylindrical tip of the young root is made up of meristem whose cells are in active division, continually adding to the number of units in the growing root. The cells at the inner, or distal, margin of this zone of division gradually become converted from small, isodiametric ones with comparatively nonvacuolate protoplasts and thin walls to larger ones with many vacuoles and slightly thicker walls. In the zone of elongation, more and more vacuoles appear in the cytoplasm as the water content of the cells increases; these vacuoles gradually run together to form the large central vacuole, pushing the protoplast back against the walls which elongate in a plane parallel to the long axis of the root, so that the cell is no longer isodiametric but several times longer than it is wide or thick. These two zones, whose combined length is only 1–10 mm., are the only regions actively concerned in the linear growth of roots of any age or size. Such linear growth is therefore the consequence of two factors, the increase in number of cells by the multiplication of those in the meristem at the extreme tip of the root and the elongation of those immediately proximal to them.

With continued growth the first cells to complete their enlargement begin to mature into the permanent primary tissues of the root. The cells in the course of such differentiation make up the zone of maturation and give rise to the mature tissues that constitute the full-grown root; these matured cells are constantly, or periodically, increased during the life of the plant by the addition of new ones from the zone of maturation. The peripheral cells in this zone follow a different course in their differentiation than do those in its center or the intermediate area so that, in the primary tissues and later youngest of these cells tubular protoplasmic processes, the root hairs, push out, their length often exceeding the diameter of the young root (Fig. 7.7). The protoplast of the cell extends into the root hair and frequently its nucleus moves into it as well.

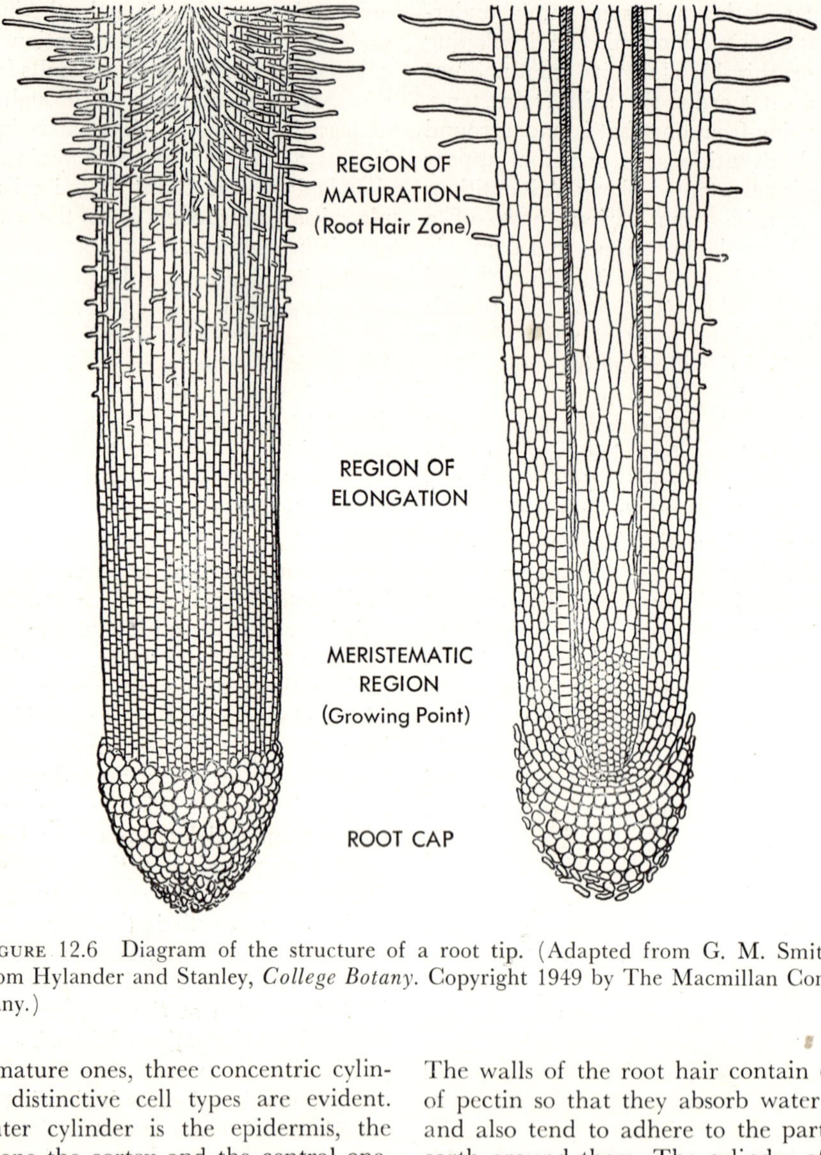

FIGURE 12.6 Diagram of the structure of a root tip. (Adapted from G. M. Smith, from Hylander and Stanley, *College Botany*. Copyright 1949 by The Macmillan Company.)

in the mature ones, three concentric cylinders of distinctive cell types are evident. The outer cylinder is the epidermis, the middle one the cortex and the central one, the stele (Fig. 12.7).

In the zone of maturation the epidermis is but one cell in thickness and its cells have comparatively thin walls which are freely permeable to water and its solutes. From the walls of the root hair contain deposits of pectin so that they absorb water readily and also tend to adhere to the particles of earth around them. The cylinder of cortex is made up of parenchyma belonging to the fundamental system; its cells are relatively widely spaced, there are many air pockets between them, and frequently they contain deposits of starch or other storage reserves.

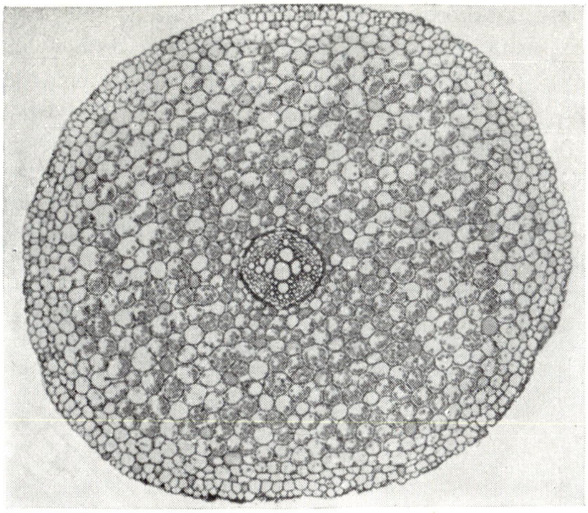

FIGURE 12.7 Tissues in the root of the buttercup (Ranunculus). (Photographs by courtesy of Dr. Norman Boke.)

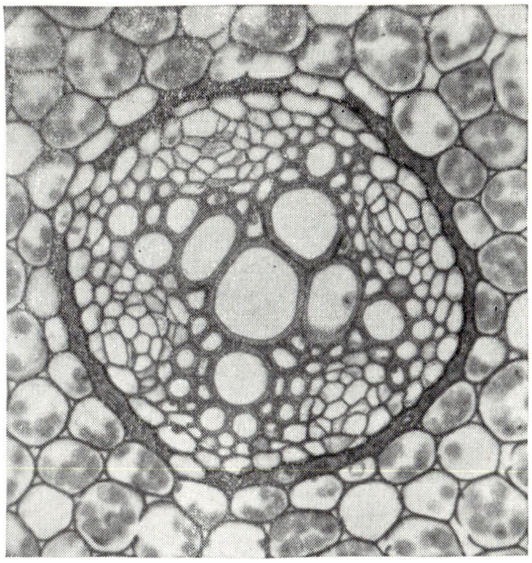

    a. Cross section of the entire root, showing epidermis, cortex and central stele.
    b. Stele under higher magnification, showing the endodermis (dark cells), the pericycle, phloem and xylem vessels.

The stele is enclosed by a cylinder of sclerenchyma, one cell in thickness, known as the endodermis, which clearly delimits it from the surrounding parenchyma. Within this is the pericycle, a cylinder of parenchyma one or two cells in thickness. Even in mature regions of a root the cells of the pericycle retain the capacity to divide and it is from them that the secondary or branch roots may arise and grow out laterally through the endodermis, cortex and epidermis (Fig. 12.8). The more central cells of the stele differentiate as xylem or phloem vessels and other tissues of the fibro-vascular system. While the cells in the roots of all vascular plants mature into conducting elements that are similar in type, there are variations in the spatial relations of these elements to each other and in their distribution within the central cylinder that are characteristic of different groups of plants. In some plants, particularly the dicotyledonous angiosperms, all the cells in the center of the stele mature as xylem elements but in the majority of spermatophytes the innermost cells develop into pith cells. Living pith cells are large parenchymatous ones which, like those of the cortical parenchyma,

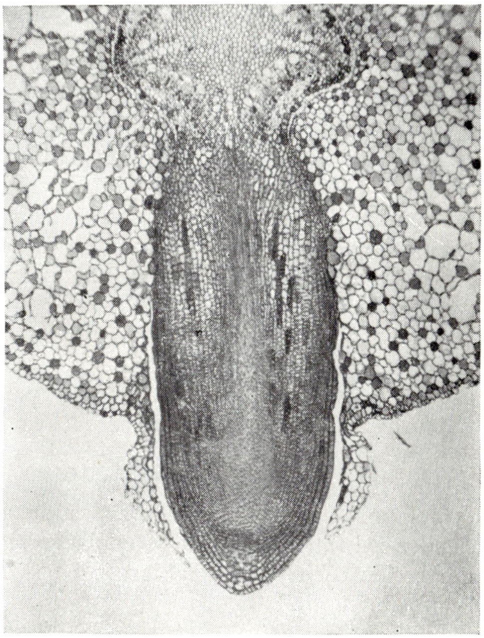

FIGURE 12.8 Branch root of a willow (Salix). (Photograph by courtesy of Dr. Norman Boke.)

are loosely assembled and often filled with storage granules (Fig. 12.9).

Just within the pericycle the cells differentiate as phloem elements. At certain points around the periphery of the stele each of the cells in a vertical row elongates markedly;

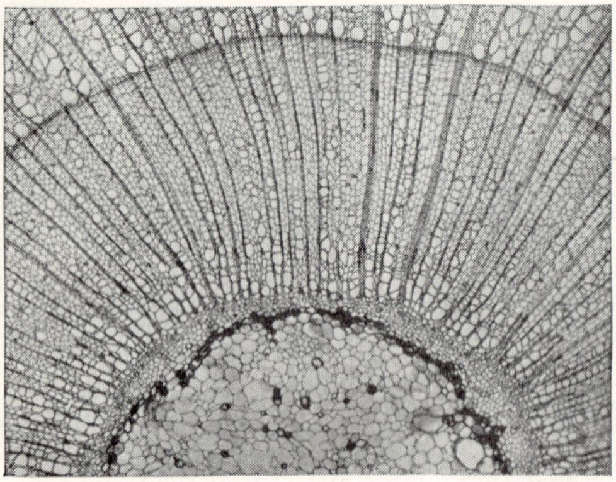

FIGURE 12.9 Cross section through the stem of a linden (Tilia), showing pith and xylem, tissues which are similar in stems and roots. (Photograph by courtesy of Dr. Norman Boke.)

its nucleus disintegrates but a layer of rather dense protoplasm remains closely applied to its walls. These walls are but slightly thickened and the terminal ones, between contiguous cells, become perforated with many small pores through which the protoplasm of adjacent cells often extends (Fig. 12.10).*  These cells form the sieve tubes, their porous terminal walls, the sieve plates across which comparatively coarse materials may quite readily pass. In the dicotyledons, the lateral walls of the sieve tubes in some cases also become perforated, so that substances may diffuse laterally across them. The cells around the sieve tubes are for the most part parenchyma, called phloem parenchyma, and are isodiametric cells with nuclei and often with many storage granules in their cytoplasm. In the dicotyledons, a long, slender cell with a complete protoplast often lies beside each unit of a sieve tube as a "companion cell."

In the more central part of the stele the cells mature into xylem elements which include the xylem parenchyma, xylem fibres,

* Cells like these are found in the blade of Laminaria and some of the other kelps.

conducting cells called tracheids and conducting vessels called tracheae. The xylem parenchyma is made up of parenchymatous cells whose walls are slightly thicker than those of the parenchyma elsewhere; the xylem fibres are long, slender cells with

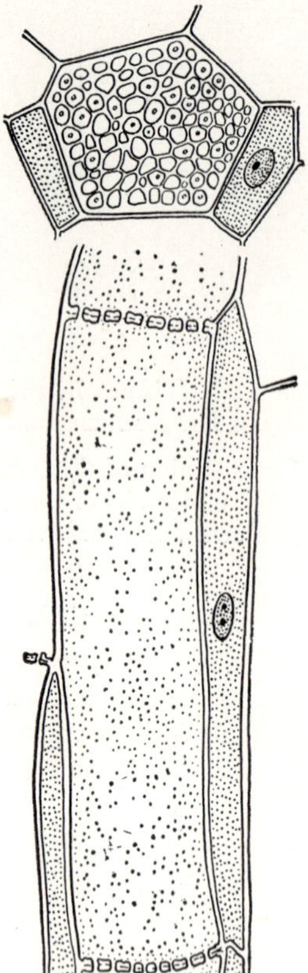

FIGURE 12.10 Sieve tubes and companion cells. (From Hylander and Stanley, *College Botany*. Copyright 1949 by The Macmillan Company.) The lower figure shows one complete cell of a sieve tube and parts of two adjacent cells separated from the complete cell by sieve plates; the sieve tube is flanked by companion cells. The upper figure represents a cross section through the sieve plate region.

lignified walls. In some plants, the cells in the core of the stele mature into pith, in others into xylem parenchyma. Like the formation of the sieve tubes, that of the tracheids and tracheae involves the enlargement and elongation of a series of cells in a vertical row but also local thickenings of

THE VASCULAR PLANTS [177]

their walls by the addition of more cellulose and the deposition of lignin in it. The thickening may take place generally over the surface of the cell, except for scattered and often numerous thin spots that become bordered pits, or in a spiral band, or in separate rings or half-rings around it (Fig. 12.11). In a fully matured cell the protoplast and thinner parts of the wall disintegrate and only the lignified parts remain. Each tracheid is an individual cell, long and slender, with walls thickened in this way; the tapering ends of successive tracheids overlap so that there is some degree of continuity between them. A trachea, or xylem vessel, is made up of a number of large, cylindrical cells whose lateral walls are similarly thickened but whose terminal walls disintegrate so that a continuous tube is formed, which according to the way the walls are lignified, is designated as a pitted, spiral, annular (Latin, anulus = ring) or scalariform (Latin, scala = ladder) vessel.

The first phloem and xylem elements to be matured become the primary vascular tissues of the root, whose formation continues throughout the life of the plant. In the ferns and monocotyledonous angiosperms, only primary tissues are produced, but in the gymnosperms and dicotyledonous angiosperms, the primary tissues are supplemented by secondary ones of different origin. In the majority of spermatophytes, the primary xylem lies along certain radii only, so that it is more or less in the shape of a star whose points are in contact with the surrounding pericycle, and the primary phloem lies between the xylem rays, separated from them by parenchyma (Fig. 12.12).

Secondary growth is brought about by the activity of certain cells in the root which do not undergo differentiation but remain per-

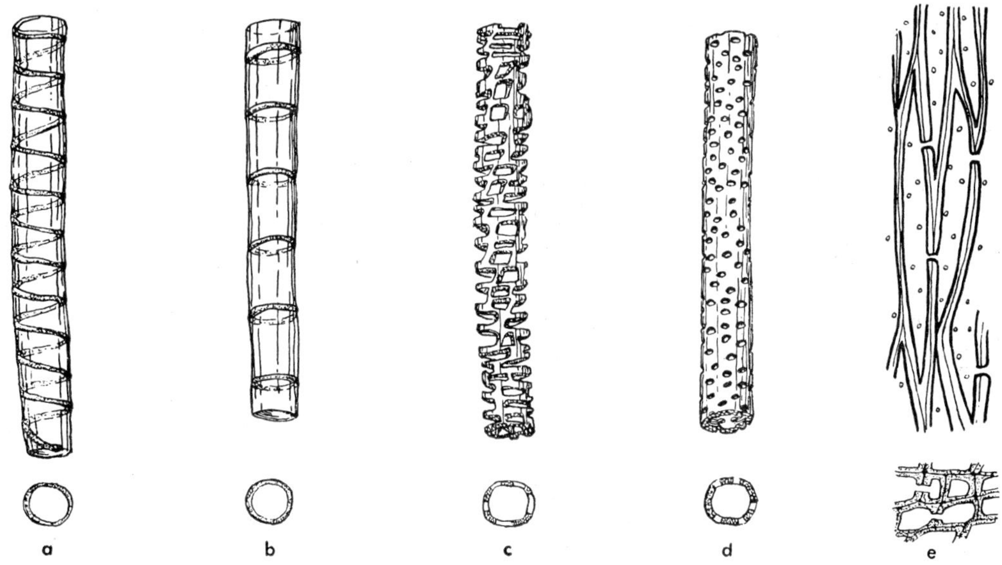

FIGURE 12.11 Types of xylem elements, essentially alike in stems and roots. (After F. Brown, in Hill, Overholts and Popp.)

  a. Segment of a spiral vessel from the stem of a balsam.
  b. Segment of a ringed vessel from the stem of a balsam.
  c. Segment of a scalariform vessel from the stem of a sunflower.
  d. Segment of a pitted vessel from the stem of an alder.
  e. Wood fibres from the stem of an ash.

The drawings at the bottom of the figure represent cross sections of the vessels and fibres.

manently embryonic and capable of division. Such cells constitute the cambium (Latin, cambium = change). The first such cells to become active in the maturing tissues lie between the patches of phloem (Fig. 12.12). As they divide, their descendants on the central side differentiate into new xylem and those on the peripheral side into new phloem. The production of secondary xylem takes place more rapidly than does that of secondary phloem with the result that the new xylem, formed in the region between the rays of primary xylem, not only converts its radial arrangement into a cylindrical one but also pushes the phloem outward so that it comes to lie on the outer circumference of the cylinder of xylem, separated from it by a cylinder of cambium usually only one cell in thickness. With the development of new sieve tubes and phloem parenchyma, the isolated patches of primary phloem are joined together so that the cylinder of xylem is surrounded by a cylinder of phloem. In many plants, however, strands of sclerenchyma cells extend between the groups of conducting cells, forming wood rays that may extend from the center of the xylem to its periphery only or as far as the pericycle, thus marking off sectors of both xylem and phloem and providing a possible pathway for the lateral diffusion of substances. Each sector of xylem and phloem is a fibro-vascular bundle; the cambium within each bundle is known as fascicular cambium (Latin, fasciculus = little bundle) and that between the bundles as interfascicular cambium. The activity of the cambium results in the formation of new xylem, new phloem and new sclerenchyma within the rays so that the diameter of the root increases in its mature regions at the same time that its length is increasing by the addition of cells from the meristem at its tip. Fibro-vascular bundles of this type are said to be "open bundles" in that they are capable of indefinite enlargement, and the roots containing them of indefinite growth; the isolated bundles of the monocotyledons, which when mature contain only xylem and phloem but no meristem, are said to be "closed bundles" since they are not open to indefinite growth. Roots with closed bundles do not increase in diameter after their cells have attained their full degree of enlargement.

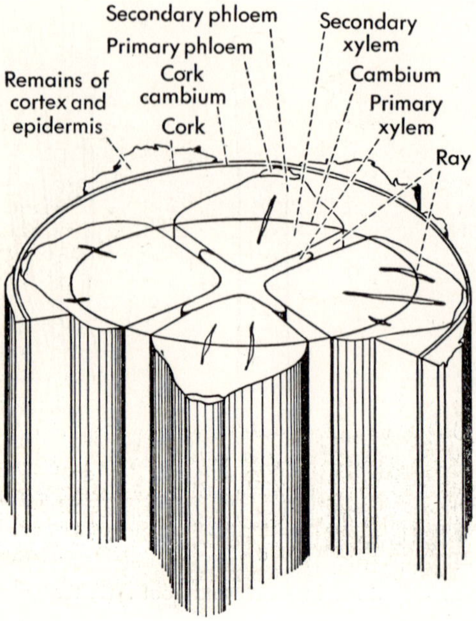

FIGURE 12.12 Tridimensional diagram of a portion of a root, showing the distribution of primary and secondary tissues. (From Smith, Gilbert, Evans, Duggar, Bryan and Allen, *A Textbook of General Botany*. Copyright 1942 by The Macmillan Company.)

The conducting tissues of the secondary xylem and phloem are similar to those of the primary, but the cells of the xylem parenchyma usually have thicker walls and in the phloem, mechanical tissue may develop, at least in the older part of the root, in the form of elongated sclerenchyma cells called bast fibres. But in many roots, even with such support, the successive masses of secondary tissues compress or crush the previously formed phloem so that the sieve tubes in it that are actually conductile are only those of more recent growth.

In many of the spermatophytes capable of secondary growth a second ring of meristem originates in the pericycle. This is known as the cork cambium because the new cells derived from it mature into large, compactly arranged ones whose walls contain deposits of a substance called suberin (Latin, suber = cork tree), a mixture of

THE VASCULAR PLANTS

waxes of different kinds. This tissue therefore becomes impervious to water and forms a water-resistant sheath between the stele and the cortex. Where such a sheath is present, the tissues enclosed within it are cut off from any soil solution that may diffuse through the epidermal and cortical cells, and those outside it from any fluid in the xylem and phloem vessels that may diffuse laterally. Entrance of water into the root as a whole is thus virtually limited to the zone of maturation where the root hairs increase the surface area for effective absorption from 5 to 18 times, and where the primary xylem is in contact with living cells not far removed from the epidermis. The development of root hairs is checked in regions where cork is laid down and there, too, the cortex and epidermis, cut off from essential supplies, die and disintegrate and in old roots may be replaced entirely by the periderm, a secondary tissue that includes the cork cells, the cork parenchyma and a layer, one or two cells in thickness, of parenchyma also derived from the cork cambium.

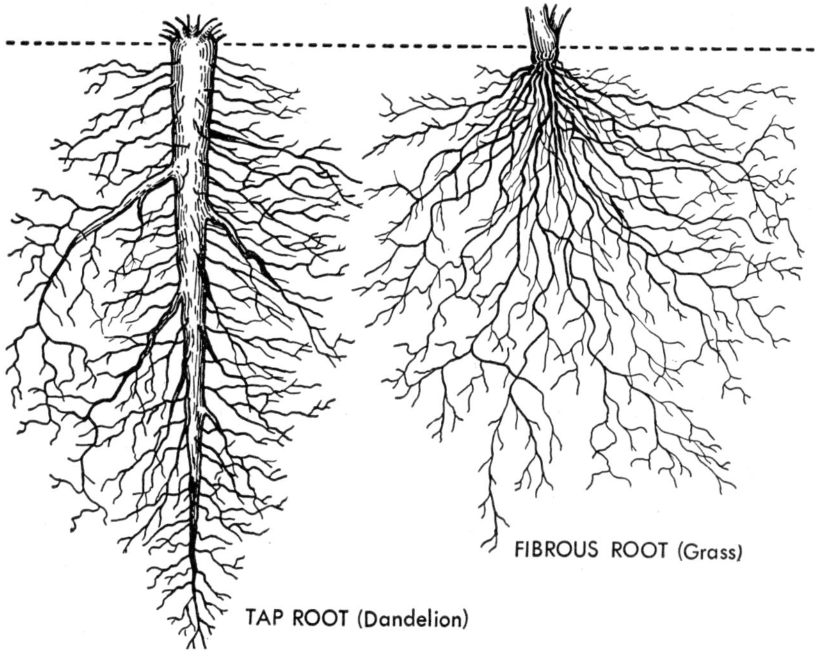

### Modifications in roots

The first, or primary, root of a terrestrial plant grows and matures in this way and from it the entire root system of the plant develops, except for whatever adventitious

FIGURE 12.13 Taproots and fibrous roots. (Adapted from E. W. Sinnott, from Hylander and Stanley, *College Botany*. Copyright 1949 by The Macmillan Company.)

roots may arise. The roots of different species vary in their growth habits as well as in their finer histological details, and any specific growth pattern may be modified by environmental conditions, such as the texture of the soil, its temperature and the moisture or nutrients that it offers. Root systems may be classified as tap, fibrous or fleshy (Fig. 12.13). In a taproot system one root, usually the primary one, remains largest and longest and becomes an axis for the secondary or branch roots; such a root system is never found in monocotyledons but is characteristic of plants like dandelions and beans, oaks, hickories and pines, although in the pines the primary root dies early in the life of the seedling plant and a secondary root becomes the taproot. A fibrous root system is made up of many small roots of nearly equal size, for secondary roots arise from the primary one which in their turn give rise to branch roots, and these to other branch roots; such a root system is characteristic particularly of grasses. Fleshy roots are modified taproots that contain much storage tissue and usually much stored material; carrots, beets and turnips are all examples of fleshy roots. Localized parts of a fibrous root system may also become fleshy, forming "tubers" (Latin, tuber = swelling) like those on the roots of dahlias and sweet potatoes. Histologically, a root may contain much storage tissue, or little, and much mechanical tissue, or little of it. For example, in the beet, successive cylinders of meristem develop outside the original cambium ring which give rise to xylem, phloem and broad bands of parenchyma in which the cells become filled with carbohydrate, much of it in the form of the trisaccharide raffinose. Or much mechanical tissue may develop in the xylem of the root with relatively little parenchyma for storage, as is the case in the long taproot of the pine which, by secondary growth, may attain a diameter as great as that of the trunk and, except for its position, be scarcely distinguishable from it. The roots of aquatic plants usually contain many air spaces which distort the typical pattern of the tissues and in which oxygen and carbon dioxide may be held and so made available to the submerged parts of the plant. The roots of some tropical plants that grow by the water's edge are flat, rather than cylindrical, and contain chlorenchyma so that superficially they resemble foliage leaves and, like them, may carry on photosynthesis. In aerial roots, like those of epiphytic orchids, there may also be chlorenchyma in which the major part of the total photosynthesis of the plant is carried on; such roots also develop an external layer called the velamen, composed of cork cells that soak up and retain moisture, and of air-filled tracheids along whose walls water vapor condenses and, as liquid, moves along them.

Specialized adventitious roots called haustoria (Latin, haurire = to drink) develop along the stems of parasitic plants like mistletoe and dodder, wherever the stems come in contact with the plant on which the parasite is growing (Fig. 12.14). These roots penetrate, like the mycelium of a mold, into the tissues of the host plant and absorb water and nutrients from them. Mistletoe is a photosynthesizing plant and so not wholly dependent upon its host for sustenance but dodder, with a body that is almost thread-like in its dimensions, is one of the few spermatophytes that never develop chlorenchyma; its haustoria penetrate into the vascular tissues of the host and drain the nutrient solutions from them.

FIGURE 12.14 Dodder entwined around the stem of goldenrod: l, scale-like leaves; r, haustoria. (From Bergen and Davis, from Woodruff, *Foundations of Biology*, 6th edition. Copyright 1941 by The Macmillan Company.)

a. Cross section of the stem of the host, showing the penetration of its tissues by the haustoria of the dodder.

b. Several seedlings of the dodder growing in the soil before attachment to the host.

## Stems

But in most plants the mature tissues of the root system are similar in type and in arrangement to those of the stem with which they are continuous. Indeed, it is often impossible to distinguish histologically between a mature stem and a mature root unless the primary xylem of the root is evident, or the section happens to pass through some structure peculiar to the stem, such as one of the small openings in the epidermis called stomata or the larger ones called lenticels. Stems arise from buds; along their length are regions of meristem often evident externally as small elevations that are called nodes, the length of stem between two nodes constituting an internode; and they serve as the axis that supports the leaves, bringing the foliage leaves into a favorable position in respect to light and the sporophylls into one that favors the transmission of their reproductive cells and the dissemination of their seeds (Fig. 12.15). Stems are, in addition, the regions from which new shoots are produced, increasing the area of the plant above the ground, and also those through which the soil solution is transferred from the roots to the leaves and the organic compounds synthesized in the leaves transferred from them to other parts of the plant and in particular to the storage areas. Young stems and some mature ones contain chlorenchyma and so act as photosynthesizing regions, and they may also be storage areas of considerable importance to the plant.

Buds are undeveloped shoots, consisting either of a mass of meristem alone or of an embryonic structure in which the primordia of the new parts are already established. There is almost always an apical bud at the tip of a stem and other buds at the nodes along its length. In spermatophytes, the main stem originates from the plumule, the primary bud at the apex of the embryo within the seed (Fig. 12.4). The growing regions of stems, like those of roots, show zones of multiplication, elongation and maturation, but in stems the zone of elongation particularly, with an average length of 2–10 cm., is much longer than it is in roots, and often includes several nodes and internodes. The linear growth of stems is brought about by the addition of new cells from the meristem of the apical bud and, for a time at least, from that at the nodes, and by the elongation of these new cells. The rapid lengthening of some stems, like those of grasses, for example, that seem to shoot up, is the consequence of cell elongation rather than of cell multiplication. But all during the life of a plant additions may be made to a stem

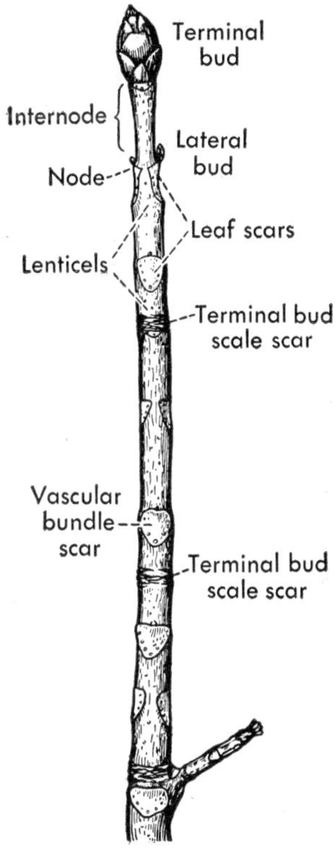

FIGURE 12.15 Stem of a horse chestnut, showing external characters typical of stems. (From Hylander and Stanley, *College Botany*. Copyright 1949 by The Macmillan Company.)

from its apical meristem that is moved further and further away from the base as the stem lengthens, as well as by the growth of lateral branches originating at the nodes.

## Growth and differentiation of stem tissues

In a growing stem the first tissue to be differentiated is sclerenchyma; the cells that give rise to this lie just beneath the epidermis and as a result of their maturation a cylinder of mechanical tissue, several cells in thickness, is developed around the softer central cells, giving some support and rigidity to the lengthening stem. The epidermis consists of a single row of flattened cells which may contain chloroplasts and which have walls that are thickened by deposits of cutin, like suberin, a mixture of waxes, that retards or prevents the passage of water. At intervals the epidermis is interrupted by small openings, the stomata (Greek, stoma = mouth), between two modified epithelial cells called guard cells, through which there may be free diffusion of atmospheric gases and water vapor (Fig. 12.30). The central part of the stem consists of parenchyma in which columns of cells destined to become the fibro-vascular bundles are variously distributed as provascular strands.

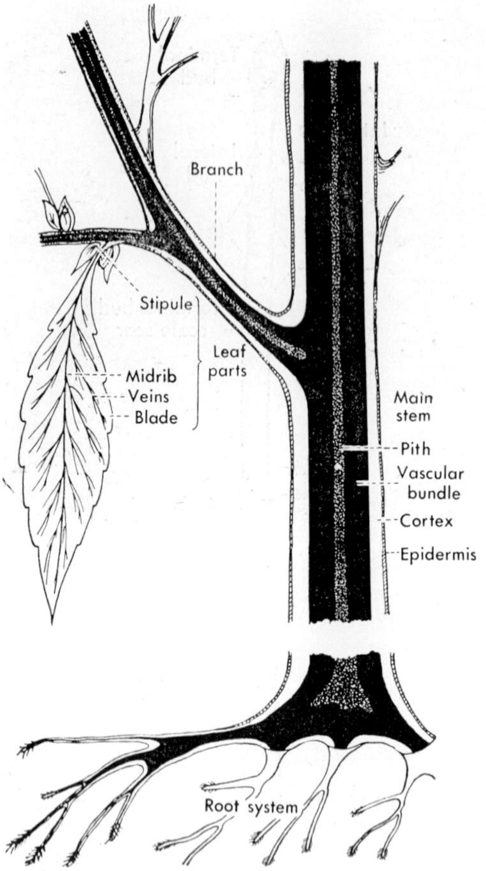

In the pteridophytes and the monocotyledonous angiosperms the peripheral cells of each provascular strand mature as sclerenchyma; the walls of the sclerenchyma cells on the outside and the inside of each bundle are slightly thicker than they are elsewhere. All the other cells of the bundle mature as xylem or phloem vessels or their surrounding tissues and, since there is no cambium, no secondary tissues are formed. In such closed bundles the xylem and the phloem may lie approximately parallel to each other in a collateral arrangement or they may be concentrically arranged, and the bundles may occupy various positions within the stem. In corn, for example, the phloem is formed by the cells in the outer half of the provascular strand and the xylem by those in the inner half so that in the mature bundle the phloem lies nearer the epidermis and the xylem nearer the center of the stem; these collateral bundles are scattered all through the parenchyma. In some ferns, phloem is formed on both the inner and the outer faces of the provascular strand, giving rise to a bicollateral bundle; in others phloem is formed all around the periphery of the strand and xylem only by the interior cells, resulting in a concentric bundle with phloem on the outside and xylem on the inside; the bundles are grouped in a ring around a central core of parenchyma. In the sweet flag, the xylem forms the outer ring of the concentric bundle and the phloem the interior; the bundles are clustered in the center of the underground stem. Whatever their arrangement, the bundles extend as vascular cylinders throughout each internode, at the nodes connecting indirectly and sometimes directly with those of the adjacent internodes (Fig. 12.16). At the nodes also are lateral extensions of the bundles, or leaf traces, where connections are made between the vascular tissues of the stem and those of the leaves; sometimes too there are cross connections there, or anastomoses, between the separate parallel bundles. In many such stems certain cells, in addition to those of the outer sclerenchyma ring, mature as sclerenchyma so that patches of mechanical tissue of various shapes and sizes are interspersed among the parenchyma cells.

FIGURE 12.16 Diagram showing the continuity of the fibro-vascular bundles in the roots, stems and leaves of a plant. (After Coulter.)

***The distribution of fibro-vascular bundles:*** In the gymnosperms and dicotyledonous angiosperms the provascular strands lie in a circle around the central cells of the stem that may mature either into pith or into xylem. The primary tissues of the stem are thus concentric in their arrangement and never radial as they are in the root. In between the phloem elements of different plants nor between those that are matured at different times in a growing season. There are, however, such differences in the xylem elements; in pines, for example, and many other gymnosperms, the only conducting

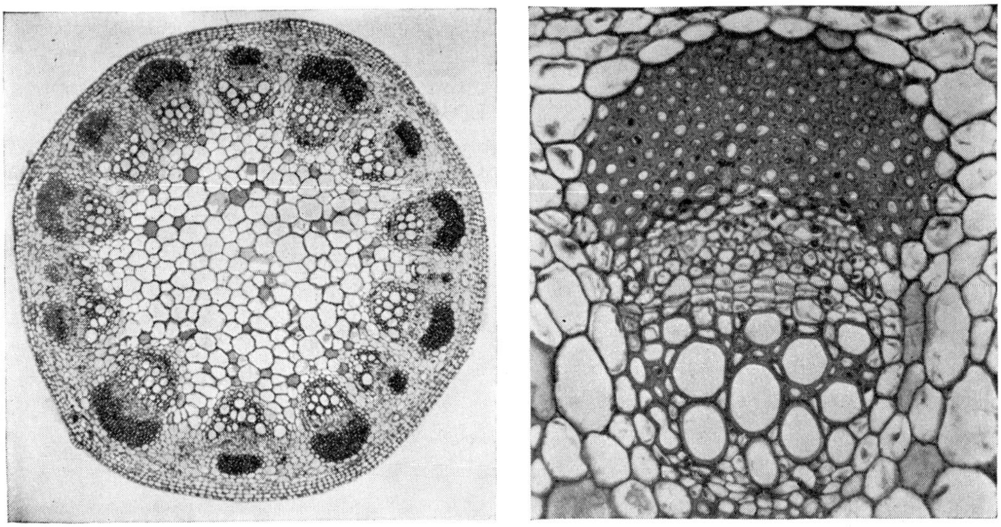

FIGURE 12.17  Stems with open fibro-vascular bundles. (Photographs by courtesy of Dr. Norman Boke.)

    a. Cross section of the stem of a sunflower, showing distribution of bundles.

    b. A single bundle at higher magnification, showing, from the bottom of the photograph upwards, primary xylem, secondary xylem, cambium, primary phloem and sclerenchyma.

only one genus of modern plants, the pteridophyte Lycopodium, are the vascular tissues of the stem developed along certain radii only and such an arrangement is regarded as a primitive one, succeeded in spermatophytes by a concentric one. In them, the differentiation of the primary xylem and phloem proceeds as it does in the root, with the phloem on the outer face of the bundle and the xylem on the inner. Secondary tissues are laid down through the activity of the cambium ring; on the peripheral side of the fascicular cambium new phloem elements are formed, during the period of growth, as they are in the root and on its central side, new xylem. Fewer cells are matured as phloem than as xylem so that there is always more xylem in a stem than phloem. There are no apparent differences vessels of the xylem are tracheids, while in angiosperms there may be both tracheids and tracheae. But in long-lived angiosperms with successive seasons of growth, tracheae predominate in the xylem that is matured in the spring, when conditions for growth are most favorable, while more tracheids are formed in the summer. Spring wood is less compact than summer wood, for it contains relatively more vessels and its cells are in general larger, and in plants that go through successive seasons of growth, spring and summer woods are macroscopically distinguishable from each other. Division of the interfascicular cambium cells leads to the formation of the wood rays, slender bands, like ribbons, of lignified cells that extend between the fibro-vascular bundles and provide a pathway for the diffusion of materials across the stem. In many stems pith cells occupy the center of the stele and may extend out between the fibro-vascular bundles as pith rays, distinct from the wood rays. In some such stems the pith acts as a storage area but in many, and especially in older stems, the protoplasts of the pith cells die and only the hollow empty cell walls remain (Fig. 12.17).

The pericycle in stems with open bundles is a thin cylinder of parenchyma alone or of parenchyma and groups of sclerenchyma fibers. These fibers may have walls that are mainly of cellulose, as they are in flax, or of cellulose with relatively large amounts of lignin, as they are in hemp; these fibers are used respectively in linen thread and in rope (Fig. 12.11e). Some of the cells of the pericycle remain capable of division as they do in the root, for from them adventitious roots may arise. A cylinder of endodermis, like that in roots and in the stems of most pteridophytes, is not often defined in spermatophyte stems. In those where it is present, like nasturtiums for example, its cells may contain starch and their walls may be distinctly thickened. In some plants only the radial and inner walls are markedly thickened by deposits of suberin and sometimes of lignin; in others, lignin is deposited along only one margin of the cell in a strip called a Casparian strip; the Casparian strips of adjacent cells make a band extending around the endodermis. The cortex of a stem often contains cells of several types. In young stems particularly, the outer layers may be of chlorenchyma and collenchyma and the inner layers of parenchyma interspersed with stone cells or sclerenchyma fibers. The secondary tissues of older stems also include a cork cambium which gives rise, as it does in the roots, to cells whose

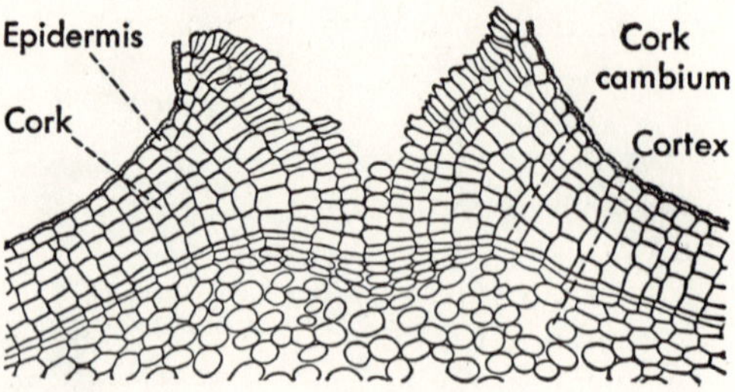

FIGURE 12.18 Lenticels.

a. The trunk of a cherry tree (Prunus avium), showing the bark with horizontal lenticels. (Photograph by courtesy of the Brooklyn Botanic Garden, Brooklyn, N. Y.)

b. Diagram of the structure of a lenticel in forsythia. (From Smith, Gilbert, Evans, Duggar, Bryan and Allen, *A Textbook of General Botany*. Copyright 1942 by The Macmillan Company.)

walls contain deposits of suberin and also to the lenticels, structures that are peculiar to stems. Although in some few plants, like currants for example, the cork cambium of the stem arises in the pericycle as it does in the roots, in the majority of plants it originates in the outer layers of the cortex, but in the members of the apple family it arises from the epidermis. In most plants the cylinder of cork is a thin one, but in some it may be an inch or more in thickness, reaching a maximum thickness in the cork oak of the Mediterranean, Quercus suber, which is the source of most commercial cork. It was such cells that Robert Hooke saw in the thin slices that he made and looked at through his microscope, actually only the skeletons around the living protoplast which, together with the wall, is, in modern usage, meant by the word "cell."

**Lenticels:** After the development of the cork the epidermis ceases to be a functional part of the stem since it is cut off from the tissues that it encloses, and some of the cells of the cork cambium, usually those lying beneath the stomata of the young epidermis, divide and give rise to a mass of loosely packed cells that push out through the epidermis, breaking it open (Fig. 12.18). These masses, like minute volcanic craters, are the lenticels through which atmospheric gases can diffuse in and out of the stem. Externally lenticels appear as round or oval elevations and sometimes make conspicuous external markings, as they do, for example, on the bark of birch and cherry trees.

**Cork:** The bark of a stem includes all the tissues peripheral to the cambium ring, that is, the phloem, pericycle, endodermis if it is present, and periderm. As the tissues central to the cork cylinder grow and enlarge, the rigid tissues of the outer layers of the bark crack open, giving it a rough and scaly appearance. The dead outer layers of the bark slough off and are replaced by new ones originating in the cork cambium. The cork cambium becomes especially active, too, when the stem is injured, for its cells are then stimulated to rapid division, providing a tissue called callus that grows over the wound; the continued formation of callus ultimately buries the cut or injured area far below the surface of the tissue covering it.

**Lactiferous and resin ducts:** Among the angiosperms there are some families of dicotyledons and some few monocotyledons

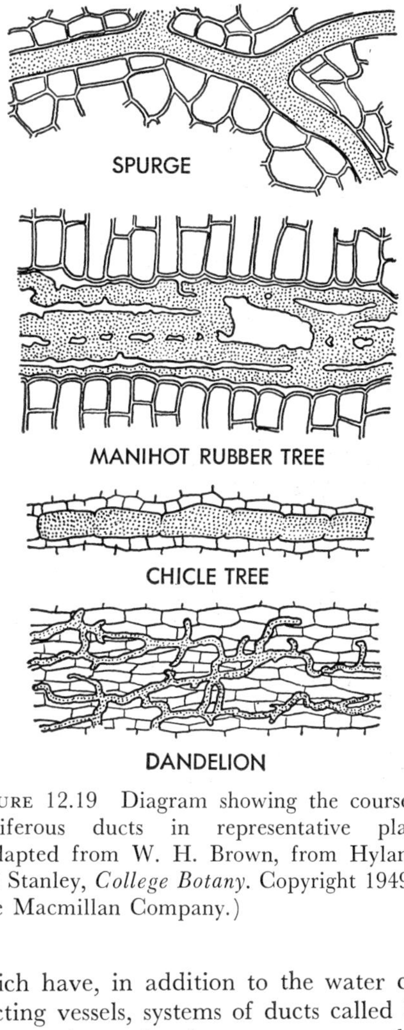

FIGURE 12.19 Diagram showing the course of lactiferous ducts in representative plants. (Adapted from W. H. Brown, from Hylander and Stanley, *College Botany*. Copyright 1949 by The Macmillan Company.)

which have, in addition to the water conducting vessels, systems of ducts called lactiferous ducts; in the gymnosperms there are comparable systems of resin ducts. The ducts, which are particularly abundant in the cortex and the pith, originate in vertical rows of meristem cells whose end walls disappear, but in which the protoplast remains alive and contains many nuclei. Such cells finally become an extensive, freely branching and anastomosing system of tubes which extend throughout the roots and stems and even into the leaves (Fig. 12.19). In the gymnosperms they are filled with resin, the general name for a group of substances about whose chemical composition but little is known; in such angiosperms as the pop-

of plants comparatively little lignin may be deposited in the walls of the xylem or in other mechanical tissues so that the stem remains permanently soft. The old distinction between trees, shrubs and herbs, which is still in popular use, was based on these

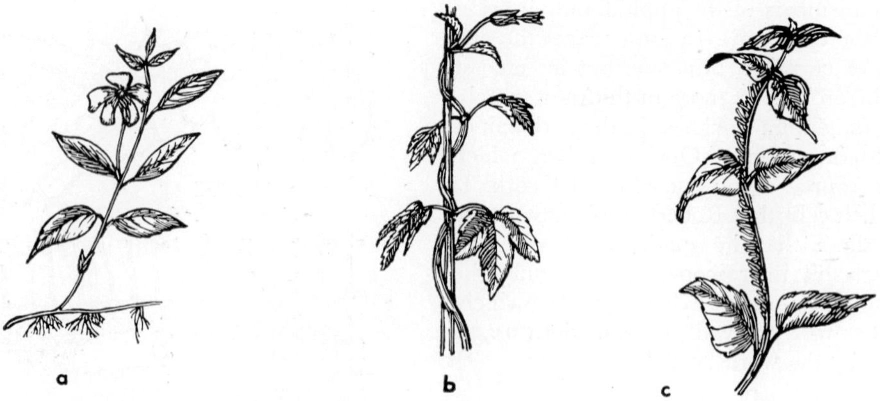

FIGURE 12.20  Devices for the support of prostrate stems.

  a. The creeping stem of the periwinkle, with roots at intervals that penetrate into the ground. (After Hylander.)
  b. The twining stem of the hop that grows in a clockwise direction around a pole. (After Poole.)
  c. Stem of the climbing hydrangea, with adventitious roots by which it attaches to a support. (After a drawing by E. M. McDougle, from Hill, Overholts and Popp.)

pies, lettuce, milkweed, bloodroot and the rubber tree particularly they are filled with latex, again a general name for an emulsion of proteins, gums, resins, oils, sugars and other organic compounds as well as some inorganic ones, viscous in its consistency and white, yellow, orange or red in color.

**Modifications in stems**

Stems vary widely in the extent and the habit of their growth, and the pattern of stem growth inherent in any plant may, like that of its root system, be profoundly influenced by environmental conditions. The stems of some plants tend to grow erect, often to considerable heights, with much wood within them so that they are capable of supporting many branches and an extensive foliage system; those of others are long and slender and, although they may be woody, unable to keep erect and so grow prostrate along the ground or become attached to some erect support. In other kinds

characters of the stem, trees being distinguished by their tall woody stems, shrubs by their shorter, freely branching ones and herbs by their soft ones with but little wood. Some plants with long, slender stems incapable of keeping erect, creep along the ground; ground pines, arbutus, periwinkle and strawberries are plants with such prostrate stems (Fig. 12.20). Others, like pole beans and morning glories, wind around some support; such plants are "twiners" and grow consistently either clockwise or counterclockwise. And others may attach themselves by means of special devices, adventitious roots or modified stems or leaves called tendrils, to upright supports; these, whether woody or herbaceous, are called vines.

In some plants certain parts of the stem are devoted principally to storage. This is the case especially in some underground stems or rhizomes where the growing end becomes greatly enlarged by the accumulation of excess or reserve materials that have been synthesized by the plant. These reserves are largely carbohydrate in the form of starch, and the regions of their accumulation may become tubers; this is the case in white potatoes and Jerusalem artichokes (Fig. 12.21). The part of a white potato a rhizome in which the leaves are fleshy and packed closely around the central axis.

Aerial stems are also modified in various ways as bulblets, tendrils and thorns; they may also be consistently reduced in their development so that the part of the plant

**ONION BULB**

**GINGER RHIZOME**

**WHITE POTATO TUBER**

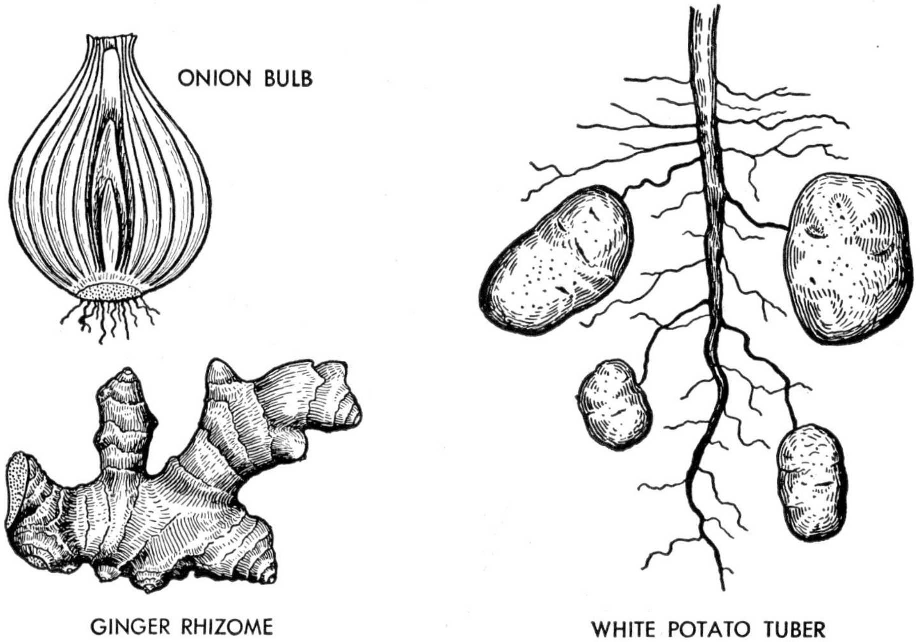

FIGURE 12.21 Rhizomes, tubers and bulbs. (Adapted from R. J. Pool and W. H. Brown, from Hylander and Stanley, *College Botany*. Copyright 1949 by The Macmillan Company.)

plant that is ordinarily eaten differs from that of a sweet potato plant both in its relation to the plant body as well as in the character of the materials within it, for a sweet potato is a root tuber and a white potato is a stem tuber. The "eyes" of a white potato are the nodes and its sprouting the development of the meristem in the buds located there.

Other modifications of rhizomes are the corms (Greek, kormos = tree trunk without boughs) and bulbs by which some plants are propagated (Fig. 12.21). The corm of a plant like the crocus or gladiolus is a very short, thick rhizome containing stored material and surrounded by the dead bases of leaves, the scales. The bulb of an onion, a hyacinth or a tulip is a single leaf bud from

above the ground is principally leaves, or they may themselves be broad and flat, resembling leaves both in shape and in chlorenchyma content. Small aerial bulbs, resembling the larger ones that develop from rhizomes, arise along the stems of tiger lilies and the flower stalks of onions and bear the same topographical relationship to the leaves as do the branch stems of all plants. The tendrils of grape vines and ampelopsis, the common Virginia creeper, are also modified branch stems which are slender and twining in their habit of growth and in the Virginia creeper provided with adhesive discs by which the vine is held to its support. The thorns of the honey locust and Osage orange are branch stems that have followed a different course in their modification; the

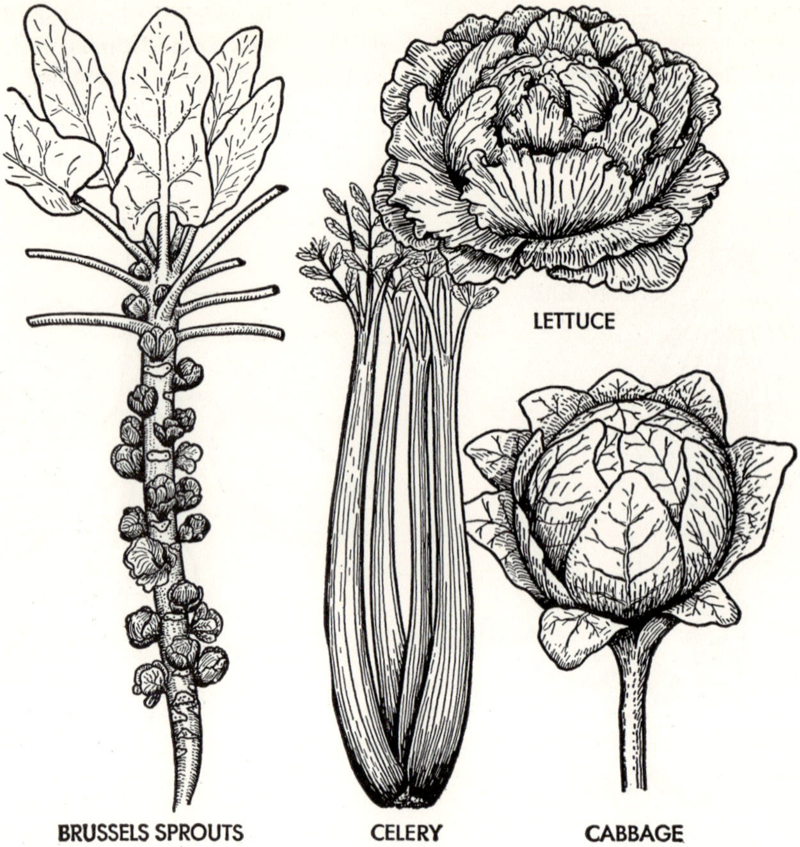

BRUSSELS SPROUTS   CELERY   CABBAGE
LETTUCE

a

GULFWEED   ASPARAGUS   PRICKLY PEAR CACTUS

- Flattened Stems
- Leaves reduced to small spines
- Leaves small and present only on young stems
- Fleshy Stem

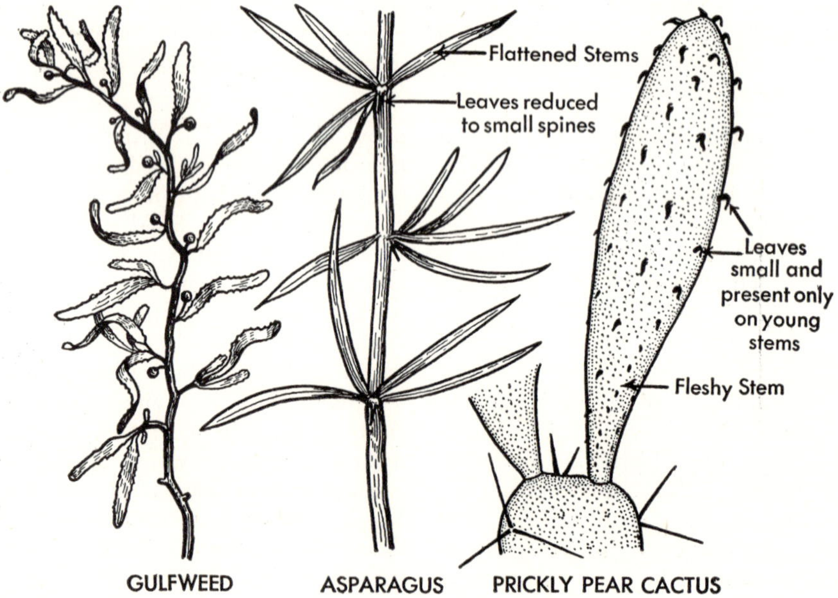

b

Figure 12.22

thorns of roses, on the other hand, are outgrowths from the cells of the epidermis. Lettuces and cabbages are common plants in which the stem is greatly reduced so that all the leaves form a cluster around it; in a plant like the dandelion, the stem is virtually absent and the leaves grow in a flat rosette. In some other plants, like asparagus and cactus, for example, the leaves are much reduced and the stem, known as a cladophyll (Greek, klados = sprout + phyllon = leaf) is the chief photosynthetic area (Fig. 12.22).

## Branches and leaves

In most plants secondary stems, or branches, arise from the primary stem and have their origin in buds that are situated at the nodes in close relationship to the position of the buds from which the leaves develop. The distribution of the leaf buds along the stem, or phyllotaxy (Greek, phyllon = leaf + taxis = arrangement) is an inherent and specific character of a plant and is one of the criteria used for the systematic classification of plants. The buds of the potential branches lie, as axillary buds, in the angle, called the axil, between the leaf bud and the primary stem so that the pattern of branching of any plant is also an expression of its phyllotaxy, but one that may be greatly modified by the failure of some shoots to develop, the loss of some that have developed or by inequalities of growth.

### Distribution of leaf buds; phyllotaxy

The leaf buds lie with mathematical precision at definite points on the nodes. In some plants there is but one bud at each node; such plants are said to show alternate phyllotaxy, for the leaves of adjacent nodes do not develop beneath each other but at different points around the circumference of the stem (Fig. 12.23). The simplest alternate arrangement is that of the elms, corn and many grasses, where each successive bud is opposite the one below it, so the third leaf is always above the first of any cycle of three, making two vertical rows of leaves along the stem, each row 180° away from the other. In beeches, the leaf buds are so arranged that each fourth leaf is over the first, making three vertical rows 120° apart. In the majority of plants with alternate leaf arrangement, the sixth leaf is over the first, so that there are five vertical rows along the stem, as is the condition in oaks and cherries, for example, but there are also cycles in which the 9th, 14th, 22nd, 35th or 56th leaf is over the first. In other plants, two leaves may arise at each node, as they do in maples and members of the mint family, and the phyllotaxy is said to be opposite, since the two buds are always 180° apart; the pair at any one node is usually at right angles to the pair above or below it. And in some plants three or more leaves originate from a single node in a whorled arrangement; the catalpa, some lilies and Elodea, the aquatic plant so commonly used in aquaria, are all plants with whorled phyllotaxy.

Other buds may also regularly arise on stems as accessory buds, like the flower buds on the sides of the axillary buds in forsythia and in peaches and plums (Fig. 12.24). Adventitious buds may also develop on leaves as they do in African violets and begonias; on the internodes of stems as they do on the cut stems of willow; and possibly even on roots, although the evidence of their origin here is not completely clear.

---

FIGURE 12.22 Modifications of leafy structures. (From Hylander and Stanley, *College Botany*. Copyright 1949 by The Macmillan Company.)

a. Edible leaves. The Brussels sprout, a member of the cabbage family (Brassica), produces many lateral leaf buds which are used as food. The "heads" of lettuce and cabbage are made up of the broad, flat leaves of the terminal bud. The "stalk" of celery is a much enlarged and blanched petiole.

b. Reduced leaves. The "leaves" of a seaweed like gulfweed are actually comparatively undifferentiated parts of the thallus. The "foliage" of asparagus is composed of enlarged stems, the true leaves being reduced to small spines. The cladophyll of a cactus is a broad and fleshy stem; the leaves, present only on young stems, are very much reduced in size.

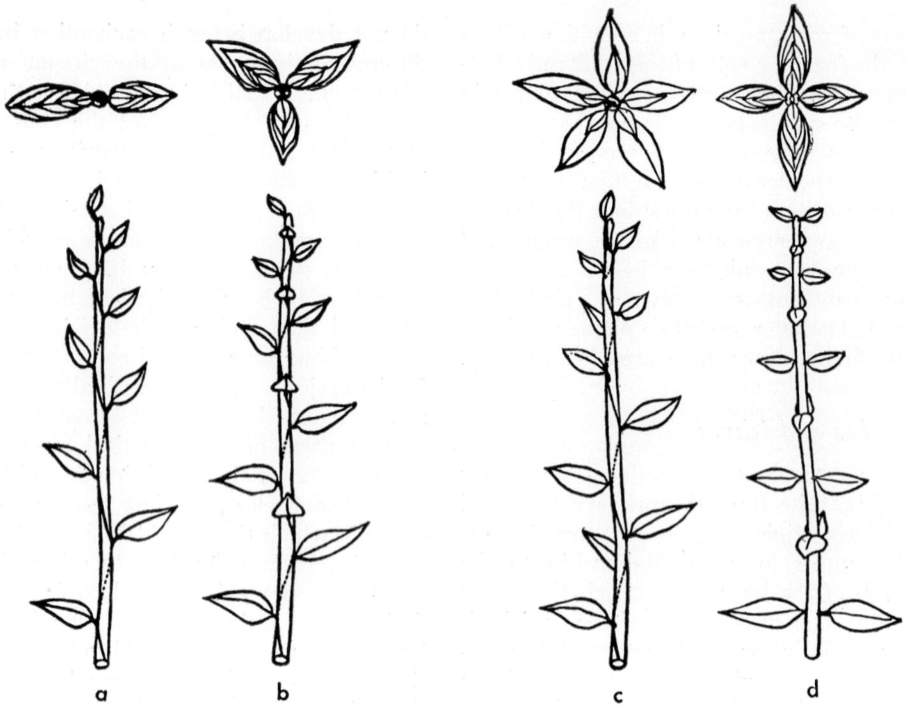

FIGURE 12.23 Types of leaf arrangement. (From Smith, Gilbert, Evans, Duggar, Bryan and Allen, *A Textbook of General Botany*. Copyright 1942 by The Macmillan Company.)

a, b, c, various alternate arrangements; d, opposite arrangement. The upper figures represent the corresponding leaf arrangement seen from above.

FIGURE 12.24 The beach plum (Prunus maritima) showing origin of flower buds directly from the main stem. (Photograph by courtesy of the Soil Conservation Service, U.S. Department of Agriculture.)

## Leaves

The leaves that arise in such definite positions along the stem are the third of the differentiated regions of the vascular plants. The foliage leaves of pteridophytes and angiosperms are broad and flat but those of most gymnosperms are slender cylinders and so commonly called needles. All typical leaves are composed principally of chlorenchyma and they are therefore the site of most of the photosynthesis that goes on in the plant; the efficiency with which such synthesis is carried out depends not only upon their own structure and internal composition but also upon their position in relation to light and the availability to them of the materials necessary to the series of reactions that make up the photosynthetic process. All the pteridophytes and the great majority of the spermatophytes, with the exception of the parasitic dodder, of Indian pipes and some few other saprophytes, are photosynthesizing systems.

*Parts of a leaf:* Typically a foliage leaf arises from a bud at the node of a stem and consists of a petiole or leaf stalk (Latin, petiolus = little foot), one or two stipules (Latin, stipula = stem) and a blade (Fig. 12.16). The petiole may be a long or a short, a stout or a slender stalk between the stem and the base of the blade through which pass a number of fibro-vascular bundles, continuous through the leaf trace with those of the stem, that spread out in the blade as its veins. The petioles also serve to hold the leaves in positions in which they will have the greatest exposure to light; those of a vine climbing against a wall, for example, bend around the stem so that the leaves that originate on its inner surface are turned outward. Some leaves have no petioles, like those of grasses and most gymnosperms, and are said to be sessile; and in some plants, like climbing nasturtiums and clematis, some of the petioles are modified as tendrils. Stipules arise either from one or both sides of the base of the petiole; they too may be absent, as they are in grasses and maples, small and inconspicuous, as they are in willows, or large, as they are in peas where they contribute as much to the total photosynthesis of the plant as do the blades themselves. Or they may become tendrils like those of smilax, or sharp and pointed spines like those of the honey locust and Euphorbia, the crown of thorns (Fig. 12.25).

The blades of leaves exhibit a wide variety and range both in shape and in size; these characters as well as their distribution along the stem and the pattern of their veins are used in the systematic classification of plants. Blades range in shape from linear ones, like the needles of gymnosperms, to broad elliptical ones as much as 10 or 20 feet in length, like those of some palms and magnolias; some, like those of water lilies, are circular and some, like those of the water plantain, are shaped like a spear or arrow head. They may be entire, with smooth margins, like those of many grasses and of lilies; notched or serrate, like those of elms; toothed or dentate, like those of hollies; or indented or lobed, like those of maples and oaks (Fig. 12.26). If the indentations are so deep that they extend to the midline, each section of the leaf is called a leaflet and the leaf as a whole is said to be compound rather than simple. If the leaflets are arranged in a series along the main fibro-vascular bundle, or midrib, of the leaf it is said to be pinnately compound (Latin, pinna = feather), since their distribution resembles that of the vanes of a bird's feather; such leaves are characteristic of many kinds of ferns and of roses. If, on the other hand, all the lobes have a common base, the leaf is said to be palmately compounded; this is the case in such leaves as the ash, the clover and horse-chestnut. Another conspicuous external feature of the blade is the distribution of the fibro-vascular bundles within it, for the larger ones at least show as elevations of its upper and lower surfaces that are called veins. The central and largest vein of a blade is its midrib; the lesser veins have either a parallel or a netted arrangement. In parallel venation, characteristic of the monocotyledons, all the veins are more or less parallel to the midrib and so to the main axis of the leaf; with netted venation, they may be either pin-

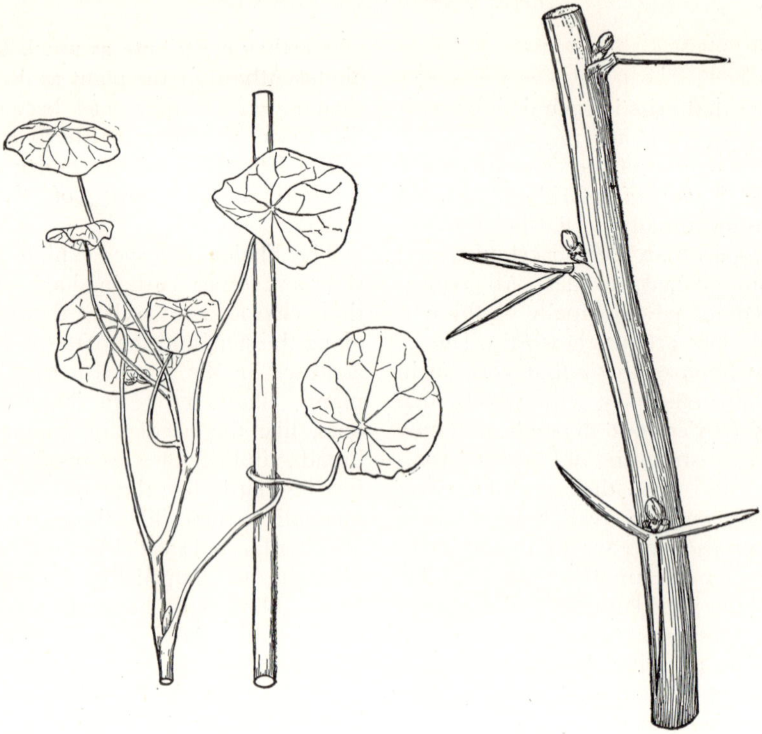

1
2

FIGURE 12.25a

1
2
3

FIGURE 12.25b

FIGURE 12.25 Modified leaves and stipules. (From Smith, Gilbert, Evans, Duggar, Bryan and Allen, *A Textbook of General Botany*. Copyright 1942 by The Macmillan Company.)

a. 1. Leaves of a nasturtium (Tropaeolum), whose petioles function as tendrils.

2. Part of the stem of a barberry (Berberis), with leaves modified as spines.

b. 1. The compound leaf of a pea (Pisum), with some of the leaflets modified as tendrils, and broad, blade-like stipules that contribute to the photosynthetic area of the plant.

2. The pinnately-compounded leaf of a rose (Rosa), with sheath-like stipules at its base.

3. Twig of a crown-of-thorns (Euphorbia), with spine-like stipules.

THE VASCULAR PLANTS [ 193 ]

nately distributed, as they are in the elms, or palmately, as they are in geraniums and maples.

The petiole of a leaf, if it has one, contains 1–5 fibro-vascular bundles surrounded by mechanical tissue and parenchyma and

characteristic size and shape it usually shows no further growth, although in the pine and in grasses there is always some meristem at its base which permits increase in its length. The absence of cambium in the tissues of leaves, one of the features that distinguishes

**SIMPLE OR COMPOUND LEAVES**

**EVERGREEN OR DECIDUOUS HABIT**

**PRESENCE OR ABSENCE OF STIPULES**

**PARALLEL OR NETTED VENATION**

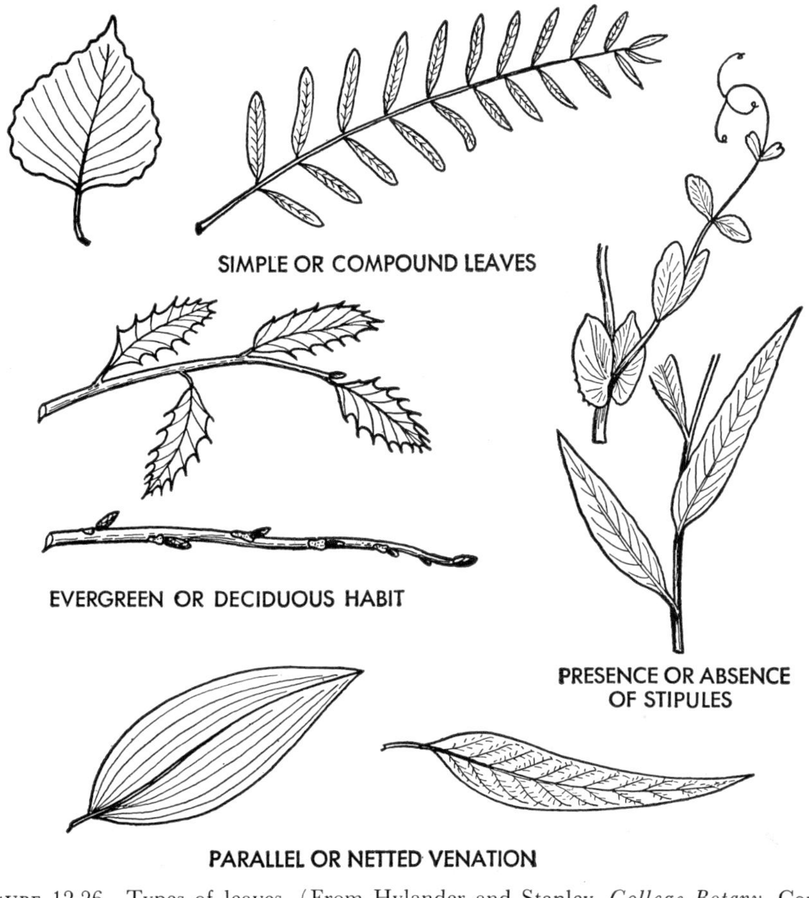

FIGURE 12.26 Types of leaves. (From Hylander and Stanley, *College Botany*. Copyright 1949 by The Macmillan Company.)

covered by epidermis. These tissues, which are continuous with those of the stem, are carried out into the stipules which may persist throughout the life of the leaf or be shed early in the development of the blade.

***Growth and differentiation of leaf tissues:*** The development, or expansion, of the blade is due almost entirely to the simultaneous enlargement and maturation of the cells already assembled in the bud (Fig. 12.27). After the blade has attained its full and

them from roots and stems, precludes their indefinite increase in size. The epidermis of a leaf blade is made up of flat cells whose lateral surfaces are usually very irregular in outline. Their walls contain cutin so that they are water-resistant and in only a few aquatic plants, habitually living below the surface of the water, do these cells contain chloroplasts. Exceptions to this are the guard cells of the stomata which are far more numerous in the epidermis of leaves than in that of stems, for there are on an average

100–300 stomata, and in some plants more than 1,000, per square millimeter of leaf surface. In terrestrial plants, the stomata are for the most part on the under surface of the blade, but in aquatic plants they may be on the upper surface, as they are in water

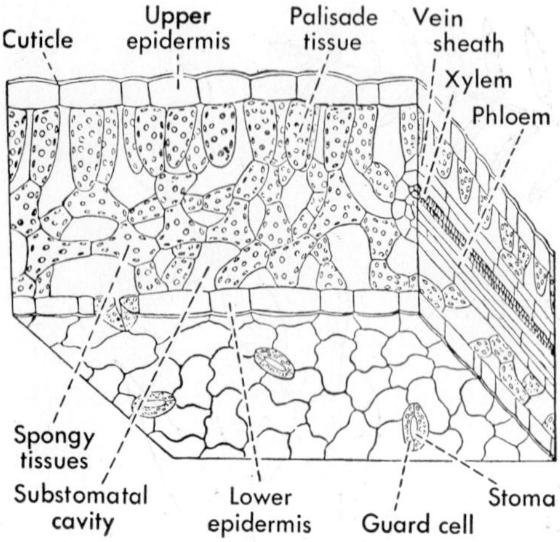

FIGURE 12.27 Stereogram showing part of the blade of a sunflower leaf. (From Smith, Gilbert, Evans, Duggar, Bryan and Allen, *A Textbook of General Botany*. Copyright 1942 by The Macmillan Company.)

lilies, and in some terrestrial ones, such as corn, for example, they are equally distributed on both surfaces. Each stoma is surrounded by two oval guard cells, containing chloroplasts and with walls that are elastic. When extended to their maximum volume, the opposing walls of a pair become arched and draw apart from each other, thus making an opening which is the stoma proper and through which air can diffuse in and out of the tissues of the leaf.

In some leaves the epidermal cells develop hairs. A hair may be a single epidermal cell elongated in a plane parallel to the surface of the leaf or a chain of two or three cells. In many cases the terminal cell of such a chain is glandular, from which the secretion may be a sticky substance that spreads over the surface of the blade as is, for example, the secretion from the gland cells on the leaves of petunias; or a volatile oil that gives the leaves a characteristic scent like those of wintergreen, mint and geranium; or an irritant substance, like that in the stinging hairs of the nettle. The tips of the hairs of nettles are bent at an angle and break easily on contact, leaving the sharp, stiff base to penetrate the skin of an animal and carry in with it the irritating secretion from the gland cell. In some other plants, like mullein, the hairs are dead and filled with air. Some leaves have an outer coating or cuticle of wax, or of a mixture of waxes, which gives them a shining or glossy appearance or, if the wax is deposited in minute plates as it is in tulips and members of the cabbage family, a grayish one, or "bloom."

The bulk of the leaf is made up of chlorenchyma called mesophyll (Greek, mesos = between + phyllon = leaf), which in addition to its chloroplasts may have other chromoplasts usually containing yellow or orange pigments of the carotenoid group. In many leaves the mesophyll cells immediately below the upper epidermis are cylindrical ones, packed closely together and forming a row of palisade cells in which chloroplasts are particularly abundant; the others, irregular in shape and with fewer chloroplasts, are loosely packed so that there are many air spaces between them. There may be several rows of these cells making up the spongy mesophyll; the lower and often larger air spaces are in direct contact with the external atmosphere through the stomata. But there are variations in the distribution of these types of mesophyll cells in different species of plants. In grasses, for example, there is no distinction between palisade and spongy mesophyll; in the rubber plant there is a layer of palisade cells just inside the lower epidermis as well as the upper; and in the eucalyptus, a tree native to Australia, all the mesophyll is of the palisade type.

The tissues of the fibro-vascular bundles are essentially the same as those in the stem and the root, except for the absence of cambium and, in the collateral bundles, the reversal of position of the xylem and the phloem. For, since the bundles in the leaf have their origin in the leaf trace that branches off at an angle from the bundles of the stem, the xylem portion of the bundle is brought uppermost in the leaf and lies toward its outer, or upper, epidermis and the phloem toward its inner, or lower, surface. Moreover, the bundles grow progressively smaller and smaller as they approach the margin of the leaf; the smallest bundles are not externally evident as veins. At the ends of the branch veins, where there are frequently junctions between them, the bundles may be represented by but a single tracheid and some surrounding sclerenchyma. The vascular tissue is always enclosed in some mechanical tissue and often in parenchyma as well, and in the larger bundles may extend from upper to lower epidermis.

**Storage in leaves; shedding of leaves:** Leaves may act as the chief storage regions of a plant as well as the principal photosynthesizing areas. This is true of plants like lettuces and cabbages where material is accumulated in the leaves all during the life of the plant. But many perennial plants are deciduous (Latin, decidere = to fall off) and in comparison to the life of the entire plant, the leaves are short-lived whether they function as storage areas or not. The leaves of some gymnosperms, like pines and firs and hemlocks, may live from three to five years and the leaves of some angiosperms, like rhododendrons, hollies and laurels, have a comparable life span. Some deciduous trees shed their leaves continually as, for example, the live oaks do, but the majority shed them at the end of each growing season and replace them at the beginning of the next one by new ones. In exceptional conditions of temperature and humidity, leaves may be shed in the course of a season. The shedding of leaves is brought about by conditions that arise in a band of cells that extends across the base of each petiole, excluding the vascular tissues, which is known as the abscission layer (Latin, ab = from + scindere = to cut). This layer develops long before the leaves actually fall; the walls of its cells are thin and the middle lamella first, and later the entire wall, disintegrates so that the leaf remains connected with the stem only by the fibro-vascular bundles. The weight of the leaf itself, or its movement by the wind, or the formation of ice crystals in the abscission layer in the early frosts of autumn causes the leaf to break off, leaving the broken and exposed fibro-vascular bundles, which are rapidly covered over by cells derived from the cork cambium, as the leaf scar. In some plants, particularly in certain varieties of oak, the abscission layer is not fully developed at the end of the summer and the leaves, although no longer photosynthetic because of the changes that have taken place in their pigments, remain on the stems all winter.

## *The vascular plant as a biological system*

The roots, the stems and the leaves with their differentiated tissues make up the body of a vascular plant to whose maintenance and growth they all contribute, and upon which it depends for the intake of materials from the environment as it depends upon its tissue systems for the distribution of these materials within its body, as well as for the distribution of the materials that it synthesizes.

### Life span

The life of a plant with closed vascular bundles is usually short, that of its aerial parts, at least, lasting at the most for one growing season, but those with open bundles may continue to grow for indefinite periods, for the meristem of the cambium and growing points remains potentially capable of continued division. But in some such plants, called annuals, the cambium is active for one season only, at the end of which the plant dies; in others, called biennials, maturity is not reached until the second year of growth, after which they, too, die; and in others, called perennials, new tissues are produced and matured season after season so that their stems may reach heights of several hundred feet and diameters of 20–30 feet. In some herbaceous perennials the stems and leaves die off each year, but the root may continue to live and send up new stems season after season. In the woody perennials each season's growth is evident in the xylem, each year's increment appearing in the cross section of a stem as a ring of spring and summer wood; the cut surface therefore shows a number of concentric rings called annual rings. The width of each annual ring is a measure of growth in any one season, which is influenced by conditions in the soil as well as by light, temperature and the composition of the atmosphere; in the fifteenth century, Leonardo da Vinci noted and recorded the effect of weather conditions upon the size of tree rings. The number of rings is also some indication of the age of a tree, although it is by no means an exact criterion, for prolonged droughts or the loss of leaves through the ravages of insects may cause additional rings to be formed in any one season. Since the addition of rings and consequent enlargement of the diameter of the stem is entirely due to secondary growth, the older or basal part of a stem is usually larger than the younger or apical part and the main stem of tall plants and the trunks of trees especially, with many annual rings, are tapering rather than straight columns. By counting the rings at the base of its trunk a fairly accurate estimate can be made of the age of a tree; by this method some of the sequoias of California, with heights of 300 feet or more and diameters of 30–35 feet, are believed to have been growing for about 4,000 years. The big cypress of Tule in Oaxaca, Mexico, 140 feet high and 50 feet in diameter, is by the same reckoning about 3,000 years old, while some pines, maples, sycamores and black walnuts in the United States have apparently been growing for at least 500 years.

### Maturation and ageing of tissues

As the tissues within a perennial plant grow older, in many cases they cease to function. The older phloem tissues become crushed by the new growth as they do in the root, and collapse. In the xylem, the older vessels may become plugged with deposits of gum or resins, or blocked by growths from adjacent parenchyma cells, so that they are no longer conductile. If they remain intact they add to the mechanical strength of the plant, enabling it to keep upright even with increasing height and to withstand the buffeting of winds; if they disintegrate through decay the center of the stem becomes hollow and the plant is not only deprived of some of its mechanical support but also open to invasion by parasites that may contribute to its decay or destroy it entirely. The older and non-functional part of the xylem is known as heartwood as opposed to the younger vessels, active in the conduction of water and its solutes, which with their surrounding parenchyma constitute the sapwood. Sapwood becomes converted to heartwood with age and is replaced by new sapwood, the xylem of the last year or two of growth. (See Fig. 18.4.)

### Relations to water

An almost continuous water supply is a prime requisite for active plants, and is the most important limiting factor of their possible habitats. In addition to its general uses by biological systems, it is essential to plants for maintenance of turgor (Latin, turgere = to swell), the degree of distention of the protoplast and cell wall that is optimal for the cell. The death of cells from desiccation has been shown to be caused indirectly by mechanical stresses resulting from the shrinking of the vacuole and the consequent stretching and tearing of the protoplasm rather than directly by the removal of water, for plants that have undergone slow and careful desiccation can be restored to full vigor by being given access to water. Turgor also imparts a certain amount of rigidity to the soft tissues of a plant, enabling many herbaceous plants to keep erect in the absence of woody tissues. Wilting in plants in an expression of loss of turgor. And all green plants have an additional demand for water and reliance upon it, since it is one of the materials used in photosynthesis, although the amount so used is less than 1 per cent of the total water absorbed.

*Translocation of dissolved substances:* The fact that the vessels of the phloem and the xylem play a major part in the distribution, or translocation, of water and its solutes throughout the plant can be shown by very simple experiments. If, for example, a plant is girdled by the removal of a ring of bark from its main stem, it does not wilt but its roots die after a short time, and ultimately the entire plant dies, showing that a supply of materials necessary to the growth and maintenance of the root system is cut off by the operation, and that a functioning root system is essential to the continued life of the plant. And if a cut stem of willow, or of any other plant that readily develops adventitious roots in water, is girdled a few inches above its cut surface, the roots will appear only above the ring; the part below it must therefore have been deprived by the operation of something necessary to root development. Such experiments make it clear that the sieve tubes function principally in the downward translocation of water and soluble substances contributed by the cells in the upper levels of the plant in which photosynthesis and other chemical reactions are going on. The factors that are involved in such transport are not clear, beyond the fact that it is favored by the gravitational pull and the structure of the sieve tubes and sieve plates, nor is the possibility ruled out that under certain conditions water and its solutes may not ascend in the conductile cells of the phloem. The direction of conduction in the xylem can be determined by putting a cut stem into water containing a non-toxic dye like neutral red or methylene blue; if the stem is sufficiently translucent the movement of the dye upward in the central vessels can be followed with the eye, but even in thick and opaque stems its presence in the xylem tubes can be seen in cross sections made at different levels of the stem. That it passes upward in the lumina rather than the walls of the tubes can be shown by putting a cut stem into warm, liquid gelatin for 30 minutes or more and then into cold water so that the gelatin solidifies. If a bit is cut off the end of the stem, exposing a new surface that has not been in contact with the gelatin, and the stem is put in water, it wilts, indicating that its cells have lost water and that none has been supplied them to replace the loss, for the tracheids and tracheae are plugged by the gelatin that rose in them. The upward conducting function of these vessels can also be shown in larger plants by cutting into a branch that is supported and removing a section of the xylem cylinder without destroying more than a small region of cortex and phloem; if this is done, the part of the plant above the removed xylem wilts.

*Entrance and movement of water and its solutes:* For aquatic plants and those that live in marshy or swampy places an adequate water supply is no problem; their need is rather for means of conveying gases around their bodies so that their submerged parts may be supplied with oxygen. But for the far more numerous species of plants which geological records show have lived on land for at least 200 million years, their water supply is a most pressing problem, especially for those that live in arid or semi-arid areas and for those that grow to considerable heights above the ground. The only effective source of water available to such plants is that which is in the soil and to which their roots alone have direct access.

This water and its solutes diffuse independently of each other through the walls of the root hairs, which are flattened against the soil particles and to some extent held there by their gelatinous walls. All ions appear to diffuse freely across these walls; the quantity of those of any one kind that enters the cell depends upon their relative mobilities and the concentration gradient, that is, their relative concentrations outside and inside the cell. $Na^+$ and $Cl^-$, for example, have been found to enter the root hairs of barley more readily than $Ca^{++}$ and $SO_4^{--}$, although the plant makes greater use of calcium and sulphate than it does of sodium and chlorine and therefore has greater need of them. There is also evidence that certain ions are concentrated, or combined, within the cell so that their diffusion into it continues long after equilibrium would otherwise be established; the concentration of chlorine in the cell sap of the fresh water alga Nitella has been shown to be 0.35 per cent when the plant was living in a medium in which the concentration was only 0.002–0.003 per cent.

Other factors than simple diffusion enter into the absorption of water, for the plasma membrane of the protoplast of the epidermal cell and its root hairs is a semipermeable one enclosing the protoplasm and the cell sap, both of which are colloidal solutions. Because of the osmotic conditions thus set up, water diffuses into the cell at a faster rate than it leaves it. The entrance of water goes on until the cell has taken up all that

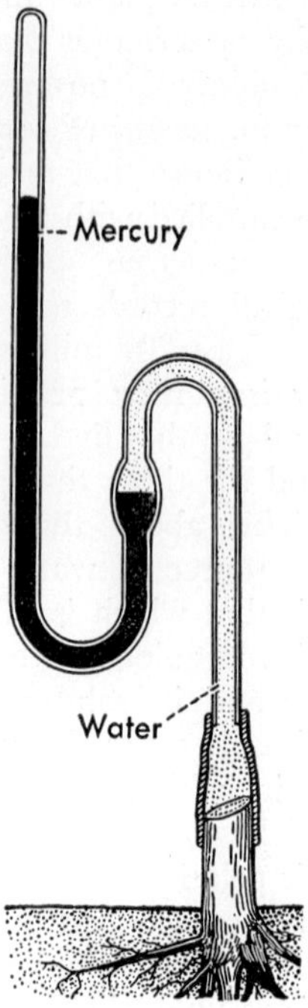

FIGURE 12.28 Apparatus for measuring root pressure. (Adapted from G. M. Smith, from Hylander and Stanley, *College Botany*. Copyright 1949 by The Macmillan Company.)

The cut end of a stem is connected to a curved glass tube partly filled with mercury. As the sap rises in the tube through the force of root pressure, the column of mercury in the other arm rises; the distance through which it travels gives a measure of root pressure.

it can and reached its maximum turgidity when water begins to pass from it to the adjoining cells, whose turgor is also increased and from which, in turn, water and its diffusible solutes move into the cells further within the roots, until they reach the primary xylem not far removed from the absorbing epidermis. And as more water is withdrawn from the soil solution by osmosis, the concentration of its solutes is increased and the concentration gradient between the soil solution and the cell sap, in respect of these solutes, becomes steeper, thus favoring their diffusion into the root.

ROOT PRESSURE: The entrance of water into its cells creates a hydrostatic pressure in the root system known as root pressure. This was recognized and demonstrated over 200 years ago by Stephen Hales. It can easily be seen in plants whose stems have been cut off a few inches above the ground level, for fluid exudes from the cut stump; if a glass tube is attached to the cut surface, the fluid can be seen to rise in it against gravity and under a pressure that has been measured and in no case found to exceed 2 atmospheres (Fig. 12.28). Calculations and experiments show that this pressure is insufficient to lift the soil solution through any but the smallest plants; it requires, for example, a pressure equivalent to about 20 atmospheres to lift it from the base to the top of a tree of ordinary height. Moreover, the fact that the presence of roots is not essential to the ascent of water is made evident by the failure of cut stems to wilt when put in an adequate amount of water. It is therefore apparent that some other force or forces must be operative in raising the soil solution through the conductile tissues of the xylem, though the nature of them is as yet by no means clear.

TRANSPIRATION: A force that might be effective in the ascent of soil solution is provided by transpiration (Latin, trans = across + spirare = to breathe), the loss of water by evaporation from the tissues of the leaves and other regions of the plant that are exposed to the surrounding atmosphere. That such water loss takes place constantly during the life of a plant can be shown by placing it under a glass dome after covering its pot with some waterproof material so that no water can escape from it or the soil in which it is growing; after a time drops of water appear on the underside of the glass dome that can only have come from the plant itself in the form of vapor which condenses into liquid when in contact with the glass. There are various ways in which the amount of water lost in this way can be measured, although the rate at which transpiration takes place fluctuates so greatly with changes in the plant itself as well as in its environment that figures of isolated transpiration rates have little significance (Fig. 12.29). Light, temperature and atmospheric humidity all influence the rate of transpiration greatly. But in general, plants growing in temperate regions lose by transpiration between 5–25 grams, equivalent to 5–25 cc., of water per square meter of leaf area per hour, and may lose as much as 50 grams (50 cc.) per square meter of leaf surface per hour. In a growing season of 100 days a sunflower plant was found to have transpired approximately 400 pounds of water, and corn plants, during an average summer season, to have removed from the soil nearly two barrels of water apiece, only a small fraction of which was used in photosynthesis.

Transpiration probably takes place in this way. The cells of the spongy mesophyll around the air spaces are in contact with the surrounding atmosphere through the stomata; this is equally true of the tissues of a stem supplied with stomata or lenticels. Unless the surrounding atmosphere is exceptionally humid, water evaporates from the walls of these cells, saturating the air in the air spaces, and, as vapor, diffuses out through the stomata; its removal from the immediate vicinity of the plant is facilitated by air currents, a dry breeze or wind. By this evaporation there is created a water deficit in the walls of the exposed mesophyll cells which is made up by diffusion of water from their protoplasts, creating a deficit there which is in turn made up by diffusion from the cell sap in their vacuoles. The concentration of the cell sap, in respect of its non-diffusible solutes, is therefore raised and the osmotic relations of these cells with those adjacent to them altered; water enters the water-deficient cells by osmosis from their neighboring cells and ultimately is drawn from the water-conducting vessels to make up this water loss, all the mesophyll cells cooperating, like a bucket brigade, in delivering water from the central supply to those that are losing it by evaporation. There is consequently a constant demand for water by the leaves, independent of that used in photosynthesis, to replace an almost constant loss of it.

If the soil solution, once it has entered a conducting tube of the xylem, can be considered as a continuous column owing to the forces of cohesion between its water mole-

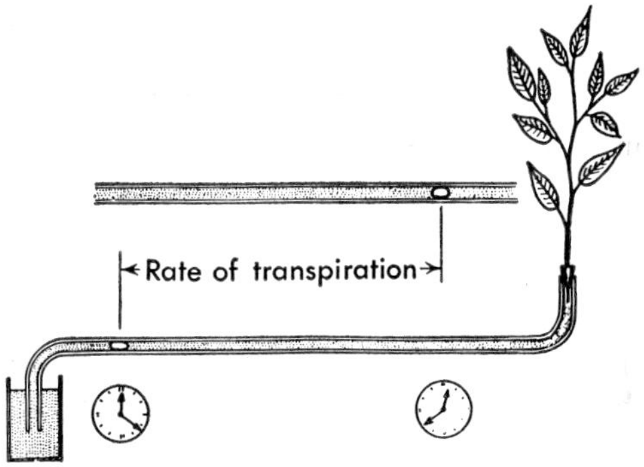

FIGURE 12.29 Apparatus (potometer) for demonstrating transpiration. (Adapted from Holman and Robbins, from Hylander and Stanley, *College Botany*. Copyright 1949 by The Macmillan Company.) An estimate of the amount and rate of water loss from the leaves of the plant inserted in one end of the tube can be obtained by measurement of the distance the air bubble moves along the tube in a given time.

cules, the water deficit created in the leaves would exert a pull upon these columns in the conducting tubes of the stem resulting in a continuous upward movement of the water, a transpiration stream. On this theory the translocation of water and its solutes is thus entirely a physical process but one that could not take place except for biological processes that go on in living tissues. The composition of the walls of the epidermal cells in the root hair region, the composition of their protoplasts and cell sap and the integrity of their plasma membranes are all factors which operate in the absorption of water by the roots and are all ones that depend upon the metabolic activities of cells and demand the expenditure of energy by them. And though evaporation is a purely physical process, transpiration is the result of biological processes, for the replacement of water so lost is also conditioned by the nature of the walls of the mesophyll cells, their membranes and their osmotic relationships which, like those of the epidermal cells of the root, are established and maintained by metabolic reactions that go on in them and the expenditure of energy by them. Whether transpiration plays any real part in the ascent of soil solution is open to question and to further investigation, especially since there is some reason to believe that the course of substances in the xylem is not exclusively upward.

Although the major part of the translocation of materials throughout the plant takes place in the vessels of the phloem and the xylem, there is undoubtedly diffusion from cell to cell, especially in the soft-walled parenchyma; the movement of substances across the stem and the root must take place in this way and there is probably also some upward and downward movement of some, if not all, of them. The upward movement of the soil solution in the xylem is at its maximum when the sun is shining and the chlorenchyma cells are photosynthesizing to their maximum capacity; as long as the stomata remain open, exposing the cells around the air spaces to the outer air, transpiration is also at a maximum and may result in the loss of more water than the roots can currently absorb or than can be drawn from any of the bound water or other reserves in the plant. The wilting of herbaceous plants in the heat of the summer sun is evidence of such a water deficit. But plants are protected to some extent from excessive water loss by various devices. Among these is the mechanism, not yet fully understood, by which the stomata are closed and opened. The stomata are open only when the guard cells are fully turgid; when water is lost from them their opposing walls are no longer arched but flat and so in contact with each other (Fig. 12.30). The plant has no control over the mechanism, whatever it may be, that effects these changes and can neither anticipate excessive water loss through transpiration nor make preparations to prevent it. In most plants, when there is an abundant water supply, the stomata are open in the light and closed in the dark so that transpiration by night is considerably less than it is by day, as little as 3–5 per cent of its daylight rate. During the night the plant has an opportunity to adjust its water balance, or the ratio between that taken in by the root system and that lost by transpiration. So important is this adjustment that it is generally believed that were it not for the intervals of darkness that night provides, vegetation could not long survive on earth. But in some plants, like potatoes, cabbages and beets, the stomata are continuously open except when the soil is deficient in water, when they close like those of other plants. The enormous number of stomata in the leaves of most plants means that there is a large surface for evaporation; measurements and calculations show that they are responsible for 80–90 per cent of the water loss through transpiration, the lenticels and the epidermal cells, whose walls are not completely impervious to water, being responsible for the remainder.

Transpiration, although it may be an effective force in raising the soil solution against the force of gravity, may also result in excessive water loss and so is a menace to the welfare of plants, for the water that is withdrawn from the cells of the leaf for photosynthesis alone is enough to exert a pull upon the water column in the xylem and to bring about its rise. It has been suggested, in order to attach some survival value to transpiration, that it is a cooling device through which the temperature of the leaf is kept below a level at which destructive changes in its cells take place. Measurements of the temperature of leaves have shown it to be consistently close to that of the atmosphere around them and seldom more than a few degrees above it. Yet leaves are exposed all day to the radiant energy from the sun, both that which strikes them directly and that which is reflected upon them. About 80 per cent of this energy is absorbed by the leaf and the remainder is reflected from it or transmitted through it. And of this 80 per cent only a very small fraction is used to initiate or to drive the reactions of photosynthesis; the remainder is dissipated as heat. It has been calculated, from determinations of the amount of radiant energy that falls upon a leaf in the noonday sunlight of summer, that this amount of dissipated energy would raise the

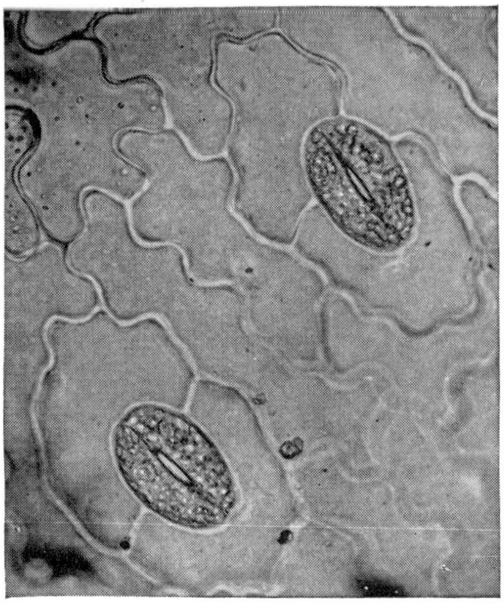

FIGURE 12.30 Guard cells.

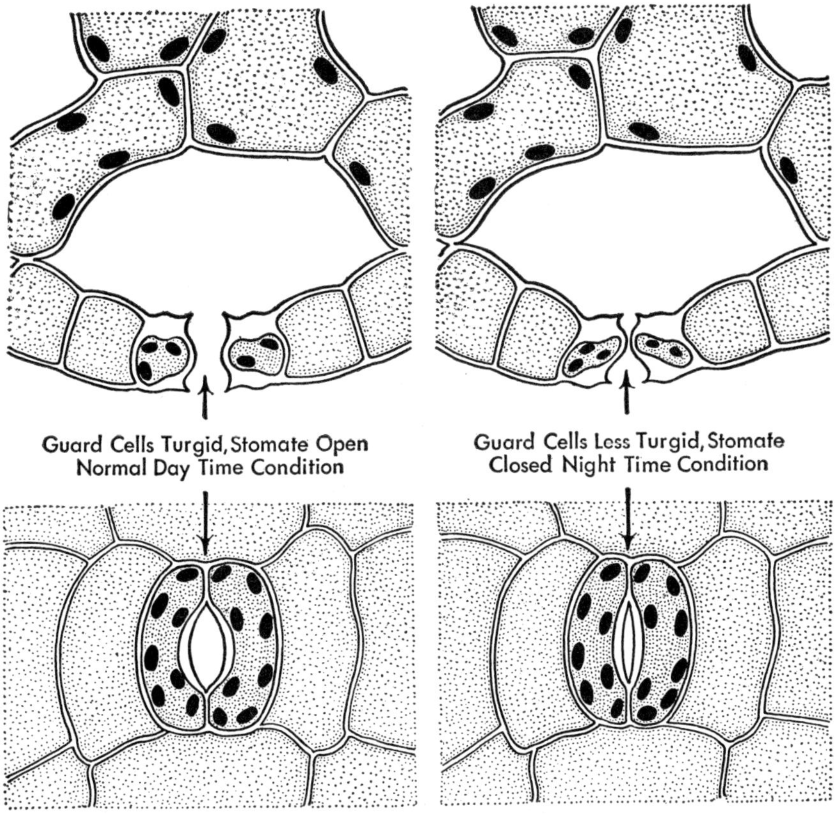

a. Guard cells from the under surface of the Boston fern (Nephrolepsis) x 500. (From Moment, *General Biology for Colleges*. Copyright 1942 by the D. Appleton-Century Company, Inc.)

b. Diagram showing open and closed guard cells. (From Hylander and Stanley, *College Botany*. Copyright 1949 by The Macmillan Company.)

temperature of the leaf about 37°C per minute so that in two minutes it could be raised more than 70°C, bringing it to a point well beyond the limit at which most plant protoplasm is killed. It is possible that transpiration is a mechanism through which the leaf is cooled and its temperature kept at its more or less constant level, for water itself can, within limits, absorb heat without much elevation of temperature and its vaporization, upon which evaporation depends, is an endothermic process requiring the expenditure of energy. But again, calculations show that if evaporation alone were responsible for the loss of heat from the leaf, water would have to be evaporated from it at a rate that exceeds any yet obtained from measurements of transpiration rates, except for very short periods of time. It therefore seems more likely that this thermal energy to a great extent is dissipated from the leaves as it is from other objects by the processes of conduction, convection and radiation and that green plants have survived as biological systems in spite of transpiration rather than because of it.

**Preservation of water balance:** Those that have survived as terrestrial systems, and attained height in their primary stems and width in the extent of their secondary ones, have been able to do so because of various devices for preserving their water balance, which either reduce the danger of water loss through transpiration or enable the plant to store comparatively large amounts of water in its tissues that can be released when need for it arises, without affecting the turgor of the actively metabolizing cells. Plants which are fitted for existence in dry regions are known as xerophytes (Greek, xeros = dry + phyton = plant); those which are fitted for existence in water or in moist situations as hydrophytes (Greek, hydor = water); and those that can exist under average conditions of atmospheric and soil humidity as mesophytes (Greek, mesos = middle). In xerophytic plants especially, the stomata are often sunk below the level of the epidermis or guarded by spines or hairs and the rate of evaporation from them thus reduced, since they are not directly exposed to the dry external air nor to the currents that accelerate diffusion of water vapor. Frequently, too, their mesophyll is a compact rather than a spongy tissue so that the number of its air spaces is greatly reduced; considerable amounts of water may also be bound in their colloids. Many such plants, too, and many mesophytes are succulent (Latin, succus = juice), with parenchyma cells in certain regions or throughout their bodies that are enlarged and contain more than the usual amount of water. The size, positions and arrangements of their leaves may also be such as to minimize transpiration, or can be adjusted to do so. The spiny leaves of cacti, for example, and the needles of pines, firs and spruces all expose a minimum of surface to the air so that cacti can live in very arid regions, and pines and similar gymnosperms high up on the slopes of mountains where atmospheric conditions favor the vaporization of water. Some xerophytic grasses and perennial xerophytes like Euphorbia, for example, shed their leaves during long, dry periods and develop new ones during the short, rainy ones.

Hydrophytes are plants that live wholly in the water, that float on its surface with their roots anchored in the soil at the bottom, like water lilies, or trailing free like the duckweed Lemna (Fig. 8.5a) or ones that inhabit swamps and marshes. In most of the vascular plants that are ordinarily wholly or partly submerged, the root system is reduced; so also is the tracheal system, and the stomata, though present, are non-functional. In all hydrophytes the part below the water usually lacks a periderm or cuticle and all its submerged parts are absorptive. Root hairs are never developed, nor in fact do they develop on the roots of terrestrial plants if they are grown in water or an aqueous nutrient solution. The parenchyma of hydrophytes is usually spongy, with large intercellular spaces filled with air, for the danger to these plants is not dehydration but asphyxiation. In the water lily, one of the most successful of the hydrophytes, there is a continuous system of air passages between the stomata on the upper surfaces of the leaves and the tissues of the parts below the water level. These air-filled spaces give the plant buoyancy and provide as well a pathway for the circulation of gases and so a means of gaseous interchange with the atmosphere; in wholly submerged plants, like Elodea, the gas that circulates within the plant can only be exchanged with that dissolved in the surrounding water.

The great majority of vascular plants are mesophytes which can endure neither prolonged drought nor an over-abundant water supply and to which the preservation of water is of vital importance. Light, a dry atmosphere, air currents or winds, warm temperatures all increase the rate of transpiration and the water loss resulting must be made up by absorption through the roots and, in them, principally through the root hair system. These delicate processes expose a comparatively enormous surface of a plant to the soil solution. In a plant of winter rye grown in soil in a greenhouse, for example, the total length of all its roots was found to be about 400 feet, with a surface area, excluding the root hairs, of about 2,550 square feet; the root hairs numbered some 14 billion and exposed a surface of over 4,300 square feet. Large plants with roots that extend below the surface layers of the soil and reach a level where the water supply is constant, can withstand temporary droughts more successfully than smaller ones with shorter roots. But even these can survive unless the drought is unusually severe, for the reduction of transpiration by the closing of the stomata safeguards them by day and the regular reduction in the rate of transpiration at night gives them an opportunity to make up the daytime deficit. Sometimes, indeed, so much water enters a plant by night that is not used in photosynthesis or transpired from it that it is given off in its liquid form in the process of guttation (Latin, gutta = drop). Some plants—cabbages, strawberries and nasturtiums for example—have water pores at the ends of their leaves, like permanently open stomata, through which this water exudes to run down the surface of the leaf and collect in drops that are often of considerable size.

## Gaseous interchange and elimination of metabolic waste

The multicellular plants, while structurally very different from multicellular animals, carry on, as animals do, a succession of chemical changes within their tissues collectively known as metabolism. Many of these reactions require molecular oxygen, although anaerobic respiration is known to take place regularly in some of their tissues and may do so under certain conditions, at least for a limited time, in most of them. Plants have no localized regions or specialized tissues for oxygen intake or carbon dioxide elimination, except insofar as stomata and lenticels may be considered as such; even those plants at the highest level of structural organization must depend upon the slow, physical process of diffusion to aerate their tissues and have no mechanism for accelerating it as many animals have. Nor have they any localized organs for the disposal of the by-products or end products of metabolism for which they have no direct use. These are frequently deposited in crystalline form between the cells or in the cell walls and quite possibly the specific products of certain plants or groups of plants, the gums and resins, the volatile or essential oils, and the alkaloids like nicotine, quinine, morphine, atrophine and strychnine represent an accumulation of substances that are intermediate or final stages of the metabolic processes that are going on in the living cells in the presence of enzymes or enzyme systems. These metabolic processes require the expenditure of energy which is derived either directly or indirectly from the food. The fact that most green plants synthesize food far in excess of their own immediate needs sometimes obscures the fact that they, too, consume some of the products of their own photosynthesis and degrade energy-rich compounds to those lower in energy value, and are, like animals, dependent upon adequate supplies of food, oxygen and water for their maintenance as well as for their growth and reproduction.

**CHAPTER 13**

# THE TUBE-WITHIN-A-TUBE PLAN OF METAZOAN ORGANIZATION

## The tube-within-a-tube plan compared to the blind-sac plan

The great majority of existing animals have bodies constructed upon the generalized architectural plan of a tube-within-a-tube. In this plan, the central cavity is an endodermal tube, open at both ends, instead of a blind sac open at only one (Fig. 13.1).

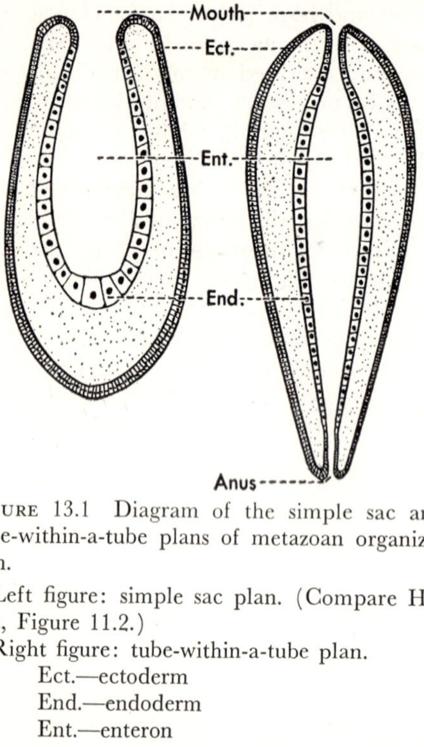

FIGURE 13.1 Diagram of the simple sac and tube-within-a-tube plans of metazoan organization.

Left figure: simple sac plan. (Compare Hydra, Figure 11.2.)

Right figure: tube-within-a-tube plan.
    Ect.—ectoderm
    End.—endoderm
    Ent.—enteron

In most animals, the openings are lined for varying distances with inturned ectoderm cells, derivatives of the embryonic stomodaeum (Greek, stoma = mouth + odaios = that which is on the road) at the anterior end, and a proctodaeum (Greek, proctos = anus + odaios) at the posterior, and the endodermal wall of the tube is supplemented by layers of cells derived from the mesoderm. There are obvious advantages in having two openings to the digestive tract; one lies in the opportunity for the development of specialized structures at the anterior opening, the mouth, for the capture, ingestion and mastication of food, a distinct asset to animals feeding upon solid material. Also, by enlargements of the tube, provision can be made for the storage of ingested food before its digestion, again an obvious asset to animals which feed periodically, and hardly possible in those in which food enters and its undigested residue leaves by the same aperture; moreover, the cells along the length of the tube can be modified in various ways for the disintegration of the ingested material. The appearance of the second opening has therefore given greater flexibility to the master pattern, but even this has not had the far-reaching consequences of a second development in the ancestral stock from which most of the tube-within-a-tube animals have evolved. This was the appearance of a fluid-filled space, the coelome, arising in connection with the third, or middle, cell layer, the mesoderm, and surrounding the endodermal cavity of the digestive tract or enteron (Greek, enteron = intestine).

## The coelome, or secondary body cavity

In order to understand the relationship of the coelome to the general body plan and the advantages that its presence confers upon animals possessing it, it is necessary to understand something of its development in the individual organism. All animals which as adults have structures derived from the three primitive cell layers—ectoderm, endoderm and mesoderm—pass through a stage early in their embryonic life when they are essentially two-layered, and when these two layers, the ectoderm and the endoderm, are separated by a fluid-filled space, the blastocoele (Greek, blastos = germ + koilos = hollow) (Figs. 25.1, 25.3). This stage may be but a brief one in their embryonic history and the appearance of these temporary two-layered systems may be quite different in different kinds of animals, for the blastocoele may be a comparatively large space, a thin slit between the ectoderm and endoderm, or combined with other embryonic structures. Whatever the conditions may be, it is this space, the primary body cavity, that is invaded by cells of the third layer and filled to a greater or less extent by them.

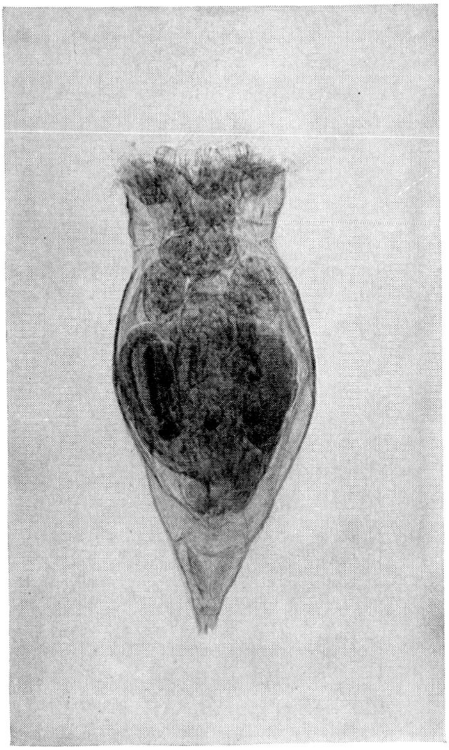

## The middle cell layer (mesoderm); acoelous and pseudocoelous animals

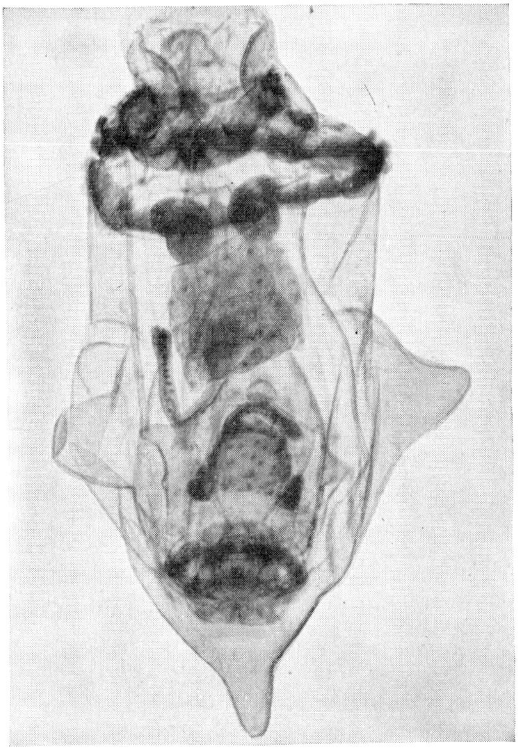

The most primitive of these invading mesodermal cells are elongated ones with several processes, often in contact with each other, known collectively as mesenchyme (Greek, mesos = in the middle + Latin, enchyma = type of tissue) (Fig. 11.1e). As development proceeds, they migrate into the blastocoele and there may differentiate in various ways, forming connective tissue, blood and lymph and in some animals, muscle, cartilage and bone. In animals like the flatworms, the mesenchyme wholly fills

FIGURE 13.2 Common rotifers. (Photographs by courtesy of the General Biological Supply House, Inc., Chicago.)

a. Hydatina.
b. Asplanchna.

The space between the enteron and the body wall is a pseudocoele, traversed by muscle strands but not lined with mesothelium.

the primary body cavity as the parenchyma, so that their bodies are virtually solid; such animals are said to be acoelous, or acoelomate. In some others, the invasion is not so complete and there are fluid-filled regions of various extent between the body wall and the enteron, so that parts of the body appear hollow; such animals are said to be pseudocoelous, or pseudocoelomate.

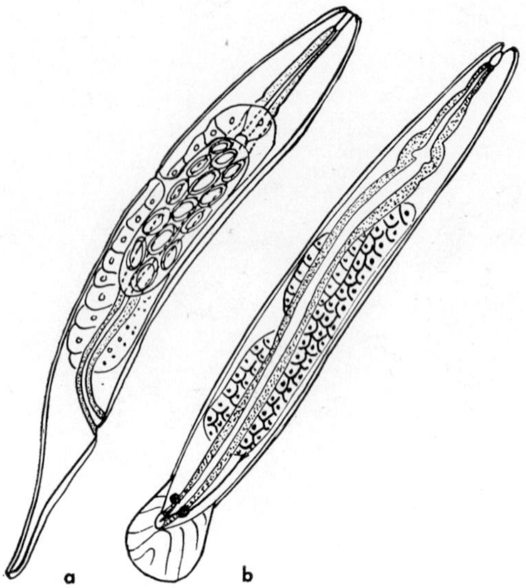

Rotifers and nematodes, both phyla of wide distribution, illustrate the pseudocoelomate condition. Rotifers are microscopic, aquatic animals, many types of which were included in Leeuwenhoek's descriptions of animalcules from rain and pond water (Fig. 13.2). Nematodes are round, unsegmented worms, living in water and other liquids, in the soil, in the air and in the bodies of other animals and plants, and ranging in size from the microscopic "vinegar eels," that live in vinegar vats, to the comparatively enormous guinea worm, a parasite in the tissues of human beings in India, Africa and South America, and recently found in the United States in dogs and mink (Fig. 13.3).

FIGURE 13.3  Nematodes. (Drawn from life.)

a. Rhabditis (female), a minute nematode that lives on decaying substances in the ground.
b. Rhabditis (male).

## Coelomate animals; origin and extent of the coelome

The majority of animal phyla inhabiting the earth to-day are coelomate, with a secondary body cavity that, in the course of growth, compresses the primary one and so reduces it to varying degrees. The coelome may originate in different ways in different kinds of animals, but always between two layers of mesoderm, properly called mesothelia. In some animals, the coelome appears first as pouches from the wall of the primitive digestive tract, its walls made of cells that have differentiated as mesothelium; in others, it appears first as a slit or a space in initially solid sheets or cords of mesoderm cells, derived from cells that have entered the blastocoele (Figs. 25.8, 25.12). As the pouch, or the slit, or the space enlarges, it occupies more and more of the area previously occupied by the primary body cavity, pushing it and whatever mesenchyme cells it may contain against the outer body wall and the inner digestive tract. The coelome itself therefore comes to be the principal space around the digestive tract and the primary body cavity occluded to a greater or less extent. In some animals, like the worms, it extends from the anterior end to the posterior, but in others, like the vertebrates, it is limited to the region of the body in which the visceral organs lie, and extends neither into the head nor the tail. It is bounded by mesothelium, modified as coelomic epithelium or peritoneum, and in the worms more or less completely divided into compartments by partitions or septa of this epithelium. In the mollusks (oysters, clams, snails, squid, etc.) and the arthropods (lobsters, crabs, insects, spiders, etc.) just the opposite conditions prevail. In them, the primary body cavity develops to greater dimensions than the secondary, forming a hemocoele (Greek, haima = blood + koilos = hollow) and reducing the true coelome to a few areas in the body—the cavity of the reproductive organs, the cavity of the excretory organs and the pericardial cavity, or space surrounding the heart. The large cavities in the bodies of these animals are therefore blood spaces or sinuses, filled with fluid

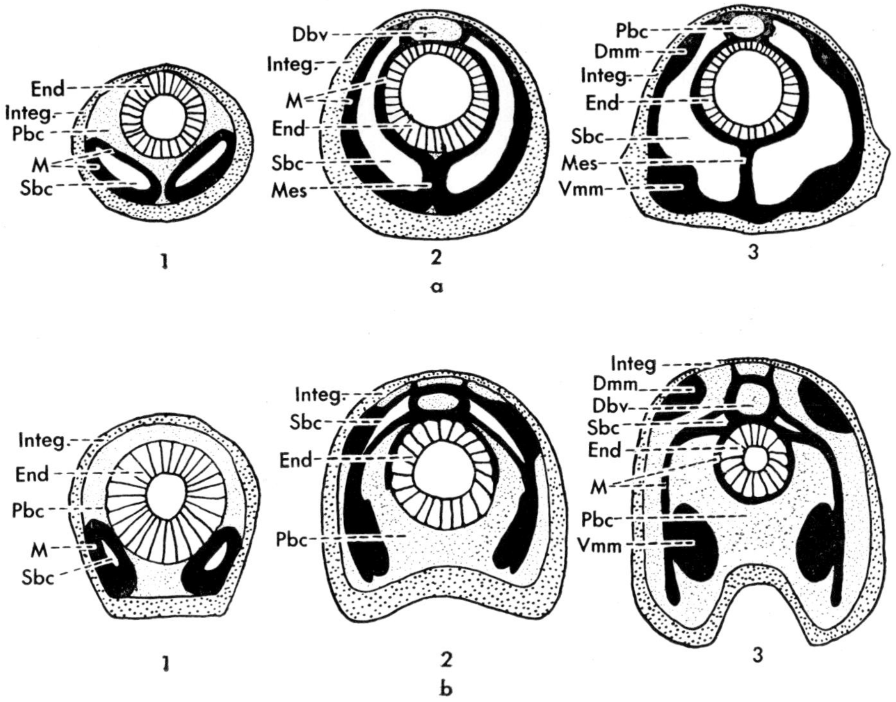

| | |
|---|---|
| Dbv | dorsal blood vessel |
| Dmm | dorsal musculature |
| End | endoderm |
| Integ | integument |
| M | mesothelium |
| Mes | mesentery |
| Pbc | primary body cavity |
| Sbc | secondary body cavity |
| Vmm | ventral musculature |

FIGURE 13.4 Diagrams of cross sections of animals constructed on the annelid and the arthropod plans at successive stages of their developmental histories to show the relations of primary and secondary body cavities. (After Borradaile.)

a. Annelid. Growth of the mesothelium and enlargement of the secondary body cavity (coelome) results in a large perivisceral cavity surrounding the internal organs. The muscles of the body wall and digestive tract, the mesenteries and the peritoneum (coelomic epithelium) are derived from the mesothelium. Through the enlargement of the coelome, the primary body cavity (blastocoele) becomes much reduced.

b. Arthropod. The secondary body cavity remains as an open space only in limited regions, its two walls elsewhere coming together as a solid sheet of mesoderm from which the muscles are developed. The primary body cavity, as a hemocoele, becomes the perivisceral cavity.

and specialized mesenchyme cells, and not coelomic spaces (Fig. 13.4).

**Advantages of a coelome:** Coelomate animals have certain structural advantages over the acoelomate. Elongation of the digestive tract and turnings and foldings in it are possible without encroachment upon other organs, since it is suspended in a cavity filled with liquid; also it may develop enlargements along its course or add accessory structures such as glands for special purposes in the digestion or assimilation of food. Moreover, it may acquire its own musculature and its movements may be independent of those of the animal as a whole; perhaps even more important, the animal possessing it may execute movements of its body without involving the digestive tract directly. The coelome therefore provides

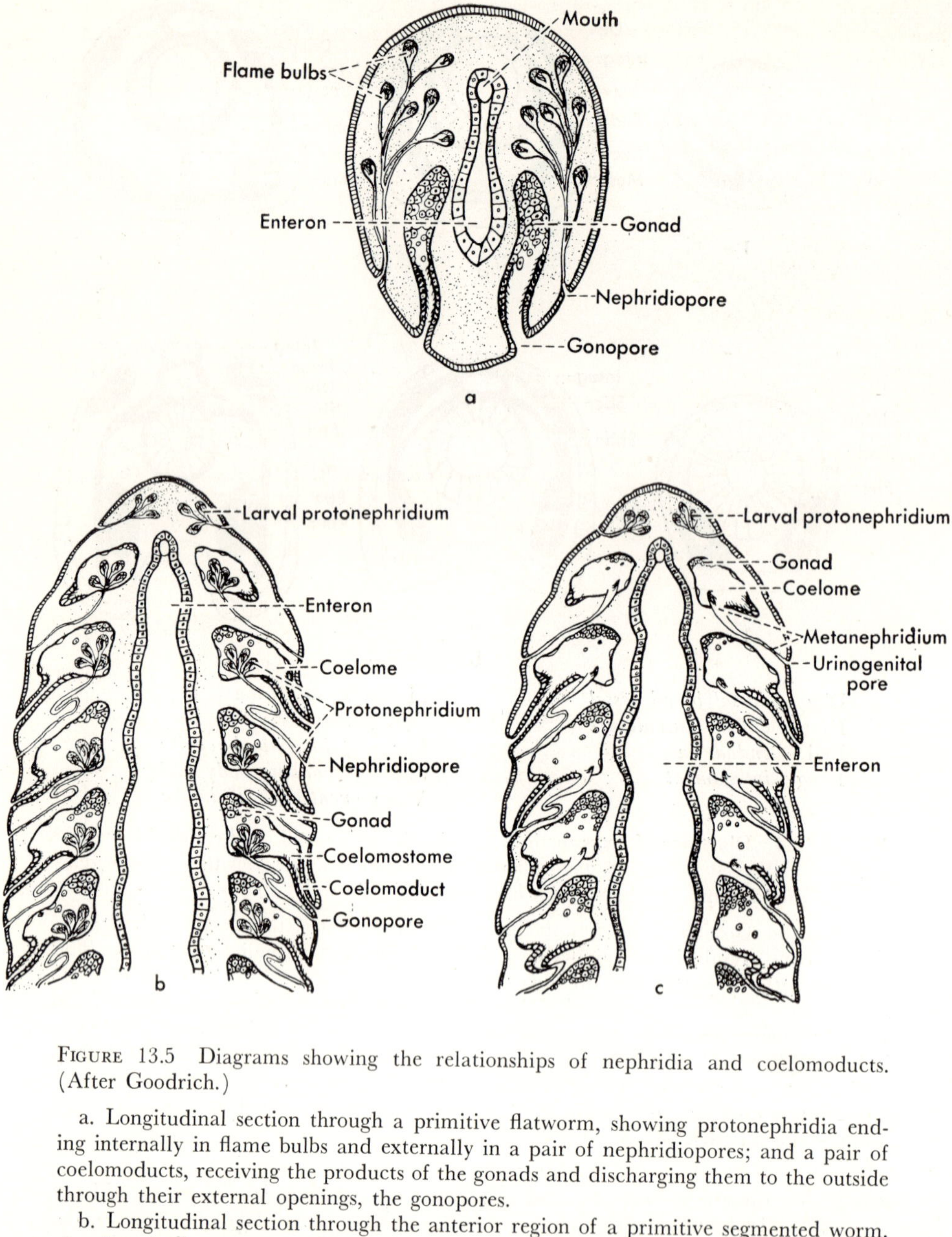

FIGURE 13.5 Diagrams showing the relationships of nephridia and coelomoducts. (After Goodrich.)

a. Longitudinal section through a primitive flatworm, showing protonephridia ending internally in flame bulbs and externally in a pair of nephridiopores; and a pair of coelomoducts, receiving the products of the gonads and discharging them to the outside through their external openings, the gonopores.

b. Longitudinal section through the anterior region of a primitive segmented worm, showing, in the most anterior segment, a pair of protonephridia draining the mesenchyme (as in the larval stages of some modern annelids), and in the posterior segments, protonephridia with flame bulbs lying in the coelomic cavity. In each segment, except the two most anterior, paired coelomoducts are shown, independent of the nephridia and opening to the outside through gonopores.

c. Longitudinal section through a primitive annelid, showing the conversion of protonephridia into metanephridia and their connection with the coelomoducts as mixonephridia.

the enteron with both stability and independence, as well as protection and space for its enlargement. It may also serve as a repository for the waste products of metabolic activity passed into it by the cells lining its walls, and as a region into which the reproductive products may be discharged.

as reproductive ducts, or gonoducts, they have been modified in most animals in the course of evolution. In some cases they have developed into the principal excretory ducts, removing waste that accumulates in the coelome and is swept into their internal openings by ciliary action or that is taken

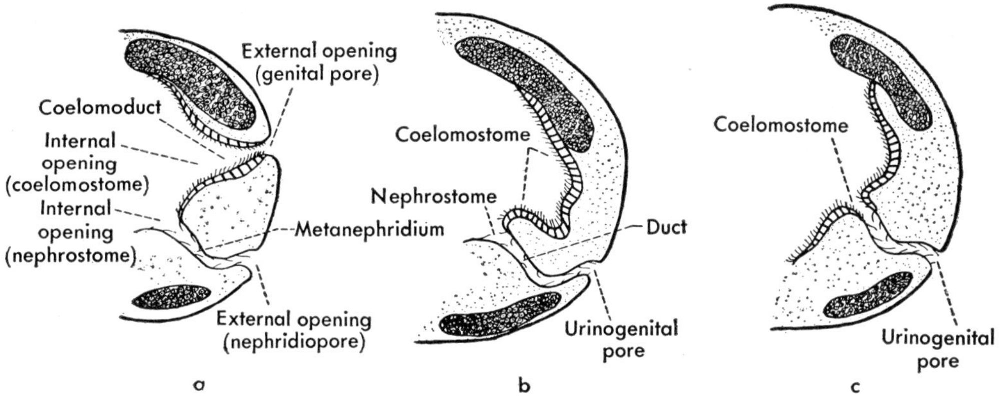

FIGURE 13.6 Diagrams showing the hypothetical derivation of a mixonephridium from an independent coelomoduct and metanephridium. Only the right half of a section across the body is represented. (After Goodrich.)

    a. Independent coelomoduct, through which reproductive cells are passed outside the body, and metanephridium, through which coelomic wastes are eliminated.

    b. Nephromixium, derived by the obliteration of the external opening of the coelomoduct; the reproductive products are removed through the nephromixium, whose external opening serves as a genital as well as an excretory pore.

    c. Mixonephridium, derived by the obliteration of the internal opening of the metanephridium; the duct and external opening have become united to the internal opening of the coelomoduct, forming a compound organ, the mixonephridium.

**Coelomoducts and nephridia:** The reproductive organs, or gonads (Greek, gone = generation), are developed from the walls of the coelome, and in most animals the reproductive cells are shed into its cavity from which they pass to the outside of the body. In some few animals the release of the reproductive cells involves the disruption of part or all of the parent body; in others, they pass to the outside without disruptive effects through permanent passages, mesodermal tubes leading from the coelome through the body wall, each opening on the surface by a pore. These passages, or coelomoducts, establish direct connection between the coelome and the exterior, providing a means of egress for the coelomic contents. While in their primitive condition they most probably functioned exclusively

up by the cells of their walls and passed by them into the lumen of the duct. In others, they have combined the function of excretory and reproductive ducts, taking up and eliminating water and soluble substances as well as conducting reproductive cells to the exterior. And in some coelomate animals, connections have been established between the nephridia and the coelomoducts, uniting them into a single organ of compound origin and common function, the mixonephridium.

    In its simplest form, as it is found in acoelomates and in the young and larval stages of some coelomates, the nephridium, primarily an excretory organ serving the mesenchyme and not the coelome, may consist of but a single pair of flame cells each connecting directly with the exterior. In most, however, there are a number of flame cells distributed throughout the body and connected with canals which are derived from ectodermal cells, hollowed out and arranged end to end like the separate pieces of a drain pipe (Fig. 13.5a). The tube itself is therefore an intracellular one, its walls those of the consecutive cells. Such an excretory organ, with no direct connection with the coelome, is known as a protonephridium; if it has acquired a connection with the coelome, it is known as a metanephridium, its internal opening as the nephrostome and its external one as the nephridiopore. In the one case the dissolved metabolic wastes are taken up from the mesenchyme by the flame cells and flushed out of the body through the tubes; in the other, coelomic fluid, containing metabolic waste and other tissue detritus, is swept into the open nephrostomes by the action of their cilia and out through the nephridiopores; in its passage along the tube the fluid may acquire some new solutes, diffusing into it from the surrounding tissues, and some of its water and possibly its solutes may pass back across the walls of the tubes to the fluid matrix of the tissue in which it lies (Fig. 13.6).

**Conditions imposed by the coelome:** But with its advantages, the presence of the coelome, and of the mesothelium, has imposed certain conditions upon the organisms possessing them which must have been met by the ancestral stock of the modern coelomates to permit their perpetuation. These conditions arise from the spatial separation of many of the tissues from the surface, primarily the region for the oxygen-carbon dioxide exchange which is fundamental to the metabolism of most animals, and from the areas in which the food undergoes chemical disintegration. In the sponges, coelenterates and ctenophores, the cells of the outer and inner layers are in contact with the external environment, and diffusion of oxygen into the cells, and of carbon dioxide and other soluble metabolic wastes from them, can take place directly from and to the surrounding medium. The process of diffusion, aided by the movements of the animal's body, and the movement of fluid by ciliary action in those species with a canalicular system, is adequate to distribute the digested nutrients from the endoderm cells to the ectoderm and the mesenchyme, and to remove metabolic waste or special products from the loosely arranged cells of this middle layer. Even in the flatworms, with a more compact middle layer, diffusion and bodily movements are sufficient to maintain these relations, for their thin, flattened bodies provide a large surface area in proportion to the volume, some of the mesenchyme cells are migratory, carrying materials around the body, and in most there is an internal system, the flame cells and the canals leading from them, through which metabolic waste can be eliminated from the body without involving the surface directly.

But with the development of the middle layer as a tissue, giving rise to organs which, as is the case particularly with the muscles, are made of close-packed cells with little intercellular substance and with a high metabolic rate, diffusion, even when supplemented with bodily movements, becomes too slow a process to be effective in the adequate distribution of materials about the body. At best it is a slow process, at least in the range of temperature that protoplasm can tolerate, and as the only distributing mechanism could hardly be adequate except for animals of small size, diffuse tissues and sluggish habits. The animals that have by-passed these limitations and attained greater size, greater structural differentiations, more compact tissues and the possibilities of more active lives are those in which a transport system has developed, by which oxygen can be carried from the regions where it can diffuse from the medium to cells not in contact with the external environment; by which nutrients can be carried from the digestive tract to outlying cells; and by which carbon dioxide and other soluble waste products of metabolism can be carried from all the cells to regions where they can be eliminated from the body. In nearly all coelomate animals there is such an accelerating transport system, the blood, a fluid tissue of mesenchymal origin, in which specialized mesenchyme cells, the blood corpuscles, float in an aqueous solution of considerable complexity. In most animals, the blood flows through definite channels or vessels, whose finest branches penetrate into all the tissues of the body, where the actual diffusion of materials takes place along the concentration gradient; in most of them, it is propelled along these vessels mainly by the rhythmical contractions of a particularly muscular region of the vascular wall, the heart. In the arthropods and mollusks, it is contained also in the blood sinuses, the hemocoele derived from the primary body cavity. The development of a blood system has permitted also the development of specialized regions for the intake of oxygen and the elimination of carbon dioxide for the body as a whole, and of specialized areas for the digestion of food, the production of specific secretions and for the elimination of excess water and soluble waste. In the more highly evolved and specialized animals, the blood has developed other functions in addition to these fundamental ones, and has also become more complex in its own constitution.

The appearance of the coelome, however it may have come about, was undoubtedly of tremendous importance to the ancestral stock from which modern animals have evolved in offering possibilities for greater elaboration of tissues and organ systems, permitting the development of massive muscle systems from the mesoderm, the enlargement and specialization of parts of the digestive and reproductive systems and indirectly, through the establishment of a vascular system, the centralization of the respiratory, excretory and nervous systems. It is scarcely surprising therefore that the most adaptable animal types, capable of making adjustments to environments of different kinds, and those most highly evolved, should be of the coelomate pattern.

## The most generalized coelomate animals: the annelids

The coelomate pattern is found in its most generalized form in the annelids (Latin, anulus = ring), bilaterally symmetrical animals whose bodies are round and made up of a series of segments (somites or metameres) which, except for the most anterior and posterior ones, are similar to each other. The many existing species of annelids are found all over the world, in salt, brackish and fresh water and in damp sea sand and in the soil; some are external parasites on the bodies of other animals. In size, they range from the fresh water Aeolosoma, about 1 mm. in length, to the giant earthworms of South America and Australia, with bodies over 7 feet in length and 1 inch in diameter. In many, some of the anterior segments bearing organs of special sense, are clearly marked off as a head.

### Nereis (Neanthes), the clam worm: external anatomy

Nereis (or Neanthes), the clam worm, common in shallow water and in burrows in the sand at tide level, is representative of the annelid plan (Fig. 13.7). Externally, the

FIGURE 13.7 Nereis (Neanthes) virens, the clam worm. (Photograph by courtesy of the New York Zoological Society.)

body is made up of a head, composed of two segments, behind which is a series of 80 or more segments all alike except for slight size differences. On the dorsal surface of the most anterior external segment are two pairs of eyes, two glandular pits called nuchal organs (French, nucal = pertaining to the nape of the neck), a pair of short, slender tentacles and a pair of thicker projections, the palps. The eyes are cups of pigmented cells sunk below the surface and covered by transparent ectoderm (Fig. 13.8); the depression of the cup is filled with gelatinous material which refracts the light rays and so serves as a lens, and the light-sensitive cells at the base of the cup terminate in nerve fibers. The nuchal organs are small pits on the dorsal surface, lined by gland cells and presumably olfactory in function. The tentacles and palps are sensitive to contact stimuli, and most probably are organs of touch. There are four pairs of tentacles on the next segment, rather longer and more slender than the anterior ones.

Each segment behind the head except the last has a broad, fleshy, blade-like extension of each lateral wall, the parapodium (Greek, parapodios = at the feet) (Fig. 13.9). Each parapodium is divided into two principal and several minor lobes; from each of the two principal lobes project tufts of stiff bristles, the setae (Latin, seta = bristle), small rods of chitin which can be retracted, projected and moved in various directions by muscle fibres attached to their bases near the cells which secreted them. In each principal lobe, there is also one larger, thicker and darker seta, the acicula (Latin, diminutive of acus = needle), which projects only a short distance from the surface and probably acts as a supporting rod. Both the dorsal and the ventral lobes have a single, short tentacle-like projection, the cirrus (Latin, cirrus = fringe), which like the tentacles of the head seems to serve as organs of touch. The terminal segment of the series, in which lies the posterior opening of the digestive tract, the anus, and in which parapodia are lacking, bears also a pair of cirri, the anal cirri, which are markedly longer than those of the parapodia. The

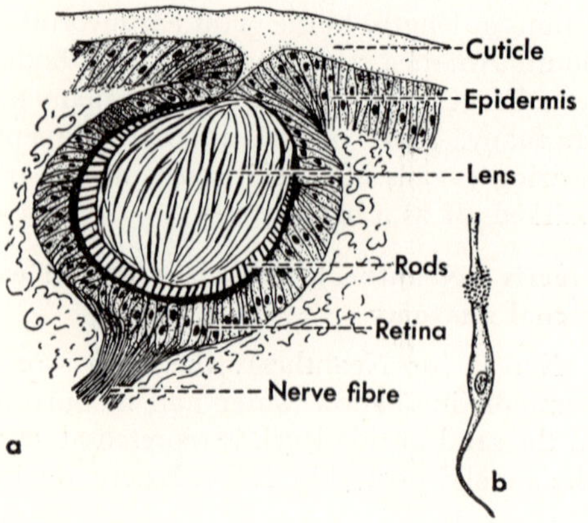

FIGURE 13.8 Eye of Nereis (after Andrews).
 a. Section through the entire eye.
 b. Isolated retinal cell and rod. x 325.

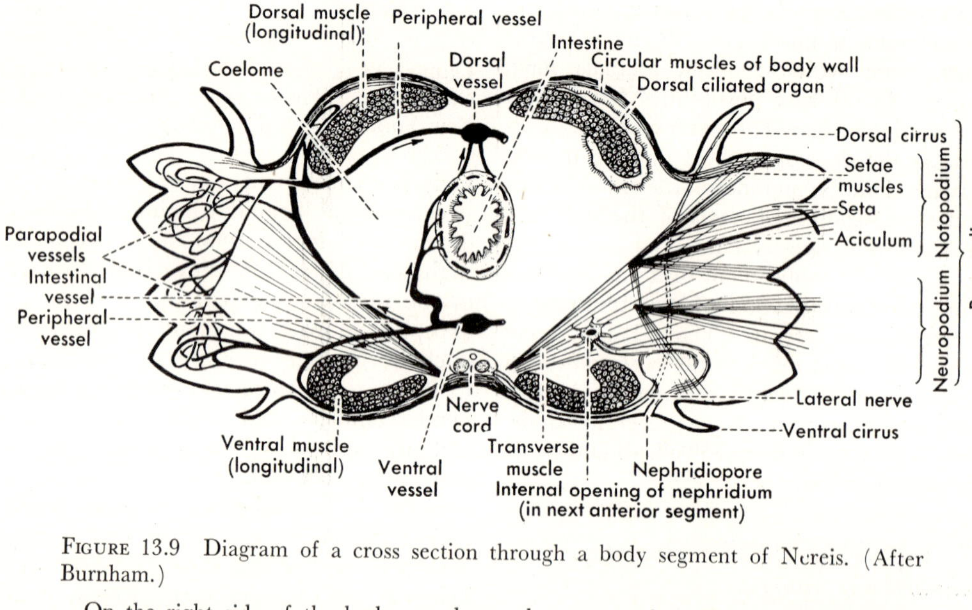

FIGURE 13.9 Diagram of a cross section through a body segment of Nereis. (After Burnham.)

On the right side of the body are shown the setae and their muscles, the lateral nerve and a nephridium, represented as lying wholly within the segment, although actually the internal opening of each nephridium (mixonephridium) lies in the segment anterior to that in which its external opening is located; on the left, the distribution of the principal blood vessels carrying blood from the ventral vessel to the various organs is shown, and that of the vessels returning it from these organs to the dorsal vessel.

## THE TUBE-WITHIN-A-TUBE PLAN    [ 213 ]

parapodia, moved by muscles, are used in crawling when the animal is in the sand, and like oars when it is swimming in the water. They also increase the surface of the body, presenting a greater area for the oxygen-carbon dioxide exchange.

mesoderm cells, differentiating as muscle cells, form also bundles of muscles that run obliquely from the dorsal to the ventral circular muscle layer in each segment, and the muscles by which the parapodia and the setae are moved.

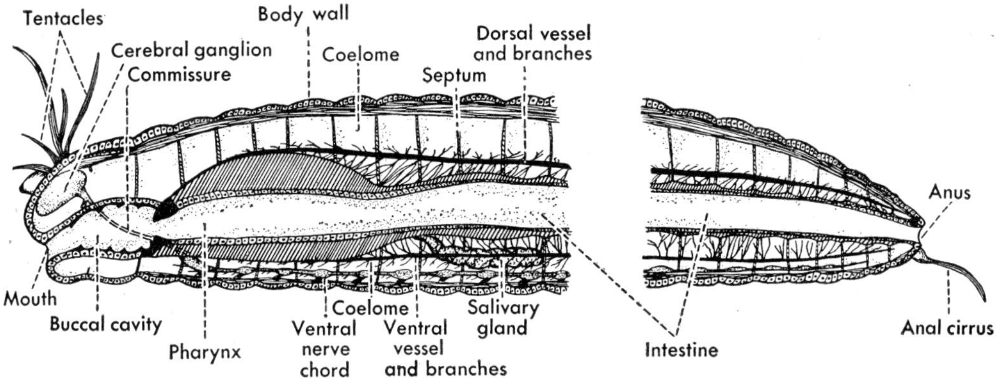

FIGURE 13.10  Diagram showing the anatomy of Nereis as represented in the most anterior and the most posterior segments. (From various sources.)

***Internal anatomy:*** The surface of the body is covered by a thin cuticle secreted by the superficial cells of the body wall and marked by fine intersecting lines which refract the light and so make the surface appear iridescent. The body wall itself is made up of many cell layers. The outer layer, or epidermis (Greek, epi = upon + dermis = skin), is thin on the dorsal surface, rather thicker on the ventral, and is made of a single layer of ectoderm cells, many of which are specialized as gland cells. Closely applied to the ectoderm is the outer sheet of mesothelium, whose peripheral cells have developed into muscle fibres, while the innermost layer, in contact with the coelome, has become a delicate epithelium, the peritoneum (Greek, peritonaion = stretched around). The muscle fibres are arranged in two layers; in the outer layer, just beneath the ectoderm, the long axes of the cells are approximately parallel to the circumference of the cylindrical body, forming a circular muscle layer; in the inner layer they are arranged in 4 thick bundles parallel to its long axis as a system of longitudinal muscles. The body wall, therefore, is of considerable thickness, and derived from the mesoderm as well as from the ectoderm. Some of the

DIGESTIVE SYSTEM: The digestive tract is a continuous tube from the mouth, a slit on the ventral surface of the externally second segment, to the anus on the most posterior segment (Fig. 13.10). Nereis possesses a retractable proboscis, which has generally been believed to represent the anterior part of the digestive tract that could be everted through the mouth, but which recent anatomical studies of the distribution of nerves to it has shown to be the first two or three segments of the body that can be withdrawn through the mouth opening or extended through it by the action of special bands of muscle fibers (Fig. 13.11). These segments are provided with several rows of short, hard, chitinous projections, the denticles, and the most anterior one with a pair of thick, curved chitinous rods with serrated or saw-toothed inner surfaces, the jaws. When the proboscis is everted, these jaws extend anteriorly and are moved in the capture of prey or to macerate the small animals upon which the worm feeds. The food so caught and broken up by the combined operations of denticles and jaws passes into the region of the digestive tract known as the oesophagus, which extends for about five segments and in which its chemical disintegration

[214] THE ORGANIZATION OF BIOLOGICAL SYSTEMS

may begin. Two sacs, occupying about five segments, lie on either side of the oesophagus and open into it by small apertures; these probably act as digestive glands. Most of the digestion, however, takes place in the stomach-intestine, which extends through- anterior to posterior. This kind of contraction is called peristalsis (Greek, peristalsis = to send around), a term that was first used by Galen. The peritoneum of the body wall, the parietal (Latin, paries = partition) or somatic (Greek, soma = body)

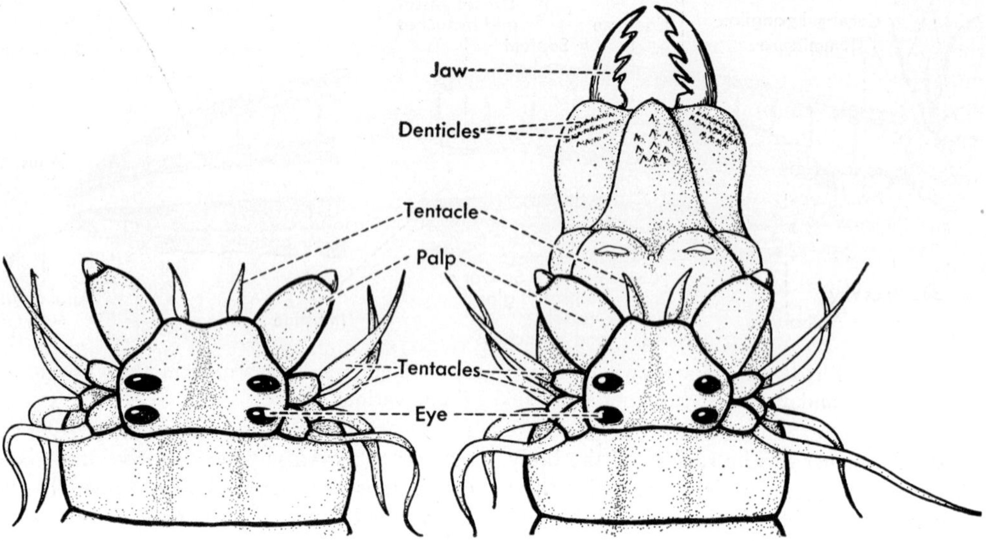

FIGURE 13.11  Head of Nereis from the dorsal aspect.
Left. Head with proboscis retracted. Right. Head with proboscis everted.

out the greater part of the worm's body and whose glandular endodermal cells secrete enzymes into the lumen to accelerate the decomposition of the food. In the final segment, the stomach-intestine becomes the rectum, lined with ectoderm, and derived from the embryonic proctodaeum.

The endodermal wall of the enteron is supplemented by tissues derived from the inner sheet of mesothelium which have differentiated as muscles and coelomic epithelium. The muscles next to the glandular endodermal cells are arranged with their long axes around the circumference of the tube; the next external layer forms a longitudinal system, outside of which lie the epithelial cells of the peritoneum, in contact with the fluid of the coelome. The food, taken in through the mouth, is propelled along the enteron by contractions of the muscles of its walls, moving like waves from layer of coelomic epithelium, is continuous with that surrounding the digestive tract, the splanchnic layer (Greek, splanchnicos = inward part), through the mesenteries (Greek, mesos = middle + enteron = intestine), double sheets of peritoneum which separate the coelomic cavity into right and left halves (Fig. 13.4). The mesenteries suspend the digestive tract, and some of the other organs, in the coelome where they carry on their own muscular movements independent of the rest of the body. Between adjacent segments throughout the body are septa of mesodermal tissue, more or less completely dividing the body transversely into compartments corresponding to the segments. In none of the annelids is the division of the coelome complete, for internal communication between the segments is provided by pores or other openings in the septa.

VASCULAR SYSTEM: The vascular system of Nereis consists of three principal longitudinal vessels with muscular walls and numerous smaller vessels. The fluid within them, the blood, contains some amoeboid cells and a dissolved protein, the red pigment hemoglobin, which has the chemical property of forming an unstable compound with oxygen and so acts as a respiratory pigment. One of the longitudinal vessels is suspended in the mesentery above the digestive tract as the dorsal vessel, running almost the entire length of the animal's body; a second is similarly suspended beneath the digestive tract as the ventral vessel, and the third, considerably smaller than the dorsal and the ventral, runs within the ventral body wall beneath the collection of nerve cells that forms the nerve cord. The muscular walls of these vessels maintain wave-like contractions, so that the blood is sent along them by peristalsis. In the dorsal vessel, the contraction waves are more powerful than in the other vessels and move from posterior to anterior, forcing the blood in this vessel forward. Peristalsis in the ventral vessel is in the opposite direction, so that the flow of blood is from anterior to posterior. Connections are established between the dorsal and the ventral vessels by two pairs of vessels in each segment which curve around the digestive tract and send branches to it, the body wall, the parapodia and other organs (Fig. 13.9). These branches divide and subdivide into vessels with finer and finer bores and more delicate walls, the finest vessels forming a network whose meshes enclose the cells of the various tissues. The exchange of materials from the blood to the cells, and vice versa, takes place by diffusion through the walls of these tiny vessels. The system is a closed one, and by peristalsis principally in the dorsal, and to some extent in the ventral, vessel, the blood is kept in constant circulation through the blood channels.

RESPIRATORY AREAS: As the blood flows through the smallest vessels in the wall of the digestive tract, the soluble end products of the digestion of the food pass into it from the endodermal cells which have absorbed them from the lumen, and are carried by the circulating blood to all the other tissues where they diffuse out into the cells along the concentration gradient. Similarly, carbon dioxide and other solutes eliminated from the cells enter the blood and are carried along in it until they reach an area where conditions are such as to bring about their release. In the case of carbon dioxide, this area is the body surface, and particularly that of the parapodia, which are richly supplied with blood vessels. When it reaches the vessels of the parapodia and the surface epithelium, the blood has a relatively high carbon dioxide and a relatively low oxygen content, so that conditions are set up for the diffusion of carbon dioxide from these vessels into the surrounding water, and of oxygen, dissolved in water, into them. Certain chemical factors are involved in this exchange as well. Among these, one of the most important is the chemical nature of the hemoglobin molecule, which reacts with oxygen in such a way that it combines readily with it at comparatively low concentrations, or pressures, of the gas, and equally readily releases it when the concentration is reduced and the pH of its medium slightly lowered. Some other pigments have this capacity as well, and so can act as respiratory pigments, but of them all hemoglobin is the most effective. The presence of such a pigment in the blood means that it can take up and carry an amount of oxygen considerably in excess of that which goes into solution, the extent of the difference depending upon the properties of the pigment and the amount of it that is present in the vascular system.

EXCRETORY ORGANS: In addition to its oxygen-carbon dioxide transport, the blood also conveys other soluble waste from the tissues to the regions from which it can be excreted. Except in a few of the most anterior and posterior segments, there is a pair of metanephridia in each segment, opening into the coelome through a ciliated funnel, the nephrostome, and to the outside by a small pore, the nephridiopore, near the ventral cirrus of each parapodium. Between the two openings the intracellular canal is ciliated through most of its course, and is twisted and doubled back upon itself so that the canal is quite long. Coelomic waste is swept into the nephrostomes by ciliary currents, and excess water and metabolic waste are passed across the walls of the canal and driven to the nephridiopore by the beating of the cilia. The coelomoducts as such in Nereis are rudimentary and have no openings to the exterior, at least no permanent ones. They are represented by short, blind, funnel-like depressions of the peritoneum, the dorsal ciliated organs, which lie in pairs in each segment near the dorsal bundles of longitudinal muscles (Fig. 13.9). Possibly they function seasonally as gonoducts, for the reproductive cells are produced from patches of peritoneum at certain times of the year and discharged directly into the coelome, from which they escape to the outside without any apparent rupture of the body wall.

NERVOUS SYSTEM: The nervous system of Nereis and the other annelids consists of special sensory regions, such as the eyes, the tentacles, the nuchal organs and other more generally distributed areas of sensitivity; nerves that connect these organs and areas with a central system; and the central system itself, consisting of a nerve cord made up of a double chain of ganglia, one pair in each segment except those most anterior, each one of which is joined to the ones immediately posterior and anterior to it by a cord, or commissure, of nervous tissue. All but the most anterior of these ganglia lie beneath the digestive tract, forming a ventral chain from which pairs of nerves extend laterally in each segment establishing connection between the central cord and the various parts of the animal's body. The most anterior of the ganglia lies dorsal to the digestive tract, connected with the ventral chain by a pair of commissures that surround the oesophagus. This is a compound ganglion, derived from the fusion of a dorsal and a ventral nerve mass, and from it and the commissure around the oesophagus nerves pass to the eyes and the tentacles, the muscles of the head segments and those of the proboscis. The nerves contain numbers of nerve cells, or their processes, some carrying stimuli from the sensory areas on the surface to the central system, and others carrying impulses from the central system to the muscles or other effector organs by which the animal makes its response to stimuli from within itself or from the outside. The first ganglion of the ventral chain, like all the rest succeeding it, is connected by lateral nerves with the parapodia, the body wall and the various organs of its segment, along which impulses travel to and from all parts of the body.

Through its organs and areas of special sense, the worm is able to receive stimuli from its environment; through its tactile organs from that with which it is immediately in contact, and through its eyes and nuchal organs from that which is at a distance. These stimuli are relayed through the central system and transmitted to the appropriate effectors. Stimuli arising within the worm itself—from the muscles, the digestive tract and other parts of the body—are similarly relayed, with the result that the animal shows coordinated responses, or behavior. With such a system, the change, or impulse, that is initiated in a nerve cell by a stimulus travels fairly definite paths and may be relayed considerable distances throughout the body instead of spreading diffusely in all directions through a nerve net like that of the coelenterates and flatworms. The annelid nervous system shows another functional property not shown by animals lower in the evolutionary scale—that of inhibition. If the dorsal ganglia are removed from a nereis, the animal moves constantly about, showing that in these nervous masses lie centers inhibiting random, undirected movements; if both the dorsal and the first ventral ganglion are removed, the animal remains quiescent unless directly stimulated, like a flatworm whose ganglia have been removed or destroyed.

## Lumbricus, the earthworm

Earthworms are land-dwelling annelids, commonly tunneling through the soil and living in burrows some distance below the surface, although emerging at times to crawl along the ground. Their bodies are segmented, with a less clearly defined head than

Nereis, no parapodia and comparatively few setae (Fig. 13.12). These are developed in pairs along the lateral and ventral surfaces of each segment, and serve to anchor the worm temporarily in its burrow, or its tunnel which it moves along by contractions of its

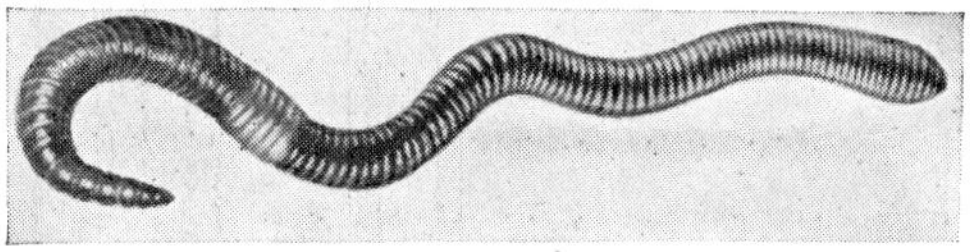

FIGURE 13.12 Lumbricus terrestris, the common earthworm. (Photograph by courtesy of the U.S. Department of Agriculture, Bureau of Entomology and Plant Quarantine.)

muscular body wall. Although there are photosensory areas on the surface of the body, particularly in the anterior region, and the first segment at least is sensitive to touch, there are no conspicuous sense organs like those of Nereis. Nor are there any denticles or jaws. Earthworms feed upon the organic material that they can extract from the soil in which they live; consequently they are most numerous in rich, loamy soil where there is much decaying vegetation. The wall of the pharynx is very muscular; through the action of these muscles, which radiate out and are attached to the body wall of the anterior segments, soil is sucked in and passed on to the oesophagus (Fig. 13.13). Posterior to the oesophagus, the digestive tract is modified as a soft-walled, slightly distensible crop in which the food may be temporarily stored. Back of the crop is another enlarged region, the gizzard, with hard, thick and muscular walls into which food is periodically passed from the crop and in which it is churned about and ground up by the fine soil particles taken in with it. Posterior to the gizzard, the digestive tract continues to the anus as the stomach-intestine, whose internal surface is increased by a longitudinal fold along the dorsal wall, the typhlosole (Greek, typhlos = blind + solen = pipe) (Fig. 13.14). In its passage, by peristalsis, along the digestive tract, the organic part of the ingested material is digested; any undigested residue is eliminated through the anus together with the particles of earth. The feeding habits of earthworms are responsible for much of the alteration that is constantly taking place in the surface layers of the earth, for they bring up to the surface, as castings, the soil from the deeper layers, sometimes burying surface structures, and always aerating and enriching, and in a miniature way plowing, the earth in which they live.

The coelome is a large space around the digestive tract, filled with fluid in which there are some cells, the coelomic corpuscles, and incompletely divided by septa into segmental compartments. The peritoneum on the surface of the stomach intes-

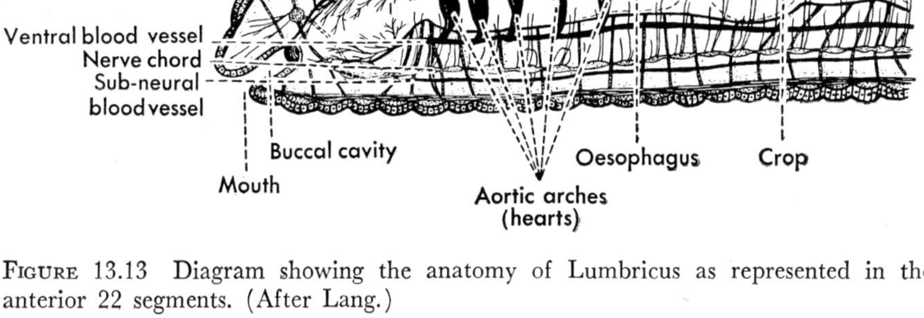

FIGURE 13.13 Diagram showing the anatomy of Lumbricus as represented in the anterior 22 segments. (After Lang.)

[ 218 ]  THE ORGANIZATION OF BIOLOGICAL SYSTEMS

tine is modified as tall, columnar cells, filled with yellow granules, the chloragogue cells (Greek, chloros = yellowish green + agoge = a leading), which have been shown to take up waste material from the coelomic fluid and so to act as storage regions for metabolic waste and cellular detritus. The tions with the coelomoducts of each segment; hence each one is a mixonephridium. The coelomoducts remain complete in only three segments as gonoducts, for earthworms have reproductive organs that are permanent in the adults, although only seasonally active.

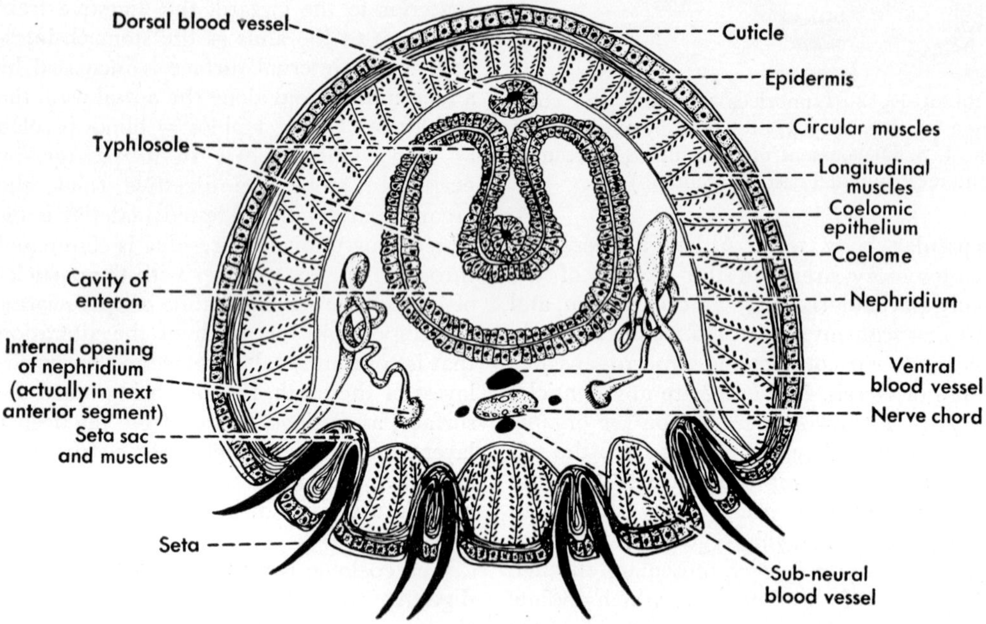

FIGURE 13.14 Diagram of a cross-section through the body of Lumbricus in the region of the stomach-intestine. (After Lang.)

The nephridia are shown in their entirety although in the animal the internal openings (nephrostomes) lie in the segments anterior to the coiled tubules of the organs and their external openings (nephridiopores).

blood system is of the same general pattern as in Nereis and the blood contains hemoglobin in solution. But in the earthworm, five of the pairs of vessels connecting the dorsal and the ventral vessels—those in the seventh to the eleventh segment—have more muscular walls and a greater diameter than the others. Contractions of the walls of these vessels, the hearts, give the main propulsive force to the blood and together with the peristalsis of the principal vessels send it along the other channels of the vascular system. The excretory organs are arranged in pairs in each segment except the first three and the last; they are compound organs, metanephridia which have acquired connec-

*Modifications for a terrestrial existence:* Earthworms show certain modifications related to their terrestrial and subterranean existence. One of these is an additional connection between the coelome and the exterior, provided by a dorsal pore on the dorsal surface of each segment. As the animal burrows deeper into the earth and is thus subjected to greater atmospheric pressure, coelomic fluid may be expressed through these pores, adjusting the internal hydrostatic pressure as well as moistening the surface. Mucus-secreting cells in the epidermis serve to keep the surface of the animal constantly moist, a condition that is essential to its existence, for there are no specialized respiratory areas and the surface of the body acts as the principal area of gaseous interchange. A fine network of blood capillaries lies just below the epidermis, from which carbon dioxide diffuses into the covering slime and into which oxygen dissolved in it passes by the same means. If the surface slime dries up, as sometimes happens when worms lose their connections with their burrows and are exposed to the sun, they die from asphyxiation. Correlated with this is also the pattern of their behavior in the avoidance of light, their burrowing existence and nocturnal habits, an adjustment of the nervous system that offers them some protection from failure of the respiratory mechanism. Water loss from the surface is minimized by the the presence of a cuticle which covers the body beneath the coat of slime, so that evaporation from the epidermis in general is but slight. Moreover, it is probable that the nephridia absorb some water from the fluid that passes along their tubules, returning it to the system as a whole, and so conserving the supply within the body.

## Segmentation

Nereis and Lumbricus, the common earthworm, are animals showing segmentation to a high degree, for the greater part of their bodies is made up of a series of apparently identical segments. Typically a segment, or a somite, is a region more or less distinctly marked off from the rest of the body by circular grooves and containing a section of the coelome, separated to a great extent from adjacent sections by transverse partitions or septa; a pair of excretory organs; a pair of ganglionic enlargements of the nerve cord; paired lateral nerves; and paired lateral extensions of the body wall, or appendages. But in few animals, even among the annelids, is there such complete serial repetition of parts as there is in Nereis and Lumbricus, or do all the segments retain all their typical features. Frequently the intersegmental grooves disappear, resulting in an apparent fusion of segments, ganglia of several segments may be concentrated in one common mass, appendages or excretory organs may be lacking in certain segments, or other modifications of a strictly segmental pattern may arise. In the leeches, for example, the segmentation is imperfect and the coelome reduced to a series of small spaces, and in two groups of burrowing marine worms, the Echiurids and Sipunculids, no segmentation is apparent in the adults although the animals in their juvenile stages may show it.

## Modifications in other annelids

Various other modifications of the annelid plan are evident in other members of the phylum. Some annelids have many setae, others few and some, none. In the most primitive members of the phylum, the nephridia are protonephridia with no opening into the coelome; the inner end of the organ, a tuft of flame cells, projects into the coelomic cavity and the passage of water and other components of the coelomic fluid takes place across the peritoneum and the plasma membranes of the flame cells. While hemoglobin is the respiratory pigment in the blood of earthworms and of Nereis, a greenish pigment called chlorocruorin, with somewhat lower capacity for combining with oxygen than hemoglobin, is present in the blood of some other marine worms, and another red pigment, erythrocruorin, in the blood of others; while in some the blood contains no respiratory pigment at all. Some, like the burrowing marine worm Arenicola, common along the Atlantic coast, have finger-like projections of the body wall, called gills, where most of the oxygen-carbon dioxide exchange takes place. But while these and the parapodia of Nereis may be particularly effective in the gaseous interchange between the animal and its environment, every free surface, including that of the coelome and the digestive tract, cooperates in it to the extent that the prevailing physical conditions permit.

# CHAPTER 14   THE ARTHROPODS

## General characters of the phylum Arthropoda

The Arthropods (Greek, arthros = joint + pous = foot) are also segmented, coelomate animals with a general body plan that is a modification of the typical annelid plan. The Arthropoda is a very large group of animals, including some 815,000 species, among which are the many different kinds of insects and spiders, the centipedes and millepedes as well as waterfleas, crayfish, shrimps, lobsters, crabs, barnacles and the worm-like Peripatus native to Australia, New Zealand and Borneo. The characteristics common to all arthropods, in addition to the jointed appendages or legs, are an exoskeleton made largely of chitin, in some members impregnated with calcium salts to form a thick outer shell; an extensive hemocoele whose growth has reduced the coelome to the cavities of the reproductive and excretory organs and some few other small spaces in the body (Fig. 13.4); and the absence of nephridia, the excretory function being taken over by modified coelomoducts, by entirely new structures or by cells distributed throughout the body and not specialized for excretory purposes. The chitinous exoskeleton of the arthropods is probably the primary factor which has permitted them to invade the land so successfully, for being light and flexible yet in most cases impermeable to water, it has diminished the danger of dehydration while not restricting too greatly the development of their bodies and limbs in different ways.

## Crustacea; segmentation and primary divisions of the body

The arthropod plan is found in its most generalized form in the Crustacea (Latin, crusta = crust or hard shell), most of which are aquatic, although some few, like the pill bugs and the woodlice, have been able to meet the conditions of terrestrial life in damp habitats. The crustacean body is bilaterally symmetrical and segmented, typically with a pair of jointed appendages attached to each segment which are used for locomotion, for feeding, for respiration and for the reception of stimuli. The anterior segments are marked off as a head, the remainder forming a trunk which in many species is divided into thorax and abdomen. In the most primitive of the crustacea, each trunk segment is covered dorsally by a skeletal plate, the tergum (Latin, tergum = back) and ventrally by a similar but usually somewhat lighter plate, the sternum (Greek, sternon = chest); these plates may be of considerable thickness, whether or not they contain calcium salts as well as chitin. They are always heavier and thicker than the covering between the segments so that the segmented trunk is flexible and can be moved dorso-ventrally and to a certain extent laterally. The external covering of the appendages is also thin over the joints, or articulations, and they can be moved not only where they join the body but also along their length. But in some, the terga of the thorax may be fused into a continuous plate, forming a dorsal shield or carapace, so that the segmentation of this region is not readily evident externally; and in others the carapace may be united to the terga of the head segments, so that there appear to be only two principal divisions of the body, the abdomen and the combined head and thorax or cephalo-thorax (Fig. 14.1).

## Appendages

The appendages of the head segments are in all modern crustacea specialized for the

FIGURE 14.1 Four species of crayfish, typical crustaceans. (Photographs by F. M. Uhler, by courtesy of the U.S. Fish and Wildlife Service.)

a. Cambarus virilis, common in large rivers and lakes in the central United States.

b. Cambarus limosus Rafinesque (Cambarus affinis Say), common in the larger rivers of eastern North America.

c. Cambarus diogenes, a burrowing species common east of the Rocky Mountains, and often found in swamps and meadows some distance from a stream. These are the "chimney crayfishes," for they often build turrets several inches high around the openings of their burrows, sometimes 2–3 feet in depth.

d. Cambarus blandingi, common in the lakes, ponds and sluggish rivers east of the Mississippi River.

[ 221 ]

reception of stimuli and at least one pair as jaws for the ingestion and mastication of food. The head always includes the first six segments of the body. In the more highly specialized crustacea, additional segments of the trunk with their appendages are included in the head, and some of the abdominal segments are reduced or lost. The appendages of the head, in addition to the eyes that are often borne on short stalks, are a pair of slender, flexible antennules and one of thicker antennae, both situated anterior to the mouth and sensitive to touch and possibly also to chemical stimuli as smells and tastes; in the less specialized types, they may combine these sensory functions with mechanical ones such as swimming, grasping and attachment. The jaws, or mandibles, enclose the mouth and serve to grind up the food or to pierce it preparatory to the animal's sucking of its juices, and parts of them may also function in setting up food currents and to a limited extent in locomotion. The remaining two primary head appendages are two pairs of maxillae which may combine the functions of locomotion, or respiration and of feeding by passing food to the mouth (Fig. 14.2).

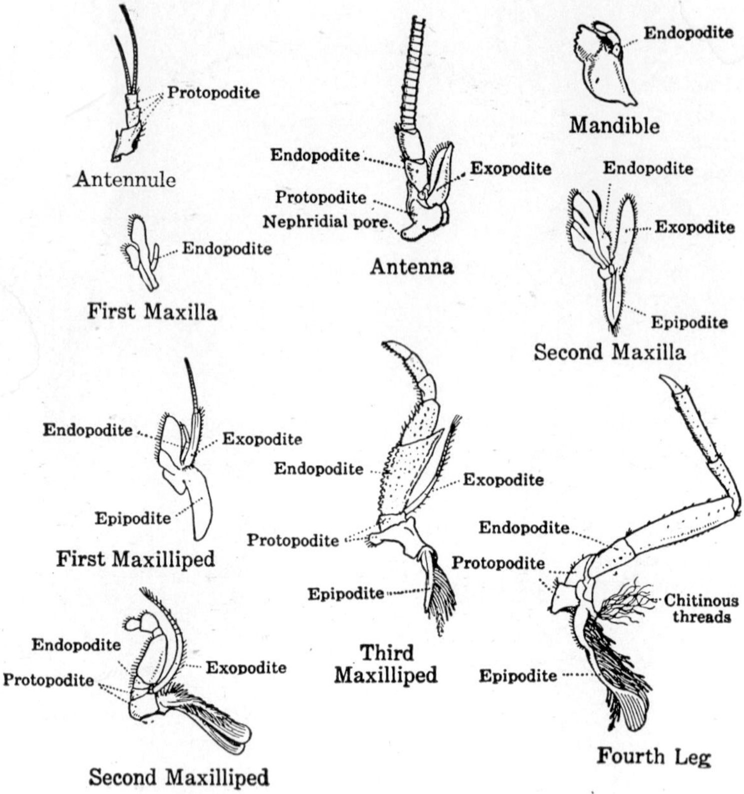

The trunk appendages may be generalized in form and in function, or, as in the more highly evolved crustacea, specialized for various purposes. The common type from which the more specialized appendages have arisen is probably that with a basal part, the protopodite (Greek, protos = first + pous = foot), which is attached to the lateral body wall in such a way as to form a movable joint or articulation and to which are attached two rami (Latin, ramus = branch); the proximal ramus, or that nearer

FIGURE 14.2  The appendages of a crayfish, seen from the ventral surface. (From Hegner, *College Zoology*, 5th edition. Copyright 1942 by The Macmillan Company.)

the midline of the body, is known as the endopodite (Greek, endon = within + pous = foot), and the distal or outer ramus as the exopodite (Greek, exo = without + pous = foot). The protopodite is usually composed of two segments but in some cases

ages, or the entire appendage may be thin-walled and serve as a respiratory area. In the latter case, the appendage is not jointed and its shape is maintained by the pressure of the blood within it which distends its walls and brings the fluid circulating within

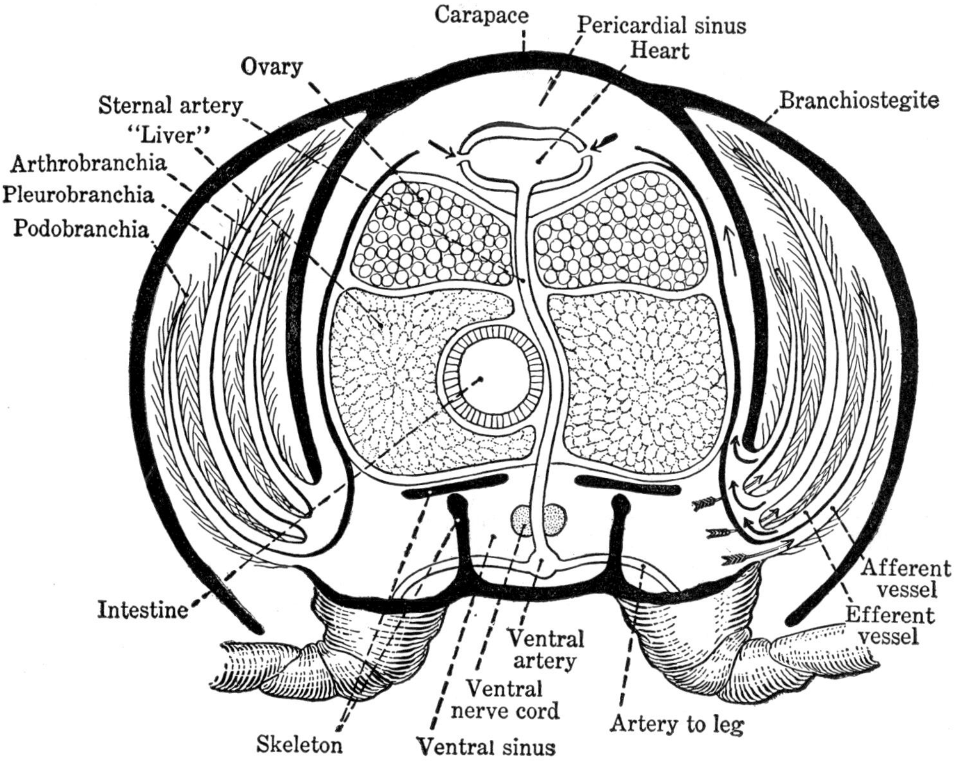

FIGURE 14.3  Cross section of a crayfish through the thoracic region, showing the arrangement of the gills and some of the internal organs. (From Hegner, *College Zoology*, 5th edition. Copyright 1942 by The Macmillan Company.)

of four; the proximal or basal segment, attached to the body, is known as the coxopodite (Latin, coxa = hip + Greek, pous = foot), the distal segment with which the endopodite and exopodite articulate as the basipodite (Greek, basis = base + pous = foot) (Fig. 14.9). The endopodite and exopodite may be many-jointed and fringed with hairs which are probably sensory in function; their movement propels the animal through the water and may also direct a food current toward the mouth and the oral appendages. Special thin-walled respiratory surfaces, the branchia or gills, may develop in connection with these appendages, or the entire appendage may be thin-walled and serve as a respiratory area. In the body close to the surrounding water. Crustacean gills are delicate, feather-shaped structures, developed as outgrowths from the basal segment of the coxopodite or from the articulating surface between the coxopodite and the body wall or from the lateral body wall itself. Structurally they are little more than a system of blood channels covered by epithelium and a thin layer of the exoskeleton across which the gaseous exchange takes place (Fig. 14.3).

### Specialization

Specialization in the crustacea has proceeded mainly in the direction of the inclu-

FIGURE 14.4 Crabs.

a. Cancer magister, an edible crab common below low-water mark along the entire Pacific coast of North America. (Photograph by V. B. Scheffer, courtesy of the U.S. Fish and Wildlife Service.)

b. Gelasimus (Uca) pugnax, the fiddler crab, common along the Atlantic coast of the United States. (Photograph by courtesy of the American Museum of Natural History, New York.)

sion of additional trunk segments in the head, and the development of appendages for particular purposes in the general activities of the animal. With the greater efficiency resulting from such specialization, some of them have been lost or reduced in the more highly evolved members. The concentration of important sensory areas and important organs in the head, or cephalization (Greek, kephale = head), evident to some extent in the annelids, has gone considerably further in the arthropods and is correlated with the condensation of the segmental ganglia of the nervous system into large masses in the anterior segments. In the specialization of the appendages, one or the other of the two rami, most frequently the exopodite, may be reduced in size or wholly lost while the other may become structurally modified in various ways for different functions. One of the most important of these modifications, from the point of view of the possibilities that it opened for crustacean development, concerns the relations of the last two segments of some of the thoracic appendages by which the terminal segment became opposable to that immediately behind it, forming a grasping organ or pincer (Fig. 14.1). With appendages of this type, the crustacean was able to seize prey and with the further development of the most anterior of these appendages as a heavy crusher claw to break it up before handing it on to the more delicate mouth parts. The crusher claw is developed on only one of the pair, usually the right one, while the terminal segments of the other appendage of the pair form a lighter pair of pincers; in those species in which the crusher claw has reached its greatest development, like the lobsters and crabs, the body is no longer strictly speaking bilaterally symmetrical, but asymmetrical. This asymmetry is most strikingly evident in the fiddler crabs, where the first thoracic appendage of the right side is greatly enlarged and, ending in a long pincer, extends across the front of the head to the left side (Fig. 14.4).

The highly specialized crustacean appendages are confined to the head and the thorax; the abdominal appendages, if present at all, are usually small and biramous, that is, retaining both the endopodite and the exopodite. Where present, they function primarily in reproduction, where they may serve to direct the distribution of the reproductive cells after they have been emitted from the animal's body or to hold, and by slow backwards and forwards movement to aerate, the eggs during the course of their embryology. In many species, abdominal appendages are entirely absent.

## Internal anatomy

Internally the crustacean plan, and that of the arthropods in general, shows marked differences from the annelid plan while retaining the general pattern of coelomate animals of a tube-within-a-tube (Fig. 14.5). The body wall is composed of an epithelium, which secretes the exoskeleton, and which in some species contains special pigment-containing cells, the chromatophores. The pigments formed by crustacea are very diverse —reds, greens, yellows, blues, violets, browns, blacks etc.—and they are found in various combinations in the different members, giving them different basic colors and different ranges of color change. Most of the pigments are contained in the chromatophores, which may lie in the subepidermal layers and in the deeper connective tissues as well as in the epidermis, but some of the blues and perhaps some of the others as well, are generally diffused throughout the tissues.

The muscles do not form a continuous layer as they do in the earthworm, nor is their segmental arrangement as regular as it is in the annelids in general, but they are distributed to the limbs and between the flexible parts of the body in such a way as to bring about the movement of these parts in different planes. In the most highly evolved crustacea, there is an internal or endoskeleton, a series of small arches over the ventral nerve cord, which offers a rigid internal area of attachment for the body muscles and consequently greater mechanical efficiency to them. Within the body wall, the space surrounding the digestive tract is a derivative of the primary body cavity, a hemocoele or blood sinus.

*Digestive system:* The digestive system runs as a tube from the mouth on the third segment to the anus, a slit on the under surface of the telson, the posterior termination of the abdomen. The stomodaeum and proctodaeum, which become the fore and hindgut

*Vascular system:* The blood system is not a closed one as it is in the annelids, but an "open" one, in which the blood comes in contact with the tissues through sinuses rather than minute vessels or capillaries. It is propelled through the body partly by con-

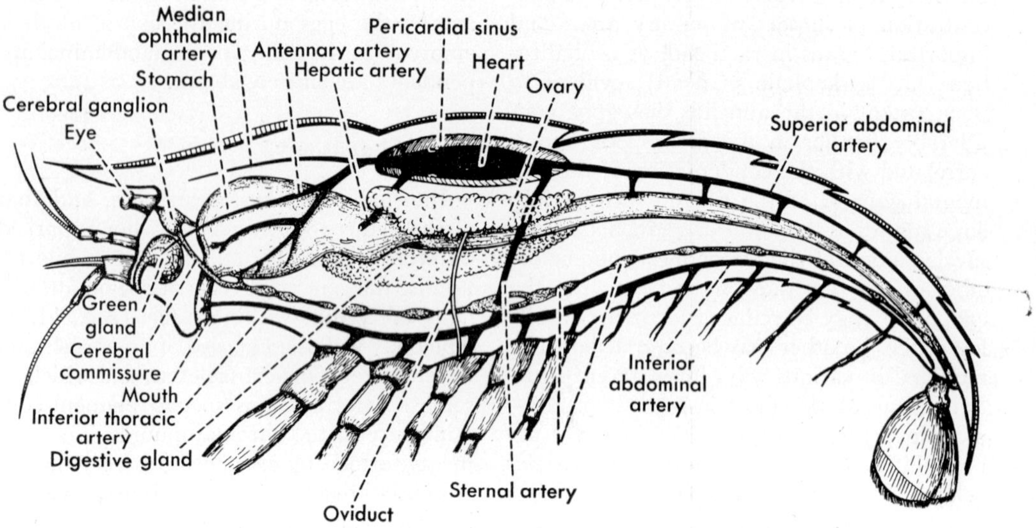

FIGURE 14.5 Diagram of the internal anatomy of a female lobster. (After Storer.)

respectively, are lined with chitinous cuticle continuous with that of the exoskeleton and represent a large portion of the tube. The foregut may be expanded into a stomach, often with elaborate thickenings and foldings of its lining to form teeth and grinding and straining mechanisms for the ingested food. The region between the foregut and hindgut, the midgut or mesenteron, where the actual digestion of the food takes place, is usually short but the area for the digestion and absorption of food is in many cases increased by lateral outgrowths or diverticula (Latin, diverticulum = bypath) from the mesenteron, forming digestive glands or hepatic caeca (Greek, hepar = liver; Latin, caecus = blind). The cells of these glands produce the enzymes that accelerate the process of digestion, which takes place in its lumen, and they also absorb the end products of the disintegration of the food; some of them store excess nutrients as glycogen or fat, breaking them down again into their constituents and releasing them to the blood when required by the organism.

tractions of a muscular sac, the heart, which lies in a blood sinus, the pericardium (Greek, peri = around + cardia = heart), and partly by the pressure exerted on the blood in the sinuses by the movements of the body and of the limbs. The blood leaves the heart through a system of vessels, the arteries, which divide and then enlarge into the various sinuses situated throughout the body, and returns to the heart ultimately via the pericardium with which the heart communicates by a number of paired openings or ostia (Latin, ostium = door). The heart lies above the digestive tract and may extend through all the trunk somites, as it does in the most primitive crustacea, or be restricted to only a few. The blood itself is a complex solution of salts and proteins; although in some few crustacea one of these proteins is hemoglobin, in the majority of them another chromoprotein, hemocyanin, is present, a respiratory pigment allied to hemoglobin, but with copper rather than iron as its metallic element. This pigment gives the circulating blood a bluish color which becomes a very deep blue when shed and exposed to air. In most species the blood also contains cells numbering 8,000–26,000 per cubic millimeter. In the crayfish, three types of cells have been identified, amoebocytes, explosive cells and thigmocytes (Greek, thigma = touch). The blood has the property of rapid coagulation when out of the body, a property which is of great importance to an animal with an open circulation, for almost any bodily injury must open a blood sinus and unless the Crustacea had had some kind of bodily protection against blood loss, they could hardly have survived the conditions of their existence as successfully as they have. The thigmocytes and explosive cells disintegrate, or explode, when exposed to air, apparently releasing a substance that brings about their agglutination, so that the fluid blood either sets to a firm jelly, or forms a clot similar to that of mammalian blood.

AREAS OF GASEOUS INTERCHANGE: While in the smaller Crustacea with thin exoskeletons, the oxygen-carbon dioxide exchange takes place over the general surface of the body, in the larger ones and those with heavy shells, there are special areas, the branchia or gills, where the exchange for the most part takes place. The gills may be freely exposed to the water, or they may be enclosed in gill chambers, made by folds of the body wall and its exoskeleton, and so protected from injury. If they are so enclosed, at least one pair of appendages is usually modified in such a way that by its movement it keeps a current of water flowing through the gill chamber, so that water with a relatively high oxygen content is swept past the gills and the water that has received carbon dioxide from them is swept away. Some of the land Crustacea have no special modifications of the respiratory mechanism, while in others like the woodlice, there are no gills but infoldings of the surface of the abdominal limbs forming a tubular system of the body surface in close contact with the blood in the sinuses of the appendages. In this, they approach the respiratory mechanism of most of the terrestrial arthropods, which reaches its fullest development in the insects.

WATER REGULATION AND EXCRETION: The principal regions of water regulation and elimination of metabolic wastes are two pairs of organs, the antennal and maxillary glands, which lie in the segments to which these appendages are attached and which open to the outside by pores on their surfaces. In only a few Crustacea are these two pairs of glands present together except during their embryonic lives; in the adults one pair only, and that usually the maxillary, remains as the primary excretory organ. The glands may be complicated in structure and elaborate in pattern, but fundamentally they can be reduced to a common plan of a mesodermal sac, probably a derivative of the coelome, with a duct or tube leading from it to the external opening. No crustacean possesses segmental nephridia like those of the annelids, although other glands and the cells of some other organs like the hepatic caeca and the midgut itself, as well as in some cases isolated groups of cells, serve also to remove waste products of metabolism from the blood and tissue fluids.

Vestiges of the coelome are also found in the reproductive organs, which like the excretory organs, may reach a considerable degree of complexity. They are permanent mesodermal structures with ducts opening to the outside on certain of the appendages and they become active seasonally, producing large numbers of reproductive cells.

*Nervous system:* The segmental pattern of the arthropods and the tendency to cephalization in them is most clearly seen in the nervous system. This consists, as it does in the annelids, of a dorsal anterior ganglion and a ventral chain of ganglia with connecting commissures and lateral nerves establishing communication between this central chain and the muscles and various organs within or on the surface of the body. In the arthropods the chain is clearly double; in some of the simplest crustacea the two longitudinal parts are separated by a distinct space. In its most primitive pattern, the dorsal ganglion, or brain, represents the fused ganglia of the segments anterior to the mouth, and in the ventral chain there is a ganglion for each segment of the trunk.

FIGURE 14.6 Insect types. (Photographs by courtesy of the U.S. Department of Agriculture, Bureau of Entomology and Plant Quarantine.)

a. Male polyphemus moth (Telea polyphemus).

b. Cockroach (Blatella germanica) with egg case. x 5.

c. Horse-fly (Tabanus).

d. Body louse (Pediculus humanis corporis). x 22.

e. Praying mantis (Tenodera sinensis).

f. Male swallow-tail butterfly (Papilio polyxenes).

In the more highly evolved crustacea, varying numbers of the anterior trunk ganglia are fused together in a single large ganglionic mass which forms the first of the ventral chain. When, as is the case in some crustacea, some of the trunk segments have fused together, their ganglia have also fused, and similarly there is a tendency for the ganglia to be lost from the segments on which there are no appendages. In addition to this central condensation of nerve cells and their processes, there is a secondary system originating from the brain and the commissures around the foregut that supplies nerves to the visceral organs and receives nerves which carry impulses originating in the viscera. Such a system is known as an autonomic one (Greek, autos = self + nomos = law) and is characteristic also of animals higher in the evolutionary scale.

## Insects

Among the arthropods, the insects and the arachnids (spiders, scorpions, ticks and mites) show the greatest divergence from the generalized plan and the greatest specialization of parts (Fig. 14.6). The insects have been the most successful of all animals in adapting themselves to varied environmental conditions and establishing new types, for they are represented in the animal kingdom by some 750,000 species, nearly nine times as many as those of any other distinct group. Most of the insects are terrestrial animals, though some are aquatic during all or the early part of their lives and many live an aerial existence. Their feeding habits are most diverse, some being omnivorous, others carnivorous and many phytophagous or exclusively plant eating and very destructive to vegetation. Some, too, are extremely limited in their choice of food, like the blood-sucking mosquitoes, lice and fleas, the nectar-feeding bees and the aphids which suck the juices from the cells of plants. Some are parasitic, living in or on the bodies of other insects or of unrelated animals and plants. They show a wide range in size; some are microscopic and some, like the beetles and moths of the tropics, have bodies 8–10 inches in length.

## Segmentation and primary divisions of the body

*The head and its appendages:* The insect body is externally marked off into three distinct regions, head, thorax and abdomen, in some cases with very narrow constrictions between the regions (Fig. 14.7). The head is made up of six segments, which are not evident externally, since it is covered by paired and unpaired plates of the cuticle which bear no relation to the segmental pattern. The number of head segments, however, can be determined from the number of paired appendages included in the head, from the ganglia represented in it and the distribution of their nerves and from the number of coelomic sacs that appear during the course of embryology but that disappear in the adult. The appendages of the head are always one pair of antennae, which may be long or short, simple jointed filaments or knobbed, branched and sometimes elaborately feathered ones (Fig. 14.8), a pair of mandibles and two pairs of maxillae. The second pair of maxillae are always fused together, as they are in some few crustacea, to form a lower lip or labium (Fig. 14.9). These, together with the first pair and the mandibles, are known as the mouth parts, which, often combined with structures derived from the upper lip, or labrum, and the floor or the roof of the mouth, are modified in various ways for sucking, lapping, sponging, piercing, biting, chewing, etc. (Figs. 14.10, 14.11). The head also bears sense organs of different kinds, most conspicuously, in the majority of insects, the compound eyes similar to those of some crustacea.

THE THORAX AND ITS APPENDAGES: Three segments are included in the thorax, each of which bears a pair of jointed legs, and typically eleven in the abdomen, although in the more highly evolved insects there is a condensation or fusion of some segments. The abdominal segments never bear appendages and the insects are sometimes known as Hexapoda (Greek, hex = six + pous = foot) because of their six thoracic legs. The legs, like the mouth parts, show great diver-

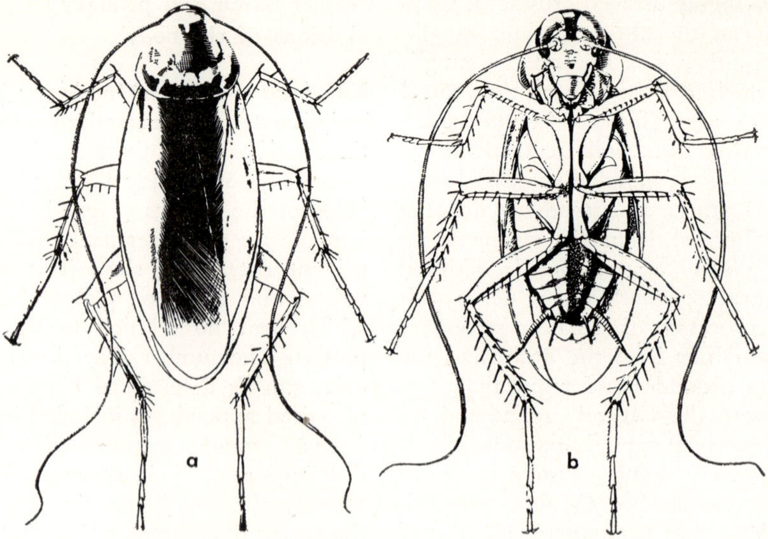

FIGURE 14.7 Cockroach (Periplaneta americana).

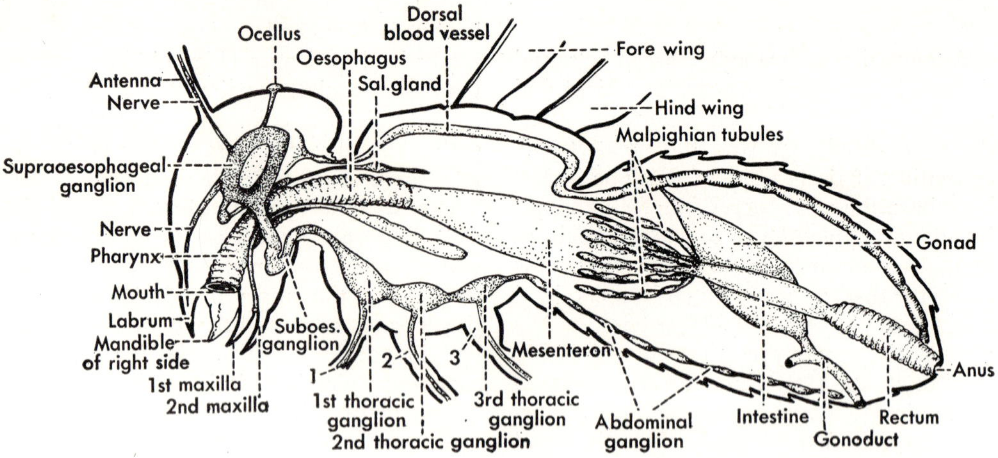

a. Dorsal (a) and ventral (b) views of the exterior of the insect. (Courtesy of the U.S. Department of Agriculture, Bureau of Entomology and Plant Quarantine.)

b. Diagram of the internal anatomy of the insect. 1, 2 and 3 indicate first, second and third thoracic legs. (After Berlese.)

sity and are adapted in various ways for running, as in cockroaches, leaping, as in grasshoppers, diving, swimming or skimming over the water, as in water beetles, etc. (Fig. 14.12). They reach perhaps the highest degree of modification in the bees, where the segments of the first pair of legs are modified to form two special structures, the pollen brushes and the antennae cleaners; those of the second pair, pollen brushes and spurs on which the wings are supported when being cleaned of pollen by the brushes; and those of the third or posterior pair, three structures, the pollen baskets, the

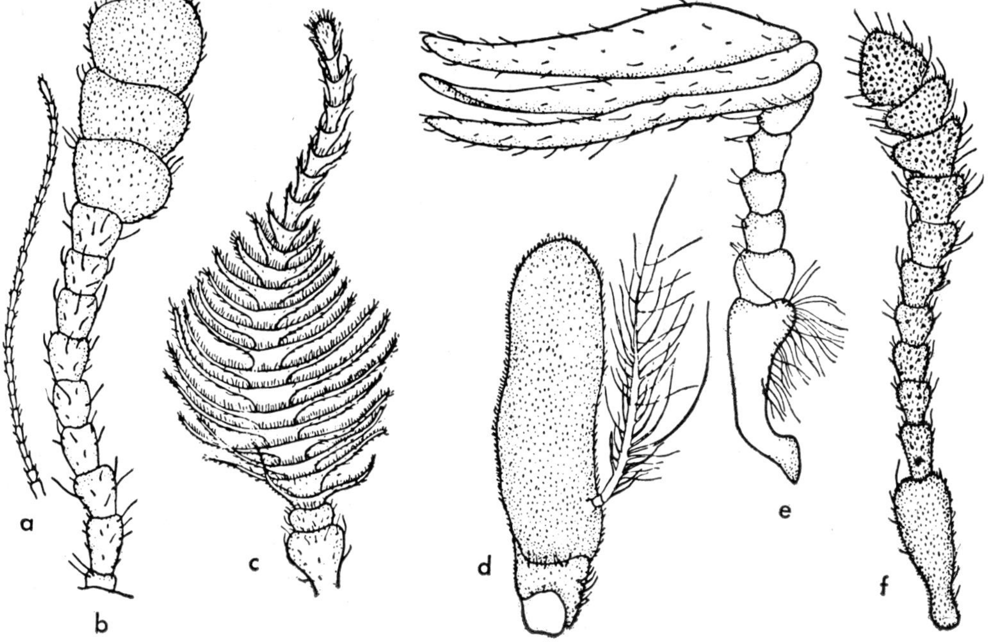

FIGURE 14.8 Types of insect antennae. (From Sanderson and Jackson, *Elementary Entomology*, by courtesy of the U.S. Department of Agriculture, Bureau of Entomology and Plant Quarantine.)

a, filiform, from grasshopper (Schistocera americana); b, clubbed, or clavate, from tenebrionid beetle (Nyctobactes pennsylvanicus); c. pectinate, or feathered, from a moth; d, aristate, with dorsal plumose aristae, from a fly; e, lamellate, from a May-beetle (Lachnosterna fusca); f, monoliniform, from a beetle.

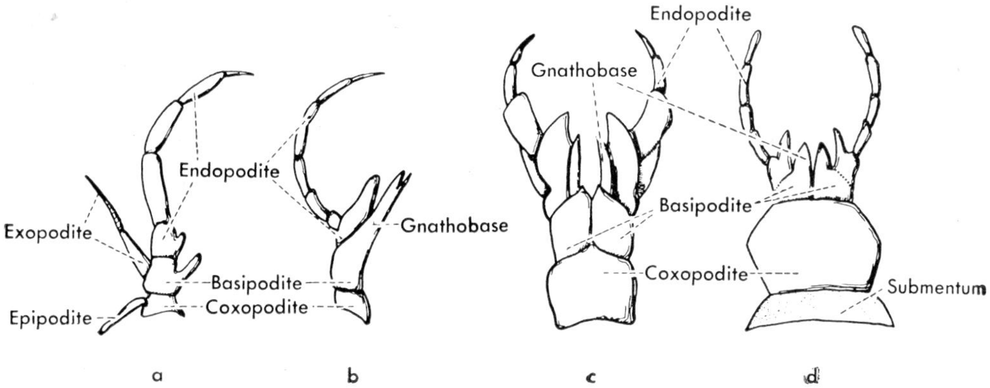

FIGURE 14.9 Diagram showing the hypothetical derivation of insect mouthparts from a crustacean pattern. (After Imms.)

a. A biramous appendage of a crustacean.
b. An insect maxilla, with the basipodite prolonged into a pincer-like structure, the gnathobase, aiding in the mastication of food.
c. Maxillipeds of a fresh water shrimp, with the coxopodites fused to form a kind of lower lip.
d. The labium, or lower lip, of an insect, derived, like that of the shrimp, by the fusion of the basal segments of the second maxillae.

[ 231 ]

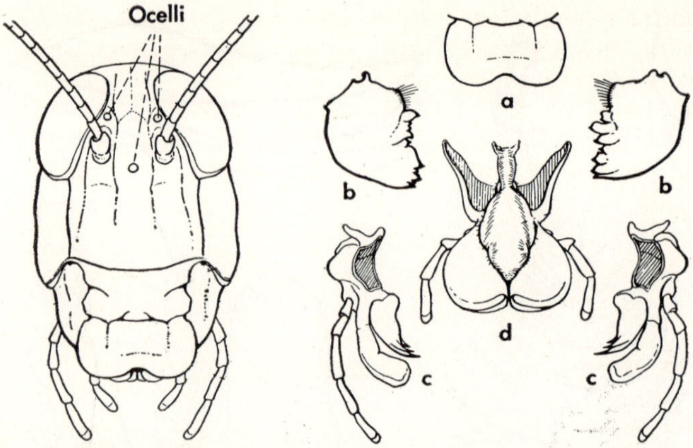

FIGURE 14.10  Diagrams of the head and mouthparts of a grasshopper. (Courtesy of the U.S. Department of Agriculture, Bureau of Entomology and Plant Quarantine.)

a. labrum, or upper lip.  
b. mandibles.  
c. maxillae.  
d. labium, or lower lip.

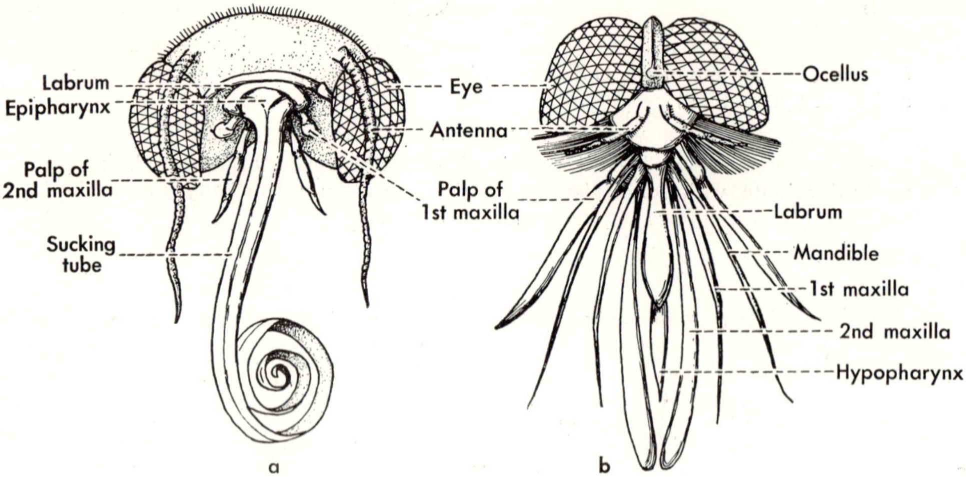

FIGURE 14.11  Modifications of insect mouthparts.

a. Mouthparts of a butterfly, adapted to siphon nectar from the base of flower petals and other fluids into the digestive tract. The mandibles are absent and the long sucking tube, coiled like a flat spring when the insect is not feeding, is made of the ridges of the first pair of maxillae fused together. The second pair of maxillae are united in the midline to form a lower lip, which is not shown. (After Lang.)

b. Mouthparts of a horse-fly, Tabanus, adapted to pierce and to suck. The mouthparts are shown as if spread apart. The labrum and hypopharynx together form a sucking tube whose upper end leads into the mouth. The mandibles are long, slender blades with sharp points; the maxillae are slender stylets and are the principal piercing organs. (After Lang.)

## THE ARTHROPODS

pollen packers and the pollen combs. All of these are brought into use in the gathering of pollen which bees collect from the flowers they visit in search of nectar and which they transport to the hive, mix with saliva and there pack into masses of "bee bread" upon which the young are fed.

to change their immediate environment for a more satisfactory one, to escape from enemies, and to make use of breeding grounds most suitable for the protection of their eggs and the rearing of their young.

While two pairs of wings are common in most insects, there is one large group, in-

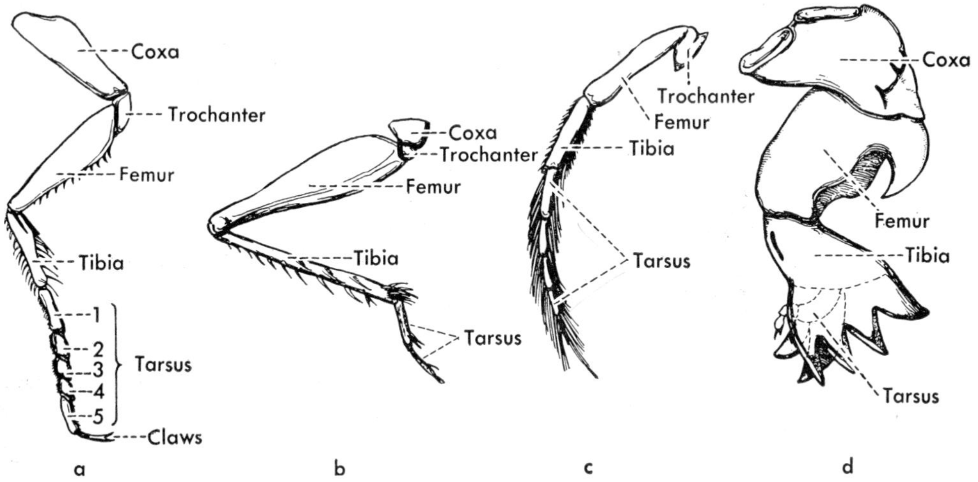

FIGURE 14.12 Legs of insects, showing adaptations to functions of different kinds. (After Berlese.)

  a. Leg of a cockroach (Blatta), adapted for running.
  b. Hind leg of a cricket (Gryllus), adapted for leaping.
  c. Leg of water beetle (Dytiscus), adapted for swimming.
  d. Foreleg of mole cricket (Gryllotalpa), adapted for digging.

*Wings and their modifications:* From the thoracic segments there are also developed, in most insects, two pairs of wings, thin lateral outgrowths of the body wall originating between the terga and the pleura (Greek, pleuron = rib or side), or lateral chitinous plates, of the middle and the posterior segments (meso- and metathorax respectively). Some insects are wingless; some, like the silver fish, Lepisma, primarily so because they are primitive in type and others, like fleas and lice, secondarily so because they are habitually parasites on the bodies of other animals and are degenerate in their locomotor structures (Fig. 14.6). The possession of wings during all or some phase of their lives has been one of the factors contributing to the success of insects, for by means of them they have been able to cover great distances in search of food or mates,

cluding the flies, midges and gnats, in which only the anterior pair is present, the posterior pair being represented by balloon-like stumps, the halteres (Fig. 14.13). The word halter is derived from a Greek word meaning to leap, and was used for the dumb-bells which Greek athletes held in their hands to give impetus in leaping. This rudimentary second pair of wings act as balancers when the fly is in flight and when it is settling on a surface; possibly also the fly's halteres, like the athlete's dumb-bells, are brought into action when it is poised to take off in flight. In most other winged insects, both wings are used in flight; in some, like the dragonflies and grasshoppers, each pair moves independently of the other, but in the better fliers there is some device by which the fore- and hindwing of each side are coupled together so that they act essentially as one. In the moths and butterflies, bristles on the posterior margin of the forewing and the anterior margin of the hindwing overlap and so hold the wings together; in the bees and wasps, a row of hooks on the anterior border of the hindwing fits into a fold on the posterior margin of the forewing when the animal is in flight. In some insects, like the grasshoppers and crickets and beetles, the forewing is heavier and thicker than the hindwing and makes a protective covering for it; when in flight, the insects hold the forewings outstretched and move only the membranous posterior pair. In others, such as the dragonflies and mayflies, both wings are membranous and sometimes, as in the lacewing flies, extremely delicate, while in the moths and butterflies, they are covered with tiny, overlapping scales and sometimes with hairs (Figs. 14.14, 14.15; cf. Fig. 14.6). Both wings and bodies of insects may be brightly colored, often multicolored. Although in some instances the color may be due to the absorption and the reflection of light rays by pigments, more often it is the result of their scattering and reflection from the surface, or to their refraction. The chemical, or pigmentary colors of insects are usually the browns and the blacks and probably the reds and the yellows; the bright metallic colors, like the gold of Cotalpa, the goldsmith beetle, the bronze of the Japanese beetle and the blue-green of the ground beetle, Calosoma, are physical, or structural, colors, as are the whites, violets and blues of butterflies and the iridescent colors of the wings of flies and bees.

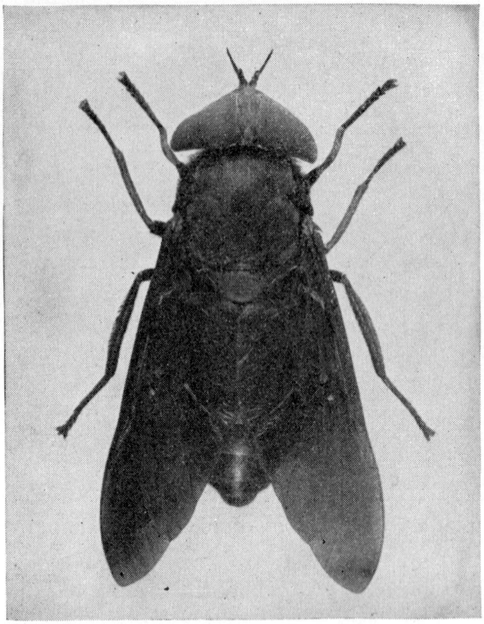

FIGURE 14.13
a. The horse-fly or blue-tailed fly (Tabanus atratus), with wings at rest. (Photograph by courtesy of the U.S. Department of Agriculture, Bureau of Entomology and Plant Quarantine.)
b. A robber fly (Atamosia puella), with wings extended showing the halteres just posterior to the bases of the full wings. (Photograph by courtesy of the Department of Agriculture, Bureau of Entomology and Plant Quarantine.)

*Thoracic muscles and the mechanism of flight:* Internally also the insects show variations of the crustacean plan. The space around the digestive tract represents the primary body cavity, crossed by muscles to the legs and wings. The wings are moved by the action of two sets of muscles, which are especially well developed and powerful in insects whose flights are long and rapid. The direct wing muscles are attached to the base of the wing and by their contraction rotate the wing slightly on its long axis. The indirect muscles are inserted on the body wall and by their action the shape of the thorax is altered. The wings, as folds of the body

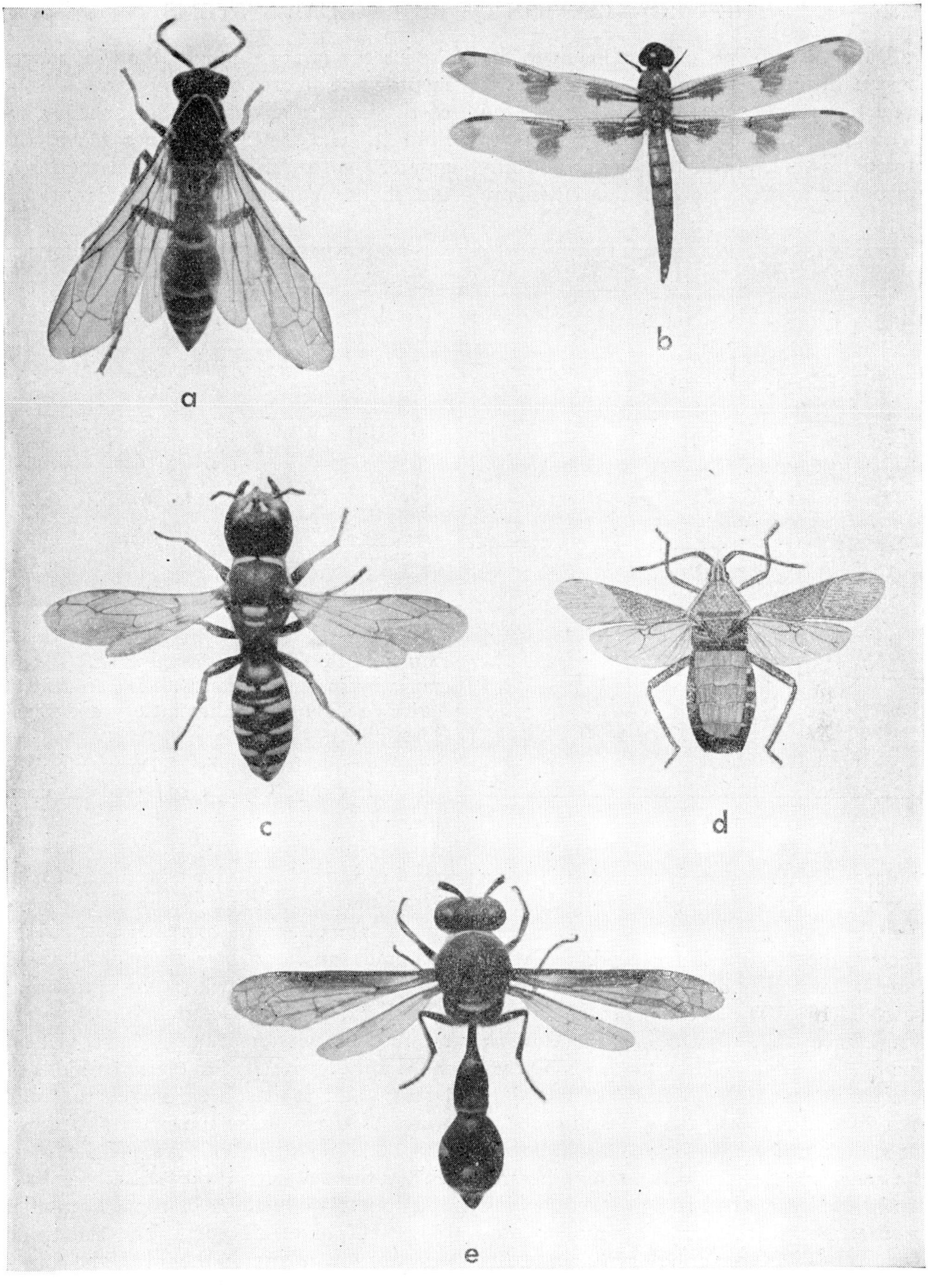

FIGURE 14.14 Types of insect wings. (Photographs by courtesy of the U.S. Department of Agriculture, Bureau of Entomology and Plant Quarantine.)

a. Wasp (Polistes fuscutus).
b. Dragonfly (Libellula pulchella).
c. "Thread-waisted" wasp (Solenius interruptus).
d. Squash-bug (Anasa tristis). (From a drawing by H. Bradford.)
e. Potter wasp (Eumenes fraternus).

wall, have two points of attachment to the thorax; their upper point of attachment is to the tergum of each side, their lower to the pleuron. One set of indirect wing muscles runs dorso-ventrally in the thorax and another longitudinally; when the latter are contracted the tergum is arched, the wing base is raised and the wing itself lowered, and when the dorso-ventral muscles are contracted, the tergum is flattened, the wing base is lowered and the wing itself raised (Fig. 14.16). The movements of insects' wings have been studied in various ways; one device is that used by the French physiologist Etienne Jules Marey (1830–1904), who gilded the tips of the wings in order to make their trajectory visible and so followed the course of their movement; another recently applied method is high-speed moving picture photography and slow motion projection. In flight, the anterior margin of the wing remains rigid, while the rest bends under the pressure of the air. As the wing moves downward, it is bent upward or cambered, and as it moves upward, its surface is bent downward, and since it is also rotated slightly, it always offers some surface to the air pressure from behind, propelling the insect forward. In flight, the wing movements cause an area of low pressure in front of the insect and one of high pressure behind it. The faster the wings move, the greater the forward pressure and the faster the flight. Various measurements of the

FIGURE 14.15 Types of insect wings. (Photographs by courtesy of the U.S. Department of Agriculture, Bureau of Entomology and Plant Quarantine.)

a. A mayfly, Irongrandis McDunnough.

b. A lacewing, Crysopa sp., predator upon aphids.

speed of insects' flight have been made with rather divergent results; houseflies, for example, are estimated to reach a speed of 4–5 miles an hour, bees from about 5–14 miles an hour and hawk moths as much as 30 miles an hour. Determinations of the rapidity of wing movement have yielded more uniform results for the same kinds of insects, and it has been found that the wings of the housefly move up and down about 333 times a second; those of the drone fly 300 times a second; those of a bee about 190 times; while those of some butterflies only 9–12 times a second. The stabilizing effect of the halteres in the flies is the consequence of their rapid vibration at the same speed as the wings, but in the opposite direction; when the wing moves up, the halter is lowered and vice versa.

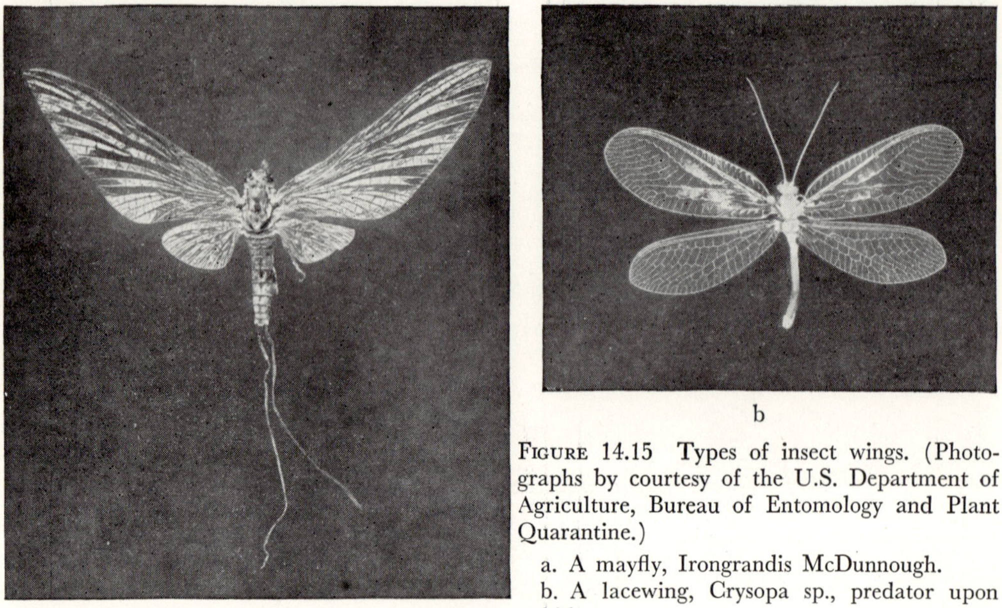

The fact that insects are capable of such rapid muscular movements which can be sustained without pausing for rest or food for long periods of time—for locusts, many butterflies and the hawk moths can travel continuously hundreds of miles—shows that they must have a very efficient mechanism for the conversion of the potential energy stored in their tissues into kinetic energy.

some insects the tract is no longer than the insect's body, although the area of the midgut may be increased by lateral pouches or caeca; in others, particularly the fluid feeders, it is much longer and bent and coiled within the perivisceral space (Fig. 14.17).

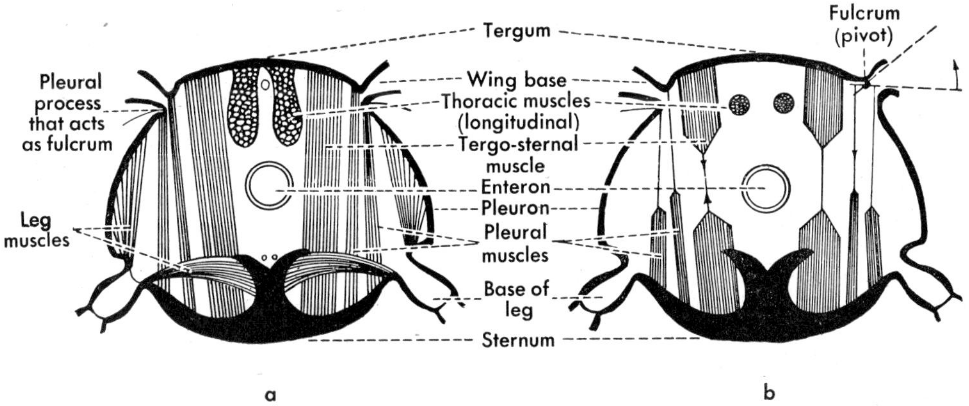

FIGURE 14.16. Diagrams of cross sections of the thorax of an insect, showing the arrangement of the muscles. (After Folsom.)

a. The muscles of the thorax that move the wings and the legs. Each wing is firmly attached to the edge of the tergum, and passes over the upper edge of the pleuron upon which, as a fulcrum, it pivots.

b. The operation of the wing muscles in flight. The longitudinal thoracic muscles act as indirect depressors of the wing, for by contraction they shorten the thorax in its anterior-posterior axis, thus arching the tergum and so raising the base of each wing and lowering the part beyond the fulcrum in a down-stroke. The tergo-sternal muscles act as indirect elevators, for by contraction they draw the tergum and sternum toward each other, thereby lowering the base of each wing and so raising the part beyond the fulcrum in an upstroke. The pleural muscles act directly upon the wing, turning it anteriorly and posteriorly upon the pivot.

That they have also a mechanism which controls their flight is shown by the ability of many of them to reverse their direction, to steer accurately and to hover, without forward or backward movement, for considerable periods of time.

### Internal anatomy

***Digestive system:*** The digestive tract is usually a complete tube running from mouth to anus, although in adult mayflies, whose life is but a few hours and which never take food, the mouth is lacking. As in the crustaceans, the lining of the foregut and of the hindgut is continuous with the external cuticle and the digestion and absorption of the food taking place in the midgut. In a number of insects, accessory digestive glands, the salivary glands, open into the foregut so that the chemical breakdown of certain constituents of the food may begin even before it reaches the midgut. Both the foregut and the midgut may be locally differentiated for particular functions, the foregut primarily into a crop for the temporary storage of food prior to its digestion and, in the case of the omnivorous and carnivorous species especially, also into a thick-walled muscular gizzard for the maceration of the ingested food. The midgut may be specialized in its anterior region for the production of enzymes to be discharged into the lumen, and in its posterior portion for the absorption of the end products of digestion, so that the two processes of digestion and absorption may go on simultaneously and not alternately as they must do in the case of animals where the endoderm cells are not so specialized. The fluid-feeding insects have a particular problem in concentrating the actual nutrients from the food they ingest and some have mechanisms derived from the midgut for this purpose. In the blood-sucking tsetse fly, for example, the anterior part of the midgut apparently functions exclusively in the absorption of water

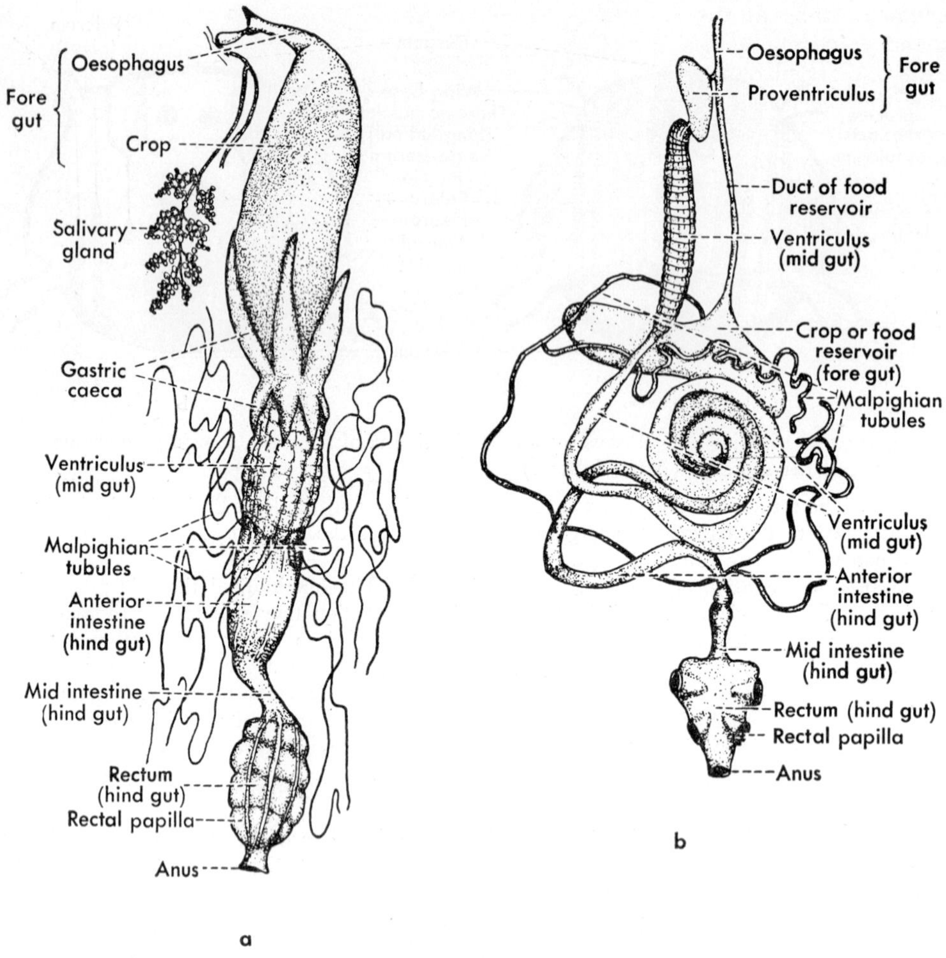

FIGURE 14.17 Digestive tracts of two species of insects, showing modifications adapting them to different kinds of life.

a. Dissection of the digestive tract of an adult grasshopper (Acridium) that feeds upon vegetation. The digestive tract is straight and no longer than the insect's body. The posterior part of the foregut is expanded into a large sac, the crop, in which the food is temporarily stored before its passage into the midgut (ventriculus), where its digestion takes place. (After Snodgrass.)

b. Dissection of the digestive tract of an adult blowfly (Calliphora) that feeds upon fluids. The food reservoir (crop) is a separate chamber of the foregut, attached to the oesophagus by a slender tube. The ingested fluids pass first into this chamber, from which they are transferred at intervals through the proventriculus to the ventriculus, a long, coiled tube in which concentration of the nutrients in the food and their digestion takes place. (After Berlese.)

from the food, for in it the blood is reduced to a viscid mass which is digested in the midregion and absorbed in the hinder portion. The cells of these three regions are microscopically distinguishable as different types. The hindgut of insects is usually composed of two regions, the intestine and the rectum, opening at the anus, and usually expanded as rectal glands. Water contained in the undigested residue of the food is absorbed by the cells of these glands, which consequently play an important part in water conservation.

*Vascular system:* The blood system is less well developed than in the crustaceans and except in a few cases the blood itself contains no respiratory pigment. In most insects, there is a heart, situated dorsal to the digestive tract just under the body wall and primitively divided into thirteen chambers corresponding to thirteen of the thoracic and abdominal segments. The contractions of the heart muscle drive the blood into a main anterior artery and then into the general blood spaces, which are very extensive so that the blood is brought into contact with all the tissues. Accessory vessels and accessory hearts are present in some insects, and the circulation of the blood is further assured by the contractions of the wing and the leg muscles. Hemocyanin as a respiratory pigment is not found in insects, and hemoglobin in only a few, notably the "blood worm," or larval stage of the midge Chironomus.

*Respiratory system:* Insects, centipedes, millepedes, some arachnids and Peripatus have developed a distinctive respiratory system, the tracheal system, found in no other group of animals. The arthropods may be classified, on the basis of their respiratory devices, into the branchiate forms, or those with gills, and the tracheate, or those with tracheae in at least the adult stage. Most of the terrestrial arthropods are tracheate, while the aquatic ones are branchiate, although some spiders possess modified gills as the principal respiratory area and some insects, like dragonflies and water beetles, have gills during their larval stages when they lead an aquatic existence.

Tracheae are fine, air-filled tubes which open to the outside by pores, the spiracles (Latin, spirare = to breathe), and which ramify throughout the animal's body, reaching all the tissues as completely as a blood capillary system. Developed as ingrowths of

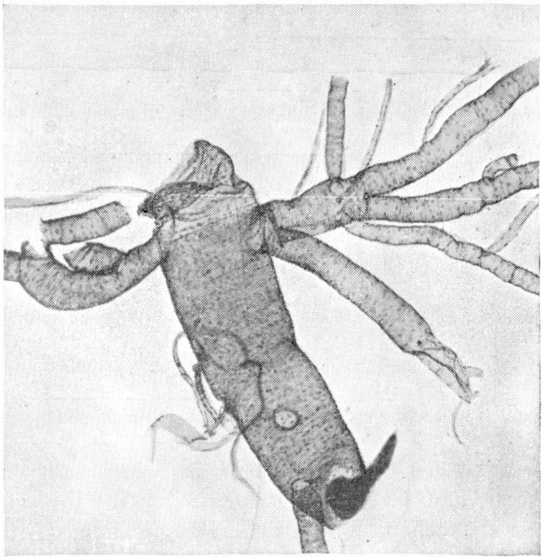

FIGURE 14.18  Insect tracheae. (Photograph by courtesy of the General Biological Supply House, Inc., Chicago.)

the body wall, their walls are continuous with the integument and lined with cuticle also continuous with that on the surface of the body. In the insects, where the tracheal system reaches its highest development, there are typically two pairs of spiracles on the thorax and eight on the abdomen, guarded by valves which can be opened or closed in accordance with the respiratory requirements. The main tubes from these openings divide and subdivide into smaller tubes, with more delicate walls and reduced diameters (Fig. 14.18); the finest of the tubes are the tracheoles, each of which terminates in a cell of the body so that the gaseous exchange occurs directly and not through an intermediate tissue like blood. In some insects, there are enlargements of the main tubes, the air sacs, distributed throughout the body.

The mechanism of tracheal respiration probably works in this way. Air is circulated through the tracheal tubes by alternate contractions and relaxations of the body. The external respiratory movements can easily be seen in a living grasshopper, whose abdomen rhythmically flattens and then returns to its original shape. The flattening is brought about by the contractions of muscles running dorso-ventrally in the abdominal cavity; the return to the original shape is due to the elasticity of the chitinous plates. When the spiracles are open, air is drawn into the main tracheal tubes at each relaxation and expelled at each contraction; if the spiracles are closed, contraction forces the air further along the internal system. The tips of the tracheoles are filled with water to which their walls are permeable. The osmotic pressure of the cell with which the tracheole is in contact is always greater than that of the water within the tracheole itself and in an actively metabolizing cell, such as those of a muscle, this difference becomes even greater as the cell constituents are broken down to release energy, and their degradation products accumulate, resulting in an even more complex and concentrated solution. Under these conditions water therefore passes from the tracheole into the cell, because of the inequality in the exchange of water molecules between them, and the column of air moves further along the tube reaching its extremity in contact with the cell (Fig. 14.19). An almost immediate exchange of gases can therefore take place, and because of the ebb and flow of air in the entire system, oxygen is brought to the cells in this way and carbon dioxide removed. Diffusion within the tracheal system and across the tracheole walls is responsible for the entrance of oxygen into the cells and the exit of carbon dioxide from them. In some insects, the physical process of diffusion within the tracheal system is supplemented by a mechanism by which circulation of air within the tubes is assured. In some grasshoppers, for instance, certain of the spiracles are used only for the inspiration, or the intake of air, and others for its expiration, or outlet. The first four pairs of spiracles are open only when the abdomen is relaxed; these are closed when it contracts and the air expired while the remaining six pairs are open, so that the air is made to circulate within the tracheal

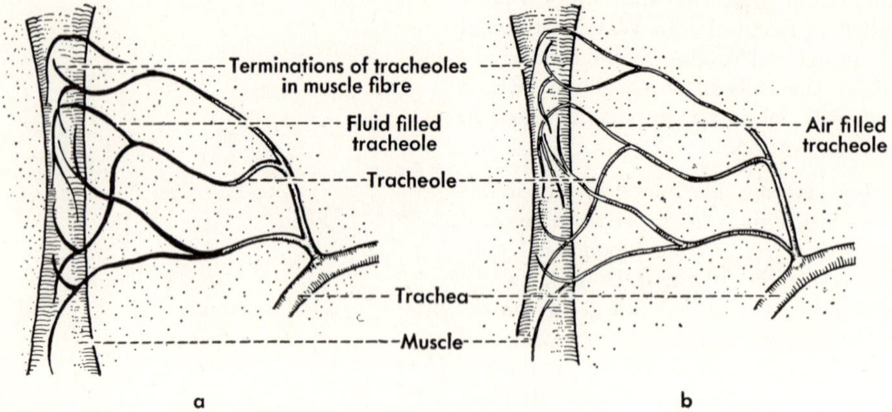

FIGURE 14.19 Diagrams showing the relation of tracheoles and muscle fibres and the mechanism of tracheal respiration. (After Wigglesworth.)

a. Resting muscle. The tips of the tracheoles are filled with fluid, from which $O_2$ diffuses into the muscle fibre and from which $CO_2$ diffuses from the muscle fibre.

b. Fatigued muscle after contraction. The osmotic relations between muscle and tracheolar fluid have been altered by chemical changes in the contracting muscle and water has been withdrawn from the tracheoles, in consequence of which the column of air has moved further along them, facilitating the gaseous interchange between muscle fibre and air tube.

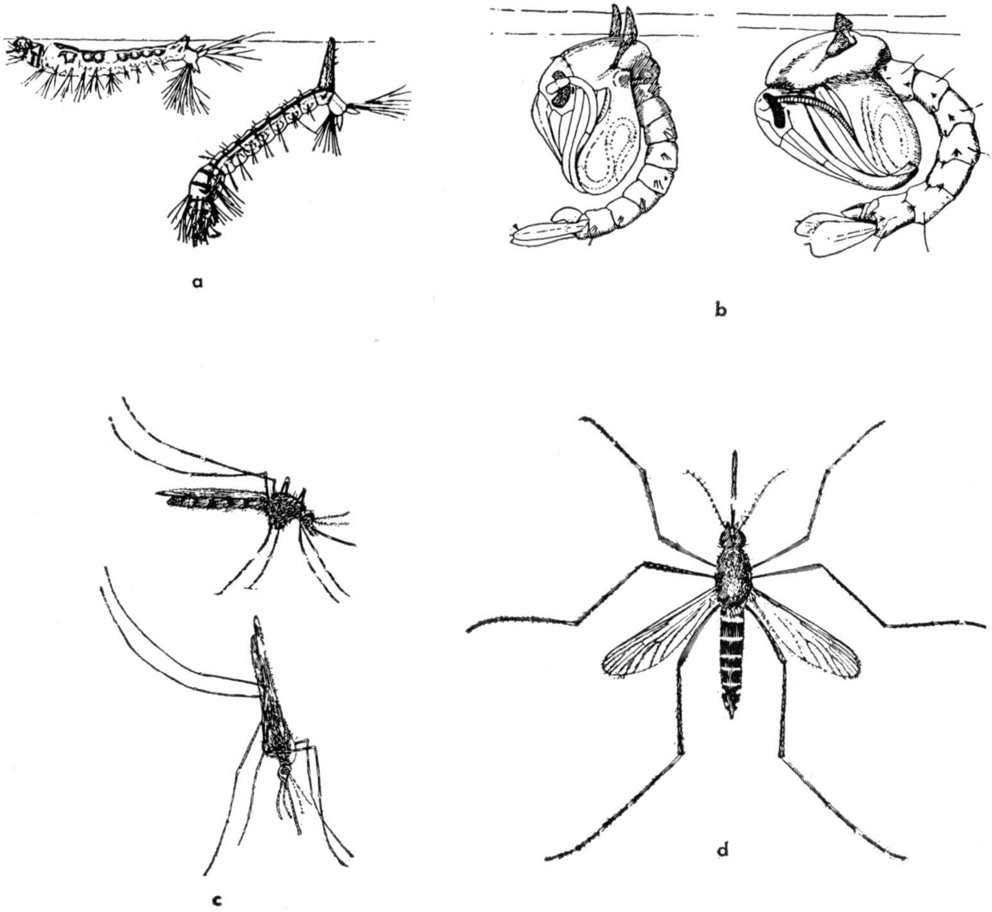

FIGURE 14.20 Life cycles of two mosquitoes, Culex and Anopheles. (Photographs by courtesy of the U.S. Department of Agriculture, Bureau of Entomology and Plant Quarantine.)

    a. Larval stages, with the ends of the tracheal tubes extending above the surface of the water. The larva to the left is that of Anopheles, the malaria carrier; that to the right is the larva of Culex.

    b. Pupation occurs in the water. The pupa to the left is that of Culex; the pupa to the right, Anopheles. Both obtain $O_2$ through the tracheal openings that extend above the water.

    c. Adult insects in resting position. Above, Culex; below, Anopheles.

    d. An adult female mosquito, Culex taeniorhynchus.

system and more effective ventilation brought about.

In aquatic insects, the tracheal system is modified in various ways to meet the conditions of their existence. In some, the number of spiracles is reduced and those that are functional are kept in contact with the air in one way or another. In the diving beetles, for example, which as adults spend relatively long periods of time under water, a bubble of air is trapped under each anterior wing whenever the animal submerges, and only the forward pair of spiracles, situated under these wings, is capable of opening and closing. When the oxygen from these bubbles is exhausted, the beetles must come to the surface again for a fresh supply of air. The aquatic larvae of mosquitoes have also but a single pair of functional spiracles, and the position of the animal in the water is always such that these project through the surface of the water and are in contact with the air (Fig. 14.20). This is the reason that spreading oil on the surface of ponds and pools where mosquitoes breed is an effective means of their control, for the oil film blocks the young mosquito's access to air, leading to its asphyxiation. In the larvae of other species, the tracheal system may be brought into contact with the water by means of tracheal gills, lateral expansions of the body wall with no functional spiracles, so that the gaseous interchange takes place wholly by diffusion across the surface epithelium and the tracheal wall. While in most cases tracheal gills are external, borne on the abdominal segments or projections from them, in the larvae of some dragonflies they are internal and made by folds of the walls of the rectum into which tufts of tracheae project. The young insect aerates its rectal gills by pumping water in and out of the hindgut by muscular movements of its abdomen. In the larvae of a few insects, such as Chironomus, the tracheal system is entirely closed and filled with fluid rather than air, and the general body surface serves as the total respiratory area, as it does also in some of the more primitive insects, like the springtails, where tracheae are wholly lacking.

**Excretory system:** The insects make use of neither nephridia nor modified coelomoducts in their elimination of metabolic wastes, but of a variety of cells. Principal among the cellular systems are the Malpighian tubules, so named because they were first demonstrated by Marcello Malpighi in his meticulous dissections of silkworms. They are slender tubules, from 2 to 100 in number in different species of insects, which originate from the wall of the digestive tract at the junction of midgut and hindgut and which twist and coil throughout the hemocoele, their cells taking up and concentrating nitrogenous waste from its fluid (Fig. 14.7b). Chemical analysis has shown the presence of crystals of uric acid in the cells of the walls of these tubules, and at times of masses of uric acid in their lumina, and by the same means it has been shown that such end products may accumulate in other regions of the body as well—in the integument, the walls of the pericardium, the fat body, the nephrocytes (Greek, nephros = kidney + kytos = cell) and the oenocytes (Greek, oinos = wine + kytos). The fat body is made up of a mass of cells, usually extending along and around the digestive tract, in which excess products of digestion are stored as fat, glycogen and albuminoids; chemical analysis has also shown the presence of salts of uric acid in the cells of the fat body. Since the storage products are often greenish or yellowish in color, the fat body showing through the transparent body wall may give a general coloration to the insect. Nephrocytes are migratory cells which are usually found in groups near the fat body and the pericardium, and which, like the cells of the walls of the Malpighian tubules, take up nitrogenous waste from the fluid in the hemocoele and concentrate it within them. The oenocytes are large cells, derived from the surface epithelium and found in masses near the abdominal spiracles, in which nitrogenous waste is also stored. The presence of such waste products in cells generally distributed throughout the body, as well as of non-nitrogenous excretory products such as the carbonates of calcium, potassium and magnesium, suggests that neither the Malpighian tubules nor the tracheae are particularly efficient in ridding the body of those products of its metabolic reactions which are useless as sources of energy and in quantity toxic to it, and that in effecting a compromise between two conditions essential to their existence—the conservation of water and the elimination of substances produced in their bodies but harmful to them—the insects have retained generalized conditions rather than developed specialized ones. In insects of some species, both tracheae and Malpighian tubules are lacking entirely and respiration and excretion are carried on by cells not set apart especially for those functions.

As in the crustaceans, remnants of the coelome are found in the reproductive system, which in most insects is elaborate in pattern and productive of large numbers of germ cells and structures accessory to them. In most insects also, the cuticular plates covering the posterior abdominal segments are modified in various ways for the transmission of the germ cells and the deposition

missures or connectives encircling the foregut just back of the mouth. In the simplest insects, the ventral chain is a segmental one, with a ganglion in each of the segments of the thorax and in all but the last of the abdomen; in the more specialized

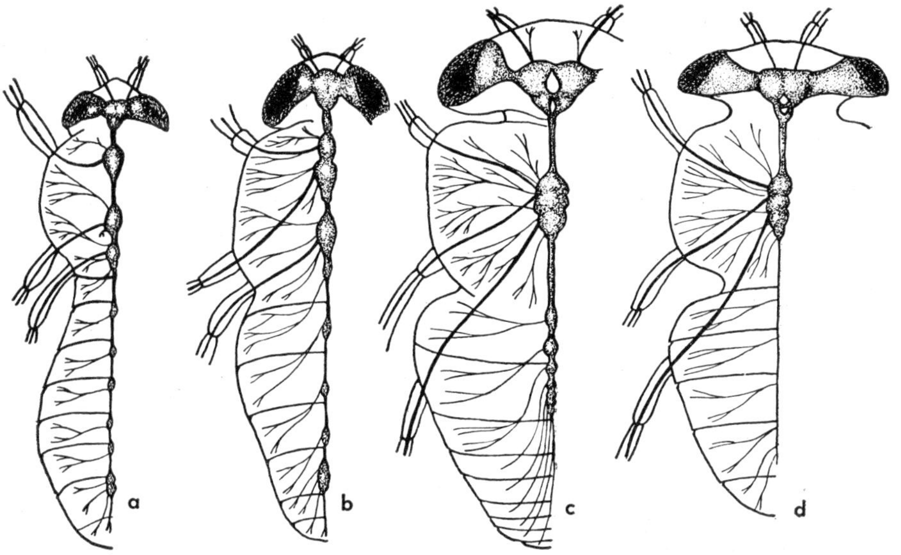

FIGURE 14.21   Diagrams of the nervous systems of four members of the Diptera, showing different degrees of concentration of the segmental ganglia. Only the left half of the body of the insect is shown in each case. (After Berlese.)

a. Nervous system of the midge, Chironomus. There is a separate ganglion in each segment of the thorax and in five of the abdominal segments; the ganglia of the two terminal segments are fused into a compound mass.

b. Nervous system of a dance fly (Empis). The ganglia of the first two thoracic segments are concentrated in a single mass, separate from that of the third. There is a separate ganglion in each of the first three abdominal segments; in the fourth segment there is a compound ganglion, representing the concentration of the three posterior ganglia.

c. Nervous system of the horse-fly (Tabanus). The ganglia of the thoracic segments are concentrated in a single mass; those of all the abdominal segments are concentrated in the first two segments of the abdomen.

d. Nervous system of a flesh fly (Sarcophaga). All the ganglia of the thorax and abdomen are concentrated in a single mass in the thorax.

and attachment of the eggs when they are laid.

**Nervous system:** The insects show still greater concentration of the segmental ganglia of the nervous system than do any of the crustacea. The dorsal ganglion, or brain, consists always of three ganglia, connected, as in the annelids and the other arthropods, with the ventral chain by com-

ones, all the ventral ganglia except the first are united in one elongated mass in the thorax, from which nerves extend to and from the abdominal as well as the thoracic organs (Fig. 14.21). There is also an autonomic system of nerves connected with the viscera and the muscles of the spiracles.

FUNCTIONAL RELATIONSHIPS WITHIN THE SYSTEM: While its basic pattern is fundamentally like that of the annelids, the nervous system of the arthropods in general shows not only a greater degree of concentration but also greater functional organization. The dorsal ganglion exercises inhibitory functions, for if it is destroyed, as has been done in experiments on bees, the insect will try to perform simultaneously all the actions for which its appendages are specialized, confusing the movements of walking, feeding, cleaning its abdomen and even of flying in uncoordinated and useless behavior. Functionally, the arthropod nervous system appears to operate as a number of units, each unit associated with a pair of appendages and each to a certain extent independent of the others. A decapitated wasp can still walk, and if one leg is removed will still walk in a straight line because of compensating movements of the other legs initiated in the functional nervous units controlling its thoracic limbs and so regulating their movement. The movements of the insect's body in respiration are directly under the control of these functional units acting as primary respiratory centers and responsible for the movements in the individual segments but responding to stimuli from secondary centers. The young dragonfly, for example, which aerates its rectal gills by pumping water in and out of the hindgut, regulates its abdominal movements in accordance with the gaseous content of the water surrounding it. Experiments have shown that these movements increase, and therefore a greater volume of water passes over the gills, if the oxygen content is low or if the carbon dioxide content is increased, while they are slowed down if the water is saturated with oxygen. But if the first thoracic ganglion is destroyed, the respiratory movements continue at a uniform rate, no matter to what extent the oxygen or carbon dioxide content of the water may be varied. While the first ganglion of the thorax in these insects acts as a respiratory center, responding to changes in the water and regulating the rate of contraction of the dorso-ventral muscles of the abdomen, other regions of the ventral chain, but apparently never the dorsal ganglion, perform this function in other species.

ORGANS OF SPECIAL SENSE: The insects, and indeed the arthropods in general, have well-developed and varied organs of special sense by which they can appreciate conditions in the environment some distance from their bodies as well as in their immediate vicinity and, through the functional neuro-muscular units of their bodies and the coordinating mechanisms of their nervous systems, they make appropriate responses to stimulating conditions. They are sensitive to light and to sound waves, to touch and to chemical stimuli with which they are in direct contact or which come to them from a distance, as in the sensations of taste and of smell respectively. In investigating the range of sensitivity of a biological system, the human experimenter can only determine its sensory discrimination by the response that it gives to an external stimulus; a response does not necessarily imply that the system has a sensation or a perception of the stimulus similar to that which the experimenter himself may have, although of course it does not preclude it. Experimental evidence has shown that insects respond to certain stimuli out of the range of human sensation, while they do not respond to all those within it. They are sensitive, for example, to sound waves not detectable by the human auditory mechanism, and while they do not respond to all the wave-lengths of light in the spectrum that are visible to humans, they do to some of those that are not.

*Photoreceptors:* The photosensitive organs of the arthropods in general are eyes which are either simple or compound. In both, the visual unit is a cup or vertical bundle of cells, over which the cuticle is transparent and elevated, forming a lens. With the exception of the median eye of some crustacea, the cells at the base of the cup, 4–8 in number, are clustered in a sheaf as they are in the vertical bundle; such a sheaf or bundle is called a retinula (Fig. 14.22). The cells of the retinula are light-sensitive and their bases are in contact with nerves connected with the cerebral ganglion and also with branches of the tracheal system. Each retinular cell secretes a crystalline substance;

THE ARTHROPODS

the secretion from all the cells in the bundle is packed together to form a rod, the rhabdome, in the center of the bundle. These cells and those surrounding them also contain dark pigment granules, whose distribution may shift under varied conditions, so that the retinula, except for its upper surface, may be completely enclosed in a light-absorbing sheath, or exposed along the greater part of its length to light waves. The eyes of arthropods consist of numbers of such units, arranged in various ways. The simple eyes of insects, called ocelli, are each a single cup made of several retinulae; the eyes of centipedes and millepedes are formed of several similar cups in contact with each other, and the lateral eyes of Limulus, the horseshoe crab, are made of a number of small cups, each with a single retinula and united into a single visual organ. The eyes of spiders and scorpions are similar to the ocelli of insects. The compound eyes of insects and of crustacea are made up of a number of units, the ommatidia (Greek, ommatidium, diminutive of oma = eye), each of which includes a retinula and cells superficial to it, which secrete a crystalline cone, and the cornea or lens individual to each unit. In many of the crustacea, these compound eyes are borne on stalks and can be turned in different directions; in the insects they are unstalked and immovable,

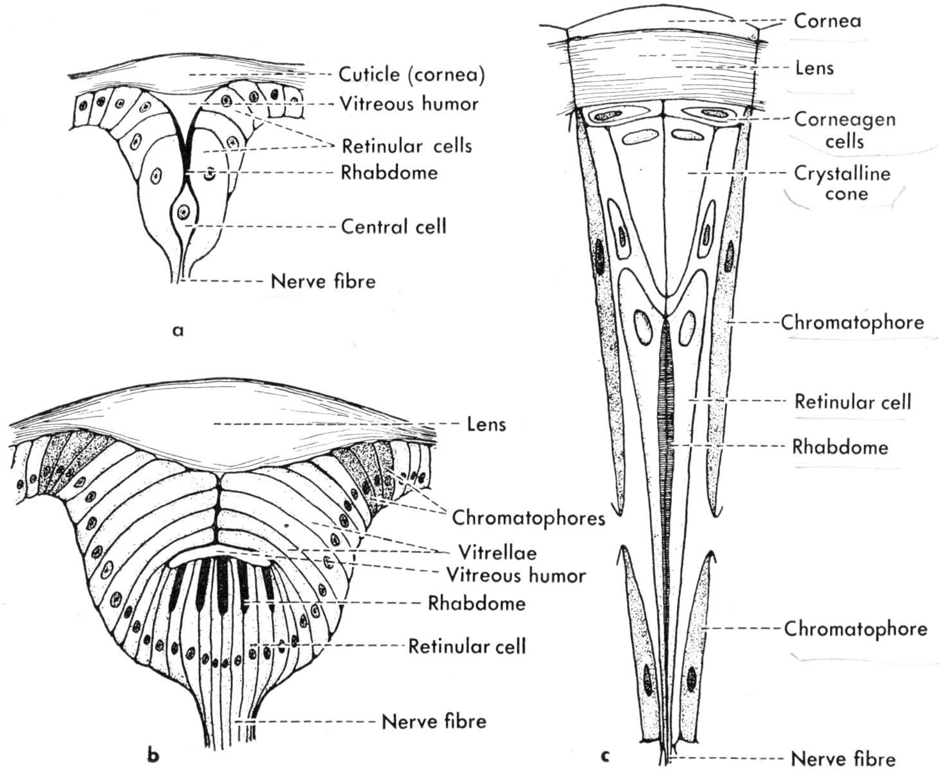

FIGURE 14.22  Diagrams of the photoreceptor organs of arthropods.

a. Visual unit from the lateral eye of Limulus (Xiphosura), the horse-shoe crab, formed by the sinking of the visual cells below the surface to form a retinula. (After Borradaile.)

b. An insect ocellus, in which the retinular cells, sunk below the surface as a cup, are covered over by cells from the side of the cup. (After Borradaile.)

c. A single ommatidium from the compound eye of a crustacean or an insect. (After Berlese.)

FIGURE 14.23   Insect eyes and images.

a. Head of a house fly (Musca domestica), showing the many-faceted compound eyes. x 24 (Photograph by courtesy of the U.S. Department of Agriculture, Bureau of Entomology and Plant Quarantine.)

b. Head of a female mosquito (Culex quinquefasciatus Say), showing the eyes and mouthparts. x 10 The paired filiform antennae and short maxillary palps are visible above the long piercing-sucking "beak," composed of labrum, epipharynx, maxillae, labium and hypopharynx. (Photograph by courtesy of the U.S. Department of Agriculture, Bureau of Entomology and Plant Quarantine.)

c. Diagram of the course of light rays through compound eyes giving (a) apposition and (b) superposition images. (After Imms.) In a, the only rays of light from the object that can reach the retinulae are those parallel to the long axes of the retinulae, indicated by broken lines; rays striking each ommatidium obliquely are absorbed by the pigment surrounding each crystalline cone when the pigment is fully dispersed in the pigment cell. In b, the oblique rays as well as those parallel to the long axis can reach the retinula, since, when the pigment granules are condensed within the pigment cells, there is no absorption of light reaching the margins of each ommatidium. Under the conditions of a, the image is a mosaic of discrete, individual images; under those of b, there is overlapping of the individual images.

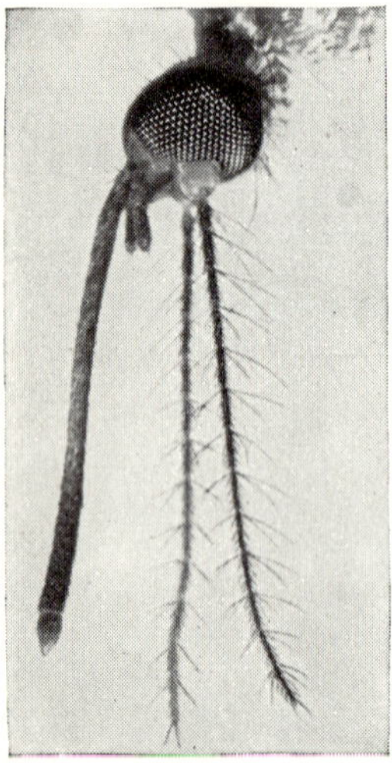

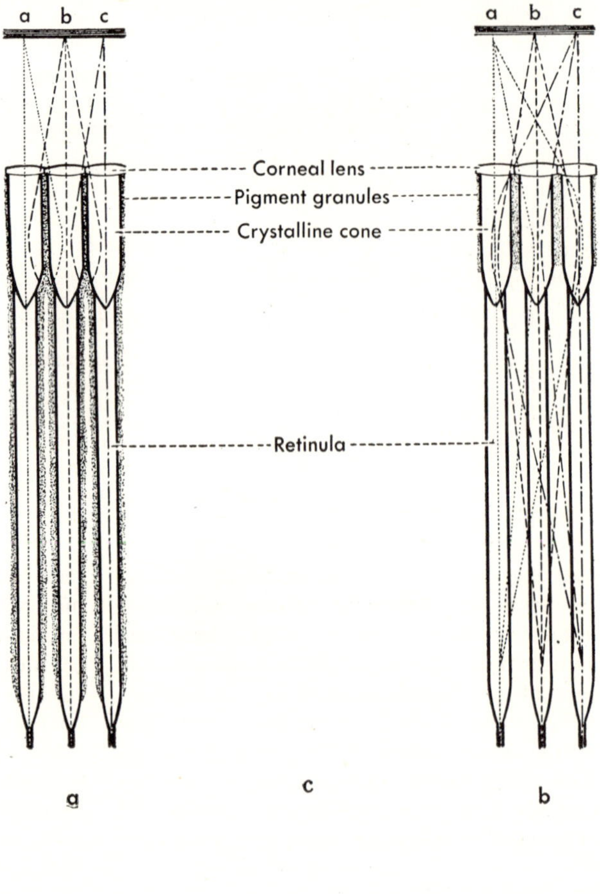

and can be differently directed only by movements of the animal's body or head.

The surface of the compound eye appears faceted; each facet is the outer surface of an individual ommatidium, of which there are about 2,500 in the eye of the crayfish, 10,000 or more in the eyes of some insects. The image that is obtained from the compound eye is an erect one, and may be either an apposition or a superposition image, depending upon the conditions of light and the extension of the pigment in the pigment cells. In either case, each ommatidium registers only a small area of the visual field so that the total image is either a mosaic of the discrete images of each ommatidium (apposition image) or else a continuous image in which the individual images overlap to a certain extent (superposition image) (Fig. 14.23). Such a photoreceptor organ is probably quick to pick up differences in light and shade and so to detect any movement, and since the ommatidia, both in crustacea and in insects, form a more or less hemispherical eye, its possessor is able to receive visual stimuli from nearly every direction at the same time.

*Tactoreceptors and statoreceptors:* Spines and hairs which are sensitive to mechanical stimuli, contact or touch, are distributed generally over the bodies of insects and other arthropods, often more abundantly on the antennae than elsewhere. While the more highly evolved crustacea possess organs of equilibration, or static sense organs, only a few aquatic insects have such specialized organs and the majority of insects maintain their positions through general neuromuscular mechanisms. The organs of equilibrium in crayfish, lobsters and similar crustaceans, the statocysts (Greek, statos = standing + kystos = cyst) are small cavities, one in the basal segment of each antennule, which are lined with sensory hairs and contain grains of sand, or other hard granules, as otoliths (Greek, otos = ear + lithos = stone) (Fig. 14.24). The function of these structures has been tested by substituting iron filings for the sand grains and bringing a magnet near the animal's head. The sensory hairs are stimulated by contact with the otoliths; under ordinary circumstances, any change from the normal position of equilibrium will be registered through these hairs and righting movements initiated. Under the experimental conditions described, crayfish in normal positions were caused to make

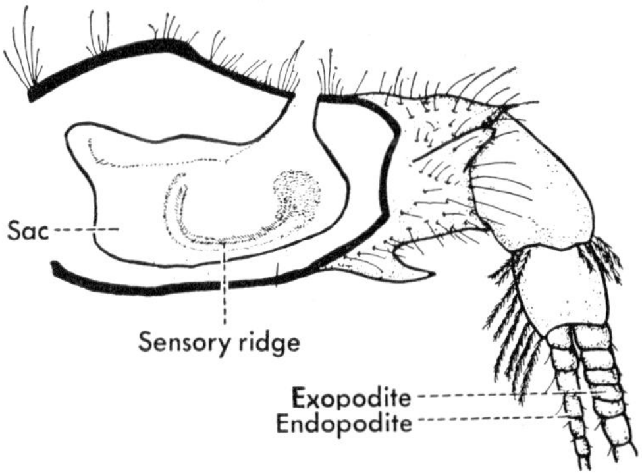

FIGURE 14.24 Statocyst from the antennule of a crustacean, showing the fluid-filled sac in the basal segment of the appendage and the ridge of sensory cells. (After Huxley and after Herrick.)

vigorous efforts to change that position when the iron filings in the statocyst were drawn about by magnetic attraction. In the larvae of one or two species of aquatic insects, there are similar statocysts on certain of the abdominal segments.

*Audioreceptors:* The finer hairs on the surface of the body which vibrate under slight differences of air pressure are probably auditory in function, for insects will respond to pressure changes in the air which humans apprehend as sound. Ants are sensitive to such sound waves as long as their antennae are intact, and it has been shown that mosquitoes will react to those that set the fine antennal hairs in motion. Such hairs may be generally distributed over the body as well as localized in the antennae and some insects, moreover, have special auditory, or tympanal, organs. In grasshoppers, there is a pair of such organs on the first abdominal segment, consisting of a thin circular or oval patch of cuticle, making a membrane which vibrates like the skin of a drum under changes in air pressure. A large air sac of the tracheal system lies on the inner surface of the membrane, and sensory nerves are either connected directly with it or lie close to it. Other insects have similar organs, in some cases more elaborate in pattern but operating on the same principle. There is a good deal of experimental evidence to show that insects possessing such organs respond to sounds audible to humans if these organs are intact, but do not respond if they are punctured or destroyed. It is also possible that they respond as well to other vibrations outside the range of human hearing.

*Chemoreceptors:* Certain sense cells on the surface of the body are sensitive to the chemical stimuli which in man produce sensations of taste and of smell. In many insects, the taste cells are associated with the mouth parts, or with the anterior part of the foregut; in others they may be situated on the antennae or on the distal segments of the legs. Discrimination between tastes has been shown in a number of insects; bees, for example, will reject honey that has been flavored with quinine or other bitter substances, and caterpillars will make spitting movements of their mouths if fed with salty or bitter food. The cells sensitive to smells are located principally on the antennae, and in some insects on the palps of the labium and the maxillae. This sense has been investigated to the greatest extent in bees, in which it seems to be very similar to that in humans, for bees respond to the same kinds of smells in the same relative strengths, and confuse smells which human beings also find similar. Insects appear to make use of their sense of smell as well as their capacity for color discrimination in selecting their food and suitable places to lay their eggs; certainly the sense of smell is valuable to social insects in distinguishing between the members of their own community and those of another. Ants of different kinds which will ordinarily fight each other will live harmoniously together if their antennae are removed, and Trichogramma, a parasitic insect that lays its eggs in the eggs of the swallow-tail butterfly, Papilio, can detect by its olfactory receptors whether or not an egg has already been laid in the butterfly egg it is walking over.

SOUND- AND LIGHT-PRODUCING ORGANS: Not only are the insects sensitive to sound waves and to light waves, but they can also produce sounds by means of special devices, and they, like many other animals and some plants, can produce light. The movements

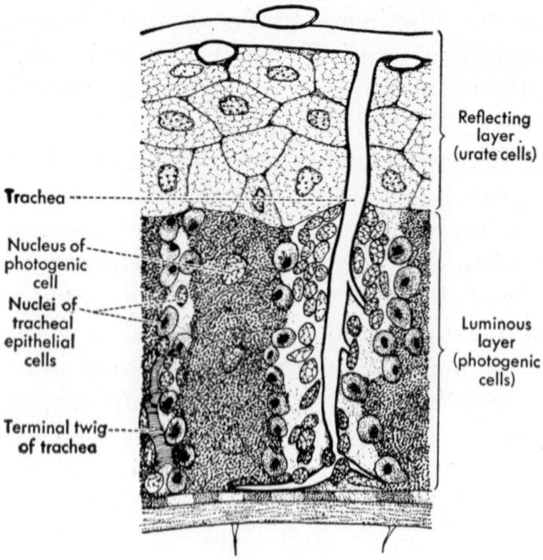

FIGURE 14.25 Section through the photogenic organ of a firefly (Photinus). (From various sources.)

of the wings of insects in flight and in hovering set up vibrations that result in high-pitched sounds which the human ear can detect; probably there are others of frequencies which the insects' sound receptors can register. The grasshoppers and katydids make sounds by rubbing parts of their bodies together; the click beetles by the impact of their skeletal plates against each other as they move the flexible parts of their bodies in jerking movements, and the termites, and deathwatch beetles by tapping the hard plates of their heads against the wood that they are living in. Cicadas move their tympanal organs by muscles, so that they make a drumming noise, like the sound of a stretched skin when struck or rubbed. A number of insects have photogenic or light-producing organs, operating by a mechanism which seems to be common to all biological systems that can produce visible light. This in an oxidative chemical reaction, in which a substance, luciferin, produced in certain cells, is oxidized through the agency of the enzyme luciferase. In this reaction, all but a small fraction of the energy is released as light, the very small remainder as heat. This "cold light" may be emitted continuously or intermittently as in the flashes of fireflies. In these insects, the cells in which this reaction takes place are situated in front of a layer of cells in which urates, or salts of uric acid, have been deposited (Fig. 14.25); this layer acts as a reflector so that the light shines from the body of the insect and may be visible at some distance from it.

**Insects as biological systems**

Insects have provided much material for biological studies of various kinds, and still offer much that is of great interest and significance for investigation and research. The identification is not yet complete of all the existing types nor of those that are in the course of being established; much of their physiology is yet to be determined and interpreted, and their sensitivities, responses and behavior patterns offer a wide field for the study of nervous stimulation, conduction and coordination. Much that relates to insects is of great practical importance to man, for they have profound effects, both beneficial and destructive, upon his welfare. Fossil remains show that insects have existed for a very long time, antedating by millions of years the advent of man upon the earth. The remains of extinct species are found in Paleozoic rocks, while some of the modern forms appeared along with the dinosaurs in the Triassic Era 200 million years ago.

*The insect cuticle:* While the properties of the cuticle with which their bodies are covered have been in many ways of particular advantage to the insects, the presence of such an investing exoskeleton has imposed certain limitations upon them, particularly in respect to their size and to their growth. Insect cuticle is made up of three layers, an epicuticle on the surface, an exocuticle and an endocuticle, all three forming an exoskeleton that is rigid yet light and flexible and variously permeable. In some insects, the cuticle is impregnated with calcium salts as it is in the crustacea, although never to such an extent. The epicuticle is a thin, refractive membrane, made of carbohydrates of high molecular weight and a substance known as cuticulin whose chemical nature is as yet unknown, but which has some properties in common with the cutin secreted by the epidermal cells of plants. The exocuticle contains cuticulin, and also chitin and protein, while the endocuticle contains only chitin and protein. These three layers refract light to different degrees, and this is one reason that light rays passing through them result in structural coloration. The endocuticle is expandable, elastic and probably freely permeable, for it is the cuticulin component of the exo- and the epicuticles that is responsible for the almost complete impermeability to water of the cuticle as a whole, a condition which prevails in the majority of insects during most of their lives. Further insurance against water loss is given by the waxy or oily coatings over the epicuticle which are secreted by the superficial glands of some insects. In many, the cuticle represents a large proportion of the total body weight, and as this in the aerial insects must be limited by the lifting capacity of their wings, their range of size is correspondingly limited. The evolutionary development of insects seems therefore to have proceeded in the direction of the specialization of parts and of behavior patterns, since the restrictions of size preclude the development of a massive brain with all the potentialities that such a development implies.

CONDITIONS IMPOSED BY A CUTICULAR COVERING; ECDYSIS: The cuticular covering has also imposed certain conditions upon the growth of the individual during its life, for while the endocuticle is expandable, the two outer layers are rigid and the growing insect, like the growing crustacean similarly enclosed in a hard case, must periodically shed its outer covering as it grows larger. So successive moults, or ecdyses (Greek, ekdyein = to put off), are customary during the life cycle of the insect, the crustacean and indeed of most arthropods, a process which is sometimes accompanied by a radical change in form, or metamorphosis

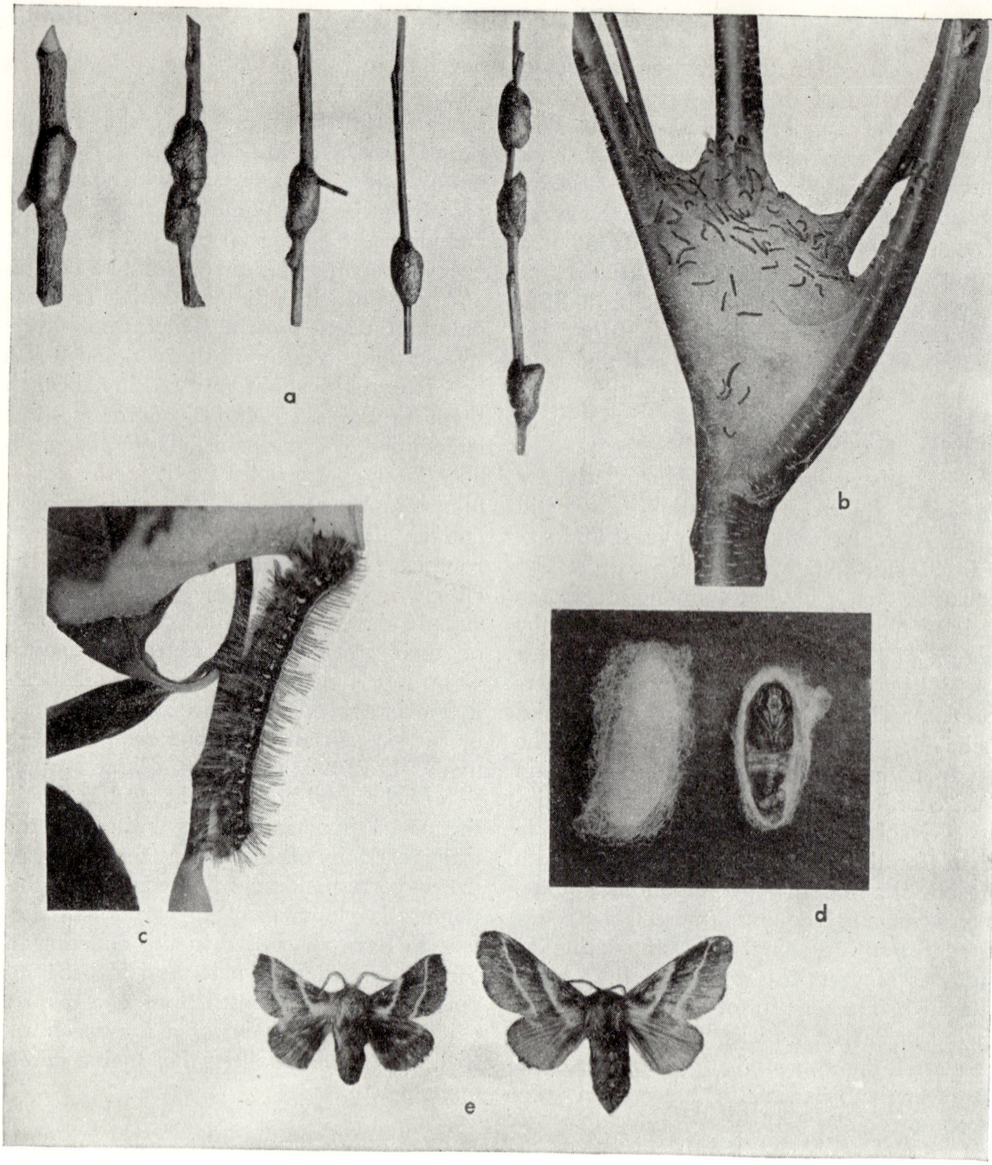

FIGURE 14.26 Life cycle of the tent caterpillar (Malacosoma americana). (Photographs by courtesy of the U.S. Department of Agriculture, Bureau of Entomology and Plant Quarantine.)

a. Egg cases. Each egg case, which is deposited by the female moth in the late summer on the twigs of such trees as wild cherry and apple, contains 300–400 eggs that undergo their early development in the autumn and remain dormant during the winter months.

b. A "tent." The larvae emerge from the egg in the spring when the leaves begin to unfold and, either over the old egg case or in a nearby fork of the tree, spin a web or "tent," which may reach a length of two feet, from which they go forth periodically to forage on the foliage and to which they return at night, or during rainstorms or periods of cold weather.

c. A foraging larva, or caterpillar.

d. Pupa. At the end of larval life, after a series of ecdyses, each larva spins a cocoon in a sheltered spot and enters a period of quiescence. The photograph at the left shows the exterior of a cocoon; that at the right, one that has been opened to show the pupa inside.

e. Adult moths (imagos) (left, male; right, female). After metamorphosis, the adults emerge from the pupal cases as flying insects, to mate and deposit eggs that will give rise to another generation of larvae, pupae and adults.

(Greek, metamorphoun = to transform), and in general habits of life. Thus the young butterfly, for example, emerges from the egg as a caterpillar, which crawls along by means of its three pairs of true locomotor appendages, the prolegs on its first three trunk segments, and various numbers of pseudolegs on the other segments and feeds on vegetation by means of chewing mouth parts. As a caterpillar it may undergo a number of moults as it outgrows its cuticular covering; each stage between moults is known as an instar (Fig. 14.26). After completing a number of larval instars, it spins a cocoon of silk fibers secreted by glands in the labium; in some beetles, the cells of the Malpighian tubules secrete the pupal covering. Within the cocoon, the butterfly enters into a period of outward inactivity; as a pupa it is quiescent and takes no food, subsisting on that which has been stored in the fat body and other tissues during the caterpillar phase. But inwardly, complicated structural changes are taking place in which the body patterns and the organs of the adult are laid down. At the end of this period, the insect emerges as an imago, its final or adult stage, with an appearance very different from that of its earlier instars. It flies rather than crawls, it feeds on the fluid secretions of plants rather than on their leaves, and it is capable of producing reproductive cells. The process of moulting is a complex one, initiated by conditions set up within the insect itself but influenced by external conditions.

THE CUTICLE AND DDT: It is the presence of a chitinous cuticle that makes insects so susceptible to DDT (dichlor-diphenyl-trichlorethane) and possibly to other insecticides as well. Studies of the comparative effects of DDT upon a wide range of animals have shown that those with chitinous coverings are the most sensitive; the coelenterates with complete perisarcs, for example, share with insects this vulnerability while other animals, with exoskeletons that do not contain chitin, escape injury or destruction from exposure to low concentrations of DDT. It is possible that a chitinous cuticle selectively concentrates the compound by adsorbing it between the micelles of which chitin is composed so that a relatively high concentration of it is built up on the surface of the animal. The mechanism of its transport into the body is not clear as yet; experiments with whole animals and with isolated parts have shown that its effect is in some way upon the neuro-muscular system, for when a sufficient quantity is introduced into the body, violent convulsive movements result ending in the death of the organism. The value of DDT as an insecticide rests upon this selective concentration by the insect cuticle so that even small amounts in the surrounding medium after a period of time accumulate to a lethal level.

## Other arthropods

While the crustacea represent the most generalized of the arthropods and the insects the most specialized, the centipedes, millepedes and Peripatus show various degrees of adaptation of the general arthropod plan, and the arachnids (spiders, scorpions and mites) the degeneration or loss of some typical arthropod features (Fig. 14.27). Peripatus, the centipedes and the millepedes are all tracheate, with bodies divided into a head and a trunk of a varying number of segments, often many. In the centipedes, each trunk segment bears a pair of jointed single appendages; in the millepedes, there are two such appendages on each trunk segment, indicating that fusion between two segments has taken place at some time in their history, and in Peripatus, while each trunk segment bears an appendage, these are not fully jointed, but are fleshy, cylindrical extensions of the lateral body wall, approximating more closely the parapodia of marine annelids than the typical arthropod appendage (Fig. 14.28).

### Arachnids

In the arachnids, the body is represented only by a cephalo-thorax of six segments and an abdomen of thirteen and a telson (Fig. 14.29). There is no head and the typical head appendages are lacking—that is, they have no antennules, antennae or true jaws.

The first pair of appendages are the chelicerae (Greek, chele = claw + keras = horn), used for grasping; the second are pedipalps, which are either sensory or prehensile and the remaining four are used for walking. All of the arachnids, except the most primitive horseshoe crabs, are fluid feeders, living principally on the juices of other animals whose integuments they pierce or crush by means of their chelicerae, and are provided with a suctorial digestive tract into which food is drawn by the action of a sucking stomach. While in some spiders and mites, and in the harvestmen, tracheae are the means of external respiration, in others, like the smallest of the mites, there is no especial respiratory surface and the exchange of gases takes place through the body surface as a whole, and in others, the terrestrial scorpions and some spiders, respiration is effected through "lung books." Lung books are pits in the integument,

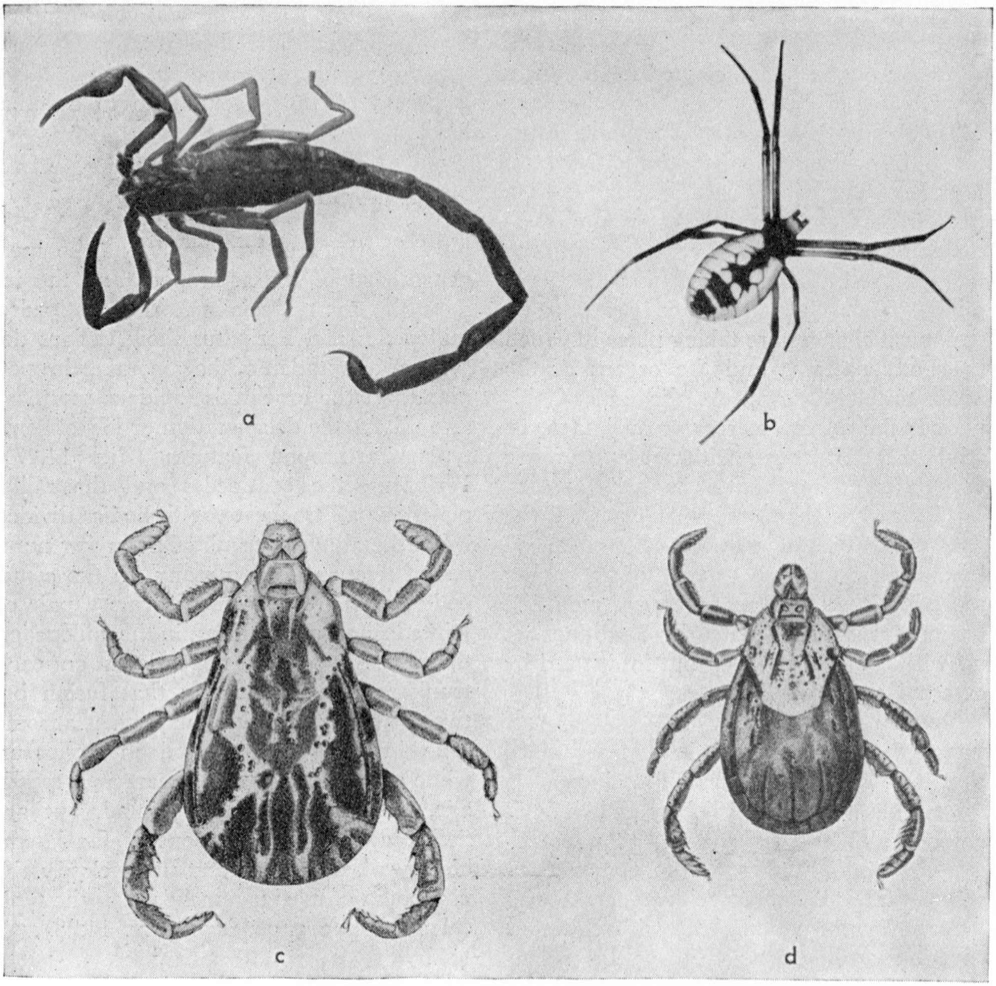

FIGURE 14.27 Types of arachnids.
 a. Scorpion (Centrurus). (Photograph of preserved specimen by D. F. Reath.)
 b. Spider (Miranda (Argiope) aurantia). (Photograph of living specimen by D. F. Reath.)
 c. Tick (Dermacentor variabilis), male much enlarged. (Photograph of drawing by courtesy of the U.S. Department of Agriculture, Bureau of Entomology and Plant Quarantine.)
 d. Tick (Dermacentor variabilis), female much enlarged. (Photograph of drawing by courtesy of the U.S. Department of Agriculture, Bureau of Entomology and Plant Quarantine.)

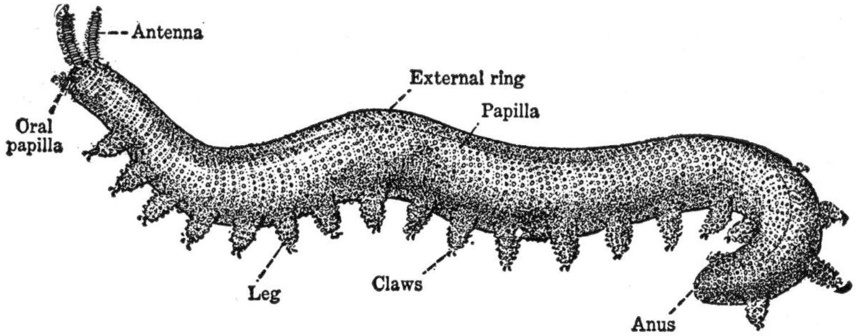

THE ARTHROPODS [253]

FIGURE 14.28 Peripatus. (From Hegner, *College Zoology*, 5th edition. Copyright 1942 by The Macmillan Company.)

whose walls are folded into thin plates or leaflets like the pages of a book, across which gases diffuse in and out of the body fluid. The pits are open to the outside through pores, and while in the scorpions the movement of air in them seems to be dependent wholly upon diffusion, in spiders there is a system of muscles by which the cavity is compressed, expelling the air from it; fresh air is drawn in when the cavity returns to its original shape due to the elasticity of its chitinous lining. On the abdominal segments of Limulus there are similar respiratory plates, but these are external and not enclosed in pits so that they form "gill books" or "book gills" across which the sea water passes as the animal slowly waves the plates back and forth.

The excretory organs of the arachnids are a pair of coxal glands, derived from the coelome and the coelomoducts of the fifth segment. Remnants of the coelome are also found in the reproductive organs but all the other coelomic spaces evident in the embryo are occluded in the adult by the growth of the hemocoele, as they are in the other arthropods (Fig. 14.30).

*Nervous system and behavior patterns:* The nervous system shows even greater concentration than in the insects, for while in the scorpions and other less highly evolved arachnids, there may be a chain of segmental ganglia, in the spiders all of the ventral ganglia have coalesced into a single one which is connected with the dorsal ganglion by commissures. Impulses from the eyes are transmitted to and relayed from the dorsal

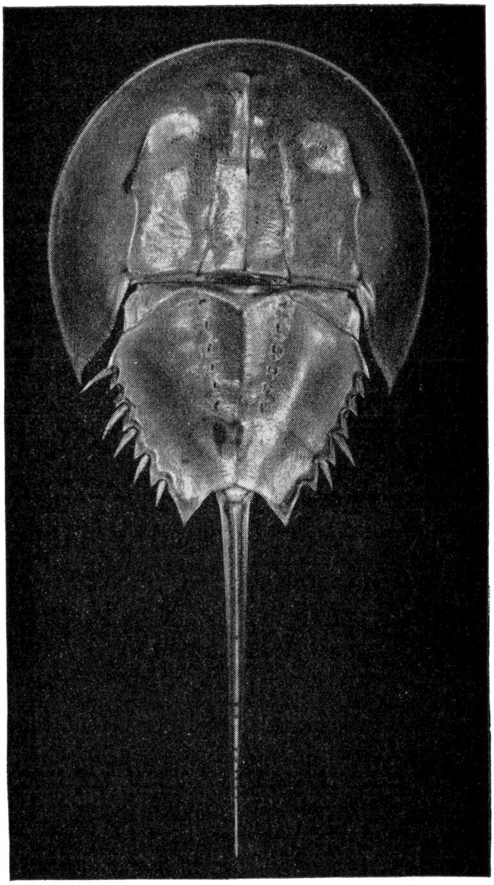

FIGURE 14.29 Limulus (Xiphosura), the horseshoe, or King, crab. (Photograph by courtesy of the American Museum of Natural History, New York.)

[254]     THE ORGANIZATION OF BIOLOGICAL SYSTEMS

ganglion; all the other sensory and effector regions of the body are connected by nerves with the single ventral ganglion. The spiders, like many of the insects, exhibit complicated and stereotyped patterns of behavior, especially in connection with the spins and anchors the radial threads, and then returns to the center of the orb and begins to spin the viscous spiral thread, making use of another set of glands to provide the sticky substance with which they are covered. Still another set of glands pro-

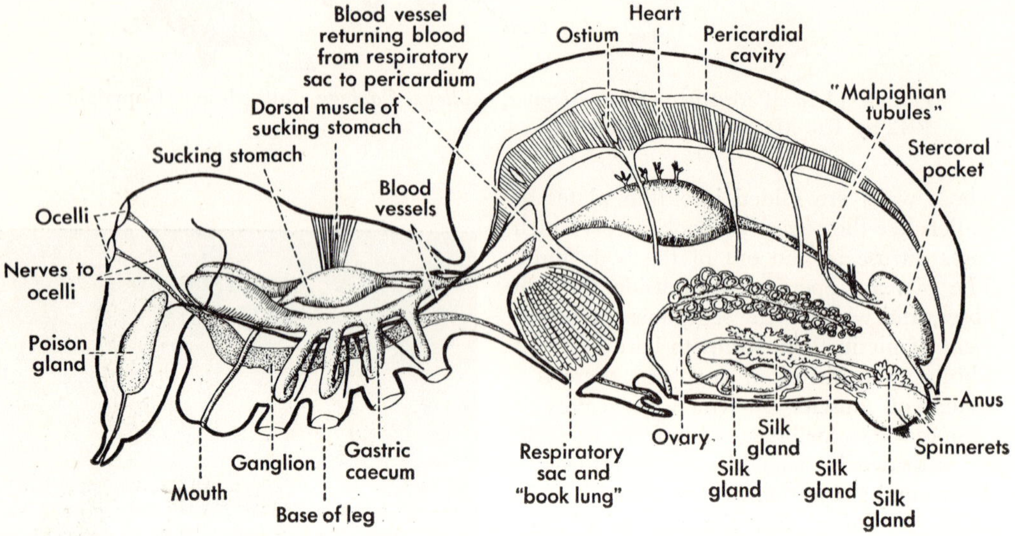

FIGURE 14.30  Diagram showing the internal anatomy of a spider (Epeira diademmata). (After Harmer and Shipley.)

spinning of their webs, the capture of their food, their mating and the laying of their eggs. The web-spinning spiders are the greatest specialists of the group. To spin an orb web like those that are so common in summer on the grass, or stretched between two upright objects, a spider makes use of the secretion from at least five different types of glands located in the abdomen, and goes through a set pattern of actions from which it cannot deviate. The glands open by tiny pores on the spinnerets, small elevations on the ventral surface of the abdomen, possibly representing vestigial abdominal appendages. The orb spider first spins a drag line between two objects; the drag line is a fairly heavy, silky thread secreted by one set of glands, and this is anchored to the supporting objects by attachment discs, secreted by another set of glands. Having blocked out the position of its web by means of drag lines which are drawn taut and anchored by attachment discs, the spider then duces the cords that are wrapped around the prey when it is finally caught in the finished web. If interrupted at any point in its spinning operations, or if any part of the web is destroyed before it is finished, most spiders cannot return to the place where they left off or repair the injured region, but must begin all over again. Once the pattern of behavior has been started, it must be carried through to completion, and the spider is incapable of changing its pattern to repeat an earlier part of it or to continue it unless each act follows almost directly upon the previous one.

### Regeneration in arthropods

The arthropods as a group have a limited capacity for regeneration, but they have some special mechanisms which minimize the effects of injury. The regenerative capacity is greatest among the crustaceans, whose lost appendages can be completely restored;

this can also be accomplished by some insects, but by others, like the cockroach, for example, a limb may be regenerated but will not be complete in all its parts. The rapidity with which arthropod blood coagulates or clots is some insurance against fatal effects from a slight injury; a further guarantee is the ability to break off a limb at a definite point, the breaking plane, usually in one of the basal segments. At the breaking plane, there is a thin layer of cuticle extending inward with only a small aperture for the passage of a nerve and a blood vessel. When injured distal to this, the arthropod flexes the limb sharply, thus compressing the blood space and producing an effect very much like the application of a tourniquet; the limb then separates from the body and the small wound quickly heals. In the crustacea and myriapods (the centipedes and millepedes) and in some insects an entirely new limb will be regenerated from the stump. This process of casting off an injured appendage, or autotomy, was first observed by Réaumur in crabs and crayfish; later it was found to take place in a number of other animals, such as starfish and other echinoderms, and even in animals as high

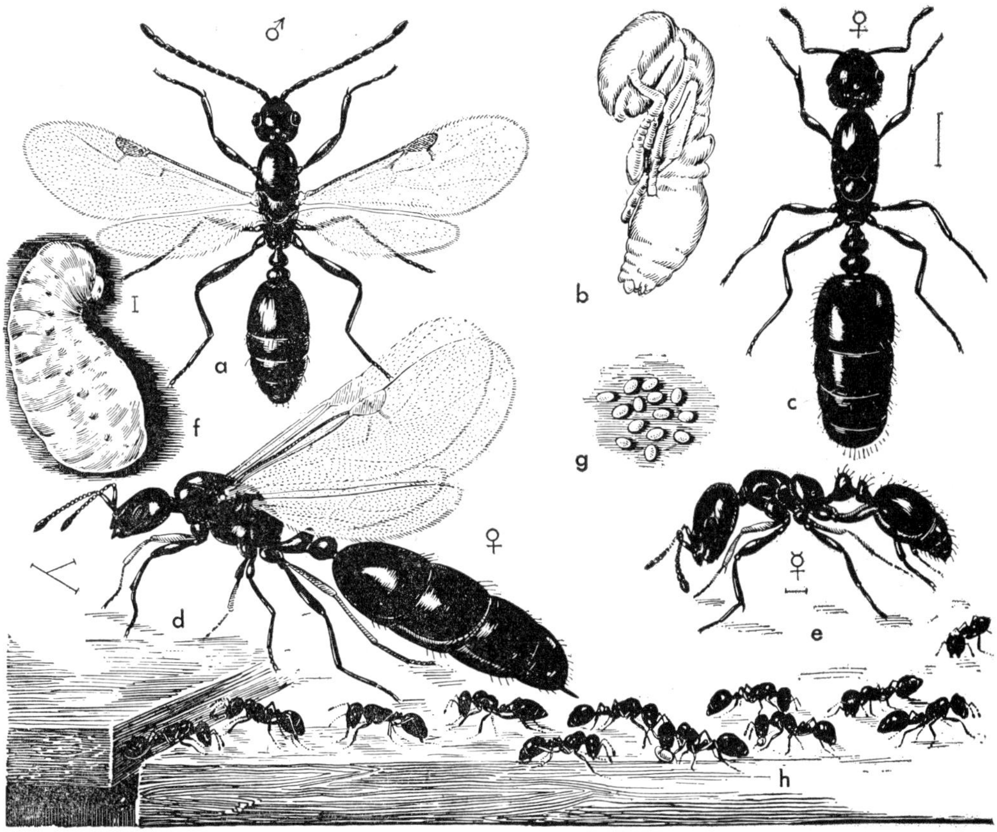

FIGURE 14.31 Life cycle and polymorphism of the little black ant (Monomorium minimus). (Photographs by courtesy of the U.S. Department of Agriculture, Bureau of Entomology and Plant Quarantine.)

a. winged male.
b. pupa, from the side.
c. wingless female.
d. winged female.
e. wingless worker (sterile individual).
f. larva (much enlarged).
g. group of larvae.
h. group of workers on the march.

in the evolutionary scale as lizards, which shed their tails after damage to them. Autotomy may also take place spontaneously, that is, without any external injury (Fig. 14.31). The winged individuals among the ants and the termites which lead but a brief aerial existence during the period of mating break off their wings when this period is over and they take up an ambulatory existence; in the termites, the wings separate from the body along a defined line, like the breaking plane of the crustacean appendage, but in ants no such definite line has been established.

CHAPTER 15

# THE CHORDATA

## The distinguishing characters of chordates

Chordates are distinguished from all other coelomate animals and from all other biological systems by the presence of an internal supporting rod, the notochord (Greek, noton = back + chorda = cord), which lies immediately dorsal to the digestive tract and from which the phylum receives its name; paired openings, the gill slits, in the lateral walls of the pharynx, connecting this region of the digestive tract directly with the exterior and between which the pharyngeal and body wall and the intervening tissues form the gill, or branchial, arches; and a hollow, tubular nerve cord, dorsal to the notochord, in most species expanded anteriorly into a bulb, the brain. Externally their bodies are more or less clearly divided into head, trunk and tail regions, and internally they all have a complete digestive tract, with anterior mouth and posterior anus, a closed circulatory system with a central muscular pump, the heart, and segmental excretory organs (Fig. 15.1). Most of them show other evidences of a basically segmental architectural plan, both during their embryonic development and as adults, evident especially in paired muscle masses, or myotomes (Greek, mys = muscle + tomos = piece), separated by connective tissue septa, the myocommata (Greek, comma = segment) and paired nerves and blood vessels corresponding to the primary body segments. These common, fundamental characters have been modified in various ways and developed to different degrees in the course of evolution of the 37,300 chordate species that have appeared upon the earth in different periods of its history.

## Chordate types

The extent of the notochord, or chorda dorsalis, a firm axial rod made of cells distended with large vacuoles and enclosed within a sheath of elastic connective tissue, in the individuals of different species, is the basis for the subdivision of the phylum into four sub-phyla, the Hemichordata (Greek, hemi = half), the Urochordata (Greek, oura = tail), the Cephalochordata (Greek, kephale = head), or Acrania (Greek, a = without + kranion = skull) and the Vertebrata (Latin, vertebratus = jointed), or Craniata.

### The lower chordates; Hemichordata, Urochordata and Cephalochordata

The Hemichordata are small, worm-like animals, the tongue or acorn worms that live in the mud and sand in shallow parts of the sea; in them the notochord is limited to a small region of the body anterior to the mouth (Fig. 15.2). The Urochordata, the tunicates or sea squirts that are widely distributed throughout the seas, all pass through a developmental stage in which, as larvae, they have a dorsal tubular nerve cord and a tail supported by a notochord; with a few exceptions, such larvae undergo regressive metamorphosis, in the course of which these chordate characters are lost and, as adults, the tunicates bear little resemblance to other chordates (Fig. 15.3). They have, moreover, certain characteristics unique among all biological systems. One of these is an investing case of tunicin, a substance that chemically resembles cellulose very closely; another is the presence of green, blue and orange cells in the fluid that circulates through their blood channels.

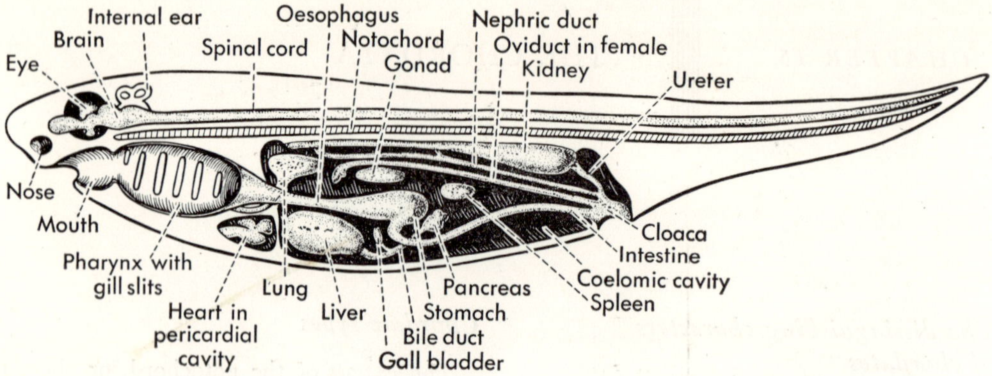

# THE ORGANIZATION OF BIOLOGICAL SYSTEMS

FIGURE 15.1 Diagrammatic longitudinal section through an "idealized" vertebrate to show the relative positions of the major organs. (From Romer, *The Vertebrate Body*. Copyright 1949 by the W. B. Saunders Company.)

Chemical analyses of the pigments in these cells have shown that they contain different oxides of the element vanadium ($V_2O_3$, $V_2O_4$ and $V_2O_5$, respectively) in combination with protein which, like hemoglobin, combine readily with oxygen and also release it readily in acid solutions. They therefore act as respiratory pigments, and probably very efficient ones, although the tunicates are the only organisms to make use of them, and it is remarkable that vanadium, whose concentration in sea water is so low that its presence cannot be directly determined by chemical means, should be selectively concentrated by this particular group of animals to such an extent that it has become part of their respiratory mechanism.

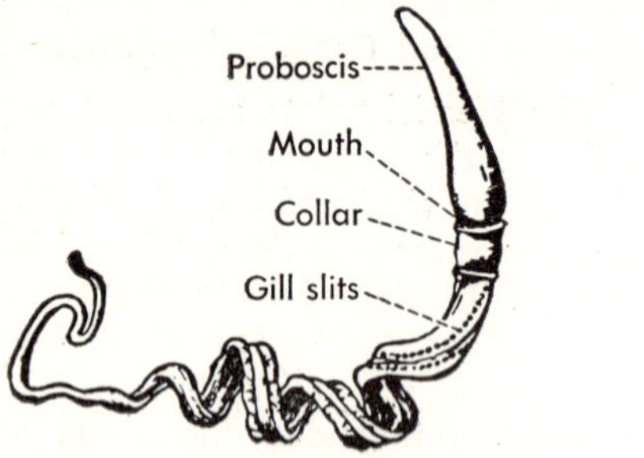

In the Cephalochordata the notochord runs the entire length of the body. The nerve cord, while very slightly expanded anteriorly, is not typically enlarged as a brain nor is it enclosed in a protective case, so that the name Acrania is also applied to them. This group includes the lancelets, small fish-like animals no more than about 100 mm. in length, which live in the shallow waters of the sea or burrow into its

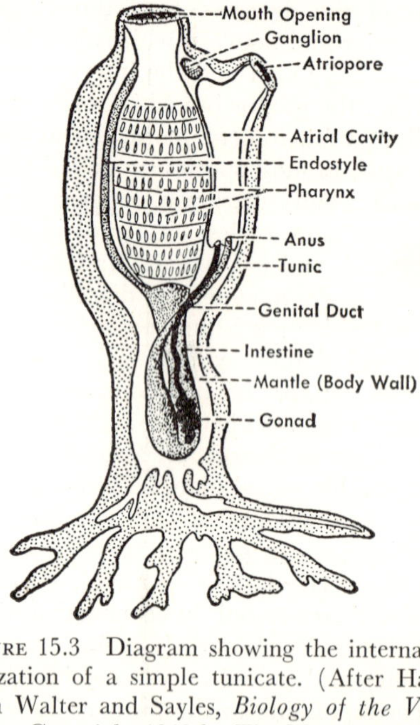

FIGURE 15.2 Dolichoglossus, a hemichordate. (From Walter and Sayles, *Biology of the Vertebrates*. Copyright 1949 by The Macmillan Company.)

FIGURE 15.3 Diagram showing the internal organization of a simple tunicate. (After Haller, from Walter and Sayles, *Biology of the Vertebrates*. Copyright 1949 by The Macmillan Company.)

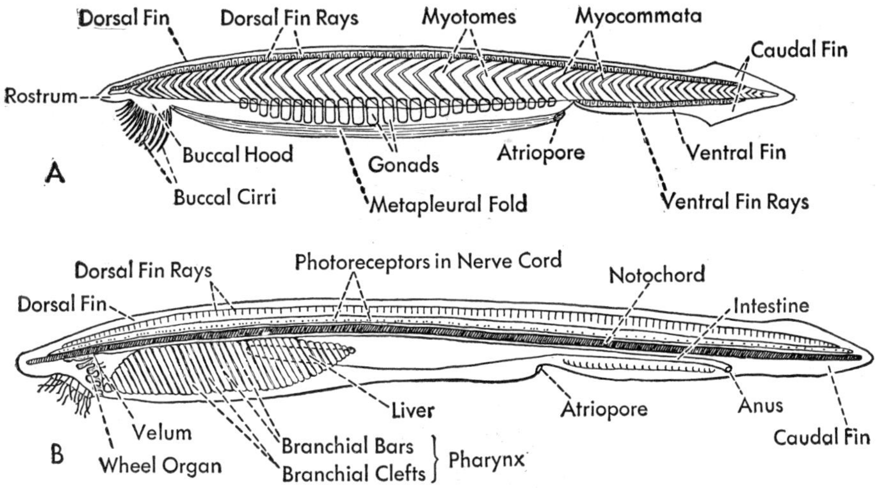

FIGURE 15.4 Amphioxus. (From Walter and Sayles, *Biology of the Vertebrates*. Copyright 1949 by The Macmillan Company.)

A. Side view of the animal. (After Kirkaldy.)
B. Side view with internal organs exposed.

sandy bottom. Amphioxus (Fig. 15.4) is a typical representative of the cephalochordates and since it has a number of features, both in its development and in its adult structure, which resemble those of the most highly evolved of the Chordates, the vertebrates, it is generally regarded as closely related to the stock from which they have evolved.

### The higher chordates; Vertebrata (Craniata)

The vertebrates have not only reached the highest degree of evolutionary development of any of the chordates, but also the widest distribution and the greatest numbers, for they are represented by some 35,000 known species, or over 90 per cent of all the chordates. In the vertebrates, the notochord serves as the main axial support only during their embryonic lives and is supplemented, or replaced, in the adults by a segmented and somewhat flexible endoskeleton surrounding the nerve cord and the brain and made of cartilage or of cartilage and bone. These cartilaginous or bony frameworks have in many cases been preserved as fossils, and the geologic record shows that vertebrates first appeared as animal types along with the giant ferns and

FIGURE 15.5 Fishes. (Photographs by courtesy of the U.S. Fish and Wildlife Service.)

a. An elasmobranch. The dogfish, Squalus acanthias.

b. A teleost. The small-mouthed black bass, Micropterus dolomieu, showing ctenoid scales.

FIGURE 15.6 Amphibians. (Photographs by courtesy of the U.S. Fish and Wildlife Service.)

a. A urodele amphibian. The marbled salamander, Ambystoma opacum. (Photograph by E. M. Kalmbach.)

b. An anuran amphibian. The green, or spring, frog, Rana clamitans. Left, male; right, female.

mosses over 240 million years ago, and that since their first appearance they have developed along various lines with various degrees of success. The most successful of these evolutionary excursions are represented to-day in the five classes of modern vertebrates, the fishes (Fig. 15.5), amphibians (Fig. 15.6), reptiles (Fig. 15.7), birds (Fig. 15.8) and mammals (Fig. 15.9), culminating in man who, by virtue primarily of his brain and his manual dexterity, has become the dominant type, largely controlling all the other forms co-existent with him in the biological world and steadily gaining more

a

b

FIGURE 15.7  Reptiles. (Photographs by courtesy of the U.S. Fish and Wildlife Service.)
  a. Alligators. Alligator mississippiensis.
  b. Gila monster, Heloderma horidum, inhabiting the deserts of Arizona and New Mexico. The only poisonous lizard in the world.

[ 262 ]  THE ORGANIZATION OF BIOLOGICAL SYSTEMS

and more control over the physical world in which he lives. How long he can maintain this supremacy seems now to depend upon the extent to which his social development keeps pace with his technological and that to which he directs his ever-increasing mastery of animate and inanimate systems to progressive construction of his civilization rather than to its deterioration or destruction.

wall, the fins. All the others are included in the superclass Tetrapoda (Greek, tetra = four + pous = foot), distinguished from the fishes by their paired fore and hind limbs, primarily locomotor in function; lungs as areas of external respiration; and the ability to live on land and in the air. They may also be subdivided into the groups Anamniota and Amniota, depending on whether or not their young are enveloped, during the course of their development, in a protective membrane called the amnion (dim. of Greek, amnos = lamb); according to this criterion, the fish and amphibia as anamniotes are distinct from the reptiles, birds and mammals as amniotes.

FIGURE 15.8 Birds. (Photographs by courtesy of the U.S. Fish and Wildlife Service.)

a. Crow, Corvus b. brachyrhynchus. (Photograph by H. H. Jackson.)

b. Great gray owl, Scotiaptex nebulosa. (Photograph taken in Alaska by O. J. Murie.)

***Distinguishing characters of vertebrates:*** The vertebrates fall naturally into two great groups, or superclasses, within each of which there is great diversity in type and in degree of evolutionary development. The superclass Pisces includes all the fishes, animals which lead an aquatic existence, which retain gill slits as adults, their external respiration being effected through branchia or gills developed in connection with them, and which steer themselves through the water and maintain their equilibrium in it by means of folds or outgrowths of the body

FINS AND LIMBS: Fishes propel themselves through the water by lateral movements of their bodies, especially of their tails, stabilize themselves in it and guide their movements by means of their fins. In all fishes except the Cyclostomes, there are two pairs of lateral fins, one single fin surrounding the

FIGURE 15.9  Mammals.

  a. Capuchin monkey, Cebus capucinus, native to Central America. (Photograph by courtesy of the Zoological Society of Philadelphia.)
  b. Rabbit, Lepus americanus. (Photograph by courtesy of the Soil Conservation Service, U.S. Department of Agriculture.)
  c. Female Hawaiian seal, Phoca sp. (Photograph by Alex Wetmore, by courtesy of the U.S. Fish and Wildlife Service.)

end of the tail as the tail fin, and one or more single fins rising from the mid-region of the back as dorsal fins (Fig. 15.5). The fins are outgrowths of the body wall, in which develop supporting rods of cartilage or bone and of keratin; the lateral fins can has reduced the effectiveness of the general body surface for the gaseous interchange and made obligatory the retention of some area where this exchange can be carried out to an extent adequate for the needs of the entire organism. In fishes, this is provided by

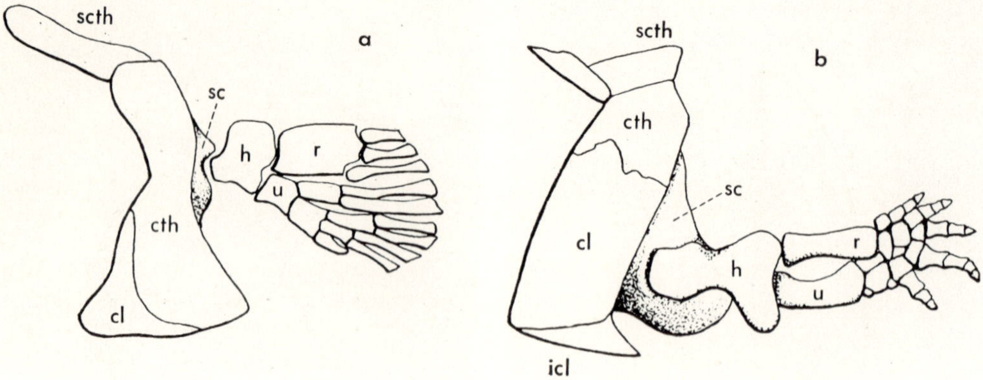

FIGURE 15.-10   The shoulder girdle and pectoral fin of a crossopterygian (a), and the same structure in an ancient fossil amphibian (b), placed in a comparable position to show the basic similarities in limb pattern.

h—humerus, r—radius, u—ulna of the tetrapod, and homologies in the fish fin.
cl—clavicle, cth—cleithrum, icl—interclavicle, sc—scapula, scth—supracleithrum.

(From Romer, *The Vertebrate Body*. Copyright 1949 by the W. B. Saunders Company.)

be turned in different directions by contractions of muscles attached to their bases, and so can direct the course of the fish to different levels in the water and help to balance it at any one level. Although no structural similarity is readily apparent between the lateral fins of modern fishes and the limbs of tetrapods, certain extinct species of the order Crossopterygii (Greek, crossoi = fringe + pterygion = little wing) furnish some evidence that they are homologous structures and that the arms and legs of modern tetrapods have evolved from such fins as these fishes possessed (Fig. 15.10).

LUNGS: The lung as an organ of external respiration has reached its highest degree of specialization in the tetrapods although it, like the tetrapod limb, may also have had its origin in aquatic vertebrates. In most of the amphibia the integument serves as the main respiratory surface, but in other vertebrates the development of water-proof coverings the gills, or branchia, developed as outgrowths along the gill slits (Fig. 15.11). Water taken in through the fish's mouth as it swims along is swept out through the gill clefts, washing over the filaments of the gills in its course. Many species of modern fish possess also an internal sac-like outgrowth of the anterior part of the digestive tube, the air or swim bladder, filled with a mixture of gases with a relatively high content of oxygen. In the more primitive of these species, this bladder remains connected with the digestive tube and functions as a respiratory area accessory to the gills, as well as a hydrostatic organ that allows the fish to adjust its specific gravity to different levels in the water. This latter function is its primary one in the more highly evolved fishes, in which the connection with the enteron has become obliterated.

Lungs are also sacs developed as outgrowths of the pharynx, with walls that are very thin and richly supplied with blood vessels. The development of the lung and the dependence of the organism upon it has proceeded to different extents in different species, but in all of them has involved modifications of the circulatory system, primarily of the vessels coursing through the gill arches between the gill slits that, in branchiate vertebrates, carry the blood past the gills.

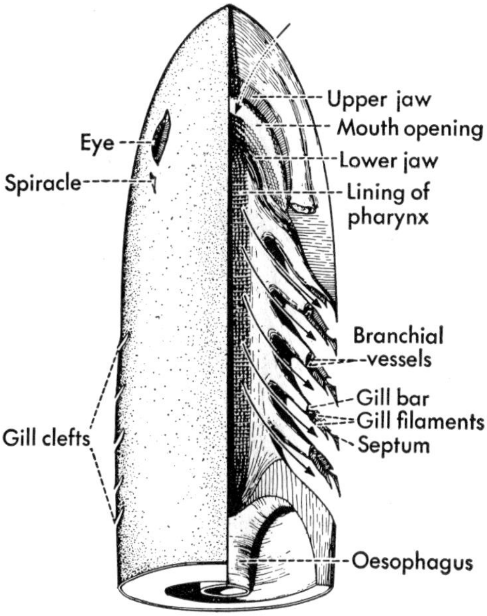

FIGURE 15.11 Diagram showing the relation of the gills to the gill clefts and the branchial chamber in an elasmobranch. (After Wilder.)

On the left, the exterior of the head region of the animal is shown; on the right, the interior as exposed by removal of the dorsal body wall. The arrows show the direction of the water current.

LIVER AND PANCREAS: Also appearing with the vertebrates and peculiar to them among biological systems are liver and pancreas, two organs developed from the enteron and functioning not only as accessory digestive glands in the production of digestive enzymes, but also as centers for the synthesis of certain specialized products and, in the case of the liver, for the storage of reserve materials. Although in many of the nonchordates there are accessory glands to which the name "liver" is frequently given, these are neither homologous nor analogous to the vertebrate liver.

## Supporting tissues of vertebrates

Both bone and cartilage are tissues of mesenchymal origin, formed by mesenchyme cells that differentiate either as chondrioblasts, or cartilage-forming cells, or as osteoblasts, or bone-forming ones. Theoretically, they are tissues that might be formed in any region of the body where mesenchyme is present, but actually they are limited to very definite areas, presumably those where mechanical strains and stresses are greatest. Cartilage, like mesenchyme, is essentially an embryonic tissue and among modern vertebrates it is only in the elasmobranch fishes that it remains as the sole supporting tissue of the adult body; in retaining it as such, these fishes—the sharks, skates and rays—exhibit the biological phenomenon of paedogenesis (Greek, pais = child + genesis = origin), or retention of an embryonic condition in adult life. In other vertebrates the cartilage that forms their internal skeletons as embryos is largely replaced, in the adults, by bone, which forms the major part of the vertebral column, surrounding the nerve cord, and of the cranium, or brain case, enclosing the brain (axial skeleton); the framework of the appendages (appendicular skeleton); and that supporting the gill arches (visceral skeleton). In addition to these regions of bone formation, common to all vertebrates, there may be others as, for example, in the tissues of the trunk where slender rods, the ribs, are formed, or in those of the integument, where dermal bones may be deposited as the scales in some fishes or the bony case that almost wholly encloses the bodies of turtles.

### Cartilage

Cartilage, commonly called gristle, is somewhat compressible and elastic and, though firm in its consistency, is not nearly so hard as bone, or dentine or enamel, the hardest substances that are produced in the animal body. Its cells lie in a solid matrix of protein chemically a good deal like mucus, and sometimes impregnated with calcium salts deposited in it in polygonal plates. This matrix may be clear or hyaline (Greek, hyalinos = of glass or crystal), as it is in the skeletons of the cartilaginous fishes, or it may be dense and fibrous, as it is on the ends of some of the bones of tetrapods or in the cartilaginous discs between the individual vertebrae of their spinal columns (Fig. 11.1g).

deposition of these salts may be due to the activity of the osteoblasts, or it may be the result of their precipitation in the intercellular substance in consequence of physical and chemical conditions there. As the matrix is deposited, the osteoblasts become further

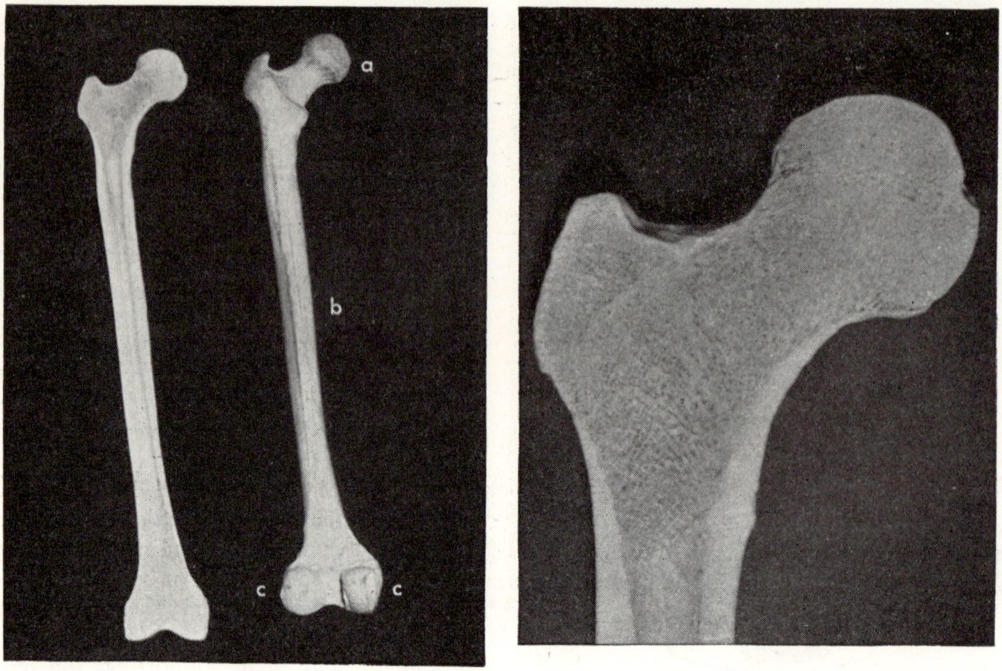

a

b

FIGURE 15.12 Structure of bones. (Photographs by D. F. Reath.)

a. A long bone (femur) of a mammal. The picture on the right shows the entire bone from its ventral aspect; that on the left, a hemisection of the bone, showing the central marrow cavity along the shaft and the cancellous bone at the upper end.
a—head; b—shaft; c—condyle.

b. The upper end of the hemisected femur enlarged to show the spongy character of the cancellous bone.

**Bone**

In the formation of bone, certain of the mesenchymal cells become differentiated and specialized as osteoblasts (Greek, osteon = bone + blastos = germ), through whose activity fibres of a protein called collogen are laid down in the intercellular substance. This organic matrix then becomes impregnated to varying degrees with calcium salts, principally phosphates, with some calcium carbonate, some magnesium phosphate and a small amount of calcium chloride. The and further removed from each other and isolated in small spaces, or lacunae (Latin, lacuna = hollow), in the hard substance (Fig. 11.1h). The finished product, of which the organic material represents about 30–40 per cent and the inorganic 60–70 per cent, is an apparently homogeneous mass of very hard material.

The relationship between the organic and the inorganic components of bone are so intimate that it is impossible to distinguish between them by any available optical means, and it may be that the ions of the inorganic compounds are adsorbed on the colloidal particles. Although so firm, on analysis mature bone has been found to contain about 50 per cent of water by weight, and sometimes as much as 24 per cent fat; the water may be to a great extent chemically or physically bound in the calcium-phosphate complex (see page 48). Certainly bone, although the most rigid tissue in the vertebrate body, is not a static one. It constitutes one of the important reserves of calcium within the organism and can be drawn upon when for any reason the current calcium supply becomes deficient. Recent studies on the metabolism of rabbits by means of radioactive isotopes have shown that radioactive phosphorus administered to adult animals entered their bone, and also the enamel and dentine of their teeth, indicating that none of these hard substances is a lifeless, inert deposit of inorganic salts but an active one, continually exchanging ions with the circulating blood.

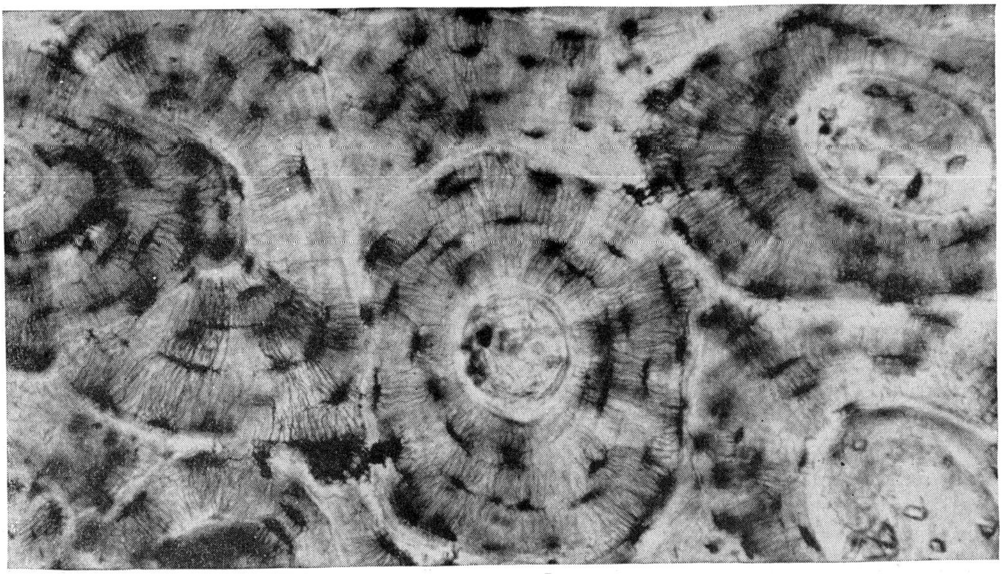

In many cases, formation of bone takes place in regions previously occupied by cartilage and is therefore endochondral (Greek, endo = within + chondrion = cartilage) in its formation. Many different specialized cells are concerned in the process, which involves the disintegration of the cartilage cells and the removal, by scavenging cells, of the cellular debris resulting, as well as the deposition of bone. But some bones, called membrane bones, are formed directly from the mesenchyme without cartilaginous precursors, and some are both endochondral and membranous in their origin. Membrane bones, which make up much of the skeleton of fishes exclusive of the elasmobranchs, and the skulls of other vertebrates, are frequently cancellous (Latin, cancellosus = covered with bars), or spongy, in appearance, for the osteoblasts are so distributed that the matrix is laid down in plates or bars which branch and join, making a meshwork of hard material with blood vessels, nerves, connective tissue cells and fluid in the interstices. This spongy bone is surrounded by compact bone of different degrees of thickness, and outside of the compact bone connective tissue cells are packed together in a firm and tough investing membrane, the periosteum (Greek, peri = around + osteon = bone). The inner layers

FIGURE 15.13 Ground section of bone from the shaft of a long bone, showing a number of Haversian systems. (Photograph by courtesy of the General Biological Supply House, Inc., Chicago.)

of the long bones of the limbs of tetrapods, endochondral in their formation, are also cancellous, while the outer layers are of compact bone, deposited in concentric rings around tubular canals that run parallel to the long axis of the bone (Figs. 15.12, 15.13). Each canal, which contains blood vessels, nerves and bone-forming connective tissue, together with its concentric lamellae of osteocytes and solid matrix, is known as an Haversian system, after a seventeenth century English physician and anatomist, Clopton Havers, whose studies first revealed the finer details of bone structure. The thicker the bone, the greater the number of Haversian systems within it. The center of the shaft of these long bones is hollow; this is the marrow cavity, in mammals especially, filled with fat, blood vessels, mesenchyme and blood cells in all stages of their differentiation, for this is the principal site of blood cell formation in adult mammals.

**Axial and visceral skeleton**

***Vertebral column:*** The major part of the axial skeleton consists of the spinal or vertebral column, made up of a series of units, the vertebrae, corresponding in number and position to the primary segments of the body. Primitively a vertebra consists of a centrum, deposited around the notochord which, in the lower vertebrates, persists as a rod running through consecutive vertebrae but, in the higher, remains as vestiges only. From each centrum a neural arch with a neural spine extends dorsally, the neural tube (nerve cord) lying in the vault made by successive neural arches in contact with each other. In the trunk, the centra are expanded laterally into short broad processes, the parapophyses of lower vertebrates and the diapophyses of higher (Greek, para = beside, dia = through + apophysis = branch), and in the tail, the ventral surface of each extends as a hemal arch and spine, similar to the neural arch and spine, through which run the principal blood vessels (Fig. 15.14). There is some freedom of movement between the vertebrae, for, except in some special conditions, they are held together, or articulated (Latin, artus = joint) in such a way that the column is flexible.

In the fishes there is little difference between the individual vertebrae, except for those of the trunk and tail where a long neural spine and modification of the lateral

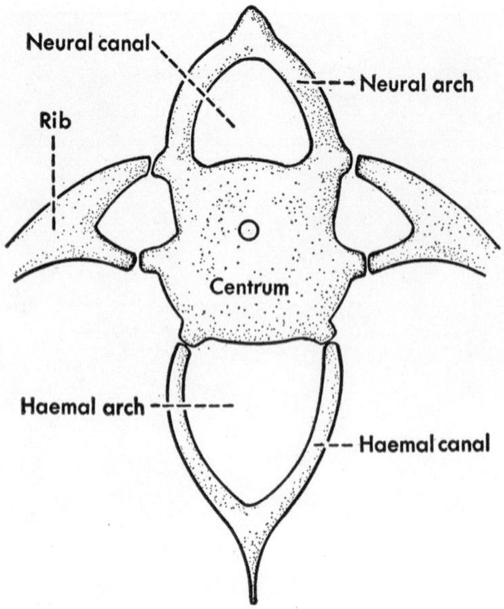

FIGURE 15.14 Diagram of a generalized vertebra of a terrestrial vertebrate. (After Kingsley.)

processes for the attachment of ribs in those of the trunk, and a complete, or closed hemal arch in those of the tail are the most prominent distinguishing features. In the trunk, the hemal arches do not meet ventrally but their sides extend around the body in the myocommata as the "fish ribs" characteristic of bony fishes. In addition to these, "true" or pleural ribs develop in the mesenchyme between the muscle segments, articulating with the lateral processes of the trunk vertebrae, so that many fishes have a double set of ribs. It is the pleural ribs and not the "fish ribs" that have their counterparts in the bodies of tetrapods.

In the tetrapods the vertebrae are neither similar in appearance nor equal in number; usually at least four different types can be identified corresponding to four different regions of the body—the cervical (Latin, cervix = neck), the most anterior of those in the column; the dorsal (Latin, dorsum =

back); the sacral (Latin, os sacrum = the lowest bone in the spine); and the caudal (Latin, cauda = tail). While in most fishes pleural ribs are attached to all the vertebrae, in the tetrapods they are completely developed only in the thoracic regions and are pattern. All modern amphibia have but one cervical vertebra; in the salamanders there may be, posterior to it, any number up to 100 depending upon the length of the body, but in the frogs and toads, the most specialized members of this class, the dorsal verte-

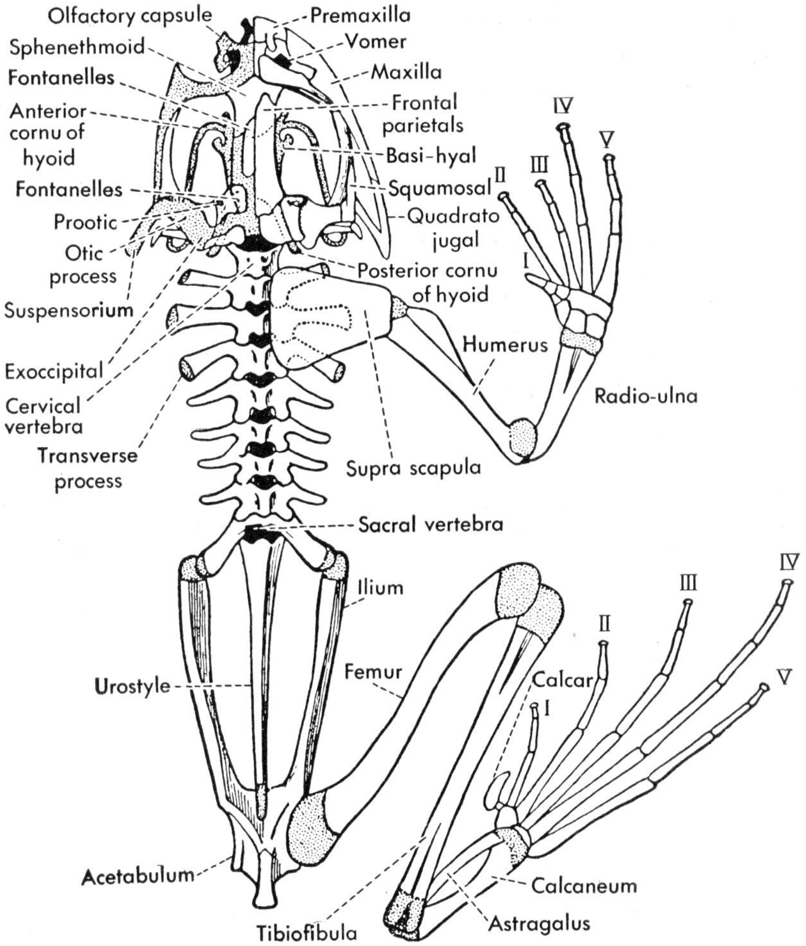

FIGURE 15.15 Skeleton of a frog from the dorsal aspect. The left half of the shoulder girdle and the left fore and hind limbs have been removed, as well as the membrane bones on the left side of the skull. (After Howes, from Woodruff, *Foundations of Biology*, 6th edition. Copyright 1941 by The Macmillan Company.)

either reduced in size, fused with the vertebrae or absent in other parts of the column.

Certain modifications of the vertebral column are characteristic of different classes of modern vertebrates, and most of these variations can be satisfactorily traced back through fossil forms to a common primitive brae are limited to eight, and those of the sacral and caudal regions fused into a long bony rod, the urostyle (Greek, oura = tail + stylos = pillar), which extends between two greatly elongated bones of the central framework of the posterior limbs, the pelvic girdle (Fig. 15.15). In the primitive amphibia there were many ribs which extended around the body like hoops, but in most modern amphibia ribs are reduced or lacking and in those that have them, short, straight rods. There are none at all in Rana, the genus of frogs that includes many of the common species.

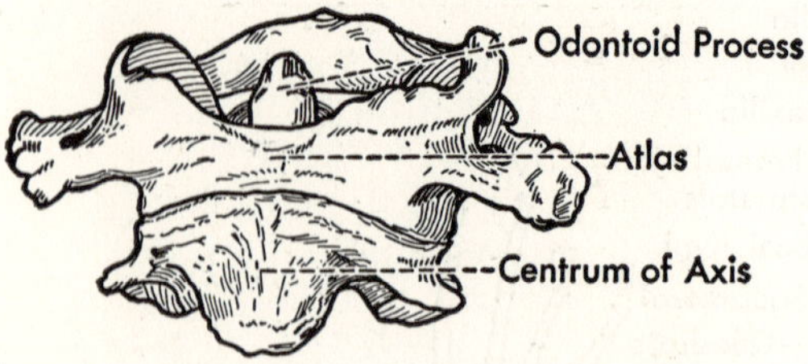

FIGURE 15.16 The human atlas and axis in ventral view. The odontoid process represents the centrum of the atlas and the anterior part of the centrum of the axis. (After Sobotta and McMurrich, from Walter and Sayles, *Biology of the Vertebrates*. Copyright 1949 by The Macmillan Company.)

In the most generalized modern reptiles cervical, thoracic, lumbar, sacral and caudal vertebrae can all be distinguished and in them, as in birds and mammals, the first two cervical vertebrae are so modified that the head can be moved independently of the rest of the body, a definite advantage to an animal in its vision as well as in food getting and other ways. The more anterior of these two vertebrae is called the atlas, so named by Vesalius, since it carries the head as Atlas carried the world upon his shoulders, and the second the axis, upon which the atlas can either rotate or pivot (Fig. 15.16). There are never more than two sacral vertebrae in modern reptiles, but the number of those in other regions varies widely, and all but the caudal vertebrae may bear ribs. Snakes have a great number of vertebrae—as many as 435 in the python—all of which bear hooped ribs; they have no limbs and the supporting girdles of the limbs are either greatly reduced or lacking entirely (Fig. 15.17). Turtles have the shortest vertebral column of any of the modern reptiles, and the further individuality of a case of dermal bones enclosing the body and united with the axial skeleton (Fig. 15.18).

The skeleton of birds is the most specialized of all vertebrate skeletons both in its form and in the composition of its bones (Fig. 15.19). The number of vertebrae is variable; in the swan, for example, there are 25 cervical vertebrae and as few as 9 in some of the smaller song birds. The thoracic

FIGURE 15.17
a. Rattlesnake (*Crotalus adamanteus*), the largest American poisonous snake, living in swamps and wet woods in the Atlantic and Gulf coastal regions, from North Carolina to Louisiana. (Photograph by F. M. Uhler, by courtesy of the U.S. Fish and Wildlife Service.)
b. X-ray photograph of a rattlesnake, showing its skeleton. (Photograph by courtesy of the Army Institute of Pathology.)

vertebrae are usually united into an elongated mass and they bear ribs; the lumbar, sacral and usually one thoracic and several caudal vertebrae are fused into the characteristic synsacrum, a common bony mass, part of which is united to the pelvis giving a firm support for the muscles of the legs which bear the whole burden of the body when the bird is on the ground or perching on a limb. A few of the caudal vertebrae behind the synsacrum are free, but the terminal ones are fused together into a single bone that is directed upward, the pygostyle (Greek, pyge = rump + stylos = pillar). The bones of birds are lighter than those of reptiles and mammals, partly because of the quality of bone that is formed and partly because of the many air spaces within them.

In the mammals, the regional differentiation of the vertebrae is quite definite and with some few exceptions, including the whales, which have no sacrum, there are usually 7 cervical vertebrae, 14–30 dorsal but usually not more than 20, 2 sacral with which others may be united, and a variable number of caudal, depending upon the presence of a tail, and its length (Fig. 15.20). In the tail-less primates the caudal vertebrae are united into a coccyx, so-called because its shape resembles the bill of a cuckoo (Greek, kokkygos = cuckoo). The thoracic vertebrae bear ribs but there are none attached to the lumbar vertebrae and those in the cervical region are reduced and fused with each vertebra.

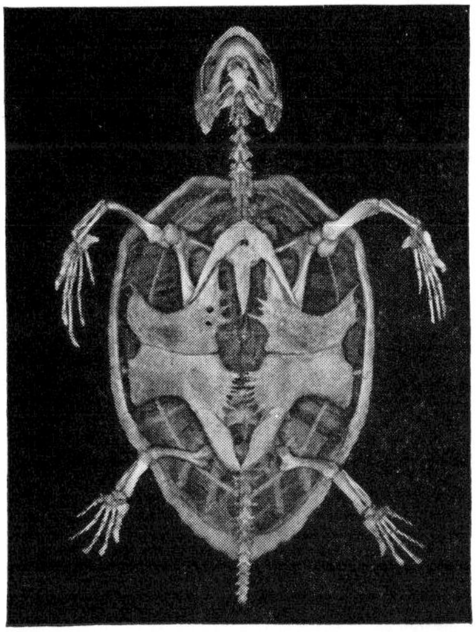

*Brain case (skull):* Except for the elasmobranchs, where it is a continuous mass of cartilage, the vertebrate cranium is made up of a number of flat bones more or less firmly joined together and in some cases completely fused. It encloses the brain, conforming to its size and shape, and is articulated with the most anterior of the vertebrae. A number of openings, or foramina (Latin, foramen = opening), in or between the bones allow for the passage of nerves and blood vessels; the largest of these is the foramen magnum, at the junction of the cranium and the vertebral column where the brain and

FIGURE 15.18 .

    a. Box turtle (Terrapene carolina). (Photograph by D. F. Reath.)
    b. Skeleton of a large marine turtle, from the ventral aspect, showing the axial and appendicular skeleton and the plates of dermal bone that lie beneath the horny scales, or scutes, and with them form the shell that encases the body. (Photograph by courtesy of the American Museum of Natural History, New York.)

cord are continuous. While the skulls of bony fishes include some 76 or more bones, either membranous or endochondral in their formation, the general tendency in the evolution of the tetrapod cranium has been toward reduction in the number of bones and

blood vessels. The prolongation of the jaws for a bill is also characteristic of birds; the bill, which is covered with a horny epidermis, may be broad and flat as it is in ducks and other fish-eaters, narrow, short and strong as it is in grain-eaters like grouse and

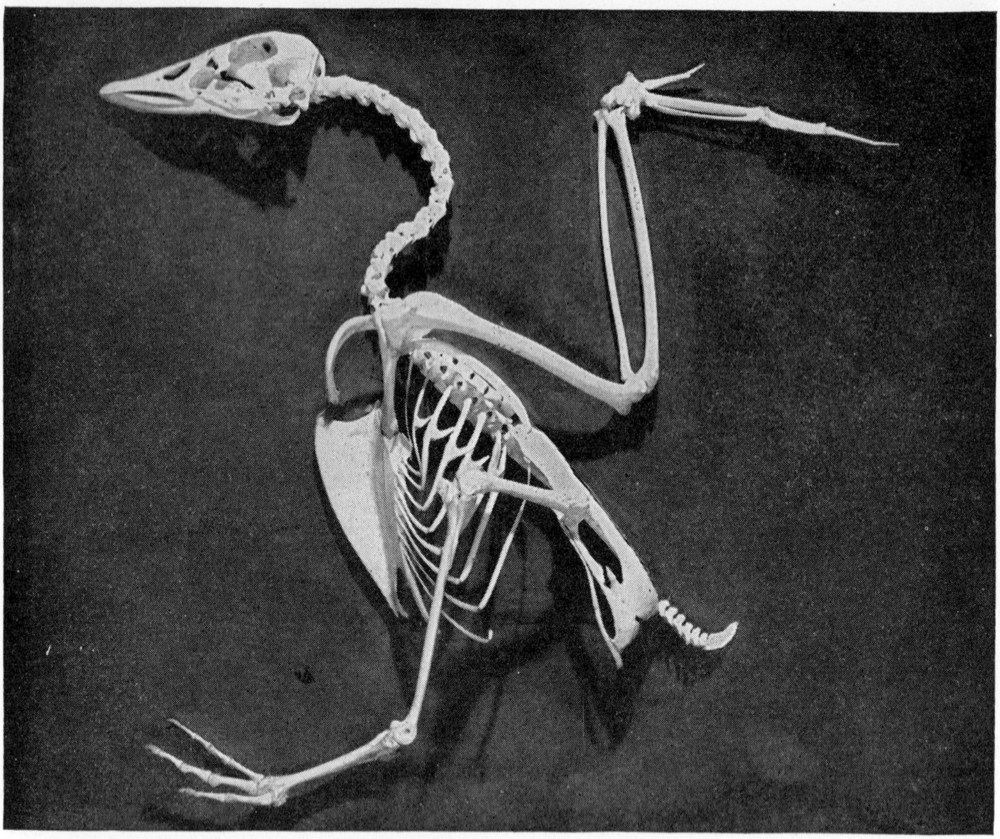

FIGURE 15.19 Skeleton of the snow goose (Branta atlantica). (Photograph by courtesy of the American Museum of Natural History, New York.)

closer union of those that persist, so that in most of them the brain is enclosed in close-set bony plates, which in some species are of considerable thickness. The maximum number of bones in the mammalian skull is, for example, 26 and these are set closely together and immovably articulated with each other, except for those of the jaw. The tendency to fusion is particularly marked in birds, whose brain case is apparently continuous except for the foramen magnum and the apertures for the cranial nerves and

sparrows, long and narrow in insect-eaters, or curved into a hook like that of a hawk or an owl, which feed upon the flesh of dead and living animals. Just as do the mouthparts of an insect, the bill of a bird gives a clue to its feeding habits and the kind of food it habitually eats. Differences such as these within a taxonomic class illustrate the structural adaptations that have arisen in closely-related animals in the course of their evolutionary development. It is through such adaptations that animals have been able to

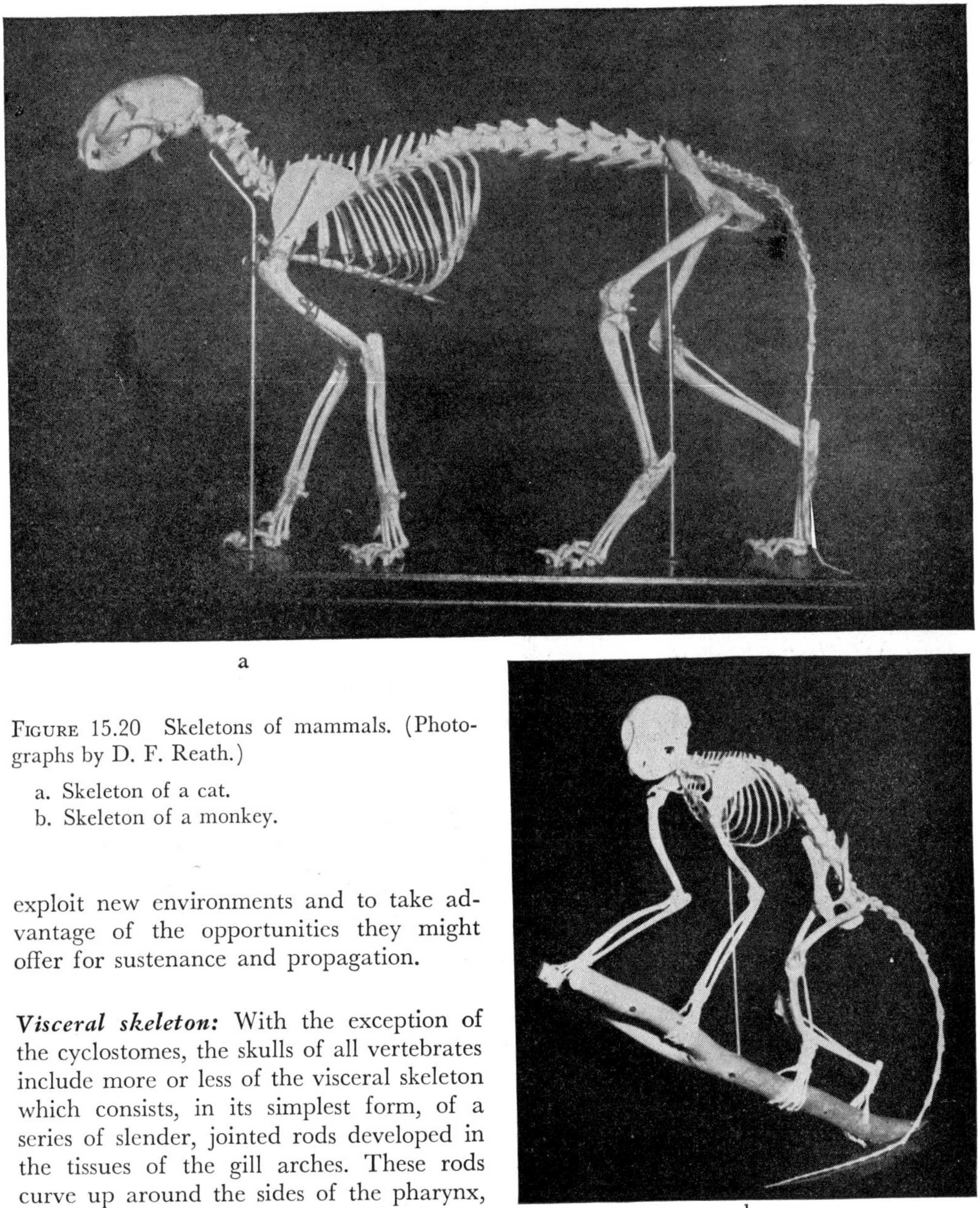

THE CHORDATA [ 273 ]

a

FIGURE 15.20 Skeletons of mammals. (Photographs by D. F. Reath.)

a. Skeleton of a cat.
b. Skeleton of a monkey.

exploit new environments and to take advantage of the opportunities they might offer for sustenance and propagation.

**Visceral skeleton:** With the exception of the cyclostomes, the skulls of all vertebrates include more or less of the visceral skeleton which consists, in its simplest form, of a series of slender, jointed rods developed in the tissues of the gill arches. These rods curve up around the sides of the pharynx, and those of each side are usually joined with one bone, or a series of bones, in the mid-ventral line (Fig. 15.21). There seems no doubt that the jaws of fishes and of tetrapods have evolved through modifications of the most anterior of these arches in their primitive ancestors, through the union of their elements to form two continuous pieces, the upper and lower jaws, which are hinged together and surround the mouth

b

opening (Fig. 15.22). The development of such a biting mouth, whose upper and lower margins can be brought together forcibly and firmly, is obviously a great asset to a heterotrophic organism and, especially in combination with strong and sharp teeth, much more efficacious in the capture and preparation of food prior to its digestion

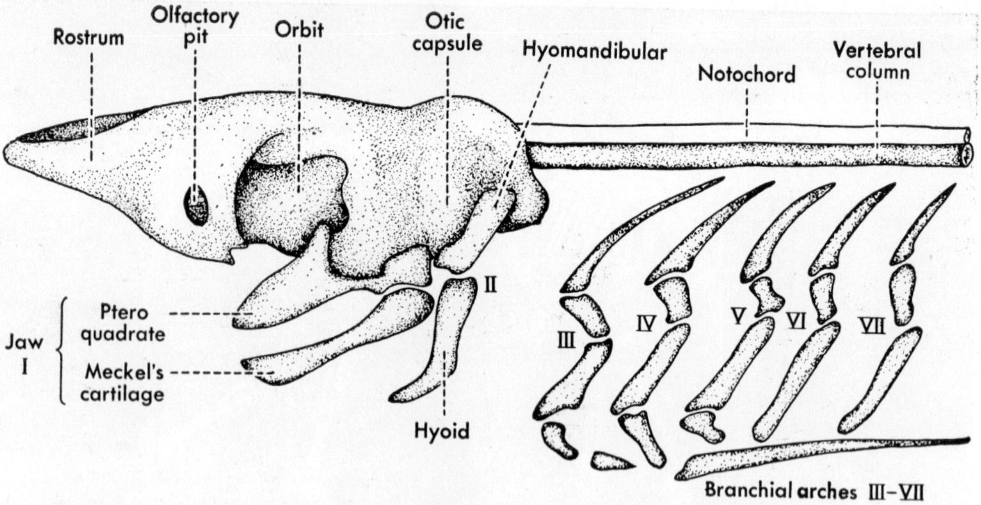

[ 274 ] THE ORGANIZATION OF BIOLOGICAL SYSTEMS

FIGURE 15.21 Skull and visceral skeleton of a dogfish. (After Little.) The branchial arches are numbered I-VII.

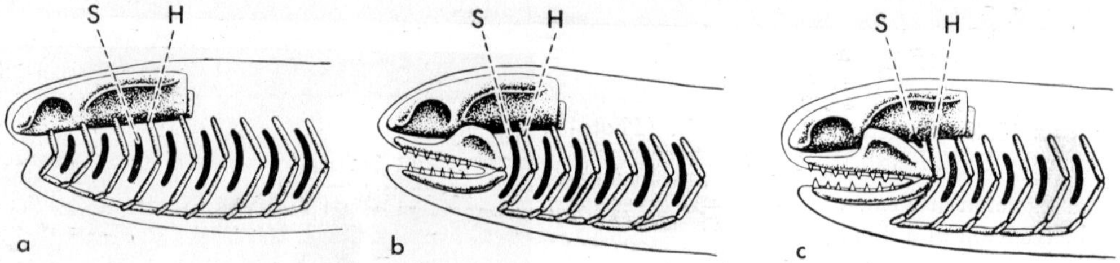

FIGURE 15.22 Diagrams showing the evolution of the jaw and hyoid region. The gill openings are represented in solid black. (From Romer, *The Vertebrate Body*. Copyright 1949 by the W. B. Saunders Company.)

H—hyomandibular, S—spiracular gill slit.

  a. Primitive jawless condition.

  b. Jaws formed from a pair of gill arches (the two anterior arches and slits may have been lost in the process). The spiracular gill slit is unreduced and the hyomandibular not modified.

  c. Condition in most jawed fishes, where the hyomandibular has become a jaw support and the intervening slit reduced to a spiracle.

than the sucking mouths of the cyclostomes or the lateral grinding and tearing mechanisms of annelids, arthropods and mollusks.

In most of the modern fishes, there remain 5 complete gill slits and one rudimentary one, the spiracle; the arch between this and the first full gill slit is called the hyoid arch (Greek, hyoeides = U-shaped), and its most dorsal segment has also become modified as a thicker and heavier hyomandibular bar. In the elasmobranchs and some of the bony fishes, the hyomandibular bar of each side articulates with the cranium in the region of the otic capsule and is bound to the jaws where they are hinged together, and so acts as a suspensor for them.

In all but the cartilaginous fishes the jaw, like the cranium, is complicated by the addition of membrane bones. The most radical change, however, has come about in the tetrapods through the inclusion of some of the bones of these first two arches in the auditory apparatus, one of the organs of special sense to which the tetrapods owe much of their success. These changes, described more fully on pages 378–382, involve the incorporation of the hyomandibular segment of the hyoid arch into the middle ear

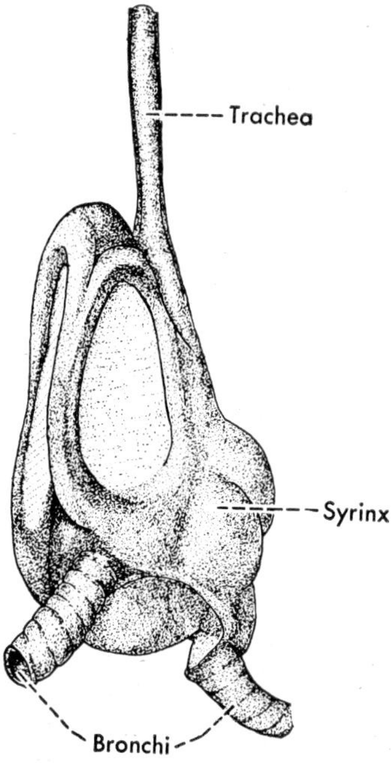

FIGURE 15.23 Trachea and syrinx of a bird (merganser). (After Ihle.)

and, in the mammals, also the vestiges of the lower jaw, for mammals are unlike all other vertebrates in having a lower jaw composed of only a pair of dermal bones, the dentaries, which articulate with another pair, also dermal in origin, the squamosals (Latin, squama = scale), fixed bones of the skull. The remainder of the hyoid arch in them and in other tetrapods has become a support for the tongue, a muscular mass in the oral cavity derived from the musculature of the second gill arch. The framework of the other gill arches has also been diverted to other uses in those tetrapods in which lungs have replaced gills for external respiratory purposes, for it is represented in them by the cartilages or bones that support the upper part of the trachea, the passage through which air is carried to the lungs, and they form also the skeleton of the larynx, the region of the trachea where vocal sounds are produced in all tetrapods but birds, in which a somewhat similar structure, the syrinx (Greek, syrinx = pipe) is located lower in the tracheal passage (Fig. 15.23).

## Appendicular skeleton

The appendicular skeleton includes the cartilages and bones that support the fins and limbs, not only those within the appendages themselves but also those of the pectoral and pelvic girdles, supporting structures that extend transversely across the body and articulate with the proximal bones of each appendage, giving greater support to them and increasing the efficiency of their movement. In the elasmobranchs, the pectoral girdle, embedded in the tissues of the ventral body wall between the anterior pair of fins, and the pelvic girdle, between the posterior pair, are curved bars of cartilage (Fig. 15.24). The fins themselves are supported by three comparatively heavy cartilaginous rods, the propterygium (Greek, pro = before + pterygion = little wing), the mesopterygium (Greek, mesos = between) and the metapterygium (Greek, meta = after), which articulate with the girdle and distal to which more slender cartilaginous rays (radialia) fan out in the broader part of the fin, while horny rays, actinotrichia (Greek, aktis = ray + thrix = hair) support the margin. The pelvic girdle is a short bar, but three regions are recognizable in the larger pectoral girdle, a ventral or coracoid portion (Greek, korax = crow + eidos = form), paired glenoid fossae (Greek, gelen = socket + fossa = ditch), where the basal cartilages of the fins articulate, and two scapulae (Latin, scapula = shoulder blade), dorsal to the glenoid fossae. In the post-embryonic stages of other vertebrates, the cartilage of the girdles is replaced by endochondral bone. The pectoral girdle is furthermore reinforced by membrane bones, of which the two principal ones, developed ventral to the coracoid, are the cleithra (Greek, kleithron = bar) and the clavicles (Latin, clavicula = little key). Both girdles show a high degree of modification in the tetrapods, correlated with the modifications of their limbs and the uses to which they have been put. In birds, for example, the two clavicles of the pectoral girdle are joined together in the furcula (Latin, furcula = little fork), the familiar wishbone of fowls. In strong fliers, this is joined to the sternum,* giving a good measure of additional support to the pectoral muscles that move the wings in flight. In the majority of mammals the girdle is considerably reduced, in most species only the scapula and clavicles remaining, the coracoid being incorporated in the scapula

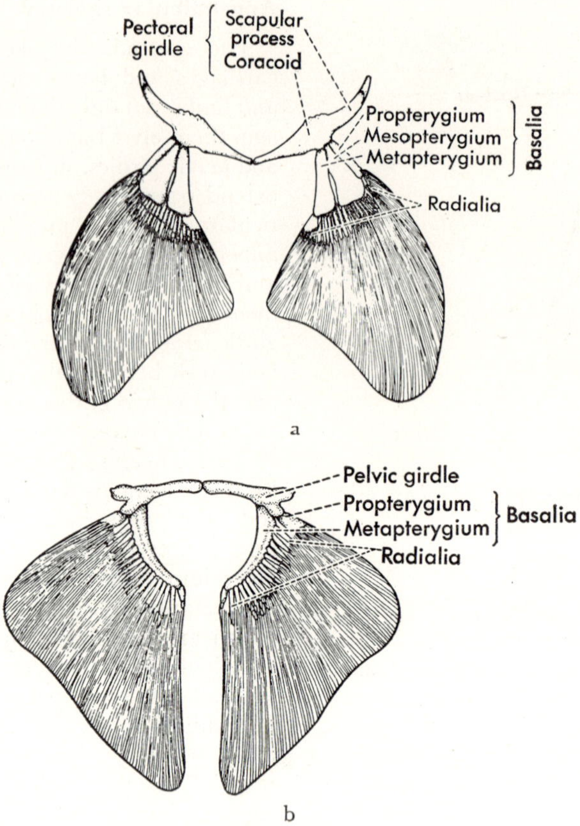

FIGURE 15.24 Appendicular skeleton of the dogfish (Squalus). (After Eddy.)
 a. Pectoral girdle and fins.
 b. Pelvic girdle and fins.

* The sternum (Greek, sternon = breast), a plate of cartilage or of cartilage and bone extending from the pectoral girdle to a greater or less extent along the midventral line of the body, is an addition to the tetrapod skeleton for which there is no counterpart in their aquatic ancestors, nor in any modern fish. Although joined with the pectoral girdle, it seems to have arisen independently of it and to be a new structure characteristic of the amniotes, where it provides protection for the organs in the interior part of the trunk, support for its muscles and attachment for the ribs. Its size and development vary greatly in different species, being entirely absent in snakes and reaching its greatest size in flying birds, where it is prolonged into a forward projecting keel that offers maximal support to the large pectoral muscles.

where it is represented by a small process forming part of the glenoid fossa. The clavicle reaches its greatest development in those that habitually climb, and in the bats, the only mammals capable of true flight, where it forms a strong brace between shoulder and sternum; it is wholly absent in whales and in rapidly running hoofed mammals, and in man it is represented by the "collar bone," extending from the scapula to the sternum, just above the first rib.

The pelvic girdle of tetrapods is greatly enlarged and strengthened in comparison to its condition in fishes, although no dermal bones are added to it and it remains deeply embedded in the tissues surrounding it. It is made up of three paired bony elements, the ilium (Latin, ilium = groin), the most dorsal piece of each side; the ischium (Greek, ischion = hip), ventral and posterior to the ilium; and the pubis (Latin, pubes = adult), ventral to both the others.

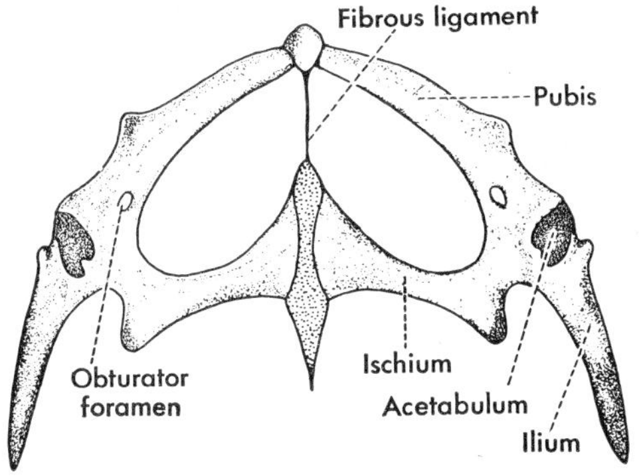

FIGURE 15.25  Pelvis of a lizard (Lacerta vivipara), showing the three bones of each side that unite to form the ring-like framework. (After Weidersheim and Parker.)

All three are more or less firmly united together, and all contribute to the formation of the acetabulum (Latin, acetabulum = little saucer), the depression, homologous with the glenoid fossa of the pectoral girdle, into which the head of the femur of the hindlimb fits (Fig. 15.25). The two ilia are united with the sacrum and the entire mass constitutes the pelvis, which may be made into a complete ring, as it is in the primates, by the union of the two pubic bones with each other. This articulation is not a rigid one, as are those between the other bones of the pelvis, but one in which slight movement is possible.

***The pentadactyl limb:*** The paired appendages of tetrapods all have a common skeletal pattern, however various their uses and however different they may externally appear to be. This pattern is shown in Figure 15.26, where the names of the homologous bones of the fore- and hindlimb are given. The primitive tetrapod limb was short and stumpy and extended outward from the sides of the body as do the limbs of modern urodele amphibia and turtles (Figs. 15.6a, 15.18). The limbs of salamanders are close to this primitive condition, although the number of their digits is four, while the primitive number of digits was probably seven. The great majority of existing tetrapods have five digits on both or on one pair of appendages, and the pentadactyl limb (Greek, penta = five + dactylos = finger) is considered the typical appendage of modern land vertebrates. In the birds and mammals the limbs show a shift in position, for they are placed under the body and turned in such a way that the joint between the bones of the upper and lower forelimb bends forwards, and that between the bones of the upper and lower hindlimb bends backwards. In consequence of this shift, the body is elevated further from the ground so that the animal commands a greater area of its environment and is also in better mechanical adjustment, leading to greater possibilities of fleetness in movement, agility in climbing and also to erect posture through which the forelimbs are freed from the function of supporting the body and can be adapted for other purposes, such as flight in birds, clinging and grasping in mammals.

The pattern of the pentadactyl limb has proved sufficiently flexible to allow modifications of its proportions, size and individuality of its bones that have led to its utilization in a number of different ways. In the wings of birds, the bones of the upper and forearm are fairly typical, but fusion of the carpals and metacarpals has taken place so that in all modern birds there are but two large, free carpals and a composite bone, the carpometacarpus, made up of the distal carpals and the three persisting metacarpals. In the hindlimb, there are no free tarsals; articulating with the femur is a long tibiotarsus and a very much reduced fibula. The tibiotarsus represents the fused tibia and proximal tarsals, and with it is articulated a long, solid piece of bone, the tarso-metatarsus, derived by fusion of the distal tarsals and the metatarsals.

In the mammals, the limbs are variously modified for swimming, flying, digging, climbing, grasping, hopping and walking. In the aquatic mammals, like whales, seals and dolphins, the anterior appendages look like fins and are used for the same purposes, but internally all the bones of the pentadactyl limb are represented with those of the upper and forearm greatly shortened and the phalanges increased in number. The hind-

rabbits, hares and kangaroos, the hindlimb is the more modified of the two, with a thick femur and long tibia and metatarsals and a powerful musculature to move them.

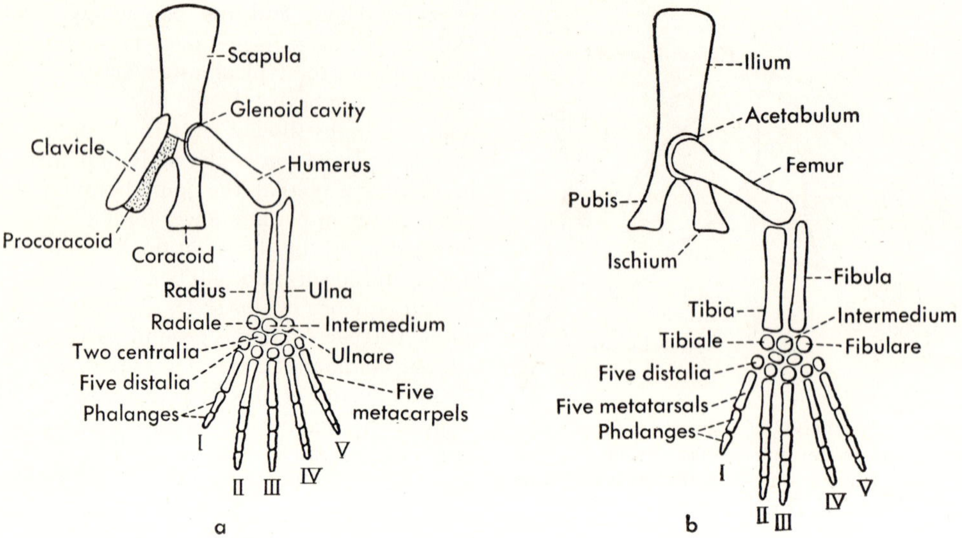

Most mammals, as indeed most modern tetrapods, are quadrupeds, supporting the

FIGURE 15.26 Plan of vertebrate limbs. (After Parker and Haswell, from Woodruff, *Foundations of Biology*, 6th edition. Copyright 1941 by The Macmillan Company.)

a. Right forelimb and right half of pectoral girdle.
b. Right hindlimb and right half of pelvic girdle.

limbs are either wholly absent or represented by two pairs of small bones embedded in the muscles of the trunk. In the bats, all the bones of the arm are elongated in proportion to those of the rest of the body; the forearm and the phalanges of the second, third, fourth and fifth digits are lengthened and provide support for the fold of skin that overlies them as the characteristic leathery wing. The hindlimbs of bats are also exceptional in that they bend forward instead of backward; bats are very poor walkers and spend most of their lives in flight, or clinging by their claws to a support of some kind. In digging mammals, like moles and the wombat of Australia, the bones of the forelimb are thick, short and broad; mammals of this habit have well-developed clavicles as have the climbing mammals whose arm bones are on the other hand relatively long and slender (Fig. 15.20). In mammals that hop, like

body on all four appendages and propelling it along by advancing them all together or in pairs; man shares with birds an exclusively bipedal mode of support and locomotion, although kangaroos and related species do not use their forelimbs in progression and some primates other than man stand erect for limited periods. In plantigrade mammals (Latin, planta = sole + gradi = to walk), the metatarsals are parallel to the ground and at right angles to the tibia; the feet of primates, bears and kangaroos are of this kind (Fig. 15.27). In digitigrade mammals (Latin, digitus = finger + gradi = to walk), the metatarsals are raised from the ground and the weight is borne on the distal phalanges; dogs, cats and rabbits are among animals with feet of this kind. In the hoofed mammals, the unguligrades (Latin, ungula = hoof + gradi = to walk), like cows, pigs and horses, there are never more than four digits and only the anterior surfaces of the distal phalanges touch the ground. Pigs stand and walk on the tips of the third and fourth digit only, the second and fifth, though present, are short and do not reach the ground; horses use only the tip of the

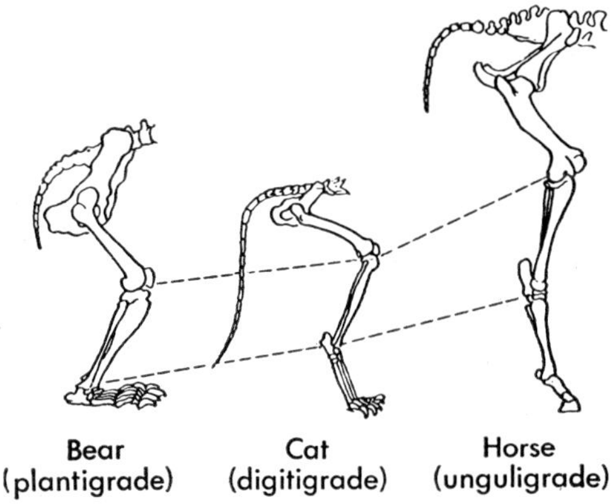

FIGURE 15.27 Plantigrade, digitigrade and unguligrade mammals. The dotted lines show the homologies between the different kinds of limbs, the upper dotted line joining the knees, the lower the ankles. (From Mavor, *General Biology*, 3rd edition. Copyright 1947 by The Macmillan Company.)

third digit, and the third metacarpal and metatarsal are strong, thick bones, while the corresponding bones of the other digits are vestigial. All mammals but the unguligrades retain a certain degree of prehensile ability in their appendages; in man this capacity is most reduced in the foot, his most specialized appendage, and well-developed in the hand where not only can all the fingers be flexed but the thumb moved laterally in all planes through the saddle joint by which it is articulated to its metacarpal. This opposable thumb, on a limb freed from the burden of supporting and moving the body, is one of man's greatest structural assets, for it has given him manual dexterity above that of any other animal and this, coupled with binocular vision and the intellectual development of his brain, gives him the advantage in meeting the conditions of life on nearly all parts of the earth, for he has been able to invent and to fashion tools with which he could cut trees or hew rocks to build houses and so protect himself, to build fires and so warm himself, to dig, sow and reap and so feed and clothe himself, and to devise and operate machines by which his own manual labor is greatly eased.

## Contractile tissues and the mechanics of movement

The bones of the vertebrate body are moved by muscles attached to them by tendons or aponeuroses, respectively cords or sheets of tough fibrous connective tissue (Fig. 15.28). These muscles are made of striated fibres, as are those of most of the other parts of the vertebrate body except the internal organs, or viscera, whose movement is brought about by the contraction of smooth muscle cells (Fig. 11.1*b, c*). The musculature of vertebrates may thus in a very general way be distinguished both by its location and its histological characters as body, or somatic, and striated muscle or visceral and smooth muscle. The contraction of smooth muscle is sluggish, compared

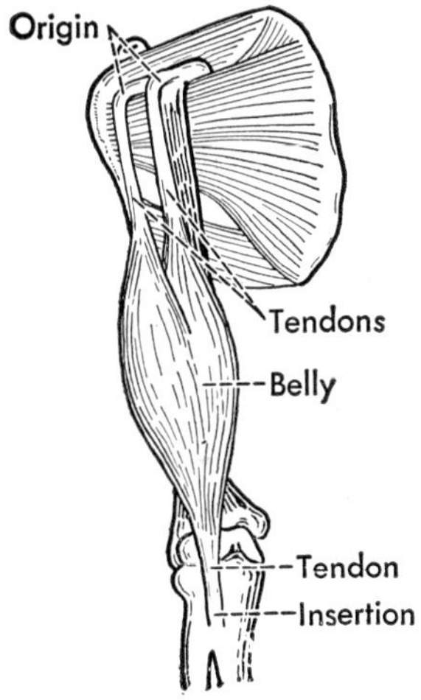

FIGURE 15.28 The biceps muscle, showing tendons attaching it to the bones at its origin and insertion. (After Mollier, from Walter and Sayles, *Biology of the Vertebrates*. Copyright 1949 by The Macmillan Company.)

to that of striated muscle, and in a number of cases it is rhythmic. In striated muscle, the unit is not a uninucleate cell, but a multinucleate protoplasmic mass, the muscle fibre, which may be as short as 1 mm. or, in some of the larger muscles, as long as 41 mm.

## The histology of muscular tissue

As it is seen under the microscope, the striated muscle fibre seems to be made up of a series of alternating light and dark discs longitudinally traversed by delicate strands, called sarcoplasm (Greek, sarx = flesh + plasma = form or mold). The sarcoplasm fills the areas between the fibrils, and the nuclei and cytoplasmic inclusions lie in it and not in the fibril proper. One can distinguish, sometimes without the aid of a

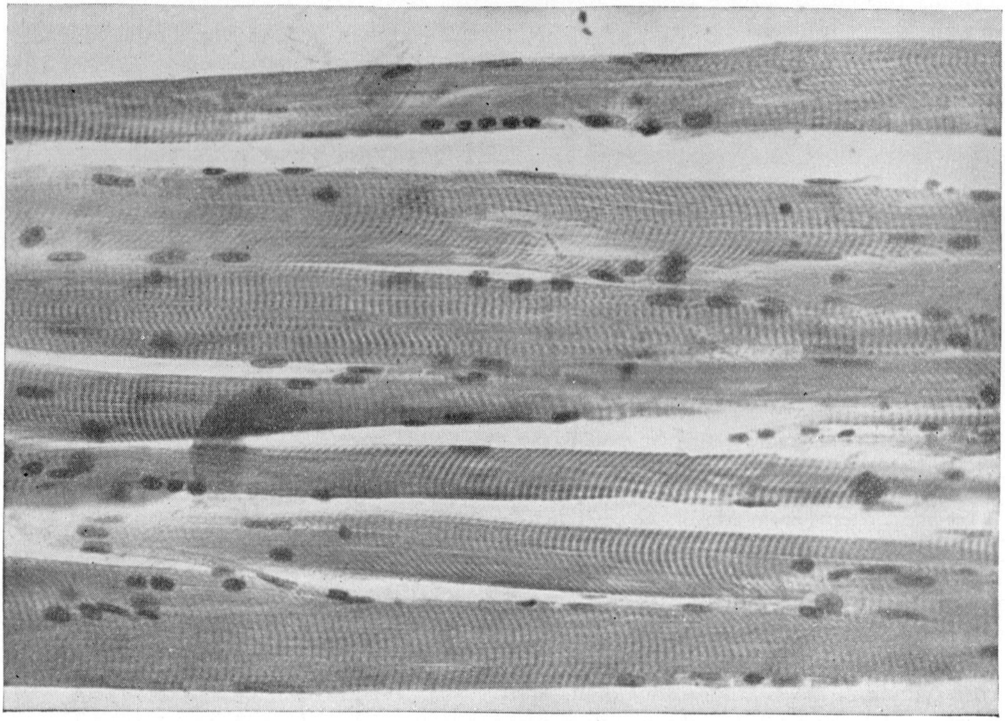

FIGURE 15.29. Striated muscle fibres. (Photograph by courtesy of the General Biological Supply House, Inc., Chicago.)

the myofibrils (Fig. 15.29). Closer microscopic analysis reveals that these areas are even more highly differentiated and that the protoplasm of the myofibrils has a different water content, refracts light to different degrees and reacts differently to shrinking and swelling agents in different regions along its length. The contractility of the muscle cell is attributed to the myofibril, and to its specific fibrous protein, myosin; the highly differentiated substance of the myofibril undergoes chemical and physical changes in the process of shortening and in the subsequent recovery of its original shape. Muscle fibres differ in the number of myofibrils in them; some contain many, while in others there are comparatively few and a greater amount of interfibrillar protoplasm

microscope, between muscles rich in sarcoplasm and those relatively poor in it, for the sarcoplasm contains an iron compound, the pigment cytochrome, which is probably present in fact in all cells and which has been found to play an important part in oxidative reactions. Muscle fibres rich in sarcoplasm and relatively poor in myofibrils look reddish or dark because of the quantity of this pigment present; those poor in sarcoplasm and with many myofibrils appear white or light. Dark muscle fibres are most effective in long and sustained contraction; they are found, for example, in the muscles of the hindlimbs of birds that must maintain a long and steady contraction when the bird is perching and, in the non-chordates, in the stout muscles that hold the two valves of the shell of an oyster or a clam together. White muscle fibres on the other hand are most effective in quick contraction and recovery and are found in the muscles that move the wings of a bird in flight, and in those that snap the shell of a bivalve mollusk together.

As an organ, a vertebrate muscle is made up of a number of muscle fibres, each within its own connective tissue sheath and bound together into a common mass with a connective tissue covering. Their function within the body is to contract; indeed, all that a muscle fibre or cell can do is to contract, reducing its linear dimensions while its volume remains approximately constant. The process of contraction is one of complicated energy changes resulting in movement that can be directly measured as work. Relaxation, or return to original shape after contraction, is a process of recovery or restoration of conditions existing before the stimulus to contraction was received.

### Muscular contraction

The chemical events that take place in the contraction and recovery of muscle, and their relation to the physical events of shortening and subsequent relaxation, are not as yet completely understood. Two substances, combinations of organic compounds with an inorganic compound, phosphoric acid, have been found in the resting muscles of vertebrates, and are known to provide energy for some of the chemical reactions that go on during their activity. One of these, adenosinetriphosphate, commonly referred to as ATP and representing about 0.25 per cent of the muscle substance, is a combination of one molecule of adenine with one of ribose and three of phosphoric acid; its structural formula is represented as

The other, phosphocreatine

$$HO-\overset{\overset{O}{\|}}{\underset{\underset{OH}{|}}{P}}\sim\overset{H}{\underset{|}{N}}-\overset{NH}{\underset{|}{C}}-\overset{CH_3}{\underset{|}{N}}-CH_2COOH$$

Phosphoric Acid Creatine

is a combination of creatine with one molecule of phosphoric acid, and represents about 0.5 per cent of the substance of resting muscle.

The conversion of adenosinetriphosphate (ATP) to adenosinediphosphate (ADP), by the splitting off of one phosphate radicle from the ATP molecule, is probably the initial one in the series of chemical changes involved in the contraction and recovery of muscle. This reaction takes place immediately the muscle is stimulated to its specific activity—contraction—it is a hydrolytic and an exothermic one, releasing energy equivalent to 12 Calories for each molecule of phosphoric acid liberated, and provides the initial energy, at the onset of contraction, for the physical process of shortening of the contractile substance. It is also a reversible reaction, and the resynthesis of ATP from its hydrolytic product, ADP, proceeds under ordinary circumstances as rapidly as it is formed. The phosphate radicle necessary for the reconstitution of ATP is contributed by phosphocreatine, which also breaks down into its organic and inorganic components with the release of energy equivalent to 12 Calories for each molecule decomposed. This decomposition of phosphocreatine is one source of the energy necessary for the reconversion of ADP into ATP, an endothermic reaction that involves the addition of one molecule of phosphoric acid to each molecule of ADP, and thus requires an expenditure of energy at least equivalent to that liberated when the bond between the phosphoric acid radicle and the rest of the molecule is broken. Energy released by the breaking of the phosphate bonds in some of these complex molecules is used to initiate the anaerobic decomposition of the polysaccharide glycogen, which represents about 1 per cent of the substance of resting muscle, into lactic acid, a reaction that is also accompanied by the liberation of energy, likewise available for the reconversion of ADP into ATP.

In the recovery process, phosphocreatine is re-formed from its decomposition products, again at the expense of energy at least equivalent to that released in its breakdown. Glycogen is also resynthesized, the energy for this being obtained from the complete oxidation, to carbon dioxide and water, of $1/5$ of the lactic acid produced from it, a reaction that may also contribute energy for the resynthesis of phosphocreatine. This oxidation requires molecular oxygen and proceeds through the series of reactions characteristic of aerobic cellular oxidations in general. It is most likely that through the energy of this reaction the rest of the lactic acid, representing $4/5$ of the total amount formed, is reconverted to glycogen and restored to the muscle for future contractions.

Muscle therefore represents a chemical and physical system in which some of the energy bound in certain of its cellular constituents—and bound there by virtue of energy expended by the tissue in synthesizing them—is released upon appropriate stimulation. Adenosinetriphosphate and phosphocreatine, with "energy-rich" phosphate bonds (designated in their structural formulae as $\sim$), represent reserves of potential energy; that bound in ATP is converted to kinetic energy directly the muscle is stimulated. ATP thus acts like a trigger mechanism in initiating the physical change of shortening of vertebrate muscle and also the series of chemical events that result in its characteristic activity. The availability of ATP is consequently of prime importance to the muscle in its functioning, an availability which is secured by the mechanisms of phosphocreatine breakdown and resynthesis of ATP from ADP which proceed simultaneously with the continued formation of ADP from ATP. A further source of energy that becomes available shortly after the onset of contraction is the breakdown of glycogen, another store of potential energy in the muscle tissue but one from which the energy is not so instantly available as it is from ATP. In extraordinary conditions of muscular activity, the additional energy demand may be met by the conversion of ADP into AMP, adenosinemonophosphate, through the breaking of a second energy-rich phosphate bond. The resynthesis of ATP then requires the addition of two phosphate radicles to each molecule of AMP, and consequently a greater expenditure of energy derived from the glycogen $\rightarrow$ lactic acid reaction.

The activity of muscle is a continuous cycle of chemical breakdown and reconstruction, catalyzed by enzymes, with the conversion of potential into kinetic energy. Some of the energy is utilized in the chemical processes of reconstruction, some to bring about the physical changes of shortening and thickening by which the muscle performs its work, and some is liberated as heat. The heat of muscular contraction is indeed the primary means by which homoiothermic animals maintain a temperature above that of their surroundings, for shivering is a direct response on the part of an animal to heat loss and a mechanism for increasing its production.

But although muscle is a specialized tissue found only in the animal body, the chemical changes that take place during its activity are not specific to it. The anaerobic decomposition of sugar into alcohol and carbon dioxide, for example, effected by the yeast cell in the process of fermentation, shown diagrammatically in Figure 17.1 on page 400, is also initiated through energy liberated from adenosinetriphosphate by breakage of its phosphate bonds. The parallelism between the chemical changes in alcoholic fermentation and anaerobic respiration in other tissues is generally recognized; the specialization of the muscle cell lies therefore not in the nature of the chemical processes themselves but in their expression in physical changes in the shape of the muscle fibre, brought about by its shortening and thickening, and in the mechanisms that insure to it an immediate and ready, as well as a continuous, supply of available energy.

**The musculature of vertebrates**

Deviations from the strictly segmental arrangement of the body muscles, evident in the lower chordates and but slightly modified in the elasmobranchs, are conspicuous in the other vertebrates, and in the higher mammals the relations of the muscles to the primitive body segments have become so altered that they are not easily recognizable. That they have their origin in segmental muscle masses is most convincingly shown by tracing their nerve supply, for the paired nerves of vertebrates are for the most part segmentally arranged and their connections with the involved and intricate musculature of the head and trunk of higher mammals gives evidence of their development from a primarily segmental plan.

In the evolution of vertebrate types, the general tendency has been toward the division of the primitive muscle masses into smaller units. The segmental muscles appear to have divided longitudinally in any plane to produce the involved patterns of small muscles, and certain of these smaller ones appear to have fused with each other to form a composite muscle representing several segments; others have atrophied so that the musculature of a segment may be greatly reduced or even wanting. Their pattern is closely related to that of the skeleton and, in the tetrapods, to the development of limbs that support the body and the change from locomotion, effected by lateral movements of the trunk and tail, to one brought about by the movement of these limbs are reflected in the development and the pattern of the muscles of the trunk and the appendages. In most of the tetrapods the tail, when it is present, is used for balancing or steering and its muscles are reduced accordingly and are no longer thick and powerful like those in the tails of fish. They are greatly reduced in the tail-less vertebrates, where the caudal vertebrae are few in number and immobile, and among mammals they are best developed in those with prehensile tails, like opossums that use them to suspend their bodies from trees and certain monkeys that hold on by them as they swing from limb to limb.

*Skeletal and dermal muscles:* As a general rule, the body muscles are attached at both ends either directly or indirectly to some part of the skeleton, but in the tetrapods some are inserted on the skin and hence are known as dermal muscles, although derived from skeletal ones. These muscles move the scales of reptiles and the feathers of birds, but they reach their greatest development in mammals where they extend widely under the skin and often can move large parts of it. It is these muscles that enable a horse to shake off a fly that has settled out of reach of its tail, or a dog to prick its ears. They are also the muscles that permit changes of facial expression in man, in whom, as in other primates, dermal muscles are confined to the head and neck, where they move the lips and the eyelids, the nose and the ears.

*Classification of skeletal muscles:* Muscular contraction always results in the movement of some part of the body so that muscles in general may be classified according to the kind of movement that they bring about, and are often so named. There are dilators which enlarge circular openings and constrictors which close them; the muscles which enlarge the pupil of the eye are dilators and the sphincter muscle (Greek, sphingter = band) at the junction of stomach and intestine is a constrictor. Those that are attached to movable bones are classified according to the direction in which they exert their pull. The flexor muscles pull on a bone in such a way that it is drawn toward another at an angle, as in bending the forearm toward the upper arm; extensor muscles straighten an angle already formed and are brought into play when a flexed limb is extended. Abductor muscles draw a bone away from the median axis of the body, as when the arm is raised from the side, or the thumb moved away from the forefinger; adductor muscles draw a bone toward the mid-line of the body, or parallel to its main axis. Elevator muscles raise a bone, and depressors lower one that has been elevated; muscles such as these open and close the mouth, the depressors of the lower jaw opening it and the elevators bringing the jaw back into position when the mouth is closed. There are muscles uppermost. The action of these muscles is not rotation, because the joint between the hand and forearm does not permit such motion and the bones of the forearm are to some extent twisted across each other in the pronation and supination of the hand.

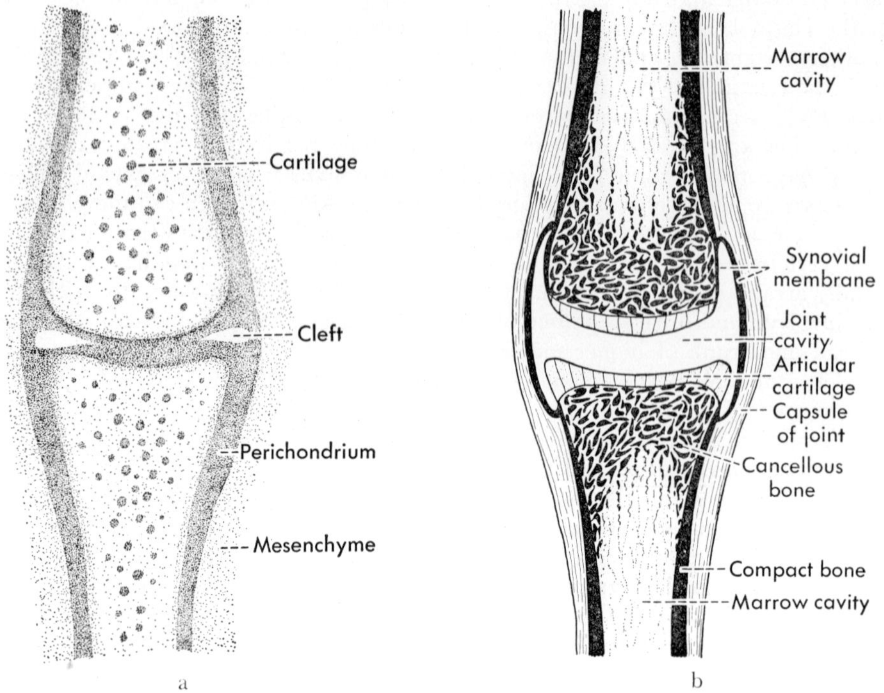

FIGURE 15.30  A diarthrosis. (After Arey.)
   a. Developmental stage.
   b. Completed joint.

which bring about the rotation of parts of the body around its main axis, such as those used in turning the head, and muscles that bring about circumduction, or circular movement of the free end of a bone or a series of bones, such as moving the arm through a full circle. The other functional types of muscles are limited to the extremities of the tetrapod limbs. These are the pronator and supinator muscles; in the forelimb, for example, the pronators turn the hand so that the thumb is directed toward the middle of the body and the palm of the hand turned downward, while the supinators move it in the opposite way so that the thumb is turned outward and the palm

## Joints

Bones can only be moved by muscles, and muscles can only effect this movement when the bones are free to move. The unions between bones are called joints, or articulations, and the nature of the joint is an important factor in determining the planes and the directions in which a bone can be moved. Joints are classified in general as synarthroses (Greek, sun = with + arthron = joint) and diarthroses (Greek, dia = through). In a synarthrosis, the mesenchyme between the adjacent bones is converted either to dense connective tissue or to cartilage so that the bones are immovably joined as are the bones of the skull; in a diarthrosis, the inner layer of mesenchyme becomes loose and discontinuous connective tissue, the space within it forming the joint cavity, and this kind of joint permits movement of the articulating bones (Fig. 15.30). The outer layers of connective tissue over the joint form the joint capsule enclosing the ends of the bones, which are covered with cartilage, as well as the loose connective tissue of the joint cavity and the lubricating fluid, or synovia, a fluid containing mucus that is secreted by the cells forming the wall of the capsule which become organized and modified as a synovial membrane.

***Types of movement at a joint:*** The type of movement permitted by a diarthrosis depends upon the relations of the end of the articulating bones to each other. Some allow more extensive motion than others, and some allow motion of one kind but not of another. The shoulder joint is the most freely movable joint in the vertebrate body and it, like that between the femur of the hind limb and the acetabulum of the pelvis, is a ball and socket joint. The proximal ends of both femur and humerus are drawn out into a rounded ball, the head, which fits into the cup-like depressions of the acetabulum and the glenoid fossa respectively (see Fig. 15.12). The shallower the cup, the greater the freedom of movement, and since the glenoid fossa is not as deep as the acetabulum the forelimb can be rotated through a full circle and moved forward and backward and raised more freely than the hindlimb. When one end of the bone is oval, not a ball but a condyle (Greek, kondylos = knuckle) and fits an elliptical depression in another, the joint is called condyloid and permits lateral motion in all planes, but not rotation; the articulation between the radius and the carpals in the forelimb and that between the tibia and the tarsals in the hindlimb are joints of this kind. A hinge joint permits movement in one plane only, as the hinge of an ordinary door allows it to be opened and shut but not to be raised or lowered; the articulations between the humerus and ulna, the femur and the tibia and between the phalanges of the digits are hinge joints and the only movements possible around them are flexion and extension (Fig. 15.31). In pivot joints, one bone remains stationary while the other rotates around it; the articulation between the

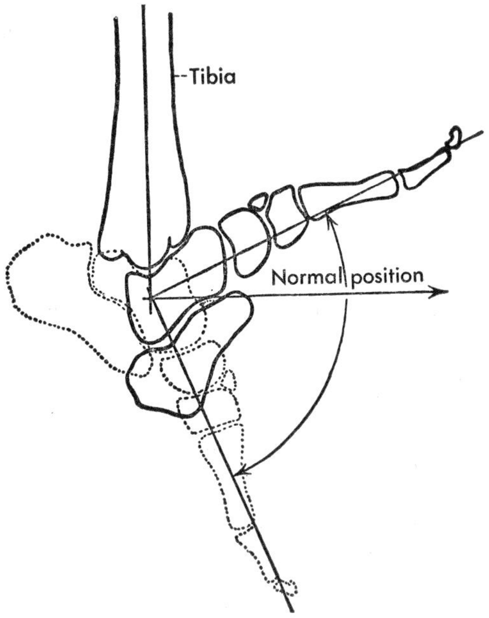

FIGURE 15.31 Diagram showing the extent of movement in a hinge joint, such as the ankle. (From Walter and Sayles, *Biology of the Vertebrates.* Copyright 1949 by The Macmillan Company.)

radius and ulna is such a joint, for the upper end of the radius, with whose lower end the carpals are articulated, rotates freely around the fixed ulna when the hand is pronated or supinated. In a saddle joint, which like a condyloid permits movement in all planes but not rotation, the articulating surfaces of both bones are saddle-shaped, concave in one direction and convex in the other; the joint between the metacarpal of the thumb and its articulating carpal is a joint of this kind. One other type of diarthrosis is found in the tetrapod body, although not in the limbs; this is a gliding joint, so called because the articulating surfaces are nearly flat, or very slightly concave-convex, so that the only possible motion is that of the simplest kind; the bones may slip along each other but cannot rotate on each other or bend at an angle. The articulations between the vertebrae of the spinal column, except for that between the atlas and axis, are of this type; the joint between these two bones is a pivot joint.

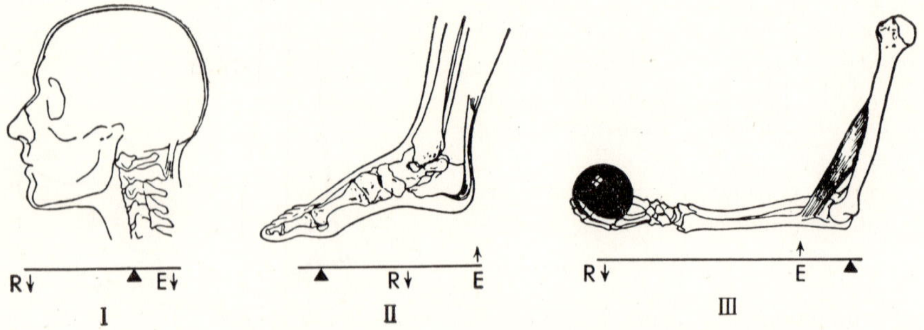

machines various devices are employed to insure the highest production of useful work with a minimal expenditure of energy. Opposing surfaces are oiled to reduce frictional resistance, ball and roller bearings are used and the machine is so constructed that the

FIGURE 15.32 Diagrams showing the application of leverage in the human body. (From Kimber, Gray and Stackpole, *Textbook of Anatomy and Physiology*, 11th edition. Copyright 1942 by The Macmillan Company.)

I. Lever of the first order, where the fulcrum (axis and atlas of the vertebral column) lies between the weight (R) and the power (E).

II. Lever of the second order, where the weight (R) lies between the fulcrum and the power.

III. Lever of the third order, where the power (E) lies between the fulcrum and the weight.

## Mechanical efficiency of movement

In moving the bones, as in moving any part of the body, the muscles do mechanical work and consequently expend energy, often of considerable magnitude. And like any machine that does work, their mechanical efficiency depends upon the relation of the work that is done to the energy that is supplied.

$$\text{Mechanical efficiency} = \frac{\text{work performed by a machine}}{\text{energy supplied to machine}} = \frac{\text{output}}{\text{input}}$$

In an ideal system, all the potential energy supplied to the machine would be converted to kinetic energy and made to do useful work, and the ratio of output to input would be unity, but no machine is perfect and some energy is always used to do useless work in overcoming friction and some is always dissipated as heat. It is most economical for the machine to keep the ratio of output to input as high as possible, and in man-made

principles of physical mechanics are applied wherever possible so that the work is done with the least amount of supplied energy. Some of these devices are also made use of in the animal body; joints and tendons that slip along bones are lubricated with synovia, and in many places in the tetrapod body the bones, joints and muscles operate on the principle of the lever, one of the oldest mechanical devices known for transmitting and modifying force and motion. Archimedes of Syracuse (287–212 B.C.) took the first step in the exact science of mechanics when he investigated the quantitative laws of lever action, although the principle of leverage and the application of it were undoubtedly known long before his lifetime. A lever is a rigid bar that can turn about one point, called the fulcrum, and along which there are two or more other points where forces can be applied; its mechanical advantage lies in the fact that through it a comparatively small force, or power, can be translated into comparatively large or comparatively speedy motion, and its application therefore results in economy of effort so that the same force can move a weight through a greater distance or with greater speed than it otherwise could. The advantage gained by the use of a lever is proportional to the length of the lever arms on either side of the fulcrum; it is primarily in speed in levers of the first and third orders, and in mechanical efficiency in those of the second. Children soon learn, when they balance on a see-saw, that the lighter child can offset the weight of the heavier one if his position on the board is further from the point on which it pivots; if set in motion, the same force will cause him to travel through a greater distance and at a greater speed than the child on the short end of the board. This same principle is applied in such aids to human labor as the crowbar, the automobile jack, the claw hammer that pulls out a nail, the can opener, the pulley and the gear. By using a crowbar, a man can lift a weight that it would be impossible for him to move by the strength of his body alone. In the vertebrate body, where leverage is used, two or more bones represent the lever bar, the articulation between them, the fulcrum, and the muscles that move them, the power applied to overcome the force of gravity acting upon the body as a whole or upon any of its parts, or the force of the muscles pulling in the opposite direction (Fig. 15.32). Levers of the first and third orders are brought into action when the limbs are extended after flexion and when they are flexed, respectively; the advantage of speed of movement is obvious for an animal that must run to catch its prey or to escape from pursuers, or to one that must strike quickly with its forelimbs in defense or attack. When the body is raised on its toes, the long bones of the foot, the articulation between them and the toes and the thick gastrocnemius muscle (Greek, gastroknemia = calf of the leg) on the back of the leg act as a lever of the second order, where the advantage is largely mechanical, making it possible by slow continuous pulling to raise the entire body against the force of gravity. The length of the bones of an animal and the points of attachment of the muscles to them are consequently factors conditioning the strength and the speed of its movements; given two animals of equal muscular development and coordination, the one with anatomically the most effective levers will have the advantage over the other for purely mechanical reasons.

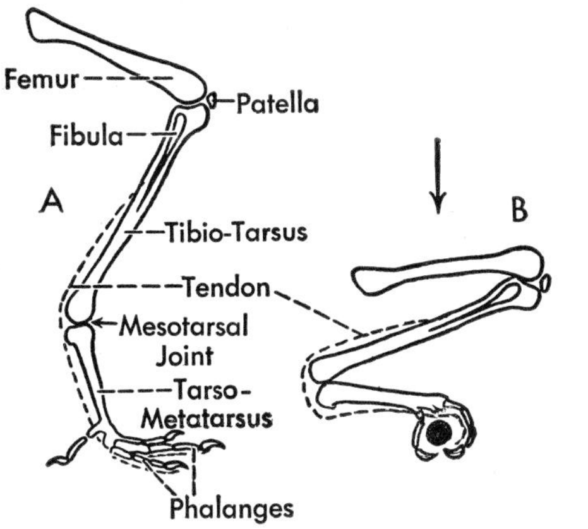

FIGURE 15.33 The perching mechanism of a bird. (From Walter and Sayles, *Biology of the Vertebrates*. Copyright 1949 by The Macmillan Company.)
A. Standing.
B. Perching.

### Specialization of muscles

In birds, certain modifications of the muscles and tendons which flex the digits of the hindlimbs have led to a perching mechanism that enables flying birds to keep their balance on a bough even when asleep. All the toes are simultaneously flexed by the pull of a common tendon attached to three flexor muscles; this tendon passes over the joints between the tibio-tarsus and the tarso-metatarsus and divides and separates into individual tendons attached to the individual digits. When the bird settles on a bough, this joint is bent and the tendon stretched, pulling on the digits and closing them around the perch, a position in which they are kept by the weight of the body (Fig. 15.33).

The highest degree of specialization of muscle tissue has been attained by some of the fishes in the electric organs derived from muscle cells arranged as separate plates or discs, and so highly modified that they are not only without the capacity to contract, but also without myosin. Yet in them the release of electrical energy, concomitant with the contraction of muscle, reaches a high level when these muscle masses are stimulated to activity.* In the electric eel of Brazilian rivers, Gymnotus, these muscle plates are in the tail and their combined voltages reach about 300, enough to stun another fish so that the eel, which is a slow swimmer, can easily catch it. In the star-gazer, Astrocopus, of North American waters, electric

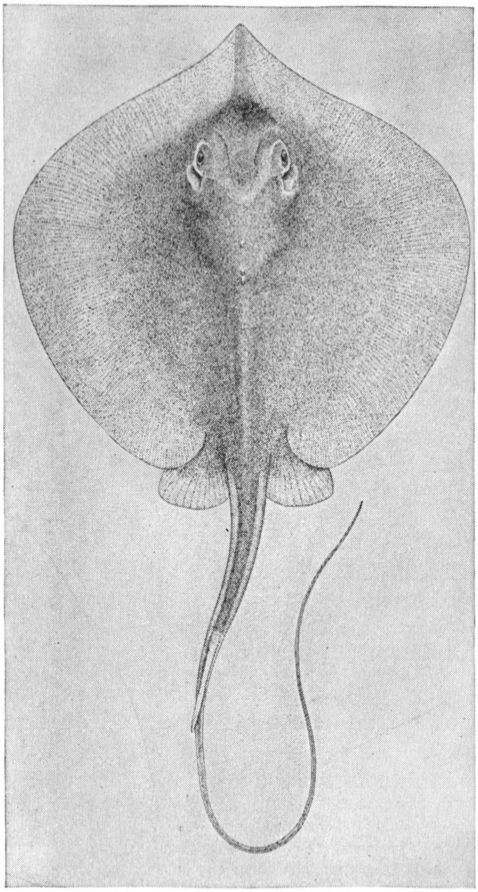

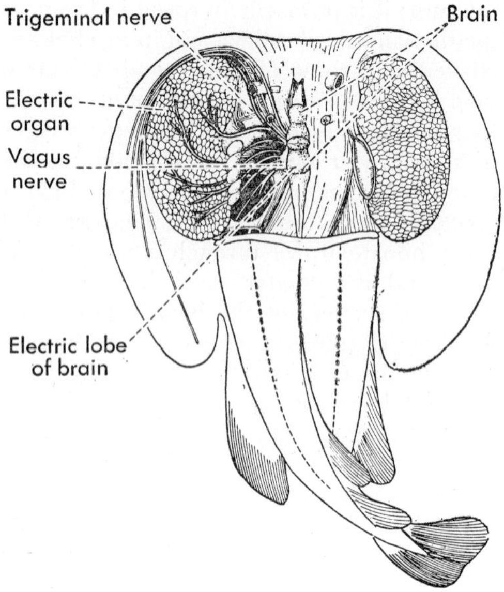

FIGURE 15.34

a. A sting ray (Dasyatus sp.). (Photograph of a drawing by courtesy of the U.S. Fish and Wildlife Service.)

b. Torpedo with electric organ and brain exposed. On the right side the dorsal surface of the organ is shown, on the left, the nerves that supply it. (After Gegenbaur, from Sedgwick.)

* The phenomenon of bio-electricity was first shown by Luigi Galvani (1737–1798) in experiments that he conducted at the University of Bologna. In the course of some of these, he and his assistants one day exposed by dissection the spinal cord of a frog and the muscles to its hind limbs. Standing on the same table as the dissected frog was an apparatus for generating static electricity, and when his assistant accidentally touched the exposed nerve with the metal blade of a bone-handled scalpel, the muscle of that leg contracted violently. Galvani immediately repeated what his assistant had done and obtained the same result, but when he brought the bone handle of the scalpel in contact with the nerve, the muscle gave no response. Although Galvani believed that the contraction on contact with a metal was due to electricity produced in the tissue itself, under the conditions of his experiment it was most probably due to potential conducted from the static machine. But he did unquestionably demonstrate animal electricity in subsequent experiments in which he laid an exposed nerve across other tissues, removed from any other electrical source, and showed that if it touched them at two points, one injured and the other uninjured, the muscle supplied by the nerve contracted. Many experiments carried on in the century and a half since Galvani's have shown that in general the more active regions of a tissue or a cell are electronegative to the less active, and that a measurable difference in potential may exist between such areas.

organs of this kind lie just behind the eyes, from which, because they are dorsal in position, the fish has got its common name. Such organs are found, too, in some of the elasmobranchs; in the electric ray, Torpedo, they are large lateral masses extending as far back as the pectoral fins and capable of producing an electrical charge of considerable intensity (Fig. 15.34). Although ordinarily these specialized muscles do not do mechanical work as other muscle fibres do, they can be made to do so experimentally; the electric organ of a fair-sized ray will, for example, ring a bell just as effectively as a couple of dry cells, or the human hand pulling a string tied to it.

## Integument

The vertebrate integument is composed of two principal layers, an inner dermis or derma (Greek, dermis = skin) or corium (Latin, corium = leather) and an outer epidermis (Greek, epi = upon + dermis). The epidermis, which is derived from embryonic ectoderm, is in turn made up of two layers, or strata, a superficial corneal layer (Latin, corneus = horny) and an underlying Malpighian layer; the dermis, which is mesodermal in origin, is essentially fibrous connective tissue, with fat and pigment cells, nerves and blood vessels distributed through it (Fig. 15.35). Although its primary functions of respiration and excretion have largely been taken over, in all the vertebrates, by specialized structures—gills or lungs in the one case and nephric organs in the other—the integument is more than a mere covering of the body. It may properly be regarded as an organ, fulfilling as the other organs do certain definite purposes in the complex body. The function of the vertebrate integument is principally one of protection, from environmental hazards such as attack by other animals, invasion by micro-organisms and dehydration, and also from dangers arising from the outward seepage of body fluids and, in the case particularly of homoiothermic animals, of heat loss. It serves also, as it does in the non-chordates, as a sensitive and secretory area, with neuroreceptor and glandular cells.

## Characters of the epidermis

In most of the vertebrates, the outer stratum of the epidermis is composed of cells particularly active in the synthesis of keratin (Greek, keras = horn), the name given to a class of fibrous proteins obtained in especially large quantities from the horns of cattle and belonging to the general group of albuminoids or scleroproteins (Greek, skleros = hard). The keratins are the most resistant of all proteins to chemical action and their disintegration is not ordinarily brought about by the reactions that go on within organisms (see page 428). The keratinization, or cornification, of the cells of this outer stratum is progressively greater from the inner layers outward, and the outermost cells on the surface of the body are no longer actively metabolizing ones but deposits of keratin and are sloughed off, either periodically in a continuous sheet, as they are in the shedding of snakes, or in strips as they are in the amphibia, or constantly in flakes as they are in most mammals. These lost cells are replaced by new ones originating in the Malpighian layer, which gives rise also to glands secreting mucus and oil, as well as to those with more specific secretions which may be poisons or volatile substances that act as scents or irritants to other animals, and in the case of the mammals, to sweat and to milk.

The cells of the Malpighian layer sometimes contain granules of melanin (Greek, melas = black), a chromoprotein synthesized by processes of cellular chemistry which have not yet been fully traced. Melanin granules may also be found between the cells, and their distribution in the epidermis is responsible in part for the coloration of vertebrate skin, and particularly of human skin. Melanin is actually a brown pigment, not a black one, and, as dispersed granules, gives a golden or brown color, while in masses it appears black. Melanin also has the property of absorbing ultraviolet light, as well as that in the visible spectrum, which has certain destructive effects upon cells, so that the presence of the pigment serves to protect the underlying cells from ranges of solar energy that are harmful to them. The

Malpighian layer is also the nutritive and generative layer of the epidermis, for it is in contact with the blood vessels and tissue fluids of the dermis beneath it and its cells multiply not only to replace the dead corneal cells but also to produce specific structures and to regenerate new cells in the healing of a wound.

### Characters of the dermis

The thickness of the dermis varies considerably in different vertebrates; it is particularly thick in mammals, and provides the leather which man has put to his use for so long in so many ways. The dermis is in contact with a layer of connective tissue which overlies the skeletal muscles and which contains fat cells and in some cases large fat deposits; often the dermis is not clearly delimited from this subcutaneous tissue, which is also very vascular; throughout the entire depth of the dermis are blood and lymph vessels, nerves and sensory nerve endings. The dermis often contains pigment cells—melanophores containing melanin granules, xanthophores containing yellow pigment granules and erythrophores containing reddish ones—and in fish especially, iridiocytes, cells that contain crystals of guanine, a colorless protein derivative, which by refraction of light rays gives the structural coloration or iridescence characteristic of so many fish. In fish, amphibia and reptiles, the pigment cells are irregular in shape with many processes through which the pigment granules flow back and forth, and the variations in distribution of the pigment brought about by different conditions result in the color changes and shifts of pattern that are so familiar in fish like the flounder, and in salamanders and chameleons (Fig. 15.36).

### Modifications of the integument

In each of the vertebrate classes there are distinctive modifications of the integument, structures that are derived either exclusively from the epidermis or from the dermis, or derived from both of these layers together. These take the form of scales, claws and nails, feathers and hairs, teeth, and the horns of some mammals; there are also specialized glands derived from the integument, and in some cases, photogenic organs and electric organs.

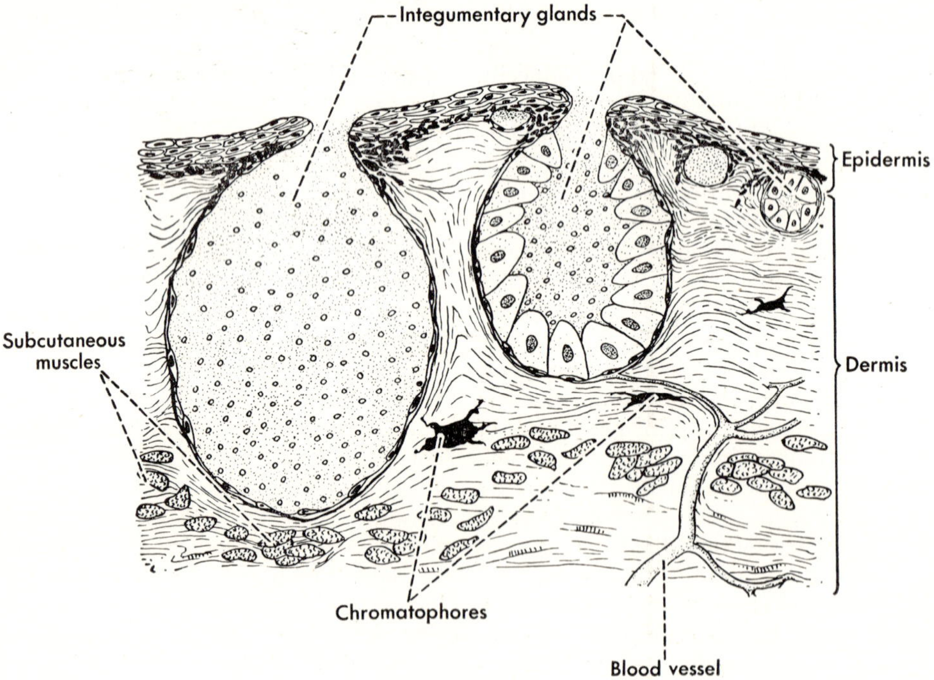

FIGURE 15.35a

**Derivatives of the epidermis:** Horny scales are particularly thick local deposits of keratin which become overlapping plates (Fig. 15.37). This kind of scale is characteristic especially of modern reptiles, but it is also found regularly on the legs of birds and the tails of some mammals, such as the marsupial opossum and rats and mice among the rodents. They are also found sporadically among the amphibia, for the warts of toads are in part horny deposits and a few species, the burrowing legless caecilians of tropical

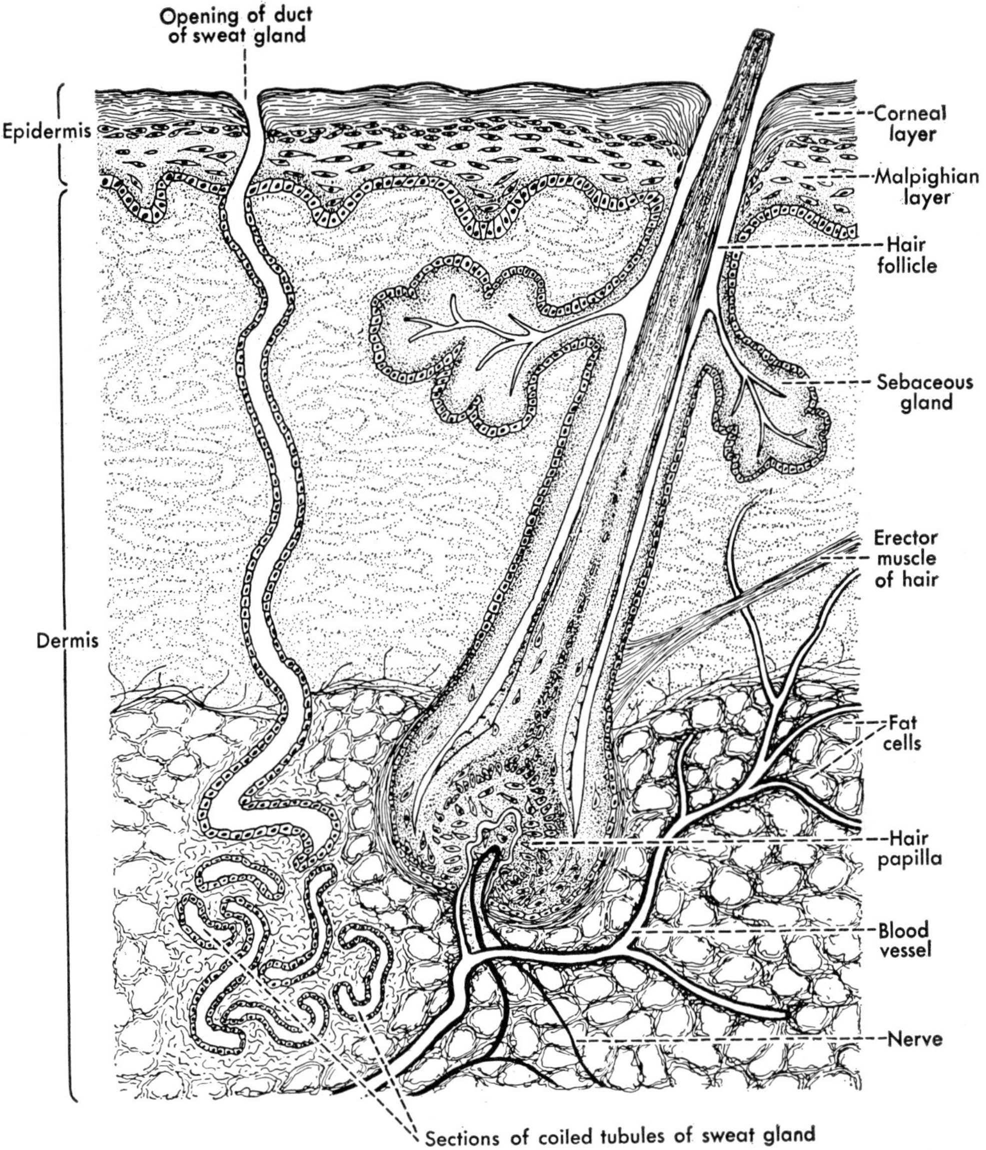

b

FIGURE 15.35  The integument of vertebrates.
    a. Section through the skin of a salamander. (After Weidersheim.)
    b. Section through the skin of the human neck. (After Little, from a preparation by R. T. Kempton.)

America, Africa and India, have typical horny scales. The claws of reptiles, birds, some mammals and two genera of Amphibia —(Onychodactylus, the land salamander of Japan and Korea, and Xenopus, the South African toad)—the nails of man and the hoofs of certain other mammals are all closely related to scales, indeed are modifications of them. These particular modifications are coverings or caps over the digits at the extremities of the limbs and are made of two scales, an unguis (Latin unguis = nail) on the dorsal surface of the digit and a subunguis on its ventral surface. The unguis is larger than the subunguis and is pushed forward over the end of the digit as it is formed (Fig. 15.38). In a claw, the unguis is curved so that its outer surface is convex and its tip bent down or hooked over the end of the digit; the subunguis forms the under surface of this free end. Human nails have the same general pattern, but in them the unguis is comparatively thin and flat and the subunguis a narrow cornified strip just beneath its tip. In a hoof, the unguis is very thick and forms a hard, heavy covering over the entire end of the digit, curving around to its under surface where the subunguis meets it as the "sole" of the hoof.

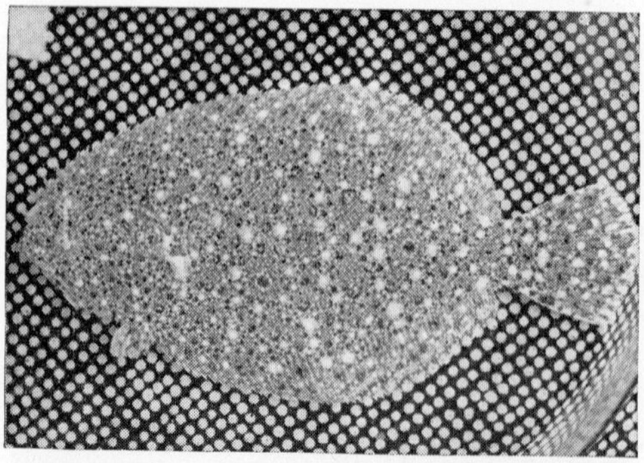

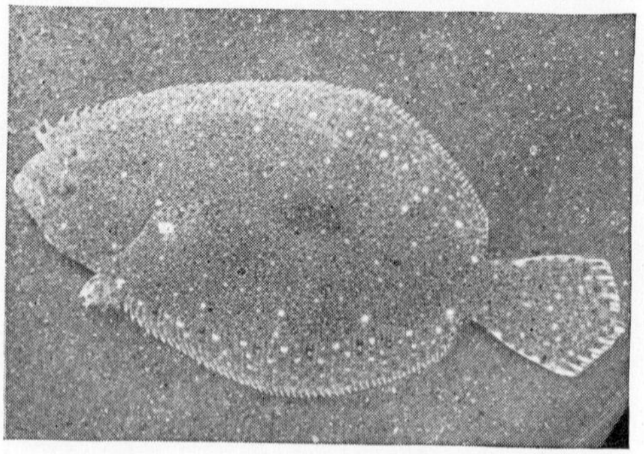

Feathers are even more greatly modified scales, developed exclusively by birds. There are in general three kinds of feathers—hair

FIGURE 15.36 Color changes in the flatfish (Paralichtys albiguttus) when placed on different backgrounds. Note the close resemblance of the fish to its natural surroundings in the above picture, where it rests on fine sand. (Photographs by courtesy of the U.S. Fish and Wildlife Service.)

feathers, down feathers and contour feathers —in which the greatest structural development is reached in the contour feather, or those that make up the conspicuous plumage of a bird and define the contours of its body. The main parts of a contour feather are the shaft and the vane, both derived from keratinized epidermis (Fig. 15.39). The base of the shaft is hollow and is known as the quill; the vane consists of fine rods, the barbs, which extend obliquely from the sides of the shaft. Each barb has smaller side branches, the barbules, provided with hooks which interlock so that the vane as a whole has an apparently continuous, but flexible, surface. A feather originates as a small elevation of the epidermis pushed up by a thickening of the dermis (Fig. 15.40). The elevation grows into a long, slender papilla which breaks through the surface of the skin, with the dermis extending some way up into it as the pulp of the developing feather. Around its base the epidermis sinks below the surface level forming a small round pit, the feather follicle (Latin, folliculus = small bag). During the course of growth, a complicated and

modifications of the keratinized epidermis, develop in a similar way. Hair covers the bodies of most mammals thickly, with notable exceptions of whales, sea cows, elephants and man among the higher mammals, armadillos and anteaters among the

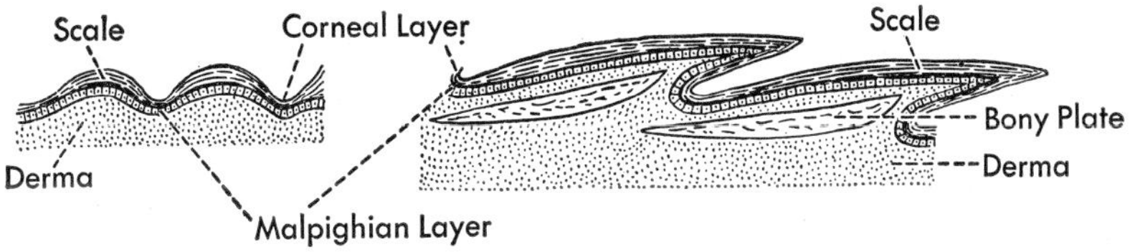

FIGURE 15.37 Horny scales. Diagrammatic longitudinal section through the integument of a reptile. (After Boas, from Walter and Sayles, *Biology of the Vertebrates*. Copyright 1949 by The Macmillan Company.)

branching system of ridges arises on the surface of the pulp, so arranged that its dorsal surface as well as its base remains smooth. These ridges grow in height and press against and through the under layers of the epidermis enclosing the pulp, with the result that the keratinized layer is divided into a number of slender rods set at oblique angles to an undivided dorsal strip and of finer rods set at oblique angles to these. When growth is complete, the pulp and Malpighian layer retract leaving a cavity in the quill, and the remainder of the epidermis, deprived of its blood supply, dries and hardens quickly. The slender rods bend back from the undivided dorsal strip, or shaft, forming the barbs of the vane, and their branches fan out as the barbules. The colors of feathers, which have a great range and often extreme brilliancy, are due in part to pigments present in the epidermal cells and in part to light refraction. The iridescence of the plumage of many birds is structural coloration of this kind. Feathers are periodically shed, or moulted, and each one so lost is replaced by a new one formed from a new papilla arising on the old site. In birds whose plumage patterns change with the seasons the colors of the new feather may be quite different from those of the old. Except in a few birds, notably ostriches, the feathers are not formed over the entire surface of the body but in definite areas called feather tracts.

Hairs, which are exclusively mammalian

lower. A hair arises from a thickening of the epidermis which grows obliquely down into the dermis and enlarges at its base into a bulb, indented as a cup on its lower, or inner, surface (Fig. 15.41). The dermis grows up into this cup and its blood vessels carry nutrients and other stimulants to growth to the cells within the epidermal cup with the result that they multiply rapidly, forming a column or shaft of cells that is pushed through the surface of the skin. The dermis forms a follicle around the bulb and, near the top of the follicle, an epidermal gland develops which secretes oil that lubricates the hair. Muscles, developed from the mesenchymal cells of the dermis, are attached to the shaft in most hairs, which by contraction bring about the elevation of the hair so that it stands temporarily perpendicular rather than oblique to the body surface. The hair itself is thus formed of a shaft of cells which in most cases contain pigments, either in solution or as solid granules. Pigment granules may also lie between the cells, and the kind and distribution of pigments within and between its cells produce the color of any particular hair; the range of color variation in individual hairs and in hair patterns is almost as great as it is in feathers. The absence of pigment, as a result of its loss or its failure to form, makes the hair appear white, an effect of structural coloration. In the fully developed hair, the cells of the shaft become keratinized and shrunken, with air spaces in and between

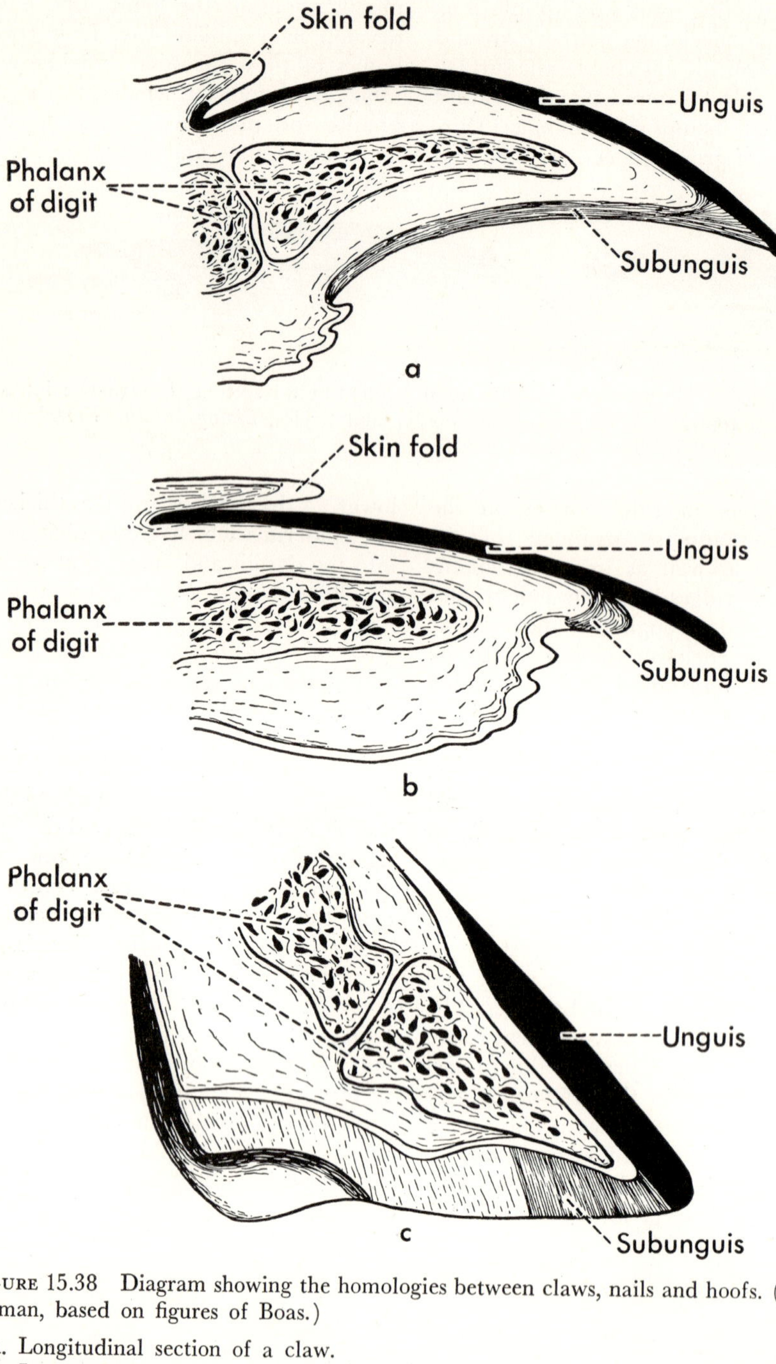

FIGURE 15.38 Diagram showing the homologies between claws, nails and hoofs. (After Hyman, based on figures of Boas.)

    a. Longitudinal section of a claw.
    b. Longitudinal section of a primate nail.
    c. Longitudinal section of a hoof.

them; the inner cells form the medulla of the hair and the outer ones the cortex. The cells of the cortex overlap like scales, and in the hairs of sheep and goats particularly, the cortical cells have processes which intertwine with those of other hairs causing the matting conditions are reflections of those within the chains of amino acids that make up the huge molecule. The two-toed sloth is unique in having hairs which are longitudinally fluted throughout their length; these long grooves offer surfaces of attachment for cer-

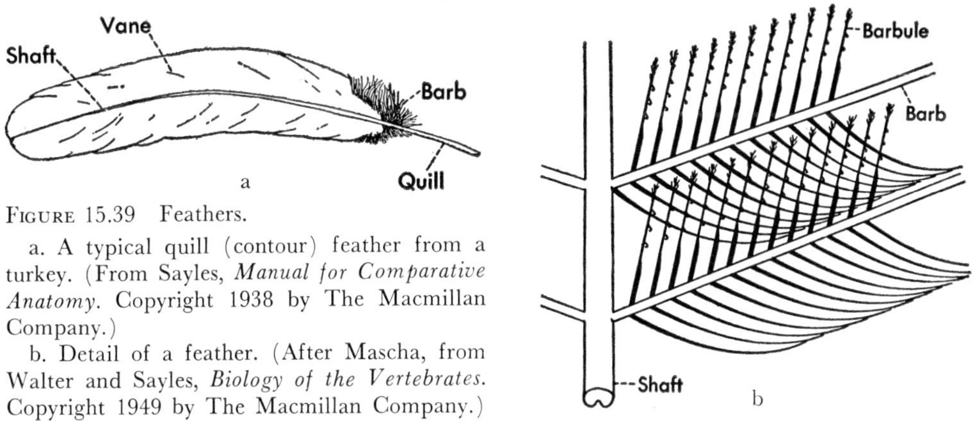

FIGURE 15.39  Feathers.

a. A typical quill (contour) feather from a turkey. (From Sayles, *Manual for Comparative Anatomy*. Copyright 1938 by The Macmillan Company.)

b. Detail of a feather. (After Mascha, from Walter and Sayles, *Biology of the Vertebrates*. Copyright 1949 by The Macmillan Company.)

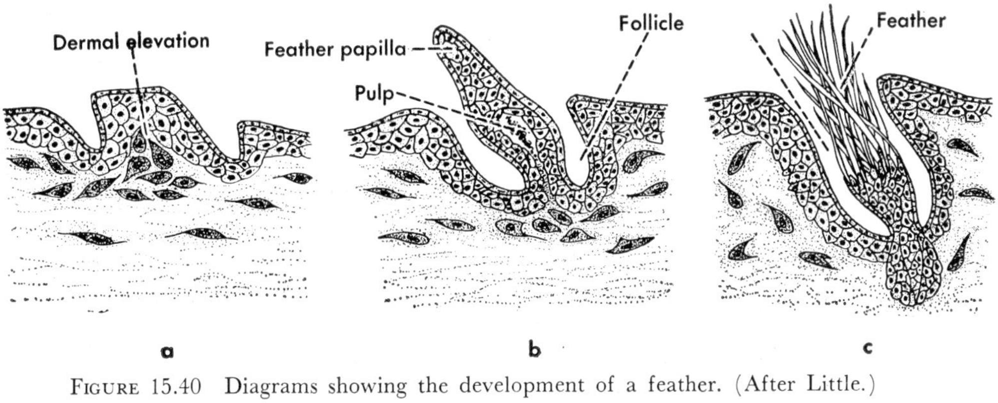

FIGURE 15.40  Diagrams showing the development of a feather. (After Little.)

or felting characteristic of wool. Hairs show greater variation in type than do feathers, scales or other integumentary structures. At one extreme of thickness and stiffness, for example, are the quills of the porcupine and the spines of the hedgehog and the anteater; at the other, the long, soft hairs of the Angora rabbit and the downy ones of the human foetus. And while most hairs are cylindrical, some are flattened either throughout their length or in certain regions; such flattenings make hair crinkly or curly and since keratin is a fibrous protein, these tain green algae which habitually live there, giving the body of the sloth a murky color, and also providing lodging for some kinds of insects, beetles, cockroaches and a species of moth which is the only representative of the Lepidoptera known to be parasitic as adults. In some species, too, certain body hairs are modified as vibrissae (Latin, vibrare = to vibrate), such as those found on the snouts or noses of dogs and cats, rats, mice and other rodents; these are usually thicker than the other hairs of the body and are sensitive to tactile stimuli, for at their

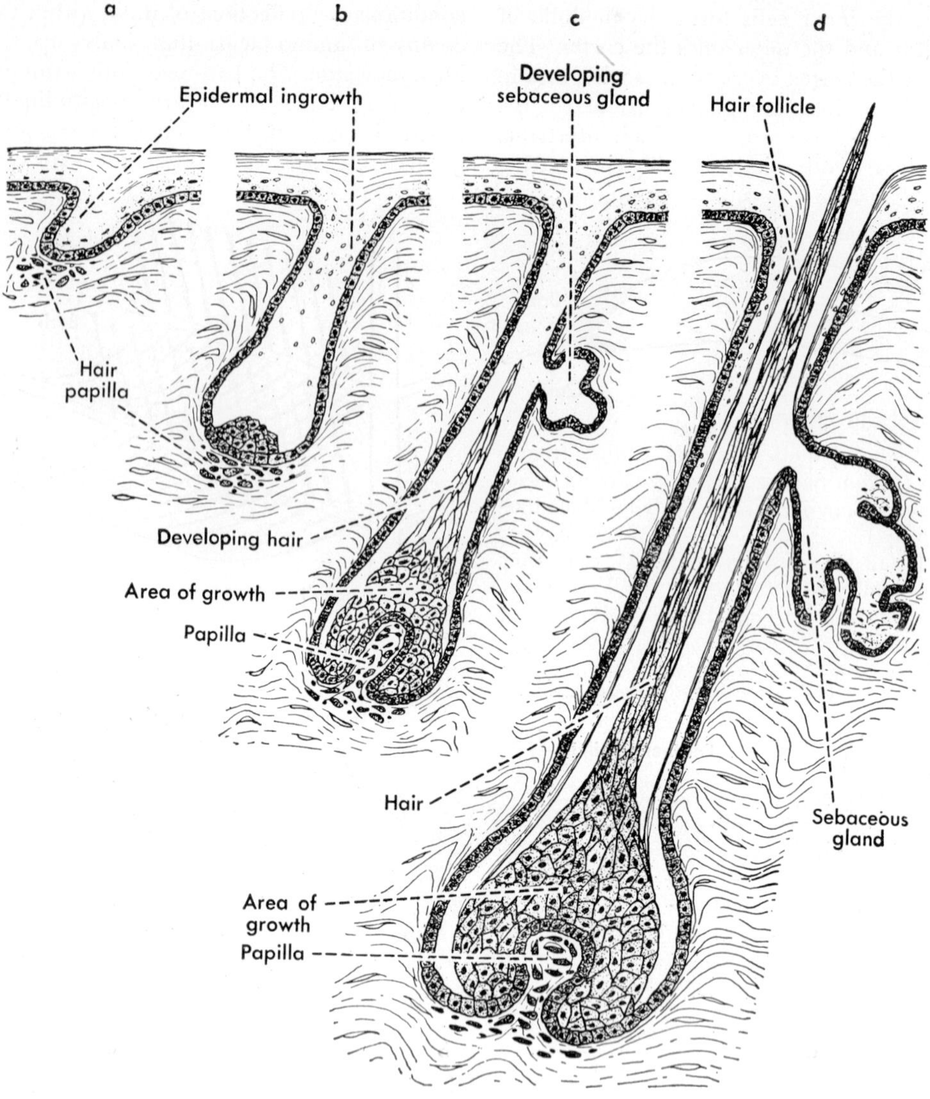

FIGURE 15.41 Diagrams showing stages in the development of a hair. (After Little.)

bases are sensory nerve endings shown by experiment to be stimulated when the hair is touched. While the capacity to produce hairs is retained by mammals throughout their whole life span under ordinary circumstances, the duration of the individual hair, with the exception of the kind known as angora, is limited, those on the scalp of man, for example, to an estimated 1600 days. Like feathers, the hairs which are periodically or seasonally lost are replaced by new ones which develop on the same site as the old, and also like feathers, the new hairs may have colors and give rise to color patterns different from those of the old.

Other epidermal derivatives, characteristic of certain groups within the vertebrate classes but not necessarily of the classes themselves, are the horns of cattle, antelopes, sheep and goats, the beaks of birds, the epidermal teeth of some larval amphibians and the highly specialized baleen of the right whales. A bovine horn is a permanent adult structure and has a core of bone, developed from a bone of the cranium and covered with heavily keratinized epidermis.* The beaks of birds are modifications of the upper and lower jaw bones with horny outer coverings which vary in thickness and in the extent to which they protrude beyond the bone. The epidermal teeth of the tadpoles of frogs and toads originate as small elevations or papillae of the integument along the margins of the mouth; the outer cells of the papillae become keratinized, forming rasping teeth, in some species fused into plates, with which the tadpole scrapes the algae on which it feeds from the objects to which they may be attached. Baleen, or whalebone, is formed from the union of greatly developed keratinized papillae at the back of the upper jaw in some whales; these papillae unite into narrow plates from two to twelve feet long which hang in rows in the oral cavity, forming a kind of fringe which strains from the sea water the minute marine organisms upon which these whales depend for food.

**Derivatives of the dermis:** Except for the elasmobranchs, the epidermis of fishes is in general soft, not keratinized, and developed as a glandular area, the principal secretion from which is mucus. But in all but a few members of the osteichthys (Greek, osteon = bone + ichthys = fish), like eels, scales are developed in the dermis, which are of three principal types, ganoid, cycloid and ctenoid, the last two showing all degrees of intergradation and often occurring together (Fig. 15.42). Ganoid scales, such as are found in sturgeons, garpikes and the crossopterygians, are separate, flat and thin plates of bone laid down by the mesodermal cells of the dermis and covered with ganoin, a hard substance something like dentine in its composition. Cycloid scales are round, ctenoid scales have jagged or toothed edges and both are made of bone with a higher content of organic material and a lower content of inorganic than most skeletal bones. These scales lie in pockets in the dermis, and increase in size during the life of the fish, successive periods of their deposition being marked as concentric rings on their surface. By counting the number of rings it is possible to determine the age of a fish, just as it is possible to determine the age of a mollusk by the lines on its shell or that of a tree by its growth rings. As they grow, the scales in most species overlap, with their free edges directed posteriorly, so that they form a complete covering for the body, like the shingles of a roof. Usually the epidermis remains as a thin covering over the surface of the scale, but in some cases it is sloughed off and the scale exposed. Some few fishes,

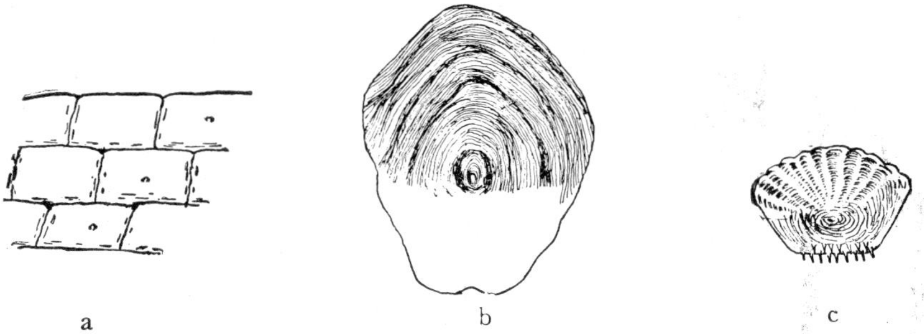

FIGURE 15.42  Types of fish scales. (From Walter and Sayles, *Biology of the Vertebrates*. Copyright 1949 by The Macmillan Company.)
  a. Ganoid scales.
  b. Cycloid scale, showing lines of growth. (After Hesse.)
  c. Ctenoid scale. (After O. Hertwig.)

* The antlers of the deer family, which grow anew every year, are entirely of bone, for the epidermis overlying them never becomes keratinized and is sloughed off as the "velvet" after the antler has completed its growth.

like sturgeons, have well-developed and thick plates of bone deposited in the dermis, called scutes (Latin, scutum = shield), which make a kind of armor over their soft bodies. Such a dermal skeleton is particularly well developed in the turtles, among the reptiles, where the body is enclosed in a bony case, or box, made up of a number of plates joined rigidly together in a dorsal carapace and a ventral plastron, which are to a great extent fused with the endoskeleton. Overlying the bony plates are typical reptilian horny scales, which provide the familiar tortoise shell of commerce. Among the mammals the armadillos alone have a similar kind of dermal skeleton, a series of bony plates covering the dorsal and lateral surfaces of the body with hairs projecting between the successive rows (Fig. 25.22).

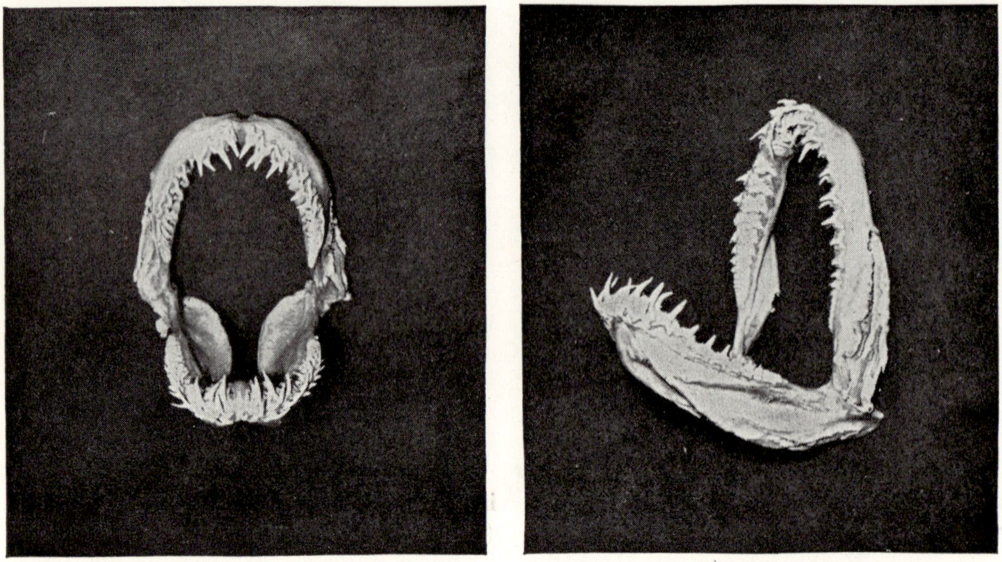

***Derivatives of both epidermis and dermis: placoid scales and teeth:*** Placoid scales (Greek, plax = flat plate) are integumentary structures characteristic of the elasmobranch fishes (Fig. 15.5a, 15.34a). Each scale consists of a basal plate of a hard substance almost like bone although non-cellu-lar, called dentine, and of a pointed spine, also of dentine, which projects through the surface of the skin. In the formation of a placoid scale, the Malpighian layer of the epidermis at first thickens and pushes down into the dermis; beneath this ingrowth, the mesoderm cells multiply and push upward forming a small papilla, which, as it grows, bends posteriorly. The dentine is laid down around the papilla as the spine of the scale and at its base cells also form the basal plate around the core of mesoderm cells which retain their connection with the dermis and also extend up into the spines of the pulp, carrying blood vessels with them. The interior of the spine is thus filled with living tissue. Such scales are developed on the integument lining the mouth, which is derived from a stomodaeum; those on its borders are longer than they are elsewhere on the body, forming diagonal rows of sharp, tearing teeth which are regularly replaced by new ones as they are worn down or broken off (Fig. 15.43).

The development of teeth is common to all vertebrates, although it no longer takes place in modern birds or the most special-

FIGURE 15.43  Jaws of a shark (a) in front view and (b) in side view, showing the rows of sharp placoid scales, or "teeth". (Photograph by D. F. Reath.)

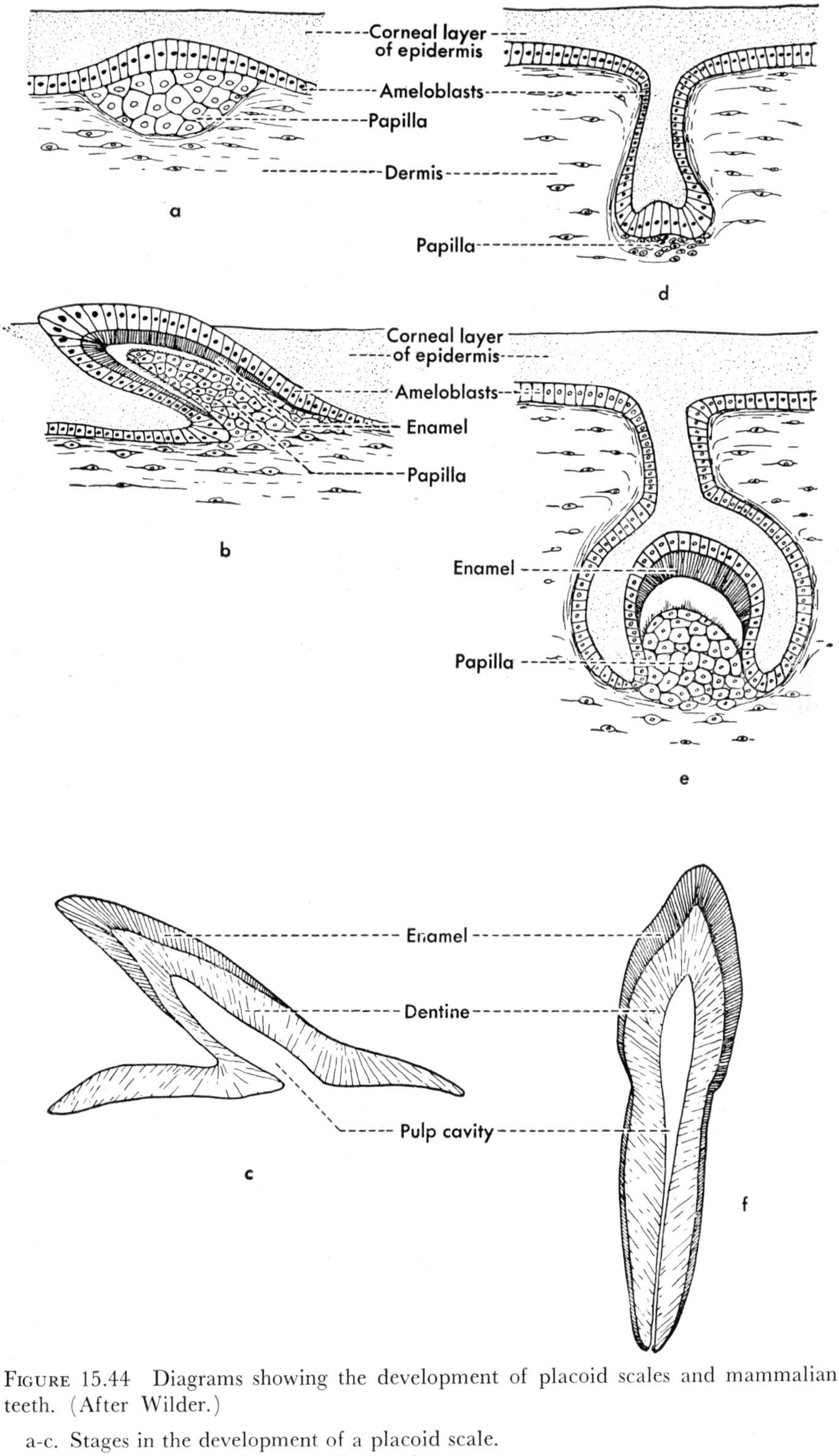

FIGURE 15.44 Diagrams showing the development of placoid scales and mammalian teeth. (After Wilder.)

a-c. Stages in the development of a placoid scale.
d-f. Stages in the development of a tooth.

ized of reptiles, the turtles. The fossils of some extinct birds, however, show that they had teeth, and modern reptiles other than turtles possess them. Teeth vary widely in size, in shape and in number among the different classes of vertebrates and, among mammals particularly, in the different orders and families, but they all have the same basic pattern which is also that of the placoid scale (Fig. 15.44). Their primitive function was presumably to prevent the escape of food from the mouth, but they have become specialized, especially in the mammals, for the biting or tearing or grinding of food and so, by breaking it up into small pieces, as structures accessory to its digestion. As in the formation of the placoid scale, the Malpighian layer of the epidermis takes the initiative in the formation of a tooth. It thickens and pushes down into the dermis; beneath this ingrowth the mesoderm cells also multiply and grow upward, indenting the mass of epidermal cells so that it becomes cup-shaped. The dermal cells inside the cup form the dental papilla which becomes the pulp of the mature tooth, and which is in contact with the underlying dermis. The papilla and pulp are supplied with blood vessels and with nerves from this layer. The outer cells of the dermal papilla become specialized as odontoblasts (Greek, odon = tooth + blastos = germ) and produce the dentine that covers the pulp. The cells of the Malpighian layer that form the lining of the cup become specialized as ameloblasts (early French, amel = enamel + blastos = germ) and secrete enamel on top of the dentine. This cap of enamel and their distribution in the body are the major points of difference between teeth and placoid scales. As the tooth grows, it pushes through the surface of the oral epithelium and its crown is exposed in the mouth cavity; the crown in most cases represents but a small part of the entire tooth, for the remainder, or root, lies below the surface, either resting on the jaw bones or embedded in them. This relation between tooth and jawbone is one of the bases for systematic distinctions between vertebrate types, distinguishing those animals in which the teeth are embedded as thecodont types (Greek, theke = case + odon = tooth) from those in which they are not, as acrodont and pleurodont types (Greek, akros = end, pleura = side).

Teeth are living, sensitive structures, nourished by the blood supply in the pulp and transmitting certain stimuli through their hard outer surfaces to the nerve endings in the pulp. The cells that make them produce the hardest materials synthesized by any biological systems, for dentine is harder than bone and enamel harder than dentine; dried enamel will spark with flint as steel does. The chemical processes by which these materials are synthesized, the elements that go into their composition or that may contribute to their formation are as yet not fully known, although it is clear that the final products are not always alike and that they are conditioned by the mineral supply available to the organism.

In all toothed vertebrates, except the mammals, the teeth are successively replaced as they are worn down or lost during the course of the animal's life, but in most mammals they are developed only twice in the lifetime of an individual and in some (whales, sirenians and monotremes) only once. Characteristically in mammals the first, or milk, teeth are lost and replaced by the second or permanent set; the eruption, loss and replacement of the milk teeth take place at different stages of development in mammals of different kinds. The number and position of their teeth is also characteristic of different groups of vertebrates. In fishes, they are usually conical and may be carried on almost any of the bones surrounding the oral cavity, as well as on those of the branchial arches; amphibian teeth are also conical, but limited in position principally to the margins of the jaws and certain regions of the roof of the mouth. Some amphibians, for example toads and one genus of frogs, lack teeth entirely as adults. Reptilian teeth show a greater variety of form than fish or amphibian teeth, although their distribution in the oral cavity is much the same as it is in amphibians. The greatest specialization of reptilian teeth is in the poison fangs of snakes. These are comparatively long teeth borne on two of the bones of the upper jaw in such a way that they are either permanently erect and so hang down into the mouth cavity, or else folded back against the roof of the mouth when it is closed and swung into position for striking when it is opened (Fig. 15.45).

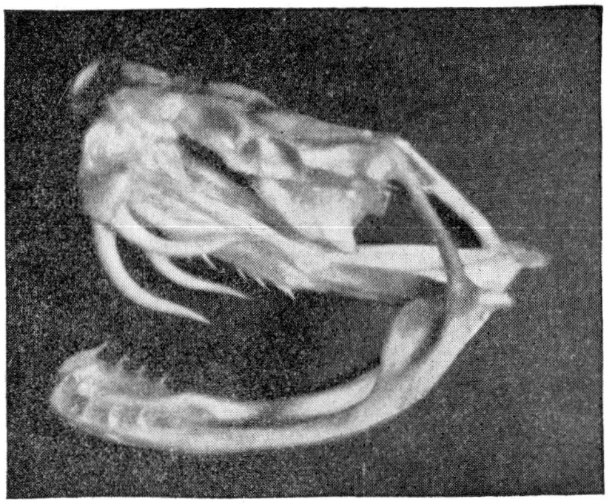

FIGURE 15.45 Fangs.

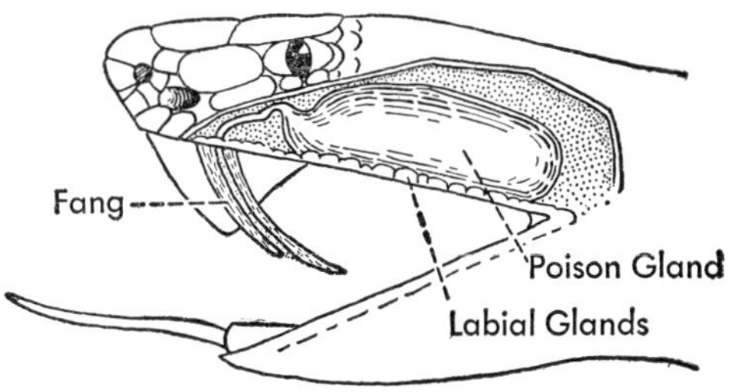

a. Skeleton of the head of a rattlesnake, showing the pivotal fangs and their replacements behind them. (Photograph by D. F. Reath.)

b. Diagram of the head of a rattlesnake, showing the poison gland with its duct passing into the fang. (After Kingsley, from Walter and Sayles, *Biology of the Vertebrates*. Copyright 1949 by The Macmillan Company.)

Pivotal fangs like these are characteristic of rattlesnakes and vipers. The teeth themselves are modified; in the erect fang, the anterior surface is grooved so that the poison secreted by a gland at the base of the tooth is directed along the groove to the puncture made by the fang, and in the pivotal fang, the edges of the groove meet so that a hollow tube is formed leading from the poison gland to an opening at the tip of the fang. Only one pair of fangs is functional at a time, but others are brought up as replacements if necessary.

With the exception of some dolphins, porpoises and types closely related to them whose teeth are conical and indefinite in number, the teeth of mammals are of four general kinds—incisors, or cutting teeth; canines, or tearing teeth; premolars and molars, or grinding teeth—and the maximum number is 44. All are embedded in sockets in the jawbones. The incisors (i), with a single root and a thin, more or less rectangular crown, are developed at the front of the jaw, the conical canines (c) lie behind them and the premolars (p) with two roots and broad, flattened, complicated crowns, and molars (m) with several roots and crowns similar to those of the premolars are placed along the sides of the jaw. The number of teeth of each kind varies in the different orders of mammals, and each variation can be expressed by a "dental formula," in which the number and kind of teeth on one side only of the jaw usually are represented, the upper figure indicating those on the upper jaw and the lower figure those on the lower jaw. The dental formula for the permanent dentition of man is, for example:

i. $\frac{2}{2}$, c. $\frac{1}{1}$, p. $\frac{2}{2}$, m. $\frac{3}{3}$   Total 32

for cats:

i. $\frac{3}{3}$, c. $\frac{1}{1}$, p. $\frac{3}{2}$, m. $\frac{1}{1}$   Total 30

for horses:

i. $\frac{3}{3}$, c. $\frac{1}{1}$, p. $\frac{4}{4}$, m. $\frac{3}{3}$   Total 44

and for rabbits:

i. $\frac{2}{1}$, c. $\frac{0}{0}$, p. $\frac{3}{2}$, m. $\frac{3}{3}$   Total 28

The type of dentition is closely related to the feeding habits of the animal, and mammals may be distinguished as herbivores (Latin, herba = plant + vorare = to devour), carnivores (Latin, carnis = flesh + vorare = to devour), rodents (Latin, rodere = to gnaw) and so on according to the type of their teeth, in much the same way that insects may be classified as suckers, lappers or chewers according to the type of their mouth parts. Tusks like those of boars, walruses and elephants represent extreme modifications of the typical mammalian tooth. The tusks of boars and walruses are greatly enlarged canines; those of the elephant are its single pair of upper incisors, which grow continually throughout its life and are made of solid dentine with only a small amount of enamel at the tip which is quickly worn away. The entire dentition of elephants is very specialized, for there are no lower incisors, no canines and six pairs of very large molars on each side, of which only one or two are functional simultaneously; as these are worn away the ones behind move up to replace them and after the last pair becomes useless, the elephant is without grinding teeth. Some few mammals are characteristically toothless as adults; these include the baleen whales, where the teeth developed during foetal life are lost soon after birth, the American and scaly anteaters and the duckbill platypus which loses its teeth when about a year old.

### Integumental glands

Epidermal glands are common to all classes of vertebrates, though reaching their highest development in the mammals. They range from single mucus-secreting cells of the epidermis and pockets of gland cells developed from the Malpighian layer, discharging their products directly to the surface, to deeper-lying tubules or sacs, which may be twisted or branched or lobulated, discharging their products through ducts that open on the surface by pores (Fig. 15.46). These products may be general in character like mucus and oil, or they may be specific secretions like the sweat of many mammals and the milk of all of them. Mucous glands are particularly numerous in the integument of fish and amphibia, where the slimy secretion keeps the body surface moist and free from micro-organisms and other foreign particles, by entrapping and entangling them. In the case of fishes, it also reduces the frictional resistance of their bodies to the water through which they move, often with great swiftness; in the case of amphibia, its advantage is largely to the process of external respiration, for in all the amphibia the skin acts to greater or less extent as a respiratory area, and in some land salamanders which are lungless it is the only one. Reptiles and birds have few epidermal glands, for their investing scales and feathers are closely placed allowing little room for the development of other structures. But all birds except ostriches have a pair of glands at the base of the tail, the uropygial glands (Greek, oura = tail + pyge = rump), which secrete an oil that lubricates the beak and also serves to dress and waterproof the feathers when the bird spreads it over them in preening. Mammals also possess such lubricating glands, the sebaceous glands which open into the hair follicles, with some few exceptions. These glands are sac-like, or alveolar, and they secret a thick fluid called sebum (Latin, sebum = tallow) containing cholesterol to which fatty acid residues are attached. (See Fig. 15.35b.) Some mammals also have sweat glands either distributed generally over the surface of the body or localized in certain areas; they are coiled tubular glands secreting a watery fluid whose composition varies in different areas of the body and under different internal and external conditions. As a rule, sweat contains sodium chloride, protein, fatty acids and urea as well as a large proportion of water. In addition to its excretory function, in the elimination of water and urea, sweat has some use as a lubricant to the skin and serves as a temperature-regulating mechanism, for its evaporation from the surface tends to lower the temperature there and hence that of the body as a whole. Modifications of both these types of glands are found along the eyelids and in the canal of the external ear where they secrete the cerumen or wax.

The most modified of the mammalian epidermal glands are the milk, or mammary, glands. These are developed to a greater extent in the females than in the males of mammals; the stimulus to their development as functional glands and to the production of their secretion is the consequence of conditions inherent in the individual. They form along two lines, the milk lines, on the ventral surface of the trunk, and they may be distributed along its length or

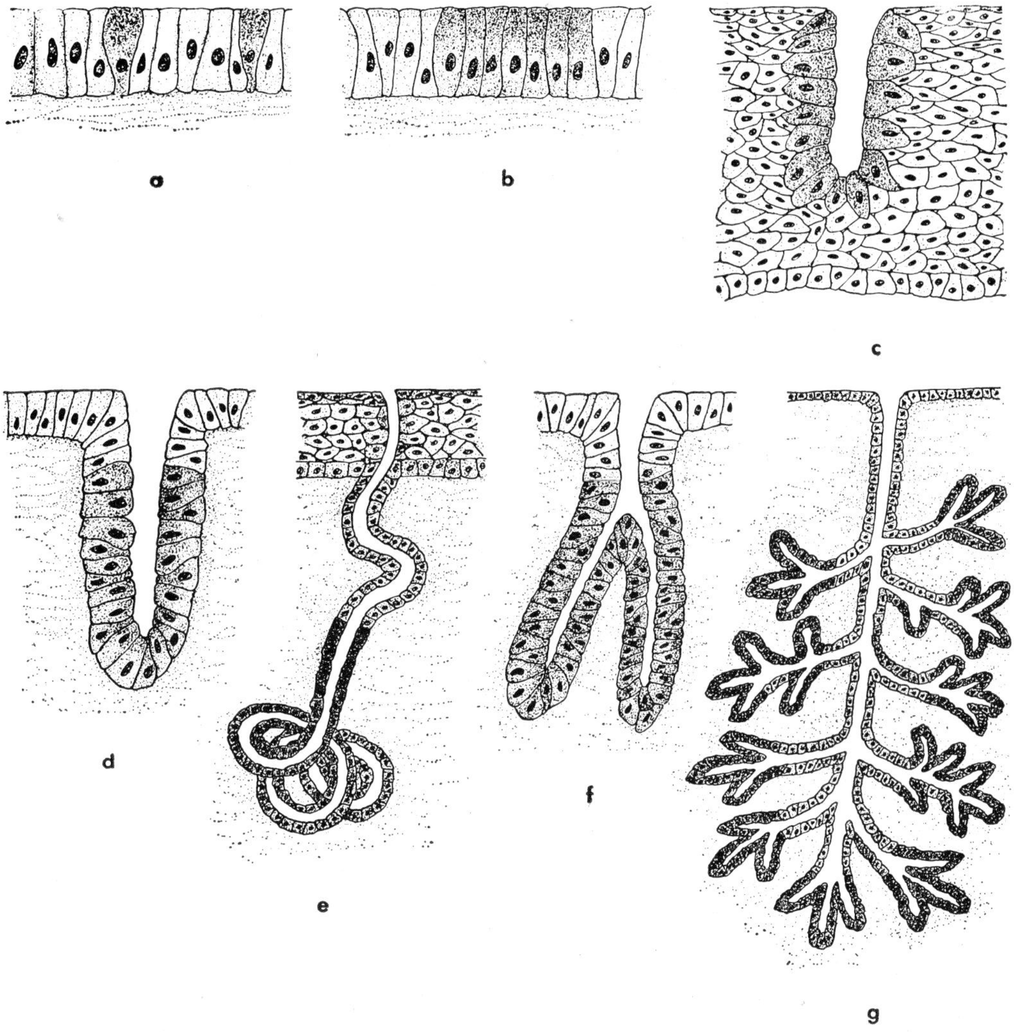

FIGURE 15.46  Types of epidermal glands. (After Kendall.)

   a. Unicellular gland (goblet cell).
   b. Secretory area, represented by a group of gland cells.
   c. Pocket of glandular cells.
   d. Simple tubular gland.
   e. Coiled tubular gland.
   f. Branched tubular gland.
   g. Compound tubular gland (secretory portions shown in black).

limited to definite areas of it. The secretion from them is an emulsion called milk, which contains fat, in droplets from 2–5 micra in diameter; albumins of which the principal one is casein; lactose or milk sugar; a derivative of nucleoprotein called nuclein; a few leucocytes; certain vitamins; and some inorganic compounds, particularly the phosphates of calcium; and some iron compounds. All of these substances are suspended or dissolved in water, making the balanced nutrient fluid on which the young of mammals are naturally fed and which, together with the products made from it, has become a staple item in the human diet at all ages. The composition of milk varies

FIGURE 15.47  Luminous deep-sea angler fish (Himantolophus azurlucens). (Courtesy of Dr. William Beebe, New York Zoological Society.) This fish, found in 500 fathoms of water off the eastern coast of Panama, is described as being about 5 inches in length, jet black in color, paling to a smoky gray along the middle of the back, with conspicuous spines, some with luminous turquoise colored bases. (Beebe and Crane, 1947.)

in different kinds of mammals; the average composition of the milk of five of them is given in Table VI.

TABLE VI

Average Composition of Milk [a]

| Animal | Water (Per cent) | Protein (Per cent) | Fat (Per cent) | Lactose (Per cent) | Minerals (Per cent) |
|---|---|---|---|---|---|
| Human | 87.5 | 1.4 | 3.7 | 7.2 | 0.2 |
| Cow | 87.1 | 3.4 | 3.9 | 4.9 | 0.7 |
| Goat | 87.0 | 3.3 | 4.2 | 4.8 | 0.7 |
| Sheep | 82.6 | 5.5 | 6.54 | 4.5 | 0.9 |
| Reindeer | 63.7 | 10.3 | 19.7 | 4.8 | 1.5 |

[a] *Proceedings of the National Nutritional Council for Defense.* From Harrow, *Textbook of Biochemistry.* Copyright 1943 by the W. B. Saunders Company.

In some vertebrates certain epidermal glands may be modified as photophores, or light-producing organs, similar in their chemical mechanism to the luminescent organs of non-chordates in that they release energy in the form of light from the oxidation of a luciferin in the presence of a luciferinase (see p. 248). Such photophores are found in some salamanders of the tropics and in some bony fish, particularly the lantern and angler fish of the deep sea, where they may lie along the sides of the body like rows of portholes in a ship or, in fish especially, may be carried on stalks arising from almost any region of the body surface (Fig. 15.47). The photophores of fish are closed sacs developed from the Malpighian layer of the epidermis and sunk in the dermis. The cells at the bottom of the sac synthesize granules of luciferin while those in the upper part are converted into a round, translucent lens and the cells of the dermis immediately surrounding the sac form a reflector layer outside of which melanophores are organized into a close-packed opaque covering so that all the light is directed outward. The whole organ operates like a bull's-eye lantern which has its own self-perpetuating and extremely efficient source of light.

Another modification of epidermal glands, which bring about the release of considerable amounts of energy in a different form, are found all over the body of the electric ference of the entire set reaches some 200 volts, enough to cause a pronounced electric shock to which the fish itself is not sensitive. Indeed none of the fish possessing electric organs of any kind appear to be affected by the shocks that they themselves produce, nor by those from other fish in their vicinity.

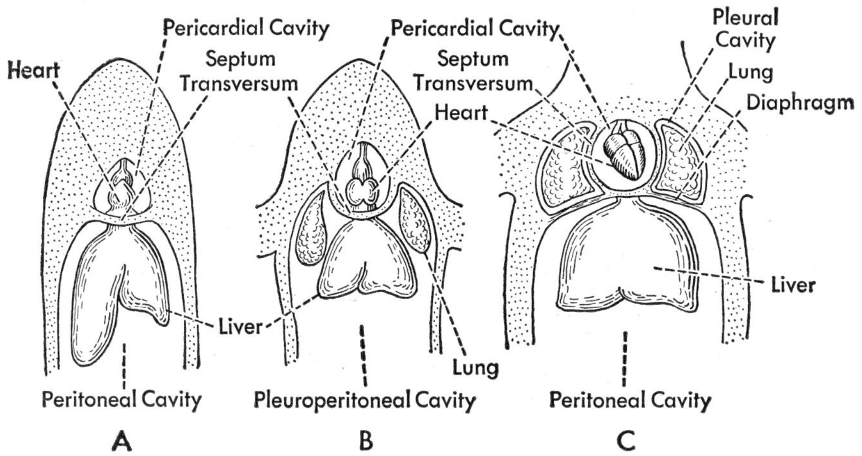

FIGURE 15.48 Diagrams showing the relations of the coelomic cavities in A, fishes; B, amphibians, reptiles and birds; C, mammals. (After Kingsley, from Walter and Sayles, *Biology of the Vertebrates*. Copyright 1949 by The Macmillan Company.)

catfish, Malapterurus electricus, which inhabits the fresh waters of northern and tropical Africa. These glands are disc-shaped and sunk below the surface of the body; they are supplied by efferent nerves and stimulated to the discharge of electrical energy by impulses initiated by sensory stimuli. While many biological processes, other than the contraction of muscle, are known to be accompanied by the release of small amounts of electrical energy—and probably all might be found to be so were it possible to record and to measure the most minute discharges —the nature of the energy-releasing reaction within these glands is not clear. It is known, however, that each disc can build up a potential difference of about 0.04 volt, and that the discs, though anatomically separate except for their nervous connections, are physically connected in such a way that their individual voltages are summated; in other words, their combined effect is like that of a number of batteries connected in series. In Malapterurus, the potential dif-

In all vertebrates the integument as a whole is greatly modified on the outer surface of the eye as the transparent tissue of the cornea. Folds of the integument also form protective coverings, or lids, for the eyes. The nictitating membrane (Latin, nictare = to connive or wink) is a fold also of transparent or translucent integument that originates at the inner angle of the eye in some elasmobranchs, the amphibia, reptiles, birds and many mammals, and that can be moved obliquely upwards to cover the eyeball. In the anamniote vertebrates, this is the only lid, but in the amniotes there is usually also a fold above and one below the eye, provided with epidermal glands and, in mammals, fringed with hairs, making the upper and lower eyelids.

## Coelome and visceral organs

The coelome in vertebrates is limited to the trunk and does not extend into the head or the tail. In the fishes, amphibia and reptiles, it is a continuous cavity, the pleuroperitoneal cavity, enclosing the digestive and reproductive organs, and in those species which have them, the lungs; in the mammals it is divided by a septum, the diaphragm, into a pleural cavity, in which the lungs lie,

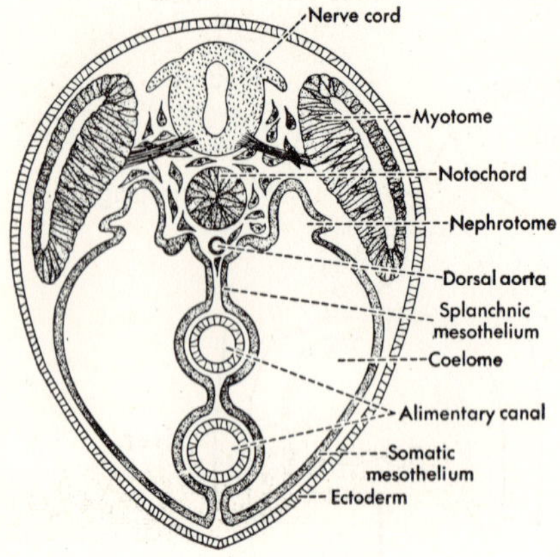

FIGURE 15.49  Diagrammatic cross-section through a vertebrate. (After Kingsley.)

and a peritoneal cavity enclosing the remaining viscera (Fig. 15.48). These cavities are lined with peritoneum, a delicate epithelium that, as parietal peritoneum, extends around the outer wall of the cavity and, as visceral peritoneum, invests the organs that lie in it. Parietal and visceral peritoneum are continuous, through the mesenteries, double sheets of peritoneum that extend from the outer coelomic wall to the viscera and that serve as supports for blood and lymph vessels, for nerves, and often as areas for the deposition of fat (Fig. 15.49).

## Lungs

In all vertebrates possessing them, the lungs arise, as do the pharyngeal pouches of the branchiate species, as outgrowths of the digestive tract. The lung first appears as a small enlargement or bud on the ventral surface of the embryonic enteron; this divides and enlarges into a bi-lobed, air-filled sac, whose walls are richly supplied with blood vessels (Fig. 15.50). In the majority of species, the connection with the oesophagus is retained as the trachea, its opening the glottis (Greek, glossa = tongue) through which the air passes, and so on into the lungs either from the mouth or from the nasal passages, for in all air-breathing vertebrates, the olfactory pits are not blind sacs as they are in the elasmobranchs and most bony fishes and open internally into a passage communicating with the pharynx (Fig. 15.51). The external openings of the olfactory organs are the external nares (Latin, naris = nostril), their internal openings, the internal nares.

The tetrapod lung shows various degrees of complexity in the different classes. In the terrestrial amphibia, it has two slender, pointed lobes arising directly from the trachea and lies in the anterior part of the coelome dorsal to the heart and the liver (Fig. 15.52). The inner walls of the two lobes are raised into folds, thus increasing the respiratory surface, and blood is conveyed to them by pulmonary arteries. They are ventilated by movements of the mouth, for muscles pulling on the hyoid bone depress the floor of the mouth, enlarging its cavity and drawing air up from the lungs to be mixed with that in the buccal cavity which has approximately the composition of external air, since it is open to the outside through the nostrils, through which the enlargement of the buccal cavity has also caused some air to be drawn. When the floor of the mouth is raised by the relaxation of the hyoid muscles, the external nares are closed and the mixed air is sent back to the lungs (Fig. 15.53). The interchange of gases between the blood and the air takes place in the mouth as well as in the lungs, and the integument as a whole acts as a large respiratory surface for all amphibia that live in moist, cool habitats; in the lungless salamanders, integumentary and buccal respiration are the only means by which the blood is supplied with oxygen and relieved of carbon dioxide, and in the dry-skinned and scaly toads pulmonary and buccal respiration alone are possible. In their aquatic larval stages, all amphibia respire externally by means of gills developed as conspicuous finger-like processes along the margins of the gill slits or concealed beneath an operculum as they are in bony fish; in some adults that live in water or in damp places, the integument may be thrown into folds resembling

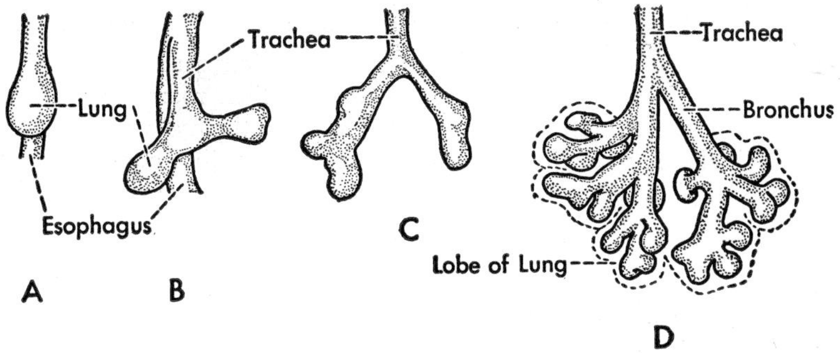

FIGURE 15.50 Stages in the development of lungs, trachea and bronchi in the human embryo. (From Walter and Sayles, *Biology of the Vertebrates*. Copyright 1949 by The Macmillan Company.)

A. 4 mm. embryo. (After Grosser and Heiss, after Arey.)
B. 5 mm. embryo. (After Heiss and Merkel.)
C. 7 mm. embryo. (After Heiss and Merkel.)
D. 10 mm. embryo. (After Heiss and Merkel.)

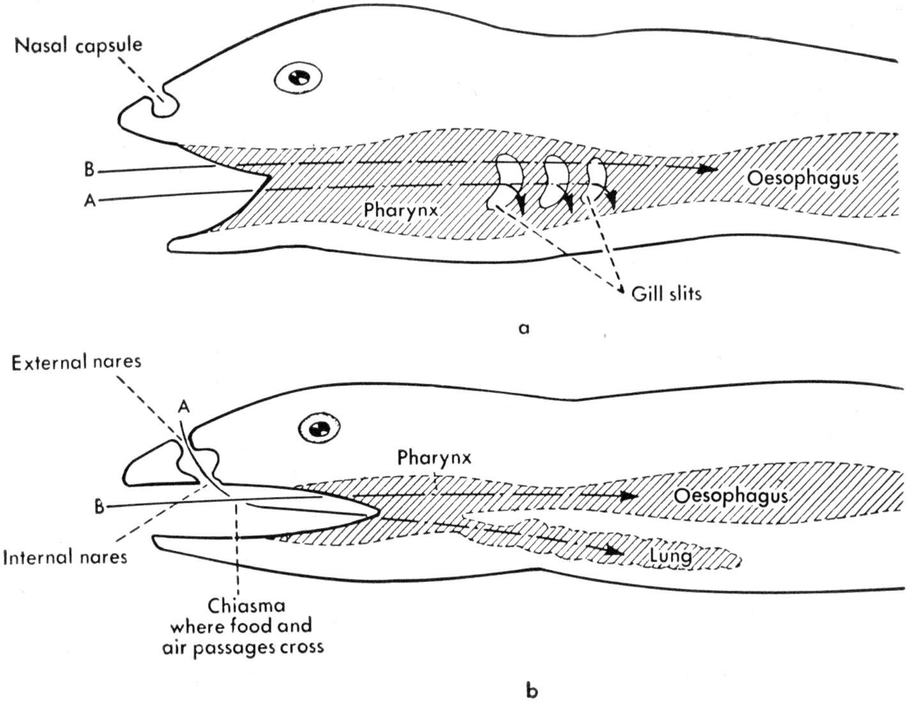

FIGURE 15.51 Diagram showing the air and food passages in aquatic and terrestrial vertebrates. (After Weidersheim.)

a. The oral cavity of a fish, showing the blind nasal capsule and the mouth opening. The arrow A shows the respiratory current; B, the food current.

b. The oral cavity of an amphibian, showing the connection of the nasal capsule with the oral cavity. The arrow A indicates the air passage; B, the food passage.

[ 307 ]

[ 308 ] THE ORGANIZATION OF BIOLOGICAL SYSTEMS

gills, but in only one species, the "hairy frog" of Africa, where in the breeding season there are a great number of fine, finger-like vascular processes on the thighs and flanks, have these diverticula any resemblance to the finer processes of gills.

brae and are covered by a modified peritoneum which is tough and fibrous and allows them little room for expansion. Nor are the organs themselves distensible sacs like those of amphibia and reptiles but spongy in their texture, showing little change of size

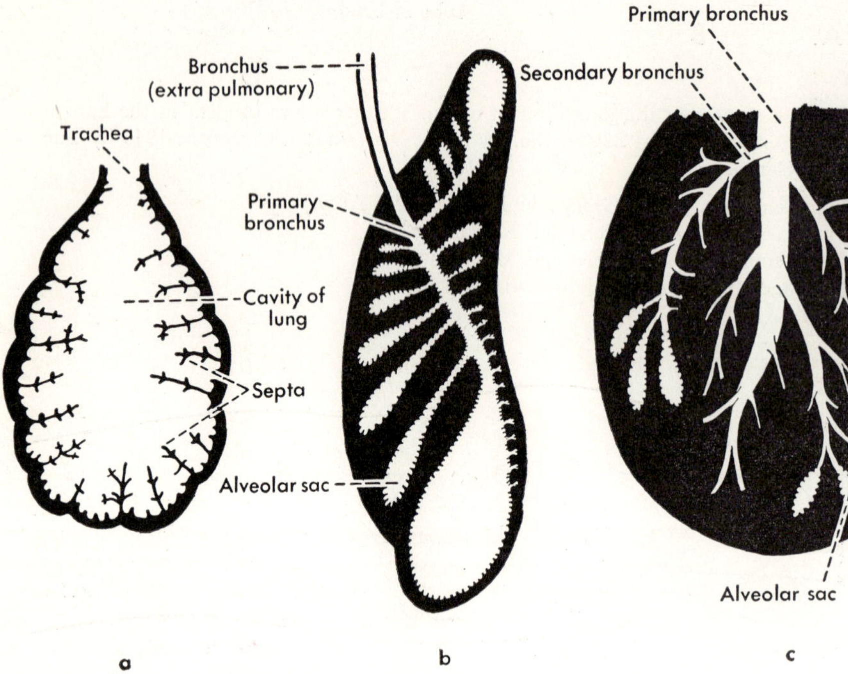

FIGURE 15.52. Evolution of lung structure. (After Ihle.)

a. Diagram of an amphibian lung.
b. Diagram of a reptilian (lizard) lung.
c. Diagram of a mammalian lung.

In many reptiles, the lungs are not symmetrical bi-lobed structures but ones in which the lobe of one side is markedly larger than that of the other. In some snakes, one lobe is entirely undeveloped, and only that on the left side becomes functional. This may perhaps be correlated with a long, slender body, for it is also the case in some few salamanders. In lizards, the lung cavity may be divided into chambers by septa which grow out from its lining and extend more or less completely from its tip to its base.

In birds, the lungs instead of lying free in the coelome with only a covering of delicate peritoneum as they do in amphibia and reptiles, are pressed against the ribs and verte-

during respiratory movements. In each lobe of the lung the tube or bronchus (Greek, bronchus = windpipe), by which it is connected with the trachea, runs the entire length of the lobe as the primary bronchus along whose length a number of secondary bronchi arise; these in turn branch into smaller tubes, or tertiary bronchi, which unite with others derived from other secondary bronchi, the whole forming a closed system of air tubes enclosed within the vascular sac (Fig. 15.54). From the walls of the tertiary bronchi radiate still finer tubes, perhaps best described as air capillaries, which also penetrate through the vascular tissue of the lung and also join end to end forming a closed system. There are no air tubes ending blindly in air spaces in the lungs of birds, a structural modification that is peculiar to them, as are the air sacs into which certain of the bronchi open. There are usually five pairs of these sacs, a cervical pair in the

Expiration; floor of mouth lowered, external nares open, lung contracted

Inspiration; floor of mouth raised, external nares closed, lung expanded

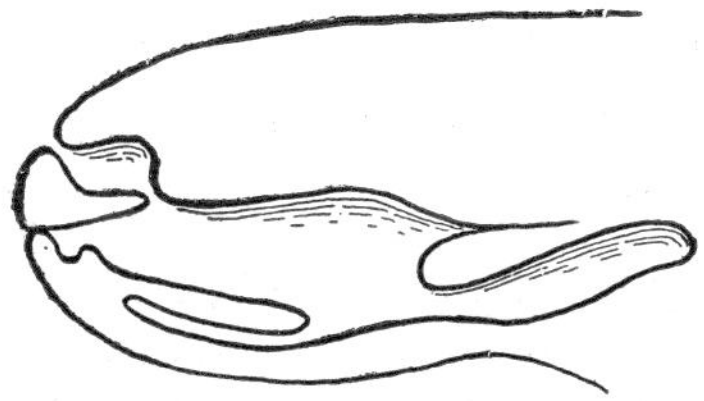

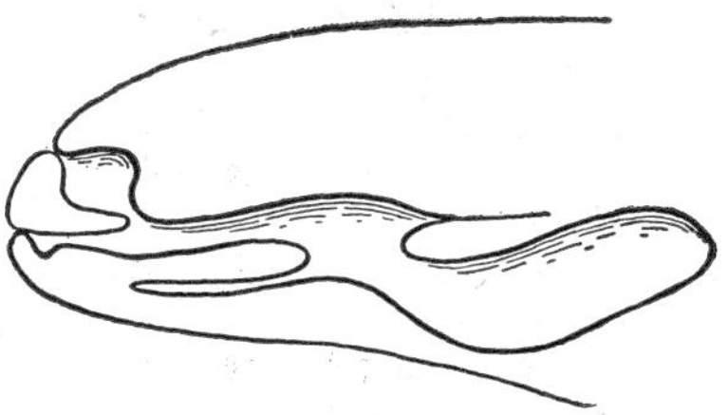

FIGURE 15.53 Diagrams showing the respiratory movements of a frog. (From Mavor, *General Biology*, 3rd edition. Copyright 1947 by The Macmillan Company.)

neck; an interclavicular pair, often fused into a single sac lying ventral to the oesophagus; an anterior thoracic pair; a posterior thoracic pair; and an abdominal pair. The primary bronchi extend beyond the tips of the vascular lobes and open into these abdominal sacs; they give off secondary bronchi along their course which in turn terminate in the other sacs, actually expansions of the ends of these bronchi. Connection with the vascular part of the lung tissue is established by other tubes, the recurrent bronchi. Air that enters the bronchi thus passes through the ramifying system of tubes within the tissues of the lung and also directly into the air sacs and bony air spaces from which it is returned to the vascular region of the lung by the recurrent bronchi; by this mechanism a continuous flow of fresh air is provided for the region in which the actual gaseous interchange takes place.

The vascular lung proper and the residual air spaces are therefore but two parts of a common structure, whose division in this way appears to be a very efficient means of insuring rapid gaseous exchange and maximum ventilation of the lung, conditions which are very important to an organism like a bird with a high metabolic rate and a habit of life that demands vigorous and often long-sustained muscular action. Possibly in addition to their respiratory function, which is certainly a principal one, the air sacs and spaces within the bones may help to lower the body temperature by offering a comparatively large internal area for the radiation of heat, for little or none can take place from the surface of the body because of the thick covering of feathers or keratinized epidermis. The sacs and the pneumatic bones have been thought, too, to aid the bird in flight by reducing its specific gravity, but some birds which are good fliers, like gulls, have bones without air spaces, although in others, like frigate birds, even the metatarsals are pneumatic. Though all the air spaces may act as hydrostatic organs in the swimming and diving birds, there is every reason to believe that their effect in raising land birds from the ground or supporting them in flight is negligible. In singing birds, whose sounds are produced in the syrinx, an enlargement of the trachea near the point of origin of the bronchi, air from the sacs may be used to set in motion the membranes that cross its cavity whose vibrations produce the notes of the songs or calls.

The lungs of mammals are constructed on a plan that has been described as that of a branching tree, for the trachea divides into two primary bronchi, making the right and left lobes of the lung, and these in turn divide within the lobes into bronchi of the second, third and successive orders up to about thirty. The finer air tubes are called bronchioles and the finest of these give rise along their length and at their tips to numerous alveoli, the ultimate air spaces (Fig. 15.55). The entire lung is divided into right and left and a number of lesser lobes and like that of a bird is spongy in its texture, although its internal construction is quite different. Originating, as do all lungs, as an outgrowth of the embryonic enteron, it is lined throughout with epithelium continuous with that of the digestive tract and endodermal in origin, with tissues derived from the mesenchyme that it has invaded in its growth applied to the epithelium to form of the bronchial tree, the bore of the divided tube is halved but the cross-sectional area of its two branches is greater than its own so that with each generation, or order, of air tubes the total air space increases. Although it is not possible to determine the area of the

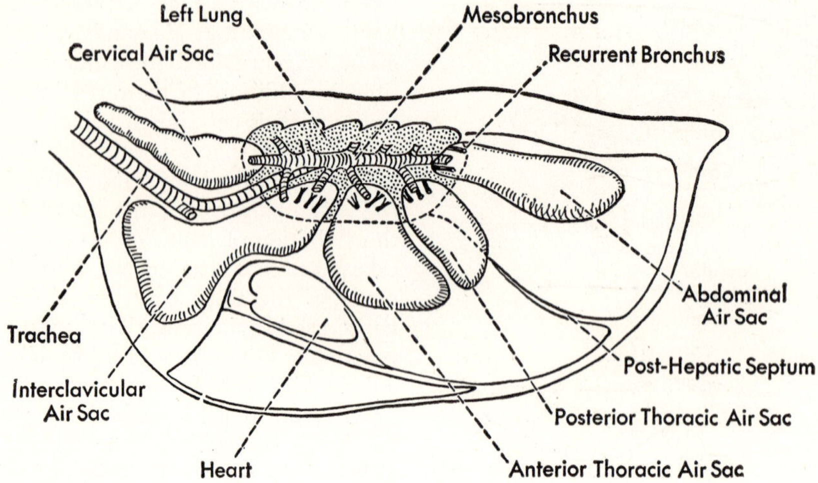

FIGURE 15.54 Diagram showing the respiratory organs of a bird from the left side. (After Goodrich, from Walter and Sayles, *Biology of the Vertebrates*. Copyright 1949 by The Macmillan Company.)

the walls of the air tubes and the covering of the organ itself. The bronchi, like the trachea, are stiffened by rings or crescentic hoops of cartilage so that they are kept permanently open; the walls of the bronchioles contain elastic fibers and so can be stretched by the incoming air but tend to collapse after such distention. The true nature of the walls of the alveoli and the alveolar ducts leading from them to the ultimate bronchioles has been extremely difficult to determine, for they are so delicate and so intimately related to the extensive system of blood capillaries that surrounds them that in sections prepared for microscopic study it is virtually impossible to determine the outlines of their slender cells or even to distinguish their nuclei from those of the capillary endothelium or the surrounding connective tissue cells. It is across these alveolar and capillary walls that the interchange of gases takes place and their arrangement is such that they provide a relatively enormous area for this exchange. With each division alveoli alone, it has been calculated that in man the total surface of the pulmonary epithelium—that is, of the bronchi and bronchioles of all dimensions as well as the alveoli—amounts to 70 square meters when expanded during the intake of air.

The lungs themselves are not active in the inspiration of air, which is drawn into them inevitably when the cavity in which they lie is enlarged. This enlargement is brought about by contraction of the muscle fibres in the diaphragm which draw it posteriorly, enlarging the pleural cavity anteroposteriorly, and of certain muscles attached to the ribs which turn them outward and upward and so increase the transverse dimensions of the thorax. In consequence of this, the air pressure in the pleural cavity becomes lower than that of the atmosphere, or negative, and since this is completely cut off from other outside communication, air rushes in through the external openings leading to the lungs, the nostrils and the mouth, and, slowed down in its passage along the bronchial tree, dilates the bronchioles and alveoli, expanding the lungs so that they fill the pleural cavity. After expansion, the elasticity of the walls of all the parts of the lung tends to bring about its collapse and this, combined with the relaxation of the diaphragm and the return of the ribs to their original positions by the inward and downward pull of another set of muscles attached to them, causes air to leave the lungs through the same passages by which it entered. The movements of the muscles leading to the intake, or inspiration, of air and to its outgo, or expiration, are the movements of breathing and are regular and rhythmical but influenced by nervous stimulation; these movements make possible and lead to the exchange of gases across the capillary and alveolar walls, or external respiration. Some such exchange between external environment and internal is an essential and universal process in all biological systems, and the mammalian lung simply provides a mechanism by which external air can be drawn into the body and air which has become charged with carbon dioxide eliminated from it; it and the blood stream which conveys the gases around the body are accessory to internal respiration, the fundamental respiratory process through which oxygen is made available to the tissues and cells for the chemical reactions that require it.

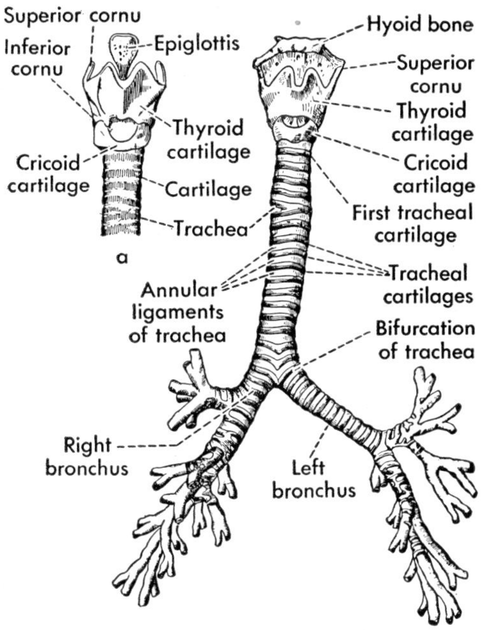

In its passage along the larger and smaller air tubes, the inspired air undergoes some physical changes, for it is filtered, moistened and either warmed or cooled very nearly to body temperature. In ordinary breathing in mammals, air is drawn in through the external nares, passes along the nasal passages into the pharynx and enters the trachea through the glottis (Fig. 15.56). This opening is protected by a cartilaginous flap, the epiglottis, which ordinarily closes down over the trachea when the animal swallows, thus directing the food into the oesophagus and preventing its entrance into the respiratory tract. The external nares are lined with keratinized epidermis and with hairs which act as filters, straining dust particles from the entering air. Further posteriorly, the cells lining the nasal passages are ciliated and glandular, secreting mucus and a watery fluid which are directed toward the pharynx by the movement of the cilia. The olfactory region of the nose is composed of neuroepithelium whose cells are sensitive to dissolved substances; it extends some distance along the nasal passage in most mammals but man, where it is limited to a comparatively small area in the upper regions of the nasal cavity. The secretions from the cells anterior to it serve to dissolve the volatile substances which are appreciated as smells and also to entangle foreign particles which have escaped the hair filter. Although essential to the sense of smell—a very important sense and one highly developed in most mammals—these secretions have also certain

FIGURE 15.55 The human larynx, trachea and bronchi. (From Kimber, Gray, Stackpole and Leavell, *Textbook of Anatomy and Physiology*, 12th edition. Copyright 1948 by The Macmillan Company.)

a. The larynx and upper part of the trachea, from the ventral side (front), showing the cartilages.

b. The larynx and trachea, showing the division of the latter into right and left bronchi, and the subdivisions of the bronchi into the finer air passages of the lung.

disadvantages to man and the primates at least, for the moist, warm surfaces of the nasal passages provide an excellent culture medium for disease-producing micro-organisms that may enter with the air. The respiratory tract is recognized as the region for the entrance into the system of certain bacteria and viruses and is suspected of being that for several others. But, ordinarily, airborne micro-organisms are entangled in the mucus mass and swept away to the pharynx by the action of the cilia. The nasal passages open by the posterior nares into the pharynx, the region common to both digestive and respiratory tracts into which open also the Eustachian tubes from the middle ear; the entrance of bacteria into these tubes, leading to infections of the middle ear in man, is not uncommon, but usually prevented by the outward beat of the cilia on the margins of the cells of the tubes. The air crosses the pharynx and enters the larynx at the upper end of the trachea, a slightly expanded region into which the vocal cords extend; these cords are folds of mucous membrane which, when brought together and caused to vibrate by air coming from the lungs, produce the characteristic sounds of mammals. The larynx as well as the trachea is for the most part lined with ciliated and glandular cells, as are the bronchi at least down to those of approximately 1 mm. in diameter, so that the protective properties of the respiratory lining are carried well down into the bronchial tree. The epithelium of the bronchioles is ciliated but not glandular, and that of the alveoli is neither.

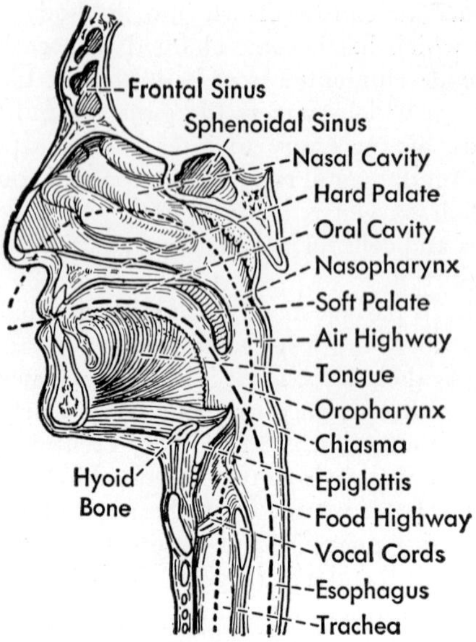

FIGURE 15.56 Sagittal section through the head and throat of a man, showing the respiratory passages and pharyngeal chiasma. (From Walter and Sayles, *Biology of the Vertebrates.* Copyright 1949 by The Macmillan Company.)

## Oral glands

With the development of lungs and of pulmonary respiration, the development of the mouth cavity as an effective secretory area became possible, a condition that cannot be attained by branchiate vertebrates in which the oral cavity is constantly washed over with water taken in for respiratory purposes. In all tetrapods, the lining of the mouth is glandular, some cells secreting a watery fluid and other mucus. The combined secretions serve to moisten and to lubricate the food; in some species these secretions have an adhesive quality which, in insect-eaters especially, helps in capturing the prey. In many, the secretory cells are localized in definite areas, in most cases sunk below the surface and opening into the mouth through ducts. These may be variously distributed throughout the oral epithelium but usually there is a pair of submaxillary glands situated below the angle of the lower jaw and a sublingual pair at the base of the tongue. In addition to these, all mammals, with the exception of whales, which lack oral glands of any kind, have a pair of parotid glands (Greek, para = beside + otos = ear) lying just below the external ears and discharging their secretions through a duct that opens near the molar teeth of the upper jaw (Fig. 19.3). These three glands are commonly known as the salivary glands, their combined secretions as saliva. In primates, pigs and some rodents, the saliva contains an enzyme called ptyalin (Greek, ptyalon = spittle), an amylase or starch-splitting enzyme, which in the presence of small amounts of salts and especially of sodium chloride, participates in the initial steps in the decomposition of polysaccharide molecules. No enzymes have been detected in the mouth secretions of any other tetrapods except in the poison glands of snakes and the Gila monster of the southwestern United States, the only poisonous lizard in the world. The poison glands of the Gila monster are specialized sublingual glands, those of the snakes a pair of modified labial glands (Latin, labium = lip), whose ducts have lost their connections with the mouth cavity proper and open at the base of the fangs (Fig. 15.45b). The venoms of cobras and rattlesnakes, introduced into the bodies of other animals, bring about the destruction of the red blood cells, or haemolysis (Greek, haema = blood + lysis = loosening), and consequent impairment of the internal respiratory processes. The enzyme responsible for this is a lipase, or fat-splitting one, called lecithinase which catalyzes the disintegration of the lecithin molecule in such a way that only one of its fatty acid chains is removed instead of two, as in the ordinary course of its degradation in the body. The product resulting from this reaction is lysolecithin which brings about the lysis of the red blood cells. The venom of vipers, on the other hand, contains a proteolytic enzyme rather than a lipolytic one, and its effect upon the proteins of the blood is to cause the formation of blood clots in the veins. The venom of other snakes affects other tissues such as the capillary endothelium and nervous tissue, causing harmful effects upon the functioning of the organism into which it is introduced when the snake sinks its fangs through the integument.

### Digestive organs

The general pattern of the digestive tract is the same in all vertebrates; it is a tube extending from the mouth to a posterior opening and so it is actually external to the body proper although enclosed within it (Fig. 15.1). There are regional modifications along its length—dilatations or especially glandular, muscular or hardened areas—in all the classes. Also all the classes have liver and pancreas as accessory digestive glands. The wall of the alimentary tube is composed throughout of an internal mucosa lining its lumen; a layer, the submucosa, of loose connective tissue supporting blood vessels and nerves that immediately surrounds the mucosa; external to that, the tunica muscularis, made up of muscle fibres, the inner ones running around the

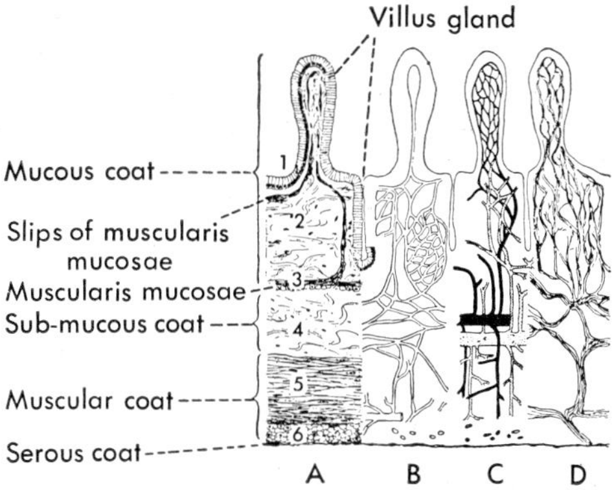

FIGURE 15.57 Diagram of a cross section of the human small intestine. (From Kimber, Gray and Stackpole, *Textbook of Anatomy and Physiology*, 11th edition. Copyright 1942 by The Macmillan Company.) In section A, the layers of the wall are shown. 1, mucosa; 2 and 4, submucosa supporting 3, the muscularis mucosa, a sheet of muscle fibres as well as blood and lymph vessels and nerves; 5, tunica muscularis; and 6, tunica serosa. In section B, the distribution of lymph vessels is shown, with a blind vessel, the central lacteal, extending into a villus, a fingerlike projection of the inner wall of the digestive tract peculiar to the intestinal region. In C, the blood supply is shown, with the arteries and capillaries in black and the veins stippled; in D, the distribution of the nerves is shown. (A and C drawn from slides of an injected specimen; B and D adapted from Mall.)

tube as circular muscles and the outer ones parallel to it as a longitudinal layer; and an external coat, the tunica serosa (Latin, serum = serum) of connective tissue covered with peritoneum (Fig. 15.57).

The oesophagus leads from the pharynx to the stomach; in fish and most amphibia it is a short, straight tube, but it is longer in animals in which the head is separated from the trunk by a well-defined neck. Its length is proportionately greater in birds as a class than in the other vertebrates, and in them it is not a straight tube but expanded at the base into a crop, which, supported by the furcula, serves in most as a reservoir for food. In pigeons, the mucous membrane of the crop is specialized as gland cells which in the breeding season secrete a milky-appearing fluid which the parents regurgitate and feed to their newly hatched young.

***The stomach:*** At the base of the oesophagus, the digestive tract enlarges into the stomach, with glandular lining and muscular walls. The shape of the stomach shows a good deal of variation in different species; it is long and slender in animals with elongated bodies and extends antero-posteriorly, but in those with greater diameter and shorter length it tends to be wider and to lie across rather than along the body. At its distal end is the pylorus (Greek, pylorus = gate keeper), the name given by Galen to the opening between stomach and intestine, which is surrounded by a sphincter muscle, and which he recognized as controlling the passage of the stomach's contents into the part of the alimentary tube posterior to it. Three regions of the stomach are generally recognized, although not clearly delimited; the cardiac region near the junction with the oesophagus; the fundus (Latin, fundus = bottom) or middle region; and the pyloric region near the junction with the intestine. In the bony fishes, there is little distinction between the stomach and the intestine, but at the pyloric end of the intestine there frequently are a number of caeca, hollow projections of its glandular wall. The greatest modification of the vertebrate stomach is in birds and in hoofed mammals like cows and sheep and in whales (Fig. 15.58). Immediately following the crop in birds is a glandular stomach, the proventriculus, in which the food is mixed with digestive juices; posterior to this is the gizzard, an expanded region of the tube in which the walls are especially muscular and the glands of the mucosa secrete a substance that hardens when it reaches the lumen of the gizzard and forms around it a tough, firm covering resistant to the action of the digestive enzymes. Here the food is further broken up and mixed more thoroughly with the secretions from the proventriculus; the gizzard is smaller in the flesh-eating birds like owls, hawks and other birds of prey, than it is in grain-eaters, where its macerating action is increased by the presence of sand grains or other sharp abrasive particles which the bird has pecked up. In whales and cows, sheep and camels the stomach is divided into four compartments. In the cow, for example, two of these compartments, the rumen (Latin,

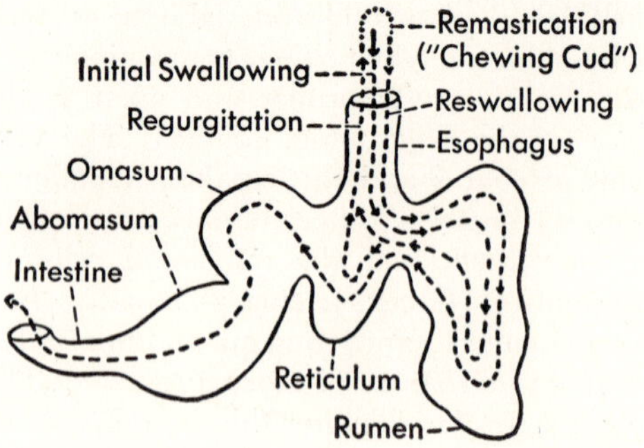

FIGURE 15.58 Diagram of a ruminant stomach. The broken lines show the course of the food. (From Walter and Sayles, *Biology of the Vertebrates*. Copyright 1949 by The Macmillan Company.)

rumen = gullet) and the reticulum (Latin, dim. of rete = net) are really expansions of the oesophagus while the other two, the omasum (Latin, omasum = tripe) and the abomasum represent the stomach proper. In eating, the cow swallows the grass or fodder without chewing it and the food mass passes directly into the rumen and reticulum where it is churned about by the action of their muscular walls and exposed to bacteria which inhabit these chambers and which can produce enzymes that bring about the decomposition of cellulose, something which the cow itself cannot accomplish. After a time the food is regurgitated into the mouth and chewed by the grinding teeth. After mastication and mixing with saliva, the food is swallowed again and this time passes directly into the omasum, where it is again churned about and broken up even more completely, and then into the abomasum where the contents of the disintegrated cells is exposed to the action of the digestive enzymes. In the camels there are a number of glandular diverticula from both the rumen and the reticulum in which water is stored. A sphincter muscle surrounds the openings of these "water cells" into the stomach, so that they may be shut off or opened.

In all vertebrates the area of the mucosa of the stomach is increased by folding, and the glandular area, even more greatly increased because the gland cells are sunk below the surface in pits, or crypts, or in longer tubules which penetrate some distance into the submucosa. The secretion in the stomach is called gastric juice, and in mammals is known to contain besides a large proportion of water (about 99 per cent) and some salts, hydrochloric acid up to 0.2–0.6 per cent; a proteolytic enzyme called pepsin; a lipase that may not be a product of its own glandular cells but of those of the pancreas; and in young mammals especially, a more specific proteolytic enzyme than pepsin called rennin, which catalyzes the conversion of casein, the phosphoprotein peculiar to milk, into paracasein, which readily forms an insoluble salt with calcium, leading to the formation of a clot. In man, the glandular cells in the cardiac region are continuous with those of the oesophagus and like them are mucus-secreting at the upper ends of the glands while along the sides and at the bases they secrete the enzymes and hydrochloric acid; the glands in the pyloric region are largely mucus-secreting. The total number of crypts in the adult human stomach has been estimated at 3,000,000 and of tubular glands at 13,000,000, providing a huge secretory area in a comparatively small organ; the secretions of all the cells during a period of 24 hours amounts to some 2–3 liters of gastric juice.

*The intestine:* The length of the intestine varies greatly in the different classes. It is nearly a straight tube in most of the fishes and one that is coiled to a greater or less extent in the amphibia and reptiles; it is longer in proportion to the body length in birds than in reptiles, and in most mammals it is a long, coiled tube with a number of regional distinctions. In general, it is longer in herbivorous animals than in carnivorous or omnivorous ones; this correlation is most striking in frogs, for in the alga-eating tadpole stages the intestine is considerably longer than the body, but after metamorphosis into the larger, flesh-eating frog, the intestine shows little increase in absolute length and is relatively much shorter. The first part of the intestine, which receives the openings of the bile and the pancreatic ducts, has a comparatively narrow bore and is known as the small intestine; posteriorly this enlarges into the colon, or large intestine with a somewhat greater diameter. In mammals three regions of the small intestine are recognized, although the differences between them are not marked and the transitions gradual; the duodenum (Latin, duodenum = twelve each), extending from the pylorus for 10–12 inches and receiving the ducts from the pancreas and liver; the jejunum (Latin, jejunus = empty), approximately the first two-fifths of the small intestine after the duodenum and so-called because it has been believed to be empty after death; and the ileum (Latin, ilium = flank), approximately the last three-fifths of the small intestine. Its lining throughout, in reptiles and birds as well as in mammals, is thrown into circular folds and is characterized especially by the presence of countless small, very active, contractile processes, from 0.5–1.5 mm. in height, which are either blunt or finger-like or leaf-like in shape. These are the villi (Latin, villus = tuft of hair), whose presence gives the intestinal mucosa the appearance of velvet or of a thick rug, the villi representing the nap or the pile (Fig. 15.57). The epithelium on the surface of the villi contains many mucus-secreting cells and at their bases are the intestinal glands, the crypts of Lieberkühn, named for a German anatomist, J. N. Lieberkühn (1711–1756). Some cells in these glands secrete mucus, while others secrete the specific enzymes of the intestinal juice, extending up from the submucosa, which supports a blind branch of the lymphatic system, the central lacteal, an artery and a vein of small dimensions, numerous blood capillaries and lymph spaces and the terminations of nerves.

In the duodenum of man and other mammals there are, in addition to the crypts of Lieberkühn, tubular glands that extend down into the submucosa. These are called Brunner's glands after a Swiss anatomist,

J. C. Brunner (1653–1737), and secrete a mucus; they are most numerous near the pylorus and the openings of the bile and pancreatic ducts. These particular glands are found only in the duodenum; elsewhere throughout its length, the mucosa of the small intestine is of the same general character, although in the posterior part of the ileum there is the greatest aggregation of lymphatic tissue, forming dull-colored, oval areas from 1–4 cm. long and therefore macroscopically visible, called Peyer's patches, after another Swiss anatomist, J. K. Peyer (1653–1712). These are found also in the duodenum and the jejunum but in those regions are more widely scattered.

The secretions from the glands of the small intestine are collectively known as intestinal juice, or succus entericus, which contains, in addition to mucus, enzymes of the general class of proteases and carbohydrases. It also contains bile, discharged into the duodenum through the bile duct, and the digestive enzymes synthesized in the pancreas,* proteases, carbohydrases and lipases. In its lumen the ingested food is reduced to molecules which can pass through the membranes of the cells covering the villi and into their blood capillaries and lymph spaces, from which they enter the portal circulation and the principal lymph vessels. The arrangement of the intestinal mucosa in folds and especially in villi increases its absorptive area enormously, and in the course of their passage along the small intestine, all the absorption of the diffusible end products of digestion takes place.

At the junction of small and large intestine there are one or more diverticula, or caeca, which are particularly large in some of the herbivorous mammals. In the rabbit, the single caecum is a long, blind pouch, capable of a good deal of distention, in which food may be stored for considerable periods of time during which the cellulose it contains is exposed, as it is in the rumen of the cow's stomach, to the action of bacteria, and so decomposed. In man and some other mammals, the caecum is a small, finger-like pouch, the vermiform appendix. The mucosa of the large intestine is not raised either in villi or in circular folds, but there are numerous glands of Lieberkühn on its smooth surface whose cells secrete mucus. It is primarily water that is absorbed from the contents of the colon, so that as the food residue passes on into the terminal part of the alimentary tube, the rectum, it is a more concentrated mass, and the water so valuable to a terrestrial animal is returned to the blood stream. In the fishes, amphibia, reptiles, birds and, among the mammals, the monotremes and certain marsupials, the rectum opens into a cloaca which receives also the products from the excretory and reproductive organs, but in the other mammals it has a separate external opening.

*The liver:* The vertebrate liver originates as an outgrowth of the embryonic enteron in a region just posterior to that which ultimately becomes the stomach (Fig. 25.14). During the course of embryonic growth and development, the liver bud grows into a compact mass of tubular glands, among which blood vessels and nerves penetrate and lymph spaces appear. Its original connection with the digestive tract is retained as the hepatic, or bile, duct, through which its specific secretion, the bile or gall, passes into the intestine, often after temporary storage in an enlargement of the duct, the gall bladder. Its cells perform functions of two general types; as gland cells, they are specialists in the production of bile, but they also remove materials from the blood and convert them in a variety of ways to a variety of substances, some of which they store. Bile is a complicated fluid, a solution of bile salts, bile pigments, the phospholipid lecithin and the sterol, cholesterol. The bile salts are sodium salts of two organic acids, taurocholic acid and glycocholic acid, and their action, when brought into contact in the intestine with food in the process of digestion, is to lower the surface tension of the fats, keeping them in a finely divided or emulsified state so that they offer a greater surface to the enzymes catalyzing the disintegration of the fat molecule (Fig. 6.4).

---

* In some bony fish, there is no connection between the pancreas and the digestive tract and any secretions from it are conveyed by the blood stream.

In addition to bile, the liver also synthesizes and stores the insoluble polysaccharide glycogen from partial decomposition products of the carbohydrates, fats and proteins digested and metabolized by the animal; this process is reversed when conditions make it necessary for the animal to call upon its carbohydrate reserves, and the glycogen stored in the liver cells is converted to a soluble product which can be transported around the body. The liver also stores some fat as well as glycogen and, in addition, plays an important part in the metabolism of both fats and proteins, for in its cells the degradation of the fat molecule is carried further toward completion, and the deamination, or removal of the $NH_2$ group, from the products of protein decomposition takes place. This reaction is one of molecular disunion, through which the amino group is set free as ammonia, leaving the carbohydrate residue of the molecule to be completely oxidized to carbon dioxide and water, with the liberation of energy, or used as any other carbohydrate may be in the body. In the majority of vertebrates, the ammonia, as soon as it is formed, is immediately combined with carbon and oxygen into urea,

$$\begin{array}{c} H_2N \\ \phantom{H_2N}\diagdown \\ \phantom{H_2N}\phantom{\diagdown}C=O \\ \phantom{H_2N}\diagup \\ H_2N \end{array}$$

or uric acid,

$$\begin{array}{c} HN-C=O \\ | \phantom{XX} | \phantom{XXX} H \\ O=C \phantom{X} C-N \\ | \phantom{XX} \| \phantom{XXX} \diagdown \\ \phantom{XXXXXX} C=O \\ H-N-C-N \\ \phantom{XXXXXXX} \diagup \\ \phantom{XXXXXXXX} H \end{array}$$

both of which are non-toxic substances.

In addition to such changes effected upon the substances conveyed to it by the blood, the liver also brings about the destruction of old blood cells and, in some vertebrates, the formation of new ones; the excretion of some substances undesirable or unneeded by the body; and the elimination of cellular detritus and foreign particles that may have found their way into it. There are in the liver certain amoeboid cells, called Kupffer cells after a German anatomist, K. W. Kupffer (1829–1902), which act as scavengers, enclosing in their cytoplasm particles of solid material—disintegrated cells, bacteria and foreign bodies of all sorts—by mechanisms similar to those by which an amoeba ingests its food. The liver is perhaps the most versatile organ in the vertebrate body, and since it is the seat of so many important reactions, it is not surprising that its total removal results in death, a fact that has been shown to be true through numerous experiments with many kinds of animals. But parts of the liver can be removed—in some experiments up to 70 per cent of the entire organ has been taken out of rats—or rendered dysfunctional by some cause or another without noticeable effect upon the animal as a whole. Experiments have also shown that it can regenerate to a remarkable degree for a tissue in a highly evolved animal, so that actual loss of a part of its substance can be compensated for not only by extra activity of the tissue remaining but also by its restoration.

*The pancreas:* The pancreas also develops as an outgrowth of the enteron slightly posterior to that which gives rise to the liver. It may be connected with the intestine by a number of ducts through which the secretions of certain of its cells pass to mix with the food in the digestive tract, or by a single one. Pancreatic juice contains a number of enzymes which catalyze the reactions in which proteins and fats are hydrolyzed into their constituent molecules. In addition to the cells that synthesize these enzymes or their precursors in a biologically inactive state, there is in the pancreas another type of gland cell that can be microscopically distinguished from them. Although these cells may lie along the ducts that lead from the groups of enzyme-secreting cells, they have no direct connection with them and the products that they synthesize are taken up directly into the blood stream and carried about the body in the blood. These cells are known as islet cells, for they lie in clusters or islands in the pancreatic tissue, and in some fishes, in the mesenteries and tissues of visceral organs other than the pancreas. Glands such as these that discharge their products into the blood stream are known as endrocrine glands (Greek, endo = within + krinein = to separate), in distinction from those whose products are discharged into a particular region of the body through tubules or ducts; such glands are known as exocrine glands, or glands of external secretion. The pancreas of most vertebrates combines the features of both types of glands, some cells acting as exocrine glands and secreting pancreatic juice and others, as endocrine glands and secreting their specific product insulin (Latin, insula = island) into the blood stream.

## Excretory and reproductive organs; urinogenital system

The development of the excretory organs and their ducts in the vertebrates is closely associated with that of the reproductive organs and their ducts, a condition that has a parallel in the relations between the nephridia and the gonoducts in the non-chordates. It is therefore logical and convenient to group both sets of organs together as a common system, the urinogenital or urogenital system. Only the excretory system will be considered in this section; the structure and functioning of the reproductive organs as such will be presented in the chapter on reproduction.

In all vertebrates, the excretory organs appear first as a series of tubules developed in the mesoderm on each side of the body and opening into the coelome at one end and into a common collecting duct on the other. Each such set of segmental tubules is known as a pronephros (Greek, pro = first + nephros = kidney), its duct as a pronephric duct (Fig. 15.59). While the pronephroi are the functional excretory organs in the adults of some of the lower chordates, collecting wastes that have accumulated in the coelome through their coelomic openings and receiving some from the blood stream as well, in the vertebrates in general they are embryonic organs only and may or may not be functional during the early life of the animal. As development progresses, the pronephros is succeeded by the mesonephros (Greek, mesos = middle + nephros = kidney), a similar set of tubules which arise in the more posterior segments and which may or may not have openings into the coelome. The mesonephroi are also called Wolffian bodies, and their ducts Wolffian ducts after a great German biologist, Caspar Friedrich Wolff (1738–1794), who first traced the development of these organs from undifferentiated tissues in the embryo chick. The mesonephric tubules are more numerous than the pronephric tubules, and they also open into a common duct; mesonephroi are the functional excretory organs of adult fishes and amphibia, but in reptiles, birds and mammals they are functional only in embryonic life and are replaced in the adult by the metanephros (Greek, meta = after + nephros = kidney), or kidney. The metanephros is also a system of tubules, but of ones that are not segmental in their arrangement and that never open directly into the coelome.

The function of such organs is primarily to maintain the water balance of the body and secondarily to eliminate from it as urine the soluble material, largely nitrogenous waste, that is useless, undesirable or even harmful to it. Except in a few cases, the mesonephric tubules, and invariably the metanephric tubules, receive such waste in solution from the blood stream. This is made possible by the development of vessels arising from the dorsal vessel which enter the mesonephros and break up into fine capillaries which loop and twist around each other in a knot, or glomerulus (Latin, glomerulus = little ball) (Fig. 15.60). These glomerular capillaries are unique in that they are inserted in the course of a small artery, and do not lie, as do other capillary systems, between an artery carrying blood from the heart and a vein returning blood to it. Each glomerulus is associated with the terminal part of a mesonephric tubule, which is indented as a cup enclosing the glomerulus and which is known as Bowman's capsule after an English surgeon, Sir William Bowman (1816–1892). The capsule and glomerulus together make up a functional excretory unit, the renal or Mal-

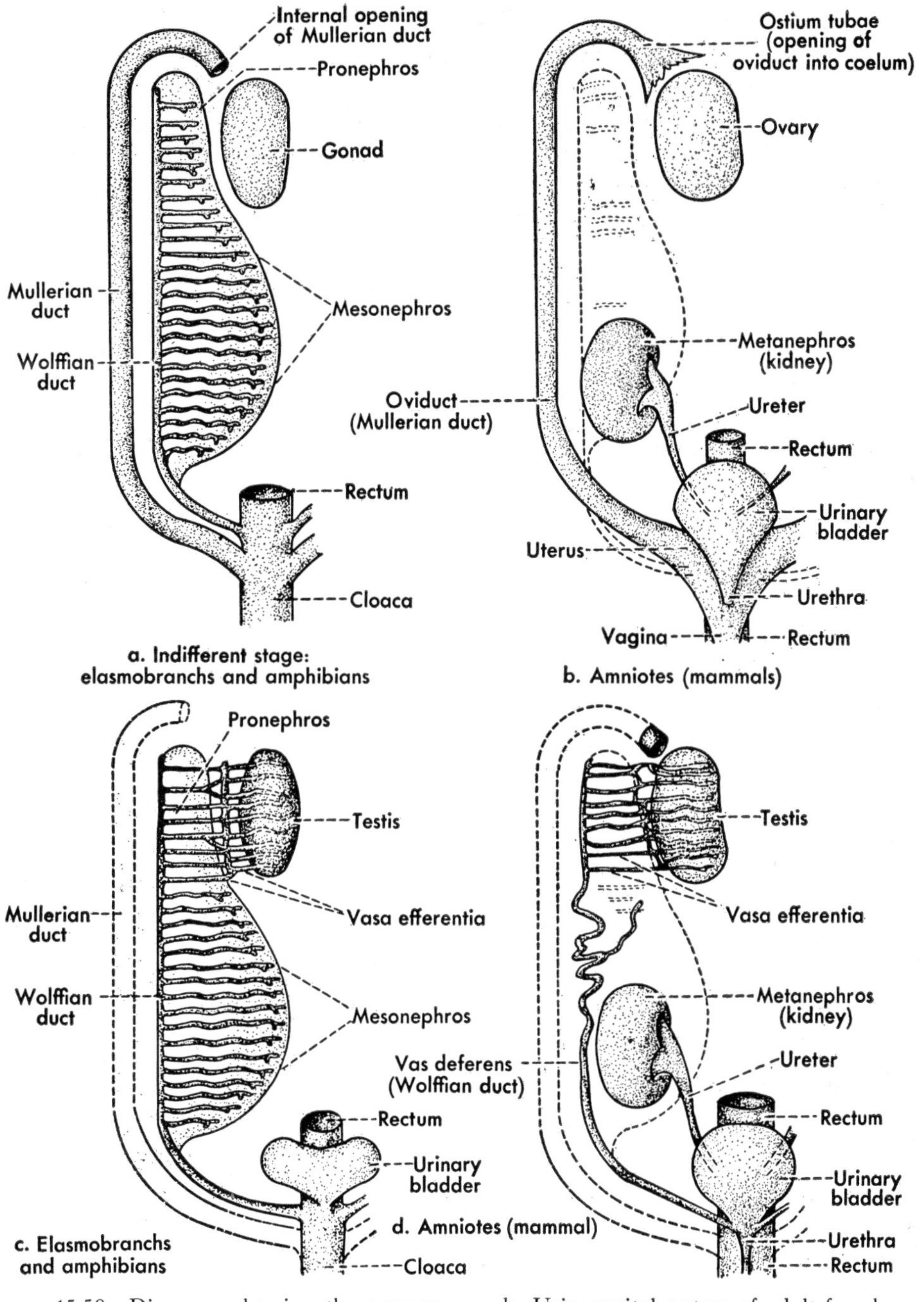

FIGURE 15.59 Diagrams showing the arrangement of vertebrate urinogenital systems. (After Kingsley.) The organs of the left side only are shown.

a. "Indifferent stage," with functional pronephric and mesonephric tubules and functional Wolffian and Mullerian ducts. This is essentially the condition in adult female elasmobranchs and amphibians, and a hypothetical one in the development of other Anamniotes.

b. Urinogenital system of adult female amniotes (mammal). The broken lines indicate the parts of the system represented in (a) that become non-functional and undergo degeneration.

c. Urinogenital system of male elasmobranchs and amphibians. The broken lines indicate the non-functional parts of the system shown in (a).

d. Urinogenital system of male amniotes (mammal). The broken lines indicate the non-functional parts of the system shown in (a).

[ 319 ]

pighian corpuscle; many Malpighian corpuscles, with the tubules leading from them, are bound together in a single mesonephros, or metanephros, as Malpighi himself described them "like apples on a tree."

The mesonephroi of fishes are two long, slender masses lying along the dorsal body wall, beneath the peritoneum and on each side of the dorsal blood vessel; a Wolffian duct lies alongside each and extends posteriorly to the cloaca. In the amphibia, they are rather more compact structures, situated more posteriorly in the pleuroperitoneal cavity. In the reptiles, birds and mammals, the mesonephros is developed and functional during embryonic life and in some for a brief period of juvenile life, but in all the Amniotes it is sooner or later replaced by the metanephros, or true kidney. The metanephroi arise posterior to the mesonephroi from paired masses of tissue at the posterior limits of the Wolffian bodies in which tubules and Malpighian corpuscles develop in much the same way that they do in the mesonephros, but without any trace of segmental arrangement. The tubules of the individual nephrons join together into larger collecting tubes, which ultimately make connection with the ureter, a tube that originates from the posterior end of the Wolffian duct draining the mesonephros and grows anteriorly and laterally toward the developing kidney. Within the tissues of the kidney, the ureter divides into a number of branches, each of which expands at the tip to form a primary renal vesicle. The region where the ureter enters the kidney becomes the pelvis of the adult organ. In the reptiles, the birds and the mammals with a cloaca, the ureters open posteriorly into the cloaca, as do the Wolffian ducts in some fishes and in amphibia, but in the adults of the higher mammals this chamber becomes subdivided into the rectum, the posterior termination of the alimentary canal which opens at the anus, and a urinogenital sinus which receives the products of both excretory and reproductive organs. In the tetrapods, a uri-

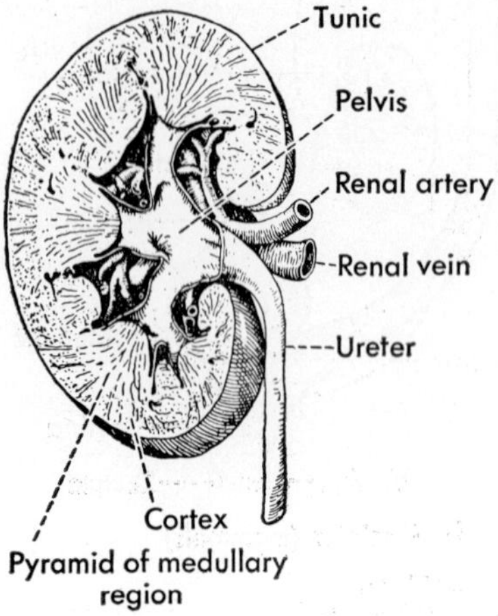

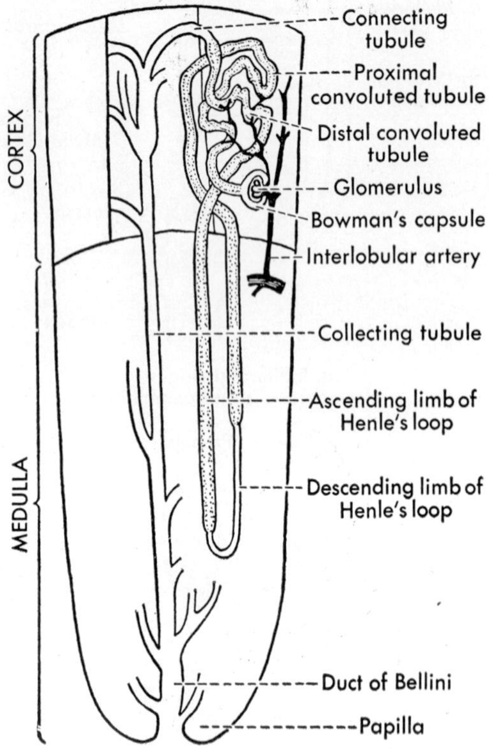

FIGURE 15.60 Structure of the metanephros.
a. Longitudinal section of the human kidney. (From Woodruff, *The Foundations of Biology*, 6th edition. Copyright 1941 by The Macmillan Company.)
b. Diagram of a urinary unit in the kidney, showing the relations of the glomerulus and Bowman's capsule to the tubules. (From Walter and Sayles, *Biology of the Vertebrates*. Copyright 1949 by The Macmillan Company.)

nary bladder, derived in part at least as an outgrowth from the embryonic cloaca, is usually present in which the urine is temporarily stored; the ureters open directly into the bladder in those amniotes possessing one and the bladder discharges its contents into the urinogenital sinus through a single tube, the urethra, but in the amphibia the ureters open directly into the cloaca and from there the urine passes into the bladder until its final elimination through the cloaca.

The adult human kidney is a bean-shaped organ which on section shows a well-defined pelvis, medulla and cortex. The pelvis, representing the expanded end of the ureter, is hollow, the cortex and medulla solid regions in which lie the tubules and the blood vessels supported by connective tissue. The Malpighian tubules and part of the system of finer tubules lie in the cortex; the main collecting ducts and their branches and the larger blood vessels in the medulla, from which a number of projections, or papillae, extend into the pelvis where connections are established between the main collecting ducts and the branches of the ureter. Each individual unit, or nephron, of which there are about 1,000,000, consists of a Malpighian corpuscle, the blind capsular end of the nephric tubule and the enclosed glomerulus, and of a long tubule with various modifications along its length. Immediately behind Bowman's capsule, the tubule is very much twisted and is known as the proximal convoluted tubule; the proximal tubule then becomes straighter and extends down into the medulla as the descending limb of Henle's loop, or the distal tubule, and in the cortex becomes again very much twisted and contorted as the distal convoluted tubule, after which it runs a short, straight course as a connecting tubule. Between the proximal and distal tubules is a region known as the thin segment where the cells are flatter and the wall of the tubule consequently thinner than elsewhere. The connecting tubules of adjacent nephrons unite into collecting tubules and those from each section of the kidney finally join in a common collecting duct that opens into a branch of the ureter which terminates in each medullary papilla. The capsules and tubules are supported by connective tissue in which there are frequently considerable accumulations of fat, and the entire kidney is invested in a connective tissue capsule and on its ventral side covered over with peritoneum.

TABLE VII

Relative Composition of Blood Plasma and Normal Urine in Man [a]

|  | Blood Plasma (Per cent) | Urine (Per cent) | Change in concentration in kidney |
|---|---|---|---|
| Water | 90–93 | 95 | ... |
| Proteins, fats and other colloids | 7–9 | .. | ... |
| Glucose | 0.1 | .. | ... |
| Urea | 0.03 | 2 | 60 |
| Uric acid | 0.003 | 0.05 | 17 |
| Na | 0.32 | 0.35 | 1 |
| K | 0.02 | 0.15 | 7 |
| Ca | 0.008 | 0.015 | 2 |
| Mg | 0.0025 | 0.006 | 2 |
| Cl | 0.37 | 0.6 | 2 |
| $PO_4$ | 0.009 | 0.27 | 30 |
| $SO_4$ | 0.003 | 0.18 | 60 |
| Creatinine | 0.001 | 0.1 | 100 |

[a] From Lovatt Evans: *Principles of Human Physiology*. Copyright 1947 by J. and A. Churchill, Ltd.

### Functions of the kidney

The excretory organs of vertebrates are of primary importance in the regulation of the internal environment of the body in that they clear the blood of certain end products of metabolism while returning to it water and other desirable materials dissolved in the blood. The fundamental contribution that these organs make to the organism as a whole is the maintenance of water balance within the body, through which the pH and solvent properties of the body fluids, their salt content and their osmotic pressures are kept within a very narrow range of variation. The end product of their activity is the urine, a fluid that contains some but not all of the solutes of circulating blood in concentrations in many cases far higher than they occur in the blood. In Table VII is given the relative composition of human blood plasma, the liquid part of the blood, and of human urine under ordinary conditions, from which it is evident that urea and creatinine, a derivative of a protein called creatine that is found particularly in muscle, are many times more concentrated in the urine than in the plasma; that the sulphate ion is more concentrated than the phosphate and that other components of the plasma are concentrated to relatively greater or less degrees.

***Experimental work on kidney functioning:*** Kidney functioning has been intensively studied for many years in many different animals and in many different kinds of ways under normal, pathological and experimental conditions. For a long time it was suspected that the Malpighian corpuscles acted like filters, straining off from the blood the molecules that could pass freely across the membranes of the vessels and the capsules and leaving behind the proteins and other non-diffusible substances. The conditions in the corpuscle made this a likely possibility, for the blood in the glomerulus is under pressure only about 20 per cent lower than it is in the arteries themselves, since the glomeruli are capillary networks within arteries whose origins are not far from the aorta; this pressure would supply the force necessary to send the diffusible substances from the blood into the capsule, a force which is ordinarily supplied by gravity in filtration processes outside the animal body. Experimental evidence also showed that an increase in blood pressure led to an increase in the production of urine. But if the function of the nephron is exclusively that of a filter, it is obvious that many substances valuable to the body would be lost, since water, glucose, inorganic salts and other diffusible materials would be taken from the blood as freely as urea or other products to be eliminated. Moreover, the composition of the urine of many different animals was found to be markedly different from that of their plasma, particularly in respect to its salt, sugar and urea content. The brilliant investigations of a group of American scientists carried on over a period of years under the leadership of Alfred N. Richards (1876–    ) have clarified many important aspects of kidney functioning. By extremely delicate techniques, using microscopic methods and an adaptation of the technique of microdissection, they were able to obtain fluid from the individual capsules of the mesonephroi of frogs and so to analyze immediately what had passed across the membranes; later, they were able also to collect samples from different regions of the tubules and so to determine what changes take place in the fluid as it passes along the nephrons (Fig. 15.61). The capsular fluid was found to be identical in its composition with the blood plasma minus its proteins; the sugars, salts and urea were present in the same concentration as they were in the circulating blood, proving the correctness of the filtration theory. Samples of the filtrate taken along the tubules showed that certain elements of the filtrate, which were of use to the animal, were resorbed in different regions, the sugars and phosphates in one region, the chlorides and water in another, so that the fluid as it passed along the tubules lost some of the solutes present in the glomerular filtrate and became more concentrated in respect to those that it retained.

These experiments have demonstrated conclusively that filtration takes place across the membranes of the Malpighian corpuscle and that some of the constituents of the filtrate are resorbed across the cells of the tubules. The high degree of selectivity that the excretory organs of all vertebrates show for the substances that they resorb, the regulation of the absorptive processes and the extent to which the cells of the tubules actively take part in the resorptive process or contribute directly to the composition of the urine by discharging materials into the fluid in the tubules are still problems that are under investigation and about which the interpretation of existing data is debatable.

Existing evidence shows that not only are water and glucose absorbed as the filtrate passes along the tubules, but also urea and certain salts. The available water supply varies greatly with the environments in which animals live, whether in fresh or salt water or in damp or arid terrestrial habitats. In a marine fish, for example, the external environment is in general more concentrated in respect to its salt content than their internal environment, and they are in danger of losing water from their bodies; in the fresh water fish, the opposite conditions prevail and their great danger is from flooding of their bodies by an excess of water which enters across their exposed semi-permeable membranes faster than it leaves. But the water that enters across these membranes in the gills and in the mouth is filtered off by the excretory organs, resulting in the production of a very dilute urine. In the bony fishes that live in the sea, on the other hand, water does not enter the body along an osmotic gradient, for the osmotic pressure of sea water is higher than that of their body fluids, and these fishes must obtain water by swallowing it. In this way, they get from the sea in which they live not only the essential water, but also the salts dissolved in it, for which they have no great need; these are removed from the blood not by the cells of the kidney but by special ones in the gills. In the dogfish and other marine elasmobranchs acquisition of water by the body is controlled by a different mechanism, for these fishes are unique in that a very large proportion of the urea filtered off from the blood by the Malpighian corpuscles is returned to it as the filtrate passes along the tubules. One segment of the nephron, just back of the glomerulus, is different histologically from the other parts of the tubule, and this is presumed to be the region where the great absorption of urea takes place. The concentration of urea in the blood is thus maintained at a high level—from 2–2.5 per cent—and is sufficient to raise its osmotic pressure above that of sea water, and water is constantly entering the body through the gills whose membranes are impermeable to urea and to salts, so that none is lost through them. Consequently marine elasmobranchs have no need to drink water as marine bony fishes, and indeed all other vertebrates, must in order to keep from desiccation.

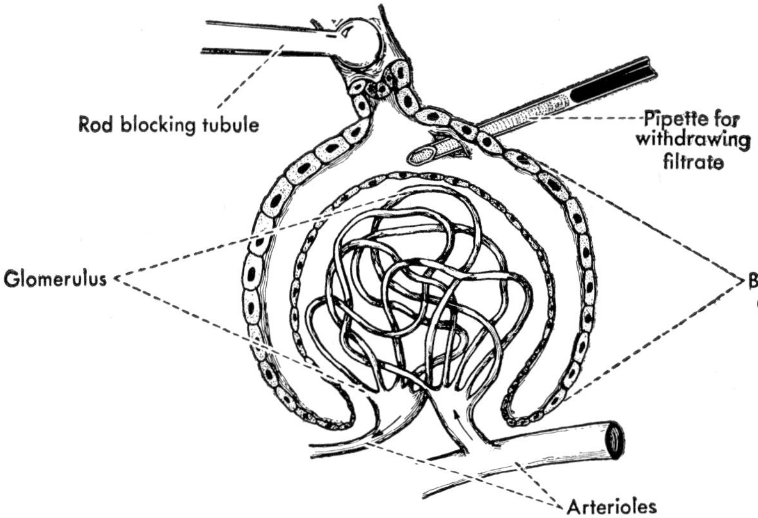

Less urea is resorbed by the kidney tubules of other vertebrates. In mammals about 50 per cent of that in the capsular filtrate diffuses back into the blood across their cells and the endothelium of the capillaries around them, and in addition, glucose, amino acids, uric acid, sodium, potassium and phosphate ions and Vitamin C, as well as water, are returned to the blood. At its ordinary concentration in the blood, which is between 0.08 and 0.2 per cent, all the glucose in the filtrate is removed across the cells of the proximal tubule, so that none is present in the urine. But if the glomerular blood, and hence the filtrate, contain glucose in concentrations above its ordinary range, which may be the case under experimental and certain pathological conditions as well

FIGURE 15.61 Diagram to show Richard's method of withdrawing glomerular filtrate from the capsule of a frog's kidney. (After Winton and Bayliss.)

as after the digestion of a meal of high carbohydrate content, the excess is retained in the tubular fluid and excreted in the urine, indicating that the cells of the tubule take up the glucose, up to a certain maximum value, as fast as it enters the capsular fluid, but that beyond this value resorption cannot keep pace with filtration and the excess is excreted. This implies an active participation on the part of the cells in removing the glucose from the tubular fluid and transferring it to the blood in the capillaries against a concentration gradient, since the concentration of glucose in the tubules is equal to that in the capillaries around them. There is further evidence for such active participation, for certain drugs have the effect of depressing or preventing this activity of the tubular cells; in animals treated with the drug phloridzin, for example, glucose is present in the urine even when its concentration in the blood is at its normal level or experimentally brought below it. This particular condition of glycosuria, or sugar in the urine, results from the failure of the tubular cells to take up the sugar from the filtrate.

Certain other substances are not resorbed at all, or to a negligible extent. Many of the experiments that have been performed in the study of kidney functioning have been by the method of perfusion, that is, by forcing a fluid of known composition through the renal blood vessels. Test substances in known amounts may thus be passed through the glomerular vessels, and assuming that they pass across the capsular membranes at a rate equal to that of the ordinary constituents of blood, the behavior of the kidney in relation to them can be determined by analysis of the urine. Test substances like inulin, a polysaccharide with a molecular weight of about 5000, and mannitol, a hexose, are quantitatively recovered in the urine, that is, the total amount that is introduced into the blood is ultimately found in the excreted urine. Students of kidney physiology speak of the "clearance values" of the constituents of blood, expressing by them the efficiency with which they are removed from a given volume of blood in a given period of time. Calculations show that under ordinary conditions of blood pressure and blood flow in the mammalian kidney, about 150 ml. of blood pass through the glomerular capillaries if they are all simultaneously in operation. Assuming that 150 ml. of blood does pass through this capillary bed in one minute, that volume of blood should be "cleared" of filterable substances like glucose, urea, inulin and mannitol in such a period of time. But at its ordinary concentration in the blood, all the glucose that is removed from it by the filtration system of Bowman's capsule is returned almost at once to the capillaries around the tubules, so that it is virtually not "cleared" of it at all, and the clearance value for glucose is thus zero. The clearance value for urea is higher, since only a part of that which enters the tubular fluid by filtration escapes from it by diffusion, and that of inulin and mannitol higher still, since none, or a negligible amount, is lost from the capsular fluid in its passage along the tubules. Observations and calculations show that in one minute's time, the kidney clears a volume of blood averaging 70 ml. of urea, but that in the same interval it clears 125 ml. of it of inulin and 175 ml. of it of creatinine.

Even higher clearance values have been obtained for other test substances. The dye phenol red, for example, has a clearance value of 400 ml. per minute and an iodine-containing compound, diodrast, one of 737 ml. per minute. Since inulin, with a clearance value of 125 ml. per minute, is known to be quantitatively removed from the blood by filtration, the possibility naturally suggests itself that there is another mechanism, additional to filtration, that operates in the removal of substances with higher clearance values. Comparative physiology has offered evidence for such a mechanism, for certain marine fishes, like the goosefish and the toadfish, have mesonephroi lacking the glomeruli of typical nephrons, yet their excreted urine contains uric acid and all the salts and other materials characteristically eliminated by the fishes. Experiments in which other substances not normally present have been introduced into the blood of these fishes show also that they are excreted by the aglomerular kidney to the same extent that they are in animals with glomerular kidneys. The only possible mechanism for the transfer of materials from the blood to the mesonephric tubules in these animals is through the cells of the tubules themselves, and while this evidence does not prove that a similar mechanism is operative in the glomerular kidney, it does show that the tubular cells can take up substances from the circulating blood and that adequate excretion for a marine vertebrate can be accomplished by mechanisms that do not include glomerular filtration. The participation of the tubular cells in the formation of urine in other vertebrates, and especially in mammals, has long been a debated question and is still regarded by some investigators as an open one. Experiments on frogs' kidneys offer some evidence, for in them the glomeruli are supplied through the renal arteries, branches of the dorsal vessel, and the tubules through vessels of the renal portal system, branches from the vessels returning blood from the posterior part of the body to the heart. If the renal arteries are tied off, the kidneys are made virtually aglomerular but they still excrete, by a mechanism that can only be tubular. Further evidence comes from experiments on the introduction of dyes into the renal circulation of animals. If, for example, the dye phenol red is injected and the animal is sacrificed shortly afterwards and its kidney examined microscopically, droplets of the dye are found to be accumulated in the cells of the proximal tubules; in animals sacrificed somewhat later in the course of the experiment, the dye is found to have disappeared wholly or to a great extent from the cells and to be concentrated in the urine.

This process of accumulation, and the ultimate elimination of the accumulated materials into the lumen of the tubule, is often referred to as secretion and a secretory activity attributed to the tubule cells. But if the word secretion is restricted to the synthesis by cells of specific products which may be discharged from them, then it is not applicable to the processes that go on in the tubular cells, for these involve only the concentration of materials received from the blood as such and their excretion into the tubules. The existing evidence seems to indicate that such excretion does take place, and that in the case of certain substances, the amount present in the filtrate is increased by contributions from the tubular cells. Whether any of the components of urine are attributable only to tubular excretion in the glomerular kidney is still problematical.

But from the present evidence it appears that the mammalian kidney performs its functions of water regulation and excretion by three principal processes—filtration across the membranes of the Malpighian corpuscle, removal of water and selected solutes from the filtrate by resorption through the cells of the proximal and distal tubules and the addition of some substances to the filtrate through the excretory activities of the tubular cells. Experimental studies on kidney clearance have so far been conducted largely with compounds that show little chemical reactivity, but this is certainly not true for many of those with which the kidney ordinarily has to deal. The presence of strong and weak electrolytes and of anions and cations carrying charges of different magnitudes complicate the situation and undoubtedly have great effect upon all aspects of kidney functioning.

Although the energy for filtration is supplied by the heart, for the amount of fluid passing across the glomerular-capsular membranes is a function of the rate of blood flow and of blood pressure, the kidney does work and expends energy, which can be measured in terms of oxygen consumption, in maintaining the integrity of its membranes and in effecting the passage of selected materials across the cells of its tubules against the osmotic gradient and the concentration of certain ones in them. This work has been calculated as equivalent to 6.7 gram calories for every milliliter of urine formed, for which the energy is derived from the oxidation of compounds within the kidney cells. As vital to the body as a whole as is the heart, the kidney does far less work and accomplishes its functions with less expenditure of energy, but with a degree of precision and finesse that has not yet been fully analyzed.

# CHAPTER 16
# INTEGRATING TISSUES OF THE VERTEBRATE BODY

*The nature of the integrating tissues*

The two great integrating tissues of the vertebrate body are those of the blood, or circulatory, system and of the nervous system. Each of these is completely distinctive histologically and each performs its function of coordinating the operation of the various organs of the body in a wholly different way, but both come into contact with nearly all its cells and so serve as links between tissues and organs that may be widely separated from each other and performing functions of quite different kinds. The blood of vertebrates, like that of non-chordates, is the medium through which materials are transported from place to place within the body; it serves also to maintain uniformity of temperature in the bodies of both poikilothermic and homoiothermic animals, just as any fluid circulating through a system tends to preserve a more or less uniform temperature throughout it. The nervous system is not only a link between the organism and its external environment, conveying the stimuli received by the superficial sensory areas to the various organs responsive to them, but also a link between different parts of the organism itself, for conditions within the organism are also stimuli to the internal receptors of the nervous system; these stimuli, when conveyed along the proper pathways, result in automatic adjustments of the body mechanisms. These adjustments are directed toward maintaining the constancy of the internal environment, in the regulation of which both nervous and circulatory systems play major roles.

*The circulatory system*
### The blood

Vertebrate blood is a tissue with two principal components—the fluid plasma and the blood cells or corpuscles. Like bone, it is derived from embryonic mesenchyme, and in its formation certain mesenchymal cells become distinguished as stem cells, or mother cells, which by division and further processes of differentiation give rise to its cellular components. The plasma represents the intercellular substance, a complex aqueous solution in which the concentration of inorganic salts, sugars and certain proteins remains at an almost constant level, while that of the various lipids, amino acids and other partial decomposition of the food, the products of the metabolic activities of the different tissues, oxygen, carbon dioxide and the other substances that it transports, fluctuates within limits according to the activities and demands of the different parts of the body.

### Components of the plasma

The inorganic salts dissolved in the plasma are ionic compounds, the chlorides, bicarbonates, phosphates and sulphates of sodium, potassium, calcium and magnesium (see Table I, page 75). Two of the dissolved proteins, fibrinogen and prothrombin, are specific ones; the others are albumins and globulins which, according to evidence that is currently accumulating from studies of their chemical and physiological properties, may also be specific to particular groups of individuals, and even to particular individuals. These plasma proteins are in general important factors in regulating the water balance within the body, for being incapable of passing across the walls of the vessels, they control to a great extent the migration of water molecules in and out of the blood. Moreover, they act as efficient buffers and so help to maintain the pH of the blood at an almost constant level, a narrow range on either side of neutrality.

## Blood cells

The cellular elements of vertebrate blood are erythrocytes (Greek, erythros = red + kytos = cell), containing the chromoprotein hemoglobin, or erythroplastids, non-nucleated corpuscles serving the same purpose, invading bacteria and foreign particles of all kinds.

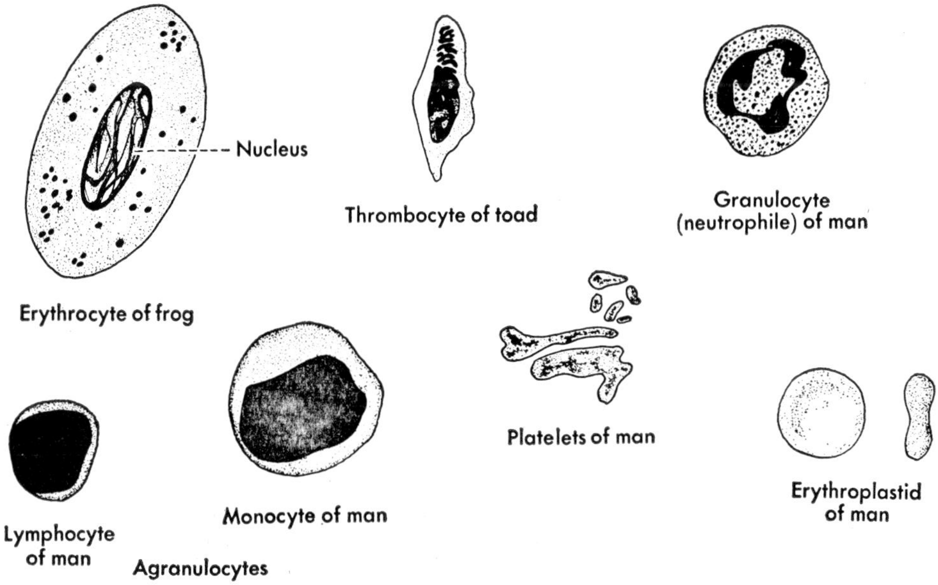

The mature leucocytes of vertebrate blood are distinguished as granulocytes or agranulocytes, depending upon whether or not their cytoplasm contains visible granules. The granulocytes are of three general types

FIGURE 16.1 Types of vertebrate blood cells. (From various sources.)

leucocytes (Greek, leukos = white) and, in all but mammals, thrombocytes (Greek, thrombos = clot) (Fig. 16.1). Erythrocytes, erythroplastids and leucocytes are not exclusively vertebrate, or even exclusively chordate, features, for similar cells or corpuscles containing hemoglobin are found in the circulating tissues of some of the echinoderms and worms, and the wandering amoeboid cells in the mesogloea of sponges and in the blood and intercellular matrices of other non-chordates resemble the leucocytes of vertebrate blood both in appearance and in behavior. For leucocytes, like these cells, are capable of active movements, and some at least of phagocytosis (Greek, phago = eating + kytos = cell), the ingestion of solid particles in an amoeboid fashion. Phagocytosis is one of the important defense mechanisms of the animal body, for the phagocytic cells rid it of tissue waste and also remove

—heterophiles, eosinophiles and basophiles —a distinction made through the staining reactions of their coarse cytoplasmic granules; they are also further distinguished by size, degree of mobility and the shapes of their nuclei, which in all three are large and irregular. Because of this, granulocytes are often referred to as polymorphonuclear leucocytes, or simply as "polymorphs." All of them are more or less mobile, the heterophiles the most active, the basophiles the least. When watched under the high magnification of a microscope, the heterophiles seem to be fairly rushing about, but actually their absolute rate of movement is comparatively slow. Measurements and calculations have shown that at 37° C., the ordinary temperature of the human body, human heterophiles may cover a distance equal to three times that of their own diameters (9–12 micra) in about a minute, a rate roughly equivalent to one inch in twelve hours. Their migrations are principally within the blood stream where they seem to be attracted or directed toward invading bacteria, to which they adhere and ultimately digest. Phagocytic activity is less marked in the eosinophiles and almost entirely absent in the basophiles; although the eosinophiles frequently make their way through the lining of the finest vessels, the capillaries, into the surrounding tissue spaces and engulf micro-organisms there (Fig. 16.2).

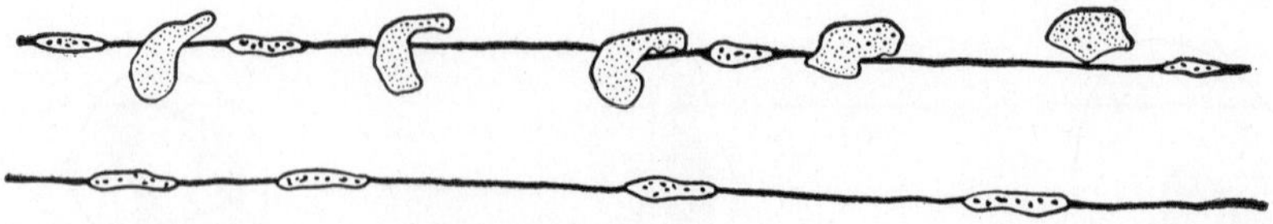

FIGURE 16.2 Migration of a leucocyte across the wall of a capillary (diapedesis). (After Clark, Clark and Rex, from Walter and Sayles, *Biology of the Vertebrates.* Copyright 1949 by The Macmillan Company.)

### Blood destruction and blood formation

Blood is not in any sense a static tissue. Not only is it being moved around from place to place within the body, but its elements are constantly shifting in position and in kind, yet under ordinary conditions remaining relatively constant in number. Its cells are short-lived, and the destruction and replacement of both erythrocytes and leucocytes are constantly going on during the animal's life. The sites of blood cell formation, potentially possible in any region of the body where there is diffuse mesenchyme, have become more and more localized during the course of vertebrate evolution. In some of the lower chordates, connective tissue within the walls of the intestine or stomach is the principal region of blood cell differentiation; in the higher vertebrates, the bone marrow has become the principal, if not the only, site of it during the adult life of the individual.

### Protective properties of the blood

In addition to the protective capacities of the phagocytic leucocytes, the blood as a whole has other properties which afford protection to the organism and for some of which the leucocytes may be at least indirectly responsible. One of these properties is its ability to coagulate when for any reason it is displaced from a vessel, and another is that of producing antibodies when it is invaded by foreign material. But although the facts of these responses which the blood makes to unusual conditions are well-established, the mechanisms by which they come about are still far from being completely known.

*Coagulation:* When a vertebrate is injured, the blood which escapes from the vessels will, under ordinary conditions, set to a jelly-like mass at the site of the injury within a few minutes—5–10 minutes in human beings. This mass temporarily seals over the open vessels and, unless dislodged, checks further blood loss until the tissues are repaired by the process of healing. Microscopic examination of the mass, or clot, shows that it is made up of fine, needle-like crystals with blood cells trapped in the spaces between them. After standing for a time, the clot shrinks and a pale, straw-colored fluid, the serum, exudes from it into which the trapped leucocytes may migrate. The material of the crystals is fibrin, and their production from some soluble component or components of circulating blood is an essential part of its coagulation. According to one theory, when blood is displaced from the vessels, a condition that must always be accompanied by some tissue injury if only to the capillary walls, a reaction is brought about between the plasma protein prothrombin (thrombogen) and the calcium ion, dissociated from the calcium salts also always present in the circulating blood, to form a substance known as thrombin. Thrombin and fibrinogen then combine to form fibrin, and the mass of fibrin crystals and blood cells becomes the clot.

The agents that initiate these changes, that prevent them from occurring in circulating blood, that control the rate at which they take place and that influence them in other ways are as yet only partly understood. It is well known that certain blood-sucking animals, such as leeches, ticks and mosquitoes, possess a substance that inhibits or prevents the coagulation of their victim's blood when injected into it from their oral glands when their mouth parts penetrate the integument of the animal they attack. This substance has been called hirudin, from the generic name for leeches, Hirudo, and it is postulated that a similar anticoagulant is present in the circulating blood of vertebrates. Such a substance has been extracted from mammalian livers and called heparin, with an anticoagulant effect so great that 1 mg. of it will prevent the clotting of 50–100 cc. of blood. Heparin is believed to be an agent that inhibits the conversion of thrombogen into thrombin. The formation of thrombogen in the blood is known to be dependent upon adequate amounts of one of the vitamins called Vitamin K, the "Koagulations vitamin" of the Danish scientist Henrik Dam, who in 1929–30 described the effects of its deficiency in chicks. The formation of fibrinogen may possibly be attributed to the white blood cells, for there is evidence that it increases in amount in the circulating blood with increase in the number of leucocytes. For the formation of the clot, calcium salts and something to remove or inactivate the inhibitors must also be present.

These inactivators presumably are derived from the injured tissues, for the blood of any vertebrate, except a mammal, will not clot if its contact with the cut tissues or rough surfaces is reduced to a minimum. Thromboplastin is the general name given to the substance, or substances, derived from the tissue cells, including those of the blood itself and, in mammals, possibly from the platelets, which cancel out the effects of the inhibitors ordinarily present. The steps in the coagulation process, so far as they are now known, may be summarized as follows:

Activators: Thromboplastin; calcium ion.

Thrombogen⟶Thrombin +
(Present in circulating blood)

Inhibitors: Antithrombogens (heparin, other substances?); deficiency of Ca; deficiency of thromboplastin.

Fibrinogen⟶Fibrin +
(Present in circulating blood)

Inhibitors: Antithrombins (hirudin; other substances?)

Cells⟶Clot.
(Present in circulating blood)

*Immune reactions:* Another property of the circulating blood, which can be protective but may also prove detrimental to the organism, is the capacity to form antibodies in response to the introduction of antigens. An antigen is defined as any substance that, when introduced into the blood stream, will provoke the formation of antibodies; it must be a substance foreign to the species, and even to the individual, producing the antibodies. Each antigen induces the formation of a specific antibody, but antibodies as a whole may be generally classified as agglutinins, precipitins, antitoxins, lysins and tropins, or opsonins, according to the gross effects that they produce. Similarly the agent inducing the formation of an antibody of any particular type is called an agglutinogen, precipitinogen and so on. In the case of agglutination, the antigen is particulate, as bacteria or other cells, and the agglutinin produced in response to their presence in the blood stream causes the agglutination or clumping of the foreign bodies, leading to a reduction in their activity and greater possibility of their elimination by the blood phagocytes. The precipitins are substances formed in response to the introduction of a soluble foreign protein which bring about the precipitation of that protein and so its removal as an effective antigenic agent, and the antitoxins are antibodies that neutralize the substances, toxic or poisonous to other organisms, that are produced by micro-organisms as by-products of their metabolic reactions. In these three responses that the blood makes to the presence of foreign material in it, only the antigen and the antibody are involved, but in the phenomenon of lysis a third substance is concerned. To bring about the lysis of invading bacterial cells, for example, the antigenic bacteria must first provoke the formation of the specific antibody, a lysin, which, however, can only effect the dissolution of the bacteria in the presence of complement, a complex substance of several components which is always present in circulating blood but whose potency is easily destroyed by heat. The tropins, or opsonins (Greek, opsonein = to buy victuals), are antibodies induced by the presence of bacteria which affect the invading organisms in such a way that they can be more readily attacked and ingested by the phagocytes. Complement is also effective here in activating the opsonins, or in otherwise facilitating their action.

The antigen-antibody reaction is one that is best known in mammals, where it can bring about the immunity, either natural or acquired, which animals may have to certain diseases caused by the presence in their bodies of pathogenic micro-organisms and of viruses. In human beings with natural immunity to a certain disease, there are in the blood at all times a sufficient quantity of antibodies specific to the agent causing the disease to bring about their elimination or destruction or the neutralization of any toxic products they may set free. Immunity to a disease may be acquired by human beings by the introduction into their blood streams of serum from another animal whose blood contains the specific antibodies necessary to combat the effects of the infection; this is called passive immunity, for the individual's own blood has taken no part in the antibody formation, and immunity of this type is of comparatively short duration. Immunization of humans against diphtheria by diphtheria anti-toxin, the antibodies produced in the blood of a horse by the presence of the diphtheria bacillus, is an illustration of immunity so acquired; so also is the resistance to measles, or the reduction in the severity of the symptoms, produced by the introduction of immune globulin. But the individual may also be made to build up a quantity of his own antibodies to a specific infective agent by introducing at intervals successively increasing amounts of the antigen until a dose sufficient to cause the symptoms of the disease produces no pathological effect. Such immunity is said to be active, and is usually long-standing and sometimes permanent. Its induction was practiced long before anything was known about antigen-antibody reactions as such. During the latter part of the Ming dynasty (1368–1644), the Chinese practiced a system of inoculation for smallpox, a disease epidemic in Asia at least as far back as the sixth century. The Chinese method was to blow some of the pulverized crusts from the vesicles, or poxes, which are laden with the infective agents, into the nostrils of healthy individuals and so to initiate a mild attack of the disease and later immunity from it. This method was practiced widely in the East, and in the eighteenth century Lady Mary Wortley Montagu saw it in operation in Turkey and wrote of it to her friends in England. Physicians in England made use of it, with success in reducing the fatality of the disease, but not in eliminating it or its disfiguring effects. The first real induction of immunity to it, by the method of vaccination, was made by an English physician, Edward Jenner (1749–1823), who carried on various biological studies along with his medical practice. In addition, for example, to investigations on the hibernation of hedgehogs and the habits of the cuckoo, he prepared and arranged the zoological specimens brought back from Captain Cook's first exploratory voyage in 1771. In his medical practice in the English countryside he had become aware of the similarity between the manifestations of three diseases, the cowpox of cows, the "grease" of horses and the dreaded and disfiguring smallpox of man, and in 1796 he was able to show that an eight year old boy, inoculated with matter taken from the vesicles on the hands of a milkmaid suffering from cowpox, did not develop the symptoms of smallpox when six weeks later he was inoculated with matter taken from smallpox vesicles. This demonstration by Jenner of the immunity acquired by the introduction into an individual of organisms which, because of their nature or their quantity, produce less severe forms of the disease became ultimately the foundation of smallpox vaccination, which is practiced in all countries with adequate public health supervision and which has reduced the incidence of the disease to a very low level throughout the world. It was also the foundation for the immunization of human beings, and of animals useful to them, against the pathological effects of many kinds of antigens.

The immune reactions of man and other organisms include some, however, that work disadvantageously for the well-being and even the preservation of the individual. Proteins of many kinds, as well as certain polysaccharides, may act as antigens, and these may not necessarily be those of bacteria, viruses or other parasites. The lecithinase in the venom of rattlesnakes and vipers is an antigen to the majority of human beings and other mammals as well; the lysolecithin that is formed in its presence is an antibody which destroys the individual's own cells (erythrocytes or erythroplastids) rather than invading ones. The proteins in the blood of some individuals are agglutinogens for the blood cells of others, a fact that has made possible the distinction between blood types, or hereditary blood groups, in man and other primates. The allergic responses of certain individuals to various kinds of plant pollens is probably an antigen-antibody reaction, the specific protein of the pollen acting as an antigen; food allergies, and other individual idiosyncrasies to particular substances, are believed to follow a similar mechanism.

It is generally accepted today that it is the chemical nature, that is to say, the atomic configuration, of the molecules of the serum proteins that is responsible for the high degree of specificity in the reactions that take place when a "foreign" substance is introduced into the body. What might be considered slight structural differences between molecules of the serum globulins may determine whether or not they will enter into an antigen-antibody reaction, and, though certain micro-organisms appear to act very generally as antigens to human beings, producing a reaction that leads to the symptoms of disease, the effect of other antigens is much more subtle and discriminating. There is reason to believe that the other tissues of the body as well as blood have a similar degree of protein specificity, and that in this may lie the basis of individuality in both plant and animal organisms. Such cellular specificity has been shown, for example, in Paramoecium, where individuals of certain strains have been found to have an agglutinating, and in some cases a lethal, effect upon those from other strains; it has also been shown in transplantation experiments where tissues grafted from one individual to another, or from an individual of one species to that of another, show various degrees of host-donor compatibility and incompatibility, from complete assimilation of the grafted tissue by the host, at one end of the scale, to its rejection with the production of unfavorable reactions at the other. These facts, together with evidence that is currently accumulating for the specificity of serum and tissue proteins from immunological studies, and chemical determinations of the nature of protein molecules, has thrown new light upon the relationships, antagonistic and otherwise, that may exist between biological systems and have provided a new tool for the taxonomist in offering him an exact basis for his groupings of plant and animal types and more fundamental explanations for relationships and differences between them, and possible lines of descent, than anatomical characters alone can offer.

**The course of blood flow**

The blood of all vertebrates flows through a closed system of connected tubes or vessels, whose lining, or endothelium, is, like the fluid within them, derived from embryonic mesenchyme. In the very smallest vessels, the capillaries, the endothelium alone separates the blood from the surrounding tissue spaces, and there is free migration of ions and other diffusible material to and fro across the plasma membranes of the flattened endothelial cells. The circulating blood of vertebrates is never in direct contact with the cells and tissues that it serves; it exchanges its materials across the capillary wall with the tissue fluid that bathes the cells (Fig. 16.3). Such an exchange is not possible in the larger vessels, for their walls are reinforced by coats of muscle and connective tissue, which in the larger vessels are thick and heavy and by their contraction help to propel the blood around the body in a steady stream. But the main impetus to its movement is given by the heart, a dilated and particularly muscular region of the vascular system that lies in a coelomic sac, the pericardial cavity (see Fig. 15.48).

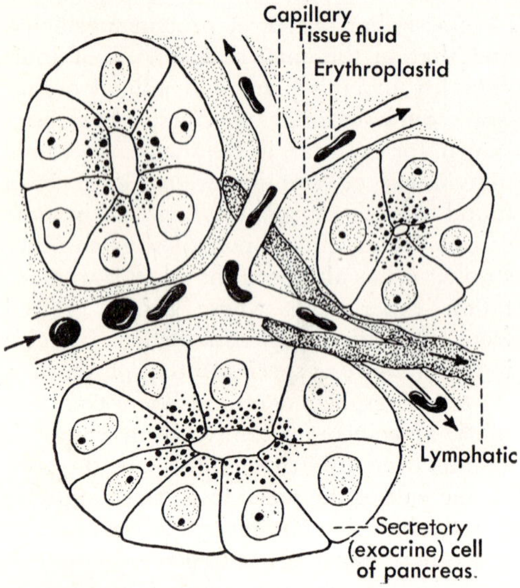

### The observations and deductions of William Harvey:

The movements of the heart and the passage of blood in the great arteries can easily be felt in an animal's body, and by simple dissections the heart can be exposed and seen in action and the larger vessels traced. But it is by no means so simple to arrive at an understanding of the course and the mechanism of blood flow throughout the body or the relations that this tissue maintains with the others through which it passes. Although the earliest students of anatomy whose records have survived had recognized the blood as a special kind of fluid and the heart as one of the most vital organs, if not the most vital organ, in the body, it was not until the early seventeenth century that William Harvey (1578–1657), an English physician, made the observations, experiments and deductions which led to a proper understanding of the heart's action and the course of blood flow through the body. The Greek and Roman scholars who concerned themselves with biological and medical studies, and those of later years who were influenced in their thinking and in their methods by their classical predecessors, had interpreted the blood as formed in the liver from the food that was eaten; it then, as they understood it, entered the heart, which passively distended to receive it and endowed it with the "vital spirit" which it carried to all the other organs along with the nutriment necessary to them. They thought of the blood as something like an agricultural irrigation system, led by conduits, the large and easily discernible vessels of the body, to the tissues into which it seeped to be built up into new flesh and so used up. Harvey watched the action of the heart in a number of animals of different kinds—shrimps, snails and shellfish, fishes, toads, frogs, serpents, pigeons, dogs and hogs—and saw that as it emptied the great arteries expanded. He felt the heart as the blood was leaving it, and found that it was hard and firm like the muscles of the upper arm when the arm is bent. He therefore concluded that the heart was muscular and that, when the blood entered it, it did more than passively dilate; it contracted and forced the blood out into the arteries. He traced the course of the blood through the hearts of different vertebrates and he reasoned that it must flow in one direction only, and more important than that, that it must flow continuously in one direction. For, he argued, the volume of the heart is limited and measurable, and the number of times that it discharges its contents to the arteries in any given period can easily be determined by counting the number of

FIGURE 16.3 Diagram showing the interrelations of cells, blood capillaries, lymphatics and tissue fluids. (After Cowdry.)

beats, reflected in the pulse rate. Assuming that the human heart holds a volume of blood equivalent to two ounces in weight— a value he had found approximately true for the heart of a dead man—then if the heart expels a quarter of its volume at each

capillaries of the web of a frog's foot. These observations can easily be made to-day by anyone with an adequate magnifying device, not only in the web of a frog's foot, but in any transparent tissue like the gill of a fish, the tail of a tadpole or salamander or

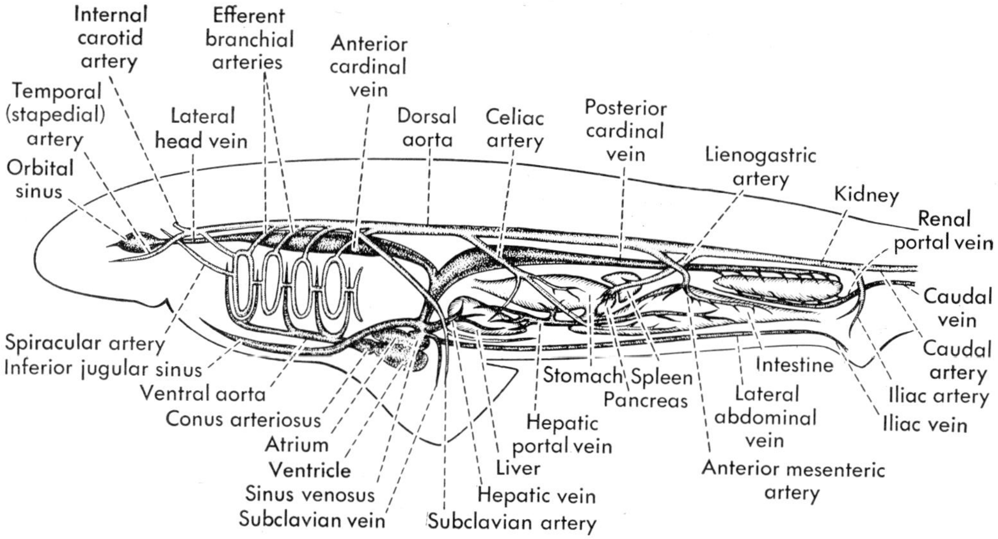

FIGURE 16.4 Diagram of the main blood vessels of a shark, as seen in lateral view. (From Romer, *The Vertebrate Body*. Copyright 1949 by the W. B. Saunders Company.)

beat and beats some two thousand or more times in half an hour, in an hour it will have pumped out into the aorta two thousand or more ounces, or some one hundred and ten pounds of blood, more than half the total body weight of even a heavy man. By a simple mathematical calculation such as this, from data that could readily be verified, Harvey showed the manifest absurdity of the current conceptions of blood formation, flow and utilization, and made the existence of connecting vessels between those obviously carrying blood from the heart and those obviously carrying blood to it a logical necessity. He thus deduced the existence of capillaries thirty years before they were actually seen, for it was not until 1660 that Malpighi (1628–1694), who bas born in the year of the publication in Frankfort-am-Main of Harvey's *An Anatomical Disquisition on the Motion of the Heart and Blood in Animals*, actually saw through his microscope the movement of the blood in the

even the skin at the base of his own fingernail. And the experiments that Harvey made to substantiate and confirm his deductions can also be easily repeated. For instance, he cut an artery in an animal and watched the blood flow from it, first in great jets, and then more and more slowly until the animal weakened and died; this must be, he reasoned, because this blood is flowing away from the heart and there is no way for it to return. He put pressure upon the veins, as his teacher, Fabricius, had done in demonstrating the action of the valves, and saw that they filled up and swelled on the side away from the heart when the blood was not allowed to flow freely through them, and he opened up a living snake and tied a ligature around its great vein and saw that the vessel emptied and grew flaccid on the heart side of the constriction and swelled up on the other; when he made the same experiment on the aorta, the opposite happened and the vessel filled up on the heart side and emptied on the other. "It is absolutely necessary to conclude," he wrote, "that the blood in the animal's body is impelled in a circle, and is in a state of ceaseless motion; that this is the act or function which the heart performs by means of its pulse; and that this is the sole and the only end of the motion and contraction of the heart." *

From these simple and straightforward experiments, and from the use of the simplest kind of quantitative methods, Harvey discovered a biological fact of the greatest importance and far-reaching significance which centuries of speculation and philosophical argument had failed to reveal. His work is a beautiful illustration of the method of the scientist; in it he fulfills the canons laid down by Francis Bacon (1561–1639)— to explain nature by experience based upon observation and experiment—and by Galileo, to measure what can be measured and to make measurable what cannot be measured. Harvey was the first man to apply these principles to an attempt to understand the animal body and his application was most fruitful, not only in the facts that he himself found out but also in the effect that it had upon his immediate successors in the study of biological systems and upon all later students of them. The demonstration of blood pressure in the horse and the measurements of the rate of flow in the capillaries of the frog's foot by Stephen Hales a century later were natural corollaries of Harvey's work; so, too, have been all the subsequent studies on the mechanism of blood flow and heart action in hundreds of research and clinical laboratories all over the world.

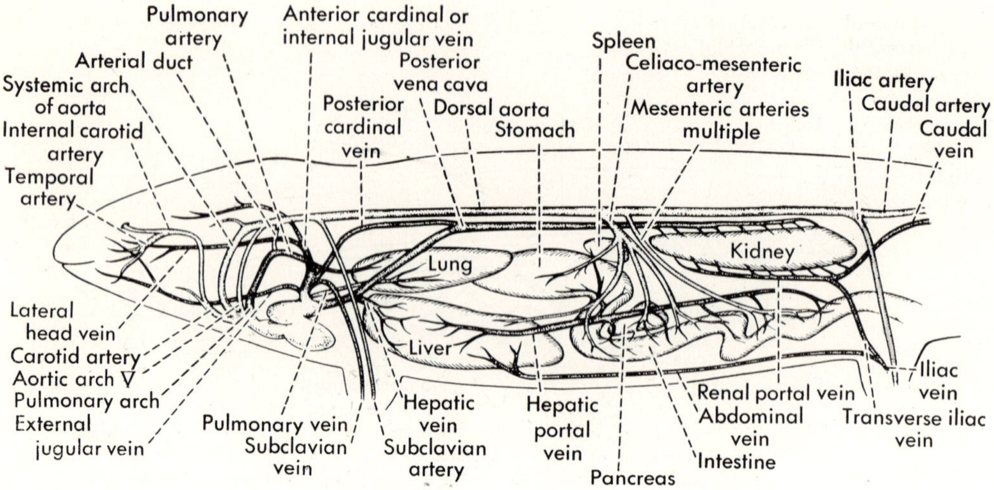

The pattern of the vessels through which the blood flows shows greater variation in the vertebrate classes than does the blood itself, at least in its more general characters (Figs. 16.4, 16.5, 16.6). These differences, as they can be traced through the different classes, are related primarily to the development of lungs and the shift from branchial to pulmonary respiration, the more complete division of the heart into separate chambers and, in the case of the veins, the assumption of an asymmetrical pattern rather than a bilateral one through the closing down of some channels, the development of new ones and the consequent redistribution of the course of the blood returning to the heart.

FIGURE 16.5 Diagram of the main blood vessels of a urodele amphibian, as seen in lateral view. (From Romer, *The Vertebrate Body.* Copyright 1949 by the W. B. Saunders Company.)

* Harvey, William: *An Anatomical Dissertation upon the Movement of the Heart and Blood in Animals* (translation, G. Moreton), facsimile edition, Canterbury, 1894.

*The heart and its development:* In all vertebrates, dorsal and ventral aortae appear as clearly defined vessels early in embryonic development. Primitively these are both paired vessels, but the fusion of the ventral aortae into a single vessel occurs very early, as does that of the two dorsal aortae in the post-pharyngeal region, although anteriorly they persist as paired vessels. The heart is differentiated along the course of the ventral aorta as an enlargement of its cavity to whose endothelial walls thick muscle coats become applied, and which is divided to greater or less extent into separate chambers. Primitively these are, from anterior to posterior, the sinus venosus, the atrium, the ventricle and the conus arteriosus (Fig. 16.7). The sinus venosus is continuous with the two great veins that return blood from the tissues and organs of the body and are called the Ducts of Cuvier after Georges Cuvier (1769–1832), the distinguished French anatomist who, above all, developed the comparative method in biology. The atrium is a comparatively thin-walled, distensible chamber receiving the blood from the sinus venosus; the ventricle is a particularly muscular one, whose contractions give the principal impetus to the blood in its course through the body. The conus arteriosus, continuous with both the ventricle and the ventral aorta, is also muscular and by its contraction helps to push the blood through the arterial channels. Backflow from one chamber to another is prevented by flaps of tissue that hang down from the inner walls of the heart and act as valves, closing off the openings between successive chambers when they are pushed upward and together by the eddying blood as it is put under increased pressure by the contraction of their walls.

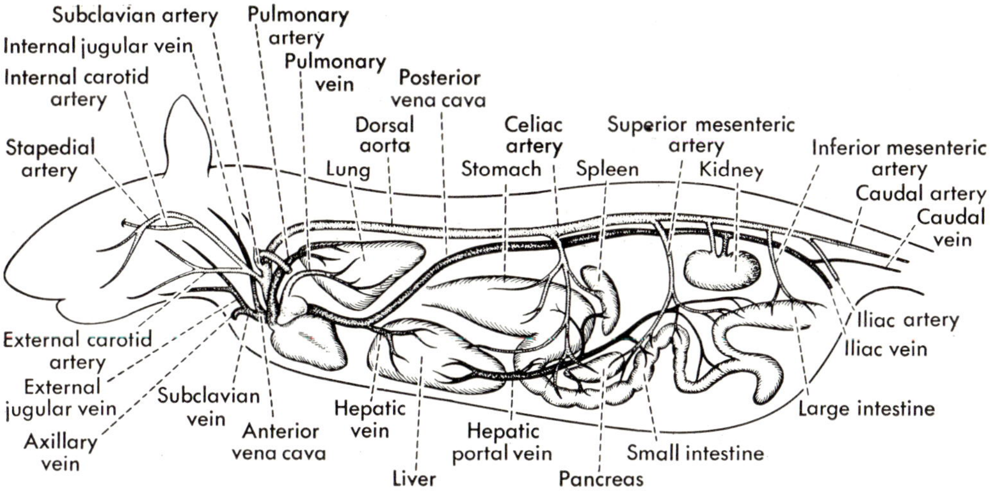

In the individual development of all vertebrates the heart passes through a stage when these chambers are more or less clearly defined in linear order, but in none does it remain in such a condition, for its growth exceeds that of the pericardial cavity to which it is confined and it becomes bent, or folded upon itself, and, in the tetrapods, partly or completely divided into right and left sides (Fig. 16.8). The adult fish heart most closely approximates the primitive condition for it is not laterally divided and, though the ventricle is under the atrium, the linear arrangement of the chambers is not greatly disturbed. But in the tetrapods it is bent into an S whose long axis is parallel to

FIGURE 16.6 Diagram of the main blood vessels of a mammal (rat) as seen in lateral view. (From Romer, *The Vertebrate Body*. Copyright 1949 by the W. B. Saunders Company.)

the long axis of the body, the atrium forming the upper curvature and the ventricle the lower one. The part of the heart that receives the blood from the great veins thus comes to lie anterior and above the ventricle, instead of posterior and in line with it, and the ventricle into right and left ventricles, the heart and the entire circulatory system gain in efficiency, for the blood becomes diverted into two main streams, one coming from the body as a whole, high in carbon dioxide and low in oxygen content, and go-

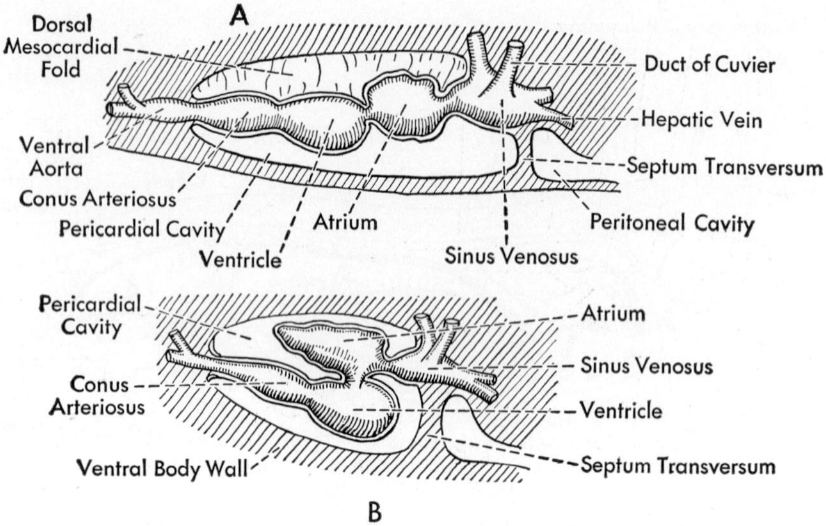

FIGURE 16.7 Diagrams illustrating the relation of the heart chambers to one another and to the pericardial cavity. (After Goodrich, from Walter and Sayles, *Biology of the Vertebrates*. Copyright 1949 by The Macmillan Company.)

A. Hypothetical primitive condition.
B. Selachian stage.

the flow of blood from atrium to ventricle has the advantage of the gravitational pull. These changes in their spatial relationships have led to the incorporation of the Ducts of Cuvier into the atrial region of the heart and of the conus arteriosus into the ventricular. The merging of the sinus venosus with the atrium is apparent in the amphibia, more complete in the reptiles, and in the birds and mammals its identity as a separate chamber is completely lost, as is that of the sinus venosus.

The division of the heart into right and left sides by the growth of septa into the cavities of the atrium and the ventricle is also complete in the birds and mammals, but partial in the amphibia and in all but the most highly evolved of the reptiles. Through such division, by which the atrium is divided into right and left auricles and ing to the areas of external respiration, and the other coming from those areas high in oxygen and low in carbon dioxide content, and going to all the other tissues and organs. In the amphibia, the atrium is only partly divided and the ventricle not at all, but in those at present at the highest levels of amphibian evolution, the frogs and toads, the blood from the integument, the principal area of their external respiration, and from the lungs, the secondary one, is effectively separated. This separation is brought about mechanically, for the force of the blood entering the right auricle from the main veins is sufficient to push the free edge of the septum against the inner wall of the left auricle, thus temporarily shutting off the connection between the two auricles, and that between the left auricle and the ventricle. The blood from the body as a whole

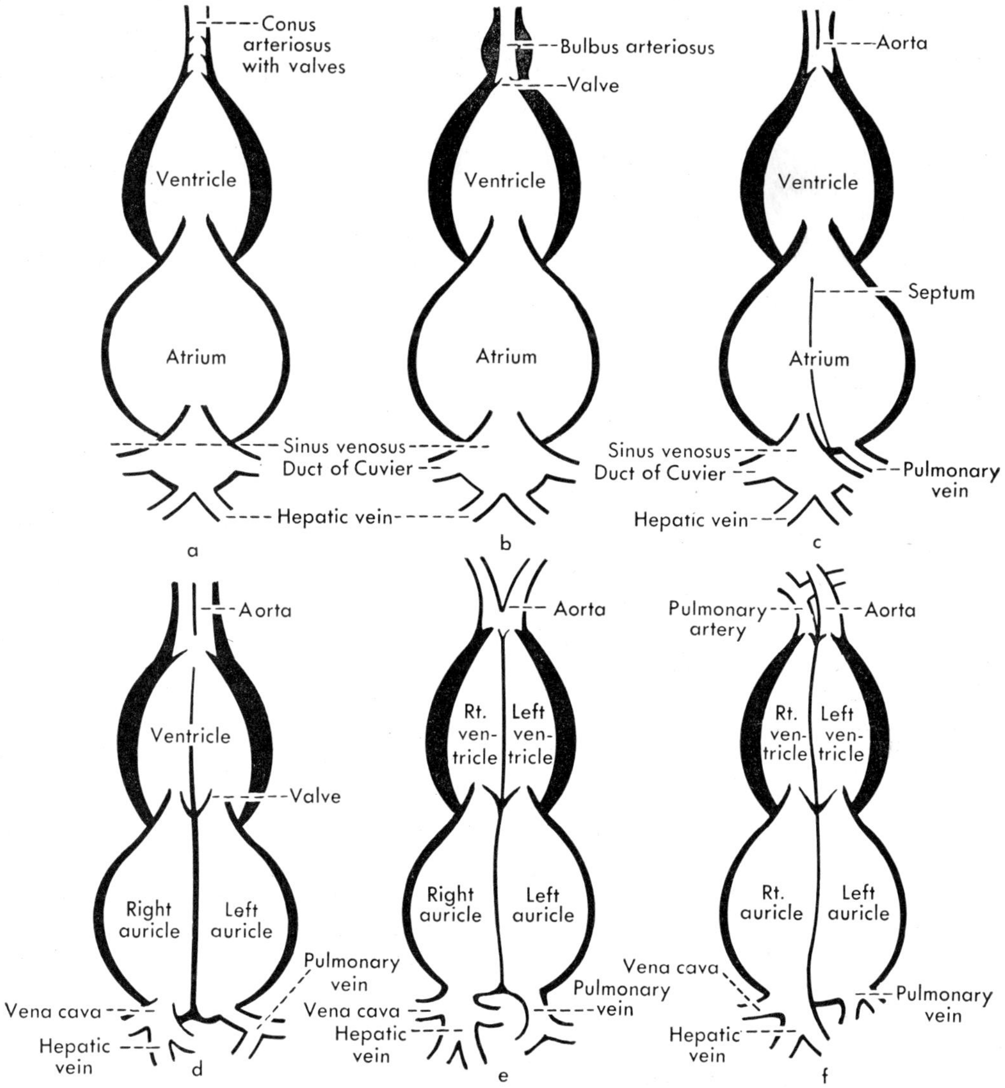

FIGURE 16.8 Diagrams showing the evolution of the vertebrate heart. (After Kingsley.)

    a. elasmobranch.

    b. teleost.

    c. amphibian, showing the partial division of the heart into right and left sides, and of the aorta into systemic and pulmonary trunks.

    d. reptile (lizard).

    e. reptile (alligator).

    f. bird and mammal, showing complete separation of systemic and pulmonary flow.

thus flows first into the ventricle, from the right auricle, after which the pressure within the right auricle becomes reduced and the septum returns to its median position so that the blood that has entered the left auricle from the respiratory surfaces can flow freely into the ventricle. The course of the blood as it leaves the single ventricle is also controlled, for the lumen of the conus is divided by a septum in the form of a loose spiral, which acts as a valve. The blood that leaves the ventricle first, which is also that which has entered it first, flows along the channels offering least resistance—the arteries to the lungs and the skin—and in so doing pushes against the spiral valve in such a way that the passages to the systemic arteries, carrying blood to the other parts of the body, are briefly closed off. After the vessels to the lungs and the skin become filled, resistance to blood flow in them increases, and the blood takes an alternative course into the main systemic artery, the aorta, and the vessels of the head and the heart itself. On purely mechanical grounds the heart of an amphibian is a more efficient organ in separating the two streams of blood than its structure alone would suggest, for although there is opportunity for the blood from the respiratory surfaces, with the maximum oxygen content, to mingle with that from the general circulation with a minimal one, the possibilities for such mixing are reduced and the blood entering the ventricle and then leaving it is so distributed that the fraction highest in carbon dioxide and lowest in oxygen is sent to the lungs and the skin through the pulmo-cutaneous vessels, that which is highest in oxygen and lowest in carbon dioxide to the head and the heart, and that which represents the greatest mixture of oxygenated and reduced blood to the general circulation.

In the reptiles, the division of the atrium into right and left halves is complete, and the partition extends also down into the ventricle, although only in the alligators and crocodiles is the ventricle completely divided (Fig. 16.8e). The aorta is divided down to its base into a pulmonary and a systemic vessel so that the channels through which the blood flows to the lungs and to the general circulation are quite separate. Valves between the ventricle and the right and left atria prevent the back-flow of blood into either chamber, and although there is some opportunity for the blood returning from the lungs to mix with that from the general circulation, in all but the crocodiles, the conditions within the heart itself reduce this possibilty even more than in the amphibian heart but do not wholly eliminate it.

It is, however, wholly eliminated under ordinary conditions in the birds and mammals, which, though of different lines of descent, have attained the same end, for in both classes the septum between the auricles and that between the two sides of the ventricle is complete, and the heart thus divided into right and left regions, insuring that the

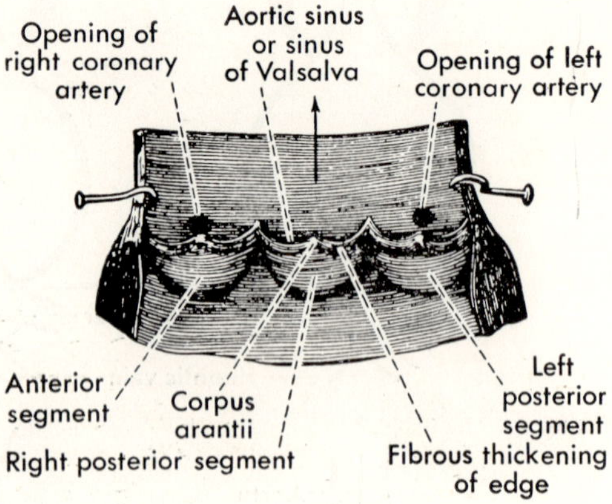

FIGURE 16.9 The aorta cut open and spread out to show the three semi-lunar valves. (After Gerrish, from Kimber, Gray and Stackpole, *Textbook of Anatomy and Physiology*, 11th edition. Copyright 1942 by The Macmillan Company.)

blood returning from the body as a whole is sent to the lungs and oxygenated before it is sent again on its course through the body (Fig. 16.8f). By this means, the tissues, except for those of the lung, receive blood with a maximal oxygen content and the efficiency of their metabolic processes is correspondingly increased. In mammals, the opening of the pulmonary artery, which leads from the right ventricle, and that of the systemic aorta, which leads from the left, are guarded by pocket-like flaps, the semi-lunar valves (Fig. 16.9). The valves between the auricles and the ventricles have additional reinforcements in the chordae tendineae, strands of firm tissue that are attached at one end to muscular elevations on the inner wall of the ventricles and at the other to the flaps, or cusps, of the valves. When the cusps are brought together, the chordae tendineae are held taut by the contraction of the muscles to which they are attached so that they hold the valves against the pressure of the blood that is being forced out of the heart when

INTEGRATING TISSUES OF THE VERTEBRATE BODY [ 339 ]

the ventricles contract. The valve between the right auricle and the right ventricle has three cusps, and is therefore known as the tricuspid valve, and that between the left auricle and left ventricle has two, and is called the bicuspid or mitral valve (Greek, which the heart may compensate by contracting more often or with greater force at each beat; in either case the muscle is made to do additional work.

During its period of relaxation the heart of both the bird and the mammal fills with

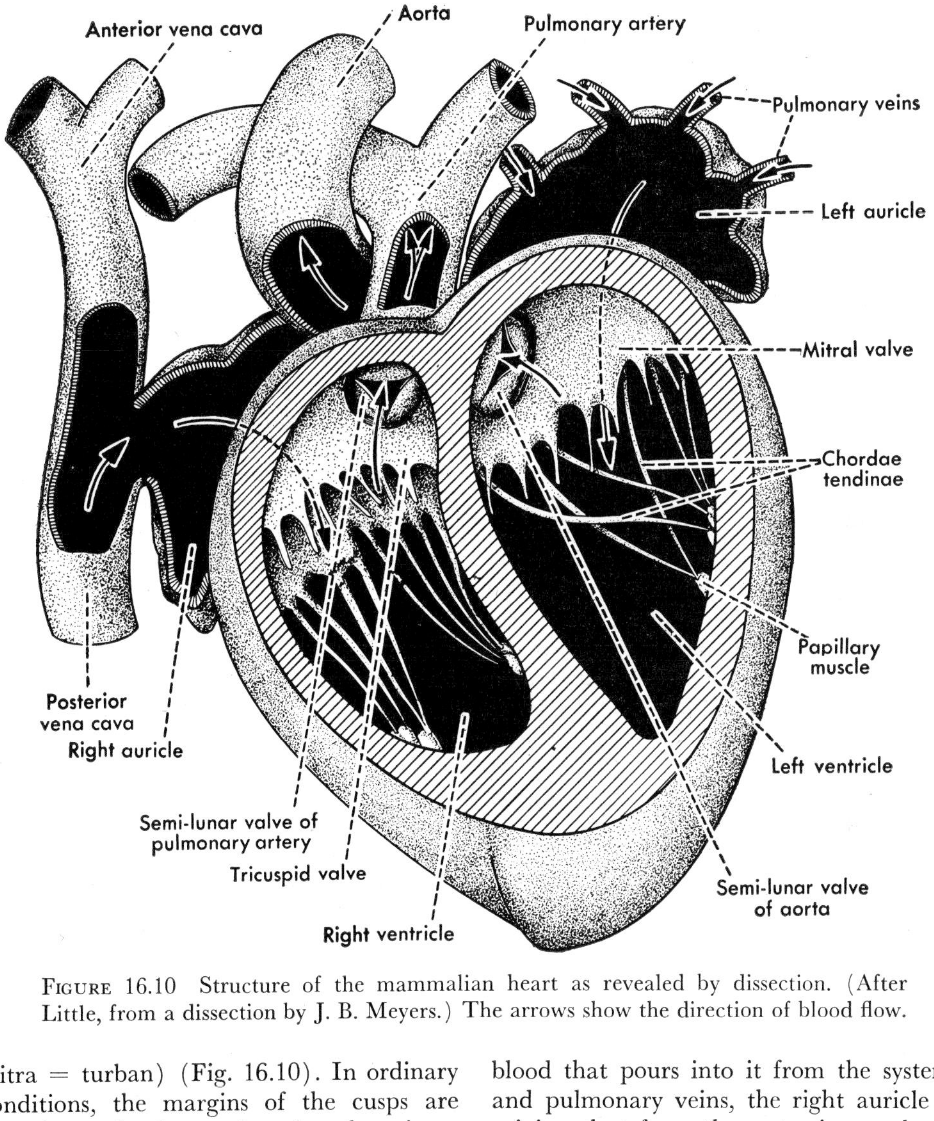

FIGURE 16.10 Structure of the mammalian heart as revealed by dissection. (After Little, from a dissection by J. B. Meyers.) The arrows show the direction of blood flow.

mitra = turban) (Fig. 16.10). In ordinary conditions, the margins of the cusps are brought so closely together that there is no backflow from ventricle to auricle and the heart is perfectly efficient in driving all the blood into the arteries at each ventricular contraction, but conditions sometimes arise to cause incomplete closure of the valves and there is leakage into the auricles, for blood that pours into it from the systemic and pulmonary veins, the right auricle receiving that from the systemic vessels and the left auricle that from the lungs; the blood flows through the auricles and past the open auriculo-ventricular valves to the ventricles, with the right ventricle receiving only the blood from the right auricle, and hence from the body generally, and the left ventricle receiving only that from the left auricle and hence exclusively from the lungs. This period, when the heart is being distended with blood, is known as diastole (Greek, diastellein = to put asunder). After a certain degree of distention, its contraction begins, originating at the bases of the great veins in the tissue that represents the vestiges of the sinus venosus. The wave of contraction spreads through the auricles, forcing the blood remaining in them into the ventricles, and with the increased pressure in the auricles the valves guarding the openings of the veins are brought together, closing their already constricted passages. The wave of contraction then spreads through the ventricles, and as the pressure in them rises, the cusps of the valves between the auricles and the ventricles which have already been pushed out from the walls by the eddying blood in the ventricles, are brought together so that each ventricle is a chamber temporarily closed off from all other parts of the circulatory system. As its walls continue to contract, the pressure within them rises until it is greater than that in the pulmonary artery and in the aorta. When this level is reached, the semilunar valves in the walls of these vessels are forced back and the blood flows into the open channels, distending the vessels to a certain extent; the elasticity of their walls allows this distention but also tends to bring about their collapse so that the flowing blood is subjected to this pressure as well as that from the contraction of the ventricles. The period of the heart's contraction is known as systole (Greek, systollein = to contract). After systole, the heart muscle relaxes and recovers from its contraction, and with the consequent enlargement of the cavities of the ventricles, the pressure within them falls so that it is lower than that in the arteries. This difference in pressure would cause the blood to flow back from them into the heart if it were not that, because of the arterial pressure, the cusps of the semilunar valves are pushed out from the walls and their edges brought together in the lumina of the vessels, sealing them off.

In ordinary circumstances, these changes in the heart occur rhythmically, ventricular systole following auricular systole and diastole following systole in regular and orderly sequence and at a characteristic rate, as a rule more rapidly in birds than in mammals and more rapidly in some groups of mammals than in others. In the fishes and amphibia, the contraction is initiated in the sinus venosus, in the other vertebrates in the sino-auricular node, the mass of tissue in the wall of the right atrium that represents the remnants of the sinus venosus. These act as "pace makers" and set the rhythm of the beat. In the mammalian heart, the continuity of the muscle fibers characteristic of heart muscle is interrupted between the auricles and ventricles by connective tissue septa which grow in between them. While both auricles and both ventricles act as units because of the syncytial nature of their muscular walls, the only muscular and nervous connection between the auricles and the ventricles is through a strand of tissue known as the auriculo-ventricular bundle, or the Bundle of His, after a Swiss anatomist, William His (1831–1904). This bundle has its origin near the point where the great veins open into the right auricle and extends in the wall between the two auricles down to the ventricles where it spreads out through their walls. Experiments have shown that if this bundle is cut, the rhythm of the heart beat is broken and though both sets of chambers continue to beat, they beat out of time with each other; the rhythm of the ventricular beat may be twice that of the auricular, or dissynchronized to any other degree. The beat of the heart as a whole is also influenced by conditions within the body, for the heart muscle responds by alterations in the rate and extent of its contractions to chemical conditions of the blood and to impulses reaching it through nerves.

*The principal vessels and their development:* In the most generalized of modern vertebrates, and at some stage in the embryological development of all of them, the blood leaves the heart through a short ventral aorta which lies just below the pharynx and gives off paired vessels that pass dorsally through the gill arches and join the

INTEGRATING TISSUES OF THE VERTEBRATE BODY [ 341 ]

paired dorsal aortae above the pharynx. These vessels, which encircle the pharynx like hoops, are called the aortic arches and their history and fate in the development of individuals of different vertebrate species have been of the greatest interest to comparative anatomists and have provided some of the most cogent evidence for the evolutionary relationships of vertebrate types and their gradual progression from a generalized aquatic ancestor (Fig. 16.11).

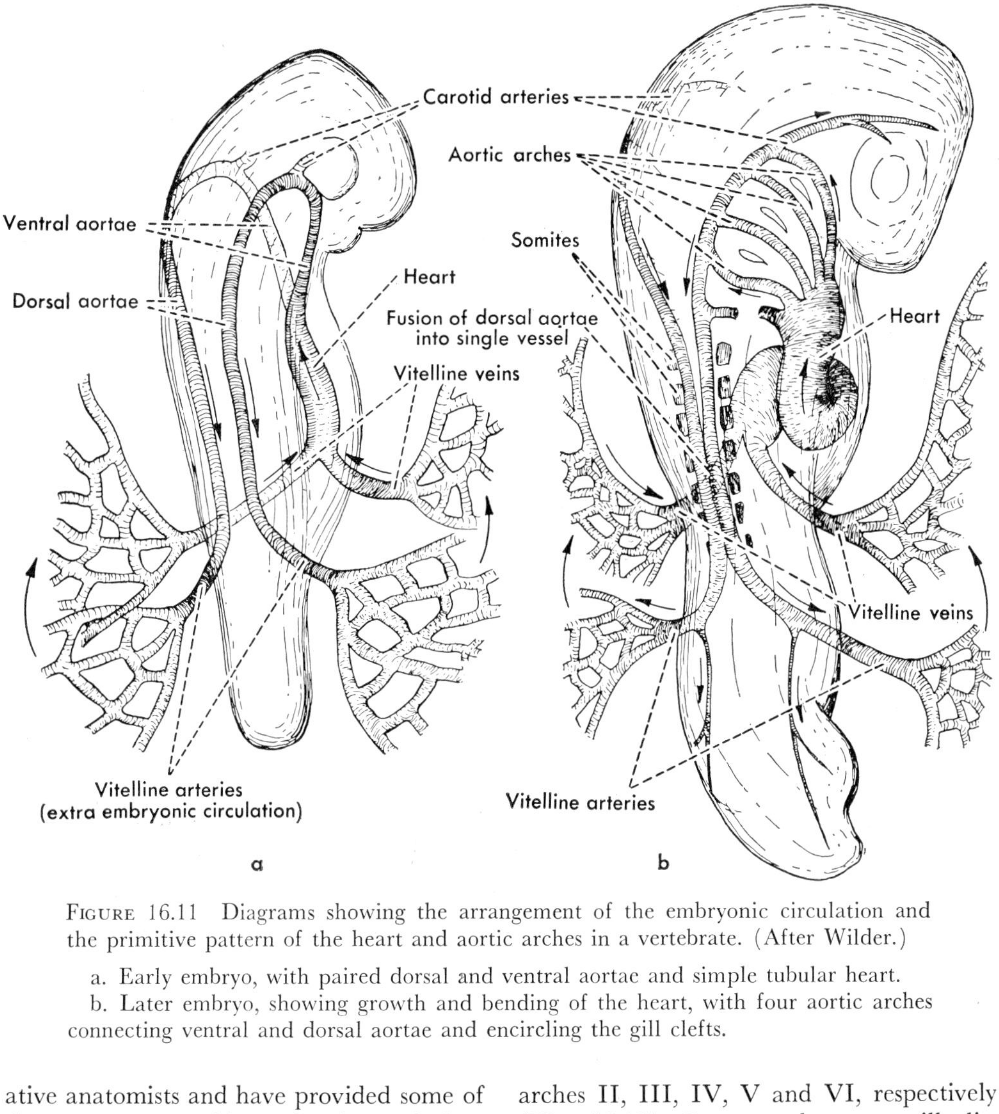

Six such aortic arches arise in all modern vertebrates, although not always at the same time or reaching the same degree of development. The first to appear in the course of a vertebrate's development is also the most anterior, arising from the end of the ventral aorta; conventionally it is designated as aortic arch I, and those that arise posterior to it, between the successive gill slits, as arches II, III, IV, V and VI, respectively (Fig. 16.12). Between the open gill slits these vessels break up into a capillary network, and where functional gills develop along the margins of the slits, as in the fishes and aquatic larvae of amphibia, a system of branchial vessels arises, carrying blood from the main trunk of each arch to the gill fila-

FIGURE 16.11 Diagrams showing the arrangement of the embryonic circulation and the primitive pattern of the heart and aortic arches in a vertebrate. (After Wilder.)

a. Early embryo, with paired dorsal and ventral aortae and simple tubular heart.
b. Later embryo, showing growth and bending of the heart, with four aortic arches connecting ventral and dorsal aortae and encircling the gill clefts.

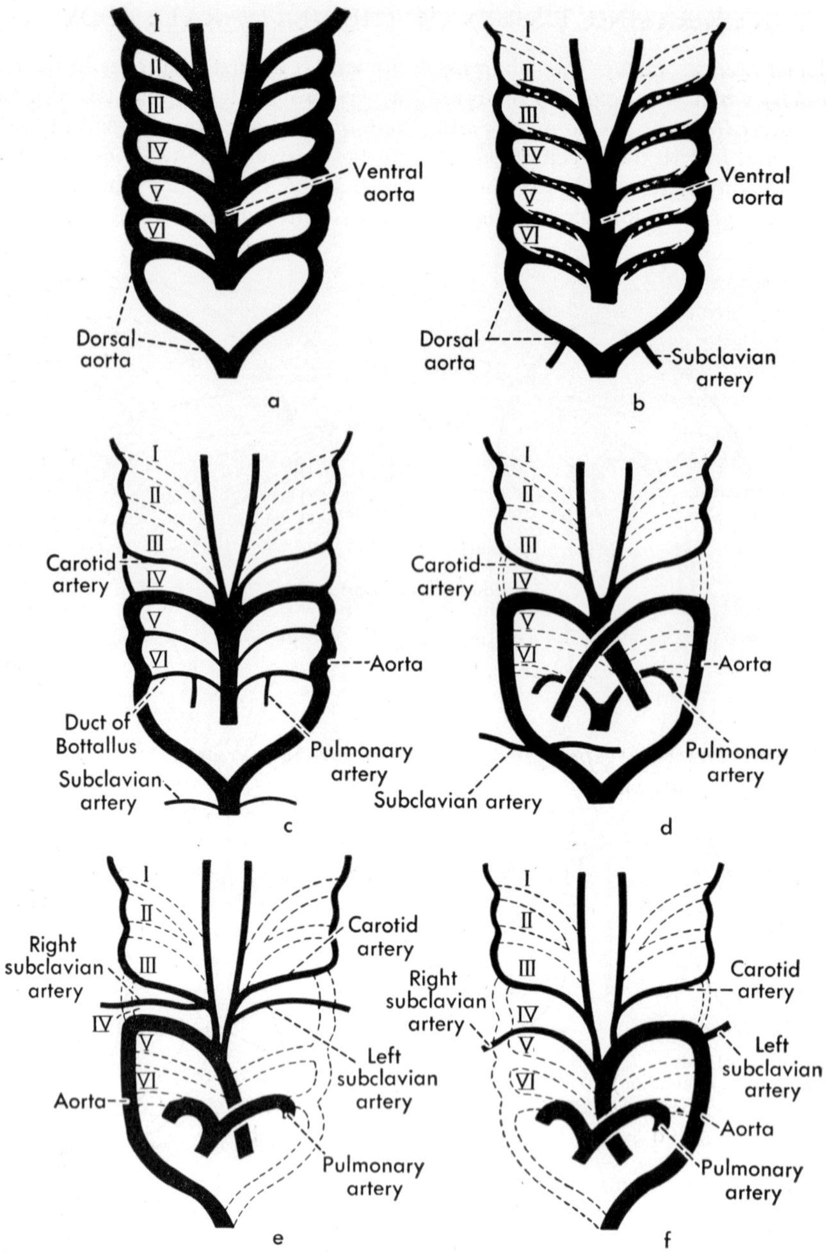

FIGURE 16.12 Diagrams showing the principal modifications of the aortic arches in the different orders of vertebrates. (After Wilder.) The successive arches are indicated by Roman numerals, the obliterated portions by dotted lines.

   a. Hypothetical condition, showing six complete arches between dorsal and ventral aortae.

   b. Condition typical of fishes, in which the most anterior arch (I) is obliterated, and a system of branchial vessels interpolated in the remaining five.

   c. Condition typical of amphibians.
   d. Condition typical of reptiles.
   e. Condition typical of birds.
   f. Condition typical of mammals.

ments and back from them to the dorsal segment of each. These vessels, the afferent branchial vessels (Latin, ad = to + ferre = to bear), carrying blood to the gills, and the efferent branchial vessels (Latin, ex = away + ferre = to bear) constitute the branchial circulation, gaseous interchange and in some fishes the migration of ions taking place across the delicate capillary walls and the surfaces of the gills exposed to the water.

In all modern vertebrates, whatever may have been the conditions in their common ancestors, the first two aortic arches are the most modified and have become wholly or partly incorporated in the carotid arteries carrying blood to the head. The first, or mandibular, is in all craniates so modified that afferent and efferent branchial vessels are never developed along its course; the second, or hyoid, although contributing to the carotid vessels is somewhat less modified in fishes where a reduced branchial circulation may arise. But in the tetrapods it is the third arch that takes over the main burden of carrying blood to the head and both sides of it are retained in all vertebrates as the roots of the carotid arteries. All or one side of the fourth arch persists in all classes of tetrapods as the systemic arch, connecting the ventral aorta with the single dorsal aorta; the fifth arch is vestigial in all but the urodele amphibia and the sixth arch gives rise to the pulmonary vessels that carry blood to the lungs (Fig. 16.12a).

With the development of the neck region characteristic of the tetrapods, evident even in the amphibia, and with the more posterior location of the heart, the spatial relations of the aortic arches to each other are altered and the carotid arteries especially are greatly lengthened. As adults, the urodele amphibia show least modification of the generalized primitive pattern; after a larval period with functional external gills, they undergo a gradual metamorphosis to the adult form during which the gills grow smaller and the branchial vessels are obliterated. The second and third arches thus lose their connection with the gills and the second virtually disappears while both halves of the third remain as the bases of the internal carotid arteries. Anterior to the origin of the third arch, the ventral aorta divides into two vessels that become the external carotid arteries, and those parts of the dorsal aortae between the carotids and the junction of the fourth arch with them become a great deal smaller and carry little blood. Both halves of the fourth arch persist, and the blood forced into them flows posteriorly into the dorsal aorta. Both halves of the fifth arch remain in some species as small vessels also carrying blood to the dorsal aorta as do those of the sixth, from which paired branches grow ventrally each of which shortly divides into a pulmonary vessel to the lung and a cutaneous one to the skin. The part of the arch on each side which lies between the origin of the pulmo-cutaneous vessels and the dorsal aorta is small and is known as the ductus arteriosus, or the duct of Botallus, after a sixteenth century Italian anatomist, L. Botallus. The blood as it leaves the heart is directed into the coronary arteries to the heart muscle, the pulmo-cutaneous vessels and then into the main trunk, where it becomes diverted into two streams, one running anteriorly in the carotids and the other posteriorly in the systemic arches. This division of the primary stream is more complete in the anuran amphibia where there is complete obliteration of the segments of the dorsal aortae between the third and fourth arches, of the entire fifth arch and of the ducti arteriosi, so that all the blood leaving the heart through the sixth arch flows into the pulmo-cutaneous artery and the rest is divided between the systemic (IV) arches and the carotid vessels (III arch). On the third arch, at the points of origin of the internal and external carotids of each side, are developed the carotid glands; these are strictly speaking not glands, but spongy and pulsating enlargements of the arch by means of which a continual flow of oxygenated blood to the head is more fully assured.

In the adult reptiles, birds and mammals there is a complete division of the ventral vessel, which becomes spirally split to its base, or junction with the heart, so that the stream of blood through the sixth arch to the lungs is quite separate from that flowing into the third and fourth arches, the carotid and systemic trunks respectively, which always remain closely associated (Fig. 16.12). Through this division, the ventral aorta becomes separated into a pulmonary and an aortic trunk, and in the reptiles and the birds the aortic trunk is also spirally divided into right and left channels. This division comes about in such a way that the smaller left arch opens from the right side of the heart and the larger right one from the left side. While in most reptiles both sides of the fourth arch remain, there is an indication of asymmetry of pattern in the difference in size of the two sides, an asymmetry that is further emphasized by the fact that in all of them, as in all the birds, the base of the carotid trunk, representing that part of the ventral aorta between the fourth and third arches, opens from the right aortic trunk. In birds and mammals, an asymmetrical pattern is definitely established but in quite different ways. In birds, only the right half of the fourth arch persists as the systemic arch, in mammals only the left. The ductus arteriosus on one or both sides remains as an open channel in the embryos of all Amniotes until the time of hatching or of birth, when the lungs fill with air and become functional respiratory surfaces; very shortly after this, the part of the sixth arch represented by the ductus becomes obliterated.

In all the vertebrates the subclavian arteries, carrying blood to the anterior appendages, arise from the fourth arch, their position shifting somewhat with the elongation of the neck and the retreat of the heart into the thoracic region of the body. In the birds, the right subclavian arises from the persistent right arch, and the base of the left subclavian represents the only remaining portion of the otherwise obliterated left arch; just the reverse is the case in mammals, where the left subclavian has its origin in the systemic arch, with which the carotid trunk is also associated, while the right subclavian appears to be a vessel whose origin is independent of the systemic trunk but which, from embryological evidence, actually represents, in its base at least, the more dorsal portion of the originally complete right arch.

The dorsal aorta is the main distributing trunk of the body; in it the blood flows posteriorly under the pressure set up by each contraction of the heart and the elasticity of the walls of the aorta itself, which tend to collapse after their distention with each new load of blood from the heart. This tendency is also a factor in keeping the blood flowing in a steady stream in the aorta and other arteries rather than in spurts coincident with each systole. From the aorta arise a number of paired and of single vessels, through whose branches blood is distributed to the organs and tissues. The principal arteries arising from the dorsal aorta are: the coeliac artery (Latin, coeliacus = belonging to the belly), which gives rise to branches supplying the liver, the anterior part of the stomach, the pancreas and other organs in this region; the anterior mesenteric artery, whose branches carry blood to the posterior part of the stomach and to the intestine; the posterior mesenteric artery which supplies, through its various branches, the posterior part of the digestive tract and the reproductive organs; paired renal arteries (Latin, renes = kidneys) to the excretory organs; paired iliac arteries (Latin, ilium = groin), that give off vessels to the rectum and body wall before entering the posterior pair of appendages as the femoral arteries (Latin, femur = thigh); and paired intersegmental arteries which, running dorsally and ventrally between the muscle segments, send branches to the muscles, the vertebrae, the neural tube and the underlying tissues of the integument.

All the larger vessels of the arterial system divide and subdivide as they reach the tissues for which they are destined, and as the vessels grow progressively smaller and smaller in diameter, their walls become progressively thinner and less muscular, until ultimately they reach capillary dimensions and their walls are composed only of endothelium. These capillaries spread through the tissues in an involved and intricate network, representing an enormous vascular area in which the rate of blood flow is considerably less than in the larger vessels; the blood in the capillaries exchanges its diffusible solutes with those of the surrounding tissue fluids. At the other end of the capillary system, the smallest vessels unite again into larger ones, the venules, and these into still larger ones, the veins, and finally into the great systemic veins through which the blood pours into the sinus venosus and so into the auricle and the ventricle to be started again on its course around the body. The blood enters the venules from the venous side of the capillary network under pressure considerably less than that on the arterial side; the blood in the veins moves more slowly than it does in the arteries but it always moves onward toward the heart, upward, downward or laterally, partly because of the pressure, though slight, that it is still under from the heart's contraction, and partly because it is squeezed along on its way by the contraction of the muscles through which the veins and venules run. Any tendency to backflow is prevented by valves, like those in the heart and the conus, which are distributed at intervals along the veins, particularly at the junctions of the large ones. In the elasmobranch fishes, the veins are often distended as large, thin-walled sinuses; these are not homologous with the blood sinuses of arthropods and mollusks, for they are not hemocoeles or derivatives of the primary body cavity but enlargements along the course of certain definite vessels.

While the course of the venules and smaller veins in general parallels that of the arterioles and small arteries, there is a good deal of difference in the pattern of the course of the large veins in the different vertebrate classes. In the most generalized of modern vertebrates, the sharks, they show a fairly regular, bilateral arrangement, the blood from the head draining into two large vessels, the anterior or precardinal veins (Latin, cardinalis = chief), and that from the posterior part of the body into two postcardinal veins. The precardinal veins run along the dorsal margins of the gill arches and each, after expanding into an anterior cardinal sinus, joins the postcardinal vein of the same side to form the Duct of Cuvier, or common cardinal vein. The posterior cardinal veins are formed by the union of a number of tributary vessels. The blood from the tail returns in the caudal vein, which forks as it enters the trunk region, one branch entering the excretory organ of each side as the renal portal vein, where it breaks up into smaller vessels that in turn unite into larger ones that unite with the posterior cardinal vein. Such a system of capillaries interpolated in the course of a vein, rather than between an artery and a vein, is known as a portal system (Latin, porta = gate). The renal portal system is peculiar to the lower vertebrates, and because of it the excretory organ receives blood from two sources—the renal portal vein and the renal artery. The blood from the pelvic fins and from the sides of the body flows into paired lateral veins that enter the common cardinal veins along with the subclavian veins carrying blood from the pectoral fins. The blood from the digestive tract is collected in the hepatic portal vein, which breaks up into a network of fine vessels and sinusoids (Greek, sinus = bay + eidos = like) that come together again as hepatic veins, emptying into the two great hepatic sinuses that unite with the sinus venosus. The walls of the hepatic sinusoids are endothelial, like those of the capillaries, but they enclose a larger space and expose a greater area of blood to the surrounding tissues.

Such an arrangement of vessels returning blood to the heart is evident during the embryological stages of other vertebrates, but in the adult tetrapods it has become considerably modified and altered. Some of these changes can be traced to the changes that take place in the heart, for, with the reduction in size of the sinus venosus and the Ducts of Cuvier and their incorporation into the wall of the atrium, there is a tendency for the veins from the head and those from the posterior parts of the body to open into the heart directly, without joining together in a common cardinal vein. The division of the atrium into two chambers, with the right one receiving blood from the systemic and portal veins and the left only that from the newly developed pulmonary vein, shifts the position of the principal vessels somewhat to the right. In amphibians, reptiles, birds and mammals a new vein arises in the posterior part of the body, its posterior limit at about the level of the anterior margins of the excretory organs; this is the postcava, or vena cava inferior, which is not found in the circulatory system of any fishes other than the Dipnoi. This vessel takes over the functions of the posterior cardinal veins, which become correspondingly reduced in size and in the higher vertebrates partially or wholly eliminated at some stage of their embryological history.

There is somewhat less change in the pattern of the anterior veins than in that of the posterior ones. In the urodele amphibia, where the resemblance to the bilateral plan of the elasmobranch venous system is closest, the blood from the head returns through the anterior cardinal veins, called in them as in all adult tetrapods jugular veins (Latin, jugulum = collar bone). These, an external and an internal jugular on each side, flow into the Ducts of Cuvier, which are still clearly defined vessels, along with, on each side, a cutaneous vessel from the body wall and a subclavian vein from the forelimb. The subclavian veins gain in size and in importance throughout the vertebrate classes with the increasing development of the anterior appendages. The right and left postcardinal veins, although considerably reduced in size, still carry blood which has passed through the renal portal system from the posterior part of the body and from the excretory organs and also enter the Ducts of Cuvier, but the new, medianly placed postcava, which receives blood also from the posterior parts of the body and from the excretory organs, enters the heart directly, at the sinus venosus. A single abdominal vein, rather than the paired lateral abdominal vessels of the sharks, carries blood directly from the iliac veins to the hepatic portal vein which, receiving also all blood from the vessels of the digestive tract, passes through the liver from which it emerges as the hepatic vein flowing into the postcava (Fig. 16.5). In the frogs and toads, the blood from the head returns to the heart in the two precavae, one on each side formed by the union of the internal and external jugular veins and each receiving as a tributary also the subclavian vessel of each side into which drains blood from the body wall. The posterior cardinal veins have become obliterated, and all the blood from the legs, the posterior part of the body, the excretory organs and the digestive tract is returned to the heart ultimately through the postcava.

In the lower orders of mammals, the Ducts of Cuvier persist but in the others, the jugular and subclavian veins of each side unite in an innominate vein (Latin, in = no + nominare = to name), and the right and left innominate veins usually join to form a single vessel, the precava, which enters the right auricle directly. The only functional remnant of the Ducts of Cuvier is the coronary vein, returning blood from the heart muscle to the right atrium. The more anterior parts of the subcardinals may persist as the azygos vein (Greek, a = not + zygon = yoke) and the hemiazygos vein, draining blood from the right and left sides of the thoracic wall respectively and emptying into the precava. In adult mammals, all the blood from the remainder of the body is returned through the postcava, and there is total elimination of a renal portal system; all the blood to the kidneys reaches them through the renal arteries, paired branches of the dorsal aorta (Fig. 16.6). The hepatic portal system on the other hand is retained and all the blood from the digestive tract passes through the liver before flowing into the postcava.

COMPARATIVE ANATOMY OF THE VERTEBRATE BLOOD SYSTEM AS EVIDENCE FOR THE "BIOGENETIC LAW": The developmental history of the heart and the principal blood vessels in vertebrates, as it is seen in the different classes and in the individuals of different classes, has offered cogent evidence for the progressive evolution of vertebrate types from an ancestral fish to successively amphibian, reptilian, avian and mammalian stages. The origin of the heart as a simple tubular structure, increasing, in the different classes and in the course of development of individuals within those classes, in complexity of structure and in its efficiency in separating the stream of reduced blood, from the body as a whole to the lungs, from that of oxygenated blood, from the lungs to the body as a whole; the development of pharyngeal pouches, some of which may, even in the human embryo, very briefly become open clefts, and of aortic arches associated with them; the gradual transition from a symmetrical venous system to an asymmetrical one by the suppression of some veins and the opening up of others; and the progressive reduction and final elimination of the renal portal system are all facts to support the argument that the development of each individual repeats, in a telescoped fashion and one greatly reduced in time, the history of the group to which it belongs. This idea, supported by other data from comparative anatomy and comparative embryology, was the keystone of the "biogenetical principle" developed by a great German biologist and natural philosopher, Ernst Haeckel (1834–1919), according to which "the development of the embryo is an abstract of the history of the genus."

VARIATIONS IN BLOOD FLOW: But blood, although a highly specialized fluid, is still a fluid and must conform to the physical laws that govern the flow of all fluids. That is to say, it is acted upon by gravity and will tend to flow downhill through the channels of minimal resistance, unless acted upon by another force that opposes the gravitational pull and is great enough to propel it along paths which offer resistance to its free flow; if there are alternative paths, it will enter that offering the least resistance. In the animal body the second force is set up by the contraction of the heart muscle, which in all vertebrates is differentiated early in the course of embryological development. The differentiation of the blood from the mesenchyme is closely associated both in time and in space with the organization of the mesenchyme cells into the endothelium of the blood vessels. At first, the channels through which the blood flows are more or less diffuse, but as the cells that will give rise to the definitive organs of the body are brought into position and the tissues of these organs differentiated, the course of the channels is increasingly restricted. Some become occluded as increasing resistance reduces the flow of blood through them or as the demand for blood supply in that region diminishes, others enlarge as more blood flows through them and new ones open up as conditions make possible the flow of blood through new areas. The mechanical and physiological conditions prevailing at any time in the course of development are basically the conditions that determine the pattern of the blood vessels, and the fact that at one stage of its embryological life an air-dwelling vertebrate has a pattern of blood vessels that resembles that of an adult water dweller does not necessarily mean that it has passed through such a stage in its evolutionary history. It may equally well mean that it has that pattern at that particular time of its life because it is the one best suited to the conditions of its structural development and its physiological demands at that time. As the definitive organs of the body are blocked out in the course of growth and their tissues take on their characteristic features and organization, the course of the blood vessels becomes more and more limited and clearly defined so that in the adult the blood flows only through definite paths which have been determined by the character of the tissues which it serves and the organization of the body as a whole. That variations should occur in the pattern of circulatory systems among individuals of the same species should not be surprising, for there may have been in the course of development just enough difference in the rate of differentiation of a tissue or of its position in relation to others to cause a shift in the direction of the blood flow which, if it occurs at a critical time of development, may result in the formation of a permanent vessel. Such anomalies are not infrequent, and the most that can be said for the plan of any circulatory system is that it has the same general pattern in the adults of a given group but that it may show great individuality in its details.

And even in any one individual the course of the blood flow is not always the same, at least as far as the finer vessels are concerned, for as conditions change with changes in the activity of different parts of the body, from hour to hour or from minute to minute, or during the growth, ageing and senescence of an individual, blood channels are shut off and the ordinary flow of blood through them is diverted to other vessels, unless conditions bring about their opening up again. Increased activity on the part of any organ is usually accompanied by increased blood flow, and since the total volume of blood within the body remains relatively constant, this increase can only be met by drawing on the supply to other organs or by tapping any reservoirs of blood that may exist; conversely the temporary disuse or permanent atrophy of an organ is accompanied by a reduction in its blood supply. The success with which the blood system can make adjustments to the varying local demands put upon it is one measure of the success of the organism as a whole. The greatest efficiency in circulatory mechanisms among modern animals has been attained by the birds and mammals, for the complete separation of the pulmonary from the systemic circulation relieves the heart of the burden of pumping around the body, against gravity and against the frictional resistance of the blood vessels and the viscosity of the blood itself, any blood but that which is highest in oxygen content; moreover, the number and distribution of the principal vessels is such that a minimal load is put upon the heart, commensurate with an adequate supply to all parts of the body and adequate drainage from them. But while a progressive relationship between the amphibia and the reptiles, the reptiles and the birds and the reptiles and the mammals seems evident from the changes that the circulatory system, especially the heart and the aortic arches, undergo in the course of individual development, it seems equally clear that the birds and the mammals have followed different lines of evolution from a probable common, reptile-like ancestor, and that both have attained similar degrees of structural complexity and physiological efficiency in their circulatory systems along different paths, determined by the conditions of their embryonic as well as their adult existence.

It is clear from a consideration of the course of the blood throughout the body of a vertebrate that its content changes appreciably as it passes through the capillary bed in the various tissues. The greatest change at any one time takes place during its passage through the organs of external respiration, for the exchange of gases is a comparatively rapid one. Blood leaving these areas is different in color, as well as in $O_2$ and $CO_2$ content, than that entering them, for oxidized hemoglobin (oxyhemoglobin) is a clearer, brighter red than it is in its reduced state, when it is a somewhat purplish-blue. The exchange of other materials that the blood carries around the body goes on more slowly, as a rule, although there is a good deal of difference in the rates at which different substances are absorbed by it from the tissues, and discharged to them by the blood. But the blood does not lose all its content of diffusible materials and acquire a new load of different ones in any one circuit of the body; its composition is constantly shifting within limits, of narrow range for some constituents, wider ones for others, and the concentration of any one substance in it at any one time must always be considered as relative to its concentration at another. After a meal, for example, the hepatic portal vein will be full of blood rich in the partial decomposition products of the food; it loses some of these as the blood flows through the liver sinusoids, and hence is reduced in viscosity as it enters the heart, but it requires a great many circuits through the liver and other tissues before the concentration of these products is lowered to the level at which they were before the food was eaten and digested.

## Lymphatic system

Closely related to the blood system and accessory to its functions is the vertebrate lymphatic system, which consists of a number of more or less clearly defined vessels and an extensive network of very delicate ones with endothelial walls like those of the blood capillaries and bores of slightly greater diameter. The larger vessels resemble the veins in the character of their walls, and their course to a great extent parallels that of the veins, into which they open at two or more points. The finer vessels form an interlacing network in the dermis and the subcutaneous tissue, and they are distributed in close association with the blood capillaries around and among the cells of nearly all the tissues (Fig. 16.13).

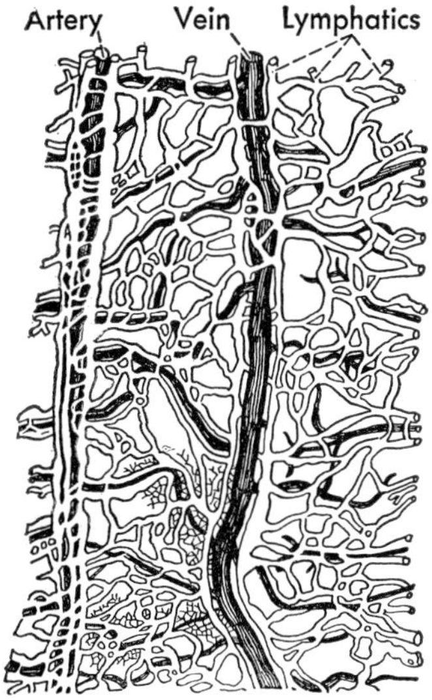

FIGURE 16.13 Distribution of lymphatics in the lung of the mudpuppy, Necturus. (After Miller, from Walter and Sayles, *Biology of the Vertebrates*. Copyright 1949 by The Macmillan Company.)

The fluid that flows through these vessels is called lymph (Latin, lympha = water), and although its composition varies in different regions of the body, and from time to time in the same region, in general it is a fluid like blood, containing salts and sugars in the same concentration as blood, apparently all the blood proteins in slightly lower concentration, relatively few erythrocytes, so that it is yellowish rather than red in color, and a preponderance of lymphocytes. Lymph will clot, although much more slowly than whole blood; this delay has been attributed to its deficiency in thromboplastin. The course of the flow of lymph is unlike that of the blood, for it flows only from the tissue spaces toward the heart, and never from the heart toward the tissue spaces; this can be shown experimentally by cutting or tying off lymph vessels, which results in an accumulation of the fluid, a condition known as edema (Greek, oidema = swelling), on the side of the block away from the heart. A similar condition sometimes arises in consequence of the occlusion of lymphatic vessels by growth or accumulations of micro-organisms or other parasites in them. The abnormal swelling of the legs of human beings called elephantiasis is attributed to blocks of this kind in the lymphatics that drain the lower limbs (Fig. 16.14). Among other things, infestation by a nematode, Filaria bancrofti, may be a cause of elephantiasis, for the parasites invade the lymphatic vessels and, if they do not block them entirely, give rise to inflammatory and other reactions that finally do cause their complete obstruction.

In birds and mammals the movement of the lymph toward the veins, against gravity, depends upon the hydrostatic pressure in the tissues relative to that in the veins, and upon the movements of the body that constrict the vessels and so propel the fluid along them. Valves in the vessels prevent the backflow of lymph so that it moves continuously, although very slowly, toward the main collecting vessels, the thoracic ducts, that run along the dorsal wall of the body cavity and open into the subclavian veins close to the entrance of the jugulars, a point where the pressure within the circulatory system is at a particularly low level (Fig. 16.15). In lower vertebrates, there are no valves and the lymph is propelled toward the veins by pulsations of lymph hearts, enlargements along the course of the lymph vessels which are sometimes divided into auricle and ventricle.

Lymphoid tissue, essentially connective tissue containing within the framework of its fixed cells and fibres quantities of lymphocytes and some blood cells, is widely distributed throughout the bodies of all vertebrates, sometimes in diffuse masses and sometimes in definite aggregates enclosed within a sheath or capsule of connective tissue. In fishes and amphibia, it is found in the liver, heart, reproductive and excretory organs but is particularly abundant in the walls of the digestive tract. The spleen, an organ found in most fishes and all tetrapods, is an elongated mass of lymphoid tissue lying along the greater curvature of the stomach; it is an important center of blood cell production in the embryonic stages of all vertebrates and in the mature ones of all but mammals.

In birds and mammals, there is a greater separation of lymphoid tissue from other organs and a diversion of its function of blood cell production to the marrow cavities of the bones, which have become the principal sites of their erythrocyte and granulocyte production, while the more definitely delimited areas of lymphoid tissue, or lymphoid organs, retain the function of lymphocyte production. In mammals, and in some birds (those of the water, marsh and shore), lymph nodes are distributed along the course of the lymphatic vessels. These originate as twisted meshworks of lymph capillaries in the connective tissue; blood vessels enter the mass, and it is further invaded by lymphocytes and becomes a compact structure supplied by afferent blood and lymphatic vessels and drained by efferent ones (Fig. 16.16). In mammals, these nodes are widely distributed through the body, and may be found as masses of varying size in the limbs, the mesenteries that support the viscera, in the nose and pharynx, in the neck and in the thorax. In the higher mammals, the nodes tend to be smaller and more numerous than in the lower. And in addition to the nodes and the spleen, the thymus gland, the tonsils and Peyer's patches in the intestinal wall all represent aggregates of lymphoid tissue. Collected together in one organ, these separate areas would be of considerable size and it has been estimated that were they all taken together, the lymphoid tissue would be about 1 per cent of the total weight of the body.

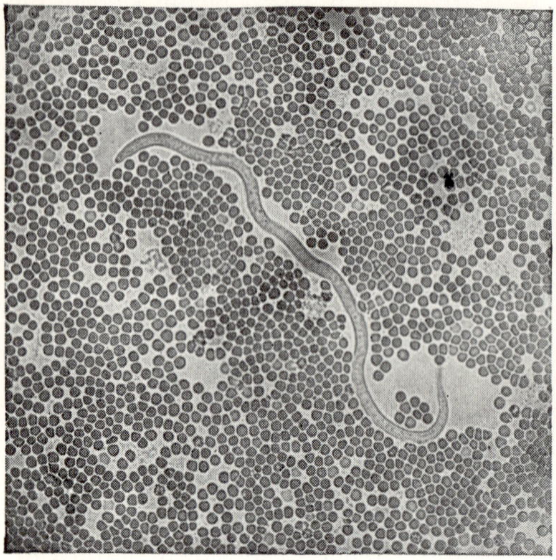

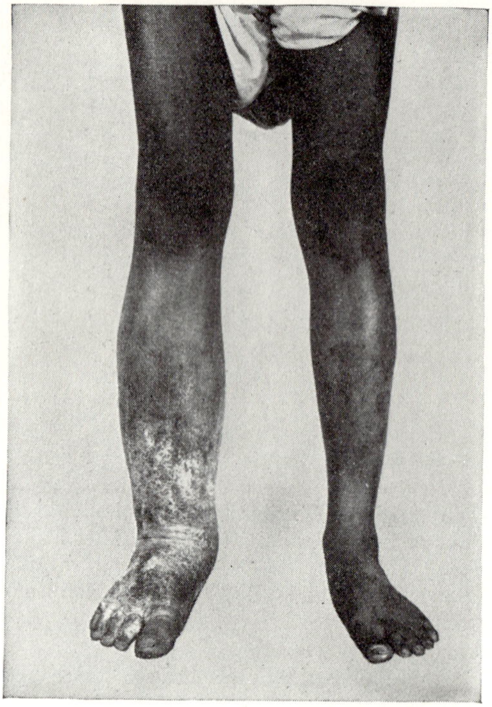

The functions of lymph have been most extensively studied in the amphibia and the mammals, but even there all the desired information is as yet far from complete. In the frog, the lymphatic system is essentially part of the circulatory system, for the water, proteins and other solutes that leave the blood capillaries and are not taken up from the

FIGURE 16.14 Elephantiasis. (Photographs by courtesy of the Army Institute of Pathology.)

a. A guinea worm (Filaria sanguinis hominis) in the blood stream of an infected human being.

b. Edematous condition of the leg of an Oriental infected with Filaria, caused by blockage of the lymph vessels.

tissue fluid by the cells pass into the lymph capillaries and are returned to the blood stream. Measurements made on the rate of lymph flow show that all the fluid volume of the blood leaves the capillaries and returns to the blood via the lymphatics 50 times within 24 hours. In these animals there appears to be a high degree of permeability on the part of the endothelium of both the blood and the lymph capillaries to the constituents of blood plasma so that there is almost free exchange across them; if the lymphatic channels of the frog are blocked, within a short period of time nearly all the blood proteins will be collected in the fluid outside the blood vessels and the animal dies.

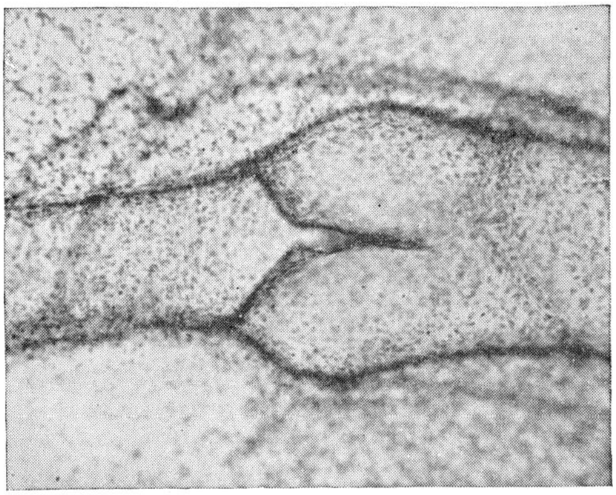

The capillary endothelium of the mammalian blood vessels and lymphatics is similarly permeable to colloids as well as to crystalloids; there seems to be a continual process of filtration of plasma across the blood capillaries into the tissue fluid, an exchange of solutes between the tissue fluid and the cells that it bathes, which is controlled by the permeability of the cell membrane, and a return of the plasma, minus these extracted substances and plus some gained from the cells, through the lymphatic channels back to the blood stream in a fairly short period of time. The pressure within the blood capillaries and the permeability of their walls and that of the lymphatic capillaries are controlling factors in this transfer of fluid from the blood stream into the tissue spaces and back to the blood stream again; the conditions within the tissues in consequence of the metabolic activities of their cells determine the amount and kind of material which will enter them from the tissue fluid and which will diffuse or be secreted from them into it. The properties of the plasma membrane of the cells, which from time to time may vary in its degree of permeability to particular substances, are of the greatest importance in this exchange, which presents to the biologist, and to the physical chemist as well, some of the most fundamental and challenging problems of biological regulation and control.

The mammalian lymphatic system shows not only more complete anatomical separation from the circulatory system than in other vertebrates, but also specialization in a number of ways. One of these is the particular capacity of the vessels in the intestinal villi to take up, in addition to the blood proteins, fats which have undergone preliminary breakdown in the lumen of the digestive tract. The finer capillaries and the central lacteals of the villi are the exclusive channels through which fat leaves the intestine, but how the microscopically visible globules of fat, or chylomicrons, in active

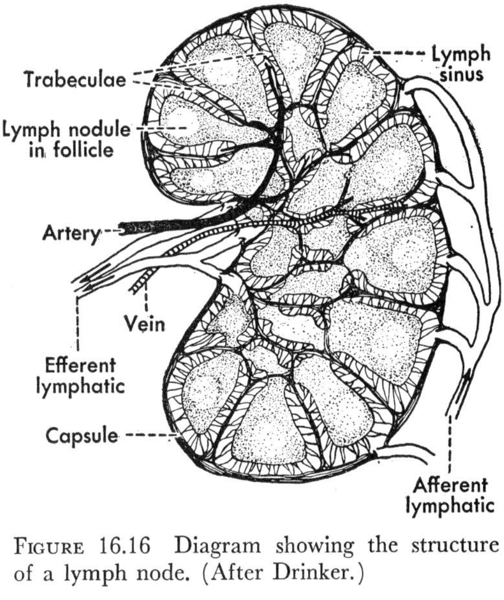

FIGURE 16.15  Valve in a lymph vessel. (Photograph by courtesy of the General Biological Supply House, Inc., Chicago.)

FIGURE 16.16  Diagram showing the structure of a lymph node. (After Drinker.)

Brownian movement get into the lymphatics is not yet known. It is quite clear that they do and that the suspension of fat droplets, or chyle (Greek, chylos = juice) is transferred to the general circulation by way of the lymphatics in the mesenteries and the thoracic duct. Indeed, the first demonstration of the lymphatics was a consequence of the distention of these particular ones with the whitish chyle, which enabled an Italian anatomist, Gasparo Aselli (Asellio) (1581–1626) to see them and to trace part of their course.

In addition to the absorption of fat, the lymphatics have been shown by numerous experiments to be able to take up particulate matter of many kinds. Mineral dusts are removed from the alveoli of the lungs by the lymphatics; dyes introduced on the membranes of the nose and pharynx appear very shortly afterwards in the cervical lymph, and graphite particles and even the red blood cells of amphibia and birds, injected into the peritoneal cavity of mammals, are recoverable from the lymph vessels of the thorax. A close relationship between lymph and the synovial fluid of the joint capsules is shown by experiments in which solid particles, such as the graphite of India ink, and certain proteins injected into the joint cavities of mammals ultimately reappear in the lymph, and finally in the blood, showing that movement of particles and of molecules can take place across the capsular lining into the lymph vessels. Bacteria and viral particles are similarly taken up by lymph, and the infective organisms finding a point of entrance in the nasopharyngeal mucous membranes may be very effectively transported to the blood stream through the lymphatics and hence generally distributed around the body. The lymph nodes appear to function as filters along the course of the lymphatic vessels as well as sites of origin or storage reservoirs for lymphocytes. The rate of flow of the slow-moving lymph is even more reduced in the twisted mass of lymph capillaries within the nodes, and the larger foreign bodies at least are crowded together and trapped within the node while the clarified lymph trickles out from the efferent lymph vessels. The nodes thus act as barriers to the further distribution of some invading particles and so as one of the organism's mechanisms of defense against them; this protective function of the nodes is extended also to the formation of antibodies, for which they are believed to be the principal site, and so, in addition to acting as barriers to the passage of infective agents, their cells operate to bring about the destruction or inactivation of them or of their products. A large number of widely distributed lymph nodes, such as are found in mammals, consequently offers a fairly efficient mechanism for the removal of micro-organisms, but a mechanism that may break down under certain conditions, such as increased lymph pressure or especial virulence of the infecting agent, or numbers of organisms too great to be held back in the filter. The nodes appear to act as much less efficient barriers in the case of viruses, for some experiments have shown that vaccinia, the virus causing cowpox, dropped into the nose of a rabbit is recoverable from the cervical lymph within nine hours, and practically continuously thereafter up to twelve days after the initial infection. The present evidence seems to indicate that the lymph nodes through which the virus must pass before reaching the main cervical channels not only fail to retard or prevent its passage but even offer areas within which it may multiply, thus increasing rather than reducing the magnitude of the infection. The lymphatics also are considered the pathway through which malignant cells, detached from a primary cancerous growth, are transported throughout the body to initiate the secondary growths, or metastases (Greek, meta = after + histanai = to place), typical of certain types of cancer.

## Reticulo-endothelial system

The close association of endothelium and reticular tissues which occurs in a number of organs in the vertebrate body—in the spleen, liver, bone marrow and lymph nodes of mammals, for example—has led to the use of the term "reticulo-endothelial system" for those regions where the phagocytic activity of cells is especially favored or especially evident, and where particulate matter of all kinds, formed in the body as well as invading it from outside, is disposed of. The Kupffer cells of the liver, the tissue macrophages as well as the cells localized in the spleen and other lymphoid organs all belong to this system, to which a wide variety of functions is attributed, including the formation and destruction of blood cells; the formation of bile pigments; the storage and metabolism of iron; fat and protein metabolism; the production of enzymes and of antibodies; and the ingestion and elimination of foreign particles of all kinds.

## The nervous system

### Structure and function

In contrast to the independence with which the blood cells perform their functions in the vertebrate body, the cellular units of the nervous system are characterized by their mutual dependence. Successful operation in the nervous system results only from the combined activity of its cells, since an impulse, to be effective, must be conducted and transmitted along a series of neurons to an effector organ. It is through the connections and interrelationships of their receptive and transmitting nerve cells and the effector organs that stumulus and response are integrated, resulting in the sum total of activities called behavior.

*The structural unit of the nervous system; the neuron:* The structural units of the vertebrate nervous system are neurons, specialized cells of different shapes and sizes in which the properties of irritability and conductivity, common to all protoplasm, reach their maximum expression. Nerve cells respond to the same agents that stimulate protoplasm in general—to energy as light, heat and electricity, to chemical agents and to mechanical ones such as contact and pressure—and they transmit the excitations aroused by such stimuli to other neurons and to other cells in the body, specifically the muscle cells and fibres and gland cells of different kinds.

A neuron consists of a cell body, or mass of protoplasm within which lie the nucleus and typical cellular inclusions, with protoplasmic processes, often of great length, extending from it (Fig. 16.17). The principal process, from the point of view of size, is the axon, or axis cylinder; this may be as

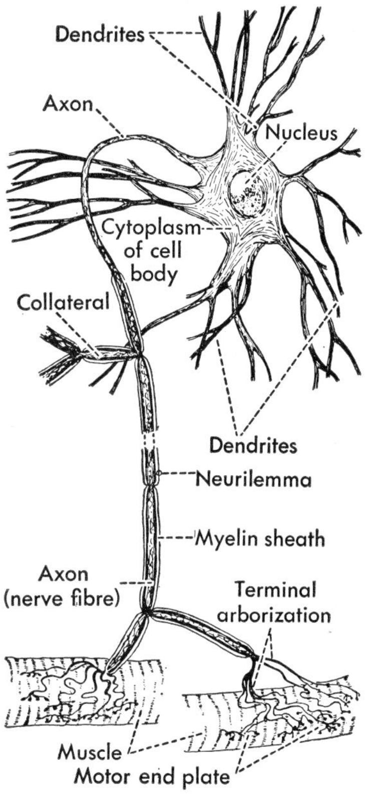

FIGURE 16.17 Diagram showing the structure of a neuron (somatic efferent). (After Jordan.)

long as a meter or more, as it is in the case of some of the neurons extending from the base of the spinal cord to the lower part of the leg in large mammals. The axon is, in many cases, surrounded by a sheath, the medullary sheath, composed of the lipid myelin, which protects the axon to some extent and may also serve to nourish and to insulate it so that the impulse travels in the main along its length, and lateral dissipation is minimized. Some neurons have an additional sheath, the neurilemma (Greek, neuron = nerve + eilema = covering), or sheath of Schwann; this is a cellular layer that may contribute to the formation of

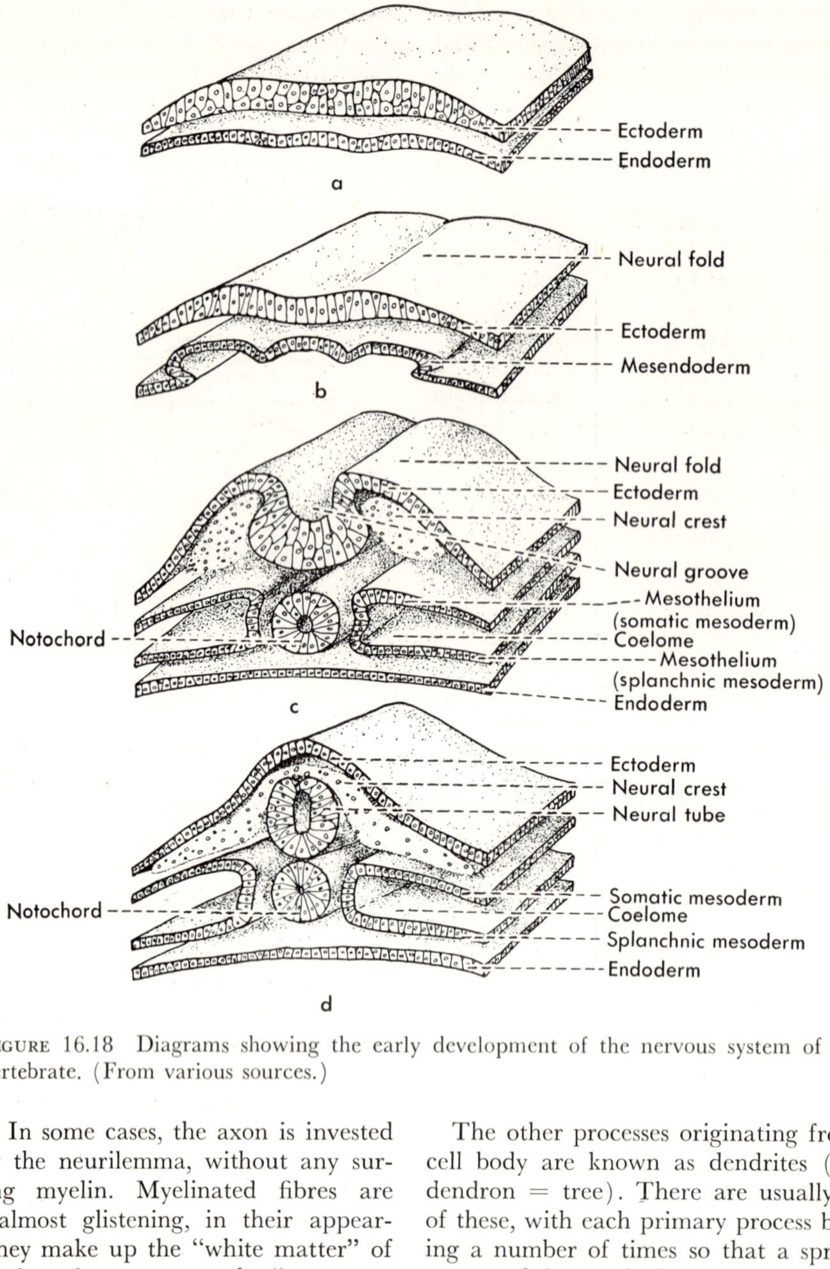

FIGURE 16.18 Diagrams showing the early development of the nervous system of a vertebrate. (From various sources.)

myelin. In some cases, the axon is invested only by the neurilemma, without any surrounding myelin. Myelinated fibres are white, almost glistening, in their appearance; they make up the "white matter" of nervous tissue in contrast to the "gray matter" of non-myelinated cells and processes. The axon gives off along its length side branches, or collaterals, terminating in relation to other cells, and, at its distal end away from the cell body, it breaks up into a large but varying number of branches, without either type of sheath, which make contact with other cells.

The other processes originating from the cell body are known as dendrites (Greek, dendron = tree). There are usually many of these, with each primary process branching a number of times so that a spreading system of fine, naked protoplasmic strands results.

*The development of the nervous system:* The greater part of the vertebrate nervous system is derived from embryonic ectoderm cells, which at an early stage in the development of the individual become depressed in a groove, or furrow, and finally sink below the surface as a hollow tube with particularly thick side walls in the midline of the dorsal region of the embryo. This is the neural tube, along whose sides extend two masses of cells, the neural crests, similarly derived from embryonic ectoderm (Fig.

meninx primitiva (Greek, meninx = membrane), but in the amphibia, reptiles and birds there are two layers, an outer dura spinalis (Latin, durus = hard) and an inner pia mater (Latin, pia = tender, mater = mother), the latter so-called because in

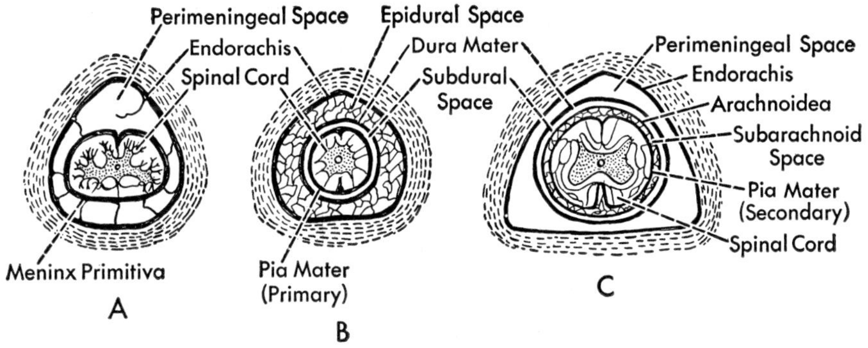

FIGURE 16.19 Diagrams showing the meninges in (A) fishes; (B), amphibians, reptiles and birds; (C), mammals. (The endorachis corresponds to the perichondrium, the dura mater to the dura spinalis, and the arachnoidea to the arachnoid membrane.) (After Weidersheim and Sterzi, from Walter and Sayles, *Biology of the Vertebrates.* Copyright 1949 by The Macmillan Company.)

16.18). From these cells, and others that migrate in from limited areas of the ectoderm along the neural tube, or placodes (Greek, plax = flat plate), and from others that remain on or near the surface and become specialized as neuroepithelial cells, the various nervous elements of the body are differentiated. Later on in the course of development, the tube becomes invested with a coat of connective tissue, supplied with blood vessels, and enclosed by the cartilage or bone of the axial skeleton, and its cells differentiated as conducting ones, the neurons, and covering or supporting ones, non-nervous in their nature, the ependymal (Greek, ependyma = upper garment) and glia (Greek, glia = glue) cells.

*The meninges:* The nerve cord is invested throughout its length by connective tissue and separated from the connective tissue that surrounds the bone and cartilage of the brain case and vertebral column by a space filled with a specialized blood filtrate, the cerebrospinal fluid, containing salts, some cells and traces of protein. In the fishes, this covering is but a single layer, called the

Arabic science it was believed to be the "mother" of the brain (Fig. 16.19). The pia mater is a delicate sheet of connective tissue supporting blood vessels that supply the central nervous system; the space between it and the dura is the sub-dural space, while that between the dura and the periosteum or perichondrium is the peri-dural space, all of which are also filled with cerebrospinal fluid. In the mammals, there are three meninges, a delicate pia mater in contact with the nervous tissue and carried down into the cavities of the brain as part of the choroid plexuses, an arachnoid membrane (Greek, arachne = spider's web), separated from the pia mater by the subarachnoid space traversed by delicate strands like a spider's web, and the dura mater, which in the primates is fused with the periosteum of the skull and the vertebral column.

## Anatomical subdivisions of the nervous system

For descriptive purposes only, the vertebrate nervous system may for convenience be considered as consisting of three parts, or divisions: the central system, including the brain and cord, the peripheral system, including the nerves that supply the skeletal muscles and the superficial sensory areas, and the autonomic system, including those nerves that supply the smooth muscles of the body, the viscera and certain of the glands. All three are so closely united, both structurally and functionally, that such a division is entirely an arbitrary one and both anatomically and physiologically meaningless.

*Central nervous system:* The nervous elements of the brain and cord are differentiated from the sides of the embryonic neural tube, while its dorsal and ventral walls, or roof and floor, are primarily non-nervous, but may secondarily become so by the migration of neurons from the side walls into them. The neurons within the brain and cord lie either with their axons parallel to the long axis of the body, and so conduct stimuli along it either anteriorly or posteriorly, or else lie transverse to the long axis, and so conduct stimuli across the tube, from one side to the other. From some of the neurons in the ventral regions of the side walls axons grow out laterally and terminate in relation to responsive cells. These are called efferent neurons for they convey impulses from the central regions outward, but they are often, less accurately, called motor neurons, since their successful operation results in the activity of an organ often expressed as movement. Other neurons, differentiated from the cells of the neural crests and sending processes both into the brain and cord and also to different parts of the body, convey impulses from the peripheral regions into the central system; these are afferent neurons, also often less accurately referred to as sensory neurons, since they convey stimuli received by sense receptors of various kinds.

THE SPINAL CORD: The spinal cord is the great central pathway along which run fibres of afferent nerves, carrying impulses from the peripheral regions of the body to other levels of the cord and the brain, and those carrying impulses from higher levels, and from the brain, to the efferent neurons; it is also a coordinating center for some of these incoming and outgoing stimuli. The core of the cord is gray matter, consisting of cell bodies and unmyelinated axons. The cell bodies are those of the efferent nerves

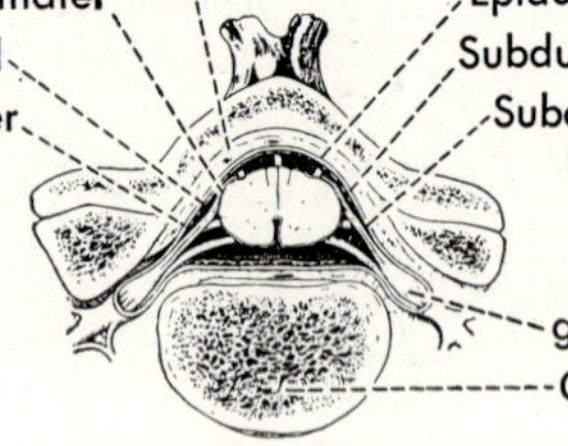

FIGURE 16.20  Cross section through a vertebra and the nerve cord within it, showing their relations to each other and the emergence of peripheral nerves from intervertebral foramina. (From Kimber, Gray and Stackpole, *Textbook of Anatomy and Physiology*, 11th edition. Copyright 1942 by The Macmillan Company.)

and of neurons that lie wholly within the cord; the unmyelinated fibres are chiefly those of these neurons and of the collaterals of the afferent nerves. The white matter surrounding the gray is made up of myelinated fibres of the afferent spinal nerves and those of connecting neurons within the cord, forming thick columns of fibres conducting impulses either anteriorly or posteriorly (Fig. 16.20). Because of the distribution of gray matter, it is possible to distinguish in many vertebrates between a dorsal and a ventral column of white matter, lying between the wings of gray matter on each side, and two lateral columns, one in the concavity of each wing. These columns can be further resolved histologically into smaller bundles of fibres, or funiculi (Latin, funiculus = little cord), whose courses and functional connections have to a great extent been traced by experimental studies. In general, the dorsal column consists of fibres that transmit impulses to the brain, or, according to the terminology of human anatomy, of ascending tracts; the ventral column consists of fibres that transmit impulses posteriorly, or of descending tracts, and the two lateral columns of some ascending and some descending tracts. Since the ascending columns are made up in great measure of the dorsal roots of the spinal nerves, or of neurons associated with them, they tend to grow larger from posterior to anterior as more fibres are added to them,

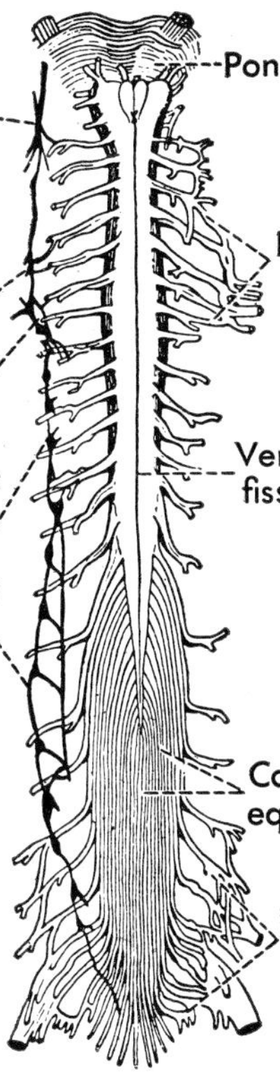

FIGURE 16.21 The spinal cord of man, showing plexuses, cauda equina and, on the left side, the chain of autonomic ganglia. (After Rauber, from Walter and Sayles, *Biology of the Vertebrates*. Copyright 1949 by The Macmillan Company.)

and conversely the descending tracts tend to grow smaller from anterior to posterior as connections are made between them and the cells of the efferent nerves in the ventral horns of the gray matter. The cord as a whole thus tends to taper toward its extremity in the posterior region of the body, although in the tetrapods with appendages it shows enlargements in the region of the fore and hind limbs where the large nerves to and from the limbs enter and leave it. Indeed, in some of the fossil reptiles that have been found, the dinosaurs, casts of the central nervous system show that there was an accumulation of nervous tissue at the level of the hind limbs that exceeded the mass and dimensions of their brains.

The spinal cord varies in its length, relative to the body length, in different vertebrates. In the fishes, caudate amphibia, reptiles and birds, it usually extends almost to the end of the vertebral column; although it is much more slender at its tip than it is anteriorly, it gives off spinal nerves along its entire length which may number more than a hundred in some of the larger fishes and reptiles. But in the acaudate amphibia and the mammals, the terminal region of the cord is non-nervous, a filum terminale (Latin, filum = thread), which does not even reach the posterior limit of the vertebral column (Fig. 16.21). The posterior nerves lie at the end of the nervous region, anterior to the filum terminale, and, bending posteriorly, form the cauda equina, or horse's tail, on the sides of the vertebral column.

THE BRAIN: The brain develops from the anterior bulbous enlargement of the neural tube; it is, like the cord, hollow and composed of nerve cells with and without investing myelin sheaths, and of glia cells. Early in the course of development it becomes marked off by transverse grooves into three primary regions, the prosencephalon (Greek, pros = near + encephalon = brain); the mesencephalon (Greek, mesos = middle) and the rhombencephalon (Greek, rhombos = wheel). As growth proceeds, the prosencephalon becomes marked off by another transverse groove into two regions, an anterior telencephalon (Greek, telos = end) and a posterior diencephalon (Greek, dia = through), and the rhombencephalon becomes similarly divided into metencephalon (Greek, meta = after) and myelencephalon (Greek, myelen = marrow) (Fig. 16.22). Each of these five regions, or chambers, develops in a characteristic way in the different groups of vertebrates, and in all of them their original linear order is more or less masked in the adults as some regions come to overlie others. In the Amniotes, the tube is folded upon itself, for some parts grow faster than others and the brain as a whole grows at a more rapid rate than the other issues of the head. A bend, the primary flexure, first appears at the level of the mesencephalon, turning the anterior cham-

As the side walls of the chambers of the brain become thickened to different degrees by the multiplication and differentiation of nerve cells in them, its central cavity becomes more or less reduced but persists in all as the ventricles, filled with cerebrospinal

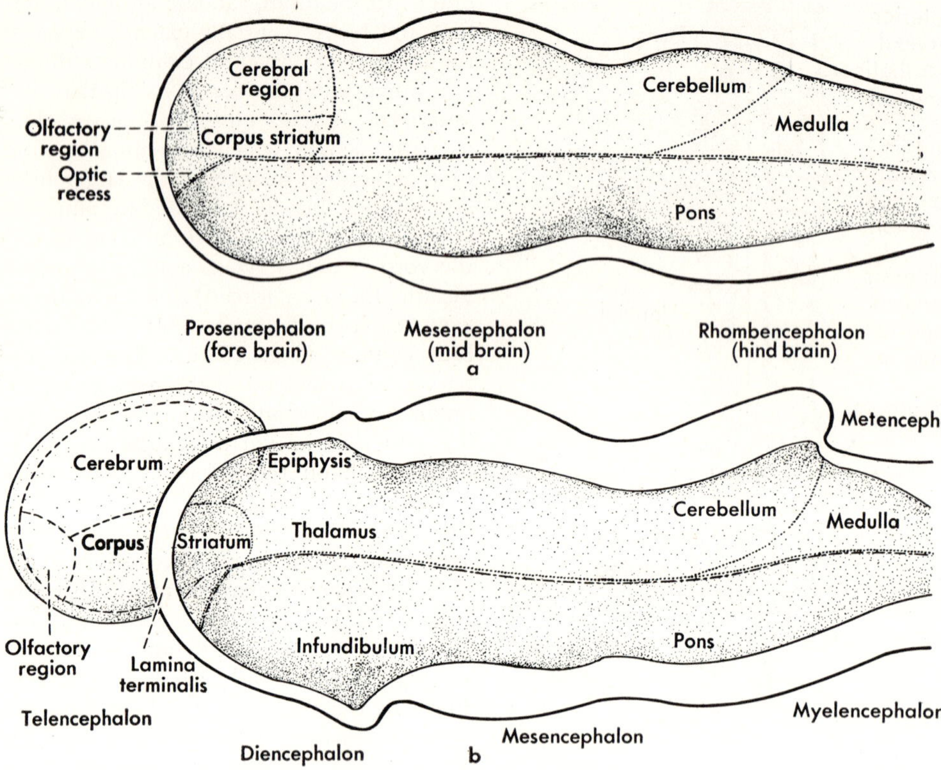

FIGURE 16.22 Diagrams showing the primary divisions of the vertebrate brain. (After Kingsley.)

a. primitive stage.
b. intermediate stage.

ber forward and at right angles to the others. The nuchal flexure, in the posterior part of the myelencephalon, bends all of the brain anterior to it forward, so that the telencephalon is directed posteriorly and its ventral surface, and that of the diencephalon, brought close to the ventral surface of the metencephalon. A third flexure, the pontine, at the junction of metencephalon and myelencephalon, bends the tube in the opposite direction, and so brings the telencephalon and diencephalon again into a dorsal position (Fig. 16.23).

fluid (Fig. 16.24). The cavity of the mesencephalon, in the adult brain connecting the third ventricle with the fourth, is called the Aqueduct of Sylvius, after a French anatomist Jacques Dubois (1478–1555), who was known as Sylvius. In general, the floor and roof of the brain remain thin and non-nervous, in comparison to its sides. This difference is particularly marked in the diencephalon and the myelencephalon, where the roof is very thin and very vascular and projects down into the ventricles as choroid plexuses, through which exchange of mate-

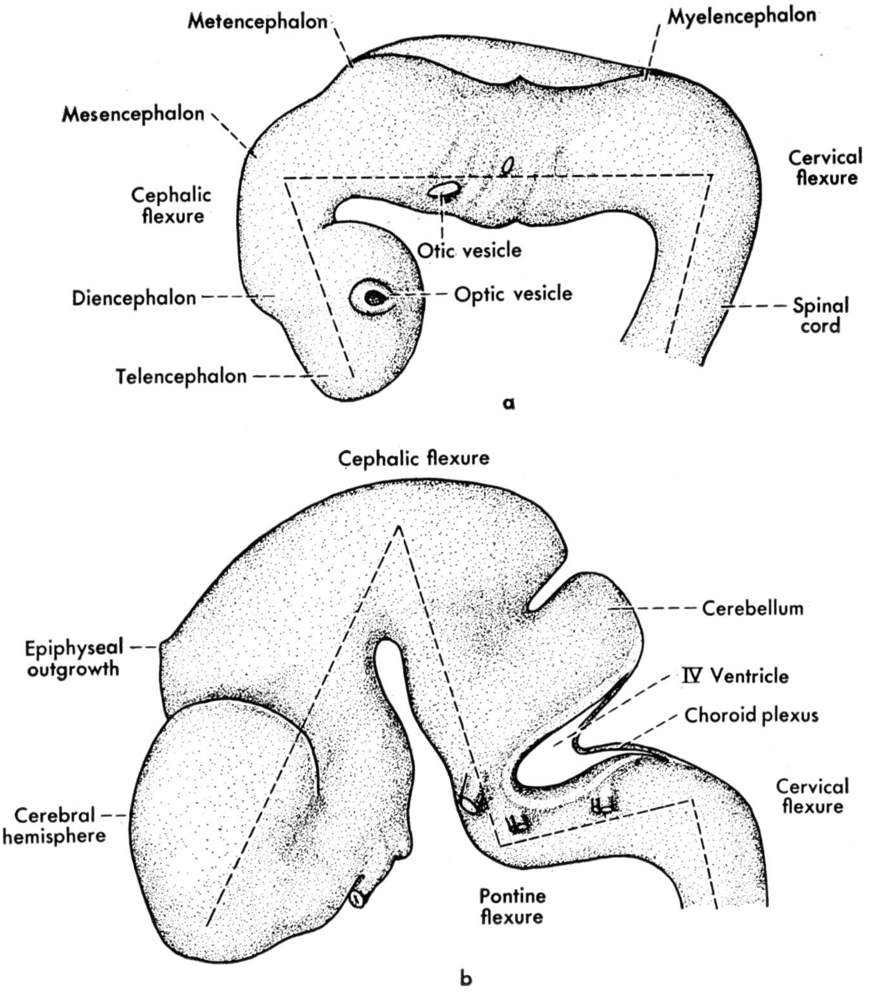

FIGURE 16.23  Flexures of the human brain stem. (After Arey.)

a. The brain of an embryo 6 mm. in length, showing cephalic and cervical flexures, both of which bend the brain ventrally on its stem.

b. The brain of an embryo 14 mm. in length, showing the position of the third, or pontine, flexure, which bends the anterior part of the brain dorsally.

rials is effected between the blood vessels and the cerebrospinal fluid (Fig. 16.25).

*Development of the telencephalon:* In all vertebrates, there is pronounced growth of the side walls of the telencephalon, forming the cerebral hemispheres, which bulge out laterally and extend anteriorly beyond the forward limit of the neural tube as it is first laid down in embryonic development. This point is marked in the adult brain by a strip of tissue, the lamina terminalis, which forms a bridge for fibres crossing from one hemisphere to the other. The position of the lamina terminalis becomes relatively more posterior with increasing forward expansion of the cerebral hemispheres, and in the mammals, where the cerebral hemispheres reach their greatest development, it is just dorsal to the point of entry of the nerves from the eyes, and makes part of the anterior wall of the third ventricle, the cavity of

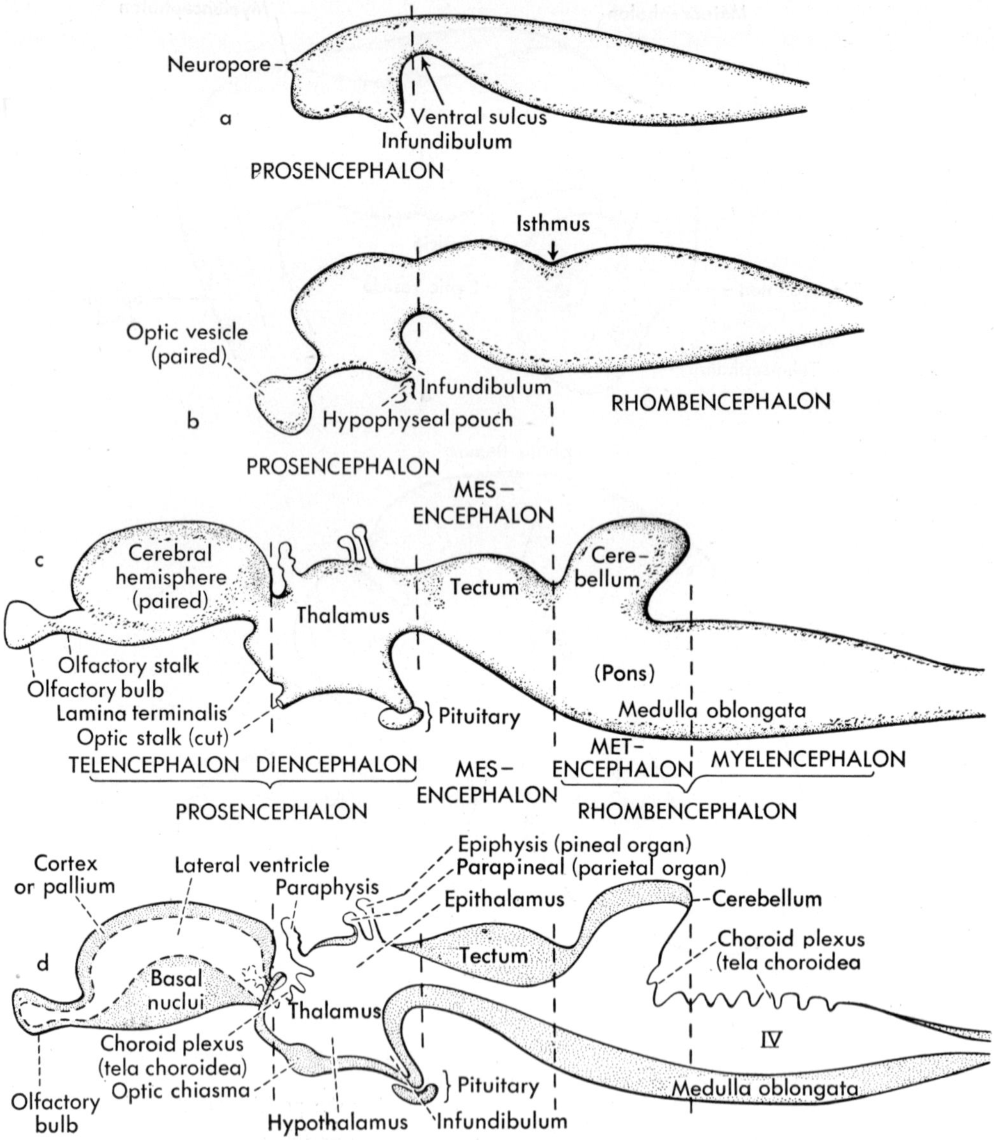

FIGURE 16.24 Diagrams showing the development of the principal brain divisions and structures. a–c, surface views; d, median longitudinal section of c. (Partly after Butschli, from Romer, *The Vertebrate Body*. Copyright 1949 by the W. B. Saunders Company.)

the diencephalon. The ventro-lateral wall of each cerebral hemisphere becomes thickened by the accumulation of nerve cells which results in the formation of a mass, the corpus striatum, on the floor of each lateral ventricle. The dorso-lateral walls of the cerebral hemispheres cover over these enlarged ventral regions as the pallium (Latin, pallium = mantle). Olfactory bulbs grow forward from their anterior surfaces toward the olfactory organs on the surface of the body in which the fibres of the olfactory nerves terminate. These bulbs are well developed in all vertebrates that rely largely upon olfactory stimuli for their awareness of objects in the world around them, but in others are relatively small and merged to greater or less extent with the cerebral hemispheres (Fig. 16.26).

These, in the course of vertebrate evolution, have become increasingly larger in size, due partly to the growth of the corpora cells, covers only the upper surfaces of the hemispheres, but in mammals it not only envelops all but their ventral surfaces but also overlies other parts of the brain (Fig. 16.27). In the higher mammals, its extent is also increased by foldings and the cerebral

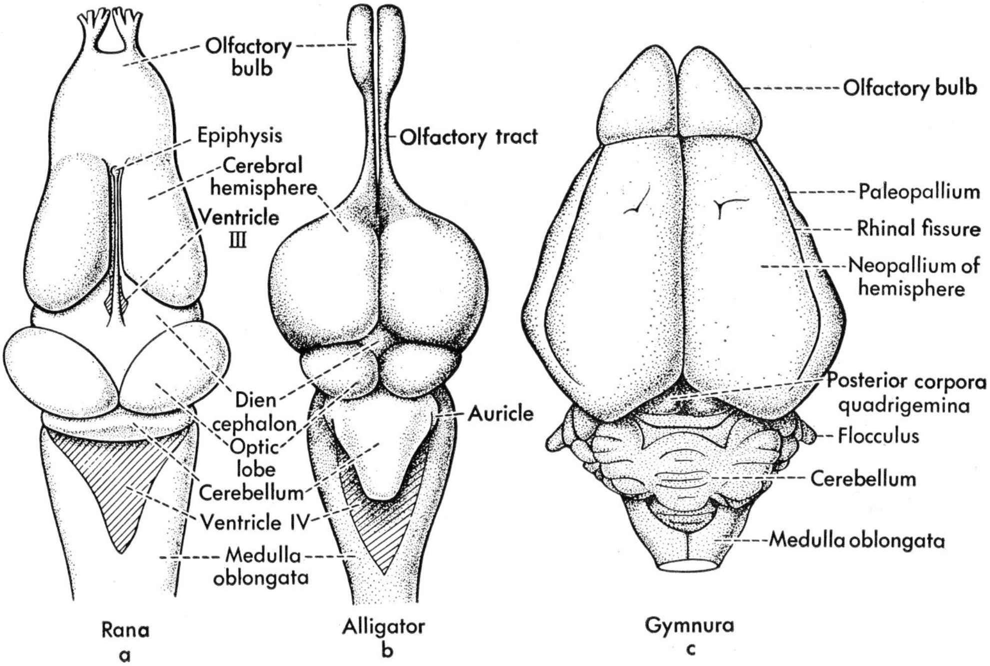

FIGURE 16.25 Dorsal views of the brains of (a) an amphibian (frog), (b), a reptile (alligator) and (c), a primitive mammal (tree shrew). Hatched areas indicate those from which the choroid plexus has been removed, exposing the underlying ventricle. (After Gaupp, Crosby, Wettstein, Clark, from Romer, *The Vertebrate Body*. Copyright 1949 by the W. B. Saunders Company.)

striata and, in Amniotes, to that of the cortex (Latin, cortex = bark). The cortex is a superficial area of gray matter derived from the pallium by the invasion of nerve cells into it; these cells are large and pyramidal in shape, with many dendrites, and are arranged in sheets or layers, histologically separate from each other but functionally interconnected by association neurons. In reptiles, there are but three such sheets, but in some mammals there are as many as ten, each one several cells in thickness and containing neurons of diverse type and extensive internal and external connections. In birds, the cortex, with four to six layers of hemispheres are externally marked by grooves, or fissures, some shallow and some deep. The development of the cortex in man is perhaps the most distinctive characteristic of the genus to which he belongs, the anatomical feature that separates him more clearly than any other from the other primates. It is the multiplicity of connections between neurons, the various paths along which the nervous impulse may travel and be guided by directing centers in the cortex, that makes possible the complicated kinds of behavior which human beings exhibit in response to stimuli reaching the central system through the afferent nerves

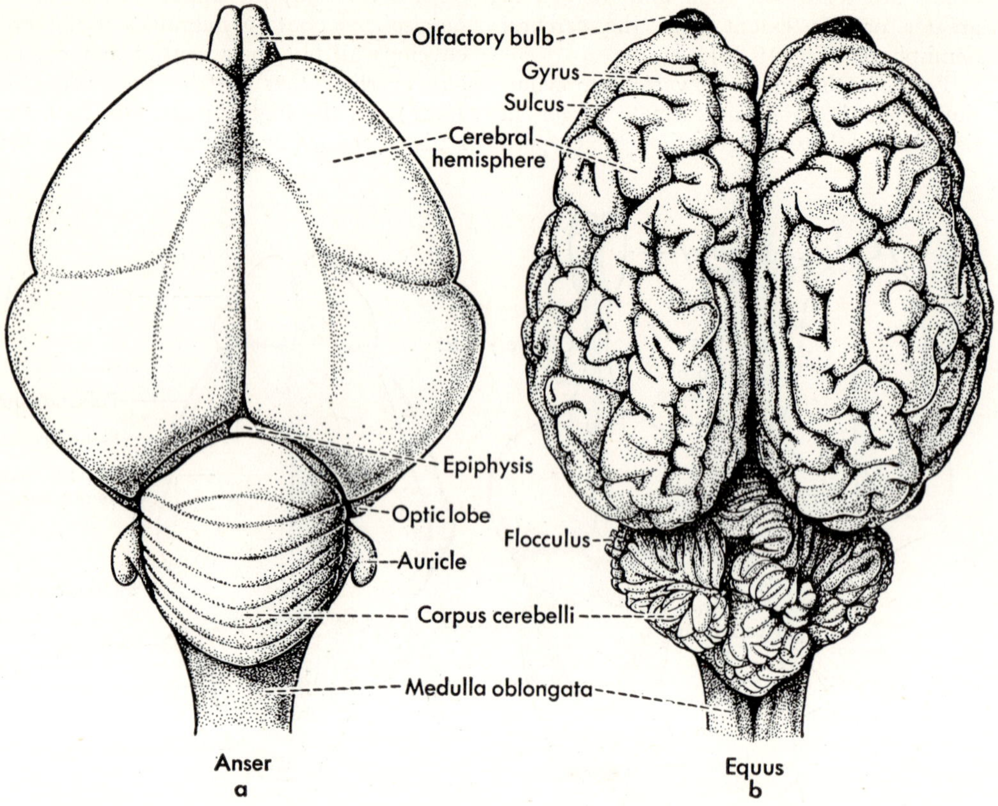

FIGURE 16.26 Dorsal views of the brain of (a) a bird (goose) and (b) a mammal (horse). After Butschli, Kuenzi, Sisson, from Romer, *The Vertebrate Body.* Copyright 1949 by the W. B. Saunders Company.)

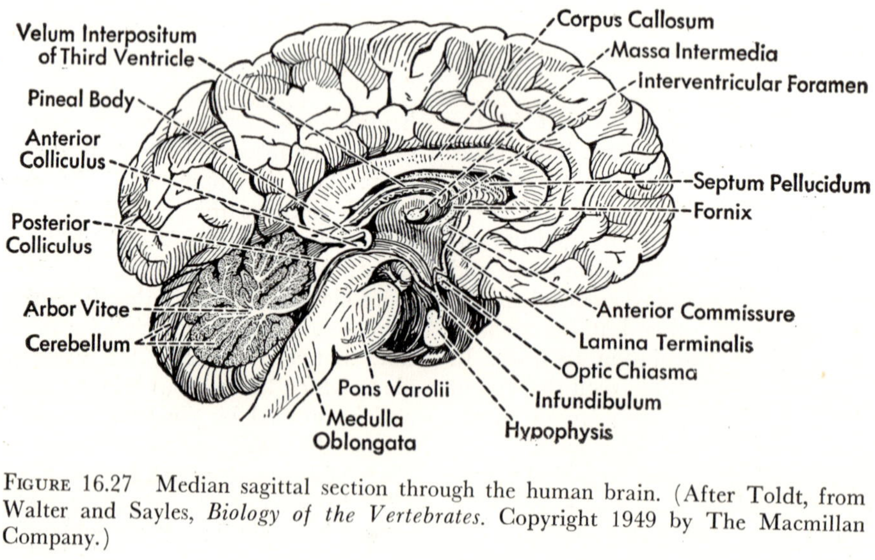

FIGURE 16.27 Median sagittal section through the human brain. (After Toldt, from Walter and Sayles, *Biology of the Vertebrates.* Copyright 1949 by The Macmillan Company.)

and also to situations arising from the mental processes of thought, reasoning and anticipation of future events.

The two cerebral hemispheres are connected by transverse commissures, strands of nerve fibres that run at right angles to their long axes and spread out in the walls of each, establishing structural and functional connections between them. One of these strands lies in the lamina terminalis, as the anterior commissure; a second tract, dorsal to this, is called the pallial commissure and connects two longitudinal tracts in the olfactory area of the telencephalon; these tracts, because of their shape, are called the hippocampi (Greek, hippocampus = sea horse). In most of the mammals, the single pallial commissure is replaced by two, of which the more dorsal and anterior is called the corpus callosum (Latin, callum = thick-skinned), connecting the cortical layers of the two hemispheres, and the more ventral and posterior one the hippocampal commissure.

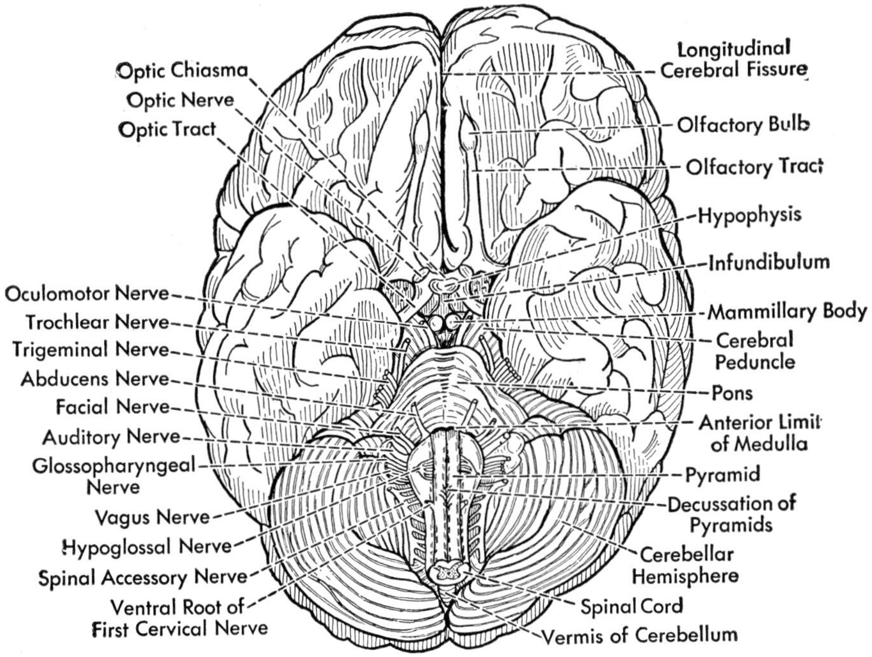

*Development of the diencephalon:* The development of the diencephalon follows quite a different course. Its side walls become thickened and extended by the massing of nerve fibres in them, but the floor and the roof as such remain relatively thin and to a

FIGURE 16.28 Basal view of the human brain. (After Toldt, from Walter and Sayles, *Biology of the Vertebrates.* Copyright 1949 by The Macmillan Company.)

great extent non-nervous. Its basal region is the site of the optic chiasma (Greek, chiasma = two lines placed crossways), where the fibre tracts from the eyes appear to cross, although actually, in mammals at least, the crossing or decussation is only a partial one, some of the fibres from each eye entering the corresponding rather than the opposite side of the brain (Fig. 16.28). This part of the brain is also known as the thalamencephalon, for Galen originally gave it the name of "thalamus," or antechamber, believing it to be the room in which the animal or vital spirits were imparted to the optic nerves. The name has been retained in modern anatomical terminology, and the adjective thalamic refers especially to nervous centers and tracts localized or originating in the diencephalon. In modern usage the word thalamus is reserved particularly for the major part of the dorso-lateral wall, the epithalamus designating a smaller, more dorsal strip and the hypothalamus the whole ventral part of the wall. In the fishes, the hypothalamus is developed to a greater extent than the thalamus proper or the epithalamus, but the whole region remains relatively small in comparison to its development and size in the reptiles and especially in the mammals, where the thalamus becomes greatly thickened and enlarged and the third ventricle, the cavity of the diencephalon, correspondingly reduced in size. Fibre tracts connecting the cerebrum with other parts of the brain and cord pass through the thalamus, and a cross connection is established through the superior commissure which runs across the roof of the ventricle. In the reptiles and mammals, a large commissure, the intermediate mass or soft commissure, crosses in the mid-region.

The greater part of the roof of the diencephalon becomes well supplied with blood vessels and forms a choroid plexus which extends down into the lateral ventricles of the cerebral hemispheres as well as into the cavity of the third ventricle. But from part of the roof of the forebrain certain structures known as the epiphyseal structures (Greek, epiphysein = to grow upon) grow upward and are developed to different degrees in the different groups of vertebrates. The most anterior of these, the paraphysis, originates at the junction of telencephalon and diencephalon and is more properly considered a derivative of the telencephalon than of the diencephalon; it is a non-nervous outgrowth with many blood vessels like the choroid plexuses which dip down into the ventricles (see Fig. 16.27). The paraphysis is well developed in adult fishes and in amphibia, less evident in the reptiles and present only during embryonic life in the mammals. Posterior to this, and clearly developing from the roof and epithalamus of the diencephalon, is the parietal organ. This appears as a dorsal outgrowth in the embryos of bony fishes but soon degenerates and disappears. It is present in amphibia and in some mammals, but not in birds, and it reaches its greatest development in certain reptiles, where it extends as a slender stalk through an opening in the cranium between the parietal bones and expands just below the integument into a sac or vesicle. The integument above this vesicle is thin and transparent, as it is on the outer surface of the paired eyes, and the cells of the vesicle itself become organized into a lens and a simple retina protected by pigment cells forming an organ resembling the eye of the mollusk, Helix. This organ, the parietal or third eye, is most highly developed in the genus Sphenodon, whose modern representatives are the two-and-a-half-foot tuataras of New Zealand, but to what extent it functions as a visual organ is problematical, since its experimental stimulation in these animals has produced no clear-cut reactions. The third outgrowth, just posterior to this and in some animals originating with it by a common stalk and later separating from it, is the pineal body (Latin, pinea = pine cone) or epiphysis proper. In some of the reptiles the pineal body may also show some of the characteristics of a visual organ, in none, however, developed to the extent of the parietal organ in Sphenodon. In birds the pineal body is rudimentary and in mammals it is small, and though attached by a stalk to the diencephalon, is non-nervous and glandular in nature, discharging its secretion as an endocrine gland into the body fluids. Neither the nature of the secretion nor its influence upon the organism is clearly defined, and the inclusion of the pineal body among the endocrine glands of the vertebrate body is open to question.

The endocrine nature of an outgrowth from the floor of the diencephalon is on the other hand clearly established. This ventral outgrowth, because of its shape, is called the infundibulum (Latin, infundibulum = funnel); growing downward and carrying with it an outpocketing of the third ventricle, it meets a dorsal and also hollow outgrowth from the roof of the oral cavity, the hypophysis (Greek, hypophysis = undergrowth), and both together form a glandular complex, the pituitary body (Latin, pituita = phlegm) (Fig. 16.29). The greater part of the hypophysis is glandular, with many blood and lymph vessels. In the amphibia, it has been shown that the development of the infundibulum is closely bound with that of the hypophysis and vice versa, for if either one is experimentally destroyed in the course of its development, the other fails to continue its growth. In the Amniotes, the hypophysis, detached from its connection with the oral cavity, differentiates into three regions, the pars anterior (distalis), the pars intermedia and the pars tuberalis. The pars anterior is the largest part and is very vascular; above it lies the smaller and less vascular pars intermedia, and close to the infundibulum and in close association with it is the pars tuberalis, lying in intimate relationship with the infundibulum which becomes the pars posterior, or pars nervosa, of the complex. The functions of these parts and the effect of their secretions upon the body as a whole are considered in Chapter 21.

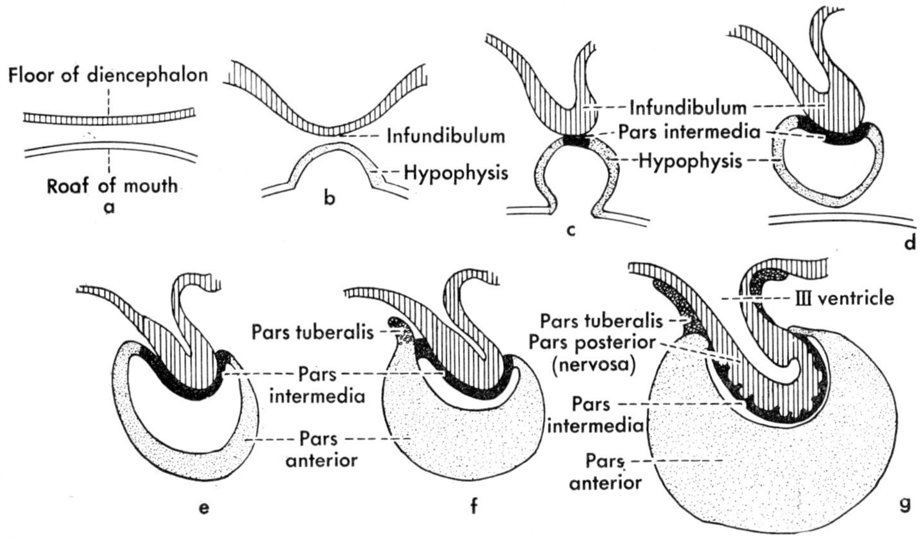

form two rounded prominences called the optic lobes, or corpora bigemina (Latin, corpus = body + bi = two + geminare = to double), of the fishes, amphibia, reptiles and birds. In mammals and in some reptiles, a transverse groove as well as the deeper

FIGURE 16.29 Diagram showing the development of the pituitary body from outgrowths of the roof of the mouth and the floor of the brain. (After Turner.)

longitudinal one marks this region off into four quadrants so that it becomes the corpora quadrigemina. The corpora bigemina are large and conspicuous, but the corpora quadrigemina are relatively smaller and are overlaid by the cerebral cortex and so not visible dorsally. The basal part of this region is thickened by strands of fibres connecting it with other parts of the brain, and the parts of the brain anterior to it with those posterior; these tracts make up the cerebral peduncles (Latin, pedunculus = little foot) or crura cerebri (Latin, crus = leg). In the mammals, the crura cerebri are particularly thick and the cavity of the mesencephalon correspondingly narrowed to a slit-like passage, the aqueduct, connecting the third and fourth ventricles. The two sides of the mesencephalon are functionally connected by the posterior commissure, a band of fibres that crosses from one side to the other in the transitional area between the diencephalon and the mesencephalon.

*Development of the mesencephalon:* The mesencephalon has undergone comparatively little external change in the different vertebrate classes. The most dorsal parts of its lateral walls become thicker, in the course of the development of the individual, and

*Development of the metencephalon:* The changes that take place in the hind brain, leading to structural developments characteristic of the different classes of vertebrates, are almost as striking as those of the forebrain. These changes center particularly around an upward growth and expansion of the dorso-lateral walls of the metencephalon, leading to the formation of the cerebellum and in mammals to the pons, a conspicuous thickening of the floor of the metencephalon composed of fibres running transversely to the long axis of the brain and of groups of connecting neurons.

In the higher reptiles, the cerebellum is large, compared to its size in the amphibia, and is even larger in birds, extending forward over the corpora bigemina as far as the posterior margins of the cerebral hemispheres, and posteriorly over the medulla, and is increased also by the addition of two small lateral lobes, the flocculi (Latin, flocculus = little flock of wool). The central part is known as the vermis (Latin, vermis = worm), for its surface is marked by a number of transverse furrows, giving it the superficial appearance of a segmented worm.

The mammalian cerebellum is much larger than that of any other kind of vertebrate; in addition to the vermis and the flocculi, there is a large cerebellar hemisphere between the vermis and the flocculus of each side, and the surface of all its parts is enormously increased by complicated and tortuous foldings, virtually occluding the cerebellar cavity. Like the cerebral hemispheres, it is covered by gray matter, but, unlike the cerebral cortex, that of the cerebellum is uniform in its composition and consists of three cellular layers whose components have extensive connections with those in their own layer as well as with those in the layers above and below them. This gray matter overlies a much smaller amount of white matter, through which run fibres connecting the cells of the cerebellar cortex with other regions of the nervous system.

The ventro-lateral walls of the metencephalon are thickened, in those animals in which the cerebellum is developed, by fibre tracts; these are the anterior continuations of afferent spinal nerves, some of which bend dorsally and establish connections with neurons in the cerebellar cortex. In most of the vertebrates, there are also a few transverse fibres connecting the two sides of the metencephalon, but in mammals this transverse band is greatly developed and is known as the pons Varolii after a sixteenth century Italian anatomist, Constanzo Varoli (1543?–1575). The pons appears as a definite enlargement on the ventral surface of the mammalian brain where it functions as a relay station for impulses passing between the cerebellar and cerebral cortex as well as a link between the two sides of the brain.

*Development of the myelencephalon:* The embryonic myelencephalon becomes the medulla oblongata of the adult vertebrate, with sides and floor much like that of the cord with which it is directly continuous. These are made up of nerve fibres, for the most part longitudinal in their course, and of masses of cell bodies of association neurons within the central system and of efferent peripheral nerves. Its roof remains permanently thin in all vertebrates, forming a choroid plexus that dips down into the fourth ventricle.

**Peripheral nerves:** The peripheral nerves are bundles of nerve fibres whose cell bodies lie either in the brain or the cord, or in ganglia peripheral to them derived from the neural crests. These fibres are bound together in a connective tissue sheath, the large bundles dividing and subdividing into smaller ones distributed to the various tissues and organs of the body, where the individual fibres in them fray out to terminate in the appropriate cells. Functionally, the fibres of the peripheral nerves fall into four categories: efferent somatic fibres, carrying impulses to the somatic muscles; efferent visceral fibres, carrying impulses to smooth muscles, to the muscle of the heart and to the glands; afferent somatic fibres, carrying impulses from the organs of special sense and sense receptors other than those in the visceral organs; and afferent visceral fibres, carrying impulses from sense receptors in the viscera.

Structurally, the peripheral nerves are

designated as spinal, or those whose fibres enter or leave the cord, and cranial, or those whose fibres enter or leave the brain. Except for some of the cranial nerves, they are fundamentally segmental in their origin, each pair corresponding to a primary segment of the body, and its efferent fibres innervating the myotomes of the corresponding segment. The modifications of the segmental plan in the adults of modern vertebrates has led to corresponding modifications in the distribution of the segmental nerves which is, however, a most valuable clue to an understanding of these modifications and to homologies between different sets of muscles particularly. For example, the same nerves that innervate the muscles of the gill arches in fishes, and so control their opening and closing and the flow of water over the gills, innervate the muscles of the pharynx in tetrapods, indicating that these different systems of muscles have their origin in the same pairs of myotomes.

SPINAL NERVES: The segmental pattern of the peripheral nerves, and of the vertebrate body, is evident particularly in the spinal nerves, each pair corresponding to a segment of the vertebral column. There is, however, a tendency for some of these nerves, especially in the regions of the appendages, to unite by cross branches into plexuses (Latin, plexus = braid), in which some of the fibres from the nerve of one segment are bound into a common bundle with those of another, or of several others (Fig. 16.21).

The spinal nerves are all designated by number and the region of the vertebral column from which they emerge, as cervical 1, 2, 3 and so on, or thoracic 1, 2, 3 and so on. They are all "mixed nerves," composed of both afferent and efferent fibres. The cell bodies of the efferent neurons lie in the ventro-lateral regions of the cord, from which their axons emerge as the ventral roots of the spinal nerve proper (Fig. 16.30). The cell bodies of the afferent neurons lie in the lateral ganglia, and send processes into the cord, to make connections with other neurons there, and away from it, as the dorsal roots of the nerve proper. These two roots converge at the sides of the cord and are united into a common bundle, which then emerges from the vertebral column through a foramen and extends to the appropriate organs. The axons of the efferent somatic neurons in the nerve run directly to the effector organs they supply,

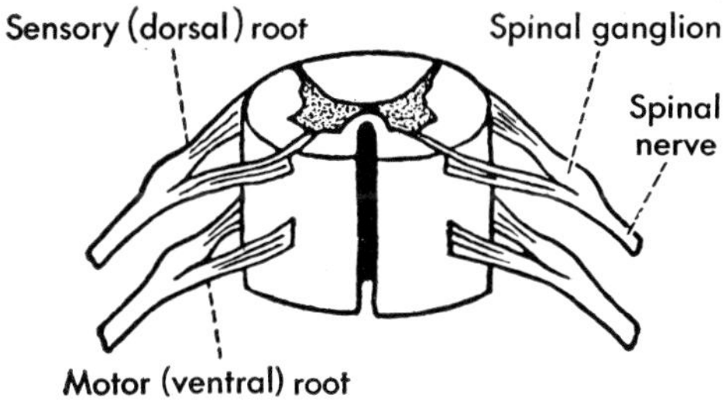

FIGURE 16.30 Diagram showing the relation of the spinal nerves to the cord. (After Piersol, from Walter and Sayles, *Biology of the Vertebrates.* Copyright 1949 by The Macmillan Company.)

their collaterals and dendrites possibly making a number of connections with cells in the central system. But the axons of the efferent visceral neurons make connections with at least one other neuron through which the stimulus is relayed to the responsive cell or cells. The cell bodies of these second, or relay, neurons, which represent nerve cells that have migrated away either from the ventral region of the neural tube or from the neural crests, lie outside the central system in an extravertebral, or peripheral, system of ganglia (Fig. 16.33). These ganglia and the nerves from them to the various organs constitute the autonomic division of the nervous system, which probably includes also some afferent visceral nerves.

CRANIAL NERVES: In the Anamniotes, ten pairs of peripheral nerves are directly connected with the brain, in the Amniotes, twelve (Fig. 16.31). Some of these, like the spinal nerves, are composed of both afferent and efferent fibres, and some also contain autonomic fibres. The distribution of the two additional nerves in the Amniotes shows that they represent the two most anterior spinal nerves of the Anamniotes, and their inclusion in the cranial set is an indication of the general evolutionary tendency toward

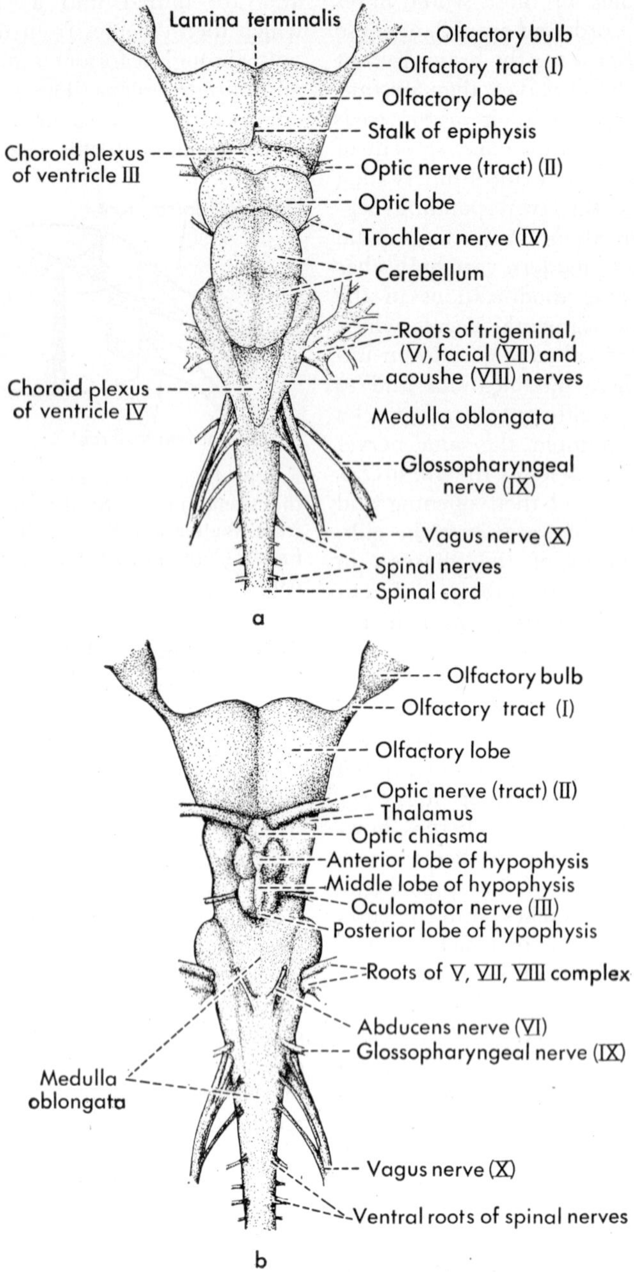

FIGURE 16.31  The brain and cranial nerves of the dogfish. (After Lazier.)

cephalization. The cranial nerves are designated either by number, from anterior to posterior, or by names more or less descriptive of their distribution or their function; they are listed, together with their location in the brain, the types of fibres known to be included in them and their principal distribution and functions in Table VIII. Those components that are related to the gill arches or their derivatives are designated as special visceral fibres, in distinction to the general visceral fibres that terminate

## TABLE VIII
### Cranial Nerves of Vertebrates

| Number | Name | Location | Types of Fibres | Principal Functions |
|---|---|---|---|---|
| I | Olfactory | Telencephalon | Special somatic afferent | Conveys stimuli from olfactory organs. |
| II | Optic | Diencephalon | Special somatic afferent | Conveys stimuli from visual organs. |
| III | Oculomotor | Mesencephalon | Somatic efferent | Innervates four of the muscles of the eye. |
| IV | Trochlear | Between optic lobes and cerebellum | Somatic efferent | Innervates one of the muscles of the eye. |
| V | Trigeminal | Myelencephalon (lateral surface) | General somatic afferent<br>Special visceral efferent | Conveys somatic stimuli from the head; innervates jaw muscles. |
| VI | Abducens | Myelencephalon (ventral surface) | Somatic efferent | Innervates one of the muscles of the eye. |
| VII | Facial | Myelencephalon (lateral surface) | General visceral afferent<br>Special visceral efferent<br>Autonomic | Conveys somatic stimuli from the head, including taste buds; from lateral line organs in aquatic Anamniotes; innervates muscles of face, jaw and mouth; innervates salivary glands. |
| VIII | Acoustic | Myelencephalon (lateral surface) | Special somatic efferent | Conveys stimuli from inner ear. |
| IX | Glosso-pharyngeal | Myelencephalon (lateral surface) | General visceral efferent<br>Special visceral efferent<br>Autonomic | Conveys stimuli from pharyngeal region and from taste buds; from lateral line organs in aquatic Anamniotes. |
| X | Vagus | Myelencephalon (lateral surface) | Special somatic efferent (Anamniotes)<br>Special visceral efferent<br>General visceral efferent<br>Special visceral afferent<br>Autonomic | Conveys stimuli from lateral line. Conveys stimuli from taste buds, thoracic and abdominal viscera; innervates muscles of gill arches and of pharynx and larynx. |
| XI | Spinal accessory | Myelencephalon (lateral surface) | Special visceral efferent<br>Autonomic | Innervates muscles of pharynx and larynx, and some of those of the pectoral girdle. |
| XII | Hypo-glossal | Myelencephalon (lateral surface) | Somatic efferent | Innervates muscles of throat and tongue and of syrinx in birds. Included with anterior cervical nerves in cervical plexus. |

in the visceral organs; those that are related to the special sense organs are designated as special somatic afferent fibres.

***The autonomic system:*** The ganglia of the autonomic system are made up of cell bodies posteriorly to run in the commissures between the ganglia, ultimately making connections with a post-ganglionic fibre at another level (Fig. 16.32). The post-ganglionic fibres usually join one of the peripheral nerves as a gray ramus communicans, and

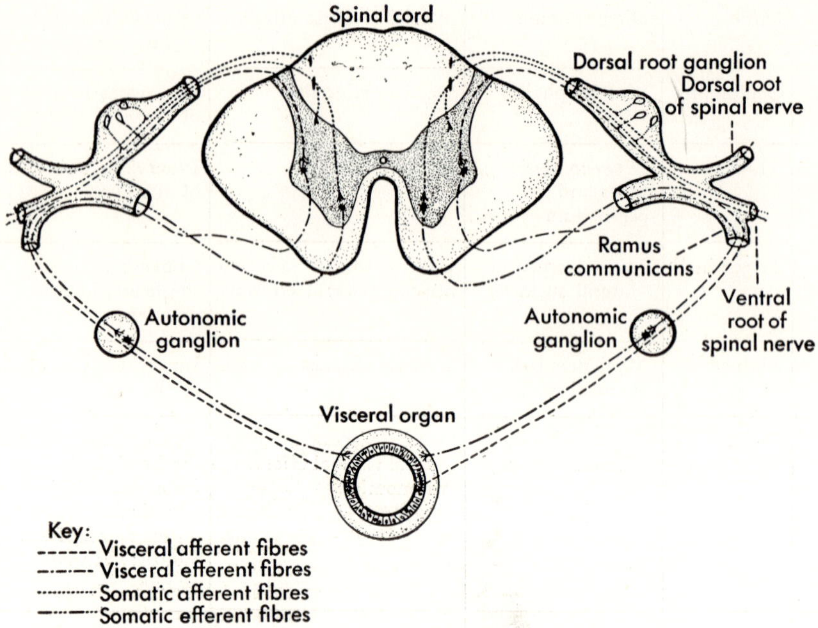

FIGURE 16.32 Diagram of a section through the human spinal cord and a spinal nerve in the thoracic region, showing the course of somatic and autonomic nerve fibres. (After Ranson.)

whose axons, often unmyelinated, are known as post-ganglionic fibres terminating in glands, both exocrine and endocrine, in the fibres of the heart muscle and in the smooth muscles of the blood vessels, the visceral, respiratory and urinogenital organs and, in mammals, the ciliary muscles that regulate the size of the pupil of the eye and the erector pili muscles that elevate the movable hairs. The post-ganglionic fibres receive the impulses they transmit from pre-ganglionic fibres which, originating in the brain and spinal cord and emerging with the efferent somatic nerves, soon diverge as part of the white rami communicantes (Latin, ramus = branch, communicans = connecting) and enter an autonomic ganglion where they make connections with the cell bodies of the post-ganglionic fibres, or turn anteriorly or run toward their destinations along with the fibres of the efferent somatic nerves. The white rami communicantes also contain afferent visceral fibres that run close to the efferent visceral fibres and pass through the ganglia without connections with other neurons there; their cell bodies are believed to lie in the dorsal root ganglia and together with those of the afferent somatic nerves and their fibres, to follow the same course into the cord. Within the cord, there are autonomic tracts and ganglia, also called nuclei, through which both efferent and afferent autonomic impulses are transmitted, coordinated and relayed.

In the higher vertebrates two divisions or sections of the autonomic system can be recognized both anatomically and functionally: the thoraco-lumbar division, also called the sympathetic, and the cranio-sacral division, known also as the parasympathetic. The pre-ganglionic fibres of the thoraco-lumbar section emerge with the ventral roots of the last cervical, the thoracic and the lumbar spinal nerves, and the postganglionic fibres originate in the chain of ganglia on either side of the vertebral column. The pre-ganglionic fibres of the cranio-sacral section leave the central nervous system in cranial nerves III (oculomotor), VII (facial), IX (glossopharyngeal), X (vagus) and XI (accessory) and with the ventral roots of the sacral nerves; their connections with the post-ganglionic fibres are made in ganglia that lie close to, or even in, the tissues which they innervate (Fig. 16.33). Most organs are innervated by nerves from both divisions, but the nerves of the cranio-sacral section do not supply the appendages or any of the glands or smooth muscle areas of the integument.

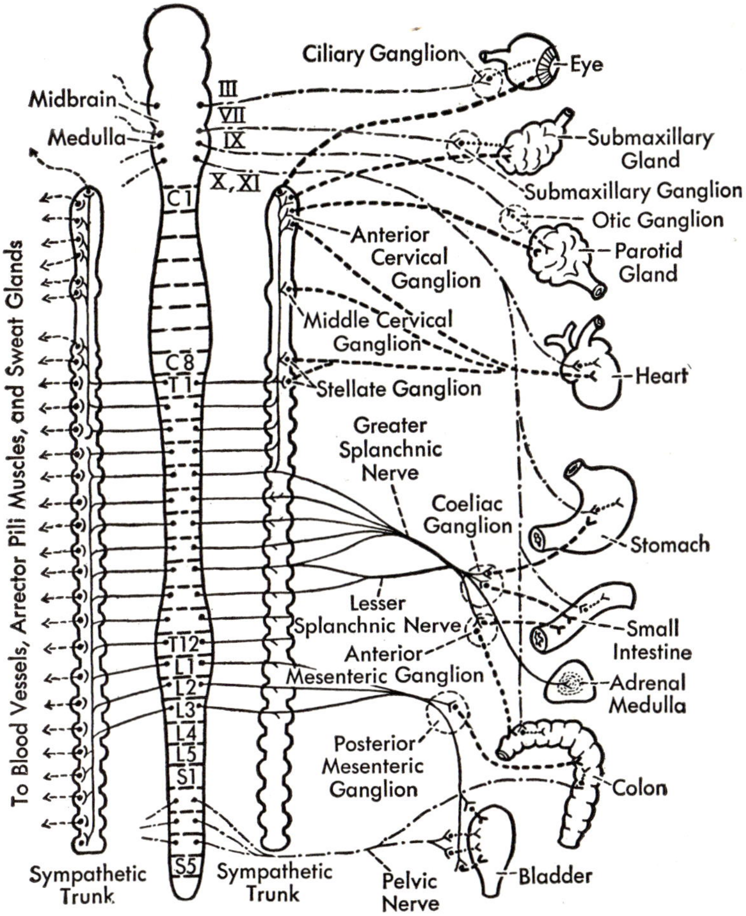

FIGURE 16.33 Diagram showing the principal autonomic pathways. The preganglionic neurones of the cranio-sacral division are represented by dash-and-dot lines; the postganglionic by dotted lines. The preganglionic neurones of the thoraco-lumbar division are represented by continuous lines; the postganglionic by broken lines. Pathways to the blood vessels and integument are shown on the left side of the diagram only; those to other visceral structures on the right side only. (After Bailey, from Walter and Sayles, *Biology of the Vertebrates*. Copyright 1949 by The Macmillan Company.)

Most organs receive a double nerve supply, one set of nerves from the thoraco-lumbar section and one from the cranio-sacral, each of which produces an effect opposite to that of the other's. The heart, for example, receives fibres from the vagus and from the anterior nerves of the thoraco-lumbar set; the impulses that pass along those from the vagus bring about retardation or inhibition of its spontaneous beat, while those that pass along the post-ganglionic fibres of the thoracic nerves cause its acceleration. These two effects appear to be antagonist to each other, and in certain circumstances one may be more in evidence than the other, but under ordinary conditions they are balanced in such a way that a uniform rate is maintained which can, however, through them be speeded up or slowed down according to conditions or demands within the organism.* In other cases, the double innervation may produce different and reinforcing, rather than opposite, effects. For example, stimulation of the submaxillary gland through its cranio-sacral supply results in the production of a watery secretion, while stimulation through the thoraco-lumbar supply results in the discharge of mucus, with the end result of a more copious flow of saliva when impulses reach the gland from both sources.

Another functional difference between the two divisions of the autonomic system is the fact that the thoraco-lumbar set of nerves tend to act as a unit, while those of the cranio-sacral set may act individually. If, for example, the organism is stimulated by the presence of an enemy, there is a generalized discharge through the post-ganglionic fibres of the thoraco-lumbar nerves bringing about characteristic reactions in the end organs in which they terminate, but all directed to preparation for the self-preserving actions of "flight or fight." The blood vessels of the skin and viscera are constricted and the blood from them diverted into the unconstricted vessels of the skeletal muscles, the brain and the heart; the heart beat is accelerated so that the blood moves more quickly around the body; and certain endocrine glands influencing metabolism are stimulated to discharge additional amounts of their secretions. On the other hand, the autonomic fibres of the third cranial nerve may be stimulated either naturally or experimentally with the result that the muscles that reduce the size of the pupil of the eye contract and this reaction is not necessarily accompanied by inhibition of the heart beat, secretion of the salivary glands, constriction of the blood vessels of the brain nor any of the other reactions attributed to the cranio-sacral division. But the combined effect of both sections of the autonomic system is to bring about automatic adjustments within the body, in human beings outside the range of their conscious control, which keep it a harmoniously working whole, with the activities of its several parts in balance and its internal environment essentially a constant one.

*Nerve endings.* EFFERENT NERVE FIBRES: The endings of the efferent nerve fibres in the effector organs may be free endings, frayed-out axons of the neurons, or looped or bulbous enlargements of these terminal strands. The histological demonstration of such endings is difficult and not entirely conclusive. The efferent fibres of the autonomic nerves often form plexuses before their terminations, and from these plexuses slender stands emerge that appear either to end alongside the gland or smooth muscle cell or cardiac muscle fibre that they innervate, or else to penetrate into its cytoplasm and end in a loop or a bulb, or a cluster of bulbs, near the nucleus. The terminations of the efferent somatic nerves in striated muscle

---

* Investigations of the innervation of organs and tissues in general point to the existence of inhibitory pathways as distinct functional components of a nervous system. For example, the flexor and extensor muscles of a joint move the bone in opposite directions and thus act antagonistically to each other; when one set is stimulated to the performance of its function in the body, the other must be suppressed or at least modulated in its activity in order to have the response an effective one. This is known as the reciprocal innervation of antagonistic muscles; the excitation of one set and the inhibition of the other combine the muscles of a joint into a functional unit and make movement through it possible. Similarly, the conditions of nervous activity throughout the body are most likely the expression of a balance between excitatory and inhibitory impulses arriving at the junctions between nerves or between nerves and the organs in which they terminate.

are rather more complicated. In some cases the fine branches of the axon end, like those of the autonomic nerves, in small loops or bulbs either on the surface of the sarcolemma or just inside it, but more often they end in motor end plates, an intimate association of nerve and muscle fibre that is essentially the same in its construction in all chordates and in all non-chordates possessing a neuro-muscular mechanism. At the junction of nerve and muscle fibre, the sarcoplasm accumulates beneath the sarcolemma and in this accumulation there are often many nuclei; within this mass the axon, divested of all its enclosing sheaths, frays out into a number of looped and twisted strands. The composite mass is a motor end plate, which in mammals appears as a distinctly enlarged area of the muscle fibre, averaging from 40–60 micra in diameter.

AFFERENT NERVE FIBRES: The sources of the stimuli received by the central nervous system may be either outside or inside the body, and the afferent nerves may terminate in organs of special sense or in relation to tissues in muscles, tendons, joints, the visceral organs or other parts of the body. The sensory areas receiving stimuli from external sources are known as exteroceptors, those from internal sources in the somatic muscles and tendons, as proprioceptors (Latin, proprius = one's own), and those from other internal tissues and organs as enteroceptors.

## Exteroceptors

The organs of special sense in vertebrates are paired eyes, paired otic organs, paired olfactory organs and, in fishes and amphibia, lateral line organs. More or less generally distributed over the surfaces of their bodies are also sensory cells, or groups of such cells, that are receptive to stimuli of touch, pressure, heat and cold and, according to human interpretation at least, of pain.

*Photoreception; the eye:* The vertebrate eye, like the photoreceptors of non-chordates, specializes in the reception of a physical stimulus, energy in the form of light.

Among visual organs it is distinctive in that its photosensitive region, the retina, is anatomically an extension of the neural tube, and not formed from superficial neuroepithelial cells as it is in the non-chordates. Early in the development of all vertebrates, outpocketings appear in the region of the future diencephalon, which extend toward the surface of the body as hollow, rounded enlargements, the optic vesicles; a little later in the course of development, the distal rim of each vesicle becomes indented and pushed back against the proximal rim, forming an optic cup, which thus has a wall of two layers from which the retina develops (Fig. 16.34). The optic cups retain their connection with the forebrain through the optic stalks. The ectoderm on the surface of the embryo outside the optic cup thickens and grows inward, filling part of the concavity of the cup and ultimately losing its connection with the surface and differentiating into the lens. The mesenchyme surrounding the optic cups forms an investing capsule of tough connective tissue, the sclerotic coat of the eyeball. Within the sclerotic coat is the choroid coat, of looser connective tissue, supporting blood vessels, smooth muscle cells and chromatophores containing the dark pigment, melanin. The wall of the optic cup in contact with this coat becomes the pigment layer of the retina, its cells developing melanin granules which are thickly distributed in their cytoplasm and which absorb the light rays that pass through the front of the eyeball. The indented rim of the cup develops into the sensory layer of the retina, the photosensitive cells lying next to the pigment layer and making connections with nerve cells distal to them, whose fibres grow in toward the brain, following the course of the optic stalk, and form the so-called optic nerves. These are therefore homologous with fibre tracts in the central nervous system and not with other peripheral nerves (Fig. 16.35).

The retina of the vertebrate eye is thus an inverted one, like that in the eyes of flatworms, for the photosensitive cells lie beneath those through which the visual stimulus is transmitted to the central system. In mammals, where the eye has reached its

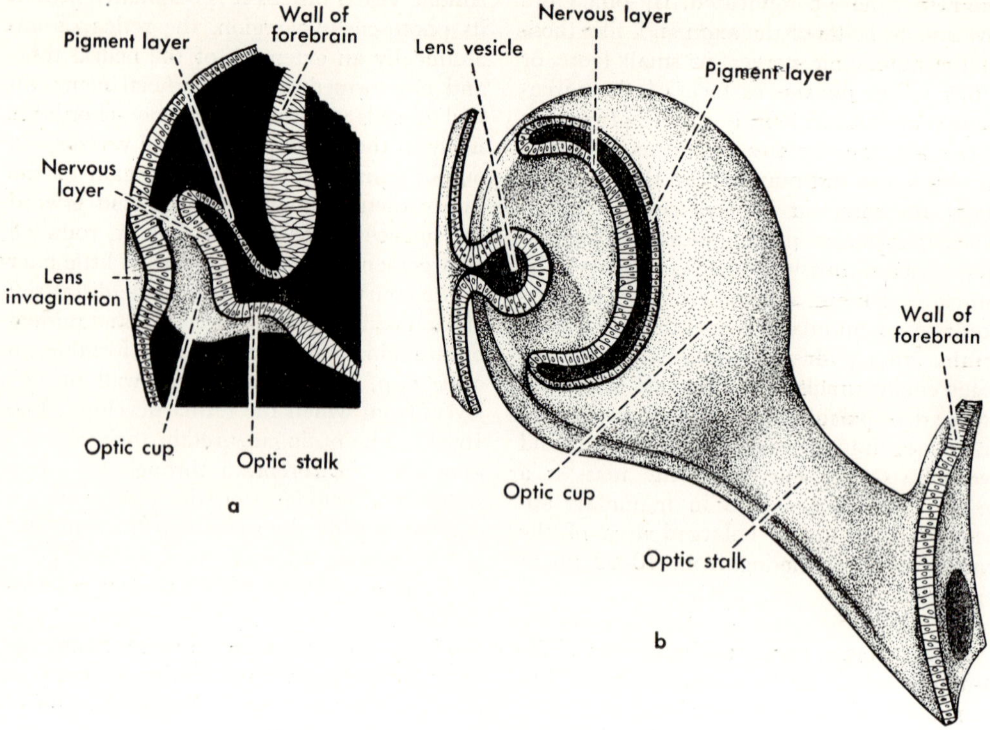

FIGURE 16.34  Diagrams showing stages in the development of the eye.

a. Early stage, showing the outgrowth of the optic cup from the wall of the forebrain and the ectodermal invagination which will form the lens. (After Kingsley.)

b. Later stage. (After Arey.)

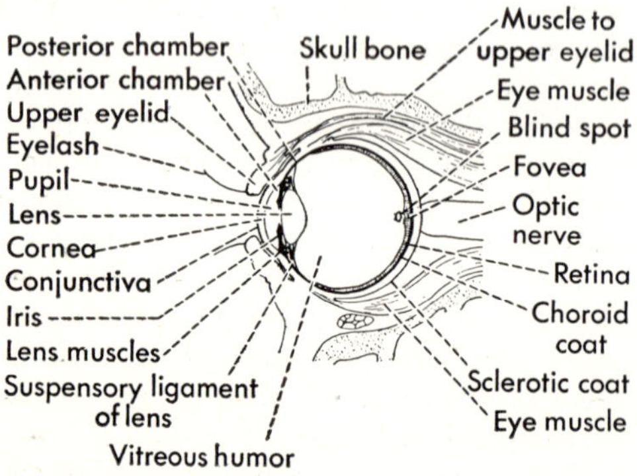

FIGURE 16.35  Diagram of a section through the human eye along the anterior-posterior axis (optic axis). (Modified after Woodruff, from Mavor, *General Biology*, 3rd edition. Copyright 1947 by The Macmillan Company.)

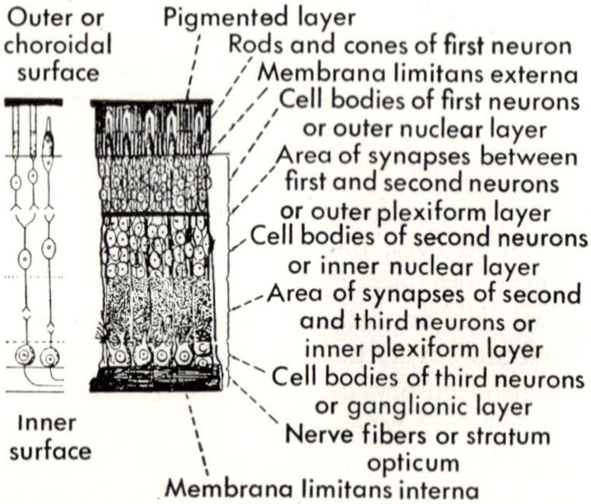

FIGURE 16.36  Diagrammatic section of the human retina. (From Kimber, Gray and Stackpole, *Textbook of Anatomy and Physiology*, 11th edition. Copyright 1942 by The Macmillan Company.)

highest level of development, the retina consists of 10 layers representing nerve cells, nerve fibres and supporting glia cells (Fig. 16.36). The photosensitive cells are the rods and cones that lie next to the pigment layer; these are neurons that are definite in their position and distinctive in their shape. The rods are long and slender and uniform in their appearance; the cones are more or less flask-shaped cells of variable dimensions. In the human eye, a small part of the central region of the retina, the fovea centralis (Latin, fovea = small pit), contains only cones; peripheral to this the number of rods in proportion to that of cones increases. The rods are further distinguished from the cones by the presence within them of a reddish pigment called rhodopsin (Greek, rhodon = rose + opsin = sight), or visual purple. This gives the retina a reddish-purple color, except for the fovea centralis where rods are absent and a narrow region just below the ora serrata (Latin, os = opening, serratus = notched) at the margin of the retina where the rods, if they are present, do not contain the pigment.

Experiments have shown that visual purple, in the cells of retinas removed from eyeballs and also when extracted from them, turns a pale yellow when exposed to light. This bleaching has been found to be the consequence of the disintegration of the rhodopsin complex into two of its components, a protein and a yellow pigment called retinene, one of the pigments in the general class of carotenoids that includes carotene, one of the most widely distributed pigments among plants and animals, and the one that gives carrots their distinctive color. In the dark, the recombination of retinene and the protein component takes place, and visual purple is thus re-formed from the products into which it was decomposed, in a reaction in which light appears to be the source of energy. It is thought that the same change takes place in the intact eye when light rays reach the retina; according to one theory, one or both of the decomposition products acts as a stimulus to the rods; according to another, only the cones are so stimulated. In either case, the photochemical change in all or part of the retina leads to impulses which are transmitted along the fibres of the optic nerve to the brain, resulting in the visual perception of an object, and in many instances also to activity in certain parts of the body or in the body as a whole. The resynthesis of retinene and the protein into visual purple is known to be related to the presence of Vitamin A, which in its molecular structure represents half of the molecule of one of the carotene pigments. In the absence of Vitamin A, less visual purple is formed and the condition known as night blindness develops. The cycle in the intact eye appears to follow this course:

$$\text{Vitamin A + protein} \xrightarrow{\phantom{xxx}} \underset{\text{dark}}{\overset{\text{Visual purple}}{\text{(rhodopsin + protein)}}} \xrightarrow{\text{light}} \text{retinene + protein}$$

The very apparent differences in the two kinds of visual cells and in their distribution in the retina suggest that they have different functions in the phenomenon of vision. The rods are presumed to be sensitive only to degrees of brightness and to be especially fitted to function in dim light, while the cones are believed to function most effectively in bright light and to be instrumental in the perception of colors. These histological and physiological distinctions have led to the Duplicity Theory (first proposed by Max Schultz in 1866)—the concept that the vertebrate retina is not one sense organ but two. The very small region of the eyeball where the fibres of the optic nerve leave it is the "blind spot," for, containing neither rods nor cones, it is insensitive to visual stimuli.

While the retina of the human eye, and that of most vertebrates, contains both rods and cones, there are some genera in all classes in which one or the other type of cell is lacking. Among the mammals, mice and dogs, for example, are deficient in cones and do not respond to color stimuli; the retinas of many fishes, reptiles and birds, on the other hand, are plentifully supplied with them, and they are, indeed, the only type of photosensitive cell in the eyes of land tortoises. Rods are particularly abundant in the eyes of deep-sea fishes, and of terrestrial animals that are active by night and quiet by day.

The vertebrate eye has been compared to a camera in which the retina represents the photosensitive plate, or film, the iris the diaphragm that regulates the amount of light admitted to the optical system, and the cornea, aqueous humor, lens and vitreous humor the focussing mechanisms by which light rays, radiated or reflected from an object, are refracted so that they form an image of it upon the photosensitive region, protected by its opaque surroundings from all other incident light. But it is a mechanism even more delicate and finely adjusted than any camera, for it has devices that automatically regulate the size of the pupil, that accommodate the system to objects at different distances from it and that move it in such ways that the image is made to fall upon the region of the retina where it will be clearest and sharpest.

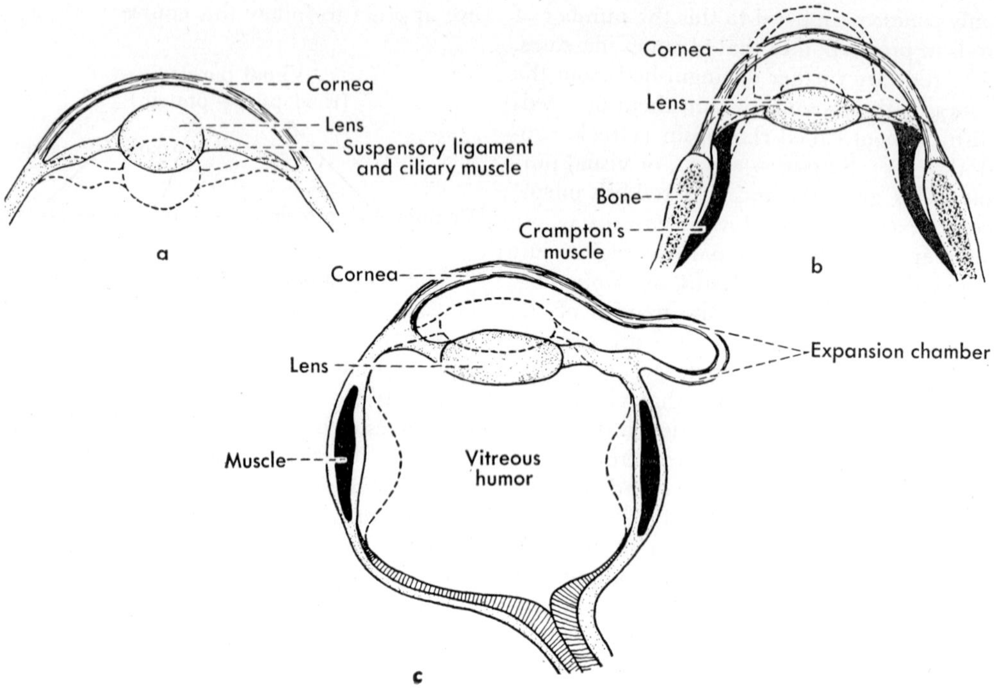

FIGURE 16.37 Diagrams showing the mechanisms of accommodation in the vertebrate eye. (After Starling.)

a. The eye of a fish, normally adjusted to focus on objects near at hand. Objects at a distance are brought into focus when the lens is drawn nearer the retina (in the position shown by the broken lines) by the contraction of the retractor lenti muscle.

b. The eye of a bird, normally adjusted to focus on distant objects. Objects near at hand are brought into focus when the curvature of the cornea and its refractive capacity are increased by the contraction of Crampton's muscle, a radially arranged muscle attached to the periphery of the cornea. Shortening of this muscle draws the margin of the cornea inward, diminishing the volume of the eye. Since its contents does not decrease in volume, intraocular pressure is increased and the most elastic areas, particularly the front of the cornea, bow outward.

c. The eye of a snake, normally adjusted to focus on objects at a distance. Objects near at hand are brought into focus when the lens is moved forward, away from the retina, by contraction of a circular muscle running around the eyeball, which compresses the vitreous humor and pushes the lens outward.

REGULATION OF VISION: The size of the pupil is regulated in most vertebrates by two sets of smooth muscle fibres in the iris, innervated by autonomic nerves. In one set, the fibres have a circular arrangement so that they form a sphincter muscle which on contraction reduces the size of the pupil; in the other, they are radially arranged and bring about the dilatation of the pupil when they contract. Accommodation, or adjustment to objects at different distances from the eye, is brought about in various ways in the different classes of vertebrates. In the elasmobranchs and in snakes, the eye is ordinarily adjusted for distant vision, and accommodation for objects closer by is brought about as it is in the squid, by compression of the eyeball which increases the pressure within it, thus pushing the lens forward. In bony fish and amphibia, the eyes are adapted for near vision, and in order to focus on objects outside this range, the lens is drawn closer to the retina by the contraction of a muscle attached to it. In birds, whose vision is ordinarily long-range, accommodation to nearer objects is effected by increase in the convexity of the cornea, thus increasing its powers of refraction. This means of accommodation in birds' eyes, not involving the lens directly, is a rapid but controllable one, and allows a bird like a hawk, for example, even while flying at a considerable height, to spot its prey upon the ground and to keep it in sight while swooping down upon it, adjusting the curvature of the cornea constantly so that the object is in focus at all levels of the downward flight (Fig. 16.37). Accommodation in mammals is brought about by changes in the shape of the lens, which is held in position in the eyeball by the suspensory ligaments radiating from its margin and merging with the membrane surrounding the vitreous humor. Processes extend between these ligaments from the ciliary body, a circular band of tissue containing smooth muscle fibres at the junction of the iris and the choroid coat proper. Contraction of these ciliary muscles, which are innervated by autonomic nerves, puts the ligaments under traction and so increases the curvature of the lens, adjusting its refractive index so that objects at different distances may be brought into focus.

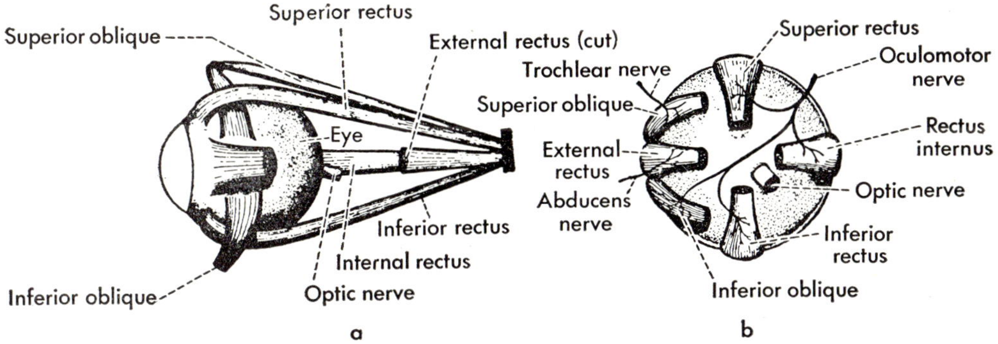

FIGURE 16.38 Diagram of the muscles moving the human eyeball. (From Neal and Rand, *Comparative Anatomy*. Copyright 1939 by The Blakiston Company. Redrawn after Warren and Carmichael, *Elements of Human Psychology*, Houghton Mifflin Company.)

   a. Left eyeball and muscles from the side.
   b. Posterior view of eyeball and muscles.

   Contraction of the superior rectus muscle rolls the eye upward; contraction of the inferior rectus rolls it downward; contraction of the internal (anterior) rectus rolls it inward; contraction of the exterior (posterior) rectus rolls it outward; contraction of the oblique muscles, acting in conjunction with the appropriate recti muscles, rolls the eyeball obliquely upward or downward.

In most vertebrates, the eyes are spherical or oval and placed on the sides of the head, either so far apart that they cannot be directed on the same object at all or else far enough removed from each other so that a single object cannot be brought into the perfectly coordinated that as the eyes move quickly from place to place, as they do, for example, in the process of reading, they converge simultaneously upon the same part of the printed page, which is thereby brought into the area of sharpest focus for each.

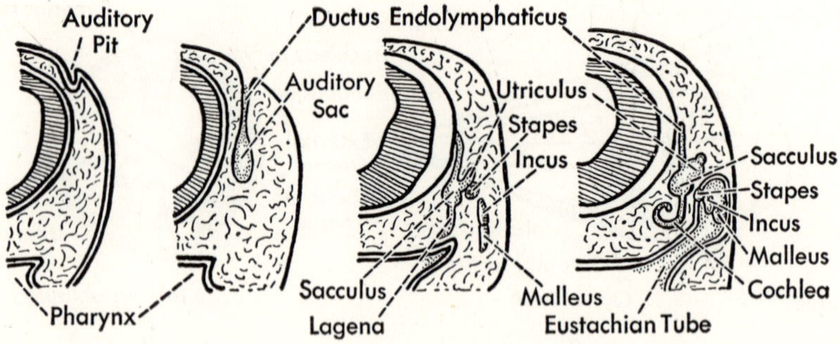

FIGURE 16.39 Diagrams showing stages in the development of the ear. (After Brandt, from Walter and Sayles, *Biology of the Vertebrates.* Copyright 1949 by The Macmillan Company.)

area of clearest vision of both eyes simultaneously. The eyes can, however, be moved in their sockets by the action of six eye muscles so that each can be directed to some extent toward the objects to be viewed. These muscles are slender strips of striated muscle fibres, innervated by the III, IV and VI cranial nerves, and by appropriate action can roll the eye upward, downward, inward or outward. In animals with flexible necks and also in those whose bodies are elevated above the ground, the range of vision without movement of the entire body is considerably greater than it is in the case of a fish, an amphibian and most of the reptiles. In primates and in owls, the eyes are close together and directed forward so that an image of an object is formed at the same time on both retinas (Fig. 16.38); these two images are only slightly different from each other but this slight difference results in stereoscopic or tri-dimensional vision, with a perception of depth as well as of height and width. The eye muscles bring about the convergence or divergence of the two eyes so that under ordinary conditions the image of the object is focussed on the fovea of each. The movements of these muscles may be extremely rapid, and are normally so

*Audioreception; the otic organs:* The paired otic organs arise from two placodes that appear as thickened regions of the embryonic ectoderm on either side of the rhombencephalon in about its midregion. These sink below the surface and become otic vesicles, initially round or oval sacs filled with fluid and, in most vertebrates, temporarily connected with the outside by narrow tubes, the endolymphatic ducts (Fig. 16.39). Some cells in the wall of each vesicle differentiate as sensory cells, and the vesicle itself becomes divided into two regions, a dorsal utriculus (Latin, utriculus = little bag) and a ventral sacculus (Latin, sacculus = little sac), connected by a narrow passage. The sensory cells are divided between the two primary chambers, and the whole structure eventually becomes enclosed within the otic capsules of the cranium.

The primary function of this sense organ is equilibration, and in the lower vertebrates statoliths of calcium carbonate are formed in both sacculus and utriculus, which thus have a similar function to the statocysts in non-chordates. But in all jawed vertebrates, three slender, hollow, arched tubes, the semicircular canals, develop from the utriculus, so arranged that they lie in three planes, one horizontal and two vertical (Fig. 16.40). Each canal, or hoop, terminates in an ampulla continuous with the chamber of the vestibule, and the whole system, called the membranous labyrinth and filled with fluid endolymph, is embedded in the cartilaginous or bony labyrinth of the skull that conforms to its contours exactly and from which it is separated by a narrow space, also filled with fluid, the perilymph. It is not yet entirely clear how this system functions in helping the animal maintain its customary position in relation to the gravitational pull, but its importance in this respect is without question.

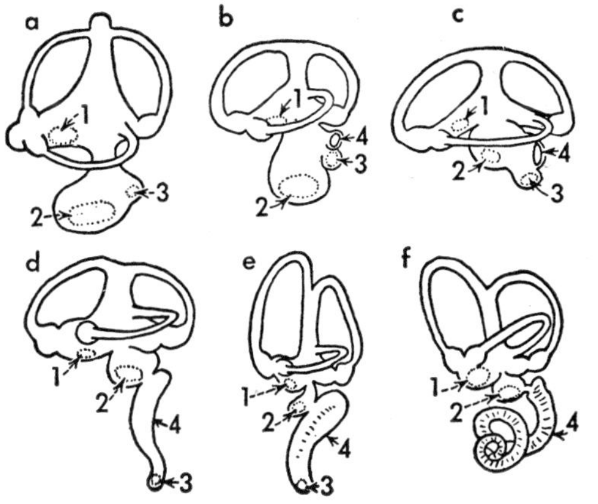

In all terrestrial vertebrates the otic organ has acquired a secondary function, that of registering slight pressure changes in the atmosphere and discriminating between them as sounds, and so also acts as an auditory organ. Audition is a most valuable asset to animals living on land, for it makes possible the apprehension of disturbances at a distance from the body, and so gives notice of neighboring benefits or dangers. These disturbances may be air currents or winds, vibrations caused by the animal's own motion and reflected from other objects, or by the movements of others, or by special sound-producing mechanisms of their bodies; sensitivity to them increases the organism's awareness of its environment, and so the possibilities of immediate and appropriate adjustment. At the highest levels of biological development, sound-producing mechanisms and sound-sensitive ones have led to means of communication between animals and, in man, to all the potentialities of speech and mutual understanding, as well as the aesthetic appreciation of beautiful or otherwise satisfying sounds.

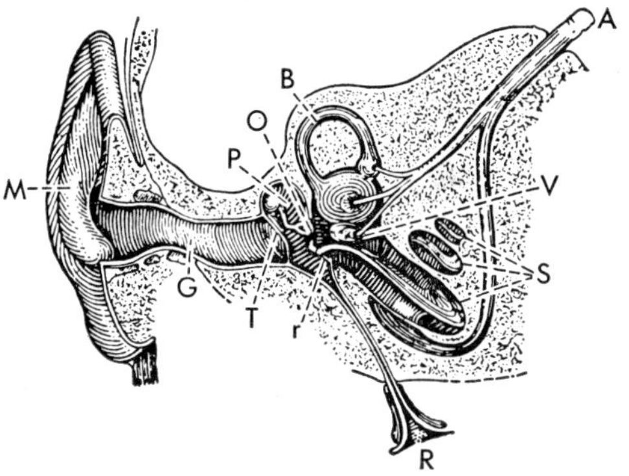

FIGURE 16.40 Diagrams showing the labyrinth of the ear and the progressive development of the lagena in vertebrates. (After Hesse, from Walter and Sayles, *Biology of the Vertebrates*. Copyright 1949 by The Macmillan Company.)

a, teleost; b, frog; c, turtle; d, crocodile; e, bird; f, mammal.

1. macula utriculi; 2. macula sacculi; 3. macula lagena; 4. basal papilla (forerunner of the Organ of Corti, which becomes incorporated within the lagena when it coils to form the cochlear duct).

FIGURE 16.41 Diagram of a section of the right ear (human). (From Kimber, Gray and Stackpole, *Textbook of Anatomy and Physiology*, 11th edition. Copyright 1942 by The Macmillan Company.)

M, concha (pinna); G, external auditory meatus; T, tympanum; P, middle ear; O, fenestra vestibuli; R, fenestra cochleae. (The chain of ossicles extends from T to O.) R, Eustachian tube; V, B, S, bony labyrinth; V, vestibule; B, semicircular canal; S, cochlea; A, acoustic nerve, dividing into branches supplying the vestibule, semicircular canals and cochlea.

The stimulus of sound waves is registered by an organ developed as an outgrowth of the sacculus, the lagena (Latin, lagena = flask), which, with the semicircular canals and their associated structures, makes up the inner ear of all vertebrates. The lagena is small in fishes, larger in reptiles and birds, where it extends ventrally as a slender tube lined with patches of sensory epithelium, and reaches its greatest development in mammals, where it becomes spirally coiled

The sensory area within the scala media is the main organ of hearing, possibly the only one, and is called the organ of Corti after an Italian microanatomist, A. Corti (1822–1876). This is a strip of neuroepithelium extending the length of the scala media and

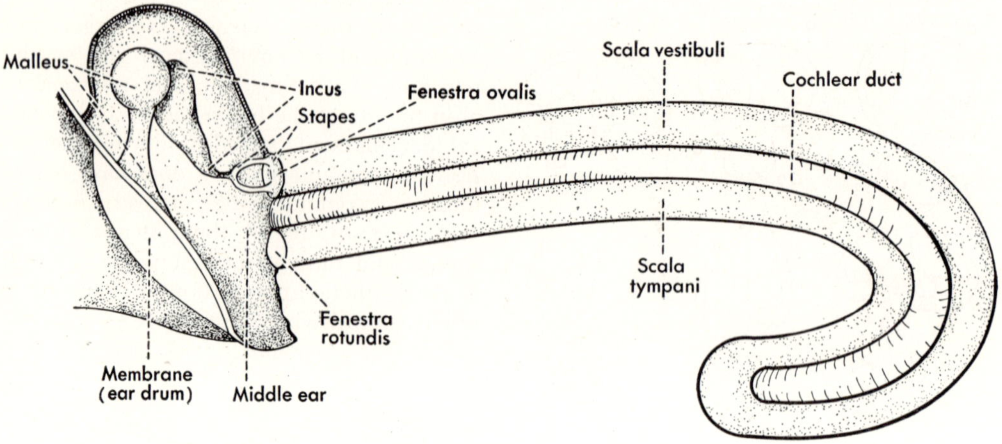

FIGURE 16.42  Diagram showing the structure of the middle and inner ear of mammals. The cochlea is drawn as if its spiral were unwound. (After Gardner.)

and contributes to the formation of the cochlea (Greek, kochlias = snail) (Fig. 16.41). In the mammals, the outer wall of the lagena makes contact along its length with the bony labyrinth around it, both on the inside and the outside of its spiral, so that the perilymphatic space around it is divided into an upper and a lower channel, communicating with each other at the apex of the spiral. The upper channel is the scala vestibuli (Latin, scala = ladder), its fluid contents separated from that of the vestibule only by a membranous covering, the fenestra ovalis (Latin, fenestra = window, ovalis = egg-shaped), a region that remains unossified. The lower channel is the scala tympani, which terminates basally in a membrane covering another unossified region of the ear capsule, the fenestra rotundum or fenestra cochleae. The lagena itself makes the scala media, filled with endolymph continuous with that in the sacculus and the semicircular canals, and all three channels, with the bony core around which they are wound, is the cochlea (Fig. 16.42).

therefore, like it, coiled and with inner and outer rows of hair cells; stimuli received by its extremely sensitive cells are transmitted to the central nervous system through fibres of the VIII cranial nerve, and registered there as sound.

A middle ear region has also been added to the tetrapod auditory apparatus and, in the mammals, an outer one as well. The middle ear is a derivative of the second gill slit, modified in the fishes as the spiracle. In the evolution of the tetrapods, this slit has become closed over externally by a membrane, the tympanum, that vibrates when sound waves strike it just as do similar membranes in some insects. The internal connection of this gill slit with the pharynx is retained as the Eustachian tube, named for an Italian microanatomist, Bartolommeo Eustachio (d. 1574), and in reptiles and birds, and also in some terrestrial amphibia, the greatly modified hyomandibular bar of the visceral skeleton extends across the cavity as the columella of the middle ear, one end of it in contact with the tympanum and the other with the membrane of the fenestra ovalis (Fig. 16.43). In mammals, a chain of three tiny bones crosses this cavity, called, because of their shapes, the stapes (Latin, stapes = stirrup), the incus (Latin, incus = anvil) and the malleus (Latin, malleus =

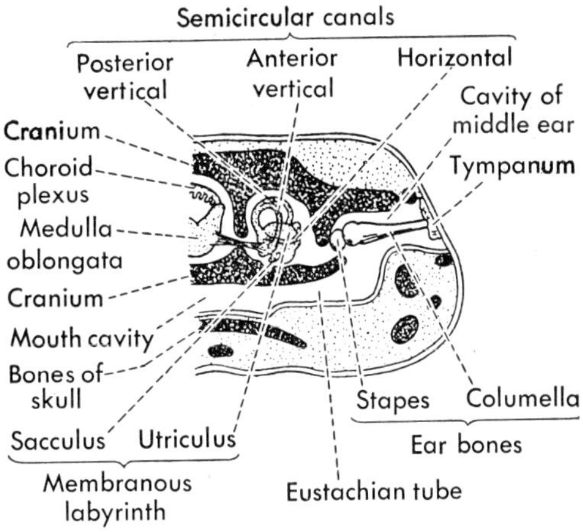

FIGURE 16.43 Cross section of the left side of the head of a frog, showing the structures of the ear. (From Mavor, *General Biology*, 3rd edition. Copyright 1947 by The Macmillan Company.)

hammer). The last two of these are derived from the mandible, which in all other vertebrates contributes to the lower jaw and in mammals alone is wholly replaced by membrane bones, the dentaries, and the vestiges of the mandibles diverted to other uses. Vibrations striking the tympanum are transmitted across the bones of the middle ear and relayed to the perilymph in the bony labyrinth surrounding the inner ear, but it is not yet clear exactly how this motion is communicated to the cells of the organ of Corti.

This chain of bones does not apparently add greatly to the efficiency or sensitivity of the mammalian ear, for sound waves are also effectively transmitted through the middle ear of amphibians, reptiles and birds by the single columella, and in pathological conditions in man, where all three bones may be ossified or immovably connected with each other by fibrous connective tissue, hearing may be but slightly affected. Moreover, the transmission of sound waves through the cranial bones rather than those of the middle ear is known to be an effective stimulus to the organ of Corti, and is the principle behind hearing aids for certain kinds of deafness.

The outer ear of mammals consists of a pinna (Latin, pinna = pinnacle), a flap or fold of the integument supported by cartilage, and a canal, the external meatus (Latin, meatus = passage), leading to the tympanum, the external surface of the middle ear. The pinnae serve to direct sound waves toward the middle ear which, like the inner ear, is enclosed in a bony case; in some mammals, the pinnae can be turned by muscles and directed toward the source of the atmospheric disturbance.

The human ear can register as sound only some of the vibrations to which the ears of other mammals are sensitive. Dogs, for instance, are known to be sensitive to sound waves of higher frequencies than those ordinarily perceived by human ears; bats guide themselves in flight by sounds detectable to man only when enormously amplified by instruments. There is, outside the world of human auditory perception, a world of sound which modern receiving and ampli-

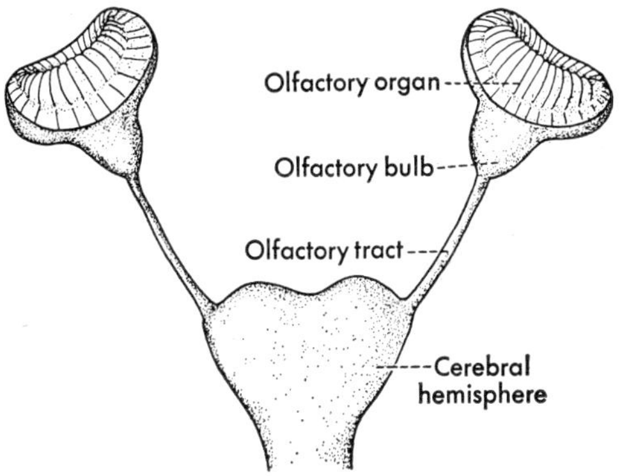

FIGURE 16.44 Olfactory organs of the shark (Carcharias), blind sacs lined with neural epithelium. (After Kingsley.)

fying devices are only beginning to reveal to human knowledge, just as three hundred years ago microscopes began to expose to human vision an unknown world of previously invisible things. Some of the instruments developed during the war (1939–

1945) for the detection of underwater sounds, primarily to register the movements of ships or of underwater missiles, disclosed the otherwise inaudible noises that are made by animals in the sea—by fish swimming through the water, by crabs and lobsters

*Chemoreception.* THE OLFACTORY ORGANS: Like the otic organs, the olfactory organs of vertebrates have their beginnings, both in the class and in the individual, as placodes in the anterior part of the head which become depressed as pits lined with neuroepi-

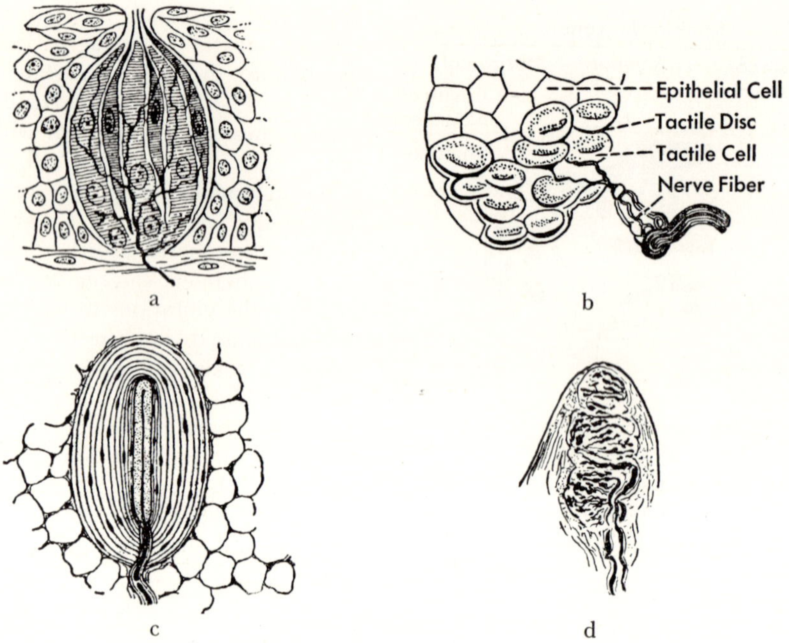

FIGURE 16.45  End Organs.

   a. Taste bud. (From Kimber, Gray and Stackpole, *Textbook of Anatomy and Physiology*, 11th edition. Copyright 1942 by The Macmillan Company.)
   b. Merkel's tactile corpuscle from the snout of a pig. (After Tretjakoff, from Walter and Sayles, *Biology of the Vertebrates*. Copyright 1949 by The Macmillan Company.)
   c. End organ of Krause. (From Kimber, Gray and Stackpole, *Textbook of Anatomy and Physiology*, 11th edition. Copyright 1942 by The Macmillan Company.)
   d. Meissner's corpuscle in the skin of a human hand. (After Ranvier, from Walter and Sayles, *Biology of the Vertebrates*. Copyright 1949 by The Macmillan Company.)

moving about, by masses of barnacles waving their appendages and even by the concerted action of the cilia on the gills of countless bivalve mollusks. The biological effects of energy manifested as sound waves of high frequency, supersonic vibrations beyond the range of unaided human detection, are only beginning to be investigated; the present evidence indicates that some of them at least are destructive to the organization of protoplasm, and of virus particles, and may become effective agents in the destruction of biological systems.

thelium. Olfactory stimuli are chemical, not physical, ones; the neuroepithelial cells of the olfactory pits are sensitive to substances brought into contact with them in solution, and unlike the sensory cells of the other sense organs that relay their message to the central system through a series of neurons, they convey it directly to the brain along their own axons which terminate in its anterior areas. All vertebrates respond to a certain extent to such stimuli, but some depend much more upon them than others for the detection of objects around them. Fishes, for example, rely far more greatly upon smell than upon sight or sound, and experiments have shown that hungry dogfish will swim over and around food if their olfactory organs are plugged with cotton, while they will find it, though hidden and even after they have been blinded, if the olfactory openings are clear. Birds and among the mammals, man, on the other hand, depend primarily upon their vision.

The definitive olfactory organs of modern fishes remain as blind sacs, whose external openings are divided by a septum so that a current of water is maintained across the olfactory membrane as the fish swims along (Fig. 16.44). But in the tetrapods the olfactory pits have acquired an internal opening in the roof of the mouth, and have become channels for the passage of air into the lungs, and so accessory to external respiration, as well as sense organs (Fig. 15.51). The olfactory membrane extends varying distances along the passage between the external and internal nares; in man, for example, it is limited to a comparatively small area in the upper regions of the nasal cavity. Other cells in these passages become mucus-secreting ones, in whose secretion volatile substances can be dissolved and so brought into contact with the sensory cells as effective olfactory stimuli.

TASTE ORGANS: Taste, like smell, results from the chemical stimulation of specialized nerve cells by dissolved substances. These cells are grouped together in clusters, as taste buds, that are sunk below the surface of the epidermis, maintaining contact with it by minute pores (Fig. 16.45). In most vertebrates, they are limited to the oral cavity and pharynx, and in mammals largely to the mouth, but in many fishes they are distributed over the surface of the head, or of the body generally.

*Lateral line organs:* Lateral line organs are found only in aquatic Anamniotes. They are clusters of sensory cells, called neuromasts (Greek, neuron = nerve + mastos = hillock), provided with hairs and sunk below the surface of the body, and so not in direct contact with the water (Fig. 16.46).

In some fishes they are distributed in isolated groups, but in most fishes and in the aquatic amphibia, they are also collected in a row, or line, along each side of the body. Communication with the external environment is established through small canals

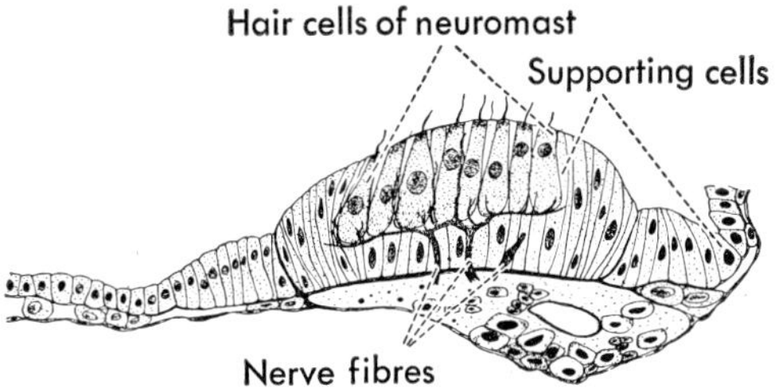

FIGURE 16.46 Transverse section of a lateral sensory canal of a dogfish (Mustelus), showing a neuromast. (After Johnson.)

opening on the surface through pores; the canals contain mucus copiously secreted by gland cells in them. The neuromasts have been proved by experiment to be sensitive to slow vibrations in the water; they transmit the stimulus so received through afferent fibres of the VII, IX and X cranial nerves that terminate in them.

*Cutaneous sensation:* Stimuli of touch, pressure, heat, cold and possibly pain are received by terminations of nerves, often enclosed within capsules of connective tissue, yet so small that their demonstration is difficult and the finer details of their structure hard to determine. Their distribution and nature are best known in mammals. Merkel's corpuscles, for example, each consisting of a modified epithelial cell and the flattened enlargement of an axon of an afferent nerve, are sensitive to tactile stimuli and are usually found in groups in the epithelial layers of mammalian skin and at the bases of the hairs (Fig. 16.45b). Meissner's corpuscles, consisting of a connective tissue capsule enclosing 1–5 nerve fibres which spiral around in the semi-fluid material within it, are also tactile in function and are found particularly in the tips of the fingers and toes and on the palms of the hand and the soles of the feet of men and apes (Fig. 16.45d).

***Proprioceptors:*** These are terminations of afferent nerves that end in close association with a muscle or a tendon (Fig. 16.47). In amphibia and amniotes, a number of such nerve endings, wound around several muscle fibres and enclosed within a connective tissue capsule, make up a neuromuscular spindle; in birds and mammals, spindles of similar construction, the neurotendinal spindles, are found in the tendons attaching muscles to bones. By responding to pressure, these nerve endings receive stimuli that, transmitted to the central system, give the organism muscle and tendon "sense," or localization of its muscles and an awareness of the degree of their contraction and so of the position of its bones.

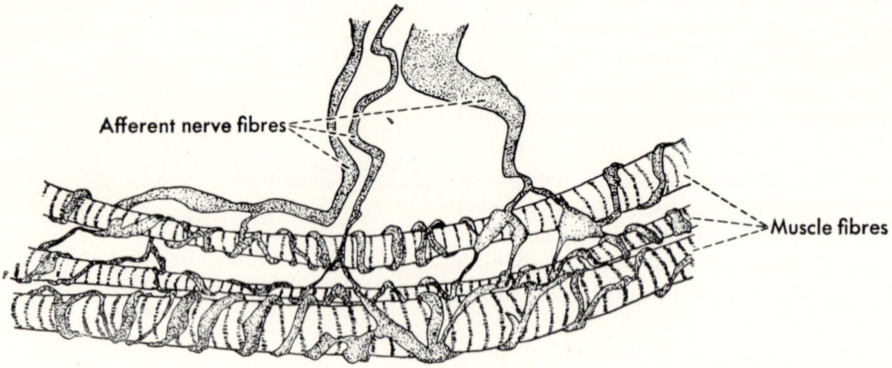

***Enteroceptors:*** These, too, are endings of afferent nerves, but in the connective tissue in the deeper regions of the body and in its various organs. Some of them are also encapsulated; the largest and most elaborate of these are the Pacinian corpuscles of mammals, which are readily visible to the naked eye, for they are 1–4 mm. long and about 2 mm. in thickness (Fig. 16.45*c*). They consist of as many as 50 concentric layers of connective tissue enclosing a single large nerve, whose fibres often pass from one end of the capsule to the other, and emerge to enter another corpuscle.

## The functional unit of the nervous system: the reflex arc

While the neuron is the structural unit of the nervous system it is not by itself a functional one, for it ordinarily does not receive

FIGURE 16.47 Muscle spindle from the muscles of a dog's foot. Three afferent fibres are shown entering the muscle spindle, branching and winding around the muscle fibres. Note that one nerve fibre is entwined around more than one muscle fibre. (After Herrick.)

a stimulus and transmit it directly to an effector organ, as some of the nerve cells in the lower non-chordates are known to do. The functional unit of the vertebrate nervous system is the reflex arc, in which at least two neurons, one afferent and one efferent, as well as receptor and effector organs are involved. The impulse always passes from the termination of the axon, or its collaterals, of one neuron to the dendrites of another, and in so doing crosses a synapse (Greek, synapsis = conjunction), for the processes of vertebrate nerve cells, while possibly in contact with each other are never united as they are in the nerve nets of some non-chordates.

At its simplest, the reflex arc consists of an afferent neuron which receives the stimulus and an efferent neuron to which the stimulus is transmitted across a synapse in the brain or cord, and which in turn transmits it to an effector organ that makes the response (Fig. 16.48). It is doubtful if conditions are actually ever so simple as this. One more neuron, and in some cases several more, may intervene between the sensory and the motor cells as connecting or associ-

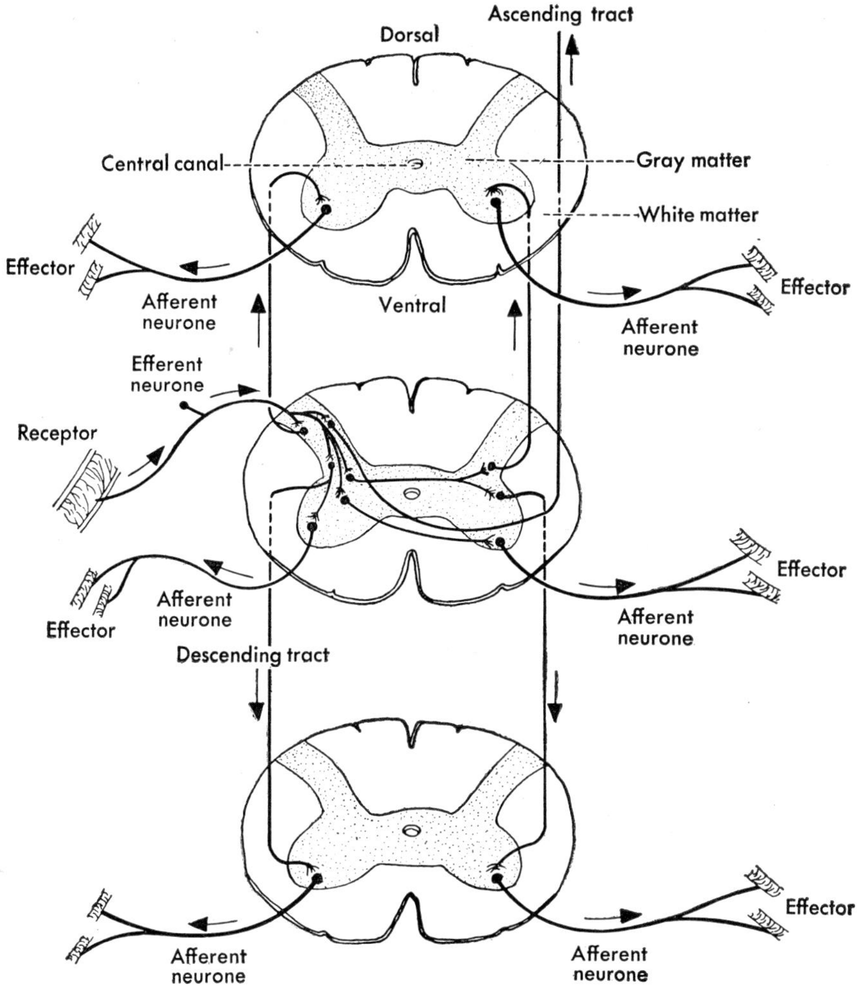

FIGURE 16.48 Diagrams showing the connections by which impulses from a receptor organ reach motor neurons at various levels of both sides of the spinal cord, resulting in multisegmental, ipse lateral (on the same side) and contra lateral (on the opposite side) reflex responses. (After Gardner.)

ation neurons through which the impulse is relayed to one, or to several, effector organs. In Figure 16.48 are shown some of the relationships that may exist between the nerve cells in reflex arcs, from which it may be seen that such arcs may also be functionally connected with each other. Except in the case of the autonomic system, these connecting neurons lie within the central system, where they constitute a large part of the tissues of the brain and the cord.

### Coordination in the nervous system

In attempting to determine the organization of the nervous system and the connections between its units, the neuroanatomist has a task somewhat comparable to that of an electrical engineer who tries to follow out the course of all the telephone, telegraph and light wires in a large and unfamiliar city, tracking down the distribution of every cable and wire through central stations and substations to every outlet in every building.

But the neuroanatomist's task is even more difficult, for his set of communications is everywhere a double one of incoming and outgoing wires, and he is, moreover, faced with all the difficulties of working with living biological systems. For only certain aspects of neuroanatomy can be studied by the dissection or histological examination of dead animals; the ultimate paths and more subtle connections of the nerves are determined only through their operation as evidenced by the behavior of the organism, a condition that demands their study in the living state. The course of the central and peripheral pathways and the functional significance of many areas of the brain and cord have been determined only by the study of the behavior of animals, including man, in which certain parts of the nervous system have been destroyed or rendered nonfunctional by injury or disease, or in which they have been experimentally removed or severed, or their action temporarily suppressed or enhanced by the use of chemical agents particularly, or by physical ones such as heat and cold or electric currents.

***Coordination in the cord:*** The cord is the center for many reflexes, for in all vertebrates in which connection between the brain and the cord has been cut, certain reflex actions can still be evoked after varying periods of time and for varying periods of time. These include flexion and extension of the limbs and certain visceral reflexes, as well as the constriction and dilatation of the blood vessels. These reflexes are intersegmental ones, for the impulse entering through afferent nerves at one level may spread through a number of anterior and posterior segments and be transmitted to effectors through afferent nerves at quite another level, as well as on the opposite side, of the cord. Association fibres within the cord, some running longitudinally and some transversely, make this possible. Behavior of a spinal animal, dependent upon the coordinating centers of its cord alone, is stereotyped, but it can respond to stimuli, except those conveyed by afferent cranial nerves; such responses are, in general, those that are directed toward self-preservation.

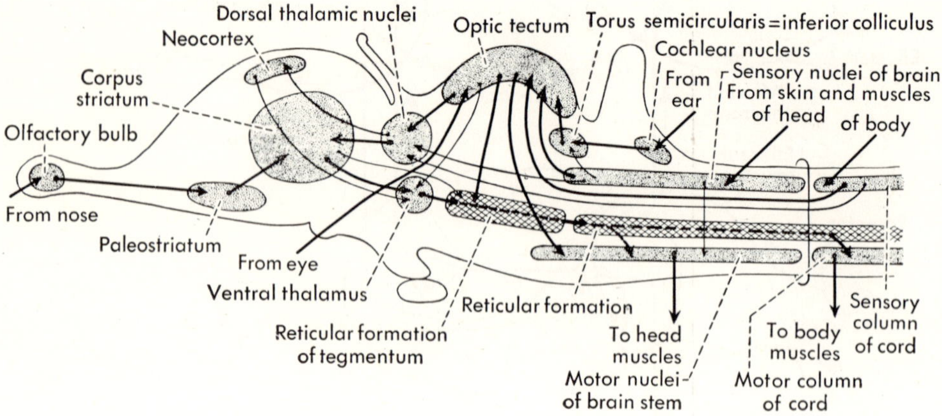

***Coordination in the brain:*** Different parts of the brain and different areas within these parts are known to serve as relay and coordinating centers for exteroceptive, enteroceptive and proprioceptive impulses. The cerebellum is primarily the center of motor coordination through which movements of the body are carried out and its equilibrium maintained; it is large in fishes, birds and mammals, all vertebrates capable of rapid and coordinated movements in swimming,

FIGURE 16.49  Diagram of the main centers and "wiring arrangement" in the brain of a reptile. (From Romer, *The Vertebrate Body*. Copyright 1949 by the W. B. Saunders Company.)

flying and running, walking or climbing, and in which such movements have distinct survival values. The dorsal part of the midbrain, the optic tectum (Latin, tectum = roof) is the end station for the fibres entering the brain through the optic nerves, from narily regulated by the hypothalamus. The thalamus is the chief end-station in the forebrain for the terminations of the sensory nerves, except for those of smell and of taste; it has close functional relationship with the cerebral cortex to which the sen-

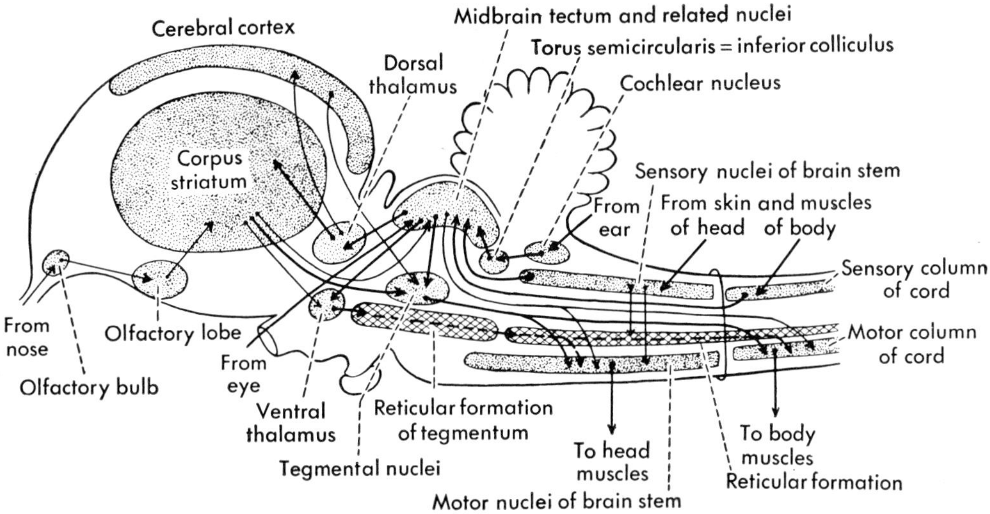

FIGURE 16.50 Diagram of the main centers and "wiring arrangement" in the brain of a bird. (From Romer, *The Vertebrate Body*. Copyright 1949 by the W. B. Saunders Company.)

which the impulses are relayed onward to other centers or to efferent nerves. This region is particularly large in reptiles and birds, but in the mammals, the visual centers are transferred to the cerebral cortex and the optic tectum serves as a reflex and relay rather than a coordinating center, with corresponding reduction in the size of the optic lobes, or corpora quadrigemina (Figs. 16.49, 16.50, 16.51). The hypothalamus is in general the principal center in the forebrain for the integration of the visceral functions and for the coordination of the impulses that travel along the autonomic nerves; it is, for example, the region controlling the constriction and dilatation of the blood vessels; the adjustment of the water balance within the organism and the level of sugar in the blood; to some extent, the control of the metabolism of carbohydrate and of fat; and in birds and mammals, the regulation of body temperature. In those mammals with sweat glands, the discharge of sweat is ordi-

sory stimuli reaching it are relayed. In the fishes, the cerebral hemispheres are concerned almost exclusively with the reception and transmission of olfactory stimuli but in the vertebrates of other classes, they receive and coordinate somatic sensory stimuli as well. With the great development of the cortex in mammals, this part becomes also the center for the final reception of impulses received from the eyes and the auditory portions of the ear, from the end organs in the integument, the muscles, tendons and joints and connective tissue, as well as the center directing the movements of the bodily muscles. It also contains large association areas, through which a great variety of functional connections may be established. In the primates, where vision is more important than the sense of smell, the visual areas in the cortex are larger and the olfactory areas smaller than in other mammals; this reduction of the olfactory areas is true also of birds where vision is also of primary importance. In man, the center for speech, as well as other consciously directed actions, is localized in the cerebral cortex whose development also gives a structural basis for memory, thought, reasoning and other intellectual capacities. The number of neu-

tem all lead to the conclusion that the conduction of the nervous impulse is an electro-chemical event, involving both the passage of a measurable electric current along a nerve and certain metabolic changes within it. The current is known as the

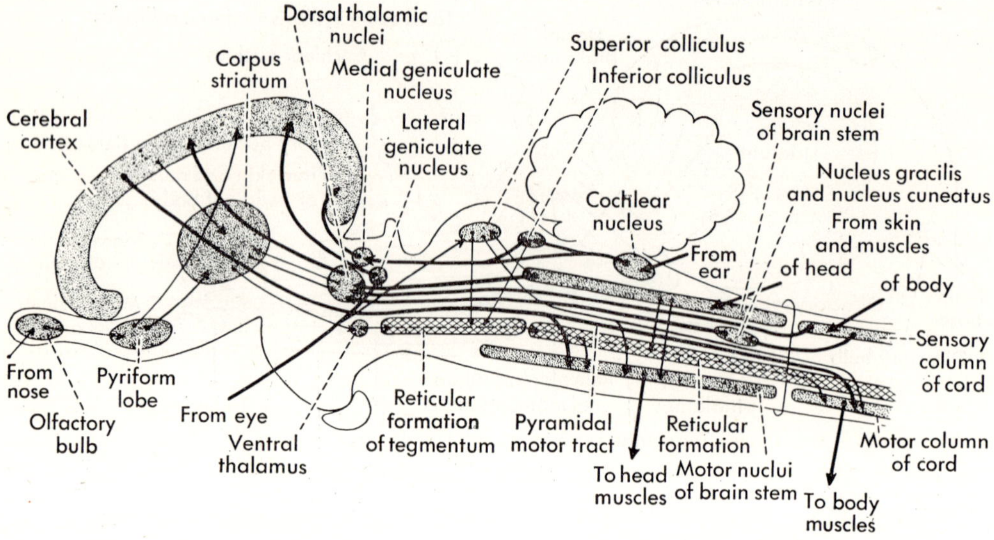

FIGURE 16.51 Diagram of the main centers and "wiring arrangement" in the brain of a mammal. (From Romer, *The Vertebrate Body*. Copyright 1949 by the W. B. Saunders Company.)

rons in the human cortex has been estimated as some 9,200,000,000, each one of which may be connected with not one but a great many others which lie in various parts of the central system as well as in the cortex. The patterns of the nervous pathways may be extremely intricate and a great variety of courses open to the passage of the nervous impulse. The final path that it travels is the resultant of many factors, both intrinsic or determined by the constitution of the animal and conditions within it, or extrinsic, determined by conditions external to it, and the end result is the response of the entire organism, or its behavior.

### Conduction and transmission of the nervous impulse

Studies of the mechanism of communication between the units of the nervous sys-

"action current" and since there are no visible changes in a nerve that is conducting an impulse, or has just conducted one, the passage of a stimulus along it can be recorded only by measurements of the action current or by responses of the end organ. The transmission of the impulse is accompanied by an increase in the consumption of oxygen and release of carbon dioxide by the nerve, and by the production of a very small amount of heat. Only repeated, steady stimulation produces a heat change large enough to be measured by the most sensitive instruments, but such determinations have shown that the heat produced is equal to $4 \times 10^{-7}$ calories per gram of nerve per second.

Measurements of the magnitude of the action current have shown that each nerve fibre, when stimulated, conducts at its max imum capacity; gradation in response to stimulation is therefore an expression of the number of fibers excited and the frequency of their excitation, and thus of the magnitude of the stimulus, rather than that of the impulse in any individual fibre. Measurements of the speed at which the impulse travels show that the rate of conduction varies for different nerves. In the dogfish, for example, at a temperature of 20°C it travels at approximately 35 meters per second; in a frog at the same temperature at approximately 30 meters per second; and in mammals, at 37°C, it ranges from a rate of 18–65 meters per second for fibres in the pyramidal tracts to an average maximum velocity of 140 meters per second for fibres in the dorso-cerebellar tract.

The impulse is a self-propagating one; that is, whatever changes take place in the nerve at the site of stimulation are initiated in the areas immediately adjacent and then in those next at hand and so on along the fibre. In an isolated nerve, it spreads as a wave of negativity in both directions away from the stimulated area. Directly after stimulation, the nerve passes through a brief period when it will not respond to stimulation; this is known as the refractory period and at its close the nerve is again in an excitable state and will respond to a stimulating agent. Given an adequate supply of oxygen, isolated nerves can conduct almost indefinitely, showing little sign of fatigue; fatigue, however, becomes apparent in a neuron-neuron-end organ sequence. The changes that go on during the passage of an impulse along a nerve must be ones that are readily reversible, for though a nerve may be in a different condition directly after its excitation, its return to the previous state is an almost immediate one.

While the impulse may propagate itself in either direction along an isolated nerve fibre, it travels from neuron to neuron in one direction only—from the terminations of the axon of one neuron across a synapse to the cell bodies or dendrites of others. The synapse thus imposes a polarity upon the nerve, for in effect it can conduct only away from its own cell body toward the cell body of another neuron. The means of transmission of the impulse across the synapse is still far from clear, although certain general characters have been established for it from studies on many different kinds of animals, including non-chordates like the squid, the cockroach and the crayfish, as well as many types of chordates. Transmission across the synapse is characterized in general not only by irreversibility, but also by delay and facilitation. That is, in addition to passing in one direction only, the impulse is always slowed down to some extent at the synapse, and its passage may enable subsequent ones to pass more readily. Moreover, while a single impulse may not of itself be strong enough to cross the synapse, a number of small ones in rapid succession may be, suggesting that some condition is set up by the first impulse that can be improved or increased by additional impulses, each in itself inadequate to produce the conditions for successful passage from neuron to neuron.

While for many years the conduction of the nervous impulse and its transmission across the synapse and finally to the end organ was thought to be a physical, or an electrical, phenomenon, yet the possibility of chemical transmission was always present and in the past thirty years much evidence has been produced in its favor. In 1921 Otto Loewi, a German physiologist working in this country, performed an experiment that gave decisive proof that a substance was liberated from nerves under stimulation which was responsible for the effect that they produced. In this experiment, he isolated the hearts of two frogs and destroyed the nervous connections of one, leaving both the vagus and the accelerator nerve to the other intact. He perfused them both with Ringer's solution, and stimulated electrically the vagus nerve of the intact heart, with the result that its beat slowed down. He then transferred the fluid from this heart to the other one with no nervous connections; its beat too slowed down. This showed clearly that in the heart stimulated through its nerve a substance was produced which was conveyed to the other in the perfusing medium, exerting an inhibitory effect upon it. He first called this the "vagus substance" (Vagusstoff); it was later identified as acetylcholine, a compound that is widely distributed in animal tissues and in those of at least some plants, and one that has great physiological potency. The smooth muscle fibre in the lung of a frog, for example, will respond to the presence of acetylcholine in amounts as minute as $1 \times 10^{-16}$ gram.

$$CH_3 \cdot CO \cdot O \cdot CH_2\!-\!CH_2\!-\!N\!\!\begin{array}{c}OH\\|\\\diagup CH_3\\\!-\!CH_3\\\diagdown CH_3\end{array}$$

Loewi continued the experiment by stimulating the accelerator nerve of the intact heart, and obtaining the expected increase in the rate of its beat, and then transferring the fluid from it to the other heart, which responded by beating also at a more rapid rate. Experiments with other organs, and other nerves, and on other animals than frogs have shown that a neurochemical mechanism of transmission is a general, and by no means an isolated, phenomenon. Acetylcholine is known to be liberated by the efferent fibres of peripheral nerves and by those of the cranio-sacral division of the autonomic system when they are stimulated to conduction; it is hydrolyzed and so disintegrated in the presence of an enzyme known as cholinesterase which has been extracted from various animal tissues such as heart, liver and intestine as well as from nerves. The afferent fibres of the peripheral nerves, on the contrary, do not produce acetylcholine to any appreciable extent, if at all, nor do those of the thoracolumbar division of the autonomic system, among which is the accelerator nerve to the heart. These latter nerves liberate a substance that is very similar to adrenalin, a compound with the formula

(structure of adrenalin with $CH(OH)CH_2NHCH_3$ substituent)

that is specifically a product of one pair of endocrine glands. The name sympathin has been proposed for this adrenalin-like substance, and also a classification of nerves into those that are cholinergic, or producers of acetylcholine, and those that are adrenergic, or producers of sympathin, a distinction that has been found also in the nerves of some non-chordates. A third category, histaminergic, has also been suggested from evidence that histamine, a substance also of great physiological potency released by practically all cells, can stimulate vaso-dilator nerve fibres to exert their effect upon peripheral vessels.

The fact that the sensory and adrenergic fibres of the nervous system, and certain other excitable tissues such as skeletal muscle fibres and unicellular algae large enough to permit measurements of an impulse passing along them, do not liberate acetylcholine on stimulation, has been offered as an argument against its significance in the conduction and transmission of the impulse in so-called cholinergic nerves. But even an elementary survey of animal and plant mechanisms makes patent the general principle that biological systems, with all their fundamental unity, frequently arrive at the same end by different routes, and it may well be found that the transmission of the nervous impulse is mediated by different chemical mechanisms in different groups of biological systems, just as, for example, respiration is so mediated.

# SECTION THREE

## THE OPERATION OF BIOLOGICAL SYSTEMS

# CHAPTER 17

# NUTRITION: THE UTILIZATION OF FOOD

## The nutrients necessary to life

To sustain life an environment must supply the nutrients necessary to the organisms that inhabit it. These nutrients include the elements of which protoplasm is made as well as those of the enzymes that catalyze metabolic reactions, the compounds called vitamins that are essential to certain of them and those called hormones that are known to influence them profoundly. There are, in addition, certain other elements known to be required in small, even minute, amounts and therefore known as "trace" elements. The food of the organism is the source from which these nutrients are obtained; to be nutritionally adequate, the food must provide them in forms and combinations suitable to the mechanical and chemical mechanisms with which the organism is endowed, as it must also provide compounds high in potential energy which will, on oxidation, yield kinetic energy adequate for the metabolic reactions carried on within the body and for the work done by its cells and tissues.

## Sources of the elements necessary to life

For the majority of organisms, the organic compounds included in the general classes of carbohydrates, lipids and proteins are their sources of carbon and nitrogen. The other elements exclusive of hydrogen and oxygen are derived largely from mineral salts, provided in the environment by the gradual disintegration of the materials of which the earth is made as well as by that of dead protoplasmic systems and the excreted products of those that are alive. These are taken into the organism dissolved in the water that it absorbs, or in solution or chemical combination in its food.

## Transformations of nutrients

*Digestion:* Since carbohydrates, lipids and proteins are compounds of considerable complexity and large molecular dimensions, they must undergo disintegration into simpler and soluble ones before they can diffuse readily into and throughout the organism. This process of disintegration is known as digestion (Latin, digerere = to separate). Digestion may be intracellular, as is the case in most plants, in the Protozoa and Porifera and some others of the invertebrates, or extracellular, as is the case in all the chordates and some of the more highly organized non-chordates. But wherever they take place, the processes of digestion are fundamentally the same in all biological systems and are preliminary to the absorption of the resulting soluble products and the further transformations of these products within the cells and tissues.

*Metabolism:* These transformations are collectively called metabolism and are either syntheses of the simpler compounds into ones of greater complexity and higher energy value, or further disintegrations of them into chemically simpler ones of lower energy value. Synthetic, or constructive, metabolism is known as anabolism (Greek, ana = up + bole = change), disintegrative or destructive metabolism as catabolism (Greek, kata = down). In consequence of either phase of metabolism, or of both of them together, substances may be set free as intermediate, end or by-products, called metabolites, that may be neutral or inert, as far as the organism is concerned, or that in quantity are toxic to it. In the latter case, the organism can survive only if it can get rid of them in some way, either by converting them into chemically inactive compounds or by eliminating them from the body by diffusion from its exposed surfaces or by flushing them out in solution through its excretory organs.

Anabolism leads to the formation of new protoplasm which may replace that which has undergone destructive changes, or may increase the mass of the body; to the formation of the specific products necessary to the functioning of the organism; to the formation of reserves that furnish stores of potential energy and of materials for future syntheses; and to that of special products that may be incorporated into the structure or substance of the organism, or that may be discharged from it. The capacity of different organisms to synthesize, from the same end products of digestion, their own particular kind of protoplasm and their own particular kind of reserves is one of their inherited and inheritable characteristics, as much a part of their genetic constitution as any of their anatomical characters. A cow and a sheep grazing in the same field, for example, eat and digest grass of the same quality and from it obtain the same materials, yet each synthesizes from these materials muscle and fat of different quality. All beef muscle and all beef fat is much the same, but quite distinct from mutton muscle and mutton fat. Similarly, two plants of different genera may grow side by side in the same soil, exposed to the same atmospheric conditions and drawing the same nutrients from the soil solution, yet from them each makes its own specific substance and its own specific products.

Catabolic changes also go on within cells and tissues, in the course of which energy is made available to the organism for its many and varied manifestations of life and vitality. These reactions are in the main of the oxidation-reduction type. The food may not be the direct source of the compounds that are degraded in catabolism, for they may come from the substance of the organism itself, or from its reserves, but the food is ultimately their source, for even if it is not directly consumed to supply the energy required, it must furnish the materials to replace those taken from the body and so utilized; otherwise the body would consume not only all its resources, but its own substance as well.

## Energy values of foods

The energy content of any given carbohydrate, lipid or protein can be experimentally determined by burning a known quantity of the pure substance outside the body under controlled conditions in a bomb calorimeter and measuring the heat evolved. The heats of combustion for a number of substances, determined in this way, are given in Table IX.

TABLE IX

Heats of Combustion of Some Common Compounds (from Sherman: *Chemistry of Foods and Nutrition*, 6th edition. Copyright 1941 by The Macmillan Company.)

| Substance | Calories per gram |
|---|---|
| Glucose ($C_6H_{12}O_6$) | 3.75 |
| Sucrose ($C_{12}H_{22}O_{11}$) | 3.96 |
| Starch ($C_6H_{12}O_6$)n Glycogen | 4.22 |
| Butter fat [a] | 9.30 |
| Edestin (protein from hemp seed) | 5.64 |
| Gliadin (protein from wheat) | 5.74 |
| Casein (protein from milk) | 5.85 |
| Carbohydrate (average) | 4.1 |
| Fats (average) | 9.45 |
| Proteins (average) | 5.65 |

[a] Butter fat is a mixture of the following fatty acids in combination with glycerol:

oleic acid ($C_{17}H_{33}COOH$), 27.4%
palmitic acid ($C_{15}H_{31}COOH$), 22.6%
myristic acid ($C_{13}H_{27}COOH$), 22.6%
stearic acid ($C_{17}H_{35}COOH$), 11.4%
lauric acid ($C_{11}H_{23}COOH$), 6.9%
butyric acid ($C_3H_7COOH$), 3%
capric acid ($C_9H_{19}COOH$), 1.8%
caprylic acid ($C_7H_{15}COOH$), 1.8%
caproic acid ($C_5H_{11}COOH$), 1.4%

### The respiratory quotient

The efficiency of the combustion can be determined by measuring the amount of oxygen consumed and of carbon dioxide evolved in the process. This is expressed as $\frac{CO_2 \text{ (output)}}{O_2 \text{ (intake)}}$; for biological systems this ratio is referred to as the Respiratory Quotient, or RQ. When carbohydrate is completely burned outside a living body, or inside it, all the carbon in the molecule is oxidized to carbon dioxide and all the hydrogen to water. But the molecule itself contains oxygen sufficient for the oxidation of the hydrogen, so that all that is required from an outside source is an amount equivalent to that necessary to oxidize its carbon content, although in the actual reaction it may be distributed between the carbon and the hydrogen. The oxidation of glucose may be grossly expressed by the equation $C_6H_{12}O_6 + 6O_2 \rightarrow 6CO_2 + 6H_2O +$ Energy, and the ratio of carbon dioxide as $\frac{6CO_2}{6O_2}$; the respiratory quotient is therefore 1. A molecule of lipid contains less oxygen in proportion to its carbon and hydrogen than a molecule of carbohydrate, so that its combustion requires more oxygen from an outside source. Triolein, one of the common fats, has, for example, the molecular formula $C_{57}H_{104}O_6$; its complete oxidation to carbon dioxide and water requires 80 molecules of oxygen for each molecule of fat, expressed by the equation

$$C_{57}H_{104}O_6 + 80O_2 \rightarrow 57CO_2 + 52H_2O + \text{Energy.}$$

In this case the respiratory quotient is $\frac{57CO_2}{80O_2}$, or 0.71, and while it varies with fats of different kinds, according to the composition of their molecules, it never reaches unity.

When protein is completely burned in a bomb calorimeter the carbon in the molecule is oxidized to carbon dioxide, the hydrogen to water and the nitrogen is evolved as nitrogen gas. The ratio of oxygen intake to carbon dioxide output depends therefore upon the amount of oxygen contained within the molecule, as it does with carbohydrate and fat, and is not affected by its nitrogen content. But in the body of a plant or animal, the nitrogen is liberated not as a gas but as ammonium compounds, urea, uric acid and other organic substances which are all capable of further oxidation and further energy release. The heat of combustion of a protein determined by calorimetry is therefore not an exact measure of its energy value to an organism when burned in its body; and since the molecular formula of proteins is unknown, it is not possible to write an equation for the oxidation of any one of them. The value of their potential energy and the respiratory quotient for their combustion must therefore be obtained indirectly. Calculated on the basis that all the nitrogen in the protein oxidized by a biological system is eliminated as urea, the energy lost by such incomplete oxidation is approximately 0.9 Calories per gram of protein, and its fuel, or energy, value is therefore not 5.65 Calories per gram, as it is when it is burned in a calorimeter but 5.65 − 0.9, or 4.75 Calories per gram. In mammals, at least, it is actually less than this, for some of the nitrogen is eliminated in organic compounds of higher energy value than urea, so that the energy loss is more nearly 1.3 Calories per gram of protein and the available potential energy content of protein on an average 5.65 − 1.30, or 4.35 Calories per gram. By indirect calculation also, the RQ of protein has an average value of 0.801.

### Heat production

The full energy value of a substance consumed within the body is never available to an organism, for some of the energy liberated is always dissipated as heat. In general, the evolution of carbon dioxide and the production of heat, however slight, by a cell, a tissue or a multicellular organism is an indication that an oxidative process, with an accompanying reduction, is going on within it either by an aerobic or an anaerobic mechanism. Such processes do not take place in a single step, as the generalized equations for the oxidation of glucose and triolein might imply, but by a series of them, each of which represents an energy change or an energy transfer. Some such processes are on the whole more efficient than others as far as the loss of kinetic energy as heat is concerned; the most efficient that is known to be carried on by biological systems is that which takes place in luminescent organisms when luciferin is oxidized in the presence of the enzyme luciferase and nearly 100 per cent of the energy so set free manifested as light. Determinations of the release of chemical energy made available to an organism by the step-wise energy exchanges that take place in oxidation-reduction reactions are far more complicated, but the loss of heat of greater or less amount by all living systems and metabolizing tissues indicates that in no case is all the energy bound in the substances that constitute its food directly available to it for the various kinds of work that it performs.

## Nutritional requirements of organisms
### Methods of determination

The chemical composition of its food is also of great importance to an organism, for the food must supply not only those substances from which the organism can synthesize the compounds necessary to its existence but such compounds that it is incapable of synthesizing. Nutritional studies of plants and animals have been numerous and varied, carried on with the purpose of determining the minimal food requirements of a given organism, the sources from which these requirements can be supplied, and the capacity of the organism to synthesize essential nutrients from inorganic compounds and from organic ones of different degrees of complexity. Such studies present many technical difficulties, for valid conclusions can be drawn only if all sources of nutrients, except those provided by the experimenter, are wholly excluded and if the composition of the materials so supplied is exactly known. The presence in the bodies of both plants and animals of benign micro-organisms that are capable of carrying out syntheses of some of the essential nutrients is a complicating factor, as is also the possibility of some slight impurity in the compounds administered as food. Studies of plant nutrition especially have been further complicated by contamination of the test solutions by the dissolution of the material of the containers or the adsorption of ions on their walls. The techniques have become more and more refined, with the use of highly purified compounds in sterile solutions and, insofar as it is possible, of organisms free from symbiotic or parasitic associations. In the case of mammals, whose nutritional needs have been more intensively studied than those of other groups of organisms because of their importance to human welfare, an exact nutritional study involves removing young animals from the uterus of the mother immediately prior to the time of their natural birth while their digestive tracts are still sterile and feeding them by aseptic methods on sterile food so that there is no opportunity for the introduction of bacteria into their intestinal tracts, an occurrence which normally takes place as soon as the young are born and begin to suckle. Under ordinary circumstances all mammals support a flourishing intestinal flora which contribute not only to the disintegration of parts of their food but to the synthesis of certain vitamins, or accessory food substances, particularly those of the B complex.

### Autotrophs and heterotrophs

While no organisms are independent of their environments as a source of food, they vary widely in the nature of the materials that they require from it. Some are less dependent than others upon organic compounds and can synthesize their food from inorganic ones; some can make use of relatively simple organic compounds as sources of carbon and nitrogen, and from these can synthesize the more complex substances that they require as nutrients; others are incapable of such syntheses and must obtain the complex compounds they need either directly or indirectly from the organisms that can make them. On the basis of their nutritional self-sufficiency, or independence of other organisms, all biological systems may be classified as autotrophs (Greek, autos = self + trophos = feeder) or heterotrophs (Greek, hetero = other). Autotrophic systems include all those that carry on photosynthesis or chemosynthesis; heterotrophic systems include all animals, whether parasitic or free-living, the parasitic and saprophytic fungi as well as angiosperms like the parasitic dodder and mistletoe and the saprophytic Indian pipe; and some few free-living angiosperms like sundews and pitcher plants which photosynthesize but also derive part of their food from the disintegrated bodies of insects caught in their leaves. But whatever the way in which they obtain their food, their utilization of it is fundamentally the same, and the processes concerned in its digestion and its metabolism, common to all living things, points again to the unity of biological processes and biological systems.

## Chemical reactions in biological systems

The chemical changes that take place within the body of an organism proceed much more rapidly than they ordinarily can be made to do outside it, and under conditions quite different from those that the chemist provides to bring about similar results in vitro. For example, the disintegration of protein to its constituent amino acids requires, in the chemist's laboratory, some twenty-four hours of boiling with 20 per cent hydrochloric acid, while in the body of a mammal it is accomplished in three to four hours at a much lower temperature and higher pH. These differences in the rates and conditions of reactions in vivo and in vitro are due to the presence of certain substances called enzymes (Greek, en = in + zyme = yeast) which are produced by living cells and which participate in the digestive and most, if not all, of the metabolic reactions that take place in the body. Knowledge of the nature and operation of these substances is still far from complete, although it has progressed with great rapidity in the past quarter of a century.

### Early experiments on digestion

The phenomenon of digestion was recognized early in man's inquiry into the conditions of life, but its nature was a mystery. Since the muscles of the stomach were seen to undergo contraction in the living animal, the disintegration of the food was believed to be a mechanical process, brought about by the grinding action of the stomach's walls. The first experiments that gave a clue to its chemical nature were those that sought to find out the qualities of the juices to which the food, once in the digestive tract, was exposed. In 1663 a Dutch physician, Regner de Graaf (1641–1673), succeeded in introducing a wild duck's quill into the pancreatic duct of a dog and in drawing out through it the fluid destined for the intestinal contents. He ascertained some of the properties of this fluid, finding that it was acid in its reaction and bitter to the taste. Nearly a hundred years late, René de Réaumur performed experiments upon birds that showed conclusively that digestion was a chemical process. Taking advantage of the habits of birds of prey to spit out any undigested parts of their food, he fed his pet kite small, perforated tin tubes filled with meat. After an interval, the kite spat the tubes out, but they were empty of their contents. Réaumur then conceived the idea of stuffing the tubes with bits of sponge to try its effect upon foods of various kinds. He found that the fluid, when brought into contact with flesh and bone, reduced them to a pulpy mass; he also found it acid when tested with litmus but salty, rather than bitter, to the taste. To his regret, his kite died before he had performed more than two experiments upon it and, since he had made no provision to replace it, he had to continue his studies upon ducks and chickens while still dreaming of the splendid amounts of experimental material that could be collected with greater ease and in greater quantity from such large birds of prey as vultures and eagles.

Later in the same century Lazzaro Spallanzani performed similar experiments upon hawks and also upon certain mammals, inducing them to swallow perforated tubes fastened to bits of string so that they could be drawn out after they had been in the stomach any determined period of time. In all these experiments he found the same softening, or dissolving, action of the stomach's juices, and in order to prove, rather than infer, that the same sort of process went on in human digestion, performed some direct experiments upon himself. Realizing that certain things, like cherry stones and plum pits, could pass through the human digestive tract without damage to it or its possessor, he resolved to swallow containers holding various kinds of food, so that after their recovery he could determine the changes that had taken place in them. He modified the procedure used with animals, however, and in his own case used small linen bags to hold the test foods. His results verified Réaumur's on the softening and disintegrative effects of gastric juice. He found, moreover, that the extent of digestion was conditioned by the thickness of the bag, and so by the accessibility of the digestive fluids to the food. If made of three thicknesses of linen, bread contained within the bag was not wholly digested while the same amount of bread disappeared entirely from bags made of one or two thicknesses. He also experimented with saliva, and found that it, too, possessed digestive potencies.

While the experiments of Réaumur and Spallanzani proved that digestion was a chemical and not merely a mechanical process, they showed nothing of the nature of the chemical changes or of the agents that brought them about. These facts could only be determined by chemical analysis of the digestive juices, the first steps toward which were taken by an Englishman, William Prout (1785–1850), one of the first men to apply pure chemistry to the operation of the animal body and so a pioneer in the development of biochemistry as a field of biology. Prout subjected the contents of a rabbit's stomach to chemical analysis, and found that it contained free hydrochloric acid. But the existence of another chemical agent in gastric juice was suspected, and its presence was deduced by William Beaumont (1785–1853), an American Army surgeon, from the extensive studies he made upon the wounded voyageur, Alexis St. Martin (see p. 428). In 1835, the German anatomist Theodor Schwann gave the name of pepsin (Greek, pepis = cooking or digestion) to a component of gastric juice that he found to be non-acid, yet chemically active in the digestion of meat.

### Studies of fermentation

In the years between Spallanzani's experiments and Schwann's description of pepsin, the digestive or disintegrative action of a number of substances of both plant and animal origin was discovered, such as the conversion of starch to sugar and dextrin by saliva as well as by material extracted from crushed wheat grains and from malt. But it was Pasteur's studies on fermentation, twenty-five years after Schwann's description of pepsin, that opened the way to the interpretation of the chemical changes that go on in digestion and metabolism.

Nearly one hundred years earlier, in 1787, an Italian naturalist, G. V. M. Fabroni (1752–1822), had defined fermentation as the decomposition of one substance by another, and in 1837 the great Swedish chemist, Jans Jakob Berzelius (1770–1848), had included fermentation among the chemical processes whose rates of reaction were markedly increased by the addition of substances known as catalysts (Greek, katalyein = to destroy or dissolve). Some reactions that would otherwise take days to come to completion are found to reach equilibrium within a few hours if an appropriate catalyst is added, the catalyst itself remaining unaltered and unincorporated in the end products, for it can be recovered quantitatively at the end of the reaction. The effect of a catalyst has been compared to the effect of oil upon an inclined plane, along which a body moves under the influence of gravity; because of the presence of the oil, the velocity of the descent is accelerated but the oil neither initiates the movement of the sliding body nor combines with it or the material of the inclined plane and remains essentially unchanged by the process in which it has been involved. Among chemical catalysts are acids and finely divided metals, like colloidal nickel and platinum, for their presence, sometimes even in minute amounts, speeds up the velocity of certain reactions several fold.

By showing that sterile sugar solutions remained unchanged, or chemically stable, if uncontaminated by yeasts or other microorganisms, Pasteur related the chemical change that takes place in fermentation to the presence of these organisms, which he called "ferments." His insistence upon the association of living organisms with these chemical "alterations" presented something of a problem to contemporary scientists, for pepsin was not a living organism yet it was known to effect a chemical change. In order to reconcile this difficulty, a distinction was made between "organized" and "unorganized" ferments, or those that were believed to be living systems, like yeast and bacteria, and those that could be isolated from them, like pepsin, trypsin,* and the starch-destroying substance obtained from saliva and from grain. Later, in 1878, a German physiologist, Willy Kühne (1837–1900), proposed the name enzyme for the unorganized ferments so that chemists and biologists had not only a conception of two different kinds of chemically active substances but different names for them as well.

That this conception was false was proved, more accidentally than deliberately, in 1897 by a German chemist, Eduard Buchner (1860–1917). Buchner planned some experiments to find out if material extracted from yeast had any medicinal value. In order to determine this he had to grind up huge quantities of yeast and press the juice out of the mass of cell fragments. Once this was accomplished, he had to find a way of preserving the juice while the experiments to test its value were being carried on. One method of preservation that he tried was one that had been used for generations by housewives—the addition of sugar. But instead of preserving the juice as he had hoped, he found that the addition of sugar resulted in fermentation; carbon dioxide was evolved from the sugary mass and alcohol collected in it, just as they might had intact and living yeast cells been introduced into it. It was therefore clear that the yeast cells themselves were not the "ferments" but material that could be separated from them and that it was nearly as active when free of the cells as it was in their presence. The extracted substance was given the name of zymase and included among Kühne's enzymes, a comprehensive term now used for all such chemically active substances,

* Trypsin is the agent in pancreatic juice whose activity in the disintegration of meat was described by a French doctor, Jean Nicholas Corvisart des Marets (1755–1821), nearly two hundred years after de Graaf had removed pancreatic juice from an animal's body.

whether operating in cells or after discharge from them.

Buchner's results made it clear that the decomposition of glucose into alcohol and carbon dioxide could be more accurately expressed by the chemical equation

$$C_6H_{12}O_6 \xrightarrow{zymase} 6CO_2 + 6H_2O + \text{Energy}$$

than by Pasteur's equation

$$C_6H_{12}O_6 \xrightarrow{yeast} 6CO_2 + 6H_2O + \text{Energy}$$

but they still revealed nothing of the process itself or of the contribution that zymase made to it. It has taken over hundreds of research workers, working in more than a dozen different countries, to unravel the sequence of events in the decomposition process and to establish the fact that zymase is not a single enzyme but a complex of several, and the fermentation of glucose a process that does not take place in one step, but in a series of steps. According to present knowledge, there are fourteen steps in the process in which at least twelve enzymes are directly involved (Fig. 17.1).

**Enzymes and enzymatic reactions**

Enzymes are considered special kinds of catalysts, or biocatalysts, the products of living cells which participate in most, if not all, of the reactions, synthetic as well as destructive, characteristic of living biological systems. Like an inorganic catalyst, a biocatalyst is not changed in the reaction in which it takes part; it does not appear in the end product and a minute amount is sufficient to influence the conversion of relatively enormous amounts of the reacting substance or substances. But a biocatalyst is far more specific in its action than an inorganic catalyst, and may also appear to initiate a reaction, in causing one to occur that would be highly improbable otherwise. While acids or finely divided metals may be equally effective agents in the reactions of a number of different reagents, an enzyme is effective in one particular kind of reaction only and with one particular kind of reagent. Meat, for example, remains unchanged in the presence of zymase, and glucose in the presence of pepsin or trypsin.

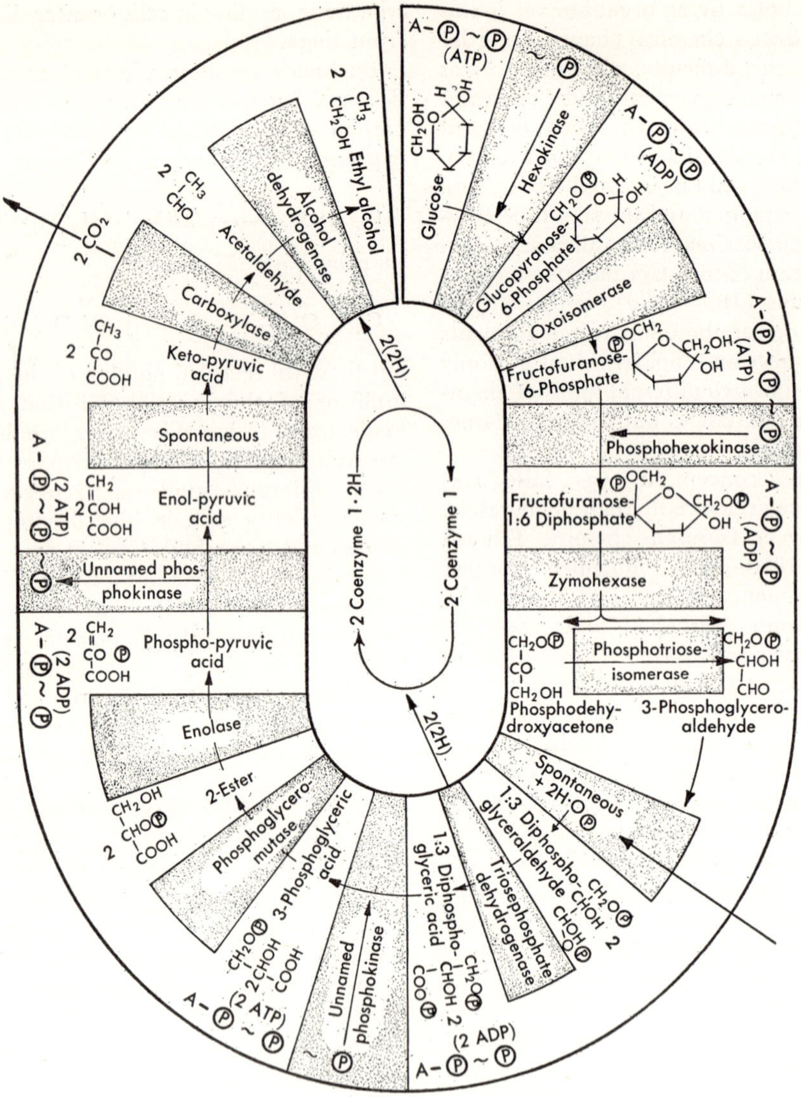

FIGURE 17.1 Diagram illustrating the 14 known steps in the conversion of glucose to alcohol in the process of fermentation. (After Pfieffer.) The 12 enzymes known to be involved are represented by stippled areas. The cycle begins at the upper right of the diagram, with the conversion of adenosinetriphosphate (ATP) into adenosinediphosphate (ADP); the phosphate radicle liberated becomes attached to the glucose molecule. The addition of phosphate radicles from another source is indicated by the arrow at the lower right; all the phosphate radicles are finally surrendered to build two extra molecules of ATP from ADP. The cycle in the center of the diagram (co-enzyme I) receives hydrogen atoms split off from the molecule of 1:3 diphosphoglyceraldehyde and holds them until they are surrendered to the acetaldehyde molecule in its conversion to ethyl alcohol.

All but the final step in this cycle are identical with the changes that go on in contracting muscle, and all the enzymes concerned, except in the initial change of the glucose molecule, are associated with mitochondria (see Figure 7.3).

Moreover, zymase is not effective on all kinds of sugars and, with those on which it is, always brings about alcoholic fermentation and none of the other kinds of decomposition possible to the glucose molecule.

The particular substance upon which an enzyme acts is called its substrate; glucose, and some of the other hexoses, furnish the substrate for the zymase complex, but each of the enzymes included in it operates only in connection with its own specific substrate which, except for the glucose molecule itself (the initial substrate for hexokinase, the first enzyme in the series), is one of the intermediate products in the progression toward alcohol and carbon dioxide. Enzymes are now commonly designated by the names of their substrates and the suffix -ase; sucrase, for example, is the enzyme that catalyzes the hydrolytic decomposition of sucrose, or cane sugar, into glucose and fructose; and urease the enzyme that brings about the decomposition of urea into ammonia and carbon dioxide. Pepsin, trypsin, now known, like zymase, to consist of several enzymes, and some others which were discovered and named before this system was in general use are still known by their original names.

Because of this specificity it is possible to classify enzymes either according to the general nature of their substrates or according to that of the reactions in which they take part. Carbohydrases include those enzymes, like sucrase, which operate upon a carbohydrate substrate; proteinases those, like pepsin, that operate upon a protein substrate, and esterases those that are effective upon compounds of hydrocarbons with acids, either organic or inorganic. Lipases, for example, are esterases, for they catalyze the hydrolysis of fats which are esters of the hydrocarbon glycerol and fatty acids. On the basis of the type of reaction in which they participate, esterases are included in the category of hydrolases, or those enzymes that cooperate in reactions involving the loss of the elements of water from the substrate or the addition of them to it. Similarly other enzymes are designated, according to the type of reaction, as phosphorylases, or those that effect the transfer of the phosphate radical $-PO_4$ from one compound to another; adding enzymes, or those that effect the union of two molecules into one, or the decomposition of one into two without the loss or addition of water; and transferring enzymes, or those that catalyze the transference of an atom or a radical from one molecule to another. In such a reaction, one molecule acts as the donator and the other as the acceptor, and the enzyme as the temporary carrier or transferring agent. Enzymes of this kind are concerned primarily in oxidation-reduction reactions, in which an enzyme may, for example, accept a hydrogen atom donated by one substance, hold it momentarily and then donate it to the final acceptor substance. One other, and much smaller group, the isomerases, are concerned in the atomic shifts by which a compound is converted to an isomeric form.

Numerous experiments have shown that enzymes are very sensitive to the physical and chemical conditions of their environment. It was found in the early studies of zymase that boiling destroyed its potency, showing that it was a thermolabile substance, or one altered by high temperatures. In 1904, two English chemists, Arthur Harden (1865–1940) and Sydney Young (1857–1937), showed that after dialysis, or the separation of the crystalloid and colloid components of yeast extract by filtration through a semi-permeable membrane, neither fraction alone could bring about the fermentation of glucose. But if a little of the crystalloid fraction, or even a little boiled yeast juice, were added to the colloidal fraction and the mixture provided with a glucose substrate, fermentation proceeded as actively as it did with freshly expressed yeast juice, and nearly as actively as with intact yeast cells. It was therefore apparent that the enzyme was effective only in the presence of another substance whose molecule was of crystalloid dimensions and thermostable, or unaffected by boiling. This substance was called co-zymase; later it too was found to be a mixture of substances, called co-enzymes, without which the enzyme proper was impotent to produce its specific effect upon its substrate. Since this discovery, a number of other enzymes concerned in oxidative reactions have been found to be equally dependent upon the presence of co-enzymes, some of which have been identified as modified forms of certain vitamins.

Many other enzymatic reactions, too, have been found to be influenced by the presence of substances more general in their nature than such co-enzymes. These may be grouped under the general heads of activators and inhibitors. Certain ions are known to be activators, although the actual role that they play is not yet clear. Many phosphorylases, for example, require the presence of magnesium ions, and the amylase of saliva, a carbohydrase, is effective only in the presence of anions, a condition which in natural conditions of the enzyme's operation is satisfied by the sodium and potassium chloride content of saliva and their dissociation into $Na^+ + Cl^-$ and $K^+ + Cl^-$. But experimentally other anions can be substituted for $Cl^-$ with similar activating effects. And some extra-cellular enzymes are discharged from the cells in inactive form, and require some change before they become effective. Trypsin is such an enzyme, for it is secreted from the cells of the pancreas as trypsinogen, an enzyme precursor or proenzyme in whose presence protein remains unchanged. The conversion of inactive trypsinogen to active trypsin takes place through the agency of enterokinase, either an enzyme itself or something very similar to an enzyme, which is secreted by the glandular epithelium of the intestine and in whose presence the enzyme proper is "unmasked" or the block to its activity removed.

Pasteur himself noted that alcoholic fermentation by yeast was depressed by the presence of oxygen; other elements or their compounds are now known to depress, or wholly inhibit, certain enzymes or enzyme systems. Among these are the ions of certain heavy metals, like $Au^{++}$, $Cu^{++}$ and $Hg^+$, and mild oxidizing agents. Bromine, iodine, chloroform and fluorides are toxic for some enzymes, and cyanides, compounds containing the $-CN$ radical, inhibit the action of most oxidases. Inorganic catalysts are known also to be poisoned by certain substances; colloidal platinum, for example, is ineffective as a catalyst in the presence of iodine, carbon monoxide (CO) and mercuric ions.

It is known, too, that organisms naturally possess, or may be caused to develop, substances that act as inhibitors, blocking the action of otherwise active enzymes. The discovery, in 1903, of inhibitors for pepsin and trypsin in extracts made from the bodies of the intestinal round worm, Ascaris, provides at least a partial answer to the long-puzzling question of the ability of parasites to survive in the digestive tracts of animals, where they are exposed to the proteolytic and other destructive enzymes of the digestive juices. But although Ascaris can exist as an intestinal inhabitant because of the particular enzyme inhibitors it possesses, it cannot escape destruction, even when alive, when exposed to proteolytic enzymes other than pepsin and trypsin, such as ficin, a proteinase obtained from the milky sap of the fig tree, or papain from the latex of the pawpaw.

Animals can also be caused to develop enzyme inhibitors by the injection of an enzyme into their blood or lymph. The development of such inhibitors is similar to the development of an antibody to an antigen, and the inhibitors themselves belong to the same class of substances as antitoxins and other antibodies. Experiments have, for example, shown that if luciferase is injected into the blood of a rabbit, serum prepared later from the blood of the injected animal will prevent the oxidation, and consequent luminescence, of luciferin extracted from the body of a luminous crustacean when mixed with luciferase from the same source.

Enzymes are also extremely sensitive to the pH of the medium in which they operate. For each there is an optimum pH, which varies from high acidity for some enzymes to high alkalinity for others, and varies also, within a narrower range, for different substrates for those enzymes that are functional with more than one. Pepsin, for example, is effective only on the acid side of the pH scale and trypsin only on the alkaline. And pepsin is most active in its decomposition of a protein like hemoglobin between pH 1 and 2, on one like gelatin between pH 2 and 3 and on casein near pH 1.5. Trypsin, on the other hand, operates most effectively on hemoglobin and gelatin in the neighborhood of pH 8, and on casein near pH 10.

There is an apparent optimum temperature range for enzymatic reactions, which lies between 30°–40° C, a range which includes the body temperature of warm-blooded animals. But this is only an apparent optimum; although the velocity of an enzymatic reaction, like that of other chemical reactions, increases with increase in temperature, or acceleration of molecular movement, the destruction or inactivation of the enzyme likewise proceeds more rapidly. The velocity is also conditioned by the concentration of the end products, for enzymatic reactions are reversible ones. If, for example, the enzyme x is one that catalyzes the disintegration of the molecule AB into A and B, the reaction proceeds until A and B have reached a certain concentration, when the disintegration of AB is suppressed and its synthesis from A and B increased. This may be expressed by the generalized equation

$$AB \underset{\longleftarrow}{\overset{\longrightarrow}{\quad x \quad}} A + B$$

and from this it is apparent that removal of the end product can cause the reaction to proceed in one direction only, from right to left or from left to right, as long as there is any substrate present. Enzymes are not exclusively disintegrative agents, as the earlier ones known were thought to be, but synthetic ones as well, as effective in the constructive metabolism of the organism as they are in the digestion of its food or its catabolism.

One of the most important milestones in enzyme research, after Buchner's discovery

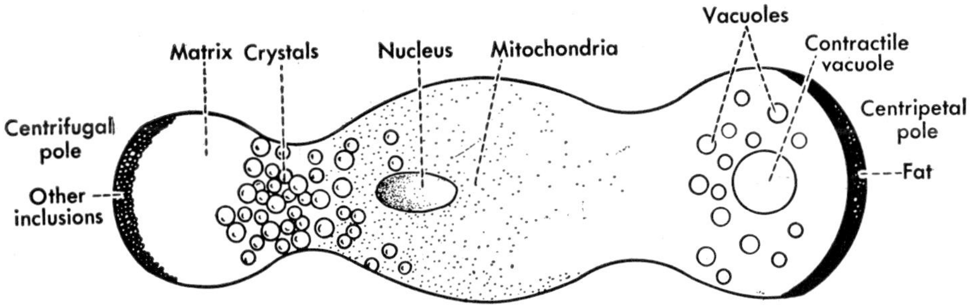

FIGURE 17.2 Diagram of an amoeba after centrifugation, showing stratification of the components of the cell. Tests for enzymatic activity of the different strata show that the region containing the mitochondria gives the greatest activity of amylase, while the region of clear cytoplasm gives the greatest activity of peptidase. (After Holter and Doyle.)

of the activity of zymase independent of the yeast cell, was the isolation of a pure enzyme and its chemical identification. This was first accomplished by an American scientist, James Sumner (1887–    ), who in 1926 succeeded in extracting urease from jack beans, a widely grown forage crop of the United States, and obtaining crystals of the pure enzyme. Upon analysis, urease was found to be a protein, with a molecular weight of about 483,000. In the quarter century following the chemical identification of urease, over thirty other enzymes have been extracted from plant and animal tissues, crystallized and analyzed. These include pepsin, trypsin, ficin and papain as well as several of those involved in the alcoholic fermentation of glucose. All of them have been found to be proteins, substantiating the inference of the protein nature of enzymes which earlier workers had drawn from certain features of their behavior, such as their colloidal properties, their sensitivity to pH and to heat and their irreversible alteration at temperatures which from the chemical point of view are comparatively low, for all but one or two of the enzymes now known are destroyed at 80° C.

The determination of the protein nature

of enzymes has opened the way to the clarification of certain facts about them as well as to theoretical explanations of their behavior. Like other proteins, they are the products of living cells, but while some seem to be common to all the cells of an organism, others are synthesized, or at least are found, only in localized tissues. All living cells of the vertebrate body, for example, contain oxidases but only the cells of the gastric mucosa elaborate the precursor of pepsin, pepsinogen, and only certain ones in the pancreas, trypsinogen, the precursor of trypsin. The intracellular enzymes also appear to be variously distributed within the individual cells. By centrifuging cells at a very rapid rate it is possible to separate them into portions containing substances of different specific gravity, and by testing the enzymatic potencies of these fragments on suitable substrates to determine whether or not certain enzymes are localized in the nucleus or in the cytoplasm, and if in the cytoplasm, whether or not they are associated with any of the microscopically visible components of the cell (Fig. 17.2). Such studies have shown the localization of some enzymes in the nucleus, of others in the optically homogeneous ground cytoplasm and the association of others with the mitochondria and Golgi substance.

***The specificity of enzymes:*** Like other specific characteristics of cells or cellular systems, the development of enzymes is under genic control; in some cases, species or groups of organisms are differentiated by the enzymes they possess. No vertebrate, for example, seems to possess the capacity to synthesize urease, although this is an enzyme found in a number of plants and in some invertebrates; pepsin, on the other hand, has not been found in any invertebrate whose enzymes have been studied and has been found in every vertebrate tested for it. Cellulase, the enzyme that makes possible the decomposition of cellulose, an invariable constituent of the food of plant-eating animals, is very limited in its distribution among multicellular animals, but very generally found in Protozoa and fungi. The most convincing evidence of direct genic control of enzyme development is currently being obtained from studies of metabolism and inheritance in the pink bread mold Neurospora, from which it is becoming increasingly clear that the loss of specific metabolic capacities, controlled by specific enzyme systems, is correlated with the loss of specific genes.

While all the studies of enzyme activity have made it clear that they direct, or control, the course of biological reactions in that they cause certain ones to take place with such rapidity that any possible side reactions are suppressed or reduced to such a degree that their effects are negligible, the actual mechanism of this control is far from clear. Like any other catalyst, an enzyme exerts its effect by lowering the activation energy of the reagent or reagents concerned. By activation energy is meant the energy that must be applied to a stable molecule to bring about its decomposition or its combination with another. How the enzyme accomplishes this is still obscure. There is evidence that a temporary enzyme-substrate union, or complex, is formed, during which it may be supposed that alterations in the position or relationships of atoms in the substrate molecule lead to distortions and consequent weakening of its structure. It may be that the effect of the enzyme is to displace some of the substrate's atoms, so that it is converted from a neutral molecule into a charged ion, or to bend its molecule in such a way that some atoms are brought closer to each other than they otherwise are, with corresponding changes in their energy relationships. In either case, there is assumed a structural or geometrical similarity or affinity between the molecule of the enzyme and the molecule of its substrate, of such a kind that the two fit together in a kind of architectural union rather than a chemical one (Fig. 17.3). The analogy of a lock and a key is often applied to the supposed enzyme-substrate relationship, an analogy which serves to explain the selectivity of all biocatalysts and the extreme specificity of certain of them. Just as one particular kind of key can be inserted into but one particular kind of lock, so one particular kind of enzyme molecule can form a complex with but one particular kind of substrate molecule. But although the general pattern of the key may correspond to the general pattern of the lock, the key will not throw the tumbler, or turn the lock, unless it is an exact fit, each one of its prongs and grooves this difference is not enough to keep the key out of the lock but is enough to prevent it from turning it. The monofluoroacetate therefore, in sufficient concentration, acts as a competitor for the enzyme, and by uniting with it blocks its union with its proper

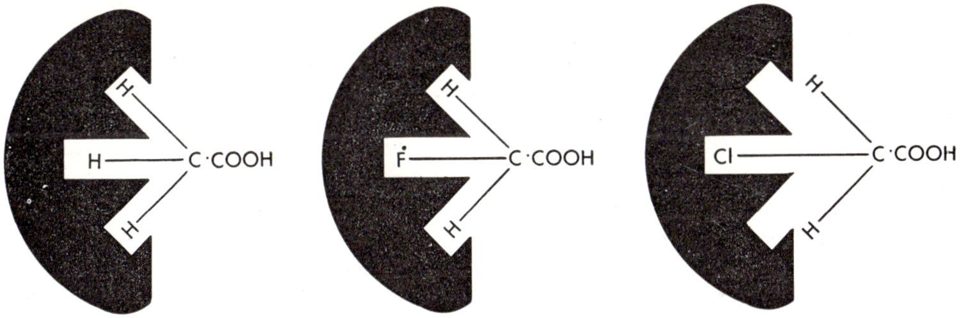

FIGURE 17.3 Diagrams illustrating the "lock and key" theory of enzyme action. The enzyme is represented by a solid black hemisphere, the substrate by the white bars that fit into it. (After Pfieffer.)

a. "Perfect fit" between an enzyme and a molecule of acetic acid.

b. Monofluoroacetate also "fits" the enzyme molecule, although the bond between the fluorine and the carbon atom in the molecule is longer than that between the hydrogen and carbon atoms in acetic acid.

c. Monochloroacetate, in which the bond between chlorine and carbon is still longer than that between fluorine and carbon, does not "fit" and the enzyme has no effect upon it as a substrate.

corresponding to grooves and prongs of identical configuration in the tumbler of the lock.

Such an assumption fits the evidence obtained from studies of the blocking effect of substances whose molecules are structurally very close to the configuration of the substrate but not identical with it. For example, the oxidation of acetic acid, $CH_3COOH$, which appears in the animal body in the course of fat metabolism, is an enzymatic reaction that can be reproduced in vitro with the extracted enzyme, under suitable conditions of temperature, pH and other conditioning factors. But if, in vitro, monofluoroacetate ($CH_3COOF$) is added to the mixture of acetic acid and enzyme, the reaction does not take place and neither compound is oxidized. The molecule of monofluoroacetate differs from that of acetic acid only by the substitution of one atom of fluorine for one of hydrogen, and apparently

substrate and so prevents its oxidation. If, on the other hand, monochloroacetate ($CH_3COOCl$) is added to the acetic acid–enzyme mixture, the oxidation of acetic acid proceeds just as it would were the enzyme and substrate alone. From these results it is evident that monochloroacetate does not unite with, or fit, the enzyme molecule and therefore does not disturb its union with, and effect upon, acetic acid. The explanation may lie in the length of the bonds between the three differing atoms and the rest of the molecule in the three different substances. Measurements have shown that in monochloroacetate the chlorine atom lies 1.76 Å from the rest of the molecule; in monofluoroacetate, the fluorine atom is 1.41 Å away from the rest of the molecule and in acetic acid the hydrogen atom corresponding in position to the F and Cl of the other compounds is 1.09 Å from the rest of its molecule. From these facts it may be postulated that there is a perfect fit between the enzyme molecule and its particular substrate, acetic acid; one between it and monofluoroacetate that is less good but still an approximation adequate to keep the acetic acid out of the combination; and none at all between it and monochloroacetate, a condition that may be attributed to the length of the monochloroacetate molecule.

A practical illustration of the enzyme-substrate competition and near-compatability is the action of sulfa drugs in the metabolic activities of bacteria. Para-amino benzoic acid is one of the compounds isolated from the complex of the so-called B vitamins that is known to be necessary to the growth of many bacteria. Structurally the molecules of para-amino benzoic acid and of sulfanilimide are very much alike:

Para-amino benzoic acid

Sulfanilimide

so much alike that sulfanilimide can take the place of para-amino benzoic acid in the enzyme-coenzyme-substrate complex and block the effective action of the enzyme. This was shown by the fact that sulfanilimide is much less potent in the destruction of bacteria grown in cultures when para-amino benzoic acid is added to the culture medium than it is in the absence of the acid, indicating that there is a similar kind of competition between the two substances for position in the enzyme-substrate complex as there is in the case of monofluoroacetate and acetic acid, but that while both of them may combine with the enzyme and its substrate only one is effective as a co-enzyme.

**The molecular structure of enzymes:** Since all the enzymes so far identified have been found to be proteins, they all have molecules of relatively enormous size, in many cases a great many times that of the substrate with which they are known to have functional affinity and are presumed to have structural affinity. It therefore seems probable that only a part of the enzyme molecule makes the combination with the substrate, and much of current enzyme research is directed toward the determination of this active part. Some enzymes are known to consist of a protein and a non-protein portion; this non-protein portion is called its "prosthetic group" (Greek, prosthetos = added on). For example, the "iron enzymes," so-called because their molecules contain iron, consist of a specific protein to which is attached hematin, also the non-protein part of the hemoglobin molecule, or a substance closely related to it. This prosthetic group is the iron-containing part of the enzyme molecule, and it is to the presence of iron that the properties of this group of enzymes are largely due. These enzymes are thus dependent upon their prosthetic groups for their activating capacities, just as some enzymes are known to be dependent upon co-enzymes or upon particular ions. Indeed, a distinction between prosthetic groups and co-enzymes, as between co-enzymes and other enzyme activators, seems to be one of degree rather than of kind, based upon the separability and degree of independence of the parts of the enzyme system rather than upon any fundamental difference in their relation to the enzyme-substrate complex. The vitamins that are included among co-enzymes act essentially as prosthetic groups of the proteins to which they become attached, and the necessity for "trace elements" may be related to their participation in enzyme reactions.

Enzymes, like other proteins, are themselves susceptible to the action of proteinases, but their digestion does not occur under natural conditions. In the case of the most vigorous proteolytic enzymes, pepsin and trypsin, the enzymes are present in the cells as inactive precursors. The enzymatic protein is believed to be enclosed within a shell, or covering, of material that is polypeptide in its nature, or made up of smaller numbers of linked amino acids than a protein molecule. The removal of this covering takes place after the enzyme has been discharged from the cell and is believed to be a process of digestion. Pepsinogen is converted to pepsin by the decomposition of the polypeptide coat, effected by the hydrochloric acid of the gastric juice; trypsinogen is similarly converted to trypsin, or the active enzyme exposed, by the action of enterokinase upon the polypeptide coat.

***The action of enzymes:*** Enzymes must, however, undergo some change or loss during the reactions in which they take part, for it is not possible to recover them quantitatively afterwards, as inorganic catalysts can be recovered. But since the union of the enzyme with its substrate is known to be, in some cases, of extremely short duration, and suspected to be nearly as brief in all, a minute amount of enzyme is adequate for an extended series of substrate activations. One of the most efficient of the intracellular enzymes, for example, is catalase, an "iron enzyme" through whose agency hydrogen peroxide is decomposed into water and oxygen.

$$2H_2O_2 \xrightarrow{\text{Catalase}} 2H_2O + O_2$$

It has been calculated that one molecule of catalase can decompose 5,000,000 molecules of hydrogen peroxide in one minute at 0° C, which means that its union with a molecule of its substrate cannot, under these conditions, last more than $\frac{1}{84000}$ of a second, during which it has accomplished its effect and after which it is free to combine with another molecule.

The action of enzymes is also known to be influenced by substances produced within the organism called hormones (Greek, hormon = exciting). These are substances synthesized in certain regions of the plant and animal body which are transferred from the sites of their origin to other parts of the body where their effects become evident. Hormones and their relations to metabolic processes are discussed in Chapter 21.

Enzymes are now known to underlie all manifestations of biological activity. They are concerned in the chemical changes that take place in the synthesis of food by autotrophic systems, in the digestion of that food by the heterotroph as well as by the autotroph and in the metabolism of the end products of digestion after their assimilation by the cells. They effect the chemical changes that take place in animal muscle leading to the physical changes in its shape on contraction and relaxation, and they effect those that take place in nerve during the passage of an impulse and the recovery of excitability afterwards. They are concerned in all the energy changes that go on within biological systems and, by doing work, they enable these systems to carry out certain functions with a minimum expenditure of energy. They are, so far as present evidence goes, the directing forces of protoplasmic organization, and operation; the extent of their direction is shown by the extent of the disturbances that arise if an enzyme is blocked and fails to do its part in the system to which it belongs.

That they themselves have some kind of organization within the cell is indicated by, for example, the difference in the amount of fermentation effected by expressed yeast juice and intact yeast cells. In the same period of time, intact yeast will ferment 10 to 20 times as much glucose as its expressed juice; this implies that the enzymes of the zymase complex are not in any haphazard arrangement within the cell, as they may be presumed to be in the juice, but that they have a definite organization and order in consequence of which their operation is more precise and efficient. One of the fundamental conditions of any molecular, or atomic, union is the proximity of the combining substances. This must be equally a condition of the enzyme-substrate association, whatever it may be. If a molecule of catalase is to associate with 5,000,000 molecules of peroxide in a minute, it is obvious that there must be a close relationship between the two substances both in time and in space. It is by an understanding of these relationships, as well as of those between the enzyme and its substrate, that one may expect to find the solution of the complex problems of protoplasmic organization and protoplasmic functioning that are the basic problems of the biologist.

# CHAPTER 18

# AUTOTROPHIC NUTRITION

## Mechanisms of autotrophic nutrition

The majority of autotrophic species make use of radiant energy for at least one of the steps in their synthesis of carbohydrate. This synthesis is thus ultimately dependent upon light and so is called photosynthesis, although some of the steps in the process are known to take place in the dark. Since the carbohydrate so formed is the basis for the construction of their lipids and proteins, nutrition in these photoautotrophic systems is conditioned by the sun's radiations and the accessibility of this energy to the plant. Some other autotrophs are able to utilize chemical energy for carbohydrate synthesis, bringing about the union of carbon dioxide and water by a series of reactions for which some, if not all, of the energy is derived from the oxidation of reduced inorganic substances. This is a process of chemosynthesis rather than of photosynthesis, since the energy necessary for it is derived from a chemical reaction and not directly from the sun.

## Photosynthesis

**Chlorophyll:** The capacity for photosynthesis is associated with chlorophyll, and in chlorophyll-containing plants takes place exclusively in the chloroplasts. Chlorophyll is the general name for at least four slightly different substances of complex molecular configuration, known respectively as chlorophylls a, b, c and d. There is not yet any exact knowledge of the physical state of these chlorophylls in the chloroplasts. But chemical analyses of the chloroplasts of a wide variety of plants have shown their contents to be a mixture of fats, waxes and salts of fatty acids as well as other pigments.

Chlorophyll a and chlorophyll b are found in the chloroplasts of green plants, in the ratios of 2 parts to 1,000 and 0.75 part to 1,000 respectively, together with the yellow carotinoid pigments, carotene and xanthophyll; chlorophylls a and c, but no chlorophyll b, are found in diatoms and brown algae, as well as the brown carotinoid, fucoxanthin; chlorophylls a and d, but neither b nor c, are found in the red algae, their green color concealed by the red pigment phycoerythrin, which is not in the chloroplast but dissolved in the cell sap. Some bacteria also contain pigment complexes, which include a green pigment closely related to chlorophyll b, called bacteriochlorophyll, and several carotinoid pigments. Different combinations of these pigments give different colors to masses of these micro-organisms, which are consequently distinguished as green, red or purple bacteria.

Something of the chemical nature and physical properties of chlorophylls a and b has been learned from studies made on extracts of chlorenchyma. The chlorophylls are insoluble in water, but readily soluble in alcohol and some other organic fluids; most of the studies have been made upon alcoholic extracts of the leaves of angiosperms. Chlorophyll a has the molecular formula $C_{55}H_{72}O_5N_4Mg$, and chlorophyll b, $C_{55}H_{70}O_6N_4Mg$. A slightly different series of degradation products is obtained from each, and each behaves characteristically in relation to light, showing differences in absorption and in fluorescence.* Alcoholic solutions of chlorophyll a show a deep red fluorescence, and those of chlorophyll b a darker, brownish-red one.

* Fluorescence is the capacity to absorb radiations and to re-radiate such energy in altered form. In the case of light, that which is re-radiated is of different wave length, usually longer, than that which was absorbed.

Extracts from chlorenchyma cells containing both chlorophyll components can be shown to absorb light energy from certain parts of the visible spectrum. If a solution of chlorophyll is placed between a source of white light and the prism or other device used to resolve it into its components of different wave length and different color, the resulting spectrum is not a continuous one, but one that is interrupted by five dark bands of varying widths (Fig. 18.1). The widest and most distinct of these bands lies in the region of red light, in the area of the spectrum represented by light of wave lengths between 510–651 millimicra; the next most evident one lies in a region of the blue and violet, or of light with wave lengths of 510–400 millimicra. The other three, all less distinct than these two, are in the orange area, between wave lengths of 620–600 millimicra; in the yellow, between wave lengths of 590–550 millimicra; and in the yellow-green, between wave lengths of 540–525 millimicra.

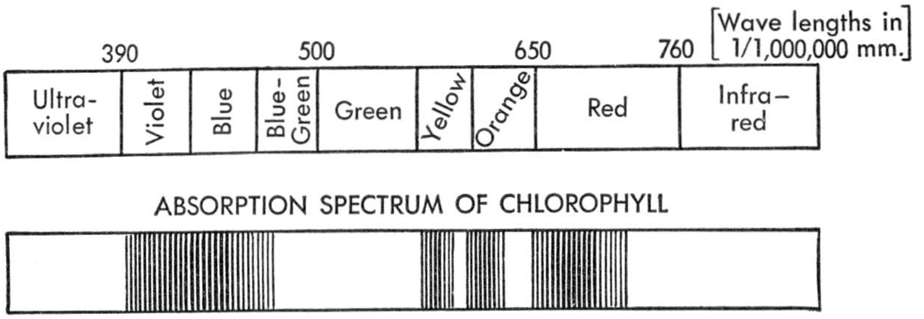

These dark bands indicate that in those regions of the visible spectrum the energy of light is not transmitted or reflected by the chlorophyll, but absorbed by it. It has also been shown that there is some absorption in the region of the ultraviolet, a range of energy radiation imperceptible to human eyes. Separately tested in this way, chlorophyll a and chlorophyll b have slightly different absorption spectra.

Synthesis and decomposition of chlorophyll are constantly going on in the green parts of plants. When the rate of decomposition exceeds that of synthesis, the carotenoids that are present are exposed and the part may turn yellow or brown, or become chlorotic (Greek, chloros = yellow-green). Such a change occurs regularly in the autumn in the leaves of perennial plants growing in limited parts of the world; at this season anthocyanins may also be formed, turning the foliage to shades of red as well as yellow. The synthesis of chlorophyll is conditioned by the genetic constitution of the plant, and by external factors, among which are water, light, temperature, oxygen, carbohydrate, the minerals supplying the elements, exclusive of carbon, hydrogen and oxygen, included in the chlorophyll molecule, and some additional ones, notably iron and manganese, that contribute to its synthesis, although in ways as yet unknown. Green plants become chlorotic if their current mineral supply is inadequate, or if their water supply is reduced; dehydration of the leaves not only inhibits the formation of new chlorophyll but accelerates the decomposition of that already in the chloroplasts. Most plants fail to develop chlorophyll if kept from the light, although its synthesis does go on in the dark in some algae, in mosses, ferns, in the seeds of conifers and in restricted parts of some angiosperms. The cotyledons in the seeds of citrus fruits, for example, often contain chlorophyll, although the flesh of the fruit and the thick coats of the seed are effective barriers to the penetration of light.

FIGURE 18.1 Absorption spectrum of chlorophyll. (From Hylander and Stanley, *College Botany*. Copyright 1949 by The Macmillan Company.)

*The photosynthetic reaction:* Analysis of the photosynthetic process has proved extremely baffling. It has never yet been possible to reproduce in vitro the synthesis of carbohydrate from carbon dioxide and water, nor to obtain from leaves in which photosynthesis is in progress substances simpler than the hexoses, glucose and fructose, and the disaccharide sucrose; these appear to accumulate temporarily in the mesophyll cells, but their precursors are still undetermined. The dependence of the process upon light can, however, be proved by very simple experiments. If some of the leaves, or parts of the leaves, of a green plant are covered with an opaque material like dark paper or a metallic foil and the plant kept in sunlight, tests for sugar and for starch in the exposed regions are positive, but in the covered parts are negative, showing that photosynthesis has been actively progressing only in the regions exposed to light and has not taken place in those from which light has been blocked off (Fig. 18.2).

Studies of the process as it takes place in the leaf have shown that it includes the diffusion, from the cell walls to the chloroplasts, of $CO_2$ either in solution in water or combined with it as $H_2CO_3$; a chemical reaction that can take place in the dark as well as in the light; and a photochemical reaction utilizing the energy absorbed from solar radiation, and consequently directly dependent upon light. At least one reaction in the series is known to be enzymatic; this may be the photochemical reaction, or it may be the one that is independent of light, or still another one whose nature is undetermined. By the use of isotopes (heavy oxygen and radioactive carbon) to tag the oxygen in the water molecule and the carbon in the carbon dioxide, it has been shown that the oxygen given off as a by-product comes from the water molecule and not from the carbon dioxide, and that the first change in the carbon dioxide molecule is its conversion to a carboxyl radicle ($-COOH$) attached to some much larger molecule. It has been postulated that the next step in the process may be the further reduction of the carbon by the addition of water to the complex and the loss of oxygen from it, a reaction that takes place only in the presence of chlorophyll. These two steps may be expressed by the equations

(1) $RH + CO_2 \rightarrow RCOOH$ (dark)
(2) $RCOOH + H_2O \xrightarrow{chlorophyll} RCH_2OH + O_2$ (light)

where R stands for a radicle of unknown composition but large dimensions, loosely bound to the carbon complex and readily detached from it. By similar successive reductions of other carbon dioxide molecules, and the release of these carbon complexes from the unknown radicles to which they are bound, chains of two or more carbon atoms with their attached hydrogen atoms and hydroxyl groups are presumably built up, the first stable configuration being a chain of six, or a hexose.

In the reduction of carbon by the photoautotrophic bacteria, the hydrogen is not derived from water but from another inorganic source, or from an organic one. The green bacteria, for instance, use hydrogen sulphide ($H_2S$) exclusively for the hydrogen donor, while the red and purple bacteria may use other inorganic sulphur com-

FIGURE 18.2 Experiment showing the effect of light upon the formation of starch in the green leaves of a plant. (From Smith, Gilbert, Evans, Duggar, Bryan and Allen, *A Textbook of General Botany*, 4th edition. Copyright 1942 by The Macmillan Company.)

A. A light screen attached to a leaf.
B. The leaf after a period of exposure to light. The dark areas show the distribution of starch as determined by the iodine test.

pounds, molecular hydrogen, or the simpler organic acids, like the lower fatty acids.

Determinations of the rate of photosynthesis and the factors that affect it have presented fewer difficulties. Like other chemical reactions, it is influenced by the availability and the concentration of the reagents involved and by temperature; in its own nature it is influenced by the chlorophyll present and the light that is available. Under ordinary favorable conditions, photosynthesis proceeds at a rate that measurements and calculations show produces, on an average, 1 gram of carbohydrate per square meter of leaf per hour; it is estimated that an acre of corn, yielding 100 bushels to the acre, makes about 200 pounds of sugar a day.

The oxygen that is a by-product of the reaction may be used, while still within the tissues, for the oxidative reactions that result in the disintegration of carbohydrate and lipid and the consequent release of energy, or it may diffuse from the cells to the air spaces, and so out through the stomata to the surrounding atmosphere. The soluble sugars may pass from the mesophyll cells to the vascular tissues and through them be transported throughout the plant body or, while still within the mesophyll cells, may be converted to insoluble polysaccharides or starches. This conversion is a process of condensation, a hydrolytic reaction in which an indefinite number of hexose molecules are combined into a single large molecule of starch with the loss of a molecule of water for each hexose union. Two hexose molecules may be united in this way to form a disaccharide as, for example, the immediate products of photosynthesis, the monosaccharides glucose and fructose, combine to form sucrose, or cane sugar, a reaction that may be expressed by the equation:

$$C_6H_{12}O_6 + C_6H_{12}O_6 \rightarrow C_{12}H_{22}O_{11} + H_2O$$

Similarly trisaccharides, composed of three hexose molecules, tetrasaccharides composed of four, and polysaccharides composed of many, are built up from the immediate products of photosynthesis, to be used at once for the plant's structural and metabolic needs or to be accumulated in its storage tissues from which, if necessary, they can be withdrawn and utilized.

***Nutrients other than photosynthetic products required by plants:*** But the carbohydrate thus provided meets only a part of the plant's nutritional requirements. Plants need, among other things, a source of nitrogen and one of sulphur for their structural proteins, of calcium for the pectin compounds in their cell walls and of magnesium for chlorophyll. Careful nutritional studies, made by observing plants grown in aqueous solutions of known mineral constitution, have shown that a number of other elements are also essential to their growth and most efficient metabolism, for the omission, the reduction or the increased concentration of certain elements result in recognizable and measurable changes in their appearance and growth rate. These necessary elements include arsenic, aluminum, barium, boron, bromine, cesium, chromium, chlorine, cobalt, copper, iodine, lithium, manganese, molybdenum, nickel, selenium, silicon, strontium, tin, titanium, vanadium and zinc, but the roles that these elements, or the compounds containing them, play in the metabolic and growth processes are at present but imperfectly understood (Fig. 18.3).

All autotrophs derive the nitrogen necessary for protein synthesis from nitrites, nitrates, ammonium salts or simple organic compounds containing nitrogen. These enter the plant in solution, absorbed from the soil water by the root hairs of terrestrial plants, and directly from the surrounding water by the exposed areas of aquatic plants. The first steps in the utilization of the nitrate ion is its reduction to nitrite and then to ammonia in the following sequence:

$$-NO_3 \rightarrow -NO_2 \rightarrow -NH_2 \rightarrow -NH_3$$

The reduction of nitrate to nitrite is known to take place principally in the roots of some plants, in the stems, leaves and cortex of the petioles and stems of others. The combination of the reduced nitrogen with carbohydrate may take place in various regions, as may the linking of the amino acids so produced into molecules of protein, a process that can also be effected by animals, the majority of which cannot, on the other hand, perform the earlier steps that lead to the formation of amino acids.

When the source of nitrogen is a simple organic compound containing the amino group ($NH_2$), or an ammonium salt, the ammonia absorbed becomes rapidly incorporated in the amino acids, the combination taking place especially in the leaves and the growing points of the plant. The carbohydrate that becomes bound with the amino group is generally believed to be an

FIGURE 18.3 The effect of mineral (boron) deficiency upon the growth of alfalfa. (Photograph by courtesy of the National Fertilizer Association.)

The plants on the left have been grown in a field near Williamsburg, Virginia, treated with 10 lbs. of borax (sodium tetraborate) per acre; those on the right in a field in the same locality without the addition of borax. The difference in growth is evident not only in the smaller size of the plants at the right, but also in the chlorotic condition of their leaves, which is striking in the living plants.

nitrogen already in its reduced form can be united with carbohydrate into amino compounds as soon as it is released from the complex in which it entered the plant. That nitrogen complexes in the soil solution are the source of this element for the protein synthesis of angiosperms has been proved by growing plants in solutions containing a stable isotope of nitrogen ($N^{15}$), bound with hydrogen and chlorine as ammonium chloride ($NH_4Cl$), and after a short time recovering the isotope from various tissues. The intermediate compound in the digestion of the more complex carbohydrates synthesized by the plant, but there is also evidence that it may be one that is intermediate in the formation of the first recoverable products of photosynthesis. It is possible, too, that the formation of fatty acids may be an intermediate step in protein synthesis, and the presence of small quantities of urea ($CO(NH_2)_2$) in angiosperms, and of considerable quantities of it in some fungi, suggests the possibility that this compound may be a starting point in the synthesis of some of the complex ring compounds that plants alone can effect.

## Chemosynthesis

The synthesis of lipid and of protein is thus dependent upon the synthesis of carbohydrate. Carbohydrate synthesis can also be carried on by some colorless, free-living bacteria by a process for which the energy is derived from the oxidation of reduced inorganic compounds or of molecular hydrogen or elementary sulphur. Since the energy for it is derived from a chemical reaction, the process is known as chemosynthesis and is wholly independent of light; the organisms capable of it are said to be chemoautotrophic rather than photoautotrophic. Such organisms are unique in that, while every biological system appears to be able to effect the oxidation of reduced carbon, at least as it is found in the sugar molecule, they alone can effect that of nitrogen, sulphur and iron as they are found in compounds in the soil and soil solution, and of free sulphur and hydrogen. To this group of micro-organisms belong the nitrifying bacteria that, in their oxidation of ammonium compounds to nitrates, release energy that becomes available to them for the synthesis of carbohydrate. Chemoautotrophic systems can exist where no others can; the decayed rocks of Alpine summits and the micaceous schists of the Pyrenees have been found to be swarming with nitrifying bacteria.

## *Utilization of products synthesized*

### Digestion

But however they are made—whether by photosynthesis or chemosynthesis—the complex molecules of carbohydrate, lipid and protein must undergo digestion before they become available for the metabolic changes that take place in the living cells. Multicellular plants, unlike the majority of multicellular animals, have no localized regions for digestion and comparatively little is known about the digestive processes that go on in them. Studies that have been made upon their enzyme systems indicate, however, that they possess enzymes of the same general types as animals and that the disintegrative changes that take place in them follow the same general pattern of those in animals. So much more is known about the digestive enzymes of animals, especially of mammals, that a consideration of them is reserved for the discussion of animal digestion. But the fact of digestion in autotrophic plants must not be overlooked. With the exception of the insectivorous plants, it is an intracellular process, taking place within the cells themselves and often to greatest extent within those in which the food was first formed. The more complex products of photosynthesis in the leaf of a green plant may, for instance, be immediately digested in situ, and the soluble end products of the process oxidized, either aerobically or anaerobically, or recombined into substances that contribute to the structure and growth of the cell, or that are stored as reserves in it. If they are not used in the cell itself, they may be translocated to others through the phloem, or by other mechanisms, and there undergo oxidation or recombination into products of one kind or another.

### Metabolic conversions

*Oxidation:* It is through the oxidation of carbohydrates principally that plants derive the energy requisite for their metabolic reactions and for their other manifestations of life. They are to a great extent dependent upon molecular oxygen for these oxidations, although some are regularly carried on anaerobically and others may be, for a time at least, when conditions make such a mechanism necessary. But external respiration, the exchange of oxygen and carbon dioxide between the organism as a whole and the atmosphere or water surrounding it, is as important to plants as it is to animals, a fact that is sometimes obscured or overlooked because of the absence of special respiratory organs and because the removal of carbon dioxide from the environment for photosynthesis and the return of oxygen to it is, in the daytime, so much in excess of the removal of oxygen and return of carbon dioxide. Although many of the fungi are anaerobes, most green plants are aerobes, incapable of surviving for more than limited periods of time if their oxygen supply is greatly reduced. Exceptions to this are cacti, which have been made to live in atmospheres of pure nitrogen and have survived for long periods during which they have given off carbon dioxide; the inner tissues of succulent plants; and the fruits and seeds of many of the flowering plants.

**AEROBIC AND ANAEROBIC OXIDATIONS**: In relation to the energy exchange, and the products consumed and released, the aerobic oxidation of carbohydrate is essentially the reverse of its photosynthesis. The energy yield from each molecule of glucose, or of any other hexose, is equivalent in amount to that which was utilized in its synthesis, and the end products of the process are qualitatively and quantitatively the same as those that were combined in it. In relation to the gaseous exchange, that which takes place in photosynthesis may be represented by the ratio $\frac{O_2 \text{ (output)}}{CO_2 \text{ (intake)}}$; that which takes place simultaneously in the tissues of the leaf and in all other living cells of the plant body in aerobic respiration as $\frac{CO_2 \text{ (output)}}{O_2 \text{ (intake)}}$.

In anaerobic oxidation, the end products are not carbon dioxide and water but carbon dioxide and more complex carbon compounds, such as ethyl alcohol ($C_2H_5OH$), acetic acid ($CH_3COOH$), formic acid ($HCOOH$), oxalic acid $\begin{matrix}COOH\\|\\COOH\end{matrix}$, lactic acid ($CH_3CHOHCOOH$), propionic acid ($CH_3CH_2COOH$), glycerol ($CH_2OHCHOHCH_2OH$) and higher alcohols collectively known as "fusel oil"  (German, fusel = bad liquor). It was Louis Pasteur who proved the connection between fermentation and anaerobic respiration, or rather the identity of the two processes, when in 1875 he showed that fermentation can take place in the absence of air and defined it as "life without oxygen." Some few organisms, like for instance the tetanus bacillus, are entirely dependent upon an anaerobic mechanism for the release of energy from carbohydrate; others, like many bacteria and yeasts, can utilize such a mechanism almost exclusively and can, moreover, withstand the effects of an accumulation of alcohol or organic acids that would be destructive to other cells. But in the majority of plants, aerobic respiration is the rule, for although the preliminary steps in the degradation of the hexose molecule may be accomplished by rearrangements of atoms and by energy transfers that do not require free oxygen, the final steps, by which the products resulting from these changes are converted to carbon dioxide and water, can be effected only if an adequate supply of molecular oxygen is available.

Anaerobic oxidation is a less efficient mechanism than aerobic. In the complete oxidation of glucose, or any other hexose, all the energy bound in the molecule is set free. But in anaerobic respiration, part of the energy remains bound in the end products, so that only a fraction of the potential energy is converted to kinetic energy. The following equations express these relationships, indicating, however, only the gross effects of the reactions, and none of the steps through which they pass.

Photosynthesis  
Chemosynthesis $\Big\}$  $6CO_2 + 6H_2O + \text{Energy} \equiv 673 \text{ Cals} \rightarrow C_6H_{12}O_6 + 6O_2$
(endothermic)

Aerobic Respiration   $C_6H_{12}O_6 + 6O_2 \rightarrow 6H_2O + 6CO_2 + \text{Energy} \equiv 673 \text{ Cals}$
(exothermic)

Anaerobic Respiration
  Alcoholic Fermentation   $C_6H_{12}O_6 \rightarrow 2C_2H_5OH + 2CO_2 + \text{Energy} \equiv 25 \text{ Cals}$
(exothermic)

  Lactic Acid Fermentation   $C_6H_{12}O_6 \rightarrow 2CH_3CHOHCOOH + \text{Energy} \equiv 18 \text{ Cals}$
(exothermic)

  Butyric Acid Fermentation
    $C_6H_{12}O_6 \rightarrow 2CH_3CH_2CH_2COOH + 2CO_2 + 2H_2 + \text{Energy} \equiv 15 \text{ Cals}$
(exothermic)

*Syntheses:* But in no case is all the energy released available to the organism carrying on the respiration. Some of it is always lost as heat and dissipated to the medium in which the plant is living. This loss is a very rapid one, for besides having no mechanism for heat regulation, the bodies of plants have a large surface compared to their mass and expose a comparatively enormous area to their environment. But except in a limited number of plants, the energy that is available to them is not expended in mechanical work in moving them from place to place, but principally in the metabolic reactions that go on within them. More of these reactions are anabolic than catabolic and the synthesis of materials exceeds their destruction; consequently the growth of plants and the accumulation of materials within them are comparatively rapid, and in general considerably more rapid than that of motile animals (Fig. 18.4).

The products of these synthetic reactions may become incorporated into the structure of the plant as new protoplasm or as new supporting substances, or they may serve as temporary storage materials or ones of indefinite duration. Synthesis of the structural products takes place primarily at the growing points, where there must exist a close relationship between cell division and the assembling of constituent molecules into the complex proteins characteristic of nucleus and cytoplasm. The condensation of molecules of the simpler sugars into the components of the cell wall—pectins, cellulose and lignin—also goes on most actively there, although the addition of cellulose and the deposition of lignin also takes place in older tissues some distance from the growing points. The materials for these syntheses must be conveyed from the sites where they were themselves first produced, either by synthesis or by digestion, but the state in which they are so conveyed and the mechanism of their translocation, at least in the multicellular plants, are still not clearly understood.

The immediate products of photosynthesis or of chemosynthesis, as well as the products of digestion, that are in excess of the needs of the plant for its maintenance and growth, are converted into storage products. In the Metaphyta, there are usually certain tissues that act as the main storage areas; these may be the reproductive structures—spores or seeds—as well as any group of tissues of the vegetative plant. But all the living cells usually contain some store of reserves, either in solution in the vacuoles or else as solid crystalline or granular inclusions in their cytoplasm. In analyzing plant products and determining the chemical nature of the substances obtained from them, exclusive of their structural components, it is in many cases impossible to distinguish between products that are the result of anabolic reactions and those that are the result of catabolic reactions. Nor is it clear in what regions the metabolic changes take place—whether the preliminary ones go on in all the living tissues of the plant body, and only the final stages in those where the products are ultimately localized, or whether these tissues are capable of conducting the entire series of synthetic or degradative reactions that result in the final product.

CARBOHYDRATES: The soluble carbohydrates that are found in the vacuoles of all plant cells, and in the conducting vessels of the vascular plants, are principally hexoses, like glucose and its isomers, fructose and galactose, and the disaccharide sucrose, the condensation product of one molecule of glucose and one of fructose. But they often also include pentoses, or sugars with a framework of five carbon atoms ($C_5H_{10}O_5$), and more rarely, heptoses with a framework of seven ($C_7H_{14}O_7$). In addition to sucrose, other disaccharides are formed, of which the most common is maltose, composed of two molecules of glucose. Trisaccharides ($C_{18}H_{32}O_{16}$) are also found; one of the most familiar of these is raffinose, the principal form of the sugar in the sugar beet and a condensation product of glucose, fructose and galactose. At least one tetrasaccharide ($C_{24}H_{40}O_{20}$) is known to be synthesized; such a sugar, called stachyose, made up of fructose, glucose and galactose molecules, is found in the members of at least four families of plants. When the concentration of these soluble sugars reaches the

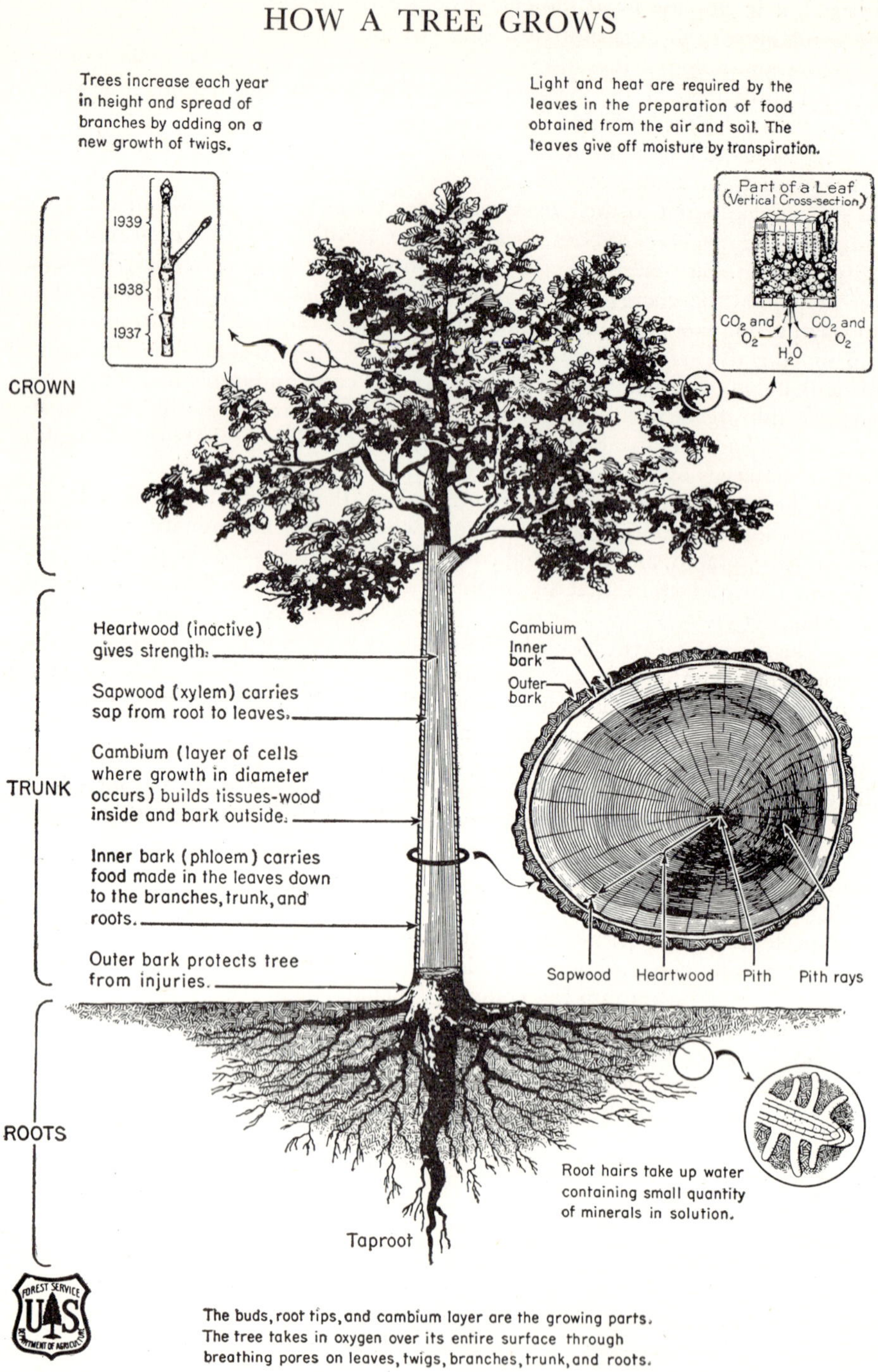
HOW A TREE GROWS
Trees increase each year in height and spread of branches by adding on a new growth of twigs.
1939
1938
1937
Light and heat are required by the leaves in the preparation of food obtained from the air and soil. The leaves give off moisture by transpiration.
Part of a Leaf (Vertical Cross-section)
$CO_2$ and $O_2$
$CO_2$ and $O_2$
$H_2O$
CROWN
TRUNK
ROOTS
Heartwood (inactive) gives strength.
Sapwood (xylem) carries sap from root to leaves.
Cambium (layer of cells where growth in diameter occurs) builds tissues-wood inside and bark outside.
Inner bark (phloem) carries food made in the leaves down to the branches, trunk, and roots.
Outer bark protects tree from injuries.
Cambium
Inner bark
Outer-bark
Sapwood
Heartwood
Pith
Pith rays
Root hairs take up water containing small quantity of minerals in solution.
Taproot
FOREST SERVICE
U S
DEPARTMENT OF AGRICULTURE
The buds, root tips, and cambium layer are the growing parts. The tree takes in oxygen over its entire surface through breathing pores on leaves, twigs, branches, trunk, and roots.

FIGURE 18.4 Diagram showing how a tree grows. (Courtesy of the U.S. Forestry Service.)

saturation point, they tend to crystallize out and are stored in solid form in the cytoplasm or the intercellular spaces.

Polysaccharides, with the general formula $(C_6H_{10}O_5)n$, are more varied in kind; some appear to be specific to particular kinds of plants. The most generally distributed polysaccharide is starch, or amylum (Greek, amylon = fine meal), which represents the union of some 24–30 glucose units into a single large molecule. The starch is deposited in grains, whose appearance is characteristic of different kinds of plants (Fig. 18.5); starch grains are found in the cells of leaves, where they may represent a temporary storage of photosynthetic products, in the living pith cells, in the cortical cells of roots and stems, in the cells of tubers and in those of seeds and fruits. The accumulation of starch may represent as much as 15–30 per cent of the dry weight of tubers, like those of the white potato for example, and 50–70 per cent of the dry weight of seeds like those of the grains. Amylum is a polysaccharide apparently peculiar to the plant kingdom, for glycogen, in whose molecule about 12 glucose units are combined, is the polysaccharide characteristic of animals. But some fungi are known to synthesize glycogen, and glycogen, along with amylum, has been isolated from the seeds of sweet corn.

Inulin (see p. 324) is another polysaccharide common in plants. It is a condensation product of fructose only; each inulin molecule consists of some thirty fructose units. It is the principal polysaccharide in the tubers of artichokes and dahlias and is found also in considerable quantities in the fleshy roots of chicory. The gums and mucilages that are found in nearly all plants are polysaccharides, condensation products either of pentose sugars, or of the hexose, galactose. Gum arabic, synthesized by certain cacti and acacias, is one of the best known of the pentosans, for it is widely used commercially in the manufacture of adhesives, inks and confectionery. All of the vascular plants seem to form "wound gum," secreted by the living cells near the site of an injury, that stops up the xylem vessels, preventing the invasion of micro-organisms into the inner tissues. Agar-agar, first introduced into bacteriological technique by Koch (see p. 133), is a galactan synthesized by certain of the red algae. Mucilages, too, are found in nearly all classes of plants—in the external walls of some algae and aquatic

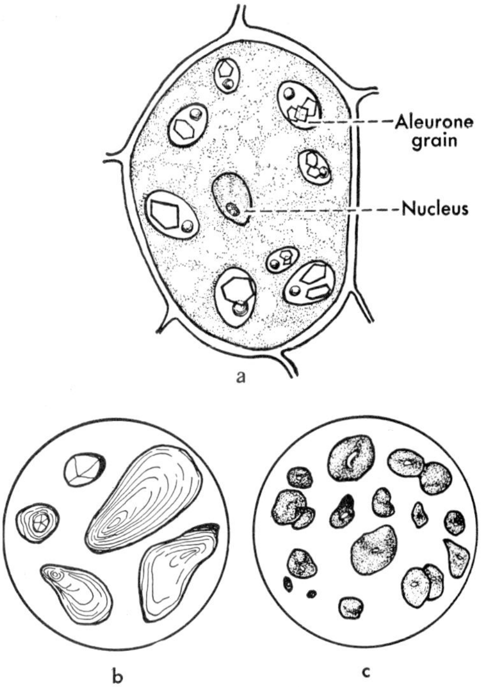

FIGURE 18.5 Storage products in plant cells.

a. Cell from the endosperm of a castor bean (Ricinus), showing aleurone grains consisting of crystals and globules of protein and deposits of amorphous protein. (After Strasburger.)

b. Starch grains from cells of potato. (After Black and Conant.)

c. Starch grains from cells of corn. (After Black and Conant.)

angiosperms and in the coats of the seeds and fruits of many terrestrial angiosperms; some mosses and ferns have mucilage-secreting hairs or mucilage sacs.

It has been shown that some bacteria, including the tubercle bacillus, the typhus bacillus, and the pneumococcus synthesize polysaccharides, included in their capsules, that are specific for each type of organism, and are therefore known as immunopolysaccharides. It is highly probable that further analysis of plant products will lead to the discovery of other substances peculiar to particular groups of plants and to individuals within those groups, and so will offer a basis for taxonomic and individual distinctions in the plant kingdom like those that are gradually being disclosed among animals.

LIPIDS: The lipids that are found in plant tissues are fats, waxes, sterols and phospholipids, principally lecithins. The fats are, like those of animal origin, esters of glycerol and fatty acids, most commonly oleic, palmitic and stearic. They are very widely distributed among the different genera of plants, where they are found in vacuoles as liquids, or in the cytoplasm as solids. Fat vacuoles, or droplets, usually containing mixtures of different fats, are often abundant in spores and seeds and may be distributed throughout the vegetative parts as well. In some of the angiosperms, they are the main form of reserve material in the seeds and replace carbohydrate as the source of energy and nutrients for the developing embryo when the seed germinates; as such, they provide a higher energy value than an equal volume of carbohydrate. The kernel of the Brazil nut is, for example, about 70 per cent fat, and that of the almond about 54 per cent. Many of these oils have been used by man for food and for the manufacture of materials useful or pleasing to him—olive oil, from the fruits of olive trees; cocoa butter, from the seeds of the cacao tree of South and Central America; cottonseed oil, from the seeds of cotton, and linseed oil, from those of flax, are but a few examples of such use. Oleomargarine is made from fats obtained from various plants; since these are chemically similar to animal fats, oleomargarine has the same energy content and much the same nutritional value as butter.

Waxes are very generally distributed throughout the plant kingdom, particularly as deposits on the surfaces of leaves, fruits and seeds, furnishing them with protective coverings. Waxes are combinations of fatty acids with alcohols other than glycerol and are of various kinds. The most prolific producer of wax is the wax palm of Brazil, Copernica cerefera, from which man obtains the carnauba wax that is extensively used in the manufacture of candles, shoe polish and varnish.

The sterols are a group of alcohol-like compounds of complex constitution. The one that is most widely distributed among plants is called sitosterol, a compound which is somewhat similar to cholesterol in its molecular configuration; cholesterol is a constituent of most, if not all, animal cells. Stigmasterol, another sterol, has been isolated from soy bean oil, and ergosterol from yeast and the fungus, ergot; ergosterol is of particular importance to man since by irradiation it can be converted to Vitamin D, one of the accessory food substances essential to him and other mammals. The lecithins are general protoplasmic components, but among plants they are accumulated as storage products particularly in the seeds of some species of pine and, among the angiosperms, in those of legumes.

Among the lipid products of plants are essential oils and resins. It is to the essential oils that many plants owe their distinctive odors and flavors, or "essences." Oil of lavender, wintergreen and lemon are all familiar essential oils, as are camphor and menthol. The essential oils vary considerably in their chemical composition, and the molecules of some of them contain sulphur. It is their sulphur-containing oils that give the characteristic odor and taste to such plants as onions, garlic, watercress and many kinds of mustard. The chemical nature of the resins is but little understood, although they are believed to be derivatives of the essential oils, or of parts of them, by a process of condensation or polymerization. They are usually found, in the plants that produce them, in association with the essential oils, either as viscous liquids or as solids. Turpentine and Canada balsam are liquid resins, and among the solid, or hard, resins are dammar and sandarac, both of which are used in the manufacture of varnish. Amber is fossilized resin, found where resinous trees have lived and perished in past eras of geologic time.

PROTEINS: The storage proteins of plants are found either in solution in the vacuolar contents or as amorphous and crystalline solids in the cells, or in the spaces between them. Proteins are generally distributed throughout the plant body, but in many genera are especially abundant in the tubers, bulbs, roots and seeds. Mixtures of proteins in an amorphous, non-crystalline state make up the aleurone grains (Greek, aleuron = flour), which constitute a large proportion of the stored materials in the seeds of grains. Aleurone grains are complicated in their structure, and in some cases may consist of a central crystalline mass surrounded by a layer of amorphous protein (Fig. 18.5). The simple proteins of plants, or those consisting of amino acids only, are

mon of the salts is calcium oxalate, frequently found in crystalline form in the intercellular spaces as well as in the cytoplasm. Glycosides are complexes of a pentose or of a hexose with some non-sugar, often a ring compound; if the sugar is glucose, the complex is called a glucoside. Phloridzin, which can be extracted in considerable quantities from the bark of plants belonging to the Rosaceae, is a glucoside which has been found to block the absorption of sugar from the tubules of the mammalian kidney; amygdalin, found in the seed of the bitter almond, is one of the cyanogenic glucosides, for on hydrolysis it yields glucose, benzaldehyde and hydrocyanic acid, which is a poison to the "iron enzymes" and so to cellular respiration.

$$\underset{\text{amygdalin}}{C_{20}H_{27}NO_{11}} + 2H_2O \rightarrow C_6H_{12}O_6 + \underset{\substack{\text{hydrocyanic} \\ \text{acid}}}{HCN} + \underset{\text{benzaldehyde}}{C_6H_5CHO}$$

classified as albumins and globulins, types of proteins that are also synthesized by animals, and as glutelins and gliadins (prolamins), types of protein peculiar to plants. There is, moreover, specificity in the particular proteins synthesized by different groups of plants. Leucosin, for example, is the protein synthesized by wheat, which has the general properties of an albumin but which yields decomposition products different from those of other albumins. Similarly, edestin is a specific globulin from hemp and amandin from almond. Among the glutelins are glutelin, synthesized by wheat, and oryzenin, synthesized by rice; and among the gliadins, gliadin, also a product of wheat, hordein, synthesized by barley, and zein, synthesized by corn. Again, as with the carbohydrates, there is reason to believe that the protoplasmic proteins, as well as those of the plant's reserves, have a high degree of individuality and specificity.

OTHER PRODUCTS: Among the other products of plant metabolism, which are found in solution in the cell sap or as solid deposits inside or outside cells, are salts of organic acids, glycosides, tannins, alkaloids, pigments and vitamins. One of the most com-

The formation of such cyanogenic glucosides is therefore a potential danger to the plant, although rarely an actual one, for emulsin, the enzyme that catalyzes the hydrolysis of amygdalin, is not formed in the same cells as the glucoside, although present in the same tissues. It may, however, be a real danger to animals which feed upon plants with cyanogenic glucosides, for crushing the tissues may bring the enzyme and its substrate together and start the reaction that ends in the release of a compound that, in sufficient quantity, is deadly to the eater.

The yellow pigments, called xanthones and flavones, and the blue, red and violet ones called anthocyanins, are all glucosides and are dissolved in the cell sap in localized regions of plants, such as the flowers and fruits of angiosperms, or more generally distributed in their tissues. The distinctive red of the beet and the purple of purple cabbage are due to the presence of anthocyanins in cells throughout the plant, and are as much an expression of the genetic constitution of the plant as are its other distinguishing characteristics. Pigments of this kind often develop seasonally in the leaves of deciduous plants growing in temperate climates, but anthocyanins especially may be conspicuous in the leaves throughout the lives of some plants and impart a distinguishing and constant character to the species. The copper beech and the red maple are examples of such permanently red-leaved plants. The development of these pigments is conditioned by the environment as well as by the inherited and inheritable constitution of the plant; light and water particularly are conditioning factors, and the acidity of the soil one that affects the color, once the pigment is formed, for the anthocyanins particularly act as natural indicators of the pH of the cell sap, and so indirectly of the environmental pH.

The tannins include a number of substances with similar properties but undefined chemical constitution. They are almost universally distributed among plants, for they are found in the leaves, wood, bark and unripe fruits of almost all species. All tannins have an astringent property and it is because of the presence of tannin that unripe fruits when eaten pucker the lining of the mouth. Tannin is much more abundant in some plants than in others, and is believed to accumulate in regions of intense metabolic activity. The galls that arise on plants, either spontaneously or in consequence of injury, contain for example 25–75 per cent tannin, and tannin accounts for 40 per cent of the dry weight of oak bark and 15 per cent of that of tea leaves. Tannin extracted from oak bark has been extensively used in the manufacture of leather; the raw dermis of animals, from which the epidermis and underlying fat and connective tissues have been scraped or digested away, is preserved from putrefaction and made less permeable and stronger by immersion in a solution of tannin.

Alkaloids, so-called because in some of their properties they resemble alkalis, are less widely distributed than tannins, but are found particularly in the seeds and fruits, and less frequently in the stems, roots and leaves of some half-dozen families of plants, including the legumes and the potato family. They are most frequently found in solution in the cell sap of young parenchyma cells or in solid form in older tissues. Their value, if any, to the plant is obscure, but many are known to have definite physiological effects upon animals, and from the earliest records of man's experimentation with drugs have been used in medical practice. Quinine, formerly more widely used to combat malaria than it is to-day, is but one of the 24 alkaloids that can be extracted from the bark of the chincona tree, and morphine one of the 20 found in the juice of poppies. Nicotine from tobacco, atropine from the deadly nightshade and cocaine from the leaves of the cacao tree are all alkaloids of common knowledge and more or less general use.

Plants are also the ultimate source, if not the direct one, of the vitamins, or accessory food substances required for adequate nutrition by man and many other animals, as well as by plants themselves. Some of these vitamins are known to be associated with the yellow pigments but the sources of others, and the position that they occupy or the role that they play in the metabolic processes of the plant, are unknown. Carotene is, for example, the precursor of Vitamin A, and Vitamin P, or citrin, is a mixture of two flavones. Other vitamins, such as thiamin, riboflavin and nicotinic acid, which are especially abundant in the seeds of grains, but present also in the vegetative parts of other plants, are known to be involved in certain enzymatic reactions and to be essential to the growth and development of some plants as well as of animals.

Substances are also formed within the bodies of plants that act as hormones, influencing the growth of roots, the enlargement of cells and other developmental processes. The chemical constitution of these substances has been studied by a number of workers; those that have been chemically identified have been found to be organic acids with molecules of varying degrees of complexity. Their formation is not peculiar to plants, for some of them at least are produced in the course of animal metabolism, but their growth-promoting or growth-inhibiting effect seems to be limited to the plant kingdom.

Many of these secondary products are believed to represent excretory products, stored in inert form in the tissues of plants. Lacking excretory organs, plants have no way of eliminating toxic substances except by diffusion through such cells as are in suitable contact with the environment. This could not be an efficient mechanism for any but the smallest of the multicellular plants, and the alternative mechanism of inactivation, rather than elimination, has become the one to take care of the potentially toxic metabolites produced in the bodies of the larger plants.

## Carbon fixation and the conversion of kinetic (solar) to potential energy

While many plant products have been found to be of use to man in his economy, his therapy and his aesthetic enjoyment, whatever may be their significance to the plants that make them or to other members of the biological world, the fundamental contribution of the autotrophic plants is their trapping of energy in the carbohydrate molecule. In this, the contribution of the photosynthesizing plants exceeds that of the chemosynthesizing, for, although they may not be so universal in their distribution as the chemosynthetic species, or so numerous, their greater size makes the contribution of each individual among them far larger; they are also more readily accessible to animals as food.

## Efficiency of the photosynthetic process

Photosynthesis is the only biological mechanism by which solar energy is trapped, but it is not one that makes use of all the energy available. A calculation of the energy budget of a green plant, for example, shows that from a mechanical point of view, photosynthesis is an inefficient process. Such a calculation has been made for a hypothetical acre of corn in North Central Illinois, the center of the corn belt of the United States.

Corn was chosen as the plant from which the figures were obtained since it probably represents the most efficient annual of temperate regions, in that at maturity its leaf area is approximately twice that of the ground of the plot on which it is growing. That is to say, 10,000 corn plants growing in an acre of land, which agriculturists have found to be the ratio from which the best crops are obtained, expose to the light a total leaf area of two acres. Analyses of individual corn plants at maturity show that the mass of each, on an average, consists of 80 per cent water and 20 per cent solid material, remaining after all the water has been evaporated off. Of this dry residue, about 95 per cent is organic material that can be burned away to carbon dioxide and water, and about 5 per cent is inorganic matter that remains as mineral ash. Practically all of the solid matter of the corn plant therefore consists of carbon compounds, for which the carbon has been obtained entirely from the carbon dioxide of the air. But this does not include all the carbon that has been incorporated into the plant during the growing season, for some of the products of photosynthesis have been oxidized and their carbon lost as carbon dioxide. The amount of this loss can be determined by measuring the respiratory exchange over a 24-hour period. Expressed in terms of glucose equivalents, or its proportion of the glucose molecule, the total carbon accumulated by such an acre of corn in the 100 days of the growing season can then be calculated to be 8,732 kg., of which 6,687 kg. represents the carbon of the organic compounds retained in the plants and 2,045 kg. that which has been lost in respiration. Determinations of the energy relationships of glucose show that the equivalent of 3,760 Calories are required for the synthesis of 1 kg., so that the energy consumed in photosynthesis can be tabulated as follows:

TABLE X
Energy Consumed in Photosynthesis [a]

| | |
|---|---|
| Glucose equivalent of accumulated carbon | 6,687 kg. |
| Glucose equivalent of oxidized carbon | 2,054 kg. |
| Total glucose manufactured | 8,732 kg. |
| Energy required to produce 1 kg. glucose | 3,760 Cal. |
| Total energy consumed in photosynthesis | 33,000,000 Cal. |

[a] Transeau, E. N., *Ohio Journal of Science*, v. 26, 1926.

The total solar energy available to this acre of corn during its growing season was determined from measurements made at the Solar Radiation Station at Madison, Wisconsin, where climate and weather conditions approximated those of central Illinois. Comparisons of the energy available and the energy consumed, or bound in the products of photosynthesis, show that less than 2 per cent of the available energy was so bound, and that photosynthesis, measured in terms of intake and output, is about 8 per cent efficient. These relationships are expressed in the following table:

TABLE XI

Efficiency of Photosynthesis [a]

| | |
|---|---|
| Total energy available on acre during growing season | 2,043 million Cals. |
| Total energy used | 33 million Cals. |
| Percentage available energy used by corn plant in photosynthesis | 1.6% |
| Percentage total light spectrum used in photosynthesis | 20% |
| Efficiency of photosynthesis | 8% |

[a] Transeau, E. N., *Ohio Journal of Science,* v. 26, 1926.

But these figures do not represent the total energy relationships between a plant and its environment, for transpiration is an energy exchange and a consumption of environmental energy. Energy equivalent to 593 Cals. is required to evaporate 1 kg. of water at the average temperature at which these plants are presumed to have been growing, and since the calculated amount of total water transpired amounts to 1.5 million kg., the total energy consumed in this process is in the neighborhood of 910 million Calories. The total energy budget of the corn field may then be summarized as in Table XII.

TABLE XII [a]

| | |
|---|---|
| Total energy available | 2,043 million Cals. |
| Energy used in photosynthesis | 33 million Cals. |
| Energy used in transpiration | 910 million Cals. |
| Total energy consumed | 943 million Cals. |
| Energy not directly used by plant | 1,100 million Cals. |
| Energy released by respiration | 8 million Cals. |
| Percentage of available energy used | 46% |
| Percentage of available energy taken up by environment | 54% |

[a] Transeau, E. N., *Ohio Journal of Science,* v. 26, 1926.

### The biological significance of autotrophs

However inefficient the photosynthetic process may appear to be when worked out on paper from data of this kind, it remains the fundamental one for the present biological world, and until it is supplanted on a large scale by some other chemical mechanism for the conversion of kinetic into potential energy, or until the present inhabitants of this planet are replaced by others with different requirements and different capacities, heterotrophs will still be dependent upon photosynthesizing autotrophs for their existence. And if one estimates the consumption of the products that plants have made through photosynthesis, by all animals as food and by man, not only for food but also to provide himself with the materials to build his houses, to warm and clothe himself and to drive the machines with which he manufactures products useful to him and transports them and himself from place to place, it becomes evident that consumption of plant products is far greater than their production. And it is greater not only than the production by plants that exist on the earth to-day, but also than that of plants that existed in past eras of the earth's history. The stores of coal and oil in the ground represent the carbon accumulations of plants that flourished and perished long before the arrival of man. It is estimated that the equivalent of $1.6 \times 10^{10}$ tons of carbon per year are assimilated by all the land plants in the world, and that the current consumption of coal and petroleum is equivalent to $1.75 \times 10^9$ tons of carbon a year. But forests are being cut down three times as fast as they grow, and even where there is not such ruthless deforestation, natural decay about equals growth so that, while these areas remain a steady source of organic material, they do not compensate for the loss elsewhere. And although the carbon assimilation of marine algae has been estimated to be four or five times that of land plants, no way has yet been devised for making use of materials from them to the extent that those from land plants have been exploited. At the rate at which these stores are being used now, it seems probable that the human population of the world will have to find other sources of energy for its material needs, if not for its nutritional ones, at some period that, at least as geologists reckon time, is not in the too distant future.

# CHAPTER 19
## HETEROTROPHIC NUTRITION: FEEDING MECHANISMS AND DIGESTION

### The dependence of heterotrophs upon autotrophs

All heterotrophic organisms are ultimately dependent upon autotrophs for the foods that supply them with energy and the nitrogen and carbon necessary for their syntheses of protein and other organic compounds. The saprophytic and parasitic plants, without the capacity for photo- or chemosynthesis, are equally as dependent upon the organic compounds constructed by green plants and chemosynthesizing bacteria as are animals which feed directly upon plants or upon other animals. The words of the prophet Isaiah, "All flesh is grass,"* are literally true, and were vegetation for any reason to disappear from the earth, or the energy of the sun to diminish appreciably, animals, insofar as we understand the conditions of their existence to-day, would also cease to populate this planet.

### Differences in the degree of complexity of compounds required by heterotrophs

But studies of the nutritional requirements of various heterotrophs have shown that differences exist in the variety and complexity of the compounds needed for their sustenance. Some free living, but not chemosynthesizing, bacteria, for example, and some of the strains of wild yeasts can use as food a carbohydrate simpler than a hexose, such as a salt of the three-carbon compound, lactic acid $(H\text{-}C\text{-}C\text{-}C = O)$, with H's and OH as shown, and an inorganic or simple organic compound containing nitrogen; if provided with these and with water and mineral salts, they will grow and reproduce. Other micro-organisms are much more exacting in their food requirements, such as strains of yeasts that have been selected for generations by brewers and bakers for their fermentative capacities and the bacteria that have adjusted to a saprophytic or parasitic existence and require a greater variety of more complex compounds for their maintenance and growth. Many experiments have been made upon animals, from protozoa to man, to test their capacities to synthesize food from inorganic or simple organic compounds. From these experiments evidence has been obtained that none of these tested can exist upon nitrogenous compounds below the level of amino acids and that most of them require at least a variety of such acids and in general much more complex organic compounds, as well as the water and mineral salts that are common needs of all biological systems.

### The feeding mechanisms of heterotrophs

The feeding mechanisms of heterotrophs, as well as their enzyme systems, impose limitations upon the kind of food that they can use as a source of nutrients. According to the way that food enters their bodies, they may be classified as those that feed by diffusion through the body surface, fluid feeders, detritus feeders, microphagous and macrophagous feeders. Those that feed by means of diffusion have no specialized region for the intake of food, which, already digested, enters their bodies through any surface area permeable to it. Among such organisms are the saprophytic yeasts and molds, whose own digestive enzymes bring

---
* Isaiah: 40.6.

about the disintegration of the substrate upon which they live; the soluble products of this digestion then diffuse into the cell, or in the case of the molds, into the hyphae that penetrate into the substrate. Included in this group are also many of the endoparasites, both protozoan and metazoan, that inhabit the digestive tracts or tissues of animals, and draw their sustenance from the end-products of the digestive processes of their hosts.

All free-living metazoa, and some parasitic ones as well, have a localized region, an oral opening or mouth, and special devices or mechanisms by which they take in food. Many of the fluid feeders are insects, with mouth parts specialized for lapping up a nutrient fluid, like the long, coiled "tongues" of butterflies (Fig. 14.11), for sponging it up like the broad labella of flies (Fig. 14.11), or for sucking it up like the proboscis of bees and mosquitoes, capable in the one case of reaching the bases of the petals in a flower and in the other of puncturing an animal's epidermis and drawing up the blood from the sub-epidermal vessels (Fig. 14.11). Spiders, too, are fluid feeders, whose sucking stomachs pull in the juices of their victims after their bodies have been crushed or punctured by the spider's claws. Some ecto- and endoparasites, still retaining mouths for the intake of food, are fluid feeders; such, for example, are fleas, lice and leeches, that live on blood; the aphids that live on the juices of plants and the liver fluke, perhaps the most specialized of all feeders since it appears to exist as an adult exclusively on bile.

Detritus feeders feed upon the organic material in soil or mud, the partial products of the decomposition of the dead bodies of plants and animals or substances that living ones have returned to their surroundings, sucking it into their mouths as earthworms, sea cucumbers and sturgeons do, or shoveling it in as they plough through it like some of the sea urchins. Such animals must ingest comparatively enormous quantities of material in order to obtain sufficient food, for much that enters their mouths is useless to them and passes unchanged out of their bodies.

Microphagous feeders subsist upon particles of extremely small size and are for the most part continuous feeders, since they too must ingest large quantities of food in order to obtain a sufficiency of nutrients. These are all aquatic animals, sweeping food into their mouths in the currents of water set up by the motion of various parts of their bodies. Ciliates like Paramoecium, for ex-

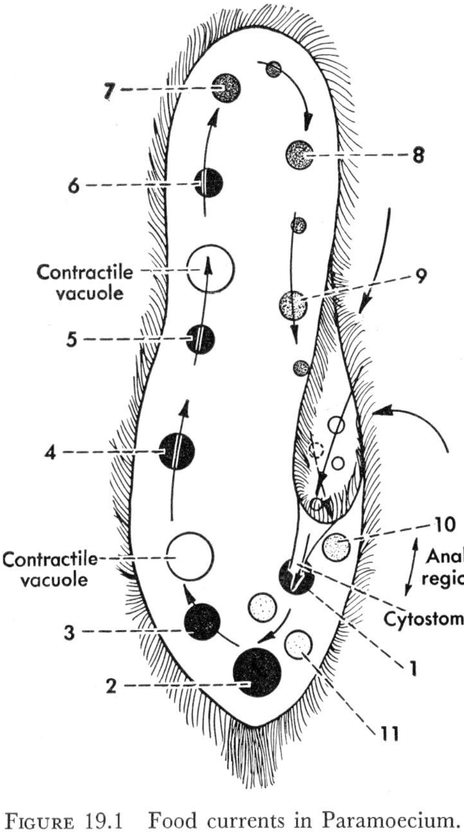

FIGURE 19.1 Food currents in Paramoecium.

The diagram shows how a current of water carrying food particles is swept into the cytopharynx by the action of the cilia, and the formation of food vacuoles at the cytostome. The course of the food vacuoles within the body of the Paramoecium is indicated by arrows, and the changes in their contents during the process of digestion by changes from uniform blackening to light and lighter stippling. The undigested residue of each vacuole is eliminated at the anal area. The numbers 1–10 indicate successive stages in the progress of a food vacuole around the body; a single vacuole may make a number of circuits before digestion and assimilation of its contents are complete.

ample, maintain a food current by the continuous beating of their cilia (Fig. 19.1); and sponges do so by the lashing of the flagella of their choanocytes. Similar mechanisms are employed by sea anemones, some marine worms and the lamellibranch mollusks. Some of the crustacea are microphagous, creating a food current, as barnacles do, by the movement of their appendages, and among the insects, larvae of the mosquito Culex have been found to do this so efficiently that they are able to keep themselves alive, although not to grow, upon particles of colloidal dimensions alone. Among the vertebrates, whales and many of the fishes live entirely upon plankton, the small and non-motile or feebly-swimming organisms near the surface of the water, straining them off from the water they take in as they swim along with open mouths.

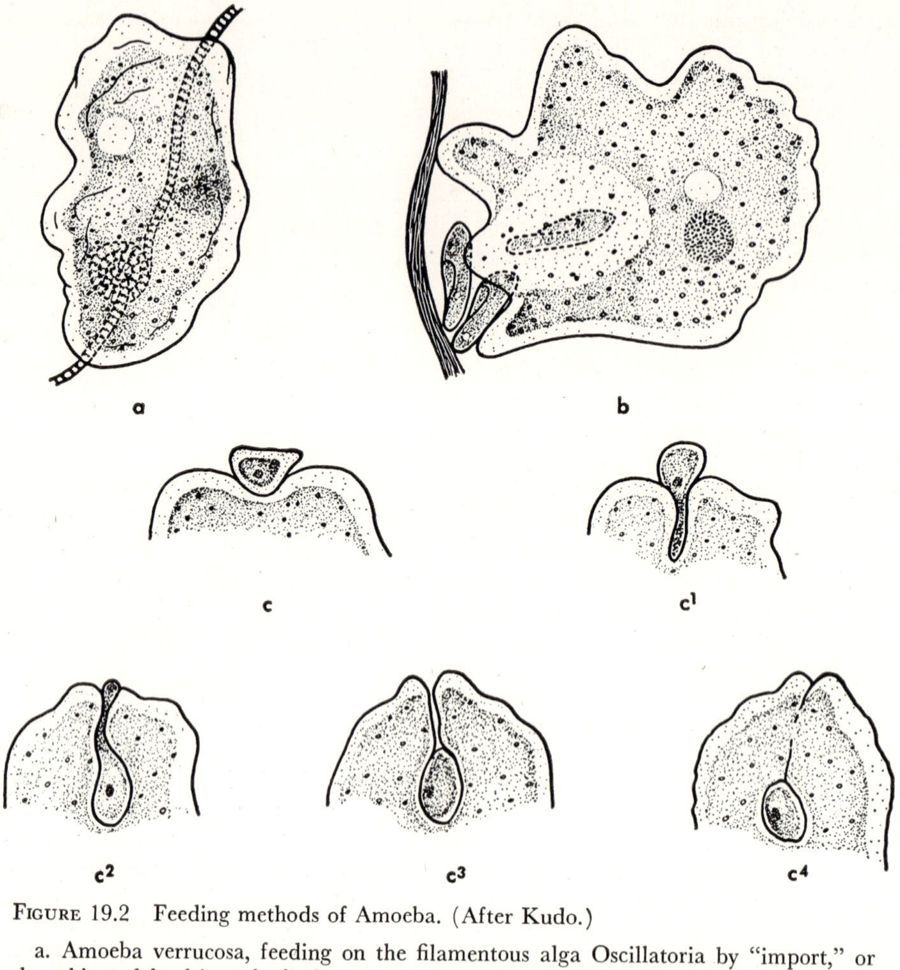

FIGURE 19.2  Feeding methods of Amoeba. (After Kudo.)

   a. Amoeba verrucosa, feeding on the filamentous alga Oscillatoria by "import," or the taking of food into the body upon contact with it. (After Rhumbler.)

   b. Amoeba proteus capturing Paramoecium by "circumvallation," or the formation of pseudopodia, without contact with the object, which they surround on all sides and ingest. (After Kepner and Whitlock.)

   $c$–$c^4$. Amoeba verrucosa ingesting a food particle by invagination, in which the amoeba adheres to the food with which it comes in contact; the ectoplasm then folds into the endoplasm as a tube, drawing the food particle in with it. The cell membrane then disappears and the particle becomes incorporated as a food vacuole in the cytoplasm.

The majority of animals are macrophagous, feeding upon comparatively large masses of solid food that they ingest only at intervals. There is considerable variation in their mechanisms for ingestion, as there is in the materials that they are both mechanically and chemically equipped to make use of as food. Amoeboid species, or species with amoeboid cells lining the cavity into which the food is taken, surround a food particle with pseudopodia and incorporate it in a cytoplasmic vacuole (Fig. 19.2); others, like the ciliate Didinium, seem to suck their prey into their bodies, or they may, like the starfish, surround it with the everted stomach and, after it has become softened by the digestive juices, draw it and the stomach back within the body. Most macrophagous feeders have some mechanism for tearing, grinding, crushing or otherwise macerating the solid food before its exposure to the digestive enzymes and consequent chemical disintegration. Aristotle's lantern in the sea-urchins, the radulae of mollusks, the gastric mills of the decapod crustacea, the mandible of the chewing insects and the teeth of the vertebrates are illustrative of such devices.

Macrophagous feeders also differ in the sources from which they derive nutrients. Herbivores (Latin, herba = herb + vorare = to devour) feed exclusively upon vegetation; these include such animals as some of the snails, grasshoppers, the grain-eating birds, rabbits, cows, sheep and horses; carnivores (Latin, carno = flesh + vorare = to devour), like starfish, lobsters, squid, some fishes, seals, birds of prey and most members of the cat and dog families, feed largely, if not exclusively, upon the flesh of other animals; and omnivores (Latin, omnia = all + vorare = to devour), like cockroaches, mice, rats and men, make use of both plant and animal tissues and products as sources of their nutrients.

## *Enzyme systems as limiting factors to the synthesis and digestion of food*

The enzymes and enzyme systems with which an organism is hereditarily endowed determine what nutrients must be obtained from external sources as well as the possible sources from which they may be drawn. The extent to which an organism is capable of synthesizing its own nutrients from inorganic or organic compounds and the extent to which it can decompose complex compounds already synthesized determine, like the regulation of its internal environment, the freedom or independence of its life. It has already been pointed out that some heterotrophs are capable of a wider range of syntheses than others, but there is also variation in their digestive capabilities. The snail, Helix, for example, can hydrolyze many more sugars than vertebrates can, and can digest tri- and tetrasaccharides; it possesses also a cellulase, so that it can derive carbohydrate from cellulose. This is true also of some locusts and some caterpillars, but not of herbivorous mammals, which must depend upon the bacterial population of their digestive tracts for what cellulose decomposition takes place there. Chitinase is found also in Helix and some insects, allowing them to make use of chitin as a food, which to other animals is only digestive waste. The presence of such enzymes, in addition to the other digestive ones common to animals of the same type, permits their possessor to exploit additional sources of food. Conversely, the absence or reduction of particular enzymes, or types of enzymes, restricts the number of possible foodstuffs.

There is still a wide field open for exploration in the comparative enzyme systems of animals, but the limited number of exact studies that have been made indicate that while animals of all species have digestive enzymes of the general type of carbohydrases, proteinases and esterases, the proportions of these and the specificity of individual enzymes among them varies in relation to their feeding habits. For example, Calliphora, the common blue-bottle or blow-fly, and Glossina, the blood-sucking tsetse fly of Africa, are both members of the family Muscidae in the insectan order of Diptera. Studies of their enzyme systems, made by grinding up the digestive tracts of adults and testing the enzymatic potencies of extracts of the cellular mass upon different kinds of substrates, have shown that while both possess carbohydrase, proteinase and lipase, the proportion of proteinase in the blood-sucking Glossina is greater than it is in Calliphora, which as an adult feeds upon liquids of all kinds and can experimentally be kept alive on a diet of dissolved sugar alone, although it will not reproduce under such conditions. The gut of the adult Calliphora is especially rich in carbohydrases, and extracts from it show but a weak proteolytic activity. Conditions in the clothes moth, Tineola biselleila, are even more specialized, for the food of their larvae consists entirely of keratin from wool, fur and feathers, a protein that is not ordinarily digested by animals. The cells in the midgut of these larvae secrete keratinase, an enzyme that brings about the disintegration of the protein molecule after its preliminary reduction by a strong reducing agent, also present in the gut, whose nature is not yet known. The effect of this reduction is to open up the sulphur-sulphur bonds holding together the chains of amino acids that make up the keratin molecule; once these linkages are broken, keratinase can effect the further disintegration of the molecule. The presence of a reducing agent in the gut and the effective operation of keratinase under conditions that inhibit the activity of proteinases such as trypsin are the unique conditions that make possible the existence of organisms like Tineola and some few other insects that feed upon wool, silk and similar substances.

Other experimental studies indicate that, at the other end of the scale, there are organisms that can call into play, or possibly even develop, enzymes other than those they ordinarily use. Some strains of bacteria and yeast, for example, naturally decompose but one kind of sugar and can be grown for generations if this alone is provided, as a carbohydrate substrate. But if they are shifted to another nutrient medium, containing a different sugar, they become capable of effecting its disintegration, and ultimately can be cultured on a medium in which the second sugar is the only carbohydrate substrate. The mechanism of such adaptations in enzymatic action is still problematical.

## Digestion in man

### The early experiments of William Beaumont

The actual course of digestion is best known in man and some few other mammals in which it has been most completely studied. The first detailed observations on a human subject were made between 1822 and 1832 by Dr. William Beaumont, a post surgeon of the American Army stationed at Fort Mackinac on the Michigan-Canadian border. Called one day to the boat landing because of an accident, he found a young Canadian voyageur, the eighteen-year-old Alexis St. Martin, terribly injured by a gunshot which had gone off less than a yard away from him. The charge, of powder and duck shot, had blown away the skin and muscles of the boy's back, and parts of his ribs and diaphragm, exposing his lungs and his stomach; his stomach had, moreover, been lacerated so that its contents were pouring out and its inner surface exposed. Beaumont replaced the organs, cleansed the wound as best he could, applied poultices according to the standard procedure of the times, and began the task of nursing the apparently mortally wounded boy back to health. Ten months after the accident, St. Martin was walking about and even able to do light work; most of the wound had healed, but there still remained an opening in his side and in the wall of his stomach through which the food that he ate flowed out unless the aperture was closed by a compress; later a flap of tissue grew along the margin of the opening, making a kind of valve which prevented the contents of the stomach from escaping.

There then began perhaps the most remarkable association between experimenter and subject ever recorded. Beaumont recognized in St. Martin perfect, and perfectly unique, experimental material for the study of digestion; he saw that not only could he recover from the boy's stomach food that had been eaten, but that he could introduce any type and quantity of food into it that he desired and leave it there as long as he chose. Moreover, he could remove gastric juice at will from the empty stomach, and even watch the gross changes of the lining of the stomach under any kind of conditions of rest or activity, emotional or other stimulation that he elected to set up. But these experiments demanded some cooperation from his subject and erstwhile patient, which understandingly enough was not always forthcoming. Beaumont engaged St. Martin as his servant as well as his subject and except for the periods when experiments were in progress, St. Martin lived an ordinary life, eating, working and living as any other man. But at times he would rebel from the conditions of his life under Beaumont's roof and scientific experimentation, and would disappear for months and even years. During one of these disappearances he married and set up his own home in the Canadian wilderness, working for the Hudson's Bay Fur Company; during another he went through a cholera epidemic, and survived the ravages of a pestilence in which many others died.

But during the periods when Beaumont did make use of him as experimental material, much important information was gathered about the nature of the gastric juice and the stomach's functioning. Beaumont was able to make an accurate description of human gastric juice, and to send samples of the pure fluid to Berzelius and other chemists for analysis. These analyses confirmed Prout's observations that its acid component was hydrochloric acid. Moreover, Beaumont was able to confirm Spallanzani's observations on the changes that take place in food exposed to gastric juice, and to make more complete comparative studies of them as they took place inside and outside the body, and to determine the types of food susceptible to the action of gastric juice and the extent of their digestion. He also made full and detailed observations on the movements of the stomach, when empty and when full, and on the effects of emotion and of pain on the secretion of gastric juice and on digestion in general.

## The course and fate of food in the human alimentary canal

An opening into a hollow organ, such as made by the gunpowder and shot in St. Martin's stomach, is called a fistula. Fistulae into any region of the digestive tract can be made by surgery, and it is by means of them, as well as by means of withdrawing the contents of the stomach and intestine by methods more refined than those of Réaumur and Spallanzani that complete studies of the digestive process have been made upon other men and upon experimental animals. As a result of these, the course and fate of the different components of the food in the digestive tracts of men and of dogs are quite fully known, and much more completely known than those in other animals.

*Ingestion and maceration:* The ingestion of food by man is a voluntary act, but once the food has reached the back of the oral cavity, its deglutition, or swallowing, and further passage along the oesophagus, stomach and intestine is involuntary. The ingested food is first subjected to maceration by the teeth, and while it is being ground up in the process of chewing, it is mixed with saliva, the combined secretions of three pairs of salivary glands, the submaxillary, sublingual and parotid. These glands are innervated by autonomic nerves (see p. 370), and are stimulated to discharge their secretions by the presence of food within the mouth and also by the sight and smell of it. Food within the mouth stimulates the taste buds and this stimulus is transmitted along the afferent fibres of the V, VII and IX cranial nerves to the salivary center in the pons and out through the efferent autonomic fibres to the salivary glands. This is a reflex stimulation, which can be elicited in a newborn baby, and is therefore known as an unconditioned reflex. Salivary secretion, resulting from the sight or smell, and indeed sometimes even by the thought of food, is a conditioned reflex, established only after taste has been associated with food. This was definitely proved by the experiments of the Russian physiologist, Ivan Pavlov

(1849–1936), and other workers in his laboratory, who were able to measure the salivary secretions of dogs by means of fistulae made in their oesophagi. Milk, which stimulates the taste buds of a newborn puppy, became a stimulus for the secretion of saliva as soon as young puppies were able to smell or see it; meat, on the other hand, was not a stimulus until they had been allowed to taste it. Moreover, if the feeding of meat to older dogs was always accompanied by a second stimulus, either visual, such as the sight of an object, or auditory, such as the ringing of a bell, after a sufficient period of association of the food as the primary stimulus and the object or the sound as a secondary one, the secondary stimulus became adequate to evoke the salivary secretion. In man, both the unconditioned and the conditioned reflexes bring about the flow of saliva into the mouth, and the psychic stimulation of food has become almost as important to him as its direct gustatory or tactile stimulation.

**Saliva and its components:** Human saliva is an aqueous solution of sodium chloride, potassium chloride, sodium bicarbonate, sodium and calcium phosphate and certain other salts, oxygen and carbon dioxide, urea, the albumin and globulin of blood serum, mucin and two enzymes of the carbohydrase class, ptyalin, or salivary amylase, and maltase in very low concentration. It is slightly acid in reaction and is produced in considerable quantity by the combined activity of the three pairs of glands. Starch is the substrate for ptyalin; in its presence, in a neutral, alkaline or slightly acid medium, the starch molecule is broken up into molecules of the disaccharide, maltose, the substrate for maltase. But it is doubtful if more than a very small amount, if any, of this digestion takes place before the food is swallowed and, passing along the oesophagus, reaches the stomach (Fig. 19.3).

**Secretions of the gastric glands:** The glands of the gastric mucosa secrete, in addition to mucin, hydrochloric acid and the enzymes pepsin, rennin and lipase. They, too, are stimulated to secretion by autonomic nerves, distributed to the stomach's wall as branches of the vagus (X cranial nerve). By means of gastric fistulae, Pavlov showed that secretion from the glands begins even before food is in the stomach, in consequence of a reflex primarily initiated by the taste of food in the mouth but secondarily, like the salivary secretion, by the sight or smell of it. Flavors that are pleasing to the individual cause a greater flow of gastric juice as a result of this psychic stimulation; conversely, unappealing food, or emotion or anxiety, may inhibit this phase of secretion. But once the food has entered the stomach, its glands are directly stimulated to discharge their contents. This stimulation is in some small part due to the mechanical stretching of its walls, but in greater measure to the effect of a substance present in the mucosa of the pyloric region of the stomach, which is absorbed into the blood stream and conveyed by it to the cells of the gastric glands, which it stimulates to secretory activity. This substance has been given the name gastrin and regarded as a hormone, for extracts of the pyloric mucosa, injected into the blood of a fasting animal, lead to a copious secretion of gastric juice. But this is also the case if the compound histamine, found in many tissues, is experimentally injected into the blood stream, a fact that has led some investigators to consider gastrin and histamine identical. Whether they are or not, the experimental data show that a chemical agent carried by the blood, as well as the autonomic nerves that reach them, stimulate the gastric glands to secretion.

Under ordinary conditions, an average adult human secretes from 2 to 3 liters of gastric juice in a twenty-four hour period. 99 per cent of this secretion is water, 0.45–0.6 per cent hydrochloric acid and the remainder the gastric enzymes and inorganic salts. The pH of the gastric juice is 0.9–1.5, a degree of acidity that is optimal for the action of pepsin, but inhibitory to that of ptyalin. The food ordinarily remains in the stomach some 3–4 hours, during which regular peristaltic contractions of the muscular walls of the distal half move it constantly in a downward path toward the closed pylorus and back again toward the proximal end of the organ, where the walls remain in a condition of continued contraction. The movement is such that the outer part of the food mass is carried toward the pylorus, while a central current moves in the opposite direction, toward the fundus. This churning serves to mix the food mass with the gastric juice, but before the mixing is complete and all the stomach's contents made acid, a considerable amount of starch has been digested to maltose.

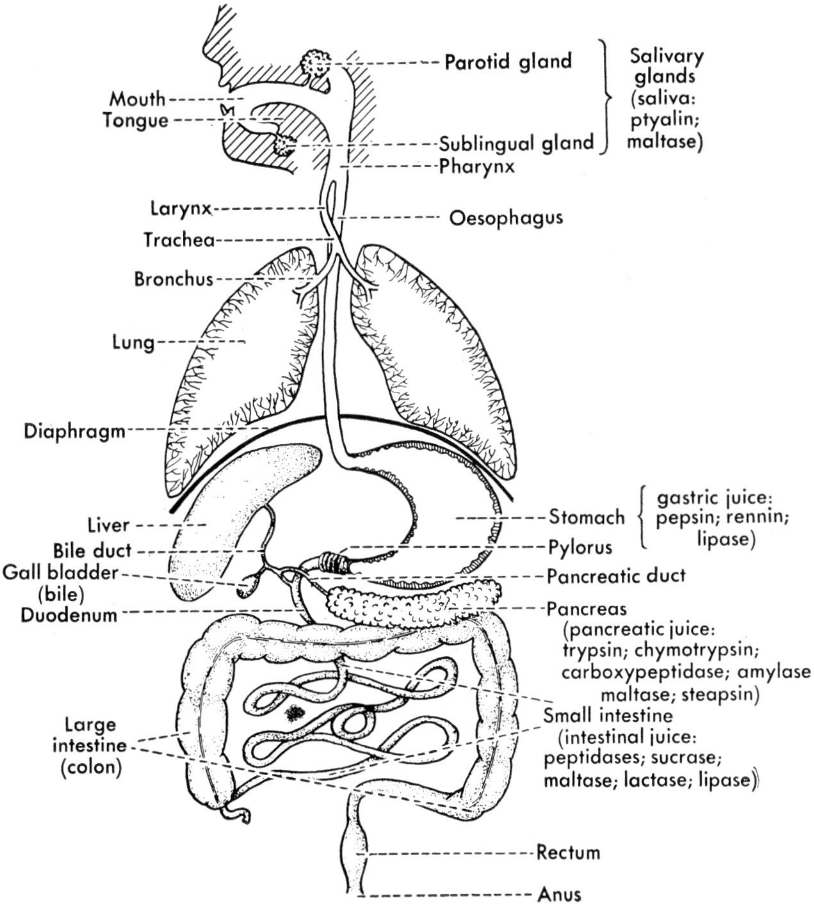

Pepsin, acting upon a protein substrate, brings about the decomposition of the protein molecule into smaller groups of amino acids known as proteoses and peptones. Rennin, which, like pepsin, is secreted in an inactive form as prorennin acts specifically upon caseinogen, a soluble protein of milk, splitting each molecule into two soluble components, whey protein and paracasein. In combination with calcium, paracasein forms insoluble calcium paracasein, which is digested by pepsin. The lipase of gastric juice is effective only upon very finely divided fats, such as those of cream and egg yolk, and its optimum pH is about 5. The digestion of the fat of an ordinary meal in the stomach of an adult is negligible in amount, and virtually all of the lipid content of the food passes through the stomach unaltered.

FIGURE 19.3 Diagram of the human digestive tract, showing the location and the principal secretions of the digestive glands. The submaxillary gland is not shown. (After Carlson and Johnson.)

The movements of the stomach and the action of the digestive enzymes reduce the solids of the food that was taken into the mouth to a fluid or semi-fluid state, and it is not until this condition has been reached that the stomach's contents can pass through the pylorus. The consistency of the food is an important factor in its passage into the intestine. From an ordinary mixed meal, fluids pass through the pylorus first, then carbohydrates, which are more rapidly softened than meat, and finally fats.

**Secretions from the pancreas:** In the intestine the soft food mass, or chyme (Greek, chymos = juice) is exposed to the action of the secretions of the pancreas and the intestinal glands, and to the bile. The enzyme-secreting cells of the pancreas are stimulated to discharge their products by impulses reaching them through branches of the vagus nerve and by a hormone, called secretin. Secretin, the first of the hormones to be discovered, is found in the cells of the intestinal mucosa; the presence of food within the intestine stimulates those cells to release the hormone into the blood, through which it is conveyed to the pancreas, leading to the secretion of pancreatic juice. By means of fistulae so made that he was able to collect this secretion as it passed from the pancreatic duct, Pavlov determined that its discharge was also evoked, as a conditioned reflex, by the sight and smell of food.

Pancreatic juice contains a fairly high concentration of sodium carbonate and sodium bicarbonate, so that its reaction is alkaline; the proenzymes, trypsinogen and chymotrypsinogen, of the proteolytic enzymes trypsin and chymotrypsin; another proteolytic enzyme called carboxypeptidase; an amylase, called pancreatic amylase or amylopsin; some maltase and a lipase, called pancreatic lipase or steapsin. Trypsinogen is converted to trypsin by the action of enterokinase and trypsin, and chymotrypsinogen to the active chymotrypsin by trypsin. Once in the lumen of the intestine, all the enzymes of the pancreatic juice are in an "unmasked" or active condition, and brought into contact with the chyme by the movements of the intestinal walls.

**Movements of the walls of the intestine:** These movements are of three kinds (1) segmenting, (2) pendular and (3) peristaltic. The segmenting movements are rhythmical annular constrictions of the intestinal wall, in consequence of which the food mass is broken up and kneaded again and again, and the flow of blood and lymph to the wall increased. The pendular movements are constrictions of the wall that move the chyme backwards and forwards within the lumen of the intestine. The combined effect of segmenting and pendular movements is to mix the food mass thoroughly with the secretions poured into the lumen of the intestine, and to bring the diffusible end products of digestion into contact with the epithelium of the villi through which they are absorbed into the blood and lymphatic vessels. The movements of the villi themselves augment those of the intestinal walls. The peristaltic movements contribute, too, to this mixing process but serve also to propel the chyme along the intestine from the pylorus toward the ilio-colic sphincter at the junction of small and large intestine.

The bile, which enters the intestine through the bile duct near the point of entrance of the pancreatic juice, contains in addition to water, inorganic salts, the bile pigments bilirubin and biliverdin, and the bile salts, sodium glycocholate and sodium taurocholate. These materials are also mixed with the chyme as it is moved about by the movements of the intestine.

**Secretions of the intestinal glands:** The secretions of the intestinal glands, the intestinal juice, are added to the mixture of chyme, bile and pancreatic juice. In addition to the enterokinase and mucus, which acts as a lubricant to the food mass, the intestinal juice contains sodium carbonate and bicarbonate, enzymes known as peptidases, the carbohydrases, sucrase, maltase and lactase; and lipase. The action of the enzymes from the pancreas and the intestine, facilitated by the bile salts, is to reduce the products of salivary and gastric digestion, and those that have escaped such digestion, to a state in which they can pass through the plasma membranes of the absorbing cells and the capillary and lacteal walls and be carried about the body and distributed to the appropriate tissues and cells.

Trypsin brings about the further disintegration of the proteoses and peptones resulting from peptic digestion, and also the decomposition of whatever protein has escaped the action of pepsin, to smaller units of protein structure, called peptides; these may be polypeptides, consisting of several amino acids; tetrapeptides, consisting of four; tripeptides, consisting of three, or dipeptides, consisting of two. Pure trypsin does not bring about the decomposition of proteins beyond the proteose or polypeptide stage; the older belief that it carried their disintegration to the amino acid stage was due to the fact that the "ferment" when first tested and named, contained at least three, and possibly more, enzymes. One of these, chymotrypsin, has the same effect as trypsin, but produces it in a different way, and the other, carboxypeptidase, is the agent that brings about the partition of the proteose and polypeptide molecules into smaller peptide units.

The disintegration of these smaller peptide units is effected by the peptidases of the intestinal juice. Aminopeptidase, like pancreatic carboxypeptidase, brings about the decomposition of molecules composed of several peptide units to the dipeptide stage; all the dipeptides are then hydrolyzed into their two component amino acids by the

**Saliva**
- ptyalin (amylase)
- maltase

**Gastric Juice**
- pepsin
- rennin — Casein — whey protein — paracasein
- lipase (negligible in adult?)

**Pancreatic Juice**
- trypsin
- chymotrypsin
- carboxypeptidase
- amylase
- maltase
- lipase

**Intestinal Juice**
- aminopeptidase
- dipeptidase
- maltase
- sucrase
- lactase
- lipase

**Ordinary Mixed Meal**

Carbohydrate
↓
disaccharides
- maltose → 2 mols. glucose
- sucrose → glucose, fructose
- lactose → glucose, galactose

Protein
↓
proteoses
peptones
↓
peptides
↓
dipeptides → amino acids

Fat
↓
glycerol, fatty acids

dipeptidases. The amino acids resulting from their progressive decomposition, or splitting of the ingested protein molecules, are capable of absorption by the cells of the intestinal mucosa and of passage across the capillary endothelium to the blood plasma.

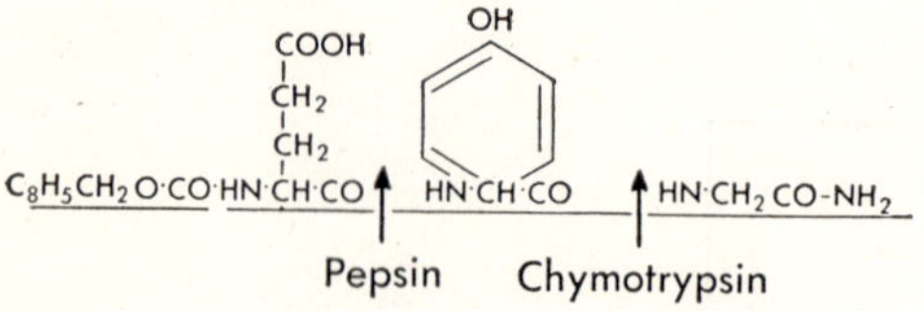

$$C_6H_5CH_2 \cdot O \cdot CO \cdot HN \cdot \underset{\underset{\underset{COOH}{|}}{\overset{\overset{CH_2}{|}}{CH_2}}}{CH} \cdot CO \underset{Pepsin}{\uparrow} HN \cdot \underset{\underset{OH}{\bigcirc}}{CH} \cdot CO \underset{Chymotrypsin}{\uparrow} HN \cdot CH_2 \cdot CO \cdot NH_2$$

FIGURE 19.4 Action of pepsin and chymotrypsin on a peptide molecule. (After Baldwin.)

Both enzymes bring about the disintegration of the molecule into two smaller ones, but split it at different bonds, indicated by the arrows.

Recent studies of the course of protein digestion have shown that each group of enzymes concerned attacks the protein molecule, or its derivative, in a different way. Each kind of enzyme is most effective in breaking the bond holding two amino acids together if the bond is of a certain type or if it has a certain position in the complex molecule. Thus pepsin and chymotrypsin may both bring about the disintegration of an amino acid complex into two parts, but the division, or splitting of the molecule takes place in each case at a different point. Trypsin and pepsin both digest the same proteins, but trypsin attacks the molecule at one point and pepsin at another, and the effect of one is complementary to that of the other (Fig. 19.4). Similarly the carboxypeptidase of pancreatic juice acts only on those polypeptides with a free carboxyl group, and the aminopeptidase of intestinal juice only on those with a free amino group. The dipeptidases of intestinal juice are specific in that they operate only upon peptides composed of two amino acids; even greater specificity for certain groups of dipeptides, or even for individual dipeptides, is suspected.

The greater part of the digestion of carbohydrate takes place within the intestine, where the pancreatic amylase has a longer time to operate than has salivary amylase, during the time the food is in the stomach, and where the maltase, sucrase and lactase of the intestinal juice, in conjunction with the small amount of maltase secreted by the pancreas, bring about the decomposition of their respective substrates into hexose molecules. It is in the intestine, too, that any appreciable hydrolysis of fat takes place, the intestinal lipase affecting the fat molecules in such a way that the bonds between the glycerol part of their molecules and the fatty acids are broken. The bile salts are accessory to this decomposition, for by lowering the surface tension of these oily substances, they reduce the chances of the coalescence of the globules into which the lipids have been divided by maceration in the mouth, as well as by the motions of the stomach and intestine. The more finely divided the globules are, the greater is the surface area that they expose to the lipase and the more rapid their hydrolysis. The bile salts, moreover, have a specific activating effect upon pancreatic lipase and the property also of keeping in solution the fatty acids liberated by lipolytic action.

## Absorption of the end products of digestion

Absorption of the digested foods also takes place in the small intestine; only alcohol is absorbed in any quantity from the stomach, while the absorption of water and, to a considerable extent, of mineral salts takes place from the large intestine. The cells of the intestinal mucosa appear to be freely permeable to hexoses, amino acids, glycerol and fatty acids, but their intake of these substances is not by diffusion alone, but by an active process of absorption, and also of selection. The work done by the intestinal epithelium can be measured by the increase in its oxygen intake and carbon dioxide output, showing the expenditure of energy. Its selective capacity has been shown by experiments in which glucose, galactose and fructose in equal concentrations have been introduced into an exposed loop of the intestine immersed in isotonic salt solution; under such conditions, glucose passes through the intestinal wall more rapidly than galactose, and galactose more rapidly than fructose. After injury or death of the cells, all three hexoses pass through the wall at an equal rate.

The bile salts also facilitate the absorption of fatty acids, uniting with them in the lumen of the intestine to form complex but temporary compounds that pass readily through the intestinal epithelial cells that overlie the lacteals, the blind lymph vessels extending into the intestinal villi. Once within the intestinal cells, the bile salt-fatty acid union is broken, and the fatty acids combine again with the molecules of glycerol that have been absorbed, so that the products of lipolytic digestion in the intestinal lumen are once again recombined as fat, a large proportion of which passes into the lacteals and so into the venous circulation through the thoracic duct. The bile salts, liberated from their union with the fatty acids, enter the portal vein, through which they are carried to the liver and again returned to the bile and ultimately to the intestinal contents.

## Egestion

Except for the fat taken up by the lacteals, which represents about 60 per cent of that resynthesized in the intestinal epithelium, the end products of digestion pass from the absorbing cells into the finer blood vessels of the intestinal wall and so to the portal vein, or the general circulation. All the remaining contents of the small intestine are moved on by its peristaltic contractions into the colon, or large intestine. This residue includes the undigested materials, those that have escaped the action of the digestive enzymes as well as those for which specific enzymes are lacking, the bile pigments, and other compounds that may have entered the intestine with the secretions that flow into it, or from the blood. Some further decomposition of the contents of the colon takes place through the activities of the bacteria inhabiting it; it is estimated that each day's food, as it passes through the digestive tract of the average adult human, is subjected to the action of over 100 billion bacteria. None of these products of bacterial decomposition is available to the body, for water and some of its mineral solutes are the only materials absorbed from the colon. The material remaining, after the absorption of water, constitutes the feces (Latin, faeces = dregs), which are eliminated from the body by the process of defecation.

## Digestive processes in other vertebrates

Digestion in other vertebrates seems to follow a similar course. Ptyalin is absent from the saliva of mammals other than the primates, pigs and some rodents, and in them all carbohydrate digestion is effected by the pancreatic amylase. The particular advantages that mammals and birds have over other vertebrates is in the nervous mechanism by which the glands secreting the digestive enzymes are stimulated to discharge their products even before the food is in the digestive tract, in a way preparing it for the reception of food and its work in the disintegration of the complex compounds. In fish and amphibia, on the other hand, the stimulation to secretion is a mechanical one only, initiated by the presence of food within the digestive tract. And the vertebrates in general have an advantage over other animals in the greater specialization of their digestive tracts, and localization of enzyme-secreting glands along it, so that digestion in them is a progressive process, and enzymes are brought together with their substrates under conditions which favor their most efficient and effective operation. In many invertebrates the digestion of all the food takes place in one common gland, a condition that is not so propitious for the operation of the enzymes and the rapid and thorough completion of their work.

# CHAPTER 20

# THE DIETARY REQUIREMENTS OF HETEROTROPHS

## *Conditions determining dietary requirements*

The dietary requirements of heterotrophic organisms are established by the use made of the digested food and the importance of that use to their growth, metabolism and maintenance. The materials necessary for their anabolic and catabolic needs must therefore not only be included in the food taken in, but must also be made available to all their cells and assimilated and utilized by them. Thus not only the content of the foodstuffs and the capacity to digest them are of primary importance for the adequate nutrition of such organisms, but also the mechanisms for their transport throughout the multicellular body and their delivery to every cell in it. Finally, the capability of the cells and tissues to make effective use of these materials is the ultimate criterion of adequate nutrition. Unless the tissues can metabolize the digested materials in such a way that they meet the architectural, energy and other metabolic requirements of the body, they might as well be absent from the diet altogether.

## *Investigations of dietary requirements*

### Methods

The most complete investigations of dietary requirements have been made on certain of the fungi and on mammals, particularly upon domesticated and laboratory animals and to some extent upon man. These requirements may be determined by feeding experiments, either by successively omitting certain kinds or categories of food from the natural diet, and observing the results, or, more accurately, by the use of synthetic diets in which only known quantities of known kinds of purified foods are fed. Among the mammals, young rats have been very widely used for this kind of study, for their diet can be controlled as soon as they are weaned, not long after their birth. Experimental studies are usually carried out on litter mates, or on individuals of the same age from the same strain, some of whom are fed a standard diet and others experimental diets. The adequacy, or inadequacy, of the experimental diet can be measured by comparisons of the rate of growth in weight and in size of the rats subsisting upon it with the controls fed a standard diet. Mineral deficiencies can also be quantitatively determined by analysis of the tissues of the control and experimental animals. Other defects appearing in the experimental animals may be attributed to their diet, provided that the other conditions of their lives are similar to those of the controls and provided that the same kind of defect appears often enough and in a large enough group of animals, so that it cannot be attributed to chance alone. But even in the most carefully controlled experiments, individual differences and idiosyncrasies introduce a source of error, and the products of the intestinal bacteria, either as direct contributions to the dietary needs of the animals or as indirect ones affecting the utilization of its food, cannot be eliminated except by elaborate techniques of sterilization. Even then it is difficult to maintain the digestive tract in a bacteria-free state for any extended period of time.

### The structural requirements of heterotrophs

The structural needs of a heterotroph are met primarily but not entirely by the proteins and minerals of its diet. The proteins must contain those amino acids, necessary to the construction of protoplasm and essential to its operation, that the organism either cannot synthesize for itself, or that it synthesizes too slowly or in too limited an amount for an adequate supply. Experiments have shown that not all proteins have these necessary constituents. Young rats, for example, fed on a mixed diet of carbohydrate, fat, vitamins and one protein of known amino acid content, showed definite differences in growth. When casein, the protein from milk, was the only one in their diet, their growth paralleled that of the controls, fed a standard, adequate diet; when gliadin, a protein from wheat, was substituted for casein, they did not grow at all and barely maintained their initial body weight; and when zein, a protein from corn, was the only protein fed, their weight fell off (Fig. 20.1). Casein, although it contains no glycine, is therefore a "complete" or adequate protein; gliadin, which contains no lysine, and zein, which has neither glycine, lysine, threonine, nor tryptophane, are deficient or inadequate ones. When these experiments were carried out it was assumed that the rat either had no need for glycine or that it could synthesize it for itself; later studies showed that the latter was the case, and that rats can synthesize this amino acid at a rate commensurate with their metabolic needs. But they cannot synthesize lysine and tryptophane, both of which are necessary to their growth, and, in the case of tryptophane, necessary even to their maintenance. These facts have been confirmed by other experiments, in which "deficient" proteins have been fed but adequate growth made possible by the addition of the missing amino acid, or acids, and by those in which the diet has included, in addition to carbohydrate, fat and vitamins, mixtures of known, purified amino acids.

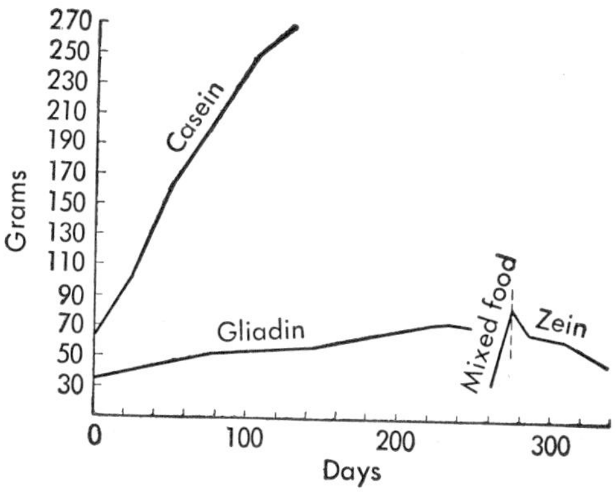

FIGURE 20.1 Curves of growth on foods containing a single protein. (Redrawn from L. B. Mendel.)

Typical growth curve of rats fed on diets containing a single protein. On casein (lacking glycocoll) satisfactory growth is obtained; on gliadin (deficient in lysine), little more than maintenance of body weight is possible; on zein (lacking lysine, glycocoll and tryptophane), even maintenance of body weight is impossible.

*Indispensable amino acids:* From feeding experiments such as these on a number of different kinds of animals it has been possible to determine the essential, or indispensable amino acids, which must be furnished by the protein of the diet to maintain the protoplasmic architecture of the body or to add to it. For the rat these are:

| | |
|---|---|
| Lysine | Phenylalanine |
| Valine | Leucine |
| Tryptophane | Isoleucine |
| Methionine | Threonine |
| Histidine | Arginine |

Experiments on dogs and humans have shown that their requirements are essentially those of rats; histidine may not be essential to man. Of these amino acids, arginine alone is known to be synthesized by animals, but not at a rate adequate to meet the demands of their bodies.

*Essential minerals:* The diet must also supply, as mineral salts or included in organic compounds, the variety of elements known to be constituents of protoplasm (see p. 16), of the body fluids, the skeletal structures and other products of cellular activity. Among these elements may be mentioned particularly calcium and phosphorus as the principal elements of cartilage, bone, dentine and enamel; sulphur, a component of the keratin of the integument and its derivatives, such as horns, feathers, hairs and claws; iron, included in the molecules of hemoglobin and the "iron enzymes"; and iodine, a constituent of the thyroxine, in the secretion from the thyroid gland (see p. 39). Other elements in combination as acids, bases or salts in solution in the body fluids determine the acidity or alkalinity of these fluids or, as buffers, serve to regulate their pH, maintain osmotic equilibrium within the body, influence the irritability, conductivity and other responses of cells and tissues, and contribute in many other ways to the functioning of the organism as a whole. Some of them are constantly being removed from the body in its excreta, and these must be replaced from ingested or imbibed materials.

### The energy requirements

***Methods of determination:*** The energy requirements of an organism can be determined from measurements of its energy exchange. These can be made either directly, as Rubner first made them (see pp. 5–6), by measuring the amount of heat given off in a given period of time, or indirectly by measuring the $O_2$–$CO_2$ exchange, and the $N_2$ content of the urine. Both methods of calorimetry have been widely used in biological experimentation with animals and plants of many different kinds. Heat production in the animal body varies with the degree of its activity; heat loss varies with the external temperature and with the amount of surface exposed to the external environment, as Rubner was able to show in his early experiments on the energy exchange of dogs, when he proved among other things that the energy lost as heat from the body surface was proportional to the body area. The conservation of body heat is a matter of considerable importance to homoiothermic animals living in a lower external temperature, for any considerable heat loss can only be compensated by a speeding up of heat-producing metabolic reactions. Among the birds and mammals there are a number of means for conserving body heat in addition to feathers, fur and, in the case of man, clothing and heated houses. In the cold, animals tend to huddle together; birds tuck their bills beneath their wings, and dogs and cats curl round so that their noses are close to their sides, drawing into their lungs air warmed by their bodies and so reducing heat loss from the pulmonary epithelium. If the heat loss is extreme the muscles respond by contracting, the result of the series of chemical reactions through which heat is evolved; this response of the skeletal muscles results in "shivering," that of the smooth muscles of the integument, in "goose flesh."

***Basal energy requirements; basal metabolism:*** The basal energy requirements of an organism are obtained by measuring, either by direct or indirect calorimetry, the heat loss when the body activity is reduced to a minimum. But even under conditions of external inactivity and of fasting, so that minimum energy is expended in movement or in the processes of digestion, some heat is given off, representing the energy expenditure of such bodily processes as maintenance of muscle tone,* circulation of the blood, ciliary movement and other kinds of cellular metabolism, including the maintenance of integrity of the plasma membranes.

This expenditure of energy is known as the basal metabolic rate, or basal metabolism. In the words of F. G. Benedict (1870–    ), one of the earliest and foremost American workers on animal, and particularly human, nutrition, "the basal metabolism of an individual is a function, first, of the total mass of active protoplasmic tissue, and, second, of the stimulus to cellular activity existing at the time that the measurement of the metabolism was made," and, further, "perhaps the most striking factors causing variations in the stimulus to cellular activity are age, sleep, prolonged fasting, character of the diet and the after effect of severe muscular work." Variations in the basal metabolic rate, as expressed by the stimulus to cellular activity, in man and other mammals tested may be the consequence also of certain pathological conditions, such as fever, increased or decreased activity of the thyroid gland and certain

---

* That every living, functioning muscle is in a permanent state of slight contraction, or tension, is evidenced by the fact that, when cut, such a muscle gapes open.

blood diseases. In man, it has been found also to vary with the sex as well as the age of the individual, being on the average somewhat higher in children than in adults and in men than in women.

**Differences in energy requirements with age and activity:** The energy requirements for man under different conditions of activity have also been determined by calorimetry. Since these will vary with the total mass of active protoplasmic tissue as well as with the work performed by the muscles, they are usually expressed in terms of unit weight, that is per pound or per kilogram, for unit time, usually taken as one hour. From these values, the total number of calories, or heat equivalents of the requisite energy, can be calculated for individuals of different weight and for any period of time (Table XIII). For human beings, the requirement is usually calculated for a twenty-four-hour period, and the average adult requirement based upon a man of 70 kilograms (175 lbs.) weight. The daily energy requirements for human beings of different ages, different sexes and different activities are given below, from the ideal dietary standards for such individuals set up by the United States Department of Agriculture.

TABLE XIII

Human Calorie Requirements at Different Ages and with Different Occupations

| | |
|---|---|
| Child under 4 years | 1200 Cal. |
| Boy 4–6 years / Girl 4–7 years | 1500 Cal. |
| Boy 7–8 years / Girl 8–10 years | 2100 Cal. |
| Boy 9–10 years / Girl 11–13 years | 2400 Cal. |
| Moderately active woman / Boy 11–12 years / Girl over 13 | 2500 Cal. |
| Very active woman / Active boy 13–15 years | 3000 Cal. |
| Active boy over 15 years | 3000–4000 Cal. |
| Moderately active man | 3000 Cal. |
| Very active man | 4500 Cal. |

**Sources of energy:** Consideration of the comparative heats of combustion of carbohydrates, fats and proteins (see p. 394) would suggest that the most economical diet to meet these energy needs would be one composed largely of fats, once the protein and mineral requirements of the organism were met, since the average heat of combustion of fat outside the body is over twice that of carbohydrate and nearly twice that of protein. But feeding experiments have shown that the digestive and metabolic changes that food materials are known to undergo in the body are of even greater importance than their theoretical energy and material value to the organism. When experimental animals are fed a diet adequate in protein and high in fat, they develop a condition known as acidosis, or one in which the alkali reserves of the blood and tissues are depleted and the acid-base equilibrium of the body disturbed. This is due to accumulation in the body of products intermediate in the catabolic metabolism of the fatty acids split off from the fat molecule in its digestion by lipase. The oxidation of one of these metabolites, acetoacetic acid ($CH_3$-$COCH_2COOH$) is known to be incomplete when the diet contains insufficient carbohydrate, presumably because its complete combustion in the body takes place only when the combustion of carbohydrate, or a carbohydrate derivative, is proceeding simultaneously.

Feeding experiments have also shown the inadequacy of diets in which carbohydrate is used as the sole source of energy. Rats fed adequate protein and carbohydrate exclusively grew more slowly than their litter mates fed a mixed diet of protein, fat and carbohydrate and moreover developed an integumentary defect, apparent in the excessive scaliness of the skins of their tails and hind legs. These effects are believed to be due to the absence of certain fatty acids that cannot be synthesized in the body, apparently of any vertebrate, as well as to that of the so-called fat-soluble vitamins. The synthesis of stearic, palmitic and oleic acids from carbohydrate seems to proceed readily in the animal body, but not that of highly unsaturated fatty acids such as linoleic acid, $C_{18}H_{32}O_2$ in which the 6th and 7th, and 11th and 12th carbon atoms in the chain of 18 are united by double bonds, or linolenic, $C_{18}H_{30}O_2$, in which there are double bonds between the 4th and 5th, the 7th and 8th, and the 11th and 12th carbon atoms in the chain. These acids, first isolated from linseed oil from which they derive their name, appear to be essential to animal nutrition, in the same sense that the indispensable amino acids are essential, in that they fill a metabolic requirement and either are not synthesized in the body, or are synthesized so slowly that they do not meet its needs. Like the essential amino acids they seem to be readily synthesized by plants, for they have been extracted from the fats of a number of plants.

**Specific dynamic action of foodstuffs:** Rubner discovered, in his feeding experiments, that the energy given off by an animal was always greater than expected, if the diet consisted exclusively of either protein or carbohydrate or fat. That is, if a quantity of protein with a heat equivalent of 100 Calories were fed, the energy of its metabolism measured calorimetrically was equal to 130 Calories. Similarly if fat or carbohydrate equivalent to 100 Calories were ingested, the metabolic energy output was equal to 113 Calories and 103 Calories respectively. These figures are probably too high, but it is well established that the mere ingestion of food, without any accompanying physical exertion, may cause the heat production of the body to rise as much as 30 per cent above its basal level. This effect is known as the Specific Dynamic Action of the foodstuffs, but it is not yet certain to what conditions it is to be attributed. It is possible that the specific dynamic action of protein represents the energy of the deamination of the amino acid molecules, and the formation of urea which takes place in the liver (pp. 316–317); that of carbohydrate, the energy of the reactions occurring in the condensation of glucose to glycogen, a conversion that also takes place to a great extent in the liver, but in other tissues as well; while that of fat may be attributable to the increased concentration of oxidizable material. But no one of these effects is independent of the other, and it is most likely that the dynamic effect of each kind of foodstuff depends on the amount of the other two that are simultaneously being metabolized. For man and other mammals that have been tested, and presumably for all other animals, the most suitable diet is a mixed one, including protein, fat and carbohydrate. Nutritionists are in general agreement that 70–75 grams of protein a day (approximately equivalent to 1 gram of protein per kilogram of body weight) is an adequate allowance for an adult human; this, if all of it is oxidized in the body, will provide him with something more than 300 Calories. The remaining energy must be furnished by the carbohydrate and fat content of his food, which will vary with his habitual amount of activity. For a grown man of average activity 80–90 grams of fat per day and 400–500 grams of carbohydrate are the accepted allowances. These quantities of protein, fat and carbohydrate will provide him with the following energy equivalents:

Energy equivalent of protein
    4.75 Cals. $\times$ 70–75 gms. 330–350 Cals.
Energy equivalent of fat
    9.5 Cals. $\times$ 80–90 gms. 725–815 Cals.
Energy equivalent of carbohydrate
    4.1 Cals. $\times$ 400–500 gms. 1600–2000 Cals.
    Total Calories 2655–3165

**The value of mixed diets:** But it is not only the quantity of the food, but also its quality, that is important in the animal diet. The protein must supply a sufficient quantity of all the essential amino acids, and the daily ideal allowance was set at 70–75 grams in order to insure that, on a diet of mixed protein, from both animal and vegetable sources, an adequate amount of each of the essential amino acids would be obtained. In general, plant proteins are incomplete ones and if they are the sole source of protein in the diet, a wide enough variety must be eaten to include all the essential amino acids. On the other hand, eggs, fish, meat and milk all provide complete proteins; for the adult human dietary, it is recommended that 50 grams of the daily allowance be of animal origin. But the quality of the fat and carbohydrate is no less important, for the former must provide those fatty acids that are necessary to the body and that it cannot make for itself, and the latter, being largely of vegetable origin, not only readily oxidizable compounds, but also the roughage, or bulk, which contributes to the more efficient functioning of the intestine. The mass of undigested and undigestible cellulose that makes up a large part of vegetable matter passes unchanged along the digestive tract, distending its walls and so stimulating them to the segmenting and pendular movements that are effective in mixing the digestive enzymes with the food mass. And with each are associated some of the vitamins, to which dietary essentials increasing importance has been attached since the beginning of the century.

## Development of the vitamin concept

The development of the concept that there are certain dietary requirements for both plants and animals outside of the general categories of protein, fat and carbohydrate, has progressed through the studies of nutritionists and biochemists in many countries for at least the past fifty years. These requirements are met by certain compounds, once called "accessory food substances," which are necessary to the growth and healthy maintenance of organisms; in their absence, or with an inadequate supply of them, characteristic structural and metabolic deficiencies arise. The chemical nature of a number of these compounds is now known; at least 16 of them have been obtained in pure crystalline form and some of them have been synthesized in the laboratory and the role that they play in the functioning of the body determined.

## The early recognition of the relationship between diets deficient in certain kinds of food and three of the "deficiency diseases"

At least three of the "deficiency diseases," as they are manifested in man, have been known far longer than their cause and cure. The symptoms of beri-beri, a disease more prevalent in the Orient than in the Western hemisphere, are related to changes in the peripheral nerves bringing about postural and behavior defects, and ultimately paralysis and wasting of the tissues. It was known in China as early as 2600 B.C. Scurvy, a disease characterized by small hemorrhages throughout the body and under the skin, particularly in the gums and the joints, soreness and pain in those regions, and general weakening of the body, afflicted the Crusaders in the thirteenth century, and was, until the early eighteenth century, a scourge for sailors, explorers and other travellers on journeys where the supply of fresh foods was limited. Rickets, manifested by bowlegs, knock-knees, swollen joints and weak and distorted limbs, was first described in detail in 1630 by an English physician, Francis Glisson (1597–1677), but the symptoms must have been known long before that.

It was first recognized in relation to scurvy that the addition of some natural foods to the diet prevented the occurrence of the disease. When Jacques Cartier made his second voyage to Newfoundland in 1535, 100 out of his crew of 103 sickened from scurvy and 25 died. One of the sailors learned that the Indians cured it by administering an infusion of the needles of spruce trees, and spruce boughs were therefore gathered, the brew made and given to the sick sailors. According to contemporary records "if all the doctors of Montpellier and Louvain had been there with all the drugs of Alexandria, they would not have done so much in a year as that tree did in six days." Other such empirical cures were reported by mariners who returned from long voyages, and from 1600 onward, sailors on the East India Company's vessels were provided with fresh fruits, principally oranges and lemons. The early colonists of North America learned to prevent scurvy by eating fruits and vegetables. When returning explorers introduced the potato into Europe, where it became a common article of diet, scurvy became much less prevalent there than before. In 1720 an Austrian army doctor reported that three or four ounces of orange or lime juice "will cure this dreadful disease without other help."

Shortly afterwards the first experimental study of the disease was made by an English naval officer, Captain Lind, who, in a Treatise on Scurvy, published in 1757, reported his treatment of twelve patients, each with an apparently equally advanced case of the disease. Two of these patients were each given a quart of cider a day; two were given twenty-five drops of elixir of vitriol (aromatic sulphuric acid) three times a day; two were given two spoonfuls of vinegar three times a day; two drank half a pint, or less, of sea water each day; two were given an elaborate concoction of garlic, mustard seed, Peruvian balsam, radish and myrrh, which they washed down with barley water; and two were given two oranges and one lemon every day. The experiment went on for six days, at the end of which one of the men given the citrus fruits was able to take his regular tour of ship's duty and the other was so much improved that he could act as nurse to the remaining patients, none of whom showed any remission of his symptoms.

Explorers and navigators took advantage of this information, and Captain Cook, on his voyage around the world in 1772–1775, made his men eat both fresh meat and fresh vegetables and also, against their protests, a pound of sauerkraut twice a week, or "oftener when it was thought necessary." In 1776 Cook reported to the Royal Society the methods he had taken "for preserving the health of the crew of His Majesty's ship the Resolution during her late voyage around the world." But it was not until 1804 that an enforced ration of lemon juice was instituted in the British Navy, and less than one hundred years ago (1865) that the same ration was made compulsory for men of the Merchant Marine. With the general introduction of an allowance of citrus fruits, or their juices, for humans who for one reason or another had to live on a diet composed largely of dried, salted and pickled foods, the incidence of scurvy was greatly reduced, but by no means eliminated from the population in general. Nor was there until recently any knowledge of the principle in those fruits active in the prevention of the disease, or the way in which it exerted its effect.

The history of the cure and prevention of rickets has much the same course. Although the malformations of rickets were well known in the seventeenth century, a cause for their development was not found until late in the nineteenth century. In 1890, an English physician, A. T. Palm, pointed out that the disease was most prevalent in those regions where there was little sunshine—in northern countries, where the winter is long and the days are short, in cities, where what sunlight there is is cut off by buildings, and in factory districts where smoke makes a screen between the sun and the earth—and of low incidence in open regions of sunny climates. He showed by examination of mummies that the ancient Egyptians had been virtually free of the disease, and he advocated the use of sunshine as a therapeutic measure for its symptoms. Some twenty years later, it was shown experimentally that the mineral content and so the firmness of the bones of puppies increased if they were exposed to sunlight.

The first steps toward a real understanding of the nature of these diseases and the development of preventive, rather than palliative or curative, measures for them came from observations on beri-beri in man and diseases with similar symptoms in animals. In 1882, a Japanese naval doctor, Baron Takaki, found that beri-beri did not appear among sailors if barley were substituted wholly or in large measure for the customary rice of their diet, and if it was augmented by an additional allowance of meat, fish and fresh vegetables. So, like scurvy, beri-beri was recognized as a disease that could be prevented and improved by a change in diet and particularly one that included fresh foods.

## Experimental production of beri-beri in fowls and of scurvy in guinea pigs

The next step in the development of the vitamin concept was, like many another scientific discovery, more or less of an accident. It was made by Christian Eijkman (1858–1930), a doctor sent by the Dutch government to study the disease in its East Indian colonies, who happened to observe that the chickens that ate little but the rice grains dropped around the kitchens and dining places developed the same polyneuritic and paralytic symptoms as humans suffering from beri-beri, while those that ate unmilled, or unpolished, rice from the fields did not show them at all. He then carried out some experiments, feeding some hens unmilled rice, with the husks still on; some, milled rice, from which the husks had been removed; and some, milled rice together with the removed husks. He found that without exception the addition of the rice husks to the fowls' diet prevented the pathological condition from appearing. Further, he tried to determine what this substance in the rice husks was, and found that it could be extracted from them by water and by alcohol, and that in solution in either case it was dialysable, that is, that it would pass through a membrane which held back particles of colloidal dimensions.

These findings of Eijkman's marked a turning point in the study of beri-beri, and indeed of all diseases, which, like it, are caused by dietary deficiency. Productive study of the nature, cause and cure of any disease can be made only if that disease can be experimentally produced in laboratory animals, so that it may be watched from its initial stages, often before any of the obvious symptoms appear, and in a large number of cases. The advantage of being able to sacrifice the animals during the course of the disease to observe any internal changes that may have taken place are obvious, as are those of testing out various therapeutic agents whose effects may be entirely speculative. But at the time that Eijkman was making his experiments upon chickens and other domestic fowls, Pasteur's influence was dominant in the scientific world, and his germ theory of disease the prevailing one. Takaki had thought that it was the addition of protein to the diet of Japanese sailors that had protected them from beri-beri and cured them when they had it; Eijkman thought that in the extract he had made from the husks of rice there was a bactericidal agent that destroyed the germs that had invaded the bodies of the diseased fowls. But only a few years later, in 1902, one of Eijkman's fellow-workers suggested that the cause of beri-beri lay, not in an infection of the nervous system, but in the absence of material needed by the nervous tissue for its effective functioning.

As chance had led Eijkman to the recognition of the causal relationship between a diet of milled rice and polyneuritis in chickens, which opened the way to the experimental production of it in birds, so chance favored two Norwegian scientists, A. Holst and T. Frölich, in the experimental production of scurvy. In 1907 they attempted to induce beri-beri in guinea pigs so that they might study it, for it was a disease fairly common among Norwegian sailors. But the guinea pigs, fed on a diet largely of refined, milled cereals and without "greens," did not develop beri-beri but instead, symptoms which Holst and Frölich recognized as those of human scurvy. So scurvy in mammals as well as beri-beri in fowls could be produced at will in the laboratory, and since the relationship between both these diseases and the absence from the diet of foods of certain kinds was well established, experimental work on their course and the nature of the substances protecting the organism against them could proceed.

Further studies of the incidence of rickets had by this time revealed the fact that the disease was practically unknown among the Eskimos, although there were long periods in the year when the regions in which they lived were virtually sunless. It was obvious, then, that sunlight could not be the only factor in its prevention. The diet of the Eskimos, far higher in fish and fish-oils than that of most peoples, offered a possible explanation, and suggested that, like beri-beri and scurvy, rickets might be related to a dietary deficiency.

### The experimental demonstration of the inadequacy of purified synthetic diets

During this period too, nutritional experiments with synthetic diets of purified proteins, carbohydrates, fats and mineral salts were being carried on in many laboratories. Workers from various countries were reporting the same results—that animals fed these purified diets did not grow and thrive as did others fed upon natural foods or living in the wild. Gradually evidence accumulated that additions of small amounts of milk, or egg yolk or even bread to the synthetic diet filled some want in the metabolic processes, and resulted in normal vitality and growth.

In 1906, the English biochemist, Sir Frederick Gowland Hopkins (1861–1947), summarized these results by saying, "No animal can live on a mixture of pure protein, fat and carbohydrate, and even when the necessary inorganic material is carefully supplied the animal still cannot flourish. The animal body is adjusted to live either upon plant tissues or the tissues of other animals, and these contain countless substances other than the proteins, carbohydrates and fats. Physiological evolution, I believe, has made some of these well-nigh as essential as are the basal constituents of the diet."

In 1912 Hopkins substantiated the first part of this statement in a report of the carefully controlled and quantitative experiments carried out in his laboratory in Cambridge. In these experiments, young rats were fed a standard diet of purified substances—starch, cane sugar, lard, casein, and mineral salts obtained from the ash of oats and dog biscuits. With highly purified casein, the animals failed to grow; with a cruder, commercial preparation, they did better, but still failed to keep pace with their litter mates, or other rats of the same age and strain, whose diet included fresh milk. But when the rats on the synthetic diet were given as little as 3 cc. of fresh milk a day, their gain in weight and general good health paralleled that of the controls.

**Extraction of an "active principle" from rice husks**

At this time a Polish biochemist, Casimir Funk (1884–    ), succeeded in extracting, first from rice husks and later from yeast, a substance that in 6–12 hours relieved the symptoms of acute polyneuritis induced in pigeons by a prolonged diet of husked grain. Funk determined some of the chemical characteristics of the substance, and found, among other things, that it contained nitrogen and that it was effective in very small doses, a quantity containing as little as 4 mg. of nitrogen producing spectacular cures in pigeons showing symptoms of advanced polyneuritis.

**The "vitamine" hypothesis of Casimir Funk:** But even more important than his chemical extraction was Funk's comprehension of the evidence that had accumulated about the three diseases suspected of being related to an incomplete or faulty diet. In 1912 he wrote: "The diseases mentioned above present certain general characters which justify their inclusion in one group, called deficiency diseases. They were considered for years either as intoxication by food or as infectious diseases, and twenty years of experimental work were necessary to show that diseases occur which are caused by deficiency of some essential substance in the food." From the chemical nature of the active substance that he had extracted from rice polishings, he postulated that these "essential substances" were all nitrogen-containing amines, and since they were necessary to life, gave them the names of "vitamines." Later, when other similarly essential substances were chemically identified, and found not to be amines, the terminal *e* was dropped to avoid misconception, and the spelling "vitamin" substituted. But the concept of deficiency diseases and the vitamin hypothesis that Funk enunciated have stimulated some of the most fruitful biological research of this century, and have led not only to theoretical conclusions of great importance and promise but to practical applications distinctly advantageous to mankind.

**"Fat-Soluble A" and "Water-Soluble B" vitamins:** Funk's vitamin hypothesis expressed the two current lines of evidence and thought in relation to the effect of diet upon the animal. It suggested that there were certain active principles included in natural foods that on the one hand promoted growth and on the other protected the animal against such diseases as beri-beri, scurvy and rickets or cured them if such protection had been lacking. Both milk and egg yolk seemed equally to contain the growth-promoting substance, while the evidence showed that at least two different substances were concerned in the deficiency diseases. The question naturally arose as to whether there was more than one growth-promoting vitamin, and it was directly answered in 1913 and 1915 by the experiments of three American scientists, E. V. McCollum (1879–    ), T. B.

Osborne (1859-1929) and L. B. Mendel (1872– ). Rats fed on synthetic diets of protein, starch, mineral salts and crude lactose showed adequate growth only if butter fat or egg-yolk extract were added; the addition of lard or of vegetable oils did not make up the deficiency. Another set of rats fed protein mineral salts and butter fat grew and exhibited no symptoms of polyneuritis if wheat or the aqueous or alcoholic extract of wheat germ, or milk, or egg yolk, or crude casein, or crude lactose (milk sugar) were added, but did not grow and showed signs of polyneuritis if the synthetic diet were augmented only by polished rice or highly purified casein or lactose. It was therefore concluded that there were two growth factors, one soluble in fat and present in butter fat and egg yolk, and the other soluble in water and present in wheat germ, milk, egg yolk, crude lactose and casein. The first of these was called "Fat-Soluble A" and the second "Water-Soluble B"; and later Vitamin A and Vitamin B. While vitamins are still conveniently classified as water or fat soluble, the investigations in the years following this initial separation of Vitamin A and Vitamin B have led to the realization that neither of these was a single substance, but a complex of several. Moreover, as analyses of these complexes have progressed and as new vitamins, or vitamin-like substances, have been discovered, the active compounds have been given distinctive chemical names, which are coming more and more into general use to replace the old alphabetical ones. The B complex, for example, is now believed to contain some 10 or more vitamins, some of which, like Vitamin $B_1$, or thiamine, have been chemically identified and synthesized in vitro, although the molecular structure of others has not yet been determined, nor indeed has a general need for them yet been finally established.

## *Vitamins and avitaminoses*

At present there are more than forty substances that are credited with the properties of vitamins, in that their deficiency or absence from the diet results in symptoms to which the general name avitaminosis has been given, first used by Funk to describe such diseases as beri-beri in man and polyneuritis in fowls. It has been recognized since the early days of vitamin study that there are degrees of avitaminosis, and while prolonged deprivation or deficiency of a vitamin may lead to symptoms associated with a particular tissue and a specific disease, and sometimes one that is fatal, a shorter period of deprivation or a lesser deficiency may result in a sub-acute or subclinical condition manifested by lowered efficiency of bodily functioning and minor, and more generalized, symptoms. The fat-soluble vitamins include the A group, all of which are derivatives of the carotene pigments; the D group, derivatives of certain sterols; the E group, all compounds containing a long chain of carbon atoms attached to two united benzene rings, the napthalene configuration; and the K group, which include a number of known and unknown substances producing similar effects in the body. The water-soluble vitamins include, in addition to those of the B complex or B family, Vitamin C, or ascorbic acid; Vitamin H, or biotin; Vitamin P, or citrin; and at least two other compounds, choline and para-aminobenzoic acid, which have always been known by their chemical names and never given an identifying letter.

## The biological properties of the six vitamins known to be required by man

Of the forty or more vitamins, or vitamin-like substances known, only six are apt to be deficient in the diet of humans. These six are Vitamin A (i.e., those of the A group); thiamine, nicotinic acid, or niacin, and riboflavin of the B group; ascorbic acid (Vitamin C); and Vitamin D, or those of the D group.

***The A group:*** Deficiency of the A group of vitamins is associated with "night blindness," or inability to discriminate between objects in dim light, and the keratinization and consequent drying of certain epithelia which are ordinarily moist, particularly those of the eyes, and of the respiratory, digestive, and genito-urinary tracts, making those regions more susceptible to infection by micro-organisms. When the conjunctiva of the eyes is keratinized, they become hemorrhagic, crusted and infected, a combination of symptoms known as xeropthalmia, the specific disease associated with this specific avitaminosis which may lead to blindness (Fig. 20.2). Not only is man sensitive to deficiency or lack of Vitamin A, but so also are all other animals that have been tested. It is known to be related to the carotinoid pigments synthesized by plants, representing a colorless part of their molecules. The carotene in plant chloroplasts acts as a provitamin, for within the animal body the carotene molecule can be split and the vitamin derived from it. Except for its connection with the re-formation of visual purple in the retina of the eye (see p. 375), in which it is known to be involved in terrestrial animals, and in some fishes, nothing definite is yet known about the role that it plays in metabolism. It can be stored in comparatively large amounts in the body, especially in the liver where in man and rats it may accumulate to the extent of 10–20 mg. per 100 grams of tissue. For this reason xerophthalmia and other symptoms of deficiency can only be produced after a considerable length of time on a Vitamin A deficient diet.

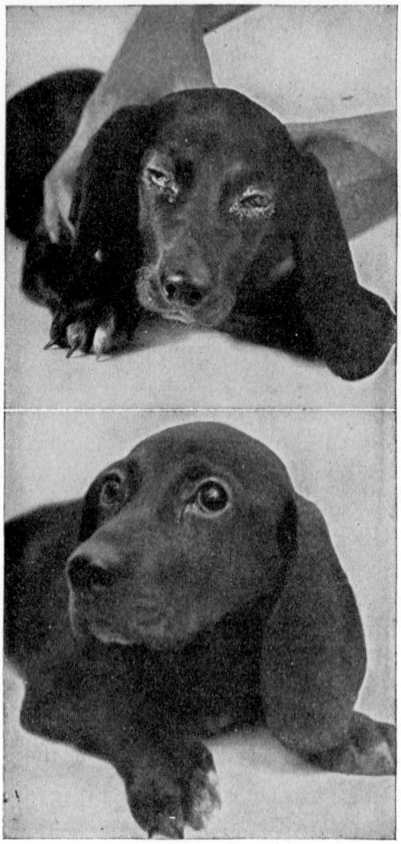

Fish livers are especially good sources of the vitamin; the livers of halibuts have been found to contain as much as 1 per cent by weight. In addition to animal livers, butter, cheese, milk and the yolks of eggs contain comparatively large amounts of it. But the animal must derive the vitamin ultimately from plants, from the carotinoid pigments associated with chlorophyll in their chloroplasts and from those that are concentrated in the storage regions of certain plants, like the roots of carrots, the tubers of sweet potatoes and the fruits of apricots, all of which provide the provitamin, or vitamin precursor, which the animal can apparently readily convert to the vitamin itself.

*The B group.* THIAMINE: Thiamine is now known to be the active principle in the husks of rice and other grains that prevents beriberi in man and polyneuritis in birds and other animals, and may cure some cases of it. Birds appear to be especially sensitive to its deficiency, but all animals that have been tested require it, showing certain defects in the functioning of their nervous and circulatory systems if deprived of an adequate supply. The nervous defects may lead ultimately to paralysis; in pigeons this is apparent first in the neck muscles, for the head is drawn back and held in a characteristic way (Fig. 20.3). The vascular symptoms are primarily slowing of the heart beat or bradycardia (Greek, bradys = slow + cardia = heart); additionally, thiamine deficiency results in loss of appetite and a general loss of

FIGURE 20.2 Xerophthalmia in a puppy due to diet deficient in Vitamin A. Full recovery after the administration of Vitamin A is shown in the lower picture. (From Bogert, *Nutrition and Physical Fitness*, 5th edition, published by the W. B. Saunders Company. Copyright 1949. Photograph reproduced by permission of Dr. H. Steenbock.)

tone of the gastro-intestinal tract. Both the chemical structure of thiamine and its role in the bodily processes are known; it was first synthesized in vitro by an American biochemist, R. R. Williams (1886– ) in 1936. Chemically it consists of a nitrogen-containing compound, an aminopyrimidine linked to a sulphur-containing one, thiazol. In the body it acts as a coenzyme, furnishing the prosthetic group for the enzyme carboxylase that catalyzes the degradation of pyruvic acid to acetaldehyde (Fig. 17.1).

$$\underset{\text{pyruvic acid}}{CH_3COCOOH} \underset{-CO_2}{\overset{\text{Carboxylase}}{\rightleftarrows}} \underset{\text{acetaldehyde.}}{CH_3CHO}$$

Pyruvic acid is an intermediate compound in the oxidation of carbohydrate; in the absence of sufficient thiamine, this metabolite is present in the blood at 2–5 times its normal concentration and increases to a similar extent in the other body fluids, reflecting its accumulation in the tissues. Administration of thiamine results in an almost immediate lowering of the concentration of pyruvates, the salts of pyruvic acid, to their normal level in the blood. These facts show that in the absence of thiamine, the succession of energy-releasing reactions through which hexose is converted to carbon dioxide and water is checked, or blocked, between pyruvic acid and acetaldehyde, and the usual pattern of carbohydrate metabolism upset. That the paralysis following extended thiamine deficiency is the result of this derangement of metabolism, and not directly of nerve degeneration, is indicated by the rapid recovery of motility after thiamine injections; pigeons in advanced stages of polyneuritic paralysis have been known to raise their heads fifteen minutes after a thiamine injection, and to appear completely normal within three hours, periods far too short for the complete regeneration of nerves.

Unlike Vitamin A, thiamine is not stored in the animal body in any appreciable amount and appears regularly in the excretion products. Therefore the animal cannot build up reserves of it, but must constantly replace it from its diet. It is synthesized by plants, and as Eijkman and others of the early workers on the anti-beri-beri factor found out, is stored by grains especially in the germ, or embryo, of their seeds and in the outer seed coats. It is also present, but in more limited amounts, in the leaves and storage regions of all plants tested; yeast can synthesize it, and so can many of the other fungi. Some fungi can synthesize one or the other part of the molecule, and if provided in the one case, with the thiazole portion, and in the other with the pyrimidine por-

FIGURE 20.3 Polyneuritis (avian beri-beri) in pigeons. (From Bogert, *Nutrition and Physical Fitness*, 5th edition, published by the W. B. Saunders Company. Copyright 1949.)

a. Characteristic attitude of a pigeon with polyneuritis after three weeks' feeding on a diet of polished rice.

b. The same pigeon three hours after feeding on a diet high in Vitamin B (rice polishings, yeast, etc.). Recovery seemed complete in twelve hours.

tion, can complete the structure of the thiamine molecule, in the absence of which they fail to grow at the standard rate. The bacteria in the rumen of such animals as cows and sheep also can synthesize it, so that it is impossible to obtain a thiamine deficiency in these animals by deficient diet alone.

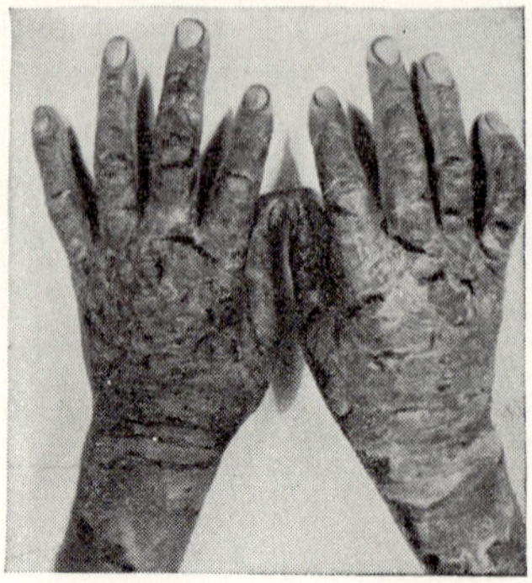

FIGURE 20.4 Pellagra in man. (From Bogert, *Nutrition and Physical Fitness*, 5th edition, published by the W. B. Saunders Company. Copyright 1949. Photograph reproduced by permission of Dr. Tom Spies.)

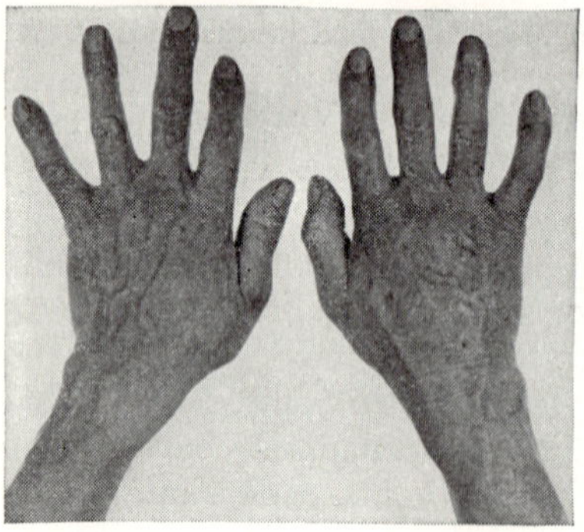

a. Hands of a pellagra patient.
b. Hands of the same patient after two weeks' diet rich in B vitamins, especially niacin.

NICOTINIC ACID (NIACIN): Deficiency in nicotinic acid (niacin) results in pellagra in man and in "black-tongue" in dogs. Pellagra, characterized particularly by special kinds of skin lesions (Fig. 20.4), has been generally known in undernourished populations but was first described in the population of southern Europe following the Napoleonic wars. About 1907 it was recognized as a disease that was especially prevalent in the mill towns in the southern part of the United States, but it was not known whether it was one of bacterial origin, spread by the unsanitary conditions and crowding of people in the industrial areas, or one of inadequate nutrition. Its inclusion among the deficiency diseases is due largely to the work of Dr. Joseph Goldberger (1874–1929) of the United States Public Health Service and his co-workers, who carried on a long and careful series of nutritional experiments, including one on a group of prisoners asked to volunteer to eat, for one year, any diet that Goldberger prescribed, including those he suspected of causing the disease. By these experiments, Goldberger was able to establish its connection with a nutritional deficiency and to relate it to a diet made up largely of corn meal, molasses and pork fat, which is still a usual one among the poorer population of the South.

He found that by adding foods rich in "water-soluble B" pellagra could be prevented and, if it had not gone too far, cured in those suffering from it. Experiments on animals indicated that foods that were rich in the anti-beri-beri vitamin were not always so effective with pellagra, and led him to suspect that "water-soluble B" was not a single vitamin, but at least two. Finally he found that yeast, kept for some time in steam under pressure, lost its anti-beri-beri potency, but was still effective in preventing and relieving the symptoms of pellagra. This was the first step toward the unravelling of the B complex. Ten years later (1937) C. A. Elvehjem (1901–    ) and his fellow workers at the University of Wisconsin showed that canine black-tongue, the counterpart of human pellagra, could be prevented and cured by a compound called nicotinic acid, which is now established as the specific preventive and possible cure for pellagra.

Nicotinic acid appears to be a dietary requirement for men, dogs and pigs, but not for rats, sheep and chicks. It is known to furnish part of the molecule of two coenzymes that are concerned in oxidation-reduction reactions, coenzyme I, or cozymase, and coenzyme II, and in its absence that part of the total respiratory process to which they contribute is defective. In addition to yeast, whole grains, such as wheat and rye, are fairly high in nicotinic acid, and some is found in leafy green vegetables and in milk.

RIBOFLAVIN: Riboflavin is another vitamin of the B complex whose isolation and chemical identification is complete and whose

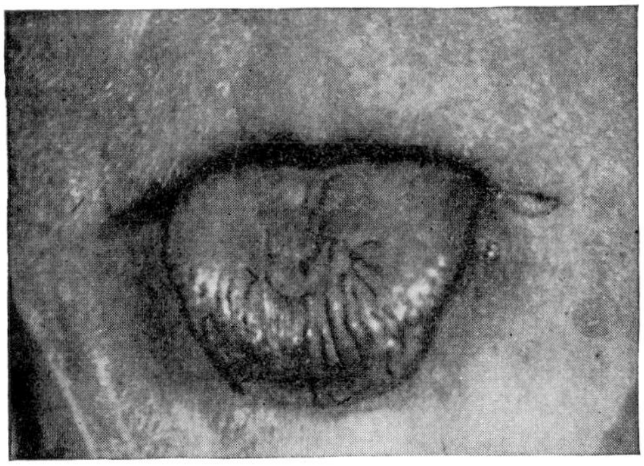

FIGURE 20.5 The effects of riboflavin deficiency, manifested by fissures at the corners of the mouth. (From Major, *Physical Diagnosis*, 3rd edition, published by the W. B. Saunders Company. Copyright 1945.)

role in metabolism is known. There is no recognized disease, like beri-beri or pellagra, that results from its deficiency but there are certain characteristic symptoms of it. These include various skin disorders, soreness of the lips and cracks or fissures at the angles of the mouth, as well as lesions of the eyes (Fig. 20.5). Chemically it is identical with the various yellow compounds, called flavines, that have been obtained from the whey of milk, the whites of eggs, animal livers and various other sources; like them, it is yellow in color with a green fluorescence. It appears to be synthesized in the leaves of plants and is very generally distributed throughout the plant kingdom; it is found, too, in relatively high concentration in eggs, meat and in milk and milk products. It is known to form part of the molecule of several of the respiratory enzymes and so, like thiamine and nicotinic acid, to be essential to the metabolism of carbohydrate. Indeed, all three of these vitamins show a certain family resemblance in their distribution, which appears to be universal, in their growth-promoting effect upon micro-organisms, and in their relation to some phase of oxidative metabolism.

*The C Group:* The compound now known as ascorbic acid has been found to be the active principal in lemon juice and other foods that prevents and relieves scurvy. Its extraction in almost pure form from lemon juice and from fresh cabbage * was accomplished by 1925, and in 1933 two teams of biochemists working independently of each other, one in England and one in Switzerland, succeeded in synthesizing it. It is very widely distributed in plants; although dry seeds contain little of it, when they are moistened and induced to sprout the vitamin appears in some quantity. Its concentration in fruits increases also with their ripening. Green peppers, for example, have been found to contain some 80 mg. per 100 grams of the fruit, while ripened red peppers contain 230 mg. per 100. Although it is established as specific for the cure, and by its absence from the body for the production, of scurvy, its actual contribution to the metabolic processes is not yet known. Guinea pigs are particularly sensitive to its deficiency, and man only slightly less so, although there is a considerable lag, in experimentally induced scurvy, between the time the diet is made ascorbic-acid-free and the appearance of the symptoms, indicating that the vitamin may be stored in the body, if not synthesized to a limited extent by it. It must be synthesized in the bodies of rats and chickens in amounts sufficient for their metabolic needs, for neither animal develops scurvy under the dietary conditions which induce it in guinea pigs. The livers of rats kept on an ascorbic-acid-free diet for extended periods of time have been found to contain appreciable amounts of the vitamin, indicating that that organ may be the region for its storage, if not the site of its synthesis. It has been found also in a variety of actively metabolizing cells, associated with the mitochondria in them, or with the Golgi substance.

* Analyses of sauerkraut have shown that contrary to Captain Cook's therapeutic principles, it contains practically none of the vitamin.

**The D group:** The D vitamins, like those of the A group, are derived from precursors or provitamins in the diet. The efficacy of sunshine and of fish liver oils in the prevention and cure of rickets, the disease of Vitamin D deficiency, was recognized before it

FIGURE 20.6 Bowlegs and knock-knees as the effects of rickets. (From Major, *Physical Diagnosis*, 3rd edition, published by the W. B. Saunders Company. Copyright 1945.)

was included among the avitaminoses. Even after it was recognized as one of them, progress in its study was slow because of the difficulty of producing it experimentally. Rickets is a disease resulting from a disturbance of the mineral metabolism of the body so that the calcification of the growing bones does not take place normally (Figs. 20.6, 20.7). It is particularly related to the available supply of calcium and phosphorus, the two minerals present in greatest proportion in bone, as well as to the mechanism of their deposition in the bony matrix. With adequate amounts and proper proportions of calcium and phosphorus, rickets may not develop even if Vitamin D, or its source, is restricted in the diet or eliminated from it entirely. But when rickets does develop, the extreme symptoms may be curving or bending of the long bones and thickenings at their extremities; X-rays of the body will reveal lesser defects, showing regions at the ends of the bones where calcification is incomplete.

The discovery, in 1924, that the acute symptoms of rickets disappeared in rats whose food had been exposed to ultraviolet radiation was a turning point in the investigation of ways to prevent and cure it. Later it was found that it was the sterol component of the fats of various foods that was converted to the active vitamin on irradiation, and in 1927 ergosterol, a sterol synthesized by the fungus ergot, was established as a provitamin. Not long after, the molecular structure of the vitamin itself was determined; at least four forms of it are now known, and a number of others postulated. While plants provide the provitamins, no significant amounts of the vitamin in any of its forms have been found in plant tissues, although they may be exposed to full sunlight. The oils from fish livers are the richest source of the vitamins as such; although cod liver oil has been very generally used to supply it, halibut liver oil contains a greater quantity per gram, and tuna and rockfish liver oils still larger amounts. The origin of the vitamin in these livers is still unknown (but see p. 126). In man and in other mammals, the skin contains greater amounts of the provitamins than the other tissues; these provitamins are converted to the active vitamin on exposure to sunshine. The conversion of the provitamin to the vitamin is a progressive process, proceeding possibly through several steps before the active compound is reached. In the case of ergosterol, for example, whose conversion to its active form or Vitamin $D_2$ has been especially studied, there are two intermediate and inactive substances formed before the vitamin itself; with longer irradiation, the conversion proceeds irreversibly and the vitamin is changed to a different kind of sterol, which in turn is converted to another form and so on. Some of these products, which succeed the vitamin, may be toxic to the organism, and so active in a different kind of way.

But the way in which the different forms of the D vitamins function in the calcification of bones and of teeth has not yet been established. It has been suggested, by certain experimental data, that the vitamin assists in the absorption of calcium and phosphorus from the intestine, and that it may, in bone, contribute in some way in the conversion of organically bound phosphorus to inorganic.

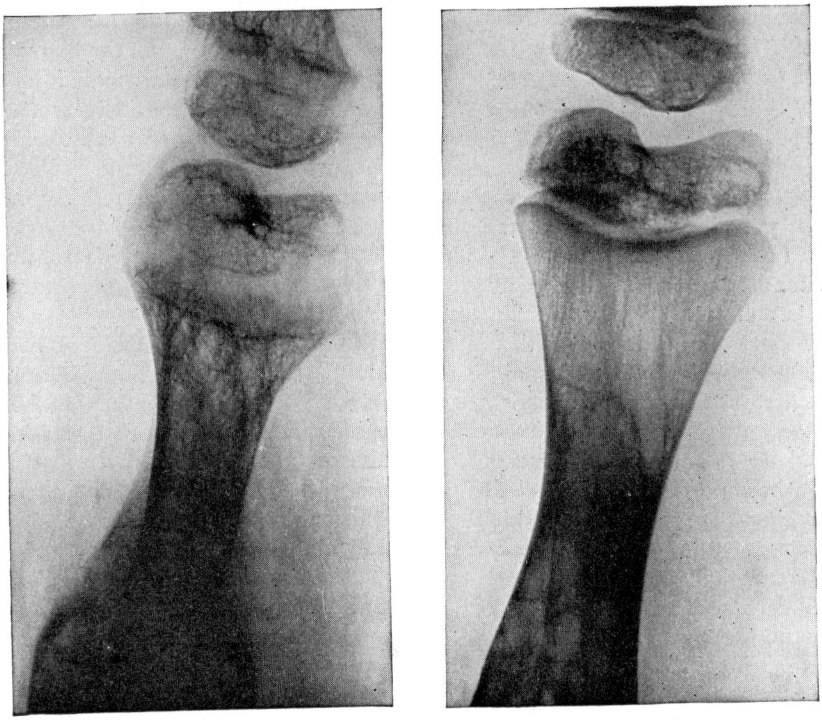

FIGURE 20.7 Deficient calcification of bone in rickets. (From Bogert, *Nutrition and Physical Fitness*, 5th edition, published by the W. B. Saunders Company. Copyright 1949.)

a. X-ray photograph of a joint that shows extreme rachitic changes.

b. The same joint after rapid healing has taken place as the result of large doses of Vitamin D over a period of one month.

### General characters of vitamins

*The active groups in their molecules:* In addition to these six vitamins, which are definitely established as dietary requirements for man, there are several others probably of equal importance to him and many others that are known to be required by other animals and by plants. Some of these, such as choline, were known chemically as tissue constituents long before any direct nutritional value was attributed to them. As work with vitamins is progressing, it is becoming increasingly clearer that they are substances not so much accessory to the metabolic machinery as integral parts of it, as choline and other such vitamin-like substances are known to be. All the fat-soluble vitamins, and at least nicotinic and ascorbic acids among those that are water soluble, owe their potency to certain atomic configurations in their molecules. In the A vitamins, it is the carbon ring to which a carbon chain (R) is attached at the free bond; in

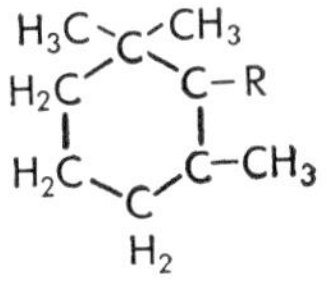

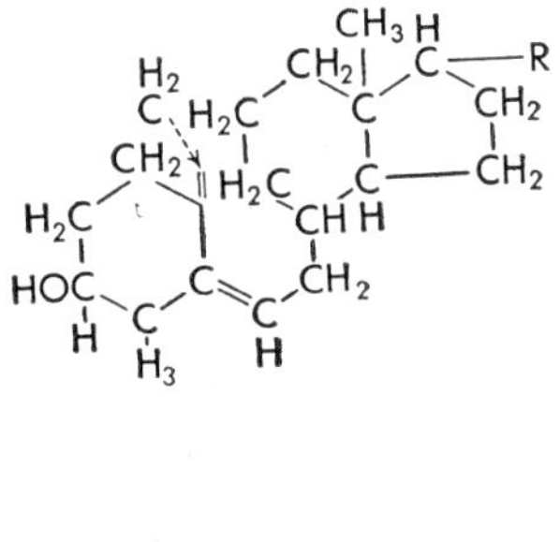

the D group it is the combination of carbon rings, characteristic of all sterols, known as the steroid configuration to which a carbon chain is attached. In either case, the carbon chains may vary without affecting the vitamin effect of the compound.

***The inhibition of vitamin activity; antivitamins:*** But close structural resemblance between a vitamin and another compound without its potency, the analog of the vitamin, may result in a competitive inhibition of the vitamin's effect. The effect of sulfanilamide upon bacteria, in blocking the action of para-aminobenzoic acid (see p. 406) is illustrative of this antagonistic action. The first such naturally occurring antivitamin to be discovered was avidin, a protein found up to the present time only in egg yolk, whose presence and effect was detected in experiments on rats in which raw white of egg was the only protein fed them. After a short time on this diet, the rats developed certain disease symptoms, including an acute dermatitis, which were called "egg-white injury." Egg-white injury was found to be due to the combination of avidin with a vitamin, then called Vitamin H, but in the newer terminology, biotin. Biotin is very generally distributed in plant and animal tissues, and has been synthesized in vitro. It is known to act as a co-enzyme in the respiratory and growth metabolism of certain bacteria, and is believed to have a similar role in all plant and animal tissues. Under ordinary circumstances, the rat has an amount of biotin in its tissues adequate to meet the metabolic demands, but with excessive amounts of egg white, much of it is inactivated by its combination with avidin, molecule for molecule, and so symptoms of its deficiency appear. The symptoms of egg-white injury are thus actually those of biotin deficiency. A compound, called 3-acetylpyridine, which is structurally similar to nicotinic acid except for the substitution of $COCH_3$ for the terminal $COOH$, acts as an antivitamin; if it is given to mice, they show typical signs of nicotinic acid deficiency, which are almost impossible to induce in them on a diet free of the vitamin. Pyrithiamine is an anti-vitamin; if fed to mice, they show signs of thiamine deficiency which can be relieved by administration of thiamine.

***Destruction of vitamins:*** Vitamins may also be destroyed within the body that needs them by substances included in its food. This was first made evident when foxes on a fox farm developed paralysis after being fed raw fish for a considerable period of time. Carp, and at least thirty other varieties of fresh water fish, have been found to contain an enzyme, thiaminase, that hydrolyzes thiamine; carp not only have no thiamine in their own tissues, but also deprive the animal that eats them of its thiamine supply. Other cases of anti-vitamin effects are known, making it clear that avitaminosis may arise from inactivation, by one mechanism or another already present in the tissues, of a vitamin as well as from a diet deficient in it. There is some evidence, too, from observations on laboratory animals particularly, that excessive amounts of vitamins may disturb the steady state of the organism, and so produce symptoms of hypervitaminosis, a condition that, along with other problems related to the vitamins, is one object of present biological inquiry.

## Biological assay as a method of determining vitamin requirements

Estimations of the amount of any given vitamin necessary for the adequate nutrition of man and a number of other animals have been made by means of biological assay—that is by determining the quantity of the vitamin that must be added to a diet made free of it, either to prevent the symptoms of the specific avitaminosis from appearing, or to bring about their remission or disappearance. In the early days of vitamin study, these amounts were expressed in arbitrary units, devised by the workers conducting the experiments; and later, an attempt was made to express them in terms of standard International Units. But with the extraction of purified vitamins, and their crystallization, these values are being expressed more and more, in an exact quantitative way by weight, as grams and fractions of grams. The vitamin content of foodstuffs has been determined, too, by bioassay, by feeding foods suspected of containing a given vitamin to animals deprived of it in their regular food; the relative quantity of the vitamin in the test food can then be determined by the rapidity and extent of the disappearance of the deficiency symptoms so caused. Other methods that are used are light-absorption ones, both of the visible and the ultraviolet spectrum; fluorescence; color changes that may take place in the combination of vitamins with other compounds; and microbiological ones. In these last methods, yeast and strains of bacteria known to need particular vitamins for satisfactory growth are used as test organisms, and grown on media made deficient in the one to be assayed; the addition of a compound suspected of vitamin potency, or of a food substance whose content is to be determined is then added to the medium and the growth of the micro-organisms measured against that of control cultures on a complete medium. In thiamine assays, alcoholic fermentation by yeast is sometimes taken as a measure of the vitamin content or potency.

**Sources of vitamins**

By tests such as these it has been shown that the vitamin content of the edible parts of plants may vary with the season, the age of the plant and the fertility of the soil. The difference in ascorbic acid content of green and ripened peppers has already been mentioned; it has been found, too, that green tomatoes ripened in storage have a lower carotene content than those that have ripened naturally in the sun on the vines. Lowered vitamin content in herbage is reflected in lower vitamin content in the tissues of the animals that feed upon it, which become correspondingly poorer sources of the vitamins for organisms that feed on them.

But whatever the vitamin, or provitamin, content of a fresh food may be, it is not always equivalent to that available to the organism after its ingestion and digestion. This is a fact of particular importance in human diet, for foods may often lose a large part of their vitamin content in their preparation, as well as in their transportation, storage and processing before storage. Ascorbic acid, for example, is very readily oxidized and even a brief exposure to air of a food containing it results in a considerable loss of the vitamin by its inactivation; thiamine, while relatively stable to heat and so not greatly reduced in quantity in the cooking of food, is very readily hydrolyzed and oxidized in alkaline solution, so that the addition of soda to water in which thiamine-containing vegetables are cooked destroys most of their possible contribution of this vitamin. And all water-soluble vitamins may diffuse out of the foods containing them with prolonged washing or soaking, or by their cooking in a large amount of water.

One of the major causes of vitamin loss from foods naturally containing them is in their processing. This was first made clear in the case of the polishing, or husking, of rice, a process designed to prevent its spoiling by fermentation and so to make possible its storage and transportation, but one that results in the removal of all its thiamine content and leads to beri-beri if the diet is not adequately supplemented. In the production of white flour, the milling process removes much of the valuable food content of the wheat and reduces its nutritional value far below the level of brown, or whole wheat, flour. Nutritionists have gradually impressed these facts upon the public, and the practice has arisen of enriching, or fortifying, such depleted foods either with synthetic vitamins or with those extracted from the husks or other discarded parts. In order to meet accepted dietary standards, the vitamin or vitamins must be added in sufficient quantity to make up the loss. White flour, and the bread made from it, is "enriched" by the addition of thiamine, nicotinic acid, riboflavin and iron, in amounts specified by amendments to the Federal Food, Drug and Cosmetic Act, and oleomargarine, made from vegetable oils, can be made to have a food value identical with butter if sufficient Vitamin A, the only essential nutrient lacking in it, is added.

*Deficiency diseases from mineral deficiencies*

"Deficiency diseases" are known to arise, too, from the absence of certain minerals from the diet, which, like the trace elements known to be required for adequate growth and metabolism in plants, are needed only in minute amounts. Such a disease is "bush sickness," a disease with symptoms similar to those of anemia which in 1895 killed thousands of sheep on the Australian ranches. Because of its resemblance to anemia, which was known to be related to an iron deficiency, iron was used for the treatment of bush sickness; in some cases it worked, and in some it failed. So important was the sheep industry to Australian economy that when it was found that the curative effects of the iron were related to the source of the ore from which it was obtained, the Australian government imported iron ores from all over the world and had the samples analyzed and compared. This led to the discovery that the effective iron contained minute amounts of cobalt as an impurity; when cobalt alone was included in the diet of sheep sick with bush sickness, they improved rapidly. Feeding experiments showed that as little as 0.0000000285 gm. ($1/1000000$ of an ounce) of cobalt per day was enough to protect a sheep against the disease, and by scattering only a few pounds of cobalt on the pastures where sheep grazed, the ranchers not only improved the vegetation but provided sufficient cobalt in the herbage upon which the sheep fed to eradicate the disease. But the actual role of cobalt, and of other mineral elements like it, in the metabolic and growth processes of the animal body is not yet fully understood.

## Human nutrition

Human nutrition has become a matter not only of national, but of international, concern since the beginning of the war in 1939, when the virtual cessation of agriculture in a large part of Europe and the Orient reduced the world's food supply drastically. Moreover, the diversion of crops from the countries producing and depending upon them to other nations and the disruption of world trade, threatened a large part of the world's population with starvation and brought thousands to their death from it. In 1941 the President of the United States called a National Nutritional Council for Defense, to discuss the problems of nutrition affecting man and his domestic animals and to formulate a program for unified national action to maintain the nutrition of the inhabitants of the United States at an adequate level. In 1943 a United Nations Food Conference was held at Virginia Hot Springs, which reviewed the world food situation, drew up a standard human dietary designed to provide adequate amounts of all the requisite structural, energy-yielding and "protective" foods, and discussed means of distributing them.

These are provided by the kinds of foods accepted by the United Nations Food Conference as the "basic seven" of the human diet, and can be met, for the average adult, by the following general dietary pattern:

| | |
|---|---|
| Milk | 1 pint |
| Egg | 1 daily (if not included somehow in each day's food, extra milk or meat should be allowed on the days omitted, or cheese, beans or peanuts substituted) |
| Meat, fish or fowl | 1 or more servings |
| Potato | 1 or more |
| Vegetables | 2 or more servings. One green and one yellow |
| Fruits | 2 or more. One should be a citrus fruit or a tomato, or other good source of Vitamin C |
| Cereals and bread | Whole grain or enriched |

This standard is far from being met in a large part of the population of the United States, partly from ignorance, partly for economic reasons and partly because of reluctance to depart from established dietary habits. Still less is it being met in other parts of the western world and huge areas of the eastern. It will take education, generosity in sharing local surpluses with those suffering from local shortages and intelligent distribution of all food supplies to bring the standard of nutrition of even the inhabitants of the United States to the adequate level. And it will take all these, and increased agricultural production besides, to bring even an approximation of this standard to the population of the world.

# CHAPTER 21

# METABOLISM AND ITS REGULATION

## *Utilization of food in the body: metabolism*

The value of any food, whatever its source may be, is measured finally by its utilization in the body. Digestion, and the absorption, transportation and assimilation by the cells of the products of digestion, are all processes accessory to those that go on in the cells themselves in the metabolic conversion of these products. A breakdown in any one of these accessory processes will result in local or general nutritional shortages, but, even if they all function together at their greatest efficiency, they are of little value if the cells cannot make use of the materials provided by them. Utilization of these materials by the cells depends primarily upon the enzyme systems with which they are endowed, and secondarily upon the efficiency with which these systems can operate under the conditions existing in the cell at any given time. The direct role that some of the vitamins play in this utilization has been indicated; equally important is that of some of the mineral salts in maintaining the intracellular pH within the optimal range and in providing some of the ions in whose presence enzymatic and other reactions are effectively carried out. In many cases among the vertebrates, although to lesser extent in other biological systems, it has been proved, too, that this utilization and the metabolic operations of cells and tissues are regulated and integrated by substances produced in other cells and tissues and conveyed by the body fluids from the site of their origin to the tissues they influence. The action of these cells and tissues is distinguished as "action at a distance" from that of nerve cells, only stimulating tissues with which they are in direct contact.

## *Substances influencing metabolic reactions*

### Chemical regulation

These substances are collectively called hormones, from the term first used by Bayliss and Starling for secretin, the substance which they found to be elaborated in the intestinal mucosa as a stimulant to the secretion of pancreatic juice. But as study of such regulating mechanisms has progressed, it has become apparent that some of the substances produced by cells that influence others are not stimulants to their activity, as the word hormone implies, but depressors of it, and that the same substance may act as a stimulant to one tissue and a depressor to another. Moreover, there are substances that are universal, or very general products of cellular activity, that influence the activities of other cells within the same biological systems. Carbon dioxide, for example, is a universal product of cellular respiration, and its accumulation in the body fluids of a multi-cellular organism has a profound effect upon all the tissues, and, in vertebrates, below a certain concentration a specific one upon the respiratory center in the medulla resulting in increased respiratory movements. Moreover, its accumulation in an environment inhabited by a number of individuals produces similar effects upon them all, in general, an initial increase in their activity and the possibility of its final cessation. Many plants liberate substances that are destructive to others in the same environment, among which are the antibiotics that have been isolated from the media in which fungi and micro-organisms have lived. Also, among the Protozoa there are some strains of Paramoecium known to produce and liberate a substance that is lethal to others, and are therefore known as "killer" strains. Influences such as these are illustrative of the biological conditioning of an external environment.

But according to present understanding and interpretation of their activity, conditioners of an internal environment, or hormones, are defined as "specific chemical substances produced by an organ or a tissue which, after being discharged into the circulating fluids (milieu intérieure), may reach all parts of the organism and in small amounts markedly influence the functions of other organs or systems without themselves contributing important quantities of matter or energy." * Their influence may be upon generalized metabolic processes, such as oxidations, or upon those that are more specialized and concern a particular compound or group of compounds; upon morphogenesis, the gradual development of the characteristic patterns or parts of an organism during its growth; upon reproduction and the development of the organs of reproduction and the distinguishing characters of males and females; upon mental and nervous functioning; upon resistance and adjustability to changes in the external environment, or to toxins or poisons formed in the body or introduced into it; and upon the other hormone-producing tissues, interrelating and balancing their action. Chemical regulation within a multicellular body seems to be a common biological phenomenon, and the primary one by which integration of its parts is brought about. In plants, it remains the primary means of metabolic coordination, but in animals, the development of nerve cells specialized for the reception and conduction of chemical as well as physical stimuli has resulted in a neural coordinating mechanism accessory to the chemical one. Nervous regulation provides for much more rapid adjustments than are possible through chemical regulation, for the nervous impulse travels at a far more rapid rate than a chemical molecule can diffuse through fluids and tissues; in the animal body, the neural mechanism operates to bring about quick adjustment of muscles and glands, while the chemical mechanism controls, to a great extent, the long-term responses of an organism, such as its metabolism, its growth and its reproduction. Complexity in regulation of this kind, and localization of the tissues producing the regulating substances seem to have progressed along with the complexity in bodily organization and bodily functioning. For example, glucose is metabolized by all biological systems, but only in the vertebrates has its metabolism been shown to be regulated by a hormone, secreted, in some of the fishes, by cells variously distributed in tissues associated with the intestine, but in the more highly evolved classes by those localized particularly in the pancreas. Reproduction, through the union of specialized cells, the eggs and the sperm, is a fundamental process common to all multicellular animals; with it is associated the development of organs, the gonads, and organ systems, for the production of these specialized cells and their passage out of the body, and also of certain features that distinguish the egg-producing members, or females, of a species from the sperm-producing members, or males. Although such a distinction is readily apparent in many of the non-chordates, it is only in the chordates that regulation and integration of the processes of reproduction and of the development of the characteristics of one sex or the other has definitely been shown to be hormonal.

## Methods for the analysis of chemical regulators

The methods used for the analysis of such chemical regulators have been primarily operative ones, in which tissues, glands or organs whose influence has been suspected have been removed from one body, grafted into another or after an interval replaced in that from which they were taken. Extracts of tissues have also been prepared and applied to parts, or injected into the bodies of individuals of the same or of different species to test their potencies; and chemical separation, or fractionation, of these extracts have been made in order to isolate the particular regulating substance. When

---

* Houssay, B. A., *Currents in Biochemical Research*, ed. D. H. Green. Copyright 1946 by Interscience Publishers, Inc.

the chemical composition of such a substance has been determined, it has in some few cases been synthesized in vitro; in many instances, compounds similar to it have been prepared and their potency in the body tested by injecting them into it. The use of tracer elements is also proving valuable in hormone research in indicating the site of their synthesis within the body and their relation to the biological mechanisms they influence.

## Biochemistry and the investigation of metabolic reactions

Investigation of metabolic mechanisms is the aim of the special field of biology known as biochemistry, where the data and techniques of chemistry are applied to the analysis and interpretation of biological activity. Animal biochemistry has progressed more rapidly than plant biochemistry, and mammalian biochemistry more rapidly than that of other animals, so that knowledge of the metabolic conversions in animals similar to man, although still far from complete, is greater than knowledge of them in other biological systems. Certain of these conversions, like certain enzyme systems, seem to be common to all kinds of organisms, and, while any detailed consideration of biochemical processes is beyond the province of an elementary text, some of the general facts concerning them underlie any understanding of biology as a science.

*Catabolic reactions:* The catabolic reactions that go on within cells are ones through which carbon compounds of high energy value are degraded to ones of lower energy value and energy made available to the organism for the various kinds of work that it performs. All of these reactions result in the oxidation of some or all of the carbon in the compound and the dissipation of some of the energy as heat. If the carbon compounds so consumed are not supplied by the food, either directly or indirectly, to replace accumulated reserves that have been used as sources of energy, they may be drawn from the substance of the body itself. This consumption of its own material results in loss of some of the body's mass, its diminution in size and its reduction in weight.

The type of carbon compound that is utilized as a principal source of energy can be determined by measurements of the RQ (see p. 394), and by analyses of the end products of the oxidative reactions. Both carbohydrate and fat can be completely oxidized to carbon dioxide and water, but only the carbon chain of the protein molecule can be, so that the amino portion in some other combination is represented in the end products of protein oxidation. The type of end product resulting from catabolism is thus related to the type of compound from which the organism derives its energy and also to the enzyme systems that it possesses and employs in its cellular oxidations. If, for example, the energy is derived from the oxidation of a hexose, the end products will be carbon dioxide and water, if the mechanism has been an aerobic one; carbon dioxide and some other compound such as alcohol, acetic or lactic acid if it has been an anaerobic one. From present evidence, plants derive their energy almost exclusively from hexose oxidations, but animals may use fat and protein as well. If their energy is derived from fat, the end products may likewise be carbon dioxide and water but may also be compounds representing an incomplete oxidation of the fatty acid molecule. These compounds, known as ketone or acetone, bodies, are acetoacetic acid ($CH_3COCH_2COOH$), and its derivatives, beta-hydroxybutyric acid

$$CH_3CH(OH)CH_2COOH$$

and acetone ($CH_3COCH_3$). And if protein is utilized, the end-products will include ammonia, which is liberated in the deamination of its constituent amino acids, or some other compound that contains the amino group as well as the possible products of carbohydrate oxidation. Ketone bodies may undergo other transformations in the body, but if they are present in excess will be eliminated from it and found in the excreta. Ammonia, on the other hand, is a very toxic substance, and unless it is rapidly eliminated from the body or inactivated in it, will have disastrous effects. According to the way in which they eliminate or convert this product, animals may be classified as ammonotelic, ureotelic or uricotelic, depending on whether they excrete ammonia as such, or convert most or all of it to urea or uric acid before its storage or excretion. The majority of aquatic non-chordates are ammonotelic, liberating ammonia directly into the water in which they live, where diffusion, augmented by movements in the water, prevents it from concentrating to any great extent in any one locality. The land-living non-chordates, such as insects and gastropods, are uricotelic, while ureotelism is limited to certain groups of the chordates; the elasmobranch and some of the dipnoid fishes; the anuran amphibia; some of the reptiles and the mammals. The remaining reptiles and the birds are uricotelic, while teleosts, some Dipnoi, the urodele amphibia and the larval (tadpole) stages of the anuran eliminate the nitrogen residue of their protein catabolism as ammonia.

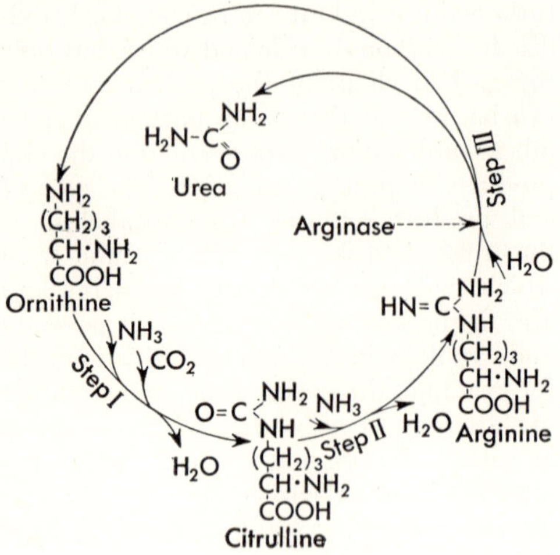

The synthesis of urea or of uric acid is essentially an anabolic process, like that of protein, carbohydrate, fat and other substances made in the body from the decomposition products of the digested food. Although urea was the first of the products of the animal body to be synthesized in vitro, an achievement of the German chemist Wöhler in 1828 (see p. 6), the course of its synthesis in vivo has only recently been made clear. Several ways of synthesis in the body are possible, but none of them the way in which Wöhler made it. According to at least one modern theory, which is acceptable to most biochemists if not to all, the usual course of the synthesis involves three amino acids, arginine, ornithine and citrulline and the enzyme arginase, which is especially abundant in the liver where urea synthesis takes place. The first step in the synthesis is the combination of the ammonia released by deamination with ornithine to form citrulline; citrulline then unites with another molecule of ammonia to form arginine, which is then split into a molecule of urea and one of ornithine through the agency of arginase. The ornithine so released is then available for combination with another molecule of ammonia, and the series of reactions can start again, the cycle repeating itself over and over (Fig 21.1). Arginase is found in the liver cells only of ureotelic animals, and without it the formation of urea in any quantity is impossible. The mechanism of synthesis of uric acid, which goes on to some extent in the liver cells of ureotelic animals and is the principal means of eliminating ammonia in those that are uricotelic, is but little understood at present.

FIGURE 21.1 Chart of the ornithine cycle. (After Baldwin.)

*Anabolic reactions:* Anabolic reactions are on the whole directed toward building up new material within the body—protein and other organic components of protoplasm; reserves of carbohydrate, of fat and in some cases of protein; other compounds that may be included in the structure of the body and those that contribute in one way or another to its functioning. The raw materials for these are provided by the food, and their direction, like that of the catabolic reactions, is controlled by intracellular enzymes and enzyme systems. Not all the material included in the end products of digestion may be used in these syntheses, for cells by virtue of their intracellular enzymes may bring about the further decomposition of these substances into products from which they select substrates for their anabolic reactions. In their reactions there may therefore be formed by-products as well as intermediate ones, which may be included in other metabolic reactions or eliminated from the body in the excreta. The intermediary metabolism of some substances is known, at least within the mammalian body, as well as the initial substrate and the final product. Stable isotopes and radioactive elements are proving to be important tools in investigations of this kind, for they can be introduced into the molecules of substances given test animals as food and the progress and fate of these tagged molecules in the body traced. Nearly ten years ago (1942), it was shown by such experiments that nothing in the animal body is static, but in a constant state of change and exchange. The storage reserves are not passive accumulations of fat or carbohydrate, but ones in which there is a continual shift of atoms between their constituents and those of the circulating fluids and other tissues. Even structures as permanent as bones and teeth are constantly exchanging atoms with other tissues (see p. 267). The use of an isotope of nitrogen, $N^{15}$, or heavy nitrogen, has given support to the probability that urea is formed through the ornithine cycle, for ammonia tagged with it and included in the diet of experimental animals was subsequently found in the arginine isolated from sacrificed animals; when this arginine was subjected to hydrolysis in vitro, the ornithine released was free of $N^{15}$, all of which was included in the urea. The isotope was also found in the urea isolated from the urine of these animals, and in an amount practically equivalent to that of the arginine obtained from their bodies.

## Regulators of metabolism
### Regulation in plants

In 1883, the great English natural scientist Charles Darwin (1809–1882), universally known for his expression of the theory of evolution through natural selection, and his son Francis produced the first evidence that growth in the stems of plants is regulated by a substance synthesized in their tips. It is a matter of ordinary observation that when a seed germinates, no matter how it may be oriented, the growing stem turns toward the light and the root usually away from the light toward the ground (Fig. 8.12). The stem thus shows positive phototropism and negative geotropism (Greek, photos = light + trope = turning), in that it bends toward the light and away from the gravitational pull, while the root shows negative phototropism and positive geotropism. Experiments have also shown that other external conditions such as the presence of water, of an electric field, or of an injury to their tissues, may influence the turning or curvature of stems and roots. Such curvature is due to inequality of growth, for the stem is longer on its outer curvature than on its inner; in plants, this may be due either to increase in number of cells or to enlargement, especially in the long axis, of cells already existing.

In many experiments on the power of movement in various plants, the Darwins found that if a growing shoot is illuminated from one side only, it bends toward the source of the light, but that if its tip is fully protected from the light and its base alone exposed, no bending takes place. They proved this by experiments on the grass Phalaris, covering the tips of young shoots with thin glass tubes, painted black, and shielding them from any light that might be radiated from the soil by black paper guards; under these conditions, the shoots did not bend when light was shown laterally on their exposed basal regions. It was therefore concluded that in these plants the tip of the shoot was the seat of the "perception" of light, and that an influence must travel from it to the basal region of the stem. Some twenty years later, a Danish botanist, Peter Boysen-Jensen (1883–    ), proved the material nature of this "influence" by experiments in which he cut off the tips of growing shoots of oats and inserted a thin block of gelatin between the cut end of the stem and the tip which he replaced upon the gelatin block. In spite of the severance of its tip and of the sheath, or coleoptile (Greek, koleos = sheath + ptilon = feather or plumule) that covers the growing tips of all monocotyledonous seedlings, these oat shoots continued growth and showed the usual tropisms of intact seedlings.

**Chemical stimulators of growth:** Following these experiments, many similar ones have demonstrated conclusively that substances are synthesized in the tips of plant stems that diffuse through the tissues basal to them and influence their growth. The mechanism of the transport of these substances is not yet clearly established; in the vascular plants, the conducting tissues may be involved, but in any case, their final distribution must be by diffusion from cell to cell. That they are responsible for growth has been shown by experiments in which the tips of decapitated seedlings have been replaced asymmetrically so that only one-half, or some other fraction, of the cut end is covered. Elongation of the stem takes place only on the covered side, and the stem is therefore bent (Fig. 21.2).

These substances have been extracted, chemically identified and given the names of Auxin A and Auxin B (Greek, auximonos = promoting plant growth). They are not species specific and are equally effective in their action upon every kind of plant tested, regardless of its species or their source. Another substance, called heteroauxin, which also influences plant growth in general, has been isolated, chemically identified and synthesized in vitro. This has been obtained from some yeasts and molds, but in greatest abundance from animal urine. It is known to be a product of the bacterial decomposition of tryptophane, an amino acid included in proteins of plant origin only; this indicates that its presence in animal urine is not due to its synthesis in the animal body as such, but to the metabolic conversion of protein included in the food.

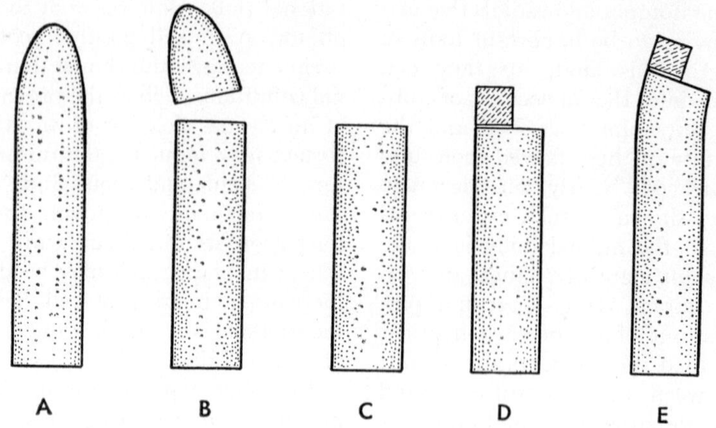

**Chemical inhibitors of growth:** While the auxins are often referred to as growth-promoting substances, it has been shown that, although they do promote some growth processes, they also have inhibitory effects upon others. They are responsible for the elongation of the stems, but they suppress elongation of roots and development of

FIGURE 21.2 Diagrammatic representation of the effect of a plant growth hormone (auxin). (After Sinnott, from Hylander and Stanley, *College Botany*. Copyright 1949 by The Macmillan Company.)

    A. Intact tip of an oat seedling, with its sheath (coleoptile) formed of the first leaf.
    B. and C. Decapitated coleoptiles.
    D. Block of agar into which growth hormone has been caused to diffuse placed on one side of the cut surface.
    E. The coleoptile grows more rapidly beneath the agar block from which the hormone has diffused into the tissues, causing the coleoptile to bend.

buds. In the dicotyledonous plants, for example, the apical bud produces an auxin which promotes the development of the stem immediately below it, but prevents that of the lateral buds along its more basal regions, so that the apical bud retains its dominance. But if the bud is removed, another one on the stem will assume dominance and control stem growth and bud inhibition by the auxin that it develops and releases to the surrounding tissues. In spite of this inhibition of other potentially dividing tissues, auxin is used for any organic substance, natural or synthetic, which, also in minute amounts, brings about the irreversible elongation of parts of plants. In animals, the distinction between hormones and vitamins is more clearly defined, for the animal depends upon its food, and so ultimately upon plant syntheses, for the source of its vitamins, but synthesizes its own hormones.

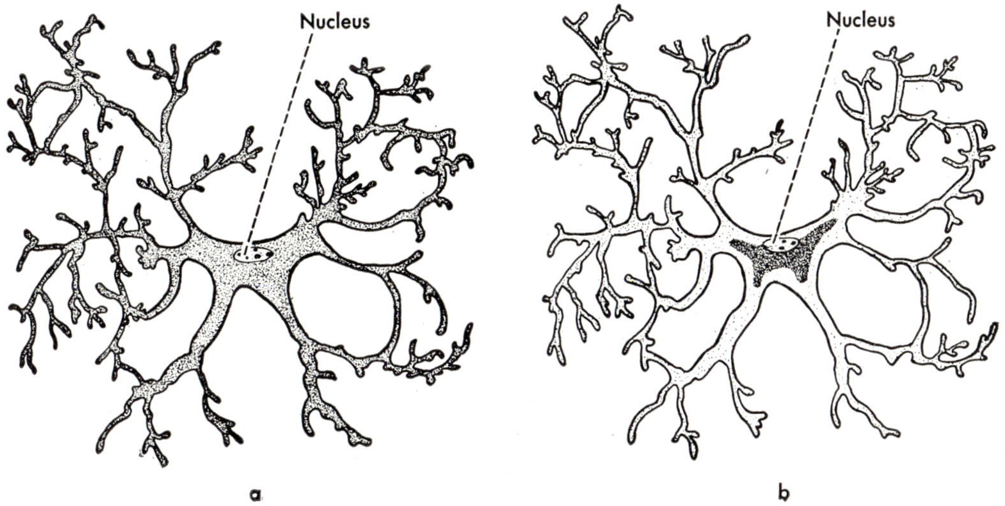

### Regulation in invertebrates

*Regulation of color changes in Crustacea:* The completely established cases of chemical regulation in invertebrates have been found among the arthropods, where the distribution of pigment in crustacean chromatophores and control of postembryonic development in insects has definitely been shown to be influenced by hormones. The chromatophores of crustaceans like crabs, lobsters, shrimps and prawns are large cells with many processes extending from them, more or less like permanently extended pseudopodia. They may contain one, two or several of the pigments common to Crustacea—yellow, orange, or red carotinoids, brown and black melanins, and white guanine. The animals show a variety of color patterns with different combinations of these pigments, and respond by color changes to differences in their backgrounds and in the intensity of the light that reaches them. These changes are brought about by alterations in the distribution of the pigment in the cells, from extreme condensation of it in the center of the cell to its extension throughout it and to the very tips of the processes (Fig. 21.3). Since no anatomical connection between these cells and the nervous system has ever been established, it was first assumed that blood flow alone controlled their activity; in 1928 it was established for the prawn, Palaemonetes, that color changes did not take place on the dorsal surface of the abdomen if the dorsal

FIGURE 21.3 Diagrammatic representation of a chromatophore showing (a) maximal dispersion of the pigment granules and (b) maximal concentration of them. (After Turner.)

abdominal vessel were tied, or blood flow through it blocked by other means. This suggested a hormonal control of pigment distribution, and various organs were removed from experimental animals to test the effect of their loss upon chromatophoric response, and extracts of various organs were injected into both intact and operated animals to test their potency. It was found that of all the experiments, only those in which the eyes and their supporting stalks were removed had any effect upon the color patterns of the animals; animals without eyes and eyestalks darkened and remained so permanently. Closer analysis of the removed part showed that the sinus gland, a small mass of tissue derived from a thickening of the neurilemma over the nerve traversing the eyestalk, was responsible for the material that, secreted into the blood, brought about the dispersal of the pigment. This substance, as yet unidentified chemically, is neither species nor genus specific; that which is extracted from a shrimp will bring about color changes if injected into a crab or a lobster, and the reverse is equally true. Present evidence indicates that there are at least three chromatophore-activating principles in it, and that the 75 species of crustaceans in which the action of the hormone has been demonstrated fall into three groups in respect to its effect upon them. In the first group, the bodies darken when the eyestalks are removed, owing to the dispersion of the dark pigments in the individual chromatophores; the bodies become lighter again, through condensation of the pigment in the cells, when the eyestalk hormone is injected into them. In the second group, removal of the eyestalks results in a mottled pattern, for in some of the chromatophores the pigment is maximally dispersed, in others maximally condensed and in others its dispersion is midway between these two extremes; injection of the hormone leads to intense blanching of their bodies, that is, to maximal pigment condensation. In the third group, removal of the eyestalk leads to blanching of the body and injection of its hormone to a general darkening or blackening.

Further studies of color changes in Crustacea have shown that there are hormones other than those of the sinus gland that affect the distribution of pigment. After removal of the eyestalks from the shrimp, Crago, the tails of the operated animals darkened rapidly but after an interval of

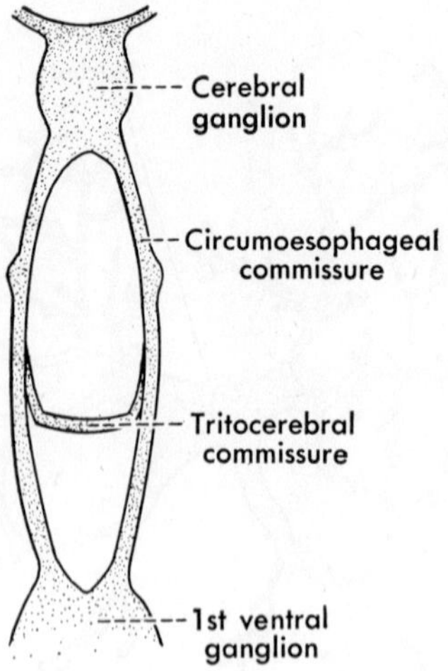

FIGURE 21.4 Diagram showing the anterior part of the central nervous system of Crago. (After Pincus.)

about an hour became much lighter owing to the concentration of the dark pigments in the chromatophores. But if the cut end of the optic nerve were stimulated, the pigment in the tail again dispersed, remained so for a time, and then concentrated again. Cutting the nerve supply to the tail made no difference to the reaction, showing that it was a response to a chemical stimulation, the source of which was finally localized in a slender strand of nervous tissue, the tritocerebral commissure, passing posterior to the oesophagus and connecting the two circumoesophageal commissures (Fig. 21.4). Extracts of this connective were specific in their effect only upon the dispersion of dark pigment in the tail, but extracts of other parts of the anterior nervous system affected the other chromatophores of the body in such a way as to bring about a general lightening of the body. In the other Crustacea that have been investigated, there appears to be a similar distinction between a tail-darkening hormone and a body-lightening one, and, though the source of both of them is also in nervous tissue, its location in the nervous system varies in different species. There is also some evidence that a hormone is derived from the sinus gland that inhibits moulting, for the succession of moults has been accelerated above the usual rate in animals deprived of it.

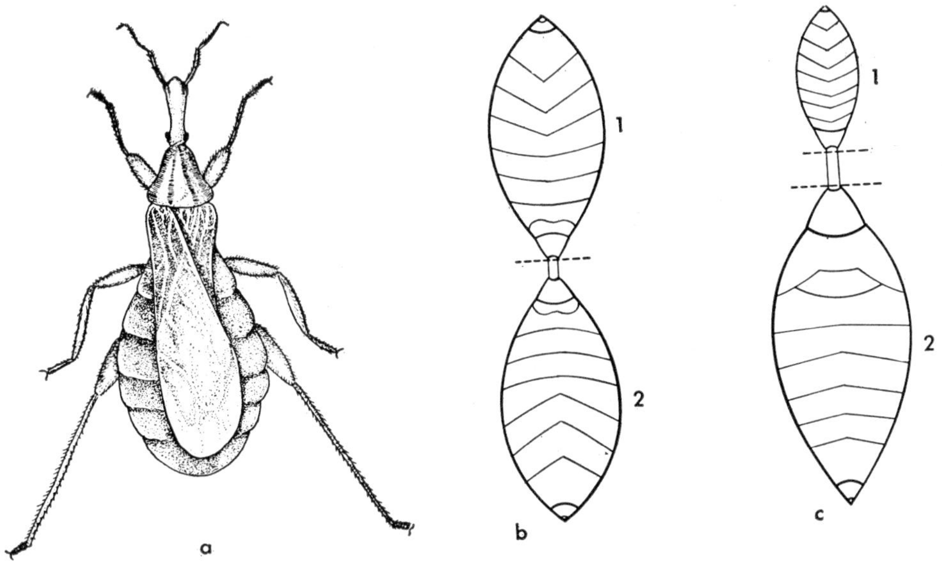

velopment was made in 1922, when it was found that the last larval instars of the gypsy moth, Lymantria, failed to pupate after removal of their cerebral ganglia, but that pupation would take place in the operated caterpillars if the ganglia were reimplanted in the abdomen. This reimplantation was effective only if done during a limited period; if performed just after the previous moult, no pupation took place, but if it were done a few days before the caterpillars would have pupated under ordinary circumstances, pupation took place as it did in intact specimens. Not long after this, conclusive evidence for a hormone controlling moulting, also derived from the cerebral ganglia, was obtained from experiments on the blood-sucking bug, Rhodnius (Fig.

FIGURE 21.5 Diagrams showing experiments with the bug Rhodnius prolixus demonstrating the effect of the moulting hormone. The broken lines show levels of decapitation. (After Turner.)

a. Adult Rhodnius.

b. Two nymphs (4th instar) united by a capillary glass tube. Number 1 was decapitated after the critical period and would not have moulted unless attached to number 2. The diffusion of moulting hormone from number 2 into number 1 causes both to moult into nymphs of the 5th instar.

c. Two nymphs of different age united by a capillary glass tube after decapitation at the levels indicated by the broken lines. Number 1 is a 1st instar decapitated before the critical period; number 2 is a 5th instar decapitated after the critical period. After union, both nymphs moult, number 1 becoming a diminutive adult without passing through the remaining nymphal stages.

***Regulation of moulting and adult differentiation in insects:*** Hormonal control of moulting has been definitely established in insects. In most species, the young emerge from the egg in a condition that differs in a number of ways from the adult, and achieve the adult condition during their post-embryonic growth (Fig. 14.26). The first demonstration of hormonal control of insect de-

21.5). This insect hatches as a nymph, and passes through several nymphal instars before reaching the adult stage; it takes but a single meal of blood in each instar, and a definite time after each meal a moult occurs. If any nymphal instar is decapitated well as by those joining together in various ways two individuals in different stages of development. Some of these experiments, particularly those upon grasshoppers, have led to the conclusion that there is also a hormone that retards, or restrains, adult

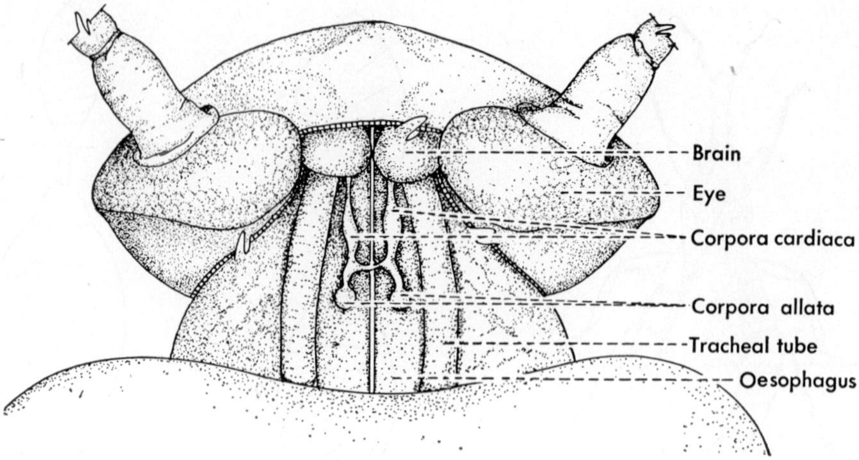

FIGURE 21.6  Head of a cockroach (Periplaneta americana) showing the relation of the corpora allata and corpora cardiaca to other organs. (After Turner.)

directly after a meal, it never moults again, although it may live for a considerable period of time, past the period when its next moult was due. But if the head is cut off an instar several days after feeding, a moult takes place at the time that it would in an intact animal. This indicates that there is a critical period when the moulting hormone is present in the body fluid. Further evidence for this has been obtained from experiments in which two nymphs, one decapitated immediately after its meal and the other several days later, were joined together by a capillary tube sealed to the cut surface of each and moulting was induced in the one that had just fed, in which, after decapitation, it would not otherwise have taken place.

Other evidence substantiating the hormonal control of insect growth and development has been obtained from removal and transplantation experiments on a number of different species, injections of extracts of organs, and of fluid from other individuals at different stages of development, as differentiation. This seems to be developed in the glandular structure found in the heads of most insects close to the cerebral ganglia called the corpora allata (Fig. 21.6), for if this structure is removed from the early nymphal instar of a grasshopper, the nymphal period is shortened, moults are suppressed and adult differentiation begins prematurely. And if the gland is transplanted into nymphs in their final instar, a succession of moults follows and they do become imagos.

The hormone from the corpora allata has been called the juvenile hormone, since its action is to cause the insect to remain in a juvenile condition throughout its entire life. The moulting and pupation hormones, on the other hand, are ones controlling progressive growth and development. Their source has been shown to be the cerebral ganglia, where there are two groups of neuro-secretory cells, one medial and one lateral. The nervous system thus affects coordination and integration within the body in two ways—by the reception of stimuli and their transmission along the nervous pathways, and by the development of chemical substances whose influence upon some, if not all, of the metabolic processes is clear. There is already some evidence that hormones also play a part in insect reproduction and fertility, although they have not been found to influence the development of characters distinguishing males and females. Like the hormones that control pigmentation in the Crustacea, the juvenile and growth and development hormones of insects, with one known exception, are not specific either for a genus or an order and, like all other hormones known, are effective in minute concentrations. The existence of other hormones and other hormone-controlled mechanisms among other invertebrates is suspected, but none of them has as yet been as fully substantiated as these cases in Crustacea and insects.

### Regulation in vertebrates

*Early observations on chemical regulation:* A hundred years ago a German scientist, Arnold A. Berthold (1803–1861), made the first experimental demonstration of the chemical influence of one part of the vertebrate body upon another. It is a matter of ordinary observation, and known long before Berthold's time, that male chickens do not develop the combs and characteristic feathering of the cock if their gonads are removed. In 1849, Berthold grafted testes, the male reproductive organs, into such castrated fowls, or capons, and observed that with the re-establishment of these tissues in their bodies, their combs grew and they took on the typical appearance of roosters. Forty years later, in 1889, two other European clinicians, Joseph von Mering (1848–1908) and Oscar Minkowski (1858–1931), indirectly produced evidence that the pancreas was a metabolic regulator, for in experiments conducted to study the effect of the removal of the pancreas on the digestion of fat, they found the concentration of glucose in the urine of the operated animal much higher than it was before the operation, or in intact animals. The demonstration of secretin by Bayliss and Starling in 1904, and their introduction of the word hormone, stimulated investigation of chemical regulation in the mammalian body and experimental verification of the idea, first expressed by Claude Bernard in 1855, that all the organs of the mammalian body liberate special substances into the tissue fluids that contribute to the maintenance of constancy in the "milieu intérieure." As the experimental work proceeded, it seemed to be evident that many of these substances were localized in particular tissues, and particular glandular areas, that discharged their products directly into the tissue fluid from which it passed into the blood vessels and was conveyed around the body. These regions were therefore called glands of internal secretion, ductless or endocrine glands, to distinguish them from those which discharged their products through ducts, the glands of external secretion or exocrine glands.

*Endocrine organs:* The mammalian tissues for which an endocrine function has been established at the present time are located in the digestive tract, including the mucosa of the intestine as well as certain cells in the pancreas, the reproductive organs, the thyroid, parathyroid, adrenal and pituitary glands. Other organs, and more or less localized cells, may also produce specific substances that contribute to the chemical regulation of the body, but the evidence for their inclusion in the endocrine system is not completely established. The study of chemical regulation in other vertebrates has shown that in general it follows the same pattern as that in mammals, although in several instances the hormone-producing cells are more generally distributed throughout the body. The various vertebrate hormones are, like those of the invertebrates, neither species nor genus specific; a purified hormone from any source is equally effective upon other animals with a similar regulatory mechanism.

THE INTESTINAL MUCOSA AND ITS ENDOCRINE SECRETIONS: The first of the mammalian hormones to be demonstrated was one of intestinal origin; in the half-century following the discovery of secretin, the site of three others has also been localized in the intestinal mucosa. The action of secretin is a direct stimulation of the enzyme-secreting cells of the pancreas, causing them to discharge their secretion into the ducts of the gland. Under experimental conditions, when the concentration of the hormone in the blood is maintained at a constant level, this response of the pancreatic cells is apparently an indefinite one, but under ordinary circumstances it is of but short duration, owing to the destruction of secretin by the enzyme secretinase present in the blood plasma and in the tissues. In 1935, secretin was isolated as a pure crystalline compound but beyond the fact that it is a protein, nothing is known of its chemical composition.

The other three hormones of the digestive tract also act in the regulation and coordination of the activities of the digestive glands. Pancreozymin stimulates the production and discharge of enzymes by the pancreas; when stimulated by pure secretin, pancreatic juice is a watery fluid poor in enzymes, but when secretin and pancreozymin act in conjunction with each other, it has a higher, or normal, concentration of enzymes. Cholecystokinin controls the discharge of bile from the gall bladder; and enterogastrone, produced almost exclusively if not exclusively by the cells in the duodenal mucosa, inhibits the secretion of gastric juice and the movements of the stomach. That these effects are the result of chemical stimulation alone has been proved conclusively by experiments in which all nervous connections to the responding organs have been cut, and the blood left as the only connecting tissue. In addition to these four intestinal hormones, five others have been postulated but not conclusively demonstrated, and two more are believed to arise in the gastric mucosa. One of these is secretin, like the intestinal secretin, and the other is gastrin, whose individuality, or identity with histamine, has not yet been established (see p. 390). Nor is it yet clear whether all the cells in the enteric mucosa elaborate these hormones, or whether they are specialized and localized like those that synthesize and discharge the digestive juices.

THE PANCREAS AND ITS ENDOCRINE SECRETIONS: Experiments following those of von Mering and Minkowski have proved conclusively that the pancreas has an endocrine as well as an exocrine function. There are in the mammalian pancreas certain cells, first

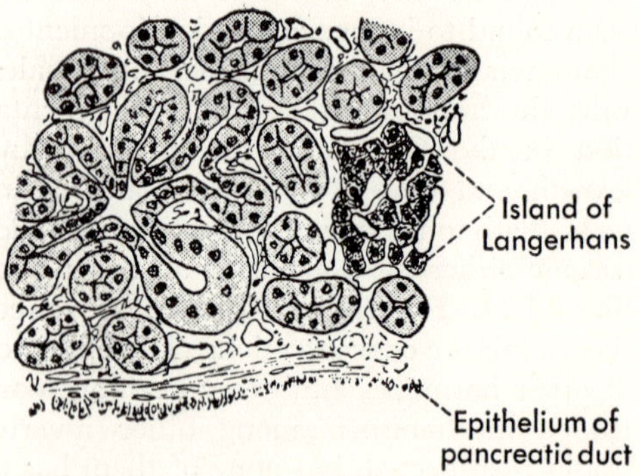

FIGURE 21.7 Section through the pancreas of a rabbit, showing the alveolar exocrine gland and the endocrine gland cells in an island of Langerhans. (After Krause, from Walter and Sayles, *Biology of the Vertebrates*. Copyright 1949 by The Macmillan Company.)

described by a German anatomist, Paul Langerhans (1847–1888), that are readily distinguishable microscopically from the enzyme-secreting cells. These are frequently clustered together in groups or patches among the other tissues of the pancreas, forming the islets of Langerhans (Fig. 21.7). These cells secrete the hormone insulin, which plays an important role in various phases of metabolism, for, by directly affecting the metabolism of glucose, it indirectly affects that of fat and protein. In animals from which the pancreas has been removed by operation, or the islet tissue made non-functional by disease, the concentration of glucose in the blood (0.2–0.5 per cent) is well above its level in intact and healthy animals (0.1 per cent), a condition that is known as hyperglycemia; the urine, ordinarily free from sugar, contains an appreciable amount of it, a condition called glycosuria. Additionally, the glycogen content of the liver and the muscles is reduced and the respiratory quotient is lowered, indicating that even with the depletion of the stored carbohydrate reserves, less carbohydrate is being oxidized; the increased production of ketone bodies and the presence of more than the ordinary amount of urea in the urine show that the catabolism of fat and of protein is proceeding to a greater extent than usual. The pathological effects of this metabolic derangement are due probably in greatest measure to the accumulation of ketone bodies, primarily acetoacetic acid, in the blood; the pH of the blood may fall to 7 or below, at which the animal falls into unconsciousness or coma. These effects are not produced if the exocrine secretion of the pancreas is prevented from reaching the lumen of the intestine by ligating (Latin, ligare = to bind) the duct or by diverting its flow through a fistula, or if all nerves to the organ are cut, so that they are attributable only to some endocrine secretion of the gland. They are relieved by injection of insulin, the active principle extracted from the tissues of the pancreas in 1922 by a team of Canadian scientists, including Dr. Frederick G. Banting (1891–    ) and Dr. J. R. Macleod (1876–1935). Insulin isolated from the islet tissue of cows, pigs, sheep, human beings and some fish has been obtained in pure crystalline form and identified as a protein, but neither its molecular composition nor its contribution in the chemical mechanisms of glycogen synthesis and disintegration and glucose oxidation have yet been determined.

THE REPRODUCTIVE ORGANS AND THEIR ENDOCRINE SECRETIONS: The reproductive organs of a male animal are called testes, or testicles; those of a female are called ovaries. These are usually paired structures, developed from the mesoderm, in which, in the one case, the male reproductive cells, or spermatozoa, are developed and matured, and in the other, the female reproductive cells, the ova or eggs. Associated with these organs, in the reproductive system, are ducts, or tubes, through which their products are conveyed to the outside, various accessory glands and, in some females, structures in which the eggs may be retained for varying lengths of time during their development and embryonic differentiation. In most of the vertebrates, too, there are certain obvious external differences between the males and the females of a species. The male fowl is distinguished from the female by its plumage and, in chickens, by its comb; color pattern and smaller size often distinguish the male from the female fish; and in mammals, differences in the external genitalia, in the development of the mammary glands, as well as in size, distinguish the two sexes. These structural differences, as well as certain metabolic ones, are known as secondary sex characters, and their development is known to be influenced by hormones originating in the gonads. The male sex hormones are known as androgens, the female sex hormones as estrogens. The first of the androgens to be isolated was obtained in 1929 from the testes of bulls and was called testosterone; when injected into capons, it produced as normal a development of the secondary characters as did Berthold's grafting of testicular tissue and its injection into young male rats, from which the testes had been removed before their secondary sex characters had developed, led to their normal development. Another androgen, androsterone, has also been obtained from the urine of both males and females; it is chemically similar to testosterone but has about one-tenth its potency. Both are sterols, containing the characteristic steroid ring (see p. 451), and both have been synthesized in the laboratory from cholesterol. The estrogens, estrone, estradiol and estriol are also sterols, and so bear a chemical relationship to the androgens and the steroid vitamins. The estrogens not only influence the development of secondary sex characters, but are also involved in the changes that take place in the reproductive organs after the discharge of the eggs from the ovary. These changes, and their hormonal regulation, will be considered in the chapter on reproduction and development.

THE THYROID GLAND AND ITS ENDOCRINE SECRETIONS: The thyroid gland, which has no counterpart in the non-chordates, develops in all classes of vertebrates from a median outgrowth of the floor of the embryonic pharynx which gradually becomes converted to a crescent-shaped mass of epithelial cells lying ventral to the trachea and transversely across it. In its development, in all groups of vertebrates with the possible exception of fishes, the thyroid is very closely associated with that of derivatives of the posterior branchial pouches, the fifth bran-

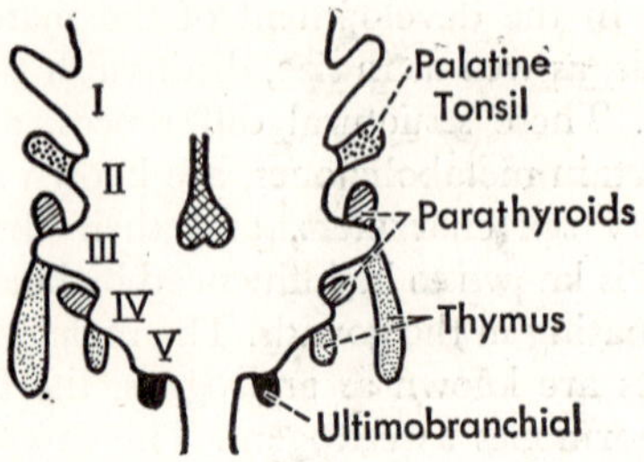

FIGURE 21.8 Diagram showing the origin of the thymus, parathyroids, ultimobranchial bodies and palatine tonsils as epithelial derivatives of the branchial pouches. (After Kohn, from Walter and Sayles, *Biology of the Vertebrates.* Copyright 1949 by The Macmillan Company.)

chial pouch developing into the ultimobranchial bodies that are incorporated into the mass of the thyroid glands, and the dorsal parts of the third and fourth giving rise to the parathyroid glands (Fig. 21.8). The thyroid gland is particularly active in the synthesis of iodothyroglobulin, a protein whose effect as a hormone is attributable to thyroxin, one of its constituent amino acids. Experiments in which compounds containing radioactive iodine have been fed to rats have shown that the thyroid gland is not the only one of their tissues which can elaborate thyroxin, for radioactive thyroxin has been isolated from their bodies even after the removal of all thyroid tissue. But the effects of the removal or decreased activity of the gland show clearly that it contains the cells in which such synthesis is carried on most effectively and to the greatest extent. The gross effect of thyroid removal is a lowering of the basal metabolic rate to 40–50 per cent of its normal value; the oxidative mechanisms and thus the metabolic rate can be restored to their normal level by transplantation of thyroid tissue or administration of its hormone. Conversely, an excessive secretion from the gland, or the experimental addition of thyroid tissue or thyroid extract to an animal, results in increased oxidative activity, fat and protein as well as carbohydrate being burned at abnormally high rates. Since its effect is upon a general and a basic metabolic process, the symptoms of thyroid excess or deficiency are generalized ones. With excessive amounts of the hormone, which may naturally result from excessive activity of the gland, or hyperthyroidism, there is a general speeding up of all the metabolic processes, with increased nervous and muscular activity; with deficiency of the hormone, resulting from removal or dysfunction of the gland, individuals become physically and mentally sluggish and lethargic. Its effects upon growth and the differentiation of adult structures are marked in all classes of vertebrates; animals deficient in it during the growth period are below the normal size and tend to remain in a juvenile condition without the full development of the reproductive organs and secondary sex characters of adults. Feeding thyroid tissue to amphibian larvae or injection of its extract into them, for example, induces their metamorphosis so that they assume the adult form earlier than they otherwise would; conversely removal of the thyroid rudiment from them prolongs their larval life indefinitely. In birds, excessive thyroid hormone increases the growth rate of feathers and induces moulting, often with changes in the patterns of feather pigmentation; reduction in the secretion retards moulting and, in males at least, the development of the reproductive cells. In mammals, its deficiency results in decreased growth and development of cerebral functions, producing in extreme cases in man the condition of cretinism, or retarded physical and mental development which can be improved by the administration of thyroid hormone during the critical periods of growth (Fig. 21.9).

THE PARATHYROID GLANDS AND THEIR ENDOCRINE SECRETIONS: The identification of the parathyroids as independent endocrine glands was first achieved through analysis of the effects of thyroid removal. In many instances, this was accompanied by convulsions from which the operated animals subsequently died. In 1891 a French investigator, E. Gley, directed attention to the two small bodies lying lateral to the thyroid gland in rabbits and it was found that if these could be dissected away from the thyroid tissue and left in the body, postoperative convulsions did not occur. Later investigations have shown that there is a drop in the calcium content of the blood following removal of the parathyroids and have related the convulsive muscular spasms to the effect of disturbances of calcium metabolism within the body. The parathyroid hormone has been isolated in pure crystalline form, and is known to be a protein and susceptible to digestion by pepsin and trypsin. Its established and recognized effect is the control of the level of blood calcium, an element that is essential to the construction of bones and teeth and to the operation of many other cellular mechanisms, including the specific responses of muscles and nerves. But calcium metabolism is very closely linked to that of other minerals, especially of phosphorus with which much of the calcium of the animal body is ionically combined as calcium phosphate. From present evidence, obtained from determinations of the elimination of radioactive phosphorus in animals in which the amount of parathyroid hormone is experimentally controlled, it is prob-

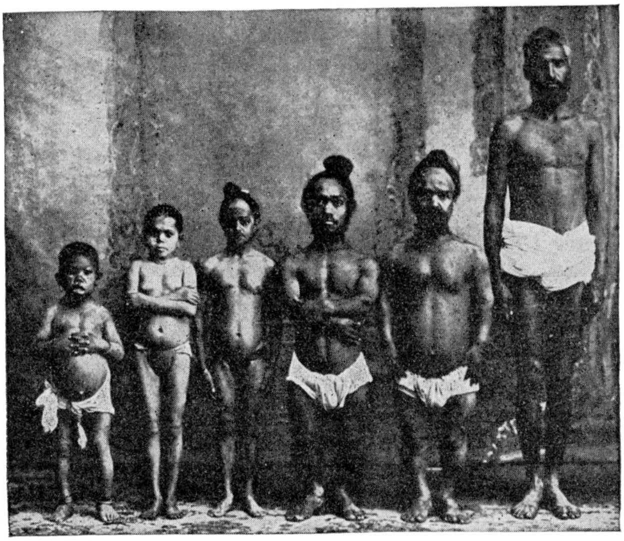

FIGURE 21.9  Various types of dwarfs. (Rischbieth and Barrington, from Major, *Physical Diagnosis,* 3rd edition, published by the W. B. Saunders Company. Copyright 1945.)

From left to right: cretin; ateleiotic dwarf; ateleiotic dwarf; achrondroplasic; achrondroplasic; normal individual.

able that the hormone acts directly upon the kidney in regulating the retention and the elimination of phosphate, and so indirectly affecting the concentration of calcium in the blood.

THE ADRENAL BODIES AND THEIR ENDOCRINE SECRETIONS: The adrenal glands of mammals are two small bodies, lying near the kidneys. In humans, each gland is actually above the corresponding kidney so that they are sometimes referred to as the suprarenals, but in other mammals they are ventral to the kidney and close to the posterior vena cava, so that the term adrenal is more generally applicable. In the mammals, each gland is a compound one, consisting of an outer region, or cortex, derived from mesoderm of the same type as that which gives rise to the gonads, and an inner region or medulla, derived ultimately from the ectoderm since it is formed from embryonic nerve cells which like those that contribute to the ganglia of the autonomic chain, migrate away from the embryonic neural tube at an early stage in the development of the individual (see p. 354). In vertebrates other than mammals, these two tissues have different relations to each other and are differently distributed in the body. In the cyclostomes and elasmobranch fishes, for example, the two types of tissue are spatially separated from each other and the cortical part of the mammalian gland is represented by small masses of tissue, the inter-renal bodies, distributed along the postcardinal veins, and the medullary part by strands of cells of neural origin lying along the dorsal aorta and near the autonomic ganglia. In most of the other vertebrates, the mesodermal and neural cells are mingled together in a common cellular mass, without localization into cortex and medulla, that lies somewhere near the kidneys.

The first descriptions of symptoms arising in human beings from disturbance of adrenal functioning were given in 1855 by an English physician, Thomas Addison (1763–1860), and characterize the disease since known as Addison's disease. Among other symptoms, such as marked anemia, loss of appetite, lassitude and finally prostration, there are distinctive changes in the pigmentation of the skin, which, generally or in localized patches, becomes yellowish or deep brown. On autopsy of the bodies of patients who had died from this disease Dr. Addison found, almost without exception, deterioration of the cortices of both adrenal glands. The suspicion that the symptoms might be due to a hormone produced by these tissues was confirmed between 1928 and 1930, when extracts of the cortex were prepared that proved to be effective in prolonging the lives of animals from which the adrenals had been removed, otherwise invariably a fatal operation. This extract, first called cortin, has been subsequently found to contain at least 26 steroids, which have been isolated and crystallized in a pure state, six of which have been found to be physiologically active in minute concentration and therefore are included among the hormones. Two of these are known to be involved in the maintenance of constancy in the distribution of water and electrolytes between the cells and body fluids, primarily by regulation of the elimination of sodium and chlorine ions through the kidneys. If proper resorption of these ions does not take place in the kidney tubules (see p. 322) the osmotic equilibrium within the body is upset by the decrease in concentration of the electrolytes in the extracellular fluids, and the water content of the cells themselves therefore increases; such conditions arise after removal of the adrenal glands, but the "leakage" of sodium chloride, and the effects attendant upon it, can be checked by the administration of these two cortical hormones. The other four are involved in carbohydrate metabolism; in their absence the blood sugar level is lowered and the glycogen reserves of the liver and muscles depleted. The synthesis of carbohydrate from lactic acid and similar carbon compounds is interfered with as is the utilization of protein as a source of carbohydrate. Moreover, the muscles become incapable of doing as much work as they can in the presence of these cortical hormones, indicating that without them the degradation of carbohydrate does not follow its normal course. With cortical insufficiency, there are also disturbances of the reproductive functions and of the development of secondary sex characters. These effects of cortical removal or dysfunction seem to be common to all animals investigated, while the pigmentation changes that accompany them in Addison's disease are peculiar to humans.

The fatal effects of removal of the adrenal glands are due to the absence of these cortical hormones, for the medulla, unlike other organs of the endocrine system, does not secrete a vital substance, although one that has widespread effects within the body. The active principle that has been isolated from it is adrenalin, or epinephrine, a comparatively simple ring compound related to the amino acid tyrosine and to the substance which has been given the name sympathin, liberated during the activity of the thoracicolumbar nerves of the autonomic system (see p. 390). The general effects of increased amounts of adrenalin in the body fluids parallel the effects of stimulation of these nerves. It is the most potent agent known in bringing about the constriction of small blood vessels; in consequence of this, the blood pressure rises and the heart beats more strongly and would beat faster if it were not for inhibitory reflexes initiated by the elevation of blood pressure that tend to slow it down. A similar reflex mechanism inhibits the respiratory movements, so that breathing becomes slower and may even stop temporarily. But adrenalin has a direct inhibitory effect upon the movements of the stomach and intestine, which cease entirely when its concentration is raised above a certain level. In its presence, also, the coagulability of the blood is increased and its glucose concentration is raised through the increased hydrolysis of muscle and liver glycogen. There is no evidence that adrenalin stimulates the oxidation of the sugar so released, as insulin does. In the lower vertebrates, the distribution of pigment in chromatophores can be controlled by injection of adrenalin. In frogs, the dark pigment in the chromatophores of the integument becomes concentrated when adrenalin is injected subcutaneously while that in the pigment cells of the retina becomes dispersed. But in any vertebrate, the effects of adrenalin are short lived, for whether it is injected into them or released naturally into their blood streams from the adrenal medulla, it is rapidly metabolized and disappears as such from the body fluids.

THE PITUITARY BODY AND ITS ENDOCRINE SECRETIONS: The pituitary body or hypophysis is also a compound structure, derived in part from an outgrowth of the roof of the mouth and in part from a downgrowth of the floor of the diencephalon (see p. 365). Vesalius is responsible for the term pituitary, believing, as did earlier and later anatomists, that the organ served as a filtration bed through which passed fluids from the brain from which the wastes were filtered out and the fluid passed on to lubricate the nasal passages. Its connection with the endocrine system was first implied in 1889 when it was found that with removal of the thyroid changes in the pituitary were apparent upon post-mortem examination. In 1895, the first experiments were made with the injection of pituitary extracts which were found to be followed by a rise in blood pressure. Subsequent studies have shown that the pars anterior, or anterior lobe, contributes at least six kinds of hormones to the mechanism of chemical regulation, the pars posterior two, and the pars intermedia, one, in those vertebrates such as fishes, amphibia, reptiles and some mammals where this region remains distinct and does not merge with the pars posterior. Moreover, functional changes in the other endocrine glands are not only reflected in the pituitary but its functioning to a great extent also influences theirs (Fig. 21.10).

The secretions of the pars anterior fall into two general categories—those that affect generalized metabolic mechanisms and those that influence specifically the activity of other organs. In the first category is a substance that regulates growth, which has been isolated in a sufficiently pure state to allow its recognition as an individual secretion in the complex of pituitary secretions. Its effects were first recognized when the condition in man known as acromegaly (Greek, akron = peak + megas = large) was found often to be associated with enlargement of the anterior lobe. In acromegaly, growth begins again in those adult tissues capable of it, and is evidenced particularly in some of the bones, whose overgrowth brings about marked changes in skeletal formation (Fig. 21.11). Deficiency of this hormone, experimentally induced or occurring naturally through malfunction of the gland, during the active growth period of young animals results in stunted individuals, or dwarfs; excess of it leads to gigantism (Fig. 21.12). The individuality of the hormones affecting metabolism are not so well established as the growth hormone, but it is clear from the effects produced by the experimental removal of the gland and by the injection of extracts of the pars anterior that carbohydrate, fat and protein metabolism are profoundly influenced by it. In the second category of anterior lobe hormones is one that seems to act specifically upon the thyroid gland, for with the removal of the pituitary the thyroid atrophies and becomes non-functional, and with implantation of the anterior lobe, or injection of its extract, is restored to functional activity. The active principle concerned in this is called thyrotropin, since it turns or directs thyroid activity; deficiency or excess of it brings about the gross effects of thyroid hypo- or hyperactivity. The anterior lobe also releases a hormone, which has a similar effect upon the adrenal cortex, called corticotropin, and several which affect the gonads and the organs of reproduction. These gonadotropic factors influence not only the development of the sex organs in young animals but their functional activity in adults and will be considered with the mechanisms of reproduction in Chapter 23. In addition to these factors, the anterior lobe secretes a substance, prolactin, which, though present in appreciable amount in the pituitaries of all classes of vertebrates, initiates the production of milk in mammals and in doves and pigeons, where the young are fed a special milky secretion from the crop glands of their parents. Prolactin is, like secretin, a hormone that influences the production of a secretion from an organ already formed, and does not, like many of the other hormones, determine or regulate the growth

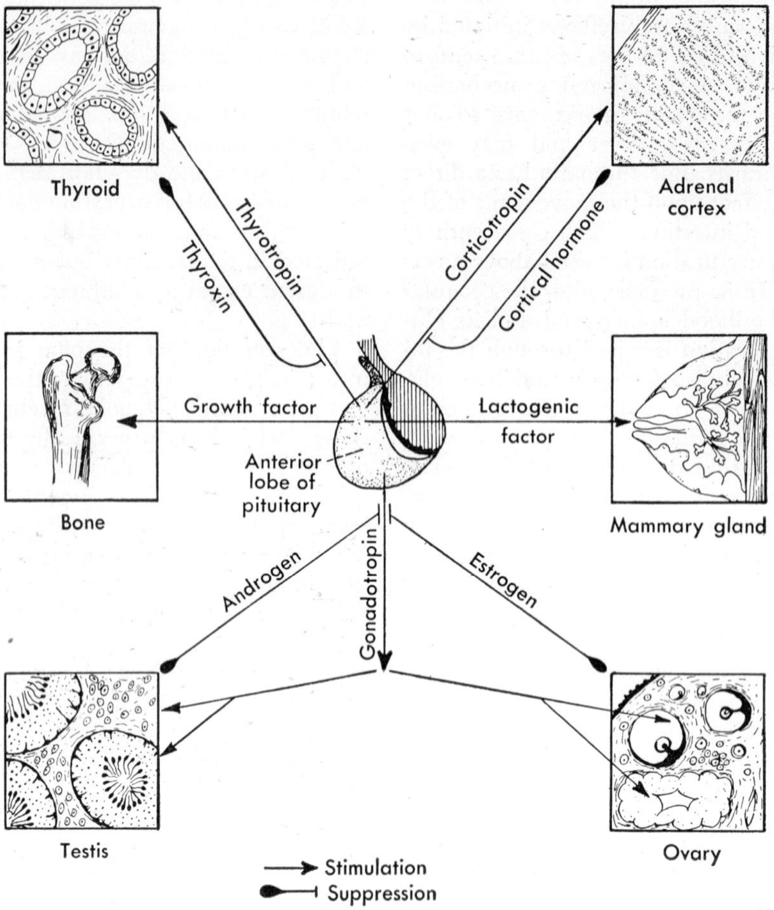

FIGURE 21.10 Diagram illustrating the action of the best-established hormones of the anterior lobe of the pituitary. (After Turner.)

and differentiation of a tissue or an organ. Prolactin is the only one of the anterior lobe hormones that has been obtained in crystalline form; it is a protein, belonging, according to present biochemical evidence, to the same category of organic compounds as the other hormones of the anterior lobe.

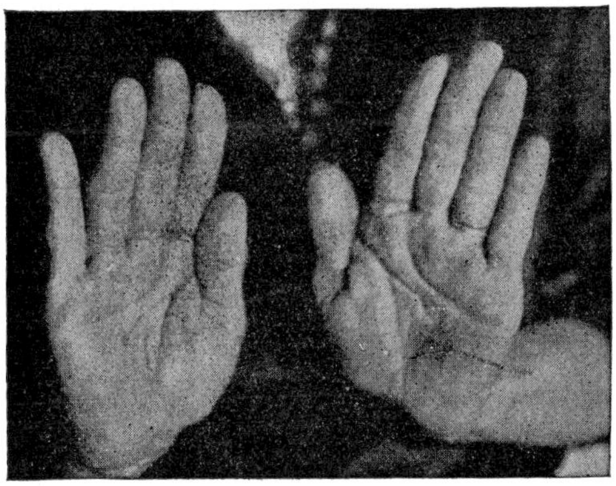

FIGURE 21.11 Spade hand in acromegaly. (From Major, *Physical Diagnosis,* 3rd edition, published by the W. B. Saunders Company. Copyright 1945.)

Two hormones of somewhat simpler chemical composition have been isolated from the pars posterior. These are apparently polypeptides, called pitressin and oxytocin (commercially pitocin). Both of these bring about the contraction of smooth muscles, oxytocin specifically those of the uterus, a part of the female reproductive system, and pitressin all those in the body, producing the same effects as a generalized stimulation of the autonomic system.

From the pars intermedia of those animals in which it can be anatomically identified has been extracted a substance called intermedin, which acts upon the chromatophores of cold-blooded animals and brings about dispersion of the pigment granules in them. Intermedin has also been obtained from pituitary extracts of all orders of vertebrates, whether they possess a chromatophore mechanism or not, which is equally potent upon those in which color changes are possible. The function of intermedin in birds and mammals, without a chromatophoric mechanism, is still undetermined. There is some evidence, too, though still inconclusive, that the intermediate lobe secretes a metabolic hormone, for when an extract of this lobe is injected into animals their RQ falls. Since this happens even after the removal of their thyroid glands, it cannot be attributed to the thyrotropic hormone. Intermedin, like the secretions of the anterior lobe, is a protein and resembles in some of its physicochemical properties the tail-darkening hormone of the Crustacea. Some similarity in action between the chromatophoric hormones of the vertebrates and invertebrates has been shown, in that the hormones of the one group of animals are

FIGURE 21.12 Russian giant, Machnow, 9 ft. 3 in. tall. (Launois and Roy, from Major, *Physical Diagnosis,* 3rd edition, published by the W. B. Saunders Company. Copyright 1945.)

effective upon pigment distribution in the other, but not always to the same extent or with the same results.

### Functional relationships between endocrine organs

The gonadotropic, thyrotropic and corticotropic hormones of the anterior pituitary are but three examples of the interaction that exists between different endocrine tissues. These three hormones control the development of the other three glands, and maintain their function. But other kinds of functional associations between endocrine organs have been demonstrated. One gland may moderate or regulate the secretion of another, as the estrogens and androgens are known to moderate the gonadotropic activity of the pituitary. Or two hormones may supplement each other, producing an additive effect, or act antagonistically to each other, maintaining a balance between two opposite effects. Some hormones increase the sensitivity of an organ to the action of others, and some, if their action is too extended, may damage the organ that is reactive to them; this latter condition is known to arise after repeated injections of anterior pituitary extract and of thyroxin, when the islet cells of the pancreas become exhausted and ultimately degenerate through continued secretion of additional amounts of insulin to combat the continuously induced hyperglycemia. But under ordinary, or so-called normal, conditions in an organism, the functional interrelationships are such that conditions within the body are kept within a narrow range of fluctuation, and, however its internal and external activity may vary, the constancy of the "milieu intérieure" is maintained.

There is also a reciprocal relationship between the hormone-producing tissues and the mechanisms that they regulate. Presumably each gland secretes continuously at a basal rate, since the removal of any one results in the characteristic symptoms of its hormonal deficiency, but can be stimulated to increased or decreased production of its hormones by conditions that arise within the body. A rise in the level of blood sugar, for example, stimulates the islet cells to an additional secretion of insulin, but when the blood sugar has fallen again to its ordinary level through the mediation of the hormone, they return to their basal rate of secretion. The adrenal medulla discharges a steady supply of adrenalin into the body fluids, but is stimulated to discharge more under conditions of hyperglycemia and asphyxia, as well as under the emotional conditions of alarm, fear, rage and pain. When these conditions are over, the secretion returns again to the basal level.

Histologically the endocrine tissues are well supplied with both blood vessels and nerves of the autonomic system, and stimuli may reach them through either medium. Nervous stimulation results in their immediate and rapid response, while chemical stimulation through the blood regulates their continuous basal functioning. That this regulation is a very precise and delicate one has been shown by experiments in which parts of an endocrine organ have been removed or additional organs implanted. As much as $6/7$ of its pancreas may be removed from an animal without affecting the blood sugar level, the islet cells of the remaining seventh combining to produce adequate amounts of insulin for its basal carbohydrate metabolism, although possibly not enough to meet any demand beyond this. Likewise, as many as four extra pancreases have been grafted into an animal without changing its blood sugar level, for the secretion of insulin by one or by five sets of islet tissue is equally controlled by the concentration of glucose in the blood. But diseased or pathological conditions of a gland may lead to a change in its basal rate of secretion, and result in the symptoms associated with deficiency or excess of its hormones, although since no one gland nor any part of the animal body is independent of the other, these symptoms are a complex of hormonal and metabolic effects and can never be reduced to a single altered biological process.

### Destruction of hormones; hormones and vitamins

Hormones themselves undergo metabolism, for they are known to disappear rapidly from the blood stream even after they have been injected in relatively large amounts. The course of this metabolism, as well as the chemical nature and molecular configuration of the compounds already identified as hormones, are problems under active investigation at present in many biochemical laboratories. From what is at present known about the composition of biologically active substances such as hormones and vitamins, it is apparent that a very slight change in the atomic groupings within their molecules may radically alter their potency, and that there is but a narrow margin of difference between an active and an inactive substance. The biological relationships between vitamins and hormones seem also to be close ones and these relationships are likewise under active biochemical investigation at present. Both Vitamin A and the estrogens, for example, may individually affect epithelia, and the question at once arises whether a relationship exists between them, or whether they are independent in their action. A number of hormones, notably the sex hormones, are sterols, and so are the vitamins of the D group, and it is possible that cholesterol, the sterol that is known to be synthesized in the animal body, is their precursor as it is believed to be that of Vitamin $D_3$. And the hormones that influence metabolism are involved in the regulation of enzymatic reactions in which vitamins are known to take part, pointing again to a possible but yet undetermined relationship between these categories of biological agents known to be essential to the functioning of the most highly evolved of existing biological systems.

# CHAPTER 22
# GROWTH AND REGENERATION; FISSION, BUDDING AND PARTHENOGENESIS

## Surface-volume relationships of cells

Growth is essentially an expression of protein synthesis. In order to grow, a cell must be supplied with material, beyond its minimal or basal needs, for the construction of the complex protein molecules of its cytoplasm and nucleus, and must have efficiently working enzyme systems to direct these anabolic reactions. When these conditions are fulfilled, the cell increases in volume. The rate of this increase is greater than that of its surface area, for the volume of a sphere, the geometric form that most closely approximates the generalized shape of cells, is proportional to the cube of the radius, while that of the surface is proportional to the square (volume = $\frac{4}{3}\pi r^3$; surface = $4\pi r^2$). And since every cell, whether an independent protoplasmic unit or one in a system of many, depends upon its surface and surface membrane for the exchange of materials with the surrounding environment, and upon diffusion between that surface and its interior, the surface area is a primary factor limiting its indefinite increase in size. For if the exchange of diffusible materials is too slow, the cell becomes starved, asphyxiated or otherwise destroyed by the accumulation of its metabolic products, after which the proteins that compose it become susceptible to the action of its own proteases, and it undergoes self-digestion or autolysis.

## The division of cells

In most instances, when the surface-volume ratio approaches a point where these limiting conditions prevail, the cell divides into two approximately equal halves, with a resulting reduction in the volume of each half, or daughter cell, in relation to its surface area. The sequence of events in such division was first followed completely by two German biologists, Walter Flemming (1843–1913) and Eduard Strasburger (1844–1912), Flemming tracing the course of division in fixed and stained cells of a number of animals, and Strasburger that in a number of plants. Their observations have since been confirmed by many others both on fixed and stained cells and on living ones, where the progress of division has been watched and photographed (Fig. 22.1). Motion picture photography has made it possible to record the process continuously and, by slow projection, to analyze its steps. Information from all these sources has made it evident that there is a general pattern of division common to all cells, although in its detail those of different tissues differ from each other.

## Mitosis

Cells divide by mitosis (Greek, mitos = thread), a term introduced by Flemming, to whom is also due much of the other terminology of the process. Mitosis involves changes both in the nucleus and the cytoplasm, a series of events that ordinarily are synchronized with each other, moving along in an harmonious rhythm. But the nucleus may divide, if not independently of the cytoplasm, at least without accompanying cytoplasmic division, so that a single cytoplasmic mass may contain two or more nuclei, and, likewise, the cytoplasm may divide independently of the nucleus. This has been shown in experiments in which the nucleus has been removed from a cell, either by centrifugal force or by operation; in such enucleated embryonic cells the cytoplasm may divide a number of times, but the cells

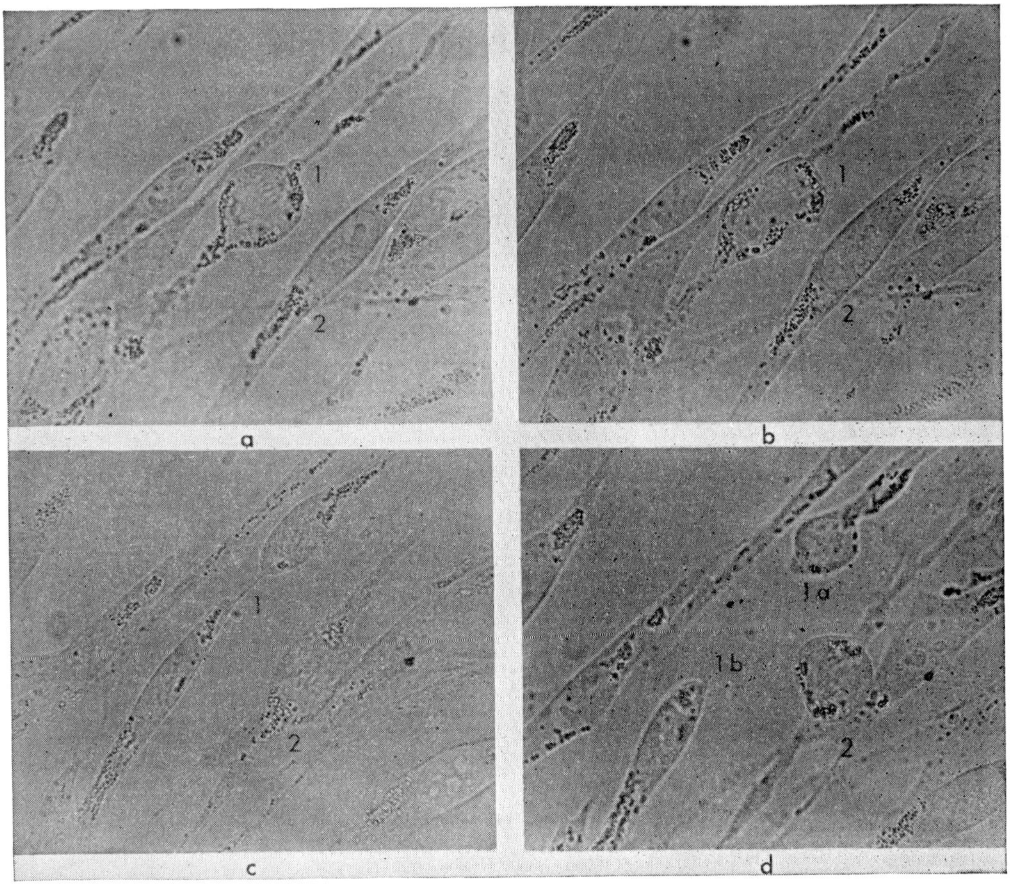

FIGURE 22.1 Mitosis in fibroblasts of mouse cultivated in vitro. (Photographs by courtesy of Dr. Warren Lewis.)

a. 2:38 P.M. The cell marked 1 is in anaphase; the cell marked 2 is in interphase.

b. 2:45 P.M. Late anaphase in cell 1; cytoplasmic constriction beginning. Cell 2 is beginning prophase.

c. 3:33 P.M. Division in cell 1 is almost complete; the two daughter cells are held together by a slender strand of cytoplasm, and their nuclei are in telophase. Cell 2 is approaching metaphase.

d. 3:45 P.M. Cell 1 has divided into two daughter cells, marked 1a and 1b. Cell 2 is in anaphase (compare cell 1 in a).

show no differentiation and ultimately division ceases. But ordinarily, in intact and growing cells, disturbances in the timing of events in either the nucleus or the cytoplasm disturb the rhythm of the division process and are reflected in abnormalities of its products.

For purposes of convenience in referring to different stages in the process, mitosis may be divided into prophase (Greek, pro = before), metaphase (Greek, meta = between), anaphase (Greek, ana = upward) and telophase (Greek, telos = end), although, except in some special cases, the process is a continuous one and one phase passes into another without any break (Fig. 22.2).

*The events of prophase:* In the nucleus the first indication of prophase is the appearance of delicate threads, or strands, often of different length which in the fixed and

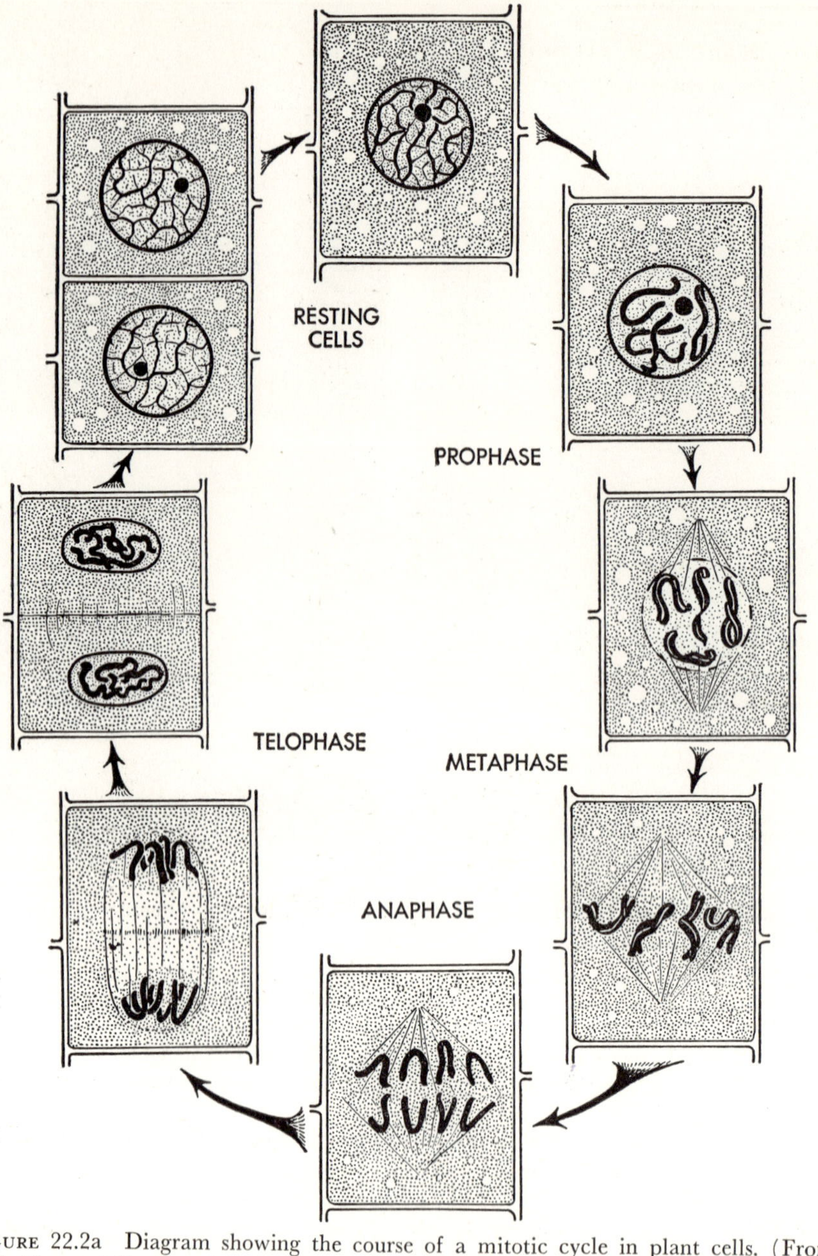

FIGURE 22.2a  Diagram showing the course of a mitotic cycle in plant cells. (From Hylander and Stanley, *College Botany*. Copyright 1949 by The Macmillan Company.)

stained cell stand out sharply against the lighter background of the rest of the nuclear contents and, in the living cell, as distinct bodies in the otherwise optically homogeneous substance. These threads are the chromosomes, given this name by the first microscopists to see them because they stained so much more readily and deeply than other elements in the cell. As the chromosomes appear in the nucleus, the nucleolus, or nucleoli, disappear, contributing their substance to the structure of the chromosomes. According to present knowledge, each chromosome consists of a coiled thread, the chromonema (Greek, chroma = color + nema = thread) of a nucleic acid-protein complex embedded in a protein matrix, and possibly wound around a protein core (Fig. 22.3). The chromonema is essentially a string of genes, a linear aggregation of large and complex molecules of nucleo-protein that can duplicate themselves through some process of nucleo-protein synthesis still to be understood, and direct the course of development of the cell that contains them. Aggregations of genic substance appear on stained chromosomes as lumps of different size, called chromomeres, distributed at different, but constant, intervals along the chromonema.

THE CHARACTERISTICS OF THE CHROMOSOMES: Counts of the chromosomes that become visible in the nucleus during mitosis have shown that there is a number characteristic for the cells of a given species and approximately constant in all of them. Some species have only a small number, others have a large one. Eight, for example, is the number characteristic of the fruit fly Drosophila melanogaster; fourteen of the garden pea; forty-eight of man; and 100 of some species of Rumex, the genus of plants that includes the docks and the sorrels. The length of the thread that first appears, the distribution of its chromomeres, and the final size and shape of each chromosome, are definite and characteristic, so that it is possible in many cases to follow the course of each individual chromosome through successive mitotic divisions.

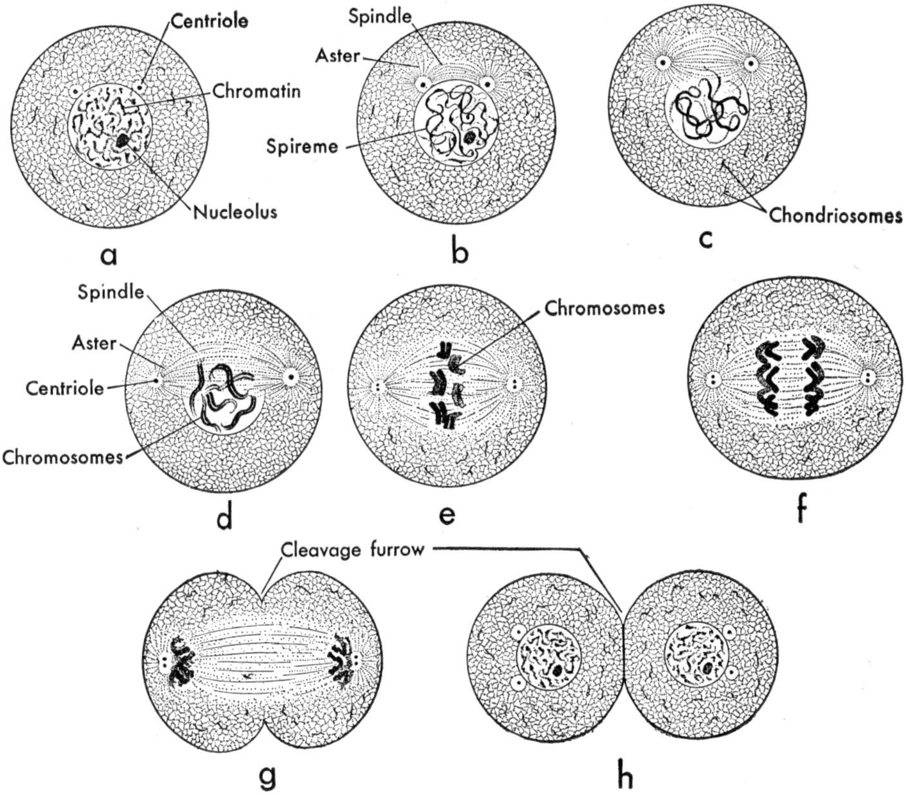

As prophase proceeds, each chromosome

FIGURE 22.2b  Diagram showing the course of a mitotic cycle in animal cells. (From Huettner, *Comparative Embryology of the Vertebrates*. Copyright 1949 by The Macmillan Company.)

a, Interphase; b–d, prophase; e, metaphase; f, anaphase; g, telophase; h, interphase.

shortens and thickens until it becomes a compact, highly refractile or, in stained cells, deeply staining body. This shortening is the result of the tightening of the coils of the chromonema, analogous to the shortening of a relaxed spring when it is again tightly wound and compressed. While these changes are going on within the nucleus, activity in the cytoplasm has been initiated in the region near the nuclear border often marked by one small body, the centriole, or by two of them. Typically in animal cells, fibres radiate out from the centrioles into the cytoplasm, forming an "aster"; if there is but a single centriole in the cell it divides before the asters appear. As prophase proceeds, the asters grow larger and more sharply defined and the two centrioles, with their radiations,

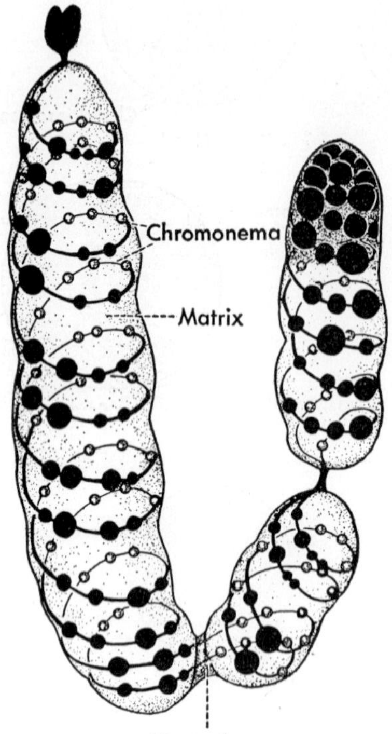

FIGURE 22.3 Diagram showing the structure of a chromosome. (After Geitler.)

Two spiraled chromonemata are shown within a matrix. One arm of the chromosome (to the left of the kinetochore, or primary constriction) shows a secondary constriction near the end with two small knobs; the other arm (to the right of the kinetochore) shows a secondary constriction about halfway along its length. Both of the knobs (or trabants) and the dark area at the end of the right arm are regions where the chromonemata remain tightly coiled throughout the mitotic cycle. The position of the kinetochore, the number and position of the secondary constrictions, the extent and distribution of the regions where the chromonemata remain tightly spiraled, are all distinguishing features of individual chromosomes.

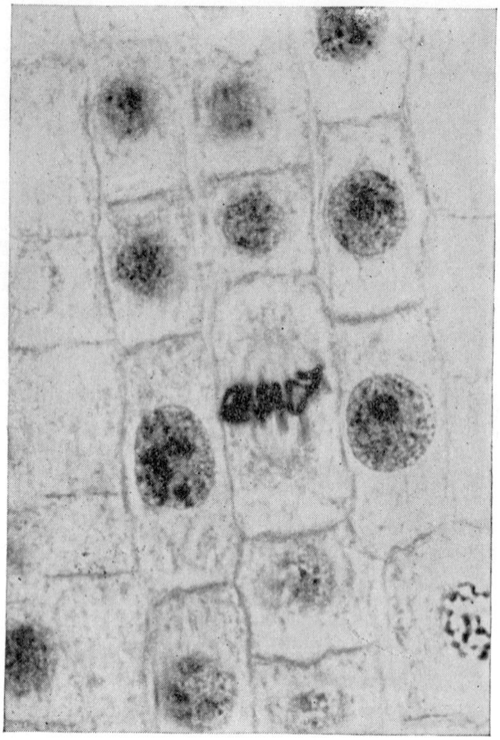

FIGURE 22.4 Dividing cells in the root tip of the onion. (Photograph by courtesy of the General Biological Supply House, Inc., Chicago.)

separate from each other, moving around the periphery of the nucleus until they lie 180° apart (Fig. 22.2b). The region of the cell between them becomes converted into an elliptical structure, the spindle, that is clearly delimited from other parts of the cytoplasm. Coincident with these changes, the nuclear membrane disappears and the spindle comes to occupy the position formerly held by the nucleus. Under some circumstances, the spindle appears to be homogeneous, under others to be traversed by fine fibrils that run lengthwise along it and converge at its poles where the centrioles lie. Such a bi-polar, astral spindle is characteristic of most animal cells; in dividing plant cells, and in some of the divisions of reproductive cells in animals, no asters are formed (Figs. 22.4, 22.5). In a few exceptional cases among animals, the spindle is regularly unipolar, and in some unusual conditions, a tripolar, or even a multipolar one, may arise.

its kinetochore; in plants, the attachment is usually around the periphery of the spindle, so that the chromosomes lie with their arms extending out into the cytoplasm and free to move with the cytoplasmic currents. In animals the chromosomes usually lie wholly within the substance of the spindle, attached to its core as well as its margin. Their migration to the equator and orientation upon it mark the metaphase of mi-

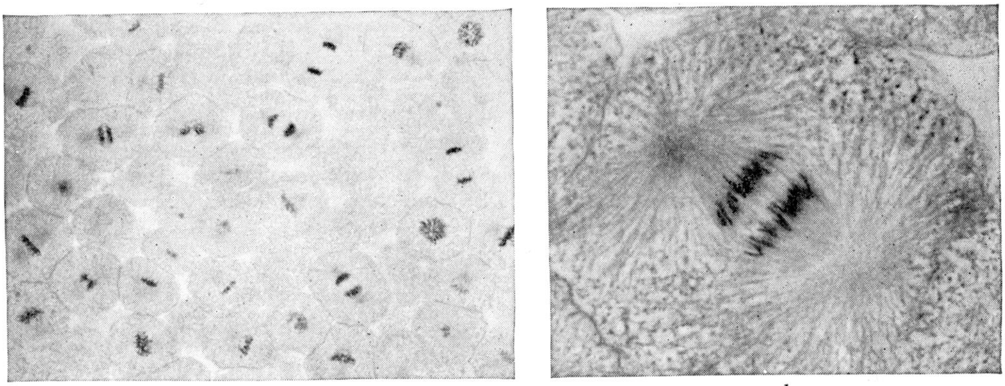

a          b

FIGURE 22.5 Dividing cells in the blastoderm of the whitefish. (Photograph by courtesy of the General Biological Supply House, Inc., Chicago.)

   a. Surface of the blastoderm showing many cells in division with well-defined spindles and asters.
   b. A single cell in early anaphase, greatly magnified.

***Metaphase:*** In each chromosome there is always one region where the chromonema remains uncoiled, or unspiralled. This region has a definite relation to the spindle and is known as the kinetochore (Greek, kinetos = moving), or centromere. It may lie near the end of the chromosome, or in the middle of it, or at any point between the middle and the end, but its position is constant for each chromosome in the nuclear set and is one of the characteristics by which individual chromosomes can be identified (Fig. 22.3). At their first appearance in the nucleus, the chromosomes are fairly evenly distributed within it, lying usually near its membrane and about equidistant from each other. But as mitosis progresses and the spindle is formed, they move toward the center of the spindle and become arranged at its equator. Each chromosome is attached to the spindle, or to a fibre of the spindle, by

tosis and the condition closest to equilibrium during the entire mitotic sequence; cells are known to remain in metaphase for extended periods of time, while the other stages are passed through with considerable rapidity.

***The events of anaphase:*** At some point during the mitotic cycle, the chromonema in each chromosome becomes duplicated, and at metaphase, each chromosome consists of two similar halves, or chromatids (Latin suffix, ides = daughters), each containing its linear aggregate of genes in an individual protein matrix (Fig. 22.3). At anaphase, the two chromatids move apart from each other and migrate toward the poles of the spindle. In every case, this separation is initiated at the kinetochore, which precedes the rest of the chromatid in its progress to the pole. Consequently the position of the kinetochore determines the shape of the chromatid during anaphase; if it is very close to the end, the chromosome will be rod-shaped; if in the middle, V-shaped; and if between these two points, J-shaped, the degree of inequality of its arms depending upon the exact location of the kinetochore. As the chromosomes move to its poles, the spindle becomes thinner and less well-defined and in most cases but a few faint fibrils and some granules mark the previous position of its equator.

**The events of telophase:** The convergence of the two sets of chromatids, or daughter chromosomes, at the poles of the spindle indicates the beginning of telophase. During this part of the mitotic sequence, the chromosomes lengthen out again into slender threads as the coils of their chromonemata relax and, surrounded by fluid, become enclosed in vesicles which gradually coalesce to form a common vesicle enclosing them all, the nucleus. As the chromosomes lengthen, they become less and less distinct, both in stained cells and in living ones, and nucleoli reappear in association with them. The individual nucleoli ultimately unite into one or two of greater volume and, except for them, the new nucleus assumes again its apparent structural homogeneity (Fig. 22.1). But several facts show that this homogeneity is only apparent. First, at the next division, the chromosomes reappear in the nucleus in the same positions they held at their disappearance; second, movements of a micro-dissection needle within an intermitotic nucleus are not free ones, but are impeded by regions of greater viscosity, corresponding to the locations of the chromosomes at their disappearance, and thirdly, in some living cells, the chromosomes or some part of each of them, even when in their most extended state, have a higher index of refraction than the nuclear material around them, and so are visible during the intervals between mitoses.

**Cytoplasmic division:** In the cytoplasm marked changes also take place during anaphase and telophase. As the daughter chromosomes move toward the poles of the spindle, the periphery of the cell often becomes lobulated; as observed in tissue cultures, this stage seems to be a period of great cytoplasmic activity, for the cell jerks and shakes as if it were in a state of internal upheaval. Toward the end of anaphase, in animal cells, a circular constriction appears around the cell called the cleavage furrow (Fig. 22.2b, g); this constriction deepens until the cytoplasm is divided into two parts, each one of which includes one of the newly formed nuclei. The cleavage furrow almost invariably lies so that it cuts across the center of the spindle; if this was located in the center of the cell, the two daughter cells are approximately even in size, but if it was eccentric in position, one daughter cell may be smaller than the other.

In dividing plant cells no such constriction appears, and the cell wall separating the two daughter cells is constructed from material that collects first in the region of the equator of the spindle and then extends to the margins of the cell (Fig. 22.2a). This material is known as the cell plate; it is first evident as granules, or small vacuoles, in the center of the cell and later as a well-defined septum or partition between the two new nuclei and their surrounding cytoplasm. Gradually, with the addition of more pectin compounds and of cellulose, the partition thickens into a typical plant cell wall and the two new cells are complete, but smaller, counterparts of the one from which they originated.

Mitosis thus results in the formation of two smaller cells from a previous larger one, each cell having approximately half the cytoplasmic contents of its parent cell and exactly the same chromosomal composition. The various cytoplasmic inclusions of the original cell are distributed fairly equally between the two new ones, but there is no conclusive evidence that any precise mechanism exists for their equal distribution, such as that which has been demonstrated for the chromosomal content of the nucleus. Additionally, mitosis results in the redistribution and reorganization of the cell's contents, for with the breakdown of the nuclear membrane, all the nuclear contents is brought into intimate relation with the cytoplasm.

## Amitosis

Occasionally, animal cells divide by amitosis, without the formation of a spindle and well-defined chromosomes. This takes place by a constriction of the cell which starts at its periphery and divides nucleus as well as cytoplasm into two approximately similar parts. There is no dissolution of the nuclear membrane, and neither a mixing of its contents with the cytoplasm nor apparently an exact distribution of the chromosomes. Amitosis has been described in some highly differentiated cells, such as bone cells and erythrocytes, but is not a common biological phenomenon, and by no means a universal one like mitosis (Fig. 22.6).

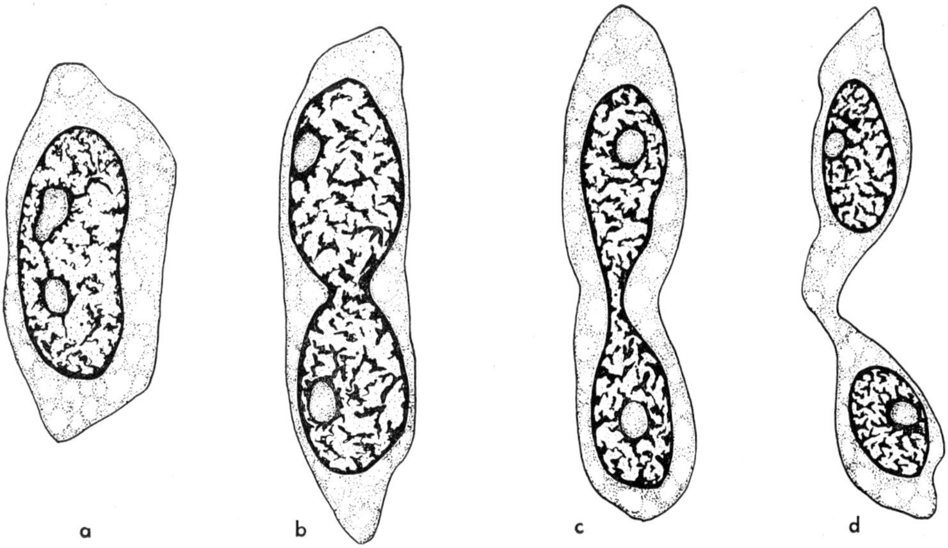

## The duration of mitosis

The duration of an entire mitotic sequence and of its different phases varies with different types of cells and under different conditions in cells of the same type. In embryonic and regenerating tissues, one division may follow another in rapid succession with only a short interval, or interphase, between them, the entire process moving rapidly from stage to stage.

FIGURE 22.6 Amitosis. Cells of the bladder epithelium in various stages of amitotic division. (After Nonidez and Windle.)

a. Cell showing elongation of the nucleus.
b. Cell showing elongation of the nucleus and cytoplasm and initial constriction of the nucleus.
c. Cell showing constriction of the nucleus.
d. Cell showing complete constriction of the nucleus and almost complete constriction of the cytoplasm.

TABLE XIV

Duration of Stages in the Mitotic Cycle [a]
(Time in Minutes)

|  | Drosophila Embryonic divisions (fixed cells) | Chick Mesenchyme (live cells in tissue culture) | Arrhenatherum (a grass) live cells |
|---|---|---|---|
| Interphase | 2.9 | 30–120 | ..... |
| Prophase | 3.6 | 30–60 | 36–45 |
| Metaphase | 0.5 | 2–10 | 7–10 |
| Anaphase | 1.2 | 2–3 | 15–20 |
| Telophase | 0.9 | 3–12 | 20–35 |
| Total | 9.1 | 67–205 | 78–110 |

[a] Schrader, Franz, *Mitosis*. Copyright 1944 by Columbia University Press, New York.

In older tissues the intermitotic interval (interphase), which represents the period of the cell's greatest synthetic activity, may be longer and in the most highly differentiated cells of a plant's or animal's body, the end cells, there is no further division.

Mitosis represents an expenditure of energy on the part of the dividing cell and is therefore an expression of energy transformations within it. As such, it is influenced by conditions that in general influence such transformations, that is, by temperature and by anaesthetics or other chemical agents that inhibit oxidations, as well as by the osmotic relationships existing between the cell and its environment. But the conditions that exist in a cell to initiate it, or to prevent its occurrence, as well as the interpretation of the events that take place in its course are still puzzles, but puzzles whose solution is of the utmost importance to an understanding of the most fundamental of all biological problems, the growth of organisms.

## Cell division and growth in multicellular systems

In multicellular systems, growth takes place through the multiplication of the cells of which they are composed and thus reflects the growth and mitotic activity of the individual cells. But every multicellular system is more than a mass of cells, for it has structural organization, expressed by its size, shape, and architectural pattern, and functional organization, expressed by the degree of differentiation, specialization and localization of its component cells. It is on the basis of such organization that taxonomic distinctions are made, but little is yet definitely known about the mechanisms that regulate and control the growth and differentiation leading to it, beyond the fact that they are part of the innate and inheritable constitution of any species and of each individual within a species, and that they may be markedly influenced by internal as well as external environmental conditions.

## Typical and atypical growth

In plants, growth is potentially unlimited because of the presence of permanent embryonic tissue in their bodies, as meristem at their growing points and, in spermatophytes, as cambium in their stems and roots as well. But although of indefinite duration, their growth is not haphazard, but ordered and regulated, for their bodies and the individual parts of their bodies show symmetry and consistency in their pattern and arrangement. But no animal is known whose natural growth is not limited both in time and in extent, although the long-term cultivation in vitro of successive generations of cells from a single piece of explanted tissue raises the possibility that under closely defined and constant conditions animal tissues may be capable of sustained existence. In nature, however, animals have a recognized life span and recognized and characteristic shapes and limitations of size. Indeed, in some of the more simply organized animals, such as rotifers and nematodes, all the cells of the body or certain organs never exceed a definite and comparatively small number. In larger and more highly organized animals, the total number of cells is indefinite yet there are checks to the unlimited growth of the whole body and of its parts, for once it has reached its characteristic size and symmetry, the rapid multiplication of cells ordinarily stops and there is no further increase in size, or addition of parts to it. A mouse, however well fed, never attains the size of a rat, nor a rat that of a woodchuck; a rabbit's external ears are always long in proportion to the rest of its body, a guinea pig's barely visible. It has already been pointed out that in both plants and animals hormones are known to regulate some aspects of morphogenesis, but how far chemical regulation can be held to account for all the phenomena of growth is still problematical. But however it may be ordered, the structural and functional development of an organism represents a balance between stimulation and inhibition of cell division. The problems of typical growth, still a long way from solution, are inseparable from those of atypical growth, in which cells seem to break loose from all the restraints ordinarily imposed upon them, dividing in a rapid and random fashion, and so giving rise to neoplasms (Greek, neos = new +

plassein = form), or tumors (Latin, tumor = swelling). Such impetus to growth is known to arise spontaneously within organisms, and also in response to certain stimuli, and may result in benign growths, or in malignant or cancerous ones. Injury to the tissue of a plant, for example, may stimulate its cells to divide; this is evident in the large callus formations of angiosperms resulting from the activity of the cork cambium in the vicinity of a wound, in the galls (Latin, galla = gallnut) developed on leaves and stems of many plants after the epidermis has been penetrated by the sting of an insect, and in the "resin galls" that arise spontaneously on the trunks and branches of various trees. In animals, neoplasms can be induced by the application of chemical agents called, because of their biological activity, carcinogens (Greek, carcinos = cancer + genes = born); such growths also arise spontaneously in every kind of tissue. Analysis of the factors that underlie neoplastic growth and that may prevent or inhibit it once it has started is one object of world-wide investigation, energetically pursued in hospital, academic and special research laboratories with every tool the scientist can provide. For an understanding of these factors lies at the root of the control and prevention of cancer, still one of the most baffling of human diseases and one that annually incapacitates and destroys thousands of human beings.

*Organizers in morphogenesis:* Typical growth is an expression of the orderly and controlled multiplication of cells that gives to an organism its characteristic size, symmetry and proportions, as well as of the differentiation of those cells into the specialized and localized tissues equally characteristic of it. This takes place during the embryonic and juvenile stages of all organisms, and in the course of such ontogeny (Greek, ontos = being + genes = born), when it follows the average or normal pattern, the new cells are brought into geographical and functional relationships with each other in a regulated time sequence. That mutual relationships exist between cells as they become organized into the definitive tissues and organs of the adult has been shown by experiments in which parts of the developing organism have been removed entirely, transplanted from place to place in a single individual, or grafted into others of the same or different species. Experiments such as these, particularly those that have been performed upon amphibian embryos, have led to the concept of "induction," first stated in 1924 by a German embryologist, Hans Spemann (1869–1941). According to this concept, localized cells in the developing individual act as organizers for others, inducing their differentiation into specific structures, either embryonic or adult. Organizers are progressively developed during the course of ontogeny, and their effect implies not only competence on the part of the inducing tissue to act as such, but also competence on the part of the responding tissue to receive and respond to the organizing stimulus. The timing of events in development is clearly of importance in such induction, for in order to be effective in the regulation of normal growth, the inducing cells must have a geographical location as well as a biological potency to act as organizers and the inducted cells must also be in a location and in a state of readiness to be receptive to their developmental influence. The fact that such competent, or receptive, embryonic tissues may be stimulated to differentiation by a variety of substances obtained from cells, some of known and some of at present unknown composition, excludes the active organizing principles from the category of recognized and accepted hormones. But the evidence of their activity makes it clear that in organic growth and development there exists a mutual relationship between the cells and cellular units, and that differentiation results from conditions external, or extrinsic, to the cells as well as internal, or intrinsic, ones. These external conditions may be mechanical ones, due to contact with neighboring cells or to stresses and strains set up in the newly formed tissues, or chemical ones, such as hormones or organizers. The intrinsic conditions are determined by the developmental potentialities with which cells are inherently endowed, conferred upon them by the chromosomal and hence the genic constitution that they have inherited from the cells preceding them in the ontogenetic sequence, and also by the physiological conditions existing within them at any given time.

**Regeneration as a manifestation of growth**

Many investigations of the problem of growth and differentiation have centered on the mechanisms of regeneration, or the restoration of parts that have been lost from an organism through injury or, in the species in which it is possible, through autotomy. Such studies offer the possibility of an experimental approach to the problem, for new growth can be initiated and its course followed under conditions that the investigator can, within limits, determine and control.

The capacity for regeneration is very general among plants but among animals, restricted, except for comparatively minor repairs of tissue injuries such as the healing of wounds or of fractured bones, to those at the lower levels of evolutionary development. In the sponges, hydroid coelenterates, planarians, starfishes and simpler annelids, almost any fragment, provided it is of adequate size, will regenerate a complete new individual, yet ctenophores and rotifers have no regenerative capacities. Only the anterior segments of earthworms can regenerate a new individual, and in the decapod Crustacea the restoration of parts is limited to the replacement of lost appendages. Among the vertebrates, the urodele amphibia can regenerate complete limbs and tails, apparently indefinitely, but the anuran cannot do so even once. There are also some lizards that break off their tails by autotomy and afterwards regenerate new, but boneless, ones, and in some few animals—sea cucumbers, Bryozoa and tunicates—disintegration, followed by regeneration, of their internal organs is a natural and spontaneous occurrence.

*Experiments on regeneration:* In experimental regeneration, when an animal has been cut into pieces, or a part removed from it, the wound is closed over by a layer of epithelium and the first sign of new growth is the appearance of a cone, or mass of tissue, called a blastema (Greek, blastema = sprout) at the new surface. The blastema is made up of undifferentiated cells that have migrated there from adjacent parts of the body, or are daughter cells, through mitotic divisions, of generalized cells in the intact part. The new structures are formed through continued divisions and rearrangements that bring the new generations of cells into positions appropriate for their differentiation and for the construction of the missing parts. That this differentiation proceeds along with the multiplication and organization of the new cells has been proved experimentally. When, for example, all the bones in the forelimb of a salamander are dissected out, the arm hangs permanently limp, for new bone does not grow within it; if it is amputated at the elbow, the stump heals over, a blastema appears and a new forearm grows, with all the bones, muscles, nerves and other parts of a normal one, although attached to a boneless upper arm. This could not have happened if the differentiated tissues of the regenerated part had been lineal descendants of those in the part immediately proximal to it, for in these experimental animals there were no bone cells in the upper arm to contribute descendants to the regenerated forearm.

HOMOMORPHOSIS AND HETEROMORPHOSIS: When the regenerated part is the replica of that which was lost, as in the restoration of the apical end of a hydroid from a basal segment, the head of a planarian from the posterior part of its body or the arm of a starfish from the disc, the conditions are those of homomorphosis (Fig. 22.7). But heteromorphic regeneration also takes place, when the restored part is not the duplicate of the missing one but of some other. If, for example, an earthworm is cut into two pieces back of the 18th somite, the posterior part will not regenerate a head, but another tail and the regenerate is not an individual, although an organized mass of cells, and having no mouth or other organs of the anterior region, does not long survive (Fig. 22.8). Removal of the crusher claw from lobsters, or of the fiddling arm from fiddler crabs, usually results in heteromorphosis, for the regenerated arm becomes the smaller of the pair and the surviving arm develops into the larger. In the Crustacea, too, an antenna may develop in the place of an eye which, with its optic ganglion, has been removed.

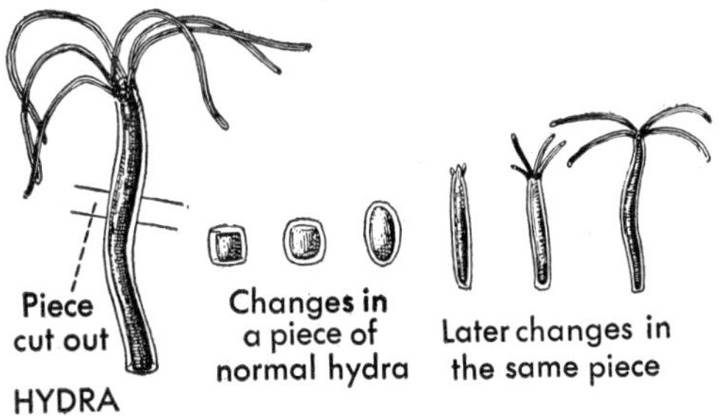

FIGURE 22.7 Experiments on regeneration in Hydra, showing homomorphosis. (From Woodruff, *Foundations of Biology*, 6th edition. Copyright 1941 by The Macmillan Company.)

THE CONCEPT OF PHYSIOLOGICAL DOMINANCE: The conditions of homo- and of heteromorphosis make it apparent that in the construction of a new part the old exerts some kind of influence upon the regenerating tissues, at least to the extent of maintaining relationships of symmetry and proportion in the body. This has been explained in terms of the physiological dominance of one part over another, and of a gradient of dominance between different regions of the body. There is no doubt that a gradient exists, when measured as relative metabolic activity, sensitivity to respiratory poisons or differences in electrical potential, but how it may act to control morphogenesis is still far from clear.

## Cell division in unicellular systems

While in multicellular systems cell division results in the growth and enlargement of the individual, in unicellular systems it results in the increase of individuals, or the enlargement of the population. Each time a unicellular plant or animal divides, a new individual is added to the total of those in the immediate environment; that is, at each fission, the population is doubled. Among the Protozoa and Protophyta, division is thus also reproduction, the means by which a species is perpetuated through the production of new individuals from those already existing.

The division, or fission, of one individual into two takes place by mitosis, in those unicellular systems in which its course has been fully followed. It has not yet been possible to trace its course in bacteria, but in yeasts, unicellular algae and Protozoa like Amoeba, Paramoecium and Vorticella, the formation of a spindle and of chromosomes and the movements of the chromosomes are in all essential respects like those of other cells. In the ciliates, whose nuclear apparatus is separated into macronucleus and micronucleus, the micronucleus alone divides by mitosis and the macronucleus divides amitotically, elongating and constricting into two parts of approximately equal size, one of which is included in each of the daughter cells. Fis-

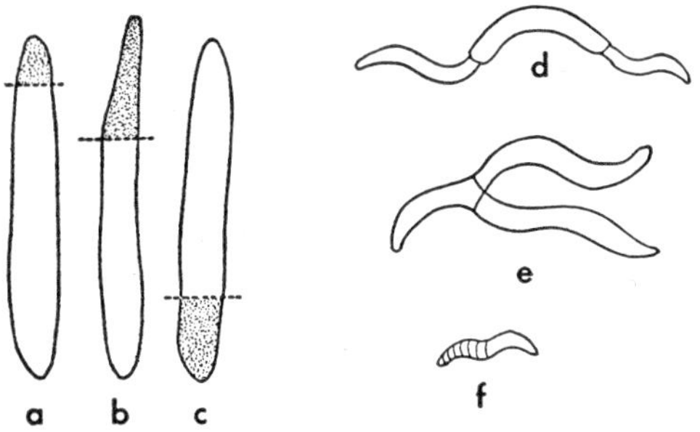

FIGURE 22.8 Experiments on regeneration and grafting in the earthworm. (From Morgan, from Woodruff, *Foundations of Biology*, 6th edition. Copyright 1941 by The Macmillan Company.) Regenerated portions are stippled.

a. Regeneration of the removed anterior segments by the posterior piece. (Homomorphosis.)

b. Regeneration of posterior segments by the posterior part, giving a "worm" with no head and two tails. (Heteromorphosis.)

c. Regeneration of removed posterior segments by the anterior piece. (Homomorphosis.)

d. Three pieces grafted together to make a single long worm.

e. Two pieces grafted to make a worm with two "tails."

f. A short anterior and a short posterior piece grafted together.

sion in bacteria may take place as often as once every twenty minutes, so that at the end of four hours a single bacterium may give rise to some five thousand descendants, and at the end of twenty-four to several million millions of them. Among the Protozoa each division occupies a longer period of time and successive divisions are further apart. Each fission, too, represents not only a nuclear and cytoplasmic division, but some sort of cytoplasmic reorganization. In Paramoecium, for example, in the new individual derived from the posterior half of the parent body, a new oral groove and other organelles of the anterior region must be constructed, and in that derived from the anterior region, those of the posterior part must be organized anew.

## Reproduction by fission, budding, fragmentation, spore formation and parthenogenesis

All the members of a species that arise from successive fissions of the descendants of a single original cell constitute a clone (Greek, clon = twig), and since each mitosis involves the duplication of material making up the chromonemata of the chromosomes, are alike in their chromosomal and genic constitution. This is equally true of new individuals that arise in some multicellular species by fission, gemmation, budding, fragmentation, the germination of spores and parthenogenesis (Greek, parthenos = maiden + genesis = origination), types of reproduction that are often referred to as asexual, since only one individual is concerned.

Fission is a very rare occurrence in multicellular systems and is not directly a mitotic process as it is in the unicellular. Flatworms, very occasionally Hydra, and some annelids may split transversely, and from each part, as in regeneration, a new individual grows. Sponges and some liverworts sometimes reproduce by gemmation, the formation of small clusters of cells, the gemmae or gemmules (Latin, gemma = bud) that, when set free, give rise to a new individual. This is closely akin to budding, common to all plants and practiced, as a method of reproduction, also by sponges and many coelenterates; gemmation is sometimes described as internal budding, rather than external. External budding, in Hydra for example, is the result of the multiplication of cells in one region of the body, and the organization of those cells into an outer or ectodermal layer and an inner or endodermal one surrounding the coelenteron (Fig. 11.9). The coelenteron of the bud is continuous with that of the parent until the bud has attained its full size, when it is constricted off from the parent body and begins its life as an independent individual. It is through successive buddings that coral colonies grow to great size and, with the deposition of a calcareous exoskeleton around each new polyp, give rise to coral islands and coral reefs. Some worms, too, reproduce by a process similar to budding, when some segments in the posterior part of the body develop as heads and they, with the segments immediately posterior to them, become detached from the rest of the body as new individuals. Reproduction by fragmentation is fairly common among plants; a filament of Spirogyra may, for example, become broken into several pieces, each of which continues its growth as a new filament, or a piece of a fern rhizome may break off the main stem and give rise to an independent plant. Many angiosperms can be propagated by slips or cuttings, a common horticultural practice; some plants, like strawberries and raspberries, do this naturally by sending out stems that grow parallel to the surface of the ground, from which adventitious roots arise and a new upright growth develops.

Reproduction by spores or by parthenogenesis involves the formation of special cells, each capable of development into a complete new individual when set free from the parent organism. In the molds, for example, a single mycelium may produce thousands of these reproductive cells either within capsules, called sporangia, at the tips of the upright hyphae, or free at their branched ends (Fig. 10.16). In either case, the spore is essentially a part of the parent plant, a tiny mass of cytoplasm, nuclei, oil droplets and other reserves that has been constricted off and become enclosed within a comparatively thick, protective wall. As the spores develop, pigments of various kinds are frequently formed in them and molds are sometimes identified as pink, blue-green, green, black and so on through the colors of their ripe spores. When set free from the parent mycelium, the spores can resist dehydration and may endure various vicissitudes for extended periods of time before they reach a medium favorable for their germination. Carried by air currents, the feet of insects or any moving object, they may finally land a long way from the place they were produced, and, germinating into a new mycelium, introduce their species of mold into an entirely new environment. Parthenogenesis is a common type of reproduction among some of the colonial algae, the rotifers, some crustaceans and some insects, in which a single cell, set apart from the others in the body for this purpose, develops through a series of embryological changes into a new individual. In multicellular systems, this cell, often called a parthenogenetic or asexual egg, is produced by the reproductive organs. But except for a few species of rotifers, in which parthenogenesis seems to be the sole method of reproduction, most multicellular systems reproduce by means of gametes and gametic union.

# CHAPTER 23 GAMETIC REPRODUCTION

## Gametes

Gametes (from Greek, gamein = to marry) are specialized cells that unite in pairs to form a single cell, the zygote (Greek, zygotos = yoked), from which the new individual arises. They are developed at the time of an organism's maturity and, in most multicellular systems, in special structures or organs. The new individual arises through successive mitotic divisions, or cleavages, of the zygote, and by the assembling of the cells so derived into regions where first the primary tissues, and later the definitive ones, are differentiated and organized into the organs and organ systems characteristic of the species. The study of the mechanisms through which the zygote is endowed with the capacity to develop along the lines common to the members of its species, and, more particularly, along those common to other individuals of the same ancestry, constitutes the division of biology known as genetics, while the study of the developmental changes through which it is converted to an independent, functioning organism, although not necessarily a full-grown one, constitutes that known as embryology.

## Sites of gamete formation

In biological systems of the simplest structural organization, gametes may be developed anywhere within the body and either continuously or seasonally. In the colonial algae, for example, any cell in the aggregate may give rise to gametes, and in the sponges and Hydra, they may be developed from undifferentiated cells in any region below the hypostome and above the base. But in more highly organized systems they are formed in localized regions, called in plants gametangia (Greek, angeion = vessel) and in animals, gonads (Greek, gone = that which generates).

## Isogametes and anisogametes

Also, in some of the simpler biological systems, one gamete may be morphologically indistinguishable from the other; in this case they are called isogametes, and the organism producing them is said to be isogamous. But the great majority of plants and animals are anisogamous, producing gametes unlike in size, in shape and in activity. The larger gamete is called the ovum, or egg; it is nonmotile and usually contains a considerable amount of reserve material, or yolk. The smaller gamete has little cytoplasm and but a small amount of reserve material, if any, and is provided with one, two or several flagella, so that it is freely motile; gametes of this kind are called sperm (Figs. 23.1, 23.2. See also Figs. 25.1, 25.5). Most species are dioecious (Latin, di = two + Greek, oikos = house), that is, the eggs and sperm are produced by different individuals, but some are monoecious, one individual producing gametes of both types, and in species with differentiated gonads and reproductive systems, those of both sexes.

*Monoecious and dioecious species:* In most dioecious species there are readily distinguishable morphological differences between the individuals that produce the eggs and those that produce the sperm. The former are designated as the female sex, and in a kind of biological shorthand represented by the symbol ♀; while the latter are designated as males and represented by ♂. And since reproduction by gametes most frequently involves those from individuals of different sexes, it is often referred to as

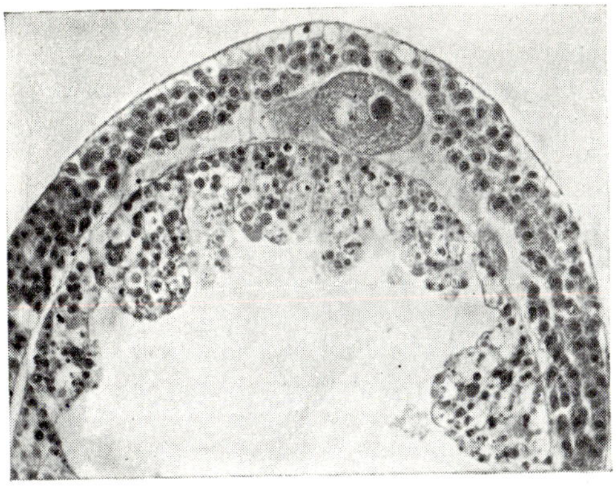

# GAMETIC REPRODUCTION [491]

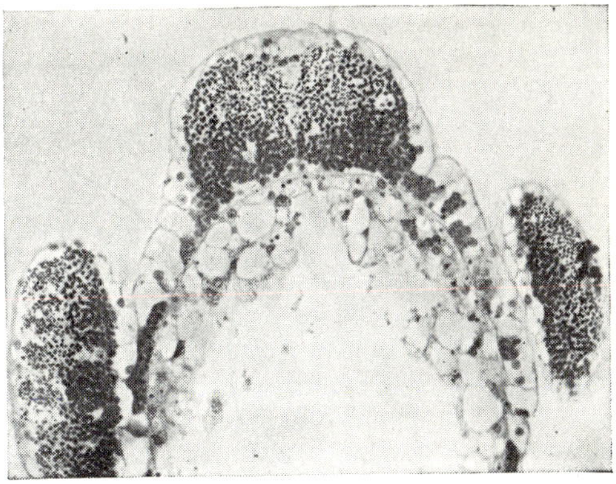

FIGURE 23.1  Anisogametes in Hydra. (Photograph by courtesy of the General Biological Supply House, Inc., Chicago.)

a. Cross section through the body of a hydra in the region of an ovary, showing an egg cell between the ectoderm and endoderm.

b. Cross section through the body of a hydra in the region of the spermaries, showing three spermaries packed with tiny spermatozoa.

sexual reproduction in contrast to the types of asexual reproduction mentioned in the previous chapter, in which but a single individual is concerned.

*Fertilization (amphimixis):* The union of two gametes to form a zygote is known as fertilization. In some cases there is complete fusion of the two cells, in others only the head of the sperm may penetrate the egg, the rest of the cell remaining outside. But in either case there is complete fusion of their nuclei, a phenomenon known as amphimixis (Greek, amphi = both + mixis = mixing) (Fig. 25.1).

*Weismann and the doctrine of continuity of the germ plasm*

The term, amphimixis, was introduced by one of the great biologists of the nineteenth century, the German scholar August Weismann (1834–1914), to whom is due also the expression of one of the most important generalizations of biology, the continuity of the germ plasm. Weismann, himself primarily a student of coelenterates and of unicellular and colonial forms, puzzled with his contemporary natural philosophers over the fate of the individual protozoan when by fission it gives

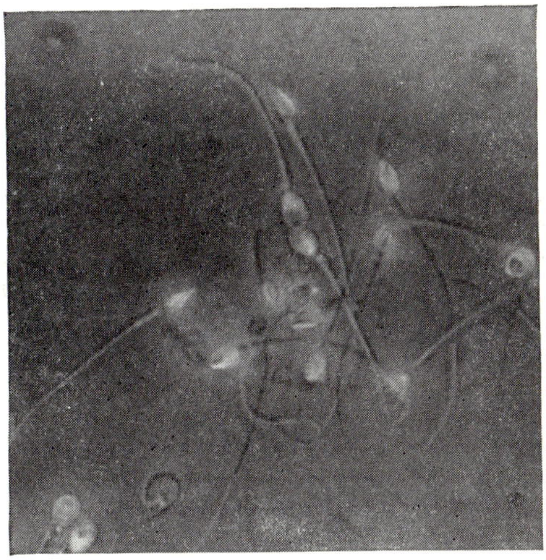

FIGURE 23.2  Human spermatozoa. Photograph of living, unstained cells taken with phase contrast microscopy (x 1250) by Dr. O. Richards, Research Laboratory, American Optical Company. (From *Cold Spring Harbor Symposia on Quantitative Biology*, vol. XI, used with permission of the Biological Laboratory.)

rise to two. But recognizing the similarity of all the individuals in a clone, and in a species, he recognized also a continuity of the individual among them, since each generation represents a segment of the preceding one. In the doctrine of the continuity of the germ plasm, he applied the same idea to

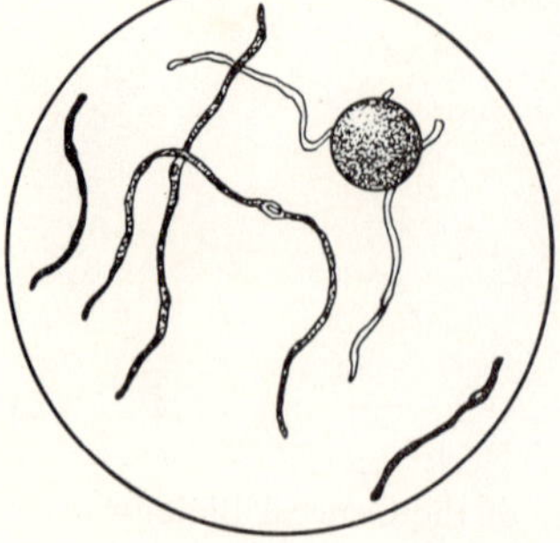

a. The diploid (2n) number of chromosomes (here represented as 6) appear in the nucleus as slender strands. Homologous chromosomes are represented by black, stippled and clear strands, and the position of the kinetochore in each chromosome by a clear area.

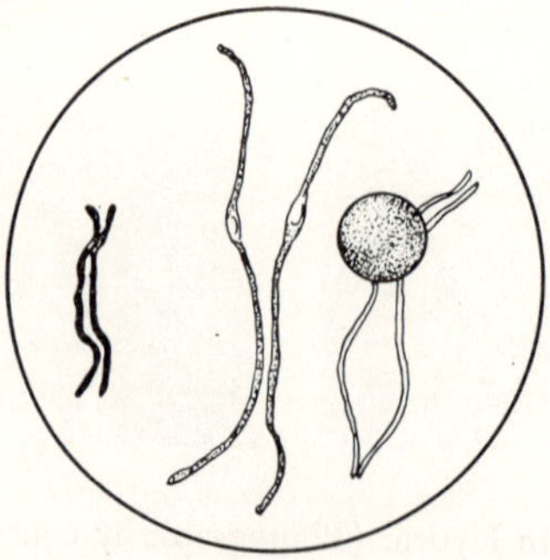

b. Synapsis: homologous chromosomes begin to pair laterally, forming double elements, or dyads, in the nucleus.

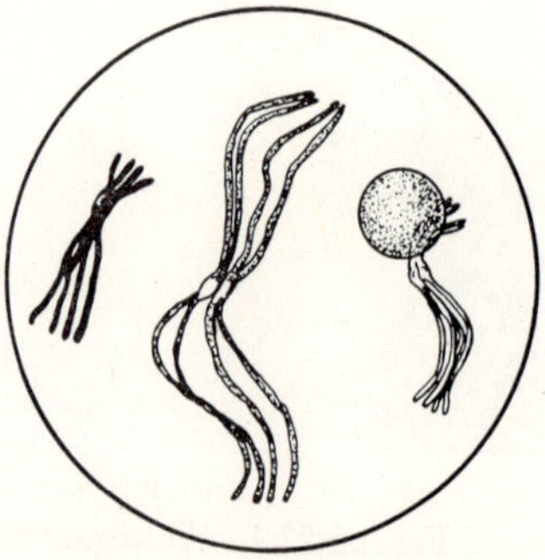

c. Synapsis: pairing of the chromosomes continues; here, or earlier in the cycle, each chromosome duplicates itself so that each dyad is composed of 4 chromatids.

1. PROPHASE

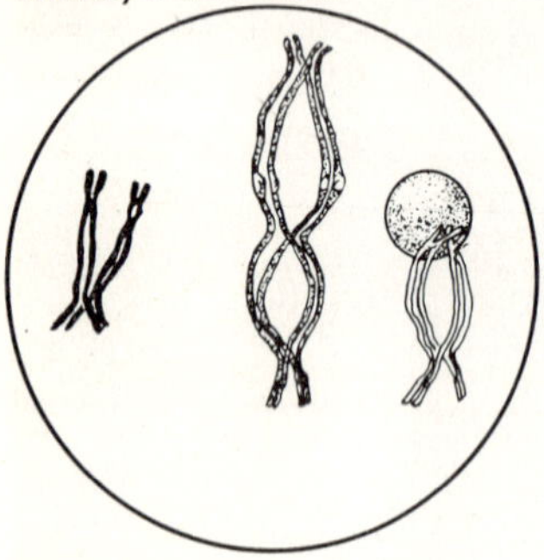

d. Diplotene Stage: the chromatids in each dyad begin to move apart. The two chromatids of each homologue are held together at the kinetochore; those of homologous chromatids may be held together by chiasmata. Compare Figure 24.4 b

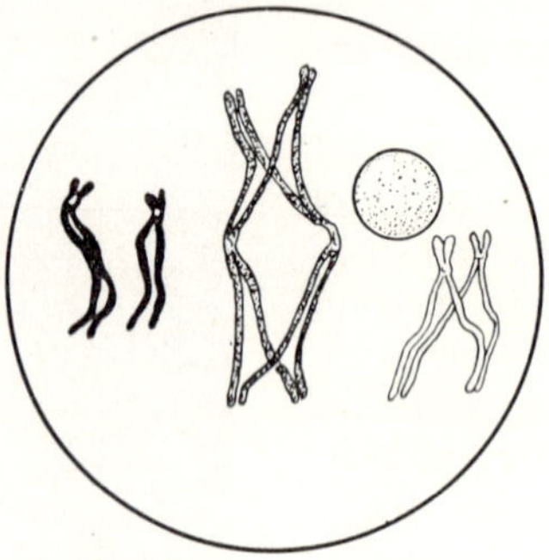

e. Diakinesis: separation of the elements of each dyad continues, accompanied by rotation of the chromatid pairs and the shortening and thickening of each chromatid.

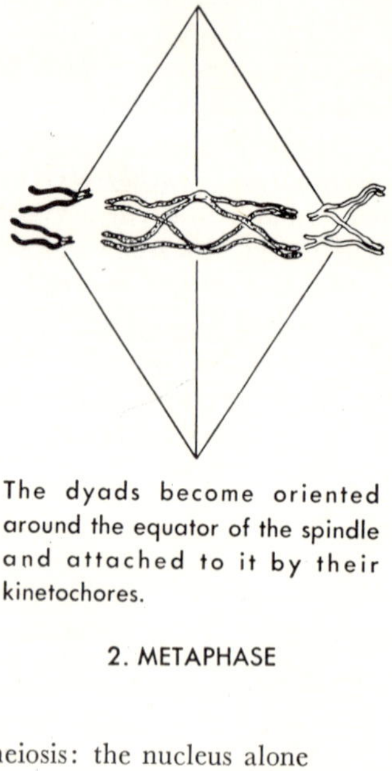

The dyads become oriented around the equator of the spindle and attached to it by their kinetochores.

2. METAPHASE

FIGURE 23.3  Diagram of the course of nuclear changes in meiosis: the nucleus alone is shown. (After Sharp.) Compare with Figure 22.2.

Two chromatids of each dyad disjoin from the other two and move toward the poles of the spindle. Compare Figure 23.4

3. ANAPHASE

a. Two nuclei, each containing half the number of chromatids of the diplotene nucleus, are formed at the poles of the spindle.

4. TELOPHASE

b. Division of the nucleus of the original cell, frequently accompanied by cytoplasmic division, is complete. The chromosomes in each new nucleus may now lengthen out into the long and slender strands characteristic of their diffuse condition in the intermitotic nucleus, or may, without such elongation, become oriented upon the spindle that forms in each new cell.

The chromosomes, each consisting of two chromatids, become oriented on the spindles arising in each of the cells formed by the previous division.

5. METAPHASE OF 2nd MEIOTIC DIVISION

The chromatids disjoin and move to the poles of the spindles.

6. ANAPHASE OF 2nd MEIOTIC DIVISION

Nuclear division completed with the formation of 4 haploid (n) nuclei, each of which contains one chromosome (chromatid) from each dyad, and therefore half the number of chromosomes of the original cell. Each homologous pair of chromosomes is represented in each of the 4 nuclei, one member of the pair in 2 of the nuclei, and the other member in the other 2 nuclei.

7. TELOPHASE OF 2nd MEIOTIC DIVISION

the sexual reproduction of multicellular systems, for he postulated that in the course of ontogeny there is a segregation of somatoplasm (Greek, soma = body), the material from which the bodily structures are derived, from the germ plasm, the material that gives rise to the germ cells. The fate of the somatoplasm is incidental in the history of the species; it perishes with the death of the body, but the germ plasm is handed down in unbroken succession from individual to individual in the germ cells or gametes. In this way continuity of the species is assured, for since each gamete represents a part of the parent organism, just as each new protozoan represents a part of the one preceding it in the succession of fissions, the zygote resulting from their fusion can only contain the potentialities of development along the lines of their ancestral germ plasms. This theory offered an explanation for the phenomenon, which must have been recognized by man as soon as he began to observe and inquire into the world around him, that "like begets like"—that the egg of a hen develops only into another chicken, that rabbits bring forth only rabbits, and cows only cows.

Weismann's theory led him to a further assumption which has since been confirmed by observation and by microchemical analysis. He believed that the germ plasm was localized in the nucleus of the germ cell, and knew that fertilization brought together the nuclei of two gametes, each from a different individual. He therefore postulated that there must be a reduction of the germ plasm to one half its bulk each time amphimixis takes place, for otherwise there would be a progressive heaping up of it from generation to generation. That such a reduction does take place has been conclusively proved by examination of the events of gametogenesis, the formation of the gametes, in microscopic studies that have been intensively carried out since the early part of this century, and by recent microchemical determinations of the nucleoprotein content of cells. The microscopic studies have shown that during gametogenesis, or at some other time in the life history of all species reproducing gametically, two modified mitotic divisions take place through which the number of chromosomes in the resulting cells is reduced to half that of the original cell, and the microchemical studies have shown that the amount of nucleoprotein in the gamete nucleus is quantitatively one-half that of the zygote nucleus, or of the nuclei of cells derived mitotically from it. The two modified mitotic divisions are known as meiosis (Greek, meiosis = making smaller) and, like mitosis, follow a common pattern but differ in their details in different species. The modification that distinguishes them from ordinary mitoses is primarily the behavior of the chromosomes in prophase, particularly in that of the first division (Fig. 23.3).

## Meiosis

Every zygote contains two sets of chromosomes, one contributed by each of the gametes united in it, and every cell derived from a zygote by mitosis has also this duplex or diploid chromosomal composition. Each member of a set ordinarily has a mate, or homologue, in the other set, so that a zygote, or diploid (2n), nucleus may be considered to be made up of a number of chromosome pairs, constant for all members of its species. These homologues sometimes can be distinguished from others in the set by similarities in their size or in the number, size and distribution of their chromomeres, but they are also known, from genetic evidence, to be similar to each other and different from the others, in the nature and location of their genes. In the prophase of the first meiotic division, the homologous chromosomes move together and pair with each other in a definite and precise longitudinal union, chromomere for chromomere, a procedure called synapsis (Greek, synapsis = conjunction). Each chromosome in a pair duplicates itself, so that each pair, or bivalent, consists of at least four chromatids. Thus the number of bivalents, and so the apparent number of chromosomes, in the late prophase nucleus is half that of the chromosomes of early prophase, but the actual number of chromatids is twice that. This becomes evident as prophase proceeds, for the chromatids of each bivalent separate slightly from each other in certain regions, showing clearly their quadripartite nature. This stage of prophase is known as diplotene (Greek, diploos = double + tainia = ribbon). The points where the chromatids remain in contact with each other are called chiasmata, and at these points exchange of substance may take place between different chromatids. Later the chromatids come together again in lateral association, shorten and thicken as metaphase approaches. The spindle appears and the bivalents arrange themselves upon it as in a mitotic division, and at anaphase half of each one separates from the other half and, migrating toward one pole of the spindle, becomes included in the nucleus of the daughter cell together with the halves of the other bivalents which have also disjoined from each other. These halves are not single chromosomes, but double units each containing two chromatids. In the second meiotic division, often following closely after the first and always without further duplication of the chromatids, these double chromosomes arrange themselves on the equator of the spindle, and at anaphase the two chromatids of each separate from each other and converge at the poles where the new nuclei are reconstructed. Each of these new nuclei therefore has half of the chromosomal content of the original cell, or the haploid (n) (Greek, haplos = single) number of chromosomes, and the mechanism of meiosis is such that this reduction in number is effected in an exact and precise way so that each cell receives a chromatid from only one member of each synaptic pair.

The position of the bivalent on the first meiotic spindle determines whether the actual "reduction" will take place in the first or the second of the two divisions. If it is oriented in such a way that both chromatids of one of the chromosomes in a pair are directed toward the same pole (Fig. 23.4), the synaptic mates are separated in the anaphase movements of the bivalents, and the two new nuclei are qualitatively different from each other, and reduced in chromosome number. But if the bivalent is oriented in such a way that its halves moving toward the poles each consist of one chromatid from each homologue, then the new nuclei are qualitatively similar and "reduction" has not taken place. Since the orientation of the bivalents on the spindle is apparently a matter of chance, the first

FIGURE 23.4 Diagram showing the possible orientations of the bivalents on the first meiotic spindle. (After Sharp.)

a. The bivalents are so oriented that the two synaptic mates disjoin from each other, effecting "reduction" at this division, since one or the other of the two homologous chromosomes (here indicated by a stippled and an unstippled rod) will be eliminated from all future descendants of the daughter cells.

b. The bivalents are so oriented that each daughter cell resulting from this division will receive one chromatid of each synaptic mate; they are therefore qualitatively alike. In the next division, the chromatids of the two homologous chromosomes will disjoin and "reduction" will be effected.

division may be a reducing one for some and not for others. But the final result is the same, for at the next division the two chromatids disjoin from each other and each is included in one of the subsequent nuclei. The distribution of chromatids from

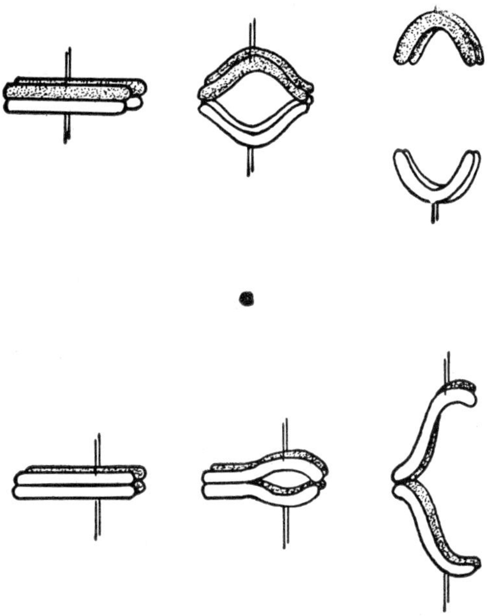

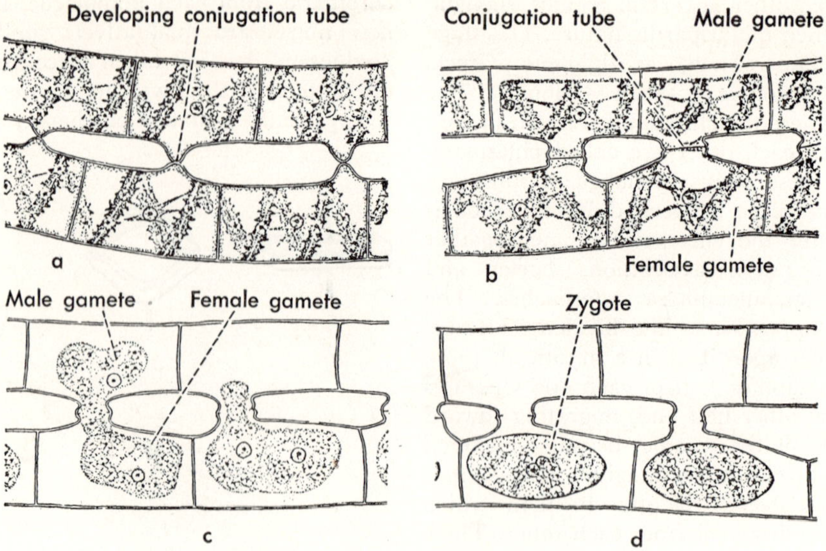

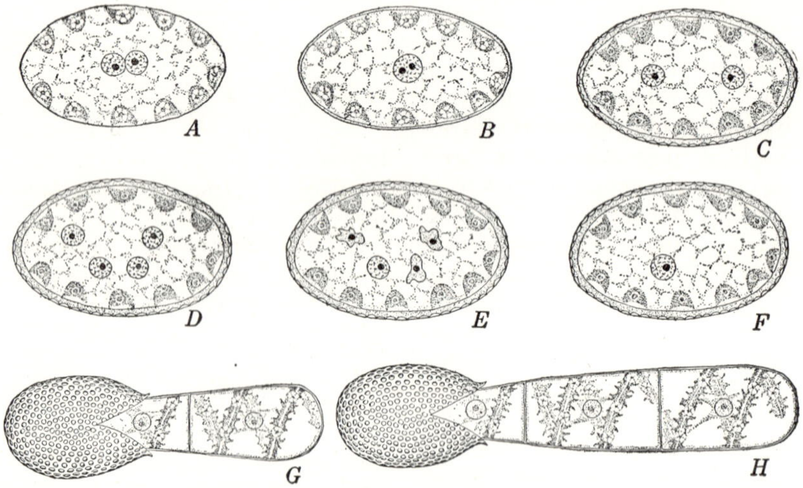

FIGURE 23.5 Conjugation in Spirogyra. (From Smith, Gilbert, Evans, Duggar, Bryan and Allen, *A Textbook of General Botany*. Copyright 1942 by The Macmillan Company.)

a. Formation of conjugation tubes and union of protoplasts as gametes.

b. Germination of the zygote. A–F in section; G and H in surface view. B, C and D show the division of the fusion nucleus into 4 daughter nuclei (meiosis); in E, the disintegration of 3 of these nuclei is indicated.

the bivalents is thus also a matter of chance, so that each haploid set resulting from meiosis may contain a new assortment of chromosomes, and each of the four cells may be qualitatively different from the others.

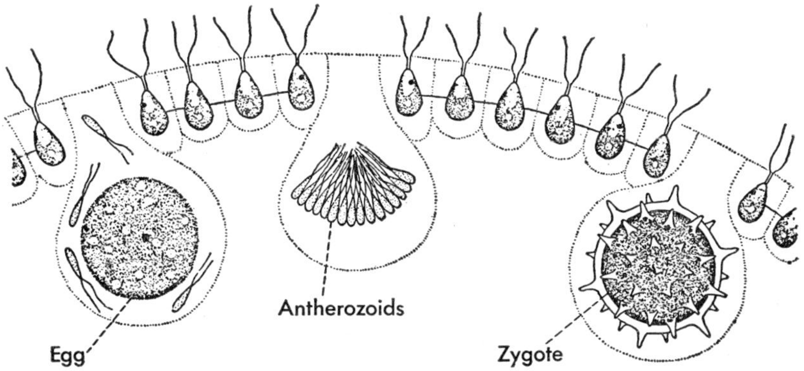

zygote nucleus then undergoes two meiotic divisions, without accompanying cytoplasmic division. Three of the resulting nuclei degenerate, leaving the fourth to divide mitotically, and with growth and division of the cytoplasm, to give rise to a new filament,

FIGURE 23.6 Reproduction in Volvox. (From Smith, Gilbert, Evans, Duggar, Bryan and Allen, *A Textbook of General Botany*. Copyright 1942 by The Macmillan Company.)

Cross section of a portion of a colony in which eggs and sperm (antherozoids) are formed and gametic union is taking place.

## Zygotic, sporic and gametic meiosis

Meiosis takes place at different times in the life history of organisms of different kinds, and, according to the time of its occurrence, is designated as zygotic, sporic or gametic. But in its essentials it is the same, no matter at what time it occurs, nor what individual differences there may be in its course.

## *Zygotic meiosis*

Zygotic meiosis is characteristic of the colonial algae, in which the cells of the vegetative individual regularly contain but a single set of chromosomes. After amphimixis, the zygote nucleus, diploid in its chromosomal constitution, undergoes meiosis before the new individual develops. In Spirogyra, for example, two cells from the same filament, or from different filaments, may unite in a process known as conjugation in which there is a fusion of the entire protoplast of the two cells (Fig. 23.5). The each cell of which has a haploid (n) complement of chromosomes, different, because of the sorting out mechanism of meiosis, from that of either of the cells to which it owes its origin. In Volvox, any cell of the colony may become a reproductive cell by growing and dropping down into the center of the hollow ball (Fig. 23.6, 10.14). Sometimes these cells are capable of parthenogenetic development, and without fertilization begin to divide mitotically, giving rise to new colonies essentially like those of which they were once a part. But sometimes they are incapable of such development and as "sexual eggs" must await fertilization before division. And sometimes they begin to divide very rapidly and give rise to clusters, or plates, of flagellate cells, the sperm. These fertilize the sexual eggs and the resulting zygotes, like those of Spirogyra, undergo meiosis before growing into a new colony. Such colonies, unlike those derived from the parthenogenetic eggs, while still possessing the general characteristics of the species of Volvox to which they belong, have the potentialities of developing, in particular ways, differently from either of the parents which contributed the gametes, since they have a new assortment of chromosomes derived in part from the egg and in part from the sperm.

in their life histories. The haploid individual is the gametophyte, or gamete-producing plant, in the series and the diploid individual is the sporophyte, or spore-producing plant. In mosses, the gametophyte is the longer-lived of the two generations, and the

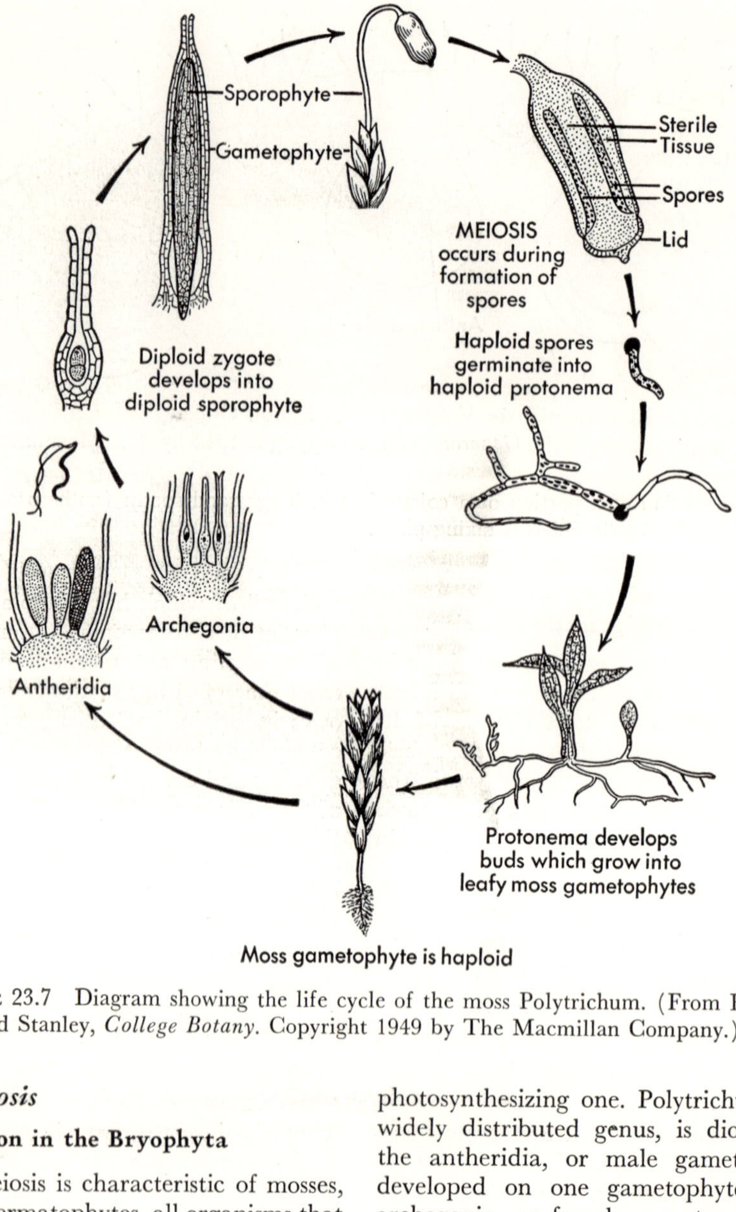

FIGURE 23.7 Diagram showing the life cycle of the moss Polytrichum. (From Hylander and Stanley, *College Botany*. Copyright 1949 by The Macmillan Company.)

## Sporic meiosis

### Reproduction in the Bryophyta

Sporic meiosis is characteristic of mosses, ferns and spermatophytes, all organisms that show metagenesis, or an alternation of generations, in that haploid (n) and diploid (2n) individuals arise in regular succession

photosynthesizing one. Polytrichum, a very widely distributed genus, is dioecious, for the antheridia, or male gametangia, are developed on one gametophyte and the archegonia, or female gametangia, on another (Fig. 23.7). A great number of sperm are formed in each antheridium by mitotic division and the organization of the resulting cells into flagellate, motile gametes. Only one egg develops in each archegonium, lying at the base of the flask-shaped structure. Fertilization of the egg depends upon the proximity of a male gametophyte to a female; and also upon the humidity of their environment, for the sperm, when released by the rupture of the antheridia, reach the eggs by swimming to the archegonia. A film of water over the plants, such as may be provided by dew or rain, is essential to the fertilization process. Once a sperm has reached a female gametophyte, it can readily move to the egg through the gelatinous mass filling the neck of the archegonium. After the union of the gametes, the zygote divides mitotically while still within the archegonium, giving rise to a long, unbranched stem at whose tip a single sporangium develops. Within this sporangium, a number of cells undergo meiosis, each such spore mother cell producing in consequence four haploid spores. When the spores are mature, the sporangium wall breaks open and they are scattered from it; those that fall upon favorable soil germinate into new gametophytes, either male or female, while the parent gametophytes continue to grow, and in the same or the following season produce new gametes and so a new sporophyte generation.

In the mosses, the sporophyte may develop chlorenchyma, but never rhizoids, so that although it can carry on photosynthesis it is dependent upon its female parent at least for anchorage and any connection with the soil solution. Although the chances are equal that all the eggs on a gametophyte will be fertilized, only one zygote is successful in its development into a sporophyte.

### Reproduction in the Pteridophyta

The sporophyte is the independent and conspicuous generation of the vascular plants and in all of them the gametophyte is a much smaller and structurally simpler plant; in the spermatophytes it is wholly dependent upon the sporophyte. The sporophyte of the fern is the leafy plant; in some species, all of the leaves are sporophylls, bearing sporangia, in others, there is a distinction between the sporophylls and the foliage leaves (Fig. 12.1a). The sporangia develop from epidermal cells in the region of the leaf called the sorus (Greek, soros = heap). In Pteris, the common bracken, the sorus is continuous along the margin of the under surface of the leaf; but in other genera it may be discontinuous and the sporangia appear in patches along the veins or near the margin of the leaves (Fig. 23.8). Each sporangium, arising by successive mitotic divisions of an epidermal cell, consists of a short stalk with a capsule at its free end. Some of the cells within the capsule become differentiated as spore mother cells, and each spore mother cell undergoes meiosis, giving rise to four haploid spores. Each spore contains a considerable amount of reserve material, and is enclosed in a thick, protective wall. When the spores are ripe, the capsule bursts open and they are scattered on the ground. On germination, each spore grows into a small, short-lived and inconspicuous plant, the gametophyte (Fig. 23.9). The gametophyte of Pteris is a heart-shaped plate of cells, a thallus only a few millimeters in height, with a few slender rhizoids anchoring it to the ground. Its central region is several cells in thickness, but the lateral parts, or "wings" consist of but a single layer of chlorenchyma (Fig. 23.10). It is, however, an independent, photosynthesizing plant. Along the mid-region are developed archegonia and antheridia, resembling those of mosses; each archegonium contains a single egg and each antheridium many sperm. Fertilization takes place, as it does in the mosses, by active movements of the motile sperm which swim in the surface film of water to the archegonia and, penetrating the gelatinous mass in their necks, reach and unite with the eggs. Only one of the zygotes develops successfully into a diploid sporophyte, temporarily parasitic upon the gametophyte until its primary root has grown and established connection with the ground and the soil solution. But after a short period of growth, the primary root system is abandoned and the stem, as a rhizome, takes over the functions of a root. In two genera of ferns, the gametophyte is even more reduced in size and in independence. In Ophioglossum, the adder's tongue, it is almost entirely buried in the ground with only a small amount of chlorenchyma exposed to the sun; in Botrychium, the grape fern, it is completely subterranean, and, with neither chlorophyll nor access to light, subsists during all its short, but extremely important, life upon the reserves stored within the spore from which it grew.

***Homospory and heterospory:*** These ferns are homosporous, for their spores not only look alike but also develop into plants that are alike. But some of the pteridophytes are heterosporous, producing spores of different size which germinate into gametophytes of different kinds. These belong to the group of plants commonly known as ground pines,

a

or club mosses. Selaginella is one of the club mosses that grows abundantly in the tropics, but is less common in temperate zones. It is a plant with small pointed leaves borne on branching stems that grow parallel to the ground, at intervals sending up erect branches whose upper leaves become sporophylls (Fig. 12.1*d*). The sporophylls of Selaginella are distinct from the foliage leaves, for instead of spreading out away from the axis of the stem, they grow almost parallel to it and are clustered together in a compact strobilus (Latin, strobilus = pine cone) (Fig. 23.11). Only one sporangium is developed on the inner surface of a sporophyll; those at the base of the strobilus contain but a single spore mother cell, from which are produced four comparatively large haploid spores, the megaspores, while in those near the top, hundreds of small spores, the microspores, are produced from numerous spore mother cells. The spores are set free from the sporangia, but the gametophytes into which they develop never escape from the spore walls. Each megaspore divides mitotically a number of times to form a plate of cells, the megagametophyte, on which several archegonia, with their contained egg cells, are differentiated from the main mass. The growth of the megagametophyte cracks open the megaspore wall, and some of the gametophyte protrudes through it, exposing the archegonia. Each microspore germinates into a microgametophyte, consisting of only a few cells and a single antheridium containing a few sperm. The microspore wall also cracks when the sperm are ripe, and, so set free, they move by means of their flagella to the megagametophytes and fertilize the eggs in the archegonia. The diploid zygote then divides to form a new plant, which will in its turn develop diploid mega- and microsporangia, diploid spore mother cells and haploid mega- and microspores.

### Reproduction in the spermatophyta

All of the spermatophytes are heterosporous, with very marked distinctions between the sporophylls and the foliage leaves, and between the sporophylls producing mega- and microsporangia. Conditions in the Cycads, among the most primitive of the modern seed plants, approximate those in Selaginella. In Zamia, for example, a cycad growing in the southernmost parts of the United

FIGURE 23.8 The undersurfaces of the sporophylls of ferns of different species, showing the distribution of the sori. (a, from Hylander and Stanley, *College Botany*. Copyright 1949 by The Macmillan Company; b, courtesy of the Brooklyn Botanic Garden, Brooklyn, New York.)

b

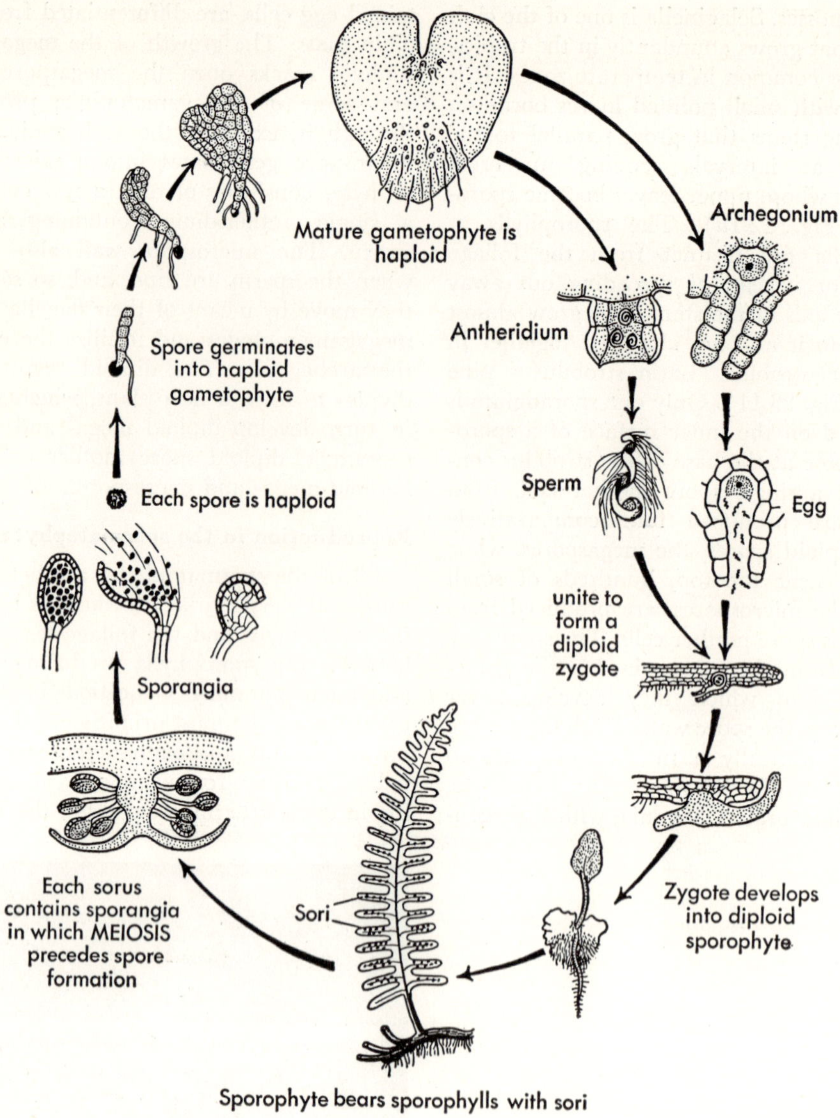

FIGURE 23.9  Diagram showing the life cycle of a fern. (From Hylander and Stanley, *College Botany*. Copyright 1949 by The Macmillan Company.)

States, in Mexico and in South America, the sporophyte reaches a height of about four feet above the ground, although a good part of the stem may be subterranean. The vegetative, or foliage leaves, resemble those of bracken, but the small and scale-like sporophylls are clustered around the axis of the stem as compact strobili (Fig. 23.12). These strobili are made up exclusively either of microsporophylls, bearing microsporangia and microspores, or of megasporophylls, bearing megasporangia and megaspores; in the first case they are known as staminate strobili, in the second as carpellate. In Zamia, therefore, as in all the seed plants, the condition of heterospory is anticipated not only in the sporangia in which the two different kinds of spores are produced, but also in the leaves from which the sporangia arise. Moreover, in Zamia, the two kinds of

sions of the epidermal cells; within each of them several hundred microspores are formed through meiotic divisions of many microspore mother cells. Each of these may begin its germination into a gametophyte while still within the microsporangium, dividing mitotically into two cells of unequal size. The smaller of these is called the prothallial cell; the larger soon divides again into two cells, a tube cell and a generative cell. This three-celled mass, within the microspore wall, is known as a pollen grain and is set free as such when the microsporophylls bend back away from the central axis of the strobilus, exposing the microsporangia whose dry walls then rupture (Fig. 23.13).

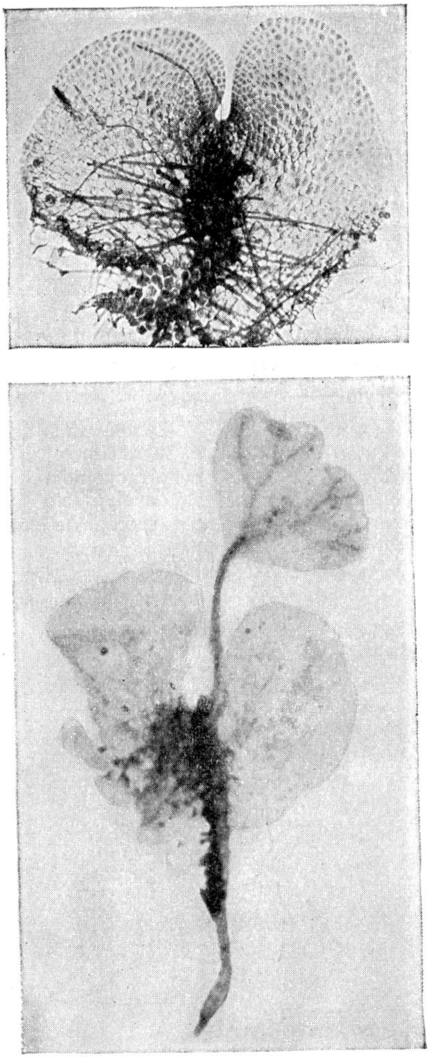

MEGASPOROGENESIS: On the inner side of each megasporophyll two ovules develop (Fig. 23.14). Ovules are structures characteristic of the spermatophytes, for it is from them that the seeds are ultimately formed. Each ovule consists of a megasporangium enclosed, except for a small opening, the micropyle, at its outer end, by an integument that has grown around it from the epidermis of the megasporophyll. In the seed plant a megasporangium is known as the nucellus (Latin, nucellus = little nut); within it only one cell becomes differentiated as a megaspore mother cell, and of the four spores resulting from its meiotic divisions, only one germinates into a megagametophyte. In Zamia and other gymnosperms, this consists of a plate of parenchymatous cells, at whose free end as many as six archegonia may develop, which are enclosed within the gametophyte as well as within the tissues of the nucellus and the integument. As the megagametophyte grows, these tissues grow along with it, so that the ovule becomes larger and larger as the structures within it mature (Fig. 23.15).

FIGURE 23.10 The gametophyte of a fern. (From Hylander and Stanley, *College Botany*. Copyright 1949 by The Macmillan Company.)

The upper photograph shows a gametophyte with antheridia and archegonia; the lower, a gametophyte with embryo sporophyte attached to it.

strobili are borne on different plants, one having at its maturity only staminate strobili and another only carpellate.

### The life cycle of a Cycad

*Microsporogenesis:* On the inner surface of each microsporophyll of a staminate strobilus 30–40 microsporangia develop by divi-

POLLINATION, FERTILIZATION AND SEED FORMATION: Fertilization of the eggs depends upon the transportation of pollen from the staminate to the carpellate strobilus, an event known as pollination, as well as upon mechanisms that bring about the actual union of gametes. Pollination is ef-

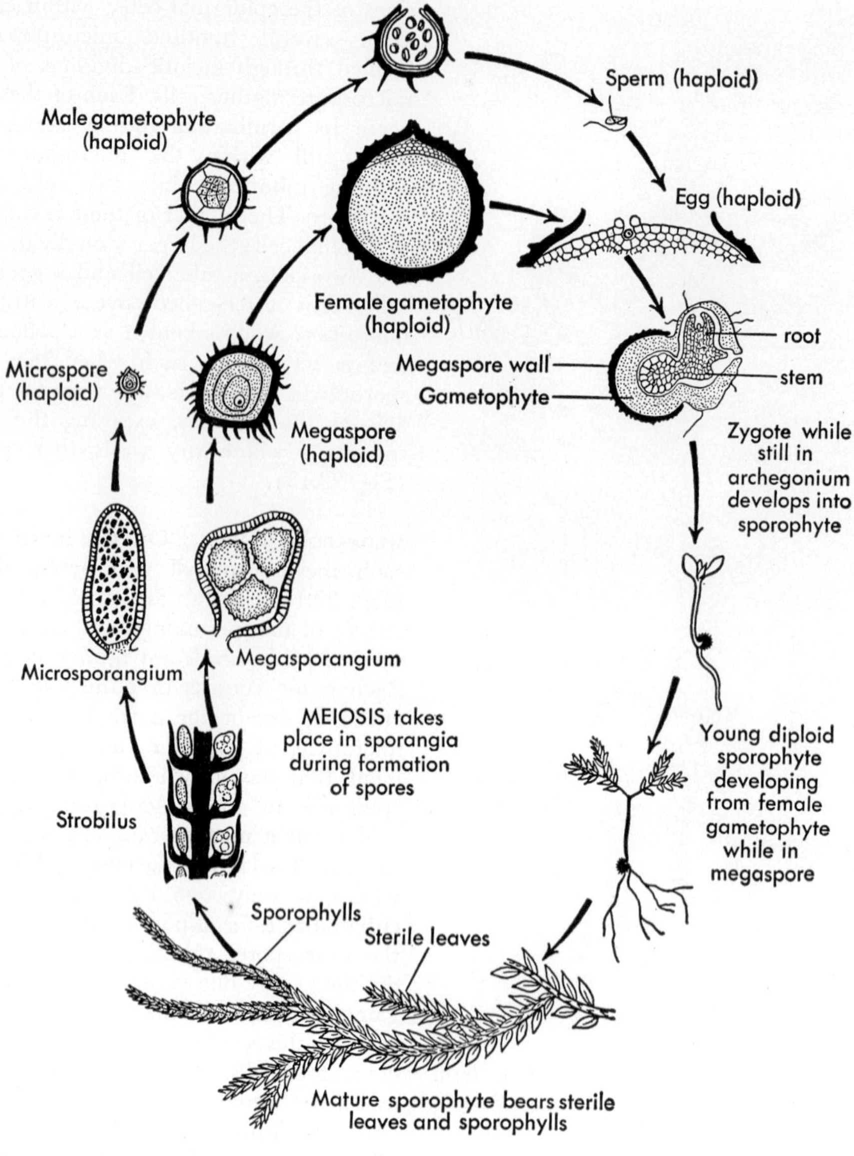

FIGURE 23.11 Diagram showing the life cycle of Selaginella. (From Hylander and Stanley, *College Botany*. Copyright 1949 by The Macmillan Company.)

fected by winds or breezes that blow dust-like pollen grains from plant to plant, where those falling at the bases of the megasporophylls may be carried by air currents through the micropyles of the ovules to the pollen chamber, a small space in each nucellus just above the archegonia. Within the pollen chamber, the immature microgametophyte of the pollen grain continues its arrested growth (Fig. 23.13). The tube cell puts out a long protoplasmic process, the pollen tube, which pushes into the tissues of the nucellus, much as the hyphae of a mold penetrate into a substrate, and absorbs nutrients from it. The generative cell divides again into two cells that differentiate as flagellate sperm. When eggs and sperm are both ripe, the tube cell sends out another process that comes in contact with the neck of an archegonium, its end bursts and the sperm are liberated to move down the neck of the achegonium and fertilize the egg at its base. Only one sperm fertilizes an egg, and only one zygote so formed is successful

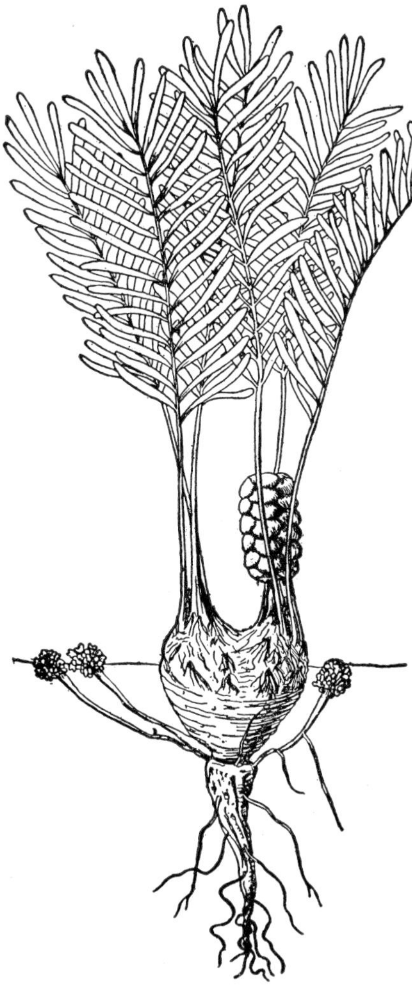

FIGURE 23.12 Sporophyte of Zamia, with one carpellate strobilus. (From Smith, Gilbert, Evans, Duggar, Bryan and Allen, *A Textbook of General Botany*. Copyright 1942 by The Macmillan Company.)

in its development into the sporophyte of the next generation. After gametic union, the tube cell, the stalk cell and the prothallial cell of the microgametophyte disintegrate, and the zygote nucleus begins a series of mitotic divisions unaccompanied by cytoplasmic divisions. This multinucleate mass is known as the proembryo; later, cell walls come in between the nuclei, and the uppermost of the cells so formed elongate, pushing the basal ones down into the tissue of the megagametophyte. These elongated cells form the suspensor, while from the mass at its base the embryo is differentiated. The embryonic cells continue to divide, deriving the energy for the series of mitoses from the breakdown of the gametophyte tissue surrounding them, and become organized into a central axis, consisting of the hypocotyl attached to the suspensor, and the epicotyl, a small mass of embryonic tissue enclosed by the two primary leaves, or cotyledons (Fig. 23.16). The embryo is embedded in the remains of the gametophyte tissue, or endosperm (Greek, endo = within + sperma = seed), which in turn is enclosed within the seed coats. The first of these coats, immediately surrounding the endosperm, is thin and delicate and represents the remains of the nucellus. The next two are derivatives of the integument, whose inner cells mature as sclerenchyma and become stone cells while the outer ones enlarge and become fleshy, making a thick outer layer. The whole matured ovule is the seed, the characteristic structure of the higher vascular plants, in which are represented three successive generations—in the seed coats, the ovule (2n) of the parent sporophyte; in the endosperm, the gametophyte (n) descended from the spore contained within the nucellus; and in the embryo, the sporophyte (2n) of the next generation, the product of the union of the gametes of two different individuals.

The series of events that culminate in the formation of a seed in Zamia occupies several months; at the end of this time, when the seed is ready, the sporophylls of the carpellate strobilus bend back from the axis and the seeds fall to the ground. After an interval the embryo begins to grow again, or germinate; the cotyledons lengthen and together with the hypocotyl and the epicotyl push out through the softened seed coats. The hypocotyl bends toward the ground and from the meristem at its tip the tissues of the primary root develop and differen-

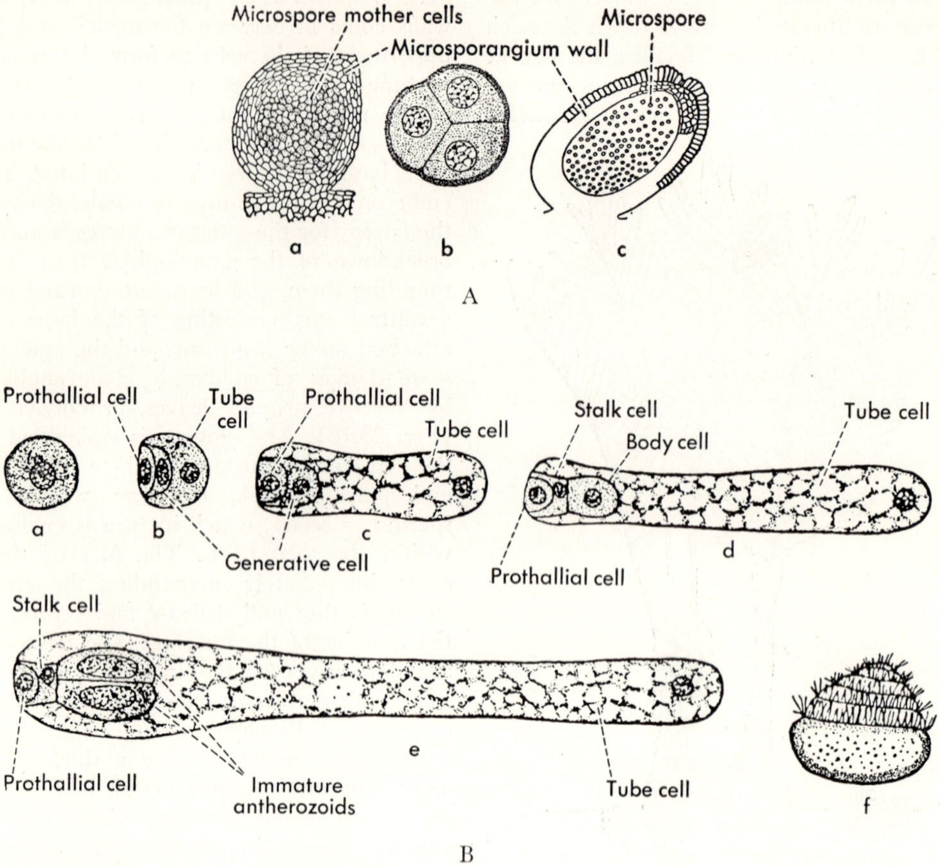

FIGURE 23.13 Development of pollen in Zamia. (From Smith, Gilbert, Evans, Duggar, Bryan and Allen, *A Textbook of General Botany*. Copyright 1942 by The Macmillan Company.)

A. Stages in the development of a microsporangium.
    a. Longitudinal section of a young microsporangium containing microspore mother cells.
    b. Three of the four spores resulting from the meiotic divisions of a single microspore mother cell.
    c. Section through a mature microsporangium, containing numerous microspores.

B. Stages in the development of a pollen grain.
    a. A microspore.
    b. Division of the microspore into prothallial, generative and tube cells: the pollen grain.
    c. and d. Growth of the tube cell and division of the generative cell into stalk and body cells.
    e. Division of the body cell into two antherozoids.
    f. Mature antherozoid.

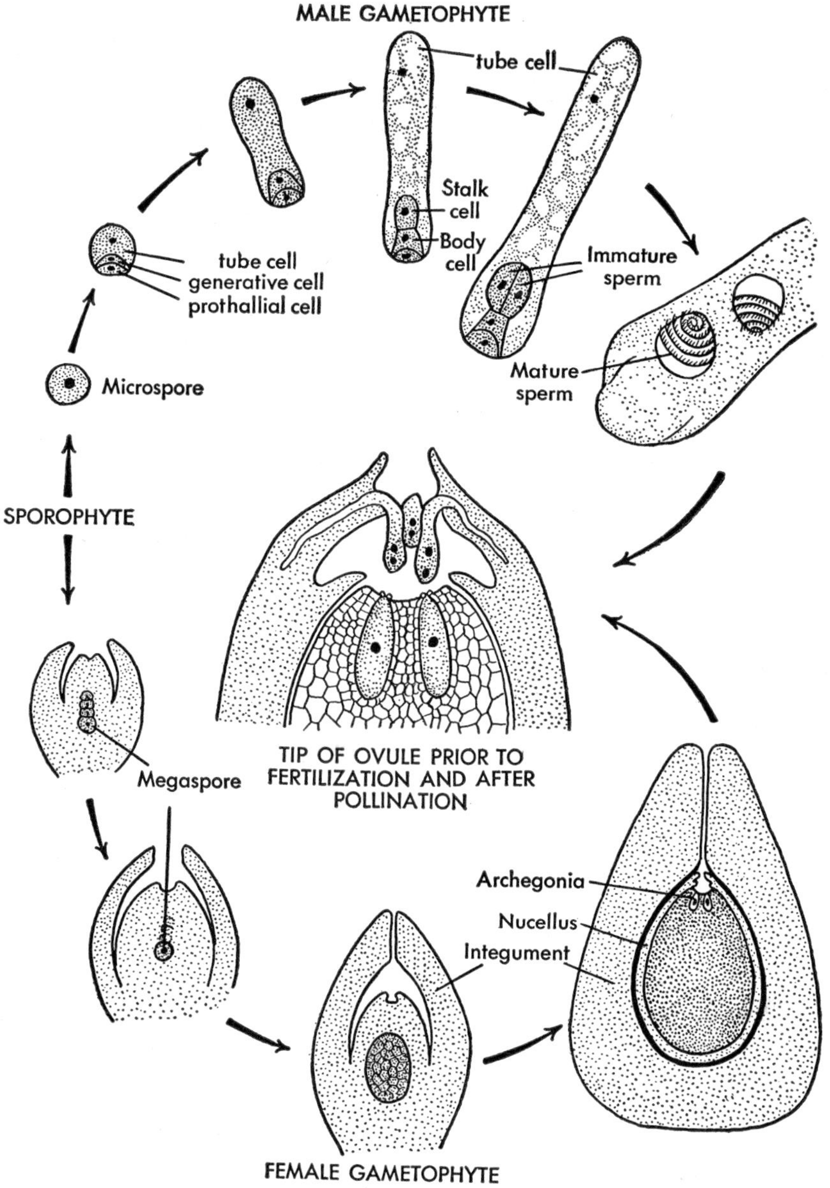

FIGURE 23.14 Diagram showing the reproductive cycle in Zamia. (From Hylander and Stanley, *College Botany*. Copyright 1949 by The Macmillan Company.)

tiate, penetrating into the soil and taking in the soil solution. The epicotyl grows more slowly into an erect stem with leaves, which begin to photosynthesize, and the new plant becomes a self-sustaining one and ultimately, in its turn, produces seeds.

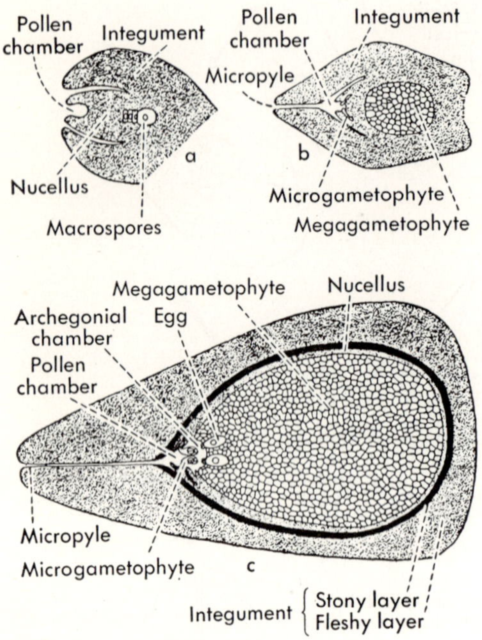

FIGURE 23.15 Stages in the development of the ovule in Zamia. (From Smith, Gilbert, Evans, Duggar, Bryan and Allen, *A Textbook of General Botany*. Copyright 1942 by The Macmillan Company.)

a. The four megaspores resulting from the meiotic divisions of a megaspore mother cell.

b. Megagametophyte formed by the germination of one megaspore.

c. Mature gametophyte, showing two archegonia, each with an egg within it ready for fertilization. Two microgametophytes (pollen grains) are shown in the pollen chamber.

**Reproduction in the pine:** The formation of the pollen and of the ovule is essentially the same in the other gymnosperms, but the mechanism of fertilization is slightly different. In the pine, for example, there is the same distinction between staminate and carpellate cones, but both are borne on the same plant, rather than on different ones (Fig. 23.17). The microspores within the microsporangia germinate into microgametophytes, each consisting of two prothallial cells, which disintegrate almost as soon as they are formed, a tube cell and a generative cell, all contained within the microspore wall. The microspore wall becomes expanded into two lateral wings, and at this stage in their development, as pollen, the microgametophytes are set free from the microsporangia and, buoyed up by their wings and sometimes in such numbers that they look like clouds of dust, are carried about by the wind. At the time of pollination, the axis of the carpellate cone lengthens, and the scales * bearing the ovules, previously closely packed together, are separated from each other.

A microgametophyte that reaches a carpellate strobilus starts growth again, and sends a pollen tube into the tissues of the nucellus where the megagametophyte is in the course of its growth from the megaspore. The prothallial cells of the pollen grain disintegrate completely and the generative cell divides into a stalk cell and a body cell; with growth of the pollen tube, the nucellus of the body cell divides into two gamete nuclei, both within the cytoplasm of the body cell. No distinct motile gametes are every produced (Fig. 23.18). The continued growth of the megaspore leads to the formation of a megagametophyte, enclosed within the spore wall and, like that of Zamia, consisting of a mass of parenchymatous cells at one end of which are, however, only 2-4 archegonia, each enclosing a single egg. The interval between pollination and the junction of pollen tube and archegonium is about a year, for pollination takes place in late May or June in the temperate regions of the United States at least, and fertilization is not effected until the following summer. But when a pollen tube finally reaches an archegonium, its tip bursts and the gamete nuclei, floating along the tube, come in contact with the egg. One of them fertilizes it; the other disintegrates. One zygote in each ovule grows into an embryo sporophyte in much the same way that

* It is not agreed among botanists whether the ovule-bearing structures of the pine are modified leaves or reduced branches.

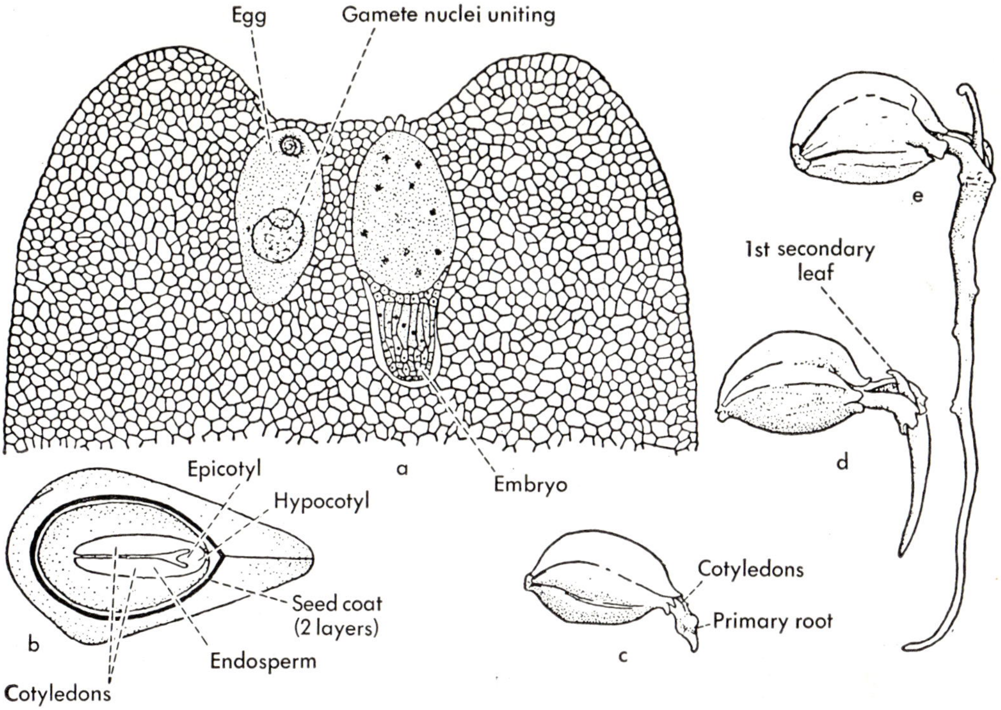

FIGURE 23.16 Fertilization and growth of the sporophyte in Zamia. (From Smith, Gilbert, Evans, Duggar, Bryan and Allen, *A Textbook of General Botany.* Copyright 1942 by The Macmillan Company.)

a. Apical portion of a megagametophyte, showing two archegonia. In the one on the left, the two gamete nuclei are uniting; in the one on the right, growth of the embryo sporophyte has begun.

b. Longitudinal section through a young seed.

c, d and e. Stages in the germination of the seed and the development of the independent sporophyte.

FIGURE 23.17 Twig of a Scotch pine (Pinus sylvestris) showing staminate cone (a); young carpellate cone (b); a mature carpellate cone (c). (From Bergen, from Woodruff, *Foundations of Biology*, 6th edition. Copyright 1941 by The Macmillan Company).

[ 509 ]

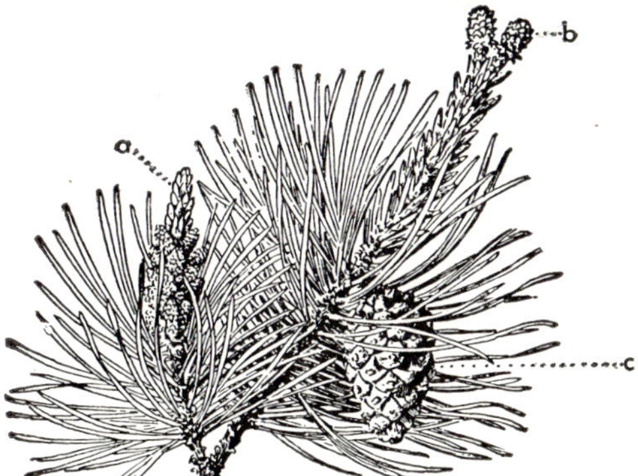

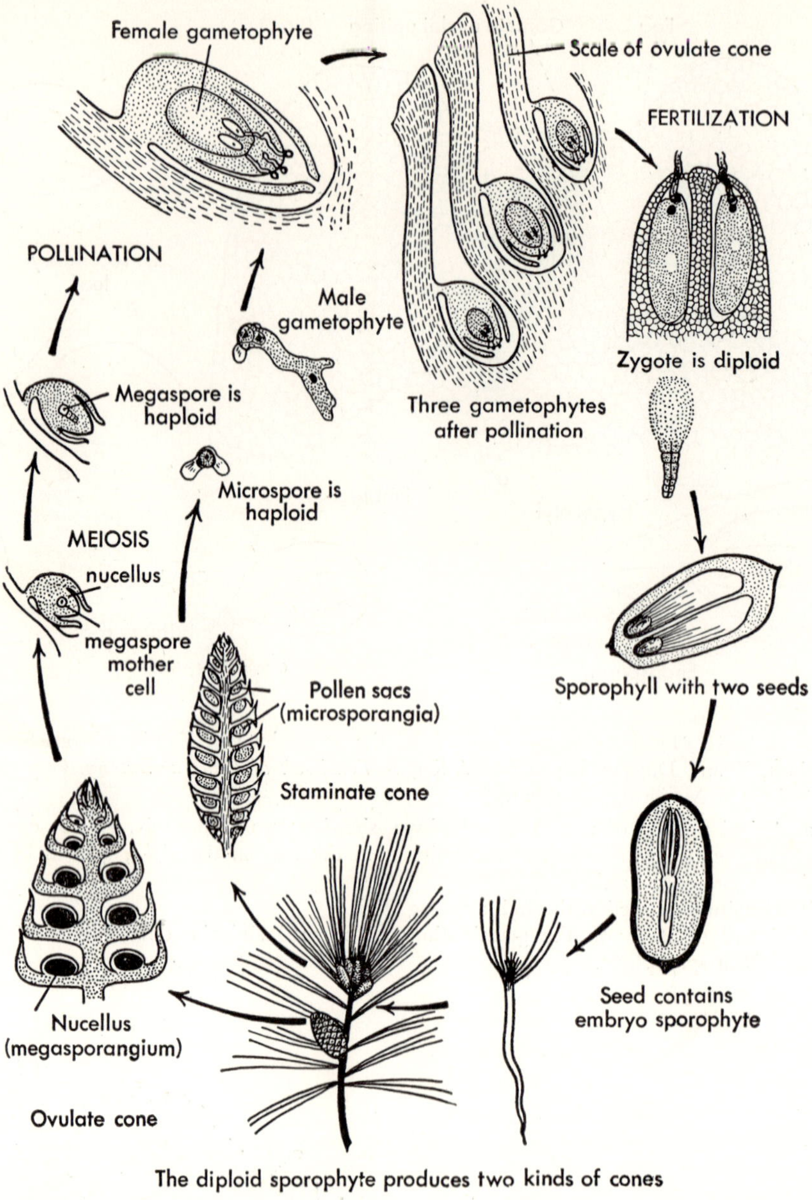

[ 510 ]   THE OPERATION OF BIOLOGICAL SYSTEMS

FIGURE 23.18 Diagram showing the life cycle of a pine tree. (From Hylander and Stanley, *College Botany*. Copyright 1949 by The Macmillan Company.)

embryogenesis takes place in Zamia, although the pine embryo has several (6–12) cotyledons instead of two. When the seed is ripe, it falls from the scale, usually carrying with it a bit of the scale as a wing, which may keep it aloft for a time and facilitate its carriage by air currents and winds to some new locality for its germination into another tree.

***Reproduction in the angiosperms:*** In the angiosperms, the distinction between microsporophyll and megasporophyll is more marked than in the gymnosperms, the gametophytes are more reduced in size and the ovule (nucellus + integument) is enclosed within the megasporophyll, whose tissues also undergo changes with the growth of the embryo and the ripening of the ovule. It is because of these additional investing tissues that the angiosperms, with "covered" seeds, are distinguished from the gymnosperms, with "naked" seeds, and that they can bear the structures known as fruits.

FLOWERS AND FLORAL STRUCTURES: The sporophylls of the angiosperms are part of the flower, which is homologous to a strobilus in that it represents a short branch with modified leaves. Primarily these leaves are arranged in concentric rings, or circlets, attached to the tip of the stem, or receptacle (Fig. 23.19). Those of the first circlet, at the base of the flower, are known as sepals and together form the corolla. They often are made up of chlorenchyma cells, but in some flowers their cells contain pigments other than chlorophyll and they may be variously colored; this is true, for example, of some varieties of clematis. The next circlet, or in many flowers series of circlets, are the petals, often brightly colored by the carotinoid pigments in their chromoplasts or the anthocyanins dissolved in their cell sap. In some species, like dogwood and bunchberries, there is an extra circlet of modified leaves, called bracts, in addition to the sepals and the petals, which, radiating from the stem, surround the flower proper; these may be white or colored, giving them the appearance of petals (Fig. 12.3c). The true petals surround the circlet of microsporophylls, or stamens, and the final, or innermost circlet, is made up of megasporophylls, or carpels. This generalized plan may be modified by the omission of some of the floral structures, or the fusion of others. The flowers of grasses, for example, have neither sepals nor petals, and consist only of stamens and carpels, enclosed by small scales, the glumes (Latin, gluma = husk). In some flowers, such as apple blossoms, the bases of the sepals, petals and stamens are united into a floral cup, surrounding the bases of the carpels and sometimes fused with them; in others, like lilies and snapdragons, the petals are united throughout their length forming a tubular flower.

The stamens usually consist of a slender, cylindrical filament, whose upper end is expanded into the gametangium, or anther, within which the microspore mother cells

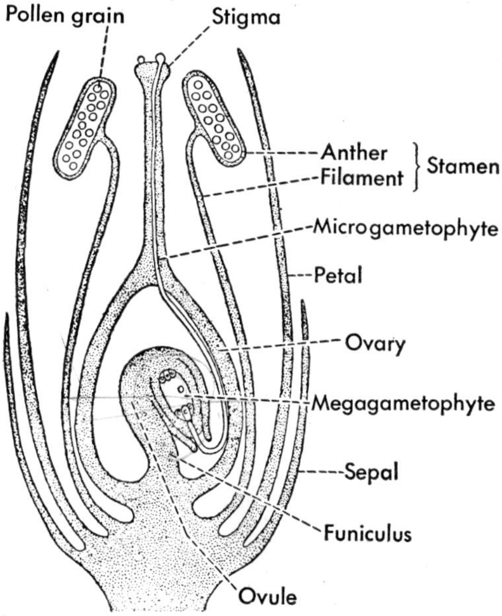

FIGURE 23.19 Diagram of a flower. (From Smith, Gilbert, Evans, Duggar, Bryan and Allen, *A Textbook of General Botany.* Copyright 1942 by The Macmillan Company.)

are differentiated, undergo meiosis and give rise to a great number of microspores (Fig. 23.20). In some species there is but a single stamen, in others two or more, a difference that was the basis for Linnaeus' original scheme of plant classification. Some flowers, too, have only one carpel, some have several that remain separate, but in the majority two or more carpels are bound together in a compact structure called the pistil. In peas, for example, and other leguminous plants, there is a single carpel but its two edges are fused together to form a cylindrical pistil which ultimately becomes the pod enclosing the seeds. In buttercups and raspberries, there are many separate carpels and in the members of the lily family, three carpels are united in a compound pistil. Each pistil usually consists of an enlarged basal region,

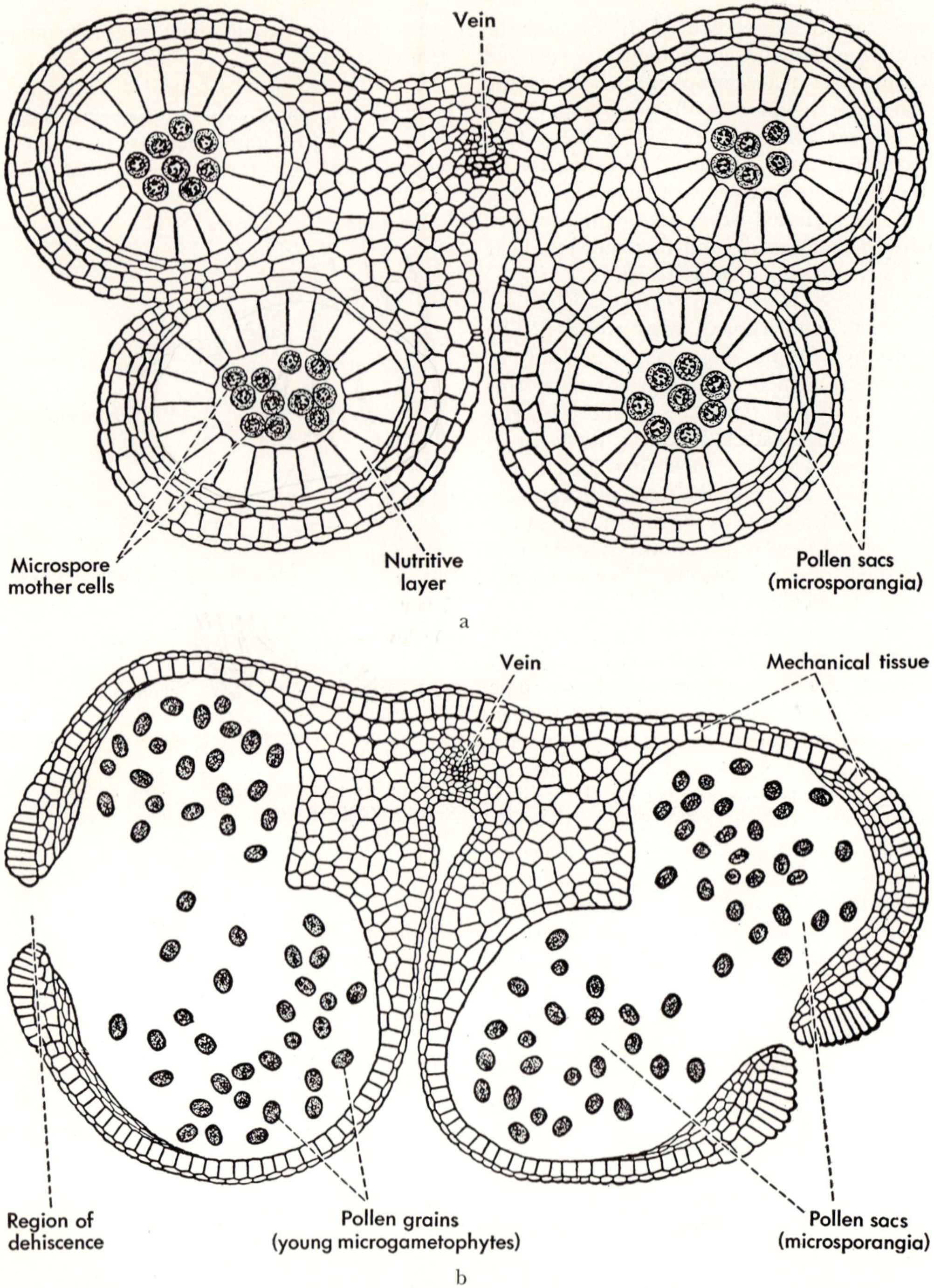

FIGURE 23.20 Diagrams showing the formation of pollen within the anthers of an angiosperm. (From Smith, Gilbert, Evans, Duggar, Bryan and Allen, *A Textbook of General Botany*. Copyright 1942 by The Macmillan Company.)

    a. Cross section of a young anther.
    b. Cross section of a mature anther with pollen grains.

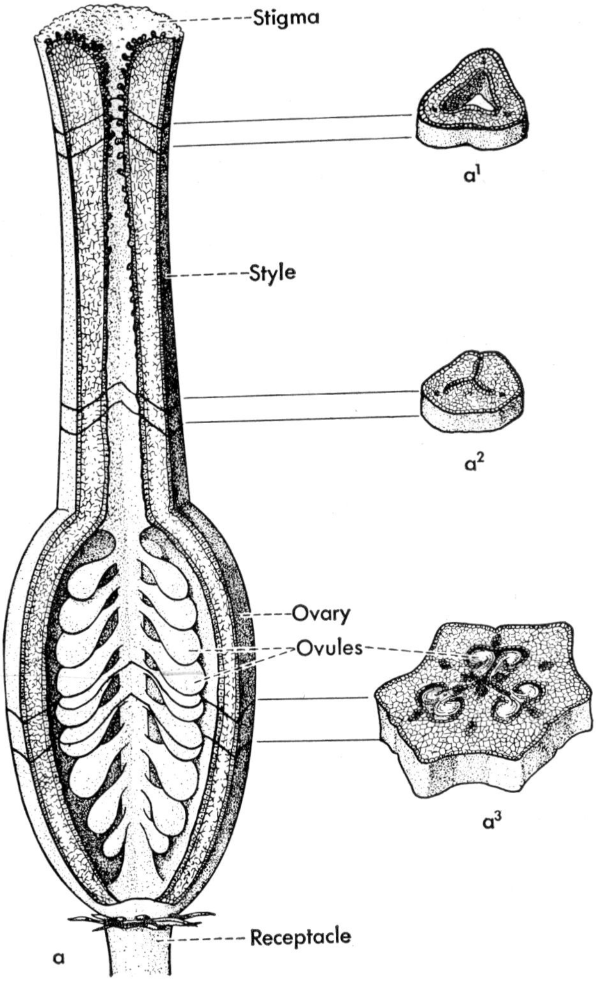

FIGURE 23.21  Diagrams showing the structure of the pistil of a lily. (From various sources).

a. Longitudinal section through the pistil, showing the tissues of the style, stigma and ovary, and the serially arranged ovules within the ovary.

$a^1$, $a^2$ and $a^3$ represent cross sections of the pistil taken at the levels indicated. In $a^3$, the tripartite nature of the pistil, composed of three carpels, is shown, with two ovules arising from the inner surface of each carpel.

the ovary, in which the ovules develop, and an elongated cylindrical style with an expanded region at its tip, the stigma (Fig. 23.21).

DIOECIOUS AND MONOECIOUS SPECIES. MECHANISMS OF POLLINATION: The enclosure of the ovules within the ovary imposes certain conditions of fertilization upon the angiosperms, since the pollen grains can have no direct access to the ovules as they have in the gymnosperms, and the pollen tube must grow in the tissues of the pistil as well as of the nucellus to bring the gamete nuclei together. But other features of the flower also affect the conditions of fertilization. In some plants, of which corn and willows are conspicuous examples, but one kind of sporophyll, either stamen or carpel, is developed in a flower, so that fertilization depends upon the transfer of pollen from one flower to another, and, in the case of willows, from one plant to another, for the staminate flowers or catkins arise exclusively on one tree and the pistillate on another. In corn, the tassel is the staminate flower, the silk the long styles of the carpels that lie in the angles between the foliage leaves and the stem, or stalk. In other angiosperms, both stamens and carpels are found in a single flower, so that self-pollination, or fertilization, is potentially possible. In the leguminous plants this is the rule, for the floral structure is such that both gametangia are enclosed within two petals that meet together to form the "keel" and the pollen, when ripe, has no ordinary means of escaping and must fall upon the pistil. But in other complete flowers, self-fertilization may be prevented by such conditions as difference in the time of maturity of the pollen and the ovules, inability of the pollen tube to grow in the tissues of the pistil of the same flower, or anatomical features that preclude, or decrease, the possibility of the pollen reaching the ovules of the same flower. In some flowers, for example, the stamens are shorter than the pistil so that the pollen does not naturally reach the stigma, and in others they may be much longer and their anthers break open with explosive force, scattering the pollen grains some distance away. Under such conditions, cross-pollinations, or cross-fertilization between different flowers of the same plant, or between those of different plants, is usual, if not obligatory. The transfer may be effected by the wind, as it is in the case of the gymnosperms, but very often it is brought about by insects that visit the flowers to obtain the sugary nectar stored in the nectaries at the base of the petals, or the pollen upon which they feed their young, to deposit eggs or simply in the course of their random excursions. In many flowers whose petals are widely spread apart, any wandering insect may be dusted with pollen grains as it walks over the anthers and may carry them by chance to the next flower it visits, but the floral structure of some flowers limits the number of insects that may be effective agents in their pollination. It was pointed out by Darwin that only the bumble bees, of the genus Bombus, have mouth parts long enough to reach the nectaries at the base of the curved petals of red clovers, while the smaller honey bees, Apis, in their search for nectar are restricted to the white varieties, with shorter petals. The bumble bee therefore is the only effective insect agent in the cross-pollination of red clover, for in its visits to one flower the pollen grains that fall on its body and escape being packed into its pollen baskets may be brushed off against the stigma of another. Still more specific is the relationship between the yucca plant and the moth Pronuba yucasella. Female moths visit the yucca flower to deposit their eggs there, thus insuring immediate access to food for their young when they hatch as caterpillars; as they leave the flower after laying their eggs, they collect some pollen from the anthers and carry it to the tip of the style, pushing it into the stigma. As a result of this pollination, the eggs are fertilized and the seeds mature, upon some of which the young caterpillars feed. In cases such as this the insect is the sole means of pollination and the plant is wholly dependent upon its visits for successful gametic reproduction.

POLLEN FORMATION: Within the anthers of an angiosperm, the haploid nucleus of each microspore divides into a tube and a generative nucleus. Usually there is no cell wall formation, and there are never any prothallial cells. At this stage of their development the microgametophytes are set free as pollen; in some plants, such as orchids, the pollen is of microscopic dimensions, in others, individual grains may be distinguished by the unaided eye.

FORMATION OF THE EMBRYO SAC: The development of the haploid megaspore, as well as the location of the ovule in which it is formed, is markedly different in the angiosperms and gymnosperms. The nucellus grows from the inner surface of the carpel, as it does in the gymnosperms, but in the angiosperms, several nucelli may develop in a row along a single carpel, instead of only two at the base, and each, attached to the surface of the carpel by a funiculus (Latin, funiculus = a little cord), may be enclosed by two integuments instead of one (Fig. 23.22). These ovules are enclosed within the pistil, in the hollow space between the united margins of the carpels composing it. Within each ovule, the single megaspore mother cell divides by meiosis into four haploid megaspores, usually arranged in linear order. Of these only one becomes functional and develops into a gametophyte, while the others undergo degeneration. The germination of the surviving megaspore involves three mitotic divisions of its nucleus, so that eight nuclei are formed; in the young gametophyte, four of these usually lie at one pole of the ovoid cytoplasmic mass, and four at the other. A little later in its development, one of these haploid nuclei from each set of four moves toward the center of the mass, and walls separate the others as individual cellular units. The middle one of the three cells nearest the micropyle is the egg cell, and the two cells flanking it, the synergids (Greek, synerges = working together); the three cells farthest from the micropyle are the antipodal cells (Greek, antipodes = with the feet opposite), and the large bi-

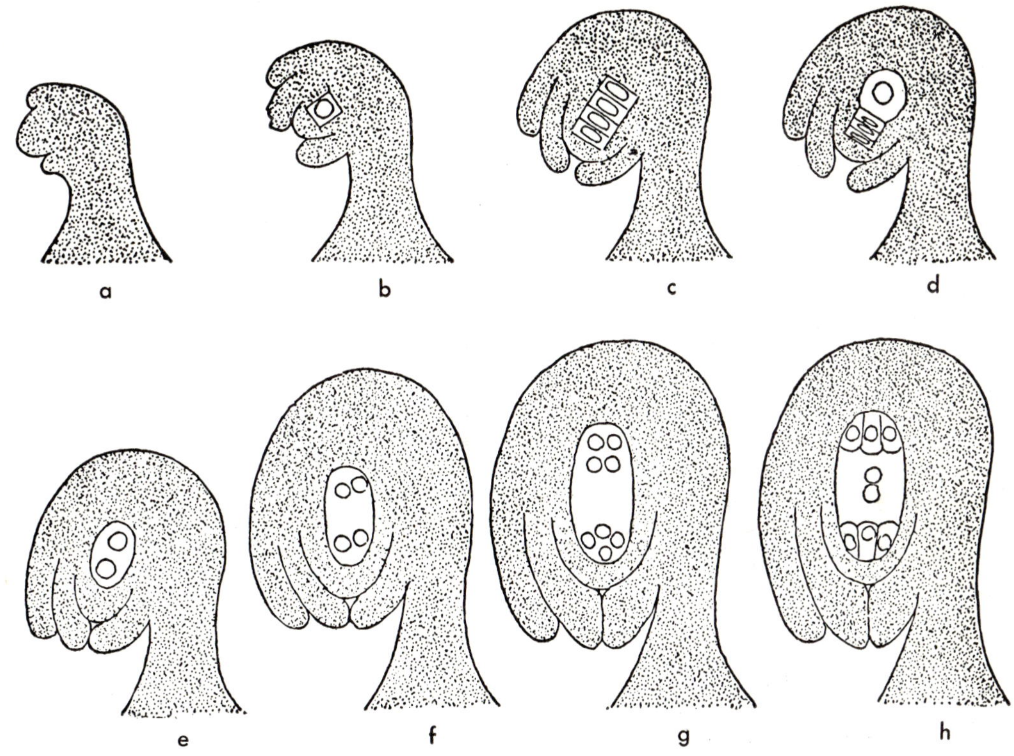

FIGURE 23.22 Diagrams showing the development of an ovule and a megagametophyte. (From Smith, Gilbert, Evans, Duggar, Bryan and Allen, *A Textbook of General Botany*. Copyright 1942 by The Macmillan Company.)

    a. A very young ovule, with inner integument only.
    b. An older ovule, showing both integuments and the differentiation of the megaspore mother cell from the other cells of the ovule.
    c. The four megaspores derived from the meiotic divisions of the megaspore mother cell.
    d. Degeneration of three of the potential megaspores.
    e-h. Development of the embryo sac (megagametophyte) from the surviving megaspore, and of the tissues around it into those of the mature ovule.

nucleate central cell, whose two nuclei ultimately fuse into one, is the primary endosperm cell. At its full development, then, the megagametophyte is a tiny group of seven cells, with no mass of gametophyte tissue and no archegonia; each contains but a single egg and is called an embryo sac (Fig. 23.23).

penetrate to the embryo sacs. Their growth may cover a period of hours, or of months; in beans for example, it is accomplished in about ten hours, in most herbaceous plants in 2–5 days, and, in woody plants, in several months. In the course of the growth of the pollen tube, the generative nucleus divides into two gamete nuclei, one of which fuses

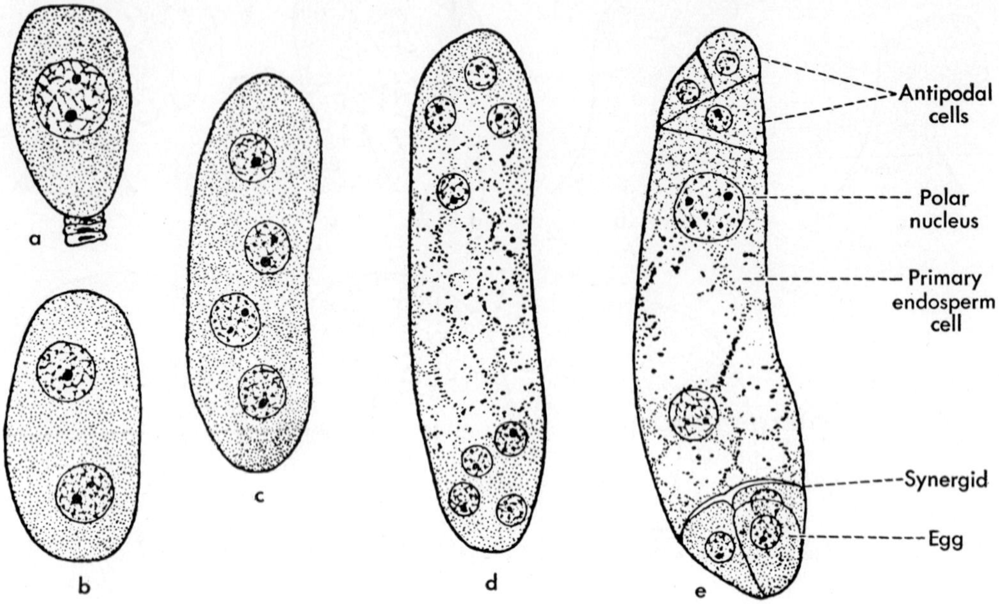

FIGURE 23.23 Diagrammatic representation of the development of a megaspore into an embryo sac. (From Smith, Gilbert, Evans, Duggar, Bryan and Allen, *A Textbook of General Botany*. Copyright 1942 by The Macmillan Company.)

a. The functional megaspore and the three degenerating megaspores.
b-d. Two-, four- and eight-nucleate stages.
e. Mature megagametophyte.

FERTILIZATION: Fertilization is effected through the medium of a pollen tube, as in the gymnosperms. In most angiosperms, a sticky, sugary secretion from the cells of the stigma favors the growth of pollen tubes; pollen from lily anthers can be seen to send out pollen tubes if mounted on a slide in a drop of the secretion from the stigma, or in a sugar solution, and watched under the microscope. Most of the pollen grains that reach a stigma send out pollen tubes. Some of these are more successful than others in making their way through the tissues of the style and reaching the ovules in the ovary. Those that do, enter the micropyles and with the egg cell, when the tip of the pollen tube bursts and sets it free, and the other unites with the nucleus of the primary endosperm cell. Thus both gamete nuclei are functional, one fusing with the haploid (n) nucleus of the egg cell to form the diploid (2n) zygote nucleus, and the other fusing with the diploid (2n) (through fusion of the two gametophyte nuclei) nucleus of the primary endosperm cell to form the triploid (3n) endosperm nucleus (Fig. 23.24).

THE DEVELOPMENT OF THE SEED: The next generation develops from the zygote nucleus much as it does in the gymnosperms, and becomes an embryo sporophyte with a hypocotyl, an epicotyl and either one or two cotyledons. A distinctive feature of the angiosperms is the concomitant development of the endosperm, a mass of cells surrounding the embryo arising from successive mitotic divisions of the endosperm cell.

content, beans contain a relatively large amount of protein and nuts have a high lipid content. In addition, vitamins and other products of the plant's metabolism are included in the seeds, either within the cells of the embryo itself or in those of the endosperm, or of the seed coats.

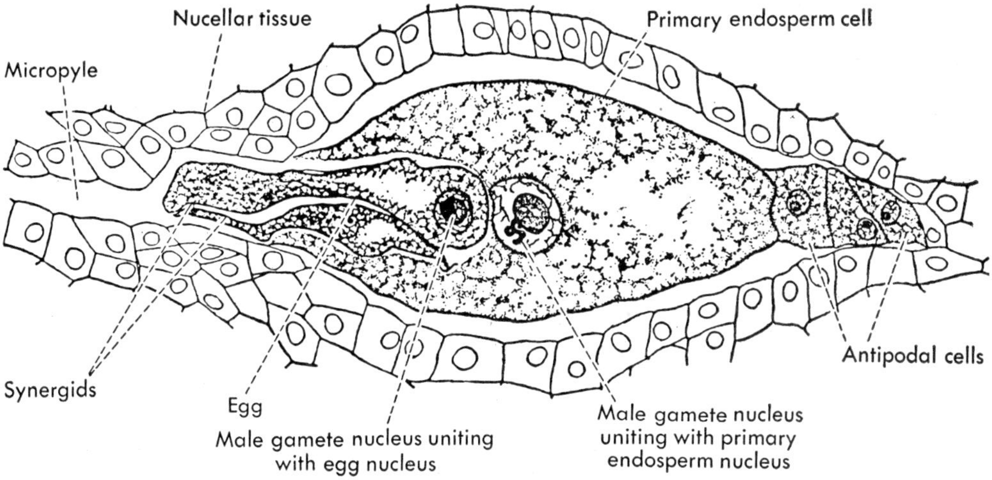

FIGURE 23.24 Fertilization in the prickly lettuce. (From Smith, Gilbert, Evans, Duggar, Bryan and Allen, *A Textbook of General Botany*, from a drawing by courtesy of K. L. Mahoney. Copyright 1942 by The Macmillan Company.)

The union of one male gamete nucleus with the egg nucleus, and of the other with the diploid endosperm nucleus, is represented diagrammatically.

The endosperm in the seeds of angiosperms is therefore quite different from that of the gymnosperms, since it represents a new tissue formed during the growth of the embryo, and not the remains of the gametophyte. In the seeds of some plants, like the grains for example, the endosperm is the main location of the stored materials; in others, like beans, the cotyledons are the principal storage areas. In either case, during the growth of the embryo and the formation of the seed, there is an active translocation of materials from other parts of the plant, and an accumulation of them in the seeds, and in the fruits that develop in connection with them. Carbohydrates, lipids and proteins may all be represented in these reserves, but often one type of compound is present in greater relative amounts than the others. Certain varieties of corn and peas, for example, are high in sugar

The seed coats of the angiosperm represent, as they do in the gymnosperm, the tissues of the nucellus and of the integument, or integuments, converted into firm coverings that protect the parts inside them from mechanical injury and from further water loss. For the formation of the seed involves not only multiplication and differentiation of cells, and the accumulation of material within them, but reduction of their water content. In the mature seed, the living cells are in a state of lowered metabolic activity, but they are still alive and still respire, although at a rate greatly below that of actively growing and synthesizing tissues. Because of this, most seeds can survive for comparatively long periods of time, one of the advantages in reproduction that spermatophytes have over other plants. But none of them can survive indefinitely, and some lose their capacity for germination very soon after they are matured. The seeds of willows and poplars, for example, are capable of germination for only a few days after they are shed, while seeds of species of Cassia, the tropical senna, taken from herbarium collections dated 1776 and 1819, germinated under laboratory conditions in 1934, over one hundred years after they had been gathered.

FRUITS: After fertilization, the petals and stamens wither and drop off, while the tissues of the ovary, and of the floral cup if one is present, are stimulated to renewed growth along with that of the zygote within the ovule. This growth results in the formation of the fruit, another distinguishing characteristic of the angiosperms. Fruits are of various kinds, characterized in general as simple, aggregate or multiple, depending upon whether they represent the development of a single ovary, with or without surrounding tissues, several separate ovaries within the same flower, or the ovaries of flowers that have grown in a cluster. Simple fruits may be fleshy, like those of apples, tomatoes or plums; dry and dehiscent (Latin, dehiscens = gaping) like those of peas, milkweed and poppies, that break open when the seeds are ripe; or dry and indehiscent, like those of the grains and nuts. A raspberry is an aggregate fruit, for each of the many separate pistils in the flower may develop as a fruit; a mulberry or a pineapple is a multiple fruit, for each represents the development of the ovaries of many flowers in a cluster (Fig. 23.25).

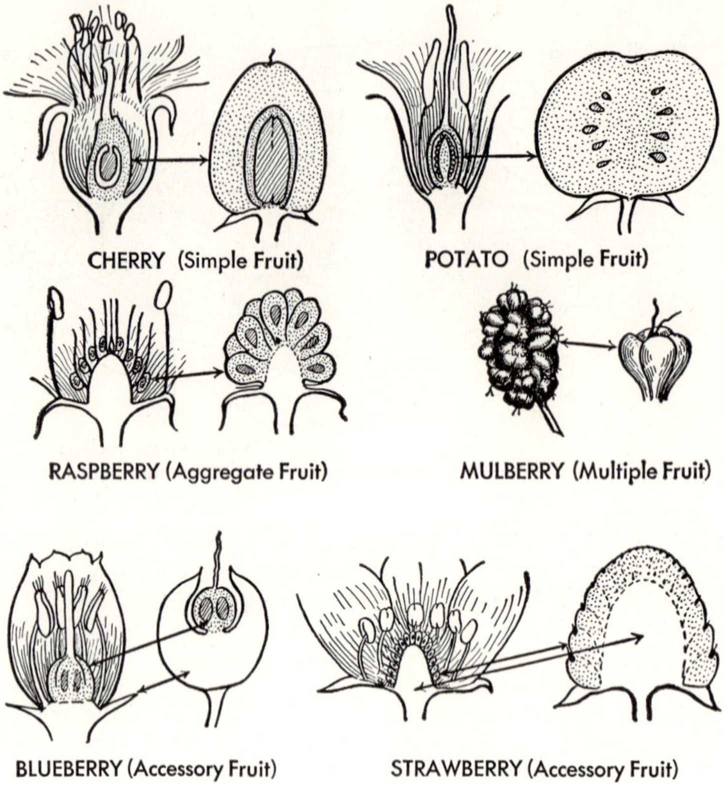

The fleshy part of a tomato is derived from the walls of the pistil, the partitions

FIGURE 23.25 Types of fruits. (Adapted from A. M. Johnson, W. H. Brown, from Hylander and Stanley, *College Botany*. Copyright 1949 by The Macmillan Company.)

between the carpels and the regions, or ridges, along them where the ovules were developed; most of that of the apple is derived from the floral tube, although the outer part of the ovary wall contributes some of it (Fig. 23.26). The development of such fruits represents growth on the part of the tissues involved, and also translocation of much of the plant's reserves to them. The transformations that these may undergo in the process of ripening of the fruit has already been mentioned.

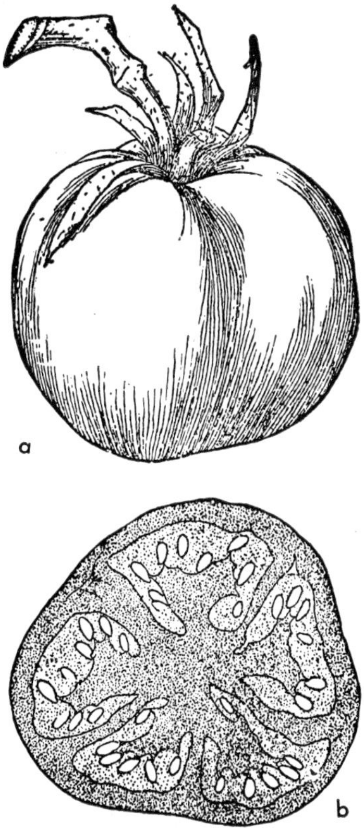

MECHANISMS OF SEED DISPERSAL: In dry fruits the tissues of the ovary may mature into a thick and hard wall around the seed, or seeds, as in nuts, or into a thin and transparent one as in the grains. In dehiscent fruits, the wall breaks open when the seeds are fully ripe, setting them free. Sometimes this happens with explosive force so that the seeds are scattered some distance from the site of their origin. In some plants there are various modifications of the walls of the fruits, or of the seed coats, that facilitate the dispersion of the seeds. The fruits of a number of common weeds are burrs, with rough outer walls that catch in the hairs of animals and so are carried from place to place; some, too, have hooks that fasten to objects and so are transported about. The seed coats of milkweeds and thistles develop fine hairs that increase the buoyancy of the seeds, and so facilitate their movement through the air by air currents, when the dehiscent fruit breaks open (Fig. 23.27). The utilization of fruits as food by many animals, as well as by man, is also a factor in seed dispersal, for birds may eat them and drop the seeds some distance away, and squirrels, mice and rats may carry them from one place to another, where if they are

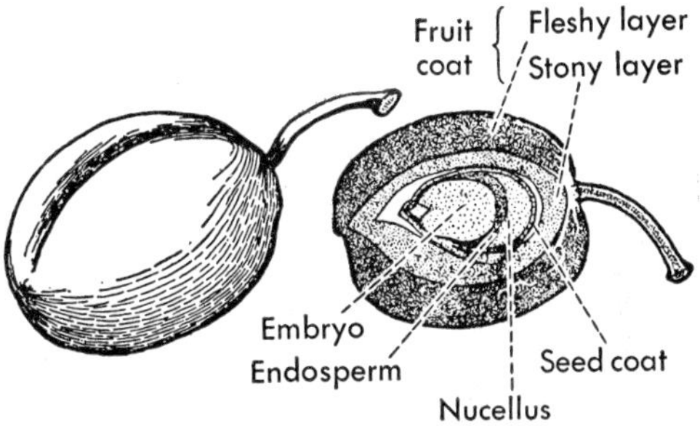

FIGURE 23.26 Types of fruits. (From Smith, Gilbert, Evans, Duggar, Bryan and Allen, *A Textbook of General Botany*. Copyright 1942 by The Macmillan Company.)

a. The tomato, a berry whose ovary wall has become greatly thickened and juicy.
b. The plum, a stone fruit (immature).

not eaten, they may germinate and grow into a new plant.

## Gametic meiosis

Gametic meiosis, with the segregation and reduction of the chromosomes in the diploid set occurring at the time of formation of the sex cells, is characteristic of all multicellular animals, and possibly also,

FIGURE 23.27 Fruit of the goatsbeard (Tragopagon pratense). (Photograph by D. F. Reath.)

The dehiscent fruit on the plant at the left has not yet broken open; that on the right has opened, exposing the seeds, each with a cluster of fine hairs at the free end.

among plants, of the diatoms and some of the more highly evolved algae. In most of these algae, however, like Laminaria, there is an alternation of generations as there is in the bryophytes and vascular plants, a diploid generation giving rise to motile haploid spores which develop into individuals producing gametes without further reduction of their chromosomal content (Fig. 23.28).

## Gametogenesis in animals

In animals, meiosis takes place in the course of oogenesis, the formation of the egg, and of spermatogenesis, the formation of the sperm (Fig. 23.29). Oogenesis involves growth of the cell destined to become the functional gamete, through the assimilation of material and its conversion to stores of protein, lipid and carbohydrate collectively known as yolk, and also the chromosomal behavior and cytoplasmic divisions that result in four cells of reduced chromosomal content. The primary germ cells from which the eggs are derived are called oogonia (Greek, oion = egg + gonos = offspring); when they start on the first of the meiotic division, they are known as primary oocytes, after the first division, as secondary oocytes, and after the second division, as ootids, which without further division become the definitive ova. In oogenesis, the first meiotic division results in two cells markedly different in size; the larger is the oocyte, the smaller, the first polar body (Fig. 23.30). In the second meiotic division, the oocyte again divides unequally, producing an ootid and another polar body, and the first polar body usually divides simultaneously. The polar bodies, while containing nuclei with reduced chromosomal content, are non-functional cells, are not fertilizable and never develop, as zygotes, into a new individual. Thus in the process of oogenesis in animals three abortive cells and only one functional egg are produced from each oogonium. But in spermatogenesis, each primary spermatocyte divides into two cells of equal size, and so does each secondary spermatocyte, so that four spermatids are produced, each of which may metamorphose into a functional sperm by rearrangement of its cytoplasmic material and the development of a flagellum. With some exceptions, gametogenesis in all animals follows this general pattern, in consequence of which four motile, functional sperm are produced to every non-motile, functional egg. In the nuclei of the sperm are represented four of the potentially possible haploid chromosomal combinations, in the nucleus of the egg but one, the other three being eliminated in the polar bodies. In every case, spermatogenesis is completed before the sperm are capable of fertilizing an egg, but in many animals, oogenesis is

In Hydra, the gametes arise from undifferentiated cells, which multiply between the ectodermal and endodermal layers, causing local swellings on the sides of the body, the temporary ovaries or spermaries (Fig. 23.1). Rupture of the ectoderm sets free the ma-

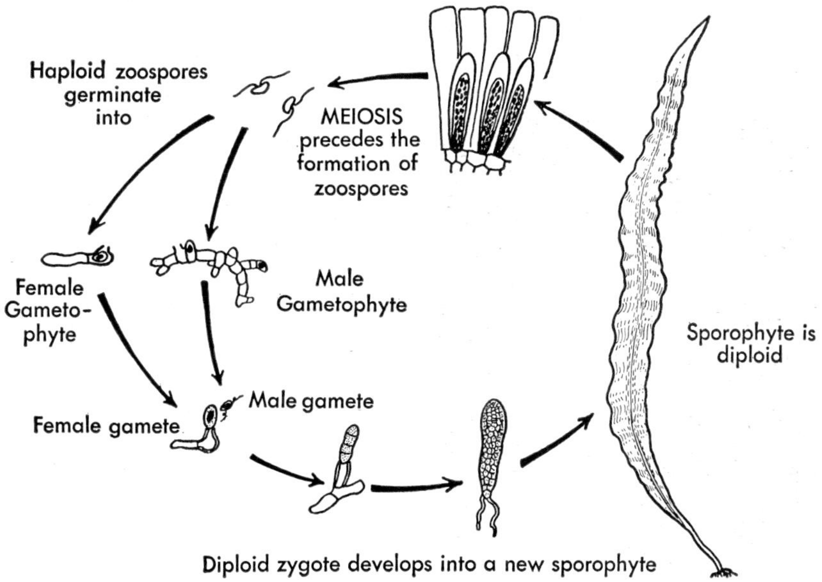

FIGURE 23.28 Diagram showing the life cycle of the kelp, Laminaria. (From Hylander and Stanley, *College Botany*. Copyright 1949 by The Macmillan Company.)

arrested at some stage in its course, usually at metaphase of the first or second meiotic division, and is not naturally completed unless a sperm penetrates the egg surface. The sperm nucleus then remains quiescent in the egg cytoplasm until the egg nucleus has completed meiosis, when fusion of the two takes place.

### Origin of the gametes

In sponges the gametes are derived from cells distributed through the mesogloea, where the eggs remain, while the sperm are set free into the gastral cavity or the flagellate chambers and are swept out through the osculum in the currents set up by the lashing of the flagella. The eggs are fertilized by sperm from other individuals, carried in with the food current, and the zygotes undergo at least the early stages of their development while still within the mesogloea.

ture sperm, which swim about in the water where they may encounter individuals bearing mature eggs. Then they move in between the ectoderm cells surrounding the egg and one may be successful in fertilizing it; the zygote then begins cleavage, usually while still attached to the parent body, but finally drops from it and completes its development free in the water. In the other coelenterates, the gametes are from the same general source, but the gonads may be more localized in position, in the medusoid members of the phylum, along the radial canals or on the margins of the manubrium, and in the anthozoan polyps, along the margins of the mesenteries that project into the coelome.

In animals with the third cell layer, the gametes are mesodermal in origin and in most are developed in gonads that are part of a permanent adult organ system, the re-

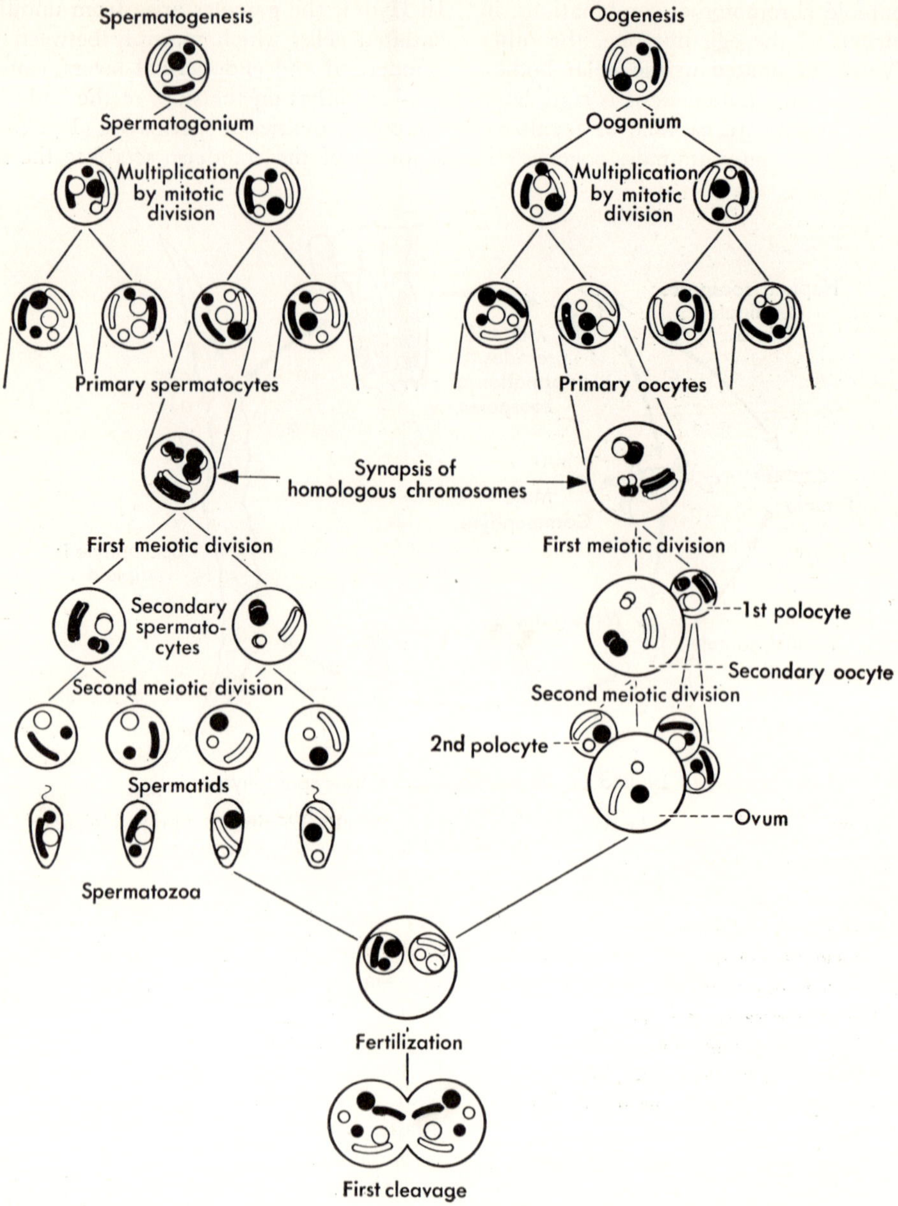

FIGURE 23.29 Diagram showing the course of spermatogenesis and oogenesis in animals. (After Shull.)

productive system. In some they may arise from non-localized mesoderm throughout the body, and in some few cases their escape to the outside is only through the rupture of the body wall and so the destruction of the parent body. This is known to occur in some few species of rotifers, and polychaete worms. In Nereis, the gametes arise from the mesoderm of the septa between the somites, which becomes mitotically active at certain seasons of the year, and drop into the coelome from which they pass to the outside either through the nephridia or the rudimentary coelomoducts, the dorsal ciliated organs (Fig. 13.9). In some species of Nereis, and in some other polychaetes, the posterior segments, with their content of ripe gametes, are detached from the anterior part of the worm's body, and after moving through the water for a time, disintegrate and so release the eggs or sperm.

FIGURE 23.30 Extrusion of a polar body during meiosis in the egg of a snail. (From Moment, *General Biology for Colleges.* Copyright 1942 by D. Appleton-Century Company, Inc.)

### Gonads and reproductive systems

But most animals have a permanent reproductive system which includes not only the gonads, but also special ducts through which their products can be transmitted to the outside without disaster to the parent body, often accessory glands of one kind or another and sacs, diverticula or expanded regions of the tubes in which gametes may be temporarily stored. In bilaterally symmetrical animals the plan of the reproductive system is usually also bilateral, but there are instances of fusion of the organs of the two sides, or obliteration of those of one side. In aquatic animals, the gametes may be released directly into the water where the chances of a motile sperm encountering an egg depend primarily upon the numbers that are released and the proximity of the males and females at the time of spawning. But this kind of fertilization is precluded for terrestrial species, which could not have survived without the development of means of internal fertilization, achieved in the process of mating or copulation. In such species, the reproductive system of the males usually includes an intromittant organ for the introduction of the sperm into the body of the female, and, in the female, often a sac for the temporary storage of the sperm that is so received.

The reproductive system of male animals consists typically of a pair of testes, from each of which a vas deferens (Latin, vas = duct + deferens = leading down) conveys sperm directly to the outside or into an ejaculatory duct, which in some species opens into a muscular organ, the penis, through which the sperm are transmitted to the female. In some species the vasa deferentia are enlarged along their course as seminal vesicles, in which the sperm may be stored, and there may be accessory glands opening into them, which in terrestrial species secrete a fluid that facilitates the transmission of the sperm, or diverticula in which the sperm are gathered into bundles or spermatophores.

The female reproductive system consists of a pair of ovaries and of oviducts, each either continuous with the ovary of the same side, or opening into the coelome near it, which unite posteriorly into a common tube, the vagina, that opens either directly to the outside or into an atrium, or a cloaca. Each oviduct may be expanded along its course into a uterus, in which the eggs may be stored before laying or in which they may be kept during all or part of their development, and accessory glands may open into the oviducts, the uteri or the vagina. These glands are either yolk glands, secreting nutritive material that surrounds the egg or is absorbed into it; shell glands, secreting capsules or other protective envelopes around the eggs; or cement glands, secreting an adhesive substance by which the eggs are attached to some external object. In species in which internal fertilization is the rule, there are frequently a pouch, the bursa copulatrix, in which the sperm from the male is received and one or two seminal receptacles in which it is stored (Fig. 23.31).

In vertebrates, the development of the reproductive system is closely bound up with that of the urinary system (see p. 318), for both arise in the same area of mesoderm. In male amphibia, the anterior mesonephric tubules make connection with the testes, as vasa efferentia, and the sperm are conveyed through them to the mesonephric duct and discharged together with the urine into the cloaca; in the females, the oviduct is separate from the mesonephric duct, although opening along with it into the cloaca.

by the beating of the cilia around its opening and along its tube. The embryonic Mullerian ducts become the oviducts of the adult, and the mesonephric ducts degenerate. In all vertebrates except the more highly evolved mammals, the reproductive,

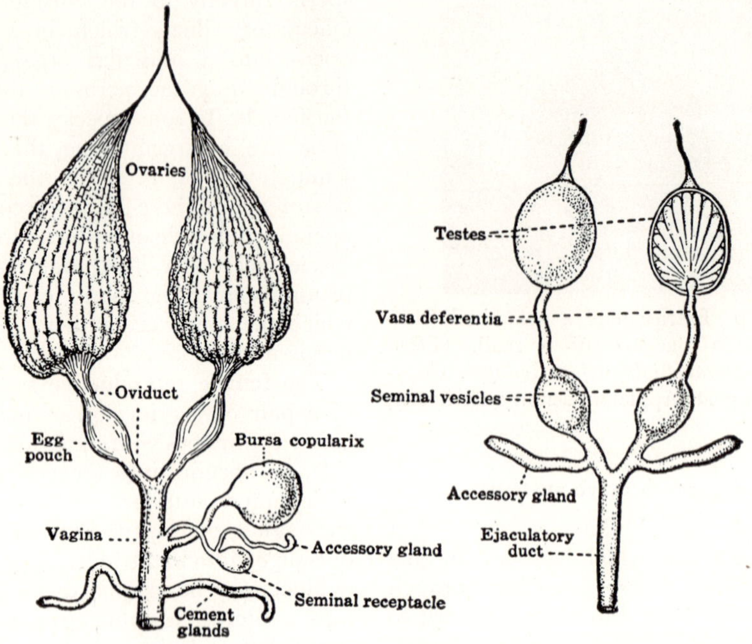

FIGURE 23.31  Reproductive organs of insects. (From Wellhouse, after Comstock, from Hegner, *College Zoology*, 5th edition. Copyright 1942 by The Macmillan Company.)

The reproductive organs of a female are shown diagrammatically in the left-hand figure; those of a male in the right-hand, with the right-hand testis shown in section.

In those vertebrates in which as adults a metanephros replaces the mesonephros, the vasa deferentia and ureters are entirely separate ducts, but the same connection is established between the anterior mesonephric tubules and the testes, before the degeneration of the rest of the mesonephros. These tubules constitute the epididymis (Greek, epi = upon + didymis = testicle); those that remain functional convey sperm from the testes to the vas deferens, to which the mesonephric duct is converted. In adult vertebrate females there is no direct connection between the ovaries and the oviducts, and the eggs are shed into the coelome and swept into the oviduct in the current set up

excretory and digestive systems open posteriorly into a common chamber, the cloaca, with a single opening to the outside; in the higher mammals, this becomes separated into rectum and urogenital sinus. The males of mammals are unique in that the testes are not within the abdominal cavity, as they are in other vertebrates, but lie in scrotal sacs outside it. In female mammals, the oviducts, which in all other vertebrates are separate throughout their length and open individually into the cloaca, unite to greater or less extent at their caudal ends; in the primates, this union is complete and there is but a single median uterus, which opens into the vagina (Fig. 15.59).

## Oviparous, ovoviviparous and viviparous species

Animals may be classified as oviparous (Latin, ovum = egg + parere = to produce), ovoviviparous (Latin, ovum = egg + vivum = living + parere) or viviparous, according to the disposition of their eggs and the relation of the female to the embryos during the course of their development. In oviparous species, which include many of the non-chordates as well as some fishes, some reptiles, amphibia and birds, the eggs, whether fertilized internally or externally, are shed from the body of the female, often enclosed in a protective membrane or shell, and develop entirely outside it; in ovoviviparous species, including also some non-chordates, as well as some fishes and reptiles, the eggs, enclosed within their shells, are harbored within the parent's body during embryogenesis and the young are hatched in a motile and independent stage of their development; in viviparous species, the eggs are not only retained within the body of the female but the embryos, during the course of their development, derive all their sustenance from her.

*Devices for safeguarding eggs, embryos and young.* IN OVIPAROUS SPECIES: Oviparous species with external fertilization usually produce enormous numbers of gametes; this is indeed essential to their survival as a species, for not only is fertilization a matter of chance, but the eggs and the sperm before they meet, and the zygotes after fertilization and the embryos developing from them are exposed to many hazards from both their physical and their biological environment. It is estimated, for example, that a single oyster may produce as many as 16,000,000–60,000,000 eggs in a season, of which only a small fraction ever succeed in completing their development to the adult stage. Codfish lay some 6,000,000 eggs a season and bullfrogs and toads may lay as many as 10,000 at a spawning; these are deposited in the water, but their chances of fertilization are better than those of many aquatic species since the males and females come together in amplexus (Latin, amplexus = encircling) when their reproductive products are ripe, and as the female sheds her eggs, the male ejects sperm upon them. Other oviparous species, both with external and internal fertilization, have various devices for protecting their eggs and embryos. The female lobster, for example, carries them entangled in the hairs of her abdominal appendages, which she gently waves back and forth, in this way aerating her eggs during the period of their incubation; the males of some marine catfish carry them in their mouths, and the male toads of the genus Alytes carry them wound around their hind legs, a habit which has earned them the popular name of "obstetrical toad." A number of animals lay their eggs in the ground, sometimes enclosing them, as earthworms and grasshoppers do, in capsules formed by the secretion of certain glands, and some cement them to leaves or other objects in the water or on land. Many insects deposit them in crevices in the bark of trees, or in fissures that they make in the stems or roots with their ovipositors, modifications of the terminal abdominal segments. Among the wasps, the females of the family Sphecidae, or "mud daubers," seal their eggs in chambers made of earth or clay and provide fresh food for the young when they hatch by sealing another insect or a spider in every chamber, having captured their prey by paralyzing, but not killing, them with a secretion they discharge when they sting. Other insects, many fishes, reptiles and birds make nests in which the eggs are deposited and guarded during the time of development by either or both parents. In ovoviviparous species, the females may carry the fertilized eggs in their uteri or in special brood pouches, or marsupia (Latin, marsupium = a pouch). The eggs of the intestinal parasite Ascaris, for example, are fertilized in the oviducts of the female, and, surrounded by a tough shell, undergo the preliminary stages of their development in the expanded regions, or uteri; a female Ascaris may contain as many as 27,000,000 eggs at one time, and shed over 200,000 a day into the intestine of her host. Among the mollusks, the mussels carry their fertilized eggs and embryos in their gills which serve as brood pouches in the reproductive season, and some of the Crustacea, like Daphnia, carry them in a brood chamber situated dorsally and just posterior to the heart.

Homoiothermic animals have a particular problem in that their eggs must be kept at the temperature of their bodies, or at least warm. Birds have surmounted this by building nests in sheltered places, often lining, and so partially insulating, them with feathers, leaves or grasses, hairs or other things that they may pick up, and by covering the eggs with their bodies from the time they are laid until they hatch. The most primitive of modern mammals, the duck-billed platypus (Ornithorhynchus) and spiny anteater (Tachyglossus) native to Australia and the neighboring islands, are also oviparous. The platypus lays eggs containing a considerable amount of yolk enclosed within a thin shell, and is believed to sit upon them and incubate them as a bird does, later suckling her young as a mammal. The anteater lays but a single egg at a time, which is probably slipped at once into the mother's abdominal brood pouch. In the marsupial mammals, like opossums of the southern United States, and the kangaroos, wallabies and other mammals of Australia, the eggs, with relatively little yolk and no shell, begin their development within the uterus of the female but in a few days the embryos emerge in a very immature condition and enter the marsupium, a furry pouch on the abdomen, where each finds a nipple, or opening of a mammary gland, and clings to it, sucking milk until its development is complete.

IN PLACENTAL MAMMALS: In all other mammals, the cleaving egg becomes more or less intimately connected with the wall of the uterus and the embryo, or fetus, completes its development within the body of the mother attached to the uterine wall by the placenta (Greek, plakous = flat cake), a composite mass of maternal and fetal tissues through which the blood vessels of the mother and of the fetus course in intimate relation with each other, but without direct connection. This anatomical arrangement makes possible the diffusion of nutrients from the maternal blood stream into the embryonic, and the transfer of respiratory gases between them. The evolutionary development of the mammals has thus included, in addition to the other features characteristic of this group of animals, a mechanism by which the eggs and embryos may be protected from chilling and from other dangers of the outside world, and the young nourished by the females during their embryonic lives, as well as for varying periods after their birth.

*Hormonal control of the reproductive cycle in placental mammals:* This mechanism is one of hormonal regulation, initiated by the gonadotropic hormones of the anterior lobe of the pituitary, which in the female stimulate the ovaries to develop and to produce and mature eggs. The mammalian egg within the ovary is surrounded by a follicle (Latin, folliculus = little bag), at first a compact mass of epithelial cells. As oogenesis proceeds, the follicle becomes filled with fluid, a mixture of water, salts, proteins and fats, secreted under the influence of a gonadotropic hormone, the follicle-stimulating hormone. The egg, embedded in a little mass of cells, becomes pushed to one side of the follicle, called a Graafian follicle after the Dutch physician Regner de Graaf, who included the examination of mammalian ovaries among his many anatomical and physiological investigations (Fig. 23.32). A quarter of a century ago a hormone called estrogen was obtained from the ovary and from the follicular fluid that stimulates the growth of the immature reproductive organs and mammary glands of young animals, and in adults induces changes in the tissue of the uterus and vagina. Later, estrogen was found to be not a single hormone, but a mixture of several.

When the ovum is ripe, the follicle ruptures and the egg is set free from the ovary and drawn into the opening of the oviduct in the current set up by the cilia lining its walls. The release of the egg is known as ovulation, and in many mammals is accompanied by willingness, or desire, to mate and behavior characteristic of sexual excitement, a condition called estrus (Greek, oistros = gadfly), or "heat." It has long been known that these periods occur cyclically, with different intervals between successive periods in different species of mammals, but their connection with ovulation has been established only as their hormonal regulation has become clear. In rats and mice, the cycle is a short one, for ovulation takes place every 4–5 days; in guinea pigs, every 15 days; in cows, horses and pigs, every 21 days; in sheep only during the late summer; in dogs and cats two or three times a year. In man and other primates, ovulation occurs about every 28 days, but is not accompanied by the external manifestations of estrus. The number of eggs ripened and expelled from the ovary at each period of ovulation varies, too, with different species. While, for example, one egg per cycle is the rule for horses, cows, sheep and primates, 4–6 are shed simultaneously by guinea pigs, mice and rats and 12, on an average, by pigs.

After the discharge of an egg, the cells lining the collapsed wall of the follicle begin to multiply under the influence of another of the pituitary hormones, the luteinizing hormone, and the empty sac is converted into a mass of cells, which have a high content of fat and are richly supplied with blood vessels that have invaded the follicle from the surrounding tissues of the ovary. In animals like cows, whose fat contains a yellow pigment, these converted follicles appear as bright yellow patches among the other tissues of the ovary, and for this reason have been given the name of corpora lutea (Latin, corpus = body + luteus = orange yellow), although they are not this color in all species. Each corpus luteum acts as a ductless gland, secreting a hormone called progesterone, which affects particularly the wall of the uterus, inhibiting the contractions of its muscles and stimulating the lining, or endometrium (Greek, endo = within + metra = womb) to thicken, by the multiplication of cells, and to become more glandular and more vascular in preparation for the reception and implantation of the embryo.

Implantation takes place only if fertilization has occurred and the egg has arrived in the uterus, after its passage along the oviduct, in a stage of its development when it can take advantage of the conditions obtaining there and when it can, on its part, influence conditions in the endometrium. If fertilization has not taken place, the eggs

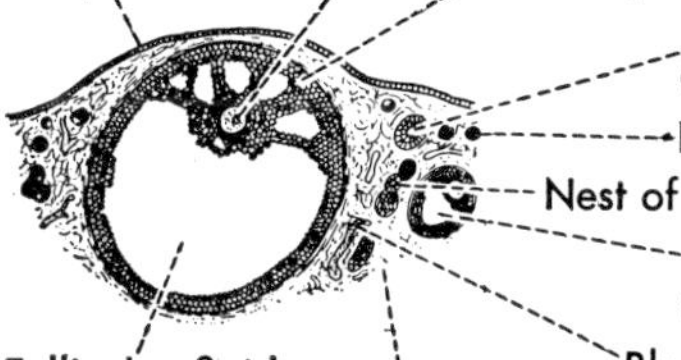

FIGURE 23.32 Diagram of a thin section of a portion of an adult mammalian ovary, showing one fully developed Graafian follicle and others in various stages of development. (From Kimber, Gray and Stackpole, *Textbook of Anatomy and Physiology*, 11th edition. Copyright 1942 by The Macmillan Company.)

and the corpora lutea degenerate, and in mammals other than the primates, the uterine wall gradually returns to its original condition and the cycle begins again. In primates, the breakdown of the corpus luteum is accompanied by a breakdown of the tissues of the endometrium, including the blood vessels, and is marked by a period of hemorrhage, or menstruation.

In the reproductive cycle of all female mammals, the pituitary and the ovaries have a reciprocal effect upon each other. As estrogen is formed, under the stimulus of the follicle-stimulating hormone of the anterior lobe, and reaches a certain concentration in the blood, it inhibits the formation of this gonadotropic hormone, but stimulates that of the luteinizing hormone which influences the development of the corpus luteum. And as the concentration of progesterone rises in the blood, the production of the luteinizing hormone is checked. If fertilization has taken place and pregnancy follows, the production of follicle-stimulating hormone is held in abeyance during the period of gestation (Latin, gestatio = bearing) through the action of estrogens pro-

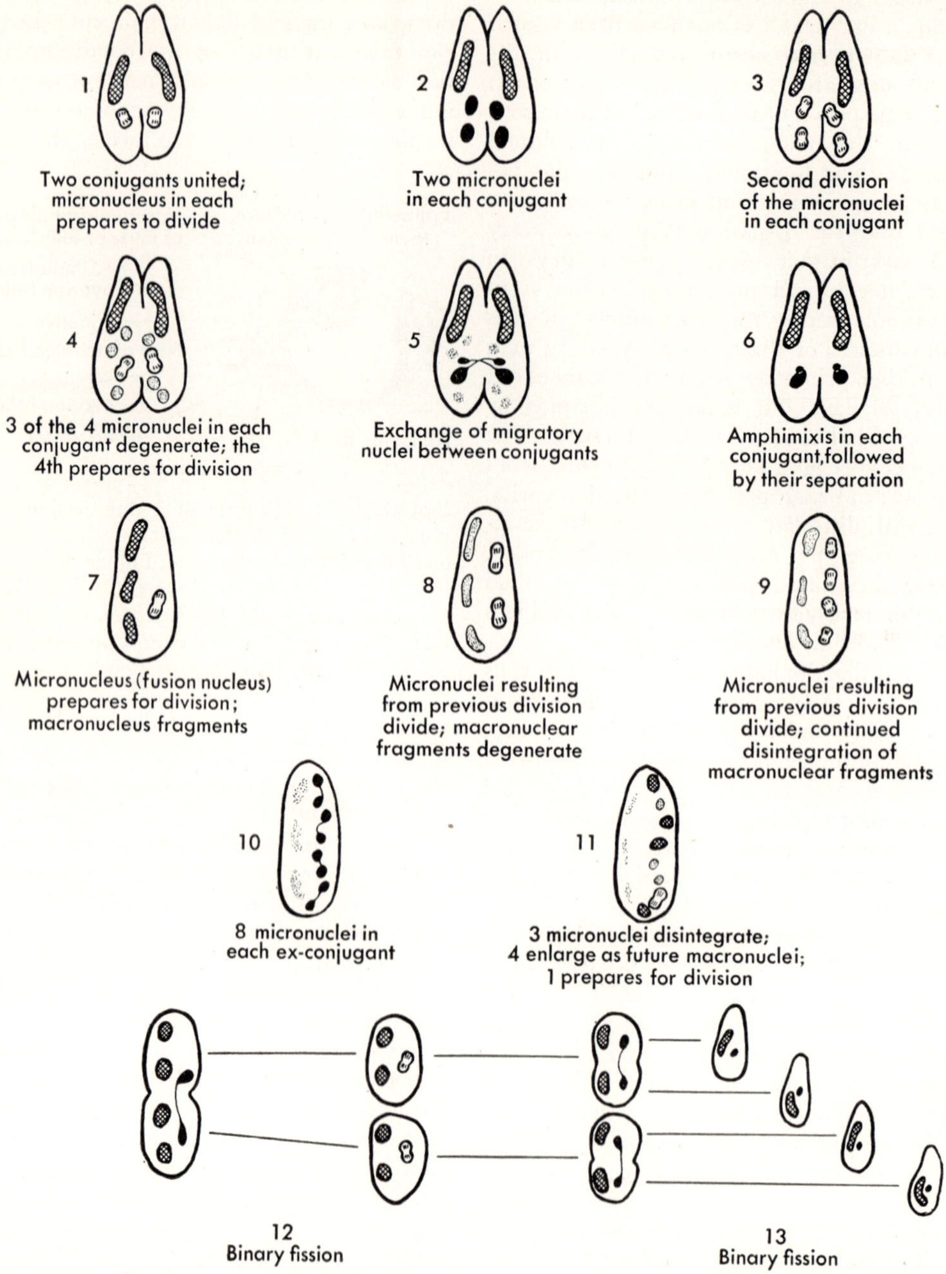

**1** Two conjugants united; micronucleus in each prepares to divide

**2** Two micronuclei in each conjugant

**3** Second division of the micronuclei in each conjugant

**4** 3 of the 4 micronuclei in each conjugant degenerate; the 4th prepares for division

**5** Exchange of migratory nuclei between conjugants

**6** Amphimixis in each conjugant, followed by their separation

**7** Micronucleus (fusion nucleus) prepares for division; macronucleus fragments

**8** Micronuclei resulting from previous division divide; macronuclear fragments degenerate

**9** Micronuclei resulting from previous division divide; continued disintegration of macronuclear fragments

**10** 8 micronuclei in each ex-conjugant

**11** 3 micronuclei disintegrate; 4 enlarge as future macronuclei; 1 prepares for division

**12** Binary fission

**13** Binary fission

FIGURE 23.33 Diagram of the sequence of events during conjugation in Paramoecium. (After Kudo.)

The macronuclei are cross-hatched; the micronuclei are solid black, except where they are shown in division. Disintegrating micronuclei are stippled.

1–6 represent changes during the period of union.

7–13 represent changes in one of the conjugants after separation, which are paralleled by those in the other conjugant.

duced by the placenta as well as by the ovary. But if fertilization has not occurred, the relatively high concentration of ovarian hormones in the blood, following on ovulation, drops to its basal level as they undergo pared for the reception of the ovum, and the release of ripe eggs from the ovary is temporarily stopped until the wall of the uterus returns once again to its previous condition.

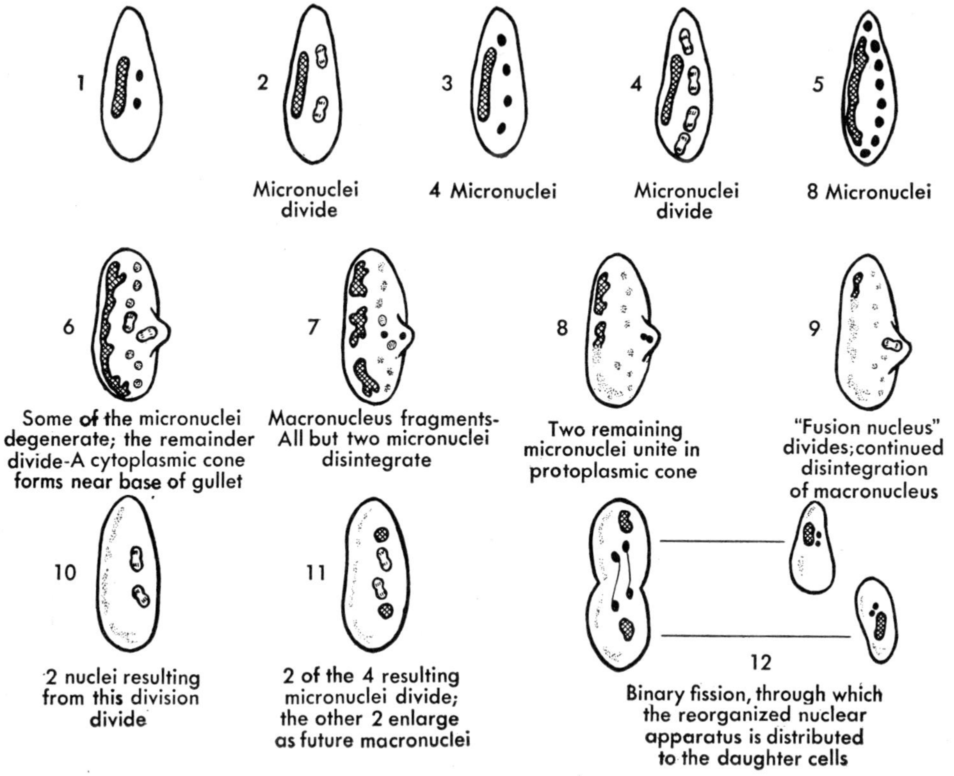

FIGURE 23.34 Diagram showing the sequence of events during autogamy in Paramoecium aurelia, a species with two micronuclei. (After Diller.) The macronuclei are cross-hatched; degenerating micronuclei are stippled.

1.
2. Micronuclei divide
3. 4 Micronuclei
4. Micronuclei divide
5. 8 Micronuclei
6. Some of the micronuclei degenerate; the remainder divide—A cytoplasmic cone forms near base of gullet
7. Macronucleus fragments—All but two micronuclei disintegrate
8. Two remaining micronuclei unite in protoplasmic cone
9. "Fusion nucleus" divides; continued disintegration of macronucleus
10. 2 nuclei resulting from this division divide
11. 2 of the 4 resulting micronuclei divide; the other 2 enlarge as future macronuclei
12. Binary fission, through which the reorganized nuclear apparatus is distributed to the daughter cells

metabolism and are excreted; thus the checks to the production of the follicle-stimulating hormone are removed, and it again exerts its effect upon the ovary and the cycle starts again. So that, in placental mammals, where the protection of the eggs and nurture of the young has reached its highest stage of evolutionary development, reproduction depends upon an ordered series of changes in the reproductive organs, as well as upon the conditions common to all animals of the successful production, and successful union, of gametes. In these changes, initiated by the discharge of the egg from the ovary and following a precisely regulated time sequence, the uterus is pre-

## Sexuality in protozoa and fungi

The fundamental sexual process of nuclear fusion, or amphimixis, is recognized as a phenomenon common to all categories of biological systems, although it is not always effected by means of gametes. It has not yet been established in Amoeba or in unicellular fungi, but in other protozoa it may take place by means of motile cells derived by successive divisions of a parent organism, or by a process of conjugation that seems to be peculiar to the ciliates. In 1692, Leewenhoek reported, in one of his many communications to the Royal Society, that he had seen Paramoecium swimming about in pairs, an observation that has since been corroborated by practically every biologist who has made any microscopic studies of these animals. The nuclear changes and the relationships between the conjugating individuals have been more completely analyzed about quite independently of each other, or they may come together in a clump or cluster, from which they later emerge in pairs. This clumping, or agglutination, is called the mating reaction, and it has been found that within the same species of

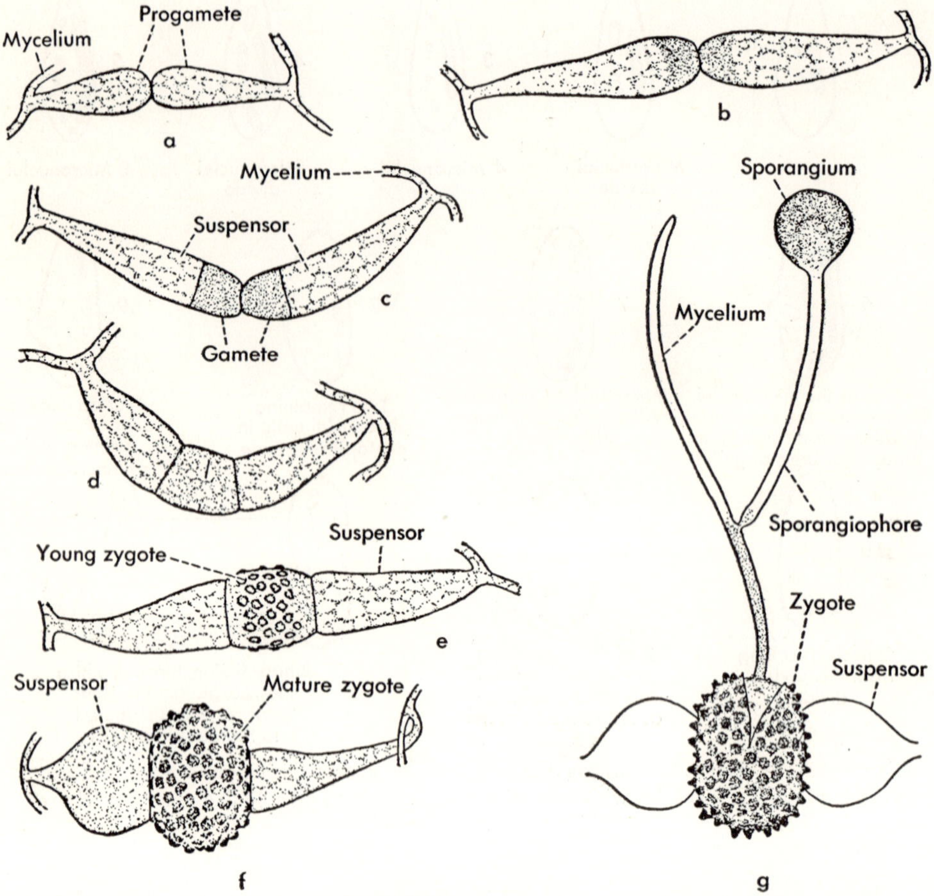

FIGURE 23.35  Conjugation in Phycomycetes. (From Smith, Gilbert, Evans, Duggar, Bryan and Allen, *A Textbook of General Botany*. Copyright 1942 by The Macmillan Company.) Stages in the formation of gametes (a-c) of the bread mold, Rhizopus. The union of the gametes is shown in d, the zygote in e and f, and the germination of the zygote into a dwarf mycelium in g.

in Paramoecium than in other genera, in some of which, however, similar conditions are known to occur.

**Nuclear reorganization in Paramoecium**

*Amphimixis:* When a number of specimens of two different races of Paramoecium are brought together in a drop of water in the field of the microscope, they may move Paramoecium there may be a number of mating types, between which conjugation will take place. Individuals of the same mating type, although of different clones, will not conjugate with each other. When conjugation does take place, the two members of a pair come together laterally, oral groove to oral groove, and the same series of nuclear changes goes on in each (Fig.

23.33). The macronucleus fragments and gradually disintegrates and becomes lost in the cytoplasm so that it is no longer recognizable as a distinct cellular entity. The micronucleus divides into two, without any accompanying cytoplasmic division, and each of these divides again, and each of these once again so that there are temporarily eight micronuclei in each conjugant. During these divisions there has been no division of cytoplasm and the two conjugants, united by a bridge of cytoplasm where their pellicles and plasma membranes have broken down, swim about and continue to sweep a food current along their oral grooves and into their gullets. Seven of the eight micronuclei enlarge and disappear, and the eighth divides again. These are the gamete nuclei. One gamete nucleus remains in each conjugant as the "stationary nucleus," and the other, as the "migratory nucleus," moves through the protoplasmic bridge connecting the two conjugants. The two migratory nuclei may pass each other in the bridge, and even come into contact with each other, but each pursues its way through the cytoplasm until it reaches the stationary nucleus of the other conjugant with which it unites to form a synkaryon (Greek, syn = with + karyon = nucleus), or fusion nucleus. After amphimixis has taken place, the two conjugants separate from each other, and reorganization of the combined nuclear material in each begins.

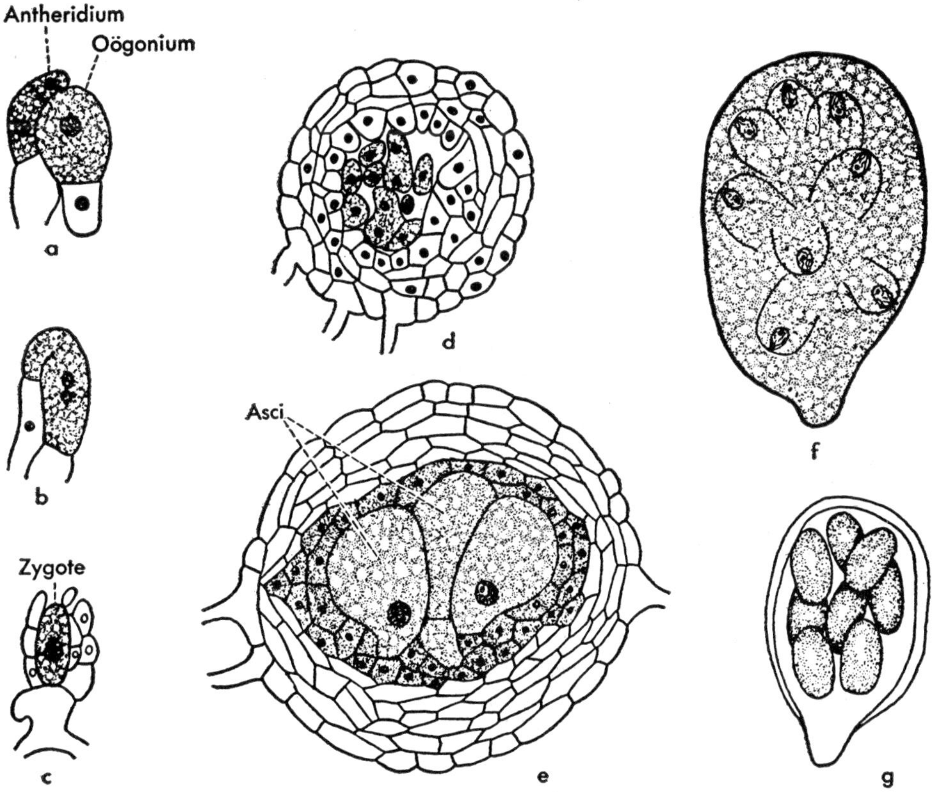

FIGURE 23.36 Gametic union and the development of the ascus in the powdery mildews (Ascomycetes). (a–e, redrawn from Harper. From Smith, Gilbert, Evans, Duggar, Bryan and Allen, *A Textbook of General Botany*. Copyright 1942 by The Macmillan Company.) a–c, Sphaerotheca; d and e, Erysiphe; f and g, Microsphaera. a and b, union of gametes; c, zygote; d, young fruiting body (the cells derived from the zygote are stippled); e, cross section of a fruiting body containing asci; f and g, the formation of ascospores.

This involves several divisions of the fusion nucleus, the disintegration of some of the resulting nuclei, the enlargement of others into macronuclei and finally the mitotic division of one, accompanied by cytoplasmic division, and another division of each of the individuals resulting. In the course of these divisions, the new macronuclei are apportioned out to the daughter cells, so that from each of the conjugants there arise four new individuals, each with a micronucleus and macronucleus that are direct mitotic descendants of the fusion nucleus. Each of the daughter cells then feeds and grows and in its turn divides by fission, giving rise to an indefinite number of descendants, or clone. These clones are similar, but different from those descended from either of the original conjugants prior to conjugation, for meiosis and so segregation and reduction of chromosomes has taken place in the course of the micronuclear divisions, and each fusion nucleus, like the nuclei of zygotes resulting from gametic union, has a complement of chromosomes qualitatively different from that of either conjugant.

***Endomixis:*** Within individual paramoecia also a process of nuclear reorganization takes place at intervals. The nuclear changes are similar to those in each member of a conjugating pair; the macronucleus disintegrates and the micronucleus divides three times, giving rise to eight (Fig. 23.34). Seven of these disintegrate and the eighth divides into two gamete nuclei, which fuse with each other. Since this fusion is between nuclei of a single individual, not of two, it is a process of endomixis rather than amphimixis, but one that likewise brings about a reassortment of the chromosomes in the diploid set. The fusion nucleus resulting from endomixis divides three times; some of the resulting nuclei degenerate, some give rise to new macronuclear material, and one remains as a micronucleus, which divides mitotically at each successive fission of the cell. In those divisions immediately following the reconstitution of the nuclear material, the new macronuclei are apportioned to the daughter cells, so that each acquires a new nuclear apparatus.

## Amphimixis in molds

Nuclear fusion has also been observed in many of the filamentous fungi. Preliminary to it, erect hyphae, or lateral branches from them, of two different mycelia growing on the same substrate come in contact with each other, the cell walls separating them disintegrate and the nuclei, or in some instances the entire protoplast, unite in a common cell. In the Phycomycetes, like the black bread mold Rhizopus, this common cell, or zygote, may develop at once into a very much reduced mycelium consisting of one or two erect hyphae and a single sporangium (Fig. 23.35), in which hundreds of spores may be formed as in the asexual process, and released when the sporangium wall breaks open. Or, as in the Ascomycetes, the zygote, formed by the union of two uninucleate cells, may divide to form a short chain of cells, enclosed, as a fruiting body, by hyphae that have grown up around the zygote from the rest of the mycelium (Fig. 23.36). From the cells derived from the zygote, there arise short branches containing some cells with two nuclei apiece. These nuclei unite, and the cell enlarges as an ascus, its nucleus dividing a number of times during the course of its growth. After a period of enlargement, cell walls are formed around each nucleus, cutting them off, with a small mass of surrounding cytoplasm, from the common cytoplasmic mass as individual ascospores, enclosed within the residual cytoplasm of the ascus. In many species the nucleus of the ascus divides three times, so that eight ascospores are ultimately formed, irregularly clustered together or arranged in linear order, as they are in the pink bread mold, Neurospora. In other species, there may be less than eight, but in any case, disintegration of the walls of the fruiting body and rupture of the enclosed asci result in the escape of quantities of ascospores, that, falling upon a suitable substrate, may germinate into new mycelia with the same species characters as their parents, but individual characters peculiar to them. Such variation inevitably results from nuclear fusion between two organisms differing in inheritable characteristics.

# CHAPTER 24
# THE INHERITANCE OF THE INDIVIDUAL

## Definition and province of genetics

The subdivision of biological science that deals with the inheritance of the individual is known as genetics (Greek, genesis = origin). That individuals resemble their parents and their more remote ancestors to a greater or less extent is a fact that man must have recognized early in his history, but it is only in this century that he has arrived at some understanding of the nature of the inheritable material and the mechanism of its transmission from generation to generation. How this material operates in shaping the qualities of organisms is a problem still to be solved, although the combined efforts of biochemists and geneticists, particularly in the past ten years, have produced valuable evidence of a close correspondence between genetic constitution and ability to carry out certain fundamental biochemical reactions.

The theory of inheritance that is almost universally accepted to-day has been derived from breeding experiments on many plants and animals, from quantitative determinations and statistical analysis of the number of types represented in the offspring of two parents that differ from each other in one or more recognizable characters and from microscopical observation of the number, kind and behavior of chromosomes in different species. According to it, the chromosomes, distributed to the cells through the mechanism of mitosis, are the principal bearers of the inheritable material, and this inheritable material incorporated in units, the genes, arranged in linear order on the chromosomes. Yet biologists have never overlooked the fact that there may also be transmission of inheritable material through the cytoplasm, and, while observations and experiments in the past fifty years have built up an impressive body of evidence in support of the chromosomes as the principal mechanism, there is also evidence that the inheritance of certain characters depends upon visible and invisible elements in the cytoplasm.

## Modern genetic theory

The chromosome theory of inheritance and its corollary, the theory of the gene, was stated in 1926 by the American scientist largely responsible for its development, Thomas Hunt Morgan (1866–1945), in the words: "the characters of the individual are referable to paired elements (genes) in the germinal material that are held together in a definite number of linkage groups; it states that the members of each pair of genes separate when the germ-cells mature in accordance with Mendel's first law, and in consequence each germ-cell comes to contain one set only; it states that the members belonging to different linkage groups assort independently in accordance with Mendel's second law; it states that an orderly interchange—crossing-over—also takes place, at times, between the elements in corresponding linkage groups; and it states that the frequency of crossing-over furnishes evidence of the linear order of the elements in each linkage group and of the relative positions of the elements in respect to each other." *

In the terminology of genetics, each member of a pair of genes is known as an allele (Greek, allelon = reciprocally); individuals in which both alleles of a pair are alike in

* Morgan, Thomas H., *The Theory of the Gene*. Copyright 1926 by Yale University Press, New Haven.

their effect upon the course of development are said to be homozygous in respect to that pair, and those in which they are unlike, heterozygous. The pair of similar alleles in the genetic constitution of a homozygous individual might then be represented as AA, and the dissimilar pair in a heterozygous individual as Aa. It follows that, if the alleles separate from each other at meiosis and are separately distributed to the germ cells, a homozygous individual will also be homogametic in respect to that particular pair of alleles, for each gamete will contain the gene A, while a heterozygous individual will be heterogametic, since half its gametes will contain the gene A, and half the gene a.

## Mendel's laws

The chromosomal theory of inheritance, although developed only through work in the past fifty years, has its foundations in experiments carried on nearly one hundred years ago by an Austrian, Johann Mendel (1822–1884). These experiments, in which different varieties of edible peas were used as experimental material, were carried on in the garden of the Königenkloster, the monastery at Brunn which Mendel entered as a young man and of which he eventually became abbot. Mendel possessed a driving scientific curiosity, and among the many natural phenomena to which he turned his attention was that of inheritance in hybrids, the offspring of parents of two different species. Such creatures as the mule, the offspring of a horse (Equus caballus) and an ass (Equus asinus), had been known since the time of Homer, and both classical and seventeenth century literature are full of allusions to the results of cross-fertilizations between animal species, for the most part fantastic ones that were supposed to have occurred naturally. Although the facts of gametic union and nuclear fusion were not established until 1875, ten years after Mendel had reported the results of his experiments and the generalizations, or "laws" that he had drawn from them, the fact that in plants fruit is produced only when pollen reaches the stigma of a flower had been known at least since the time of the Assyrians, 1000 years before Christ. Using this knowledge, and taking advantage of the fact that cross-fertilizations between plants of different varieties, and even of different species, often result in offspring that are fertile and not, like the mule, incapable of reproduction, horticulturists and scientists before Mendel and contemporary with him had made numbers of experimental crosses and gained some knowledge of the characters of hybrids in relation to those of their parents. It was generally recognized, as a result of these crossings, that the characters of a hybrid may closely resemble those of one or the other of its parents, or may be intermediate between them, and that all members of the first generation of offspring of parents of different kinds are, in general, alike in appearance, but that members of later generations, the offspring of the hybrid parents, are different and diverse in appearance.

## Mendel's experiments and their results

None of these experimenters succeeded in finding general principles that applied equally well to the interpretation of hybrids of all kinds. Mendel undertook his experiments with full realization that all of the previous work on plant hybridization had been purely qualitative, dealing with general descriptions of the hybrids and their offspring, but neither with the analysis of the individual characters of the plants nor with the numbers of different types that were obtained. He saw that the answer to the problem of the formation and development of hybrids could be reached only through quantitative study of the number of types represented in their offspring, the exact identification of these types with their separate generations and the determination of their statistical relations. Here he was, like Harvey, fulfilling Galileo's canon of scientific experimentation (see page 334), and by so doing, he discovered the secret that had eluded his predecessors. His success lay partly in this clear conception of the requirements of a scientific experiment, partly in the care and precision with which he carried out his experiments and analyzed the results from them, and partly in the importance that he attached to the individual characters of each member of every generation of peas that he grew and harvested.

In making his experiments, he determined first that each of the varieties of peas he used bred true to its type, reaching, for example, an average height of 6–7 feet or no more than 3/4–1 1/2 feet, producing exclusively either round seeds or wrinkled ones, or yellow or green ones, or any other of the seven pairs of alternative characters whose inheritance he had chosen to follow. Then, in each hybridization experiment, he pulled the stamens, before their pollen was ripe, out of all the flower buds on some of the plants of the varieties he intended to use as parents, and dusted the stigmas of such emasculated flowers with pollen from others he had left intact. He made reciprocal crosses in each experiment, that is, he used the same variety both as the pollen-contributing, or male, parent, and as the ovule-contributing, or female, parent, so that he could determine the inheritance of parental characters entering either through the pollen or the egg. In this way he brought together the germ cells of plants that differed in one, two or three pairs of characters. Figures 24.1 and 24.2 show the results of his experiments in crossing round and wrinkled seeded varieties, and round, yellow and green, wrinkled seeded ones. In these, whose results are typical of the others that he made, the character of one parent only is apparent in the first generation of hybrids, whether introduced through pollen or ovule. Following the terminology of other hybridizers, Mendel called this the dominant character, and the other, which was concealed in the hybrid but reappeared unchanged in its offspring, the recessive.

From the results of his experiments, Mendel saw that by grouping together the types, on the basis of their apparent characters and of the constancy with which these characters were reproduced in the offspring, it was possible to express in a series all the kinds of offspring that could be derived from a hybrid, according to the mathematical laws of combination and recombination. He saw, further, that, since constant forms could be produced only through the union of egg and pollen (gamete nucleus) of like type, within the ovaries of the hybrid, and likewise within its anthers, there must be formed as many kinds of egg cells, and as many kinds of pollen, as there are constant combining forms, and he devised an experiment to test this hypothesis. He made a cross between a round, yellow seeded variety and a wrinkled, green seeded one. The hybrid seeds, which were round and yellow, were planted and the stigmas of all the flowers on some of the plants grown from them pollinated with pollen from

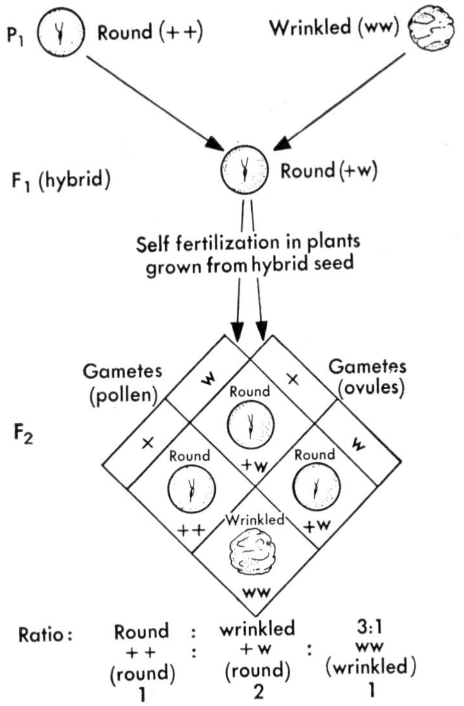

FIGURE 24.1 Diagram illustrating Mendel's one-factor crosses (here of round seeded x wrinkled seeded peas). The external characters of the peas (phenotype), as Mendel distinguished them, are written beside the seeds of each generation, their genic constitution (genotype), as it is now understood, in parentheses beside them. (The diagonal representation of the conventional Punnett square is taken from charts in the Mendel Museum at Mary Washington College, Fredericksburg, Virginia under the direction of Dr. Hugo Iltis.)

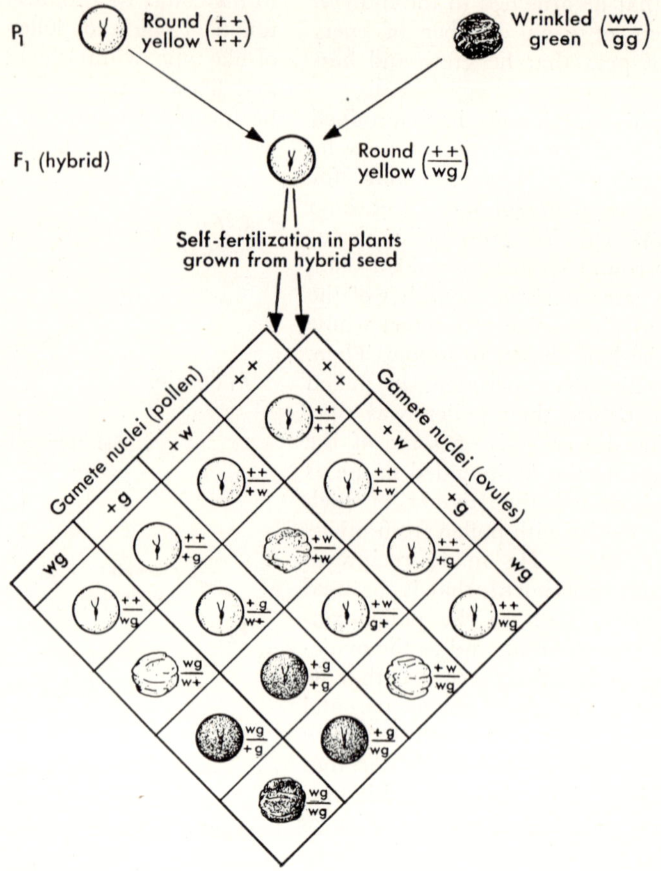

# THE OPERATION OF BIOLOGICAL SYSTEMS

FIGURE 24.2 Diagram illustrating Mendel's two-factor crosses (here of round, yellow × wrinkled, green seeded peas). Symbols as in Figure 24.1. In the sporogenesis of the hybrid ($\frac{++}{wg}$) resulting from the cross, the four different genes, on four different chromosomes, segregate at random, giving four classes of pollen and four classes of egg cells, and sixteen possible recombinations in the zygote.

plants of a pure round, yellow seeded variety; the stigmas of all the flowers on others were pollinated with pollen from plants of a pure wrinkled, green seeded variety. At the same time, pollen from some of these hybrid plants was transferred to the stigmas of flowers of the round, yellow and wrinkled, green seeded strains. If Mendel's hypothesis were correct, the hybrid plants should produce egg cells of the four classes, AB, Ab, aB and ab, where A stands for roundness, a for wrinkledness, B for yellowness and b for greenness, and the plants from the pure stocks gametes of only one type, AB or ab respectively. The possible combinations, when the eggs of the hybrids were fertilized by AB or ab pollen, and when the eggs of the pure stocks were fertilized by the hybrid pollen could then be expressed as follows:

1. Hybrid egg cells AB, Ab, aB and ab $\times$ AB pollen from a pure round, yellow strain.
    Possible zygotic combinations
    AABB, AAbB, aABB and aAbB.
2. Hybrid egg cells AB, Ab, aB and ab $\times$ ab pollen from a pure wrinkled, green seeded strain.
    Possible zygotic combinations
    AaBb, Aabb, aaBb, and aabb.
3. Egg cells of pure AB variety $\times$ hybrid pollen AB, Ab, aB and ab.
    Possible zygotic combinations
    AABB, AABb, AaBB and AaBb.
4. Egg cells of pure ab variety $\times$ hybrid pollen AB, Ab, aB and ab.
    Possible zygotic combinations
    aABb, aAbb, aabB and aabb.

The results of these crossings fulfilled his predictions exactly, for from experiments 1 and 3 he obtained only round, yellow seeds, and from experiments 2 and 4, round, yellow, round, green, wrinkled yellow and wrinkled green seeds in approximately even numbers, since all possible combinations of gametes in 1 and 3 include the dominant A and B, while those in experiments 2 and 4 contain aa and bb combinations as well.

Two general principles can be deduced from these experiments that apply not only to the reproduction of hybrids but to that of all individuals arising from the union of an egg and a sperm. According to the first of these, the two differentiating characters brought together in the zygote separate, or segregate, from each other in the course of the formation of the gametes of the individual into which the zygote develops, without contamination during their association within it. According to the second, the distribution of these segregating characters is a random one, so that when a number of them are concerned, they may be present in the gametes in all possible combinations, according to the mathematical laws of probability. These two general principles are known as the Law of Segregation and the Law of Independent, or Random, Assortment, or as Mendel's Laws.

Mendel presented the results of his experiments to the Brunn Society for the Study of Natural Science in February, 1865, but they received scant attention either from those present or from the few European scientists outside Brunn who heard of them. It was not until the early 1900's that their implications were understood and Mendel, diverted from his experiments on peas by the advice of the leading contemporary European botanist, Karl Nägeli (1817–1891), to those on hawkweed, a plant far less satisfactory for this kind of study, died sixteen years before his work received the recognition it merited.

### Mitosis, meiosis and fertilization as mechanisms for Mendelian inheritance

At the beginning of this century, when improvements in the techniques of microscopical study had made possible detailed observations of cell constituents, individual differences between chromosomes and between the sets of chromosomes of different species were recognized, and the course of events in mitosis, meiosis and fertilization were followed. It became evident, to those who knew about Mendel's experiments, that meiosis would provide a mechanism for the segregation and random assortment of the inheritable units, and fertilization one for their recombination, that he had deduced from his breeding experiments. It had been shown, too, by experiments on sea urchin eggs, that at least one complete set of chromosomes is necessary for normal development, and that individual chromosomes have specific effects upon specific characters. The chromosomes therefore came to be regarded as the physical basis of inheritance, as protoplasm was regarded as the physical basis of life.

### Modification of the law of random assortment

But as genetic studies progressed it became evident that Mendel's Laws required a certain amount of modification. There was not, for example, in all cases the free assortment of the characters known to be

[ 538 ]  THE OPERATION OF BIOLOGICAL SYSTEMS

included in the hybrid that he had found, but a tendency for certain ones to be linked together and so inherited in groups, or blocks. Nor did the numbers of different kinds of offspring of hybrids invariably fulfill the expected Mendelian ratios. Studies of linked characters showed that they fell into a number of groups that never exceeded the haploid number of chromosomes, from which it was concluded that they were transmitted from generation to generation by the same chromosome. But in some instances, it was found that linked characters entering a hybrid in one combination reappeared in its offspring in a different one, indicating that an exchange, or shift, of alleles between homologous chromosomes had taken place.

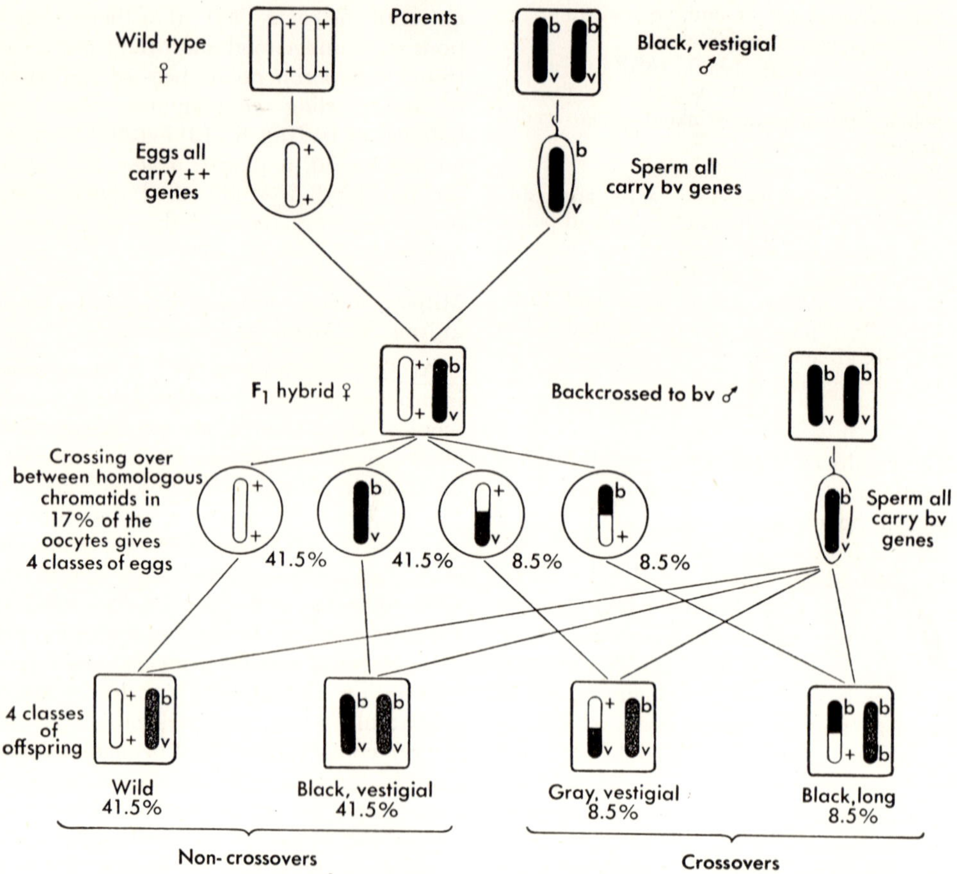

*Linkage and crossing-over:* For example, in the fruit fly Drosophila, an animal that has been widely used for genetic studies and which has furnished much of the evidence for modern genetic theory, body color and length of wing are characters ordinarily inherited together. If a wild fly, which has a grayish-yellow body and wings that extend slightly beyond the tip of the abdomen, is mated to a fly with a black body and short, or vestigial, wings, all the offspring in the first generation are so-called wild-type flies, with gray bodies and long wings (Fig. 24.3).

FIGURE 24.3 Diagram showing the mechanism of inheritance in a heterozygous fly derived from the mating of a wild-type fly (++) with one with black body and vestigial wings (bv). (After Altenburg.)

Flies of this generation would be expected to produce only two classes of gametes, in respect to these two pairs of characters, one containing the chromosome with the genes for long wings and gray body color and the other, the chromosome with their vestigial and black alleles. But when females of this generation are mated to black, vestigial males from a stock known to breed true for these characters, it is found that their gametes are of four kinds, not two, for among their offspring are not only flies with long wings and gray bodies, and flies with vestigial wings and black bodies, as would be expected, but also a small proportion of those with vestigial wings and gray bodies, and long wings and black bodies, representing a new combination of the parental characters. That such recombinations do arise through exchange of segments, or of genes, between homologous chromatids during meiosis has been proved by cytological examination of marked chromosomes, correlated with genetic data, both in Drosophila and in maize, or corn (Zea mays), and is known as crossing-over (Fig. 24.4).

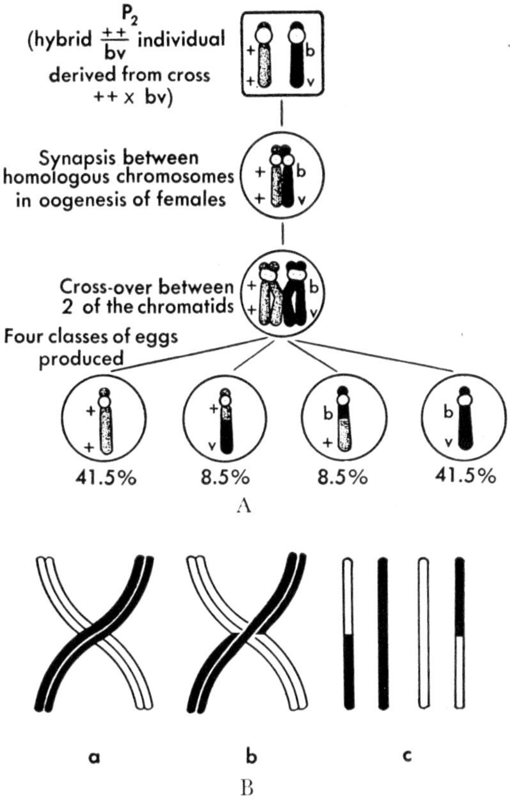

*Evidence for the linear order of the genes; chromosome maps:* It has been found, further, that while there is consistency in the frequency with which crossing-over takes place between any two given pairs of alleles, there are great differences in the frequencies with which it occurs between others in the same linkage group. This fact has been used to advantage in determining the order of the genes on the chromosomes, and their relations to each other. On the assumption that their arrangement is a linear one, and that crossing-over takes place less frequently between the alleles of linked genes that are close together than between those that are separated by a greater length of chromosome, it has been possible to plot the locations of the genes from measurements of the frequency of crossing-over between any two pairs. In this way very complete maps of the chromosomes of Drosophila and of Zea have been made, in which all the genes so far identified are assigned positions, or loci, on particular chromosomes of the haploid set, and somewhat less complete ones for a great many other species. The theoretical accuracy of these maps has been confirmed, in Drosophila at least, by microscopic examination of the chromosomes in the nuclei of the salivary glands of the larvae. These chromosomes, about one hundred times longer than the length at metaphase of those in most of the other tissues of the body, show linear differentiations that correspond to the locations of genes determined by this method (Fig. 24.5).

FIGURE 24.4 Crossing-over.

A. Diagram showing the mechanism of inheritance, with crossing-over, in a heterozygous female fly, derived from a cross between one wild-type parent, and one with black body and vestigial wings. Only the pair of chromosomes carrying the genes affecting body color are represented.

B. Diagram showing how the exchange may take place between homologous chromosomes during meiosis. The four chromatids of one bivalent with a single chiasma are shown.

## Sex inheritance

Early in the study of the chromosome content of the cells of different species a correlation was discovered between the sex of the individual and its complement of chromosomes. In Protenor, for example, a genus of bugs, all females have a diploid number of 14, or 7 pairs, while the males have only 13, 6 pairs and one odd chromosome, or heterochromosome; in another genus, Lygaeus, both males and females have 14, or 7 pairs, but while in the females both members of each pair are similar in size and shape, in the males one pair consists of a large chromosome and a very much smaller one. In both insects, all the eggs are alike in containing a haploid set of seven similar chromosomes, but in each the males produce sperm of two kinds. During spermatogenesis in Protenor, the unpaired chromosome is duplicated, as are the members of each of the pairs, and in the first division its two chromatids separate, or disjoin, and move to the two poles of the spindle with the bivalents, so that each secondary spermatocyte has seven bivalent chromosomes and one univalent one; in the next division, the univalent goes to one pole, and so is included in only two of the four spermatids derived from each spermatogonium (Fig. 24.6). In Lygaeus, the members of the dissimilar, or heteromorphic, pair come together in synapsis like the others in the set, and their chromatids disjoin in a similar fashion, so that half the sperm receive the large member and half the small (Fig. 24.7). When, in Protenor, a sperm with 7 chromosomes fertilizes an egg the resulting zygote, with 14, develops into a female; when a sperm with 6 chromosomes fertilizes an egg, the resulting zygote, with 13, develops into a male. Similarly in Lygaeus, fertilization of an egg by a sperm containing the large chromosome results in the development of a female, and by a sperm containing the small chromosome, in the development of a male.

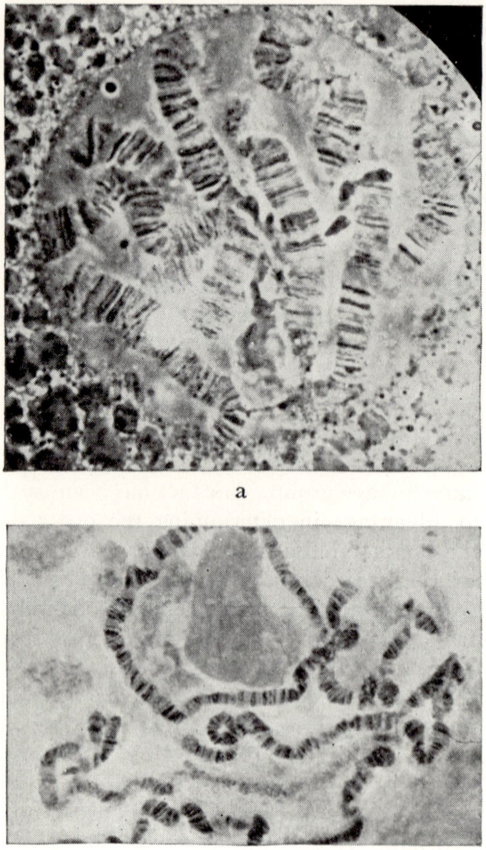

Such differences in number of chromosomes, or in the visible characteristics of one pair, and a similar mechanism of sex determination have been demonstrated in a great variety of animal species and, among plants, in at least 55 species of angiosperms. But in moths, caddis flies, birds and some fishes, it is the female that has the heteromorphic pair of chromosomes, and so it is the eggs, and not the sperm, that are of two classes and are the sex-determining gametes. And it is only in dioecious plants, where there is a sex distinction between individuals, one producing only carpellate and another only staminate flowers, that the

FIGURE 24.5 Salivary gland chromosomes of Drosophila. (Photographs taken with phase contrast microscopy, by courtesy of Dr. Jack Schultz.)

a. Nucleus of a salivary gland cell, at high magnification, showing the chromosomes as striped, ribbon-like bands coiled within it.

b. Chromosomes pressed out of the nucleus of a cell of a salivary gland in an aceto-orcein smear preparation.

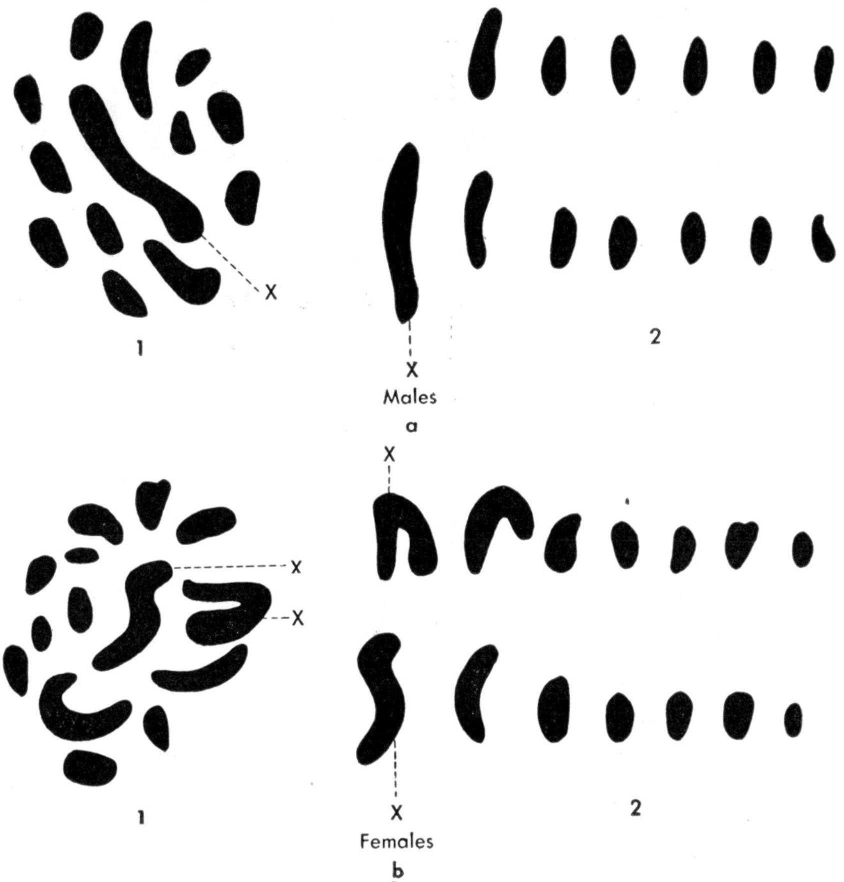

FIGURE 24.6 Chromosome complements of Protenor. (After Morgan, after Wilson.)

a(1) The chromosomes are shown as they appear in division in the cells of a male. (2n = 13.)

(2) The chromosomes are arranged in two sets, showing the homologues as they pair in synapsis. In the meiotic divisions, the large X, having no mate, accompanies one or the other set of autosomes to the pole of the spindle, so that two classes of sperm result, one with the X chromosome (n = 6A + X), and one without it (n = 6A).

b(1) The chromosomes are shown as they appear during division in the cells of the female (2n = 14).

(2) The chromosomes are arranged as in a (2). In meiosis, the two X chromosomes pair, and disjoin, each egg receiving one (n = 6A + X).

mechanism has been shown to operate as it does in animals.

The chromosomes, whose presence is associated with the development of one or the other sex, were called "sex chromosomes" and believed to carry the genes for maleness or femaleness, and so to be different from the others in the set, believed to carry only genes directing the development of bodily, or somatic, characters and collectively called "autosomes." Although so definite a distinction has since been found to be false, and the term sex chromosome to a great extent abandoned in favor of heterosome, the mechanism of sex determination through the distribution of these chromosomes to the gametes and so to the zygotes is well established. The heterosomes are generally referred to as X or Y chromosomes, the Y indicating the dissimilar member of a hetero-

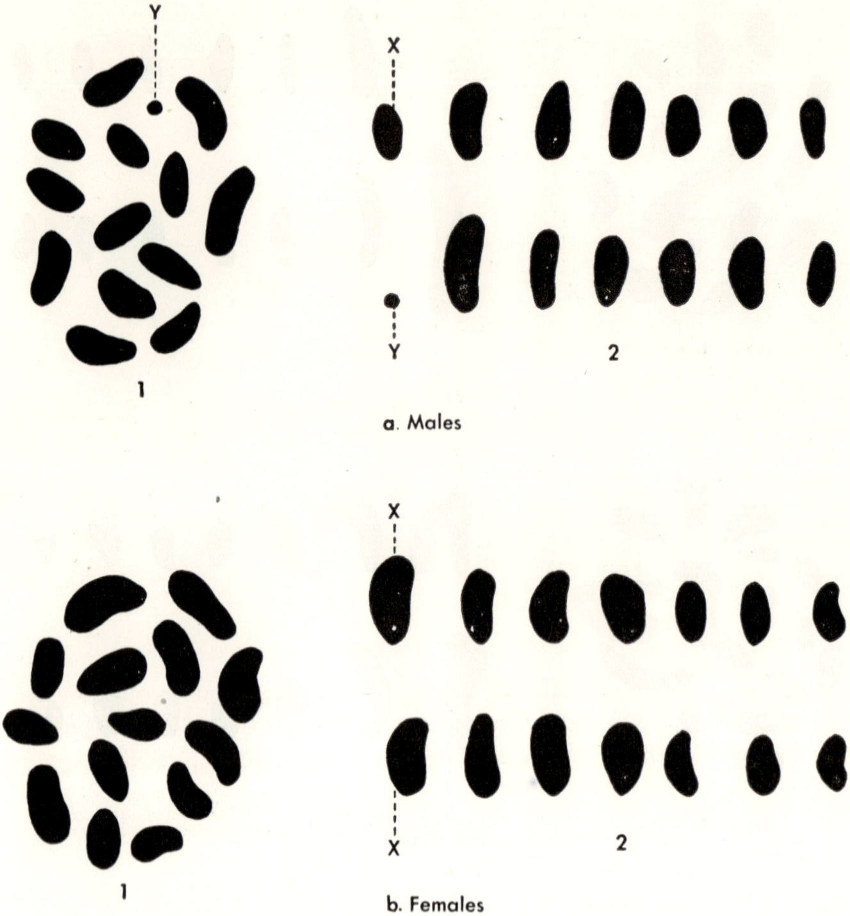

FIGURE 24.7 Chromosome complements of Lygaeus. (After Morgan, after Wilson.)

a(1) All 14 chromosomes are shown as they appear during division in the cells of the male (2n = 14).

(2) The chromosomes are arranged as in 24.6 a (2). After meiosis there are two classes of sperm, each with 6 autosomes and one with the large X chromosome (n = 6A + X) and one with the small Y chromosome (n = 6A + Y).

b(1) All 14 chromosomes are shown as they appear during division in the cells of the female (2n = 14).

(2) The chromosomes are arranged in sets of 7. After meiosis, all the eggs contain 6 autosomes and 1 X chromosome (n = 6A + X).

morphic pair; in moths and birds, Z may be used to designate the X chromosome, and W the Y, of other species.

### The mechanism of sex inheritance

This mechanism of sex determination can be expressed in four general formulae, which numerous investigations of representatives of all the principal groups of sexually reproducing organisms have shown apply to all species in which there is a morphological distinction between males and females. Sex in such organisms is determined at the time of fertilization, although differentiation of the characters associated with it may be greatly modified by conditions within the organism as well as by those outside it. These formulae, where A stands for the full

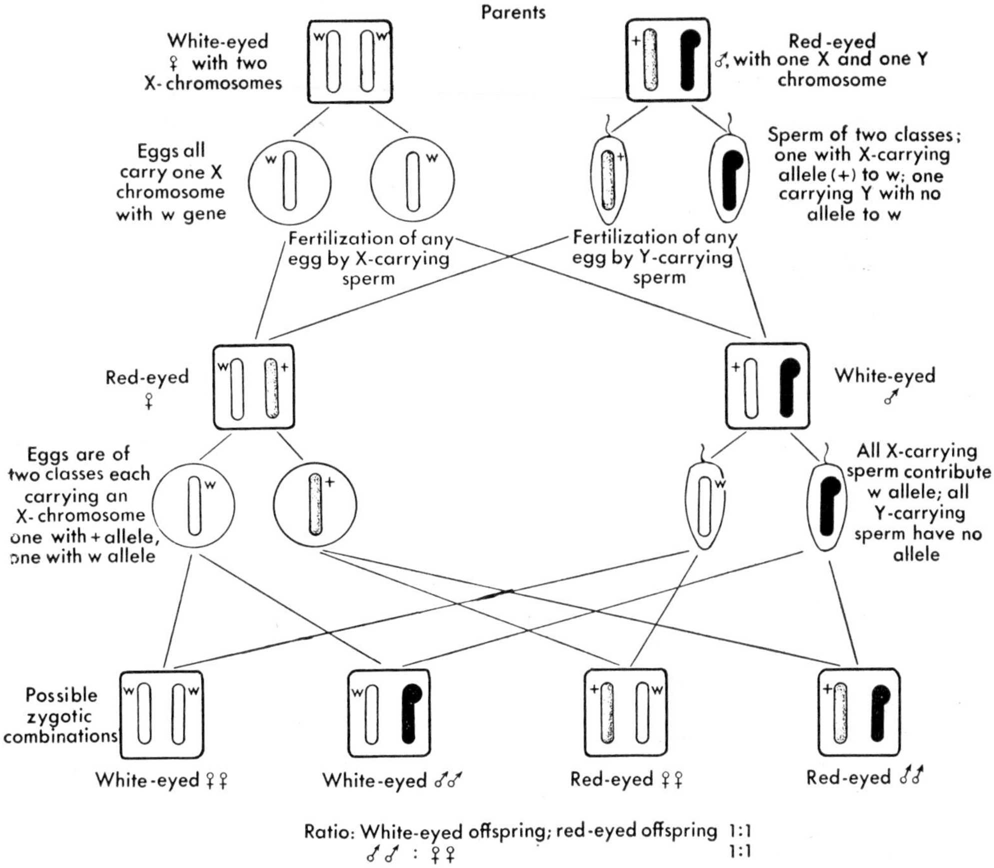

FIGURE 24.8 Diagram showing the inheritance of a gene located on the X chromosome of Drosophila. (After Morgan.)

complement of autosomes, X or Z, Y or W for the heterosomes, and O for the absence of a homologue for any one of them are:

1. Male heterogametic, characteristic of most animals and of dioecious plants.

   | | Female | Male |
   |---|---|---|
   | a. | A + XX | A + XY |
   | b. | A + XX | A + XO |

2. Female heterogametic, characteristic particularly of moths and birds.

   | | | |
   |---|---|---|
   | a. | A + XY (ZW) | A + XX (ZZ) |
   | b. | A + XO (ZO) | A + XX (ZZ) |

It follows, if these mechanisms operate consistently, that males and females will be represented in equal numbers in the offspring of any two parents, provided that the total number of their progeny is large enough to insure an equal representation of all possible gametic unions.

In Drosophila melanogaster, both males and females have a chromosomal complement of 8. The two X chromosomes of the female are rod-shaped, the Y in the male is hook-shaped and in meiosis pairs with the single X. Breeding experiments have shown that some 200 genes associated with the production of bodily characters are located on the X chromosome, while very few are on the Y. These genes are therefore said to be sex-linked, and their location is proved by their distribution in the first generation of offspring of males and females differing in one or more of the characters whose development they direct. If, for example, a female with white eyes is mated to a male of the wild type, with red eyes, her sons are all white-eyed and her daughters red-eyed. And if one of these daughters is mated to a white-eyed male, approximately fifty per cent of her sons and daughters are red-eyed and fifty per cent white-eyed. The mechanism of this inheritance is shown in Figure 24.8, from which it is also evident that a female may transmit to her sons a characteristic that she herself has not shown, because it is the expression of a recessive gene for which she is heterozygous, her other X chromosome carrying its dominant allele. Half of her eggs will, however, contain the X chromosome with this gene, and when these are fertilized by sperm carrying the Y chromosome the resulting zygotes will develop into males showing this recessive character, since the Y chromosome carries no alternative allele to it.

Instances of such sex-linked inheritance have been shown in a great number of animal species and in some plants. In man, red-green color blindness, at least one kind of hemophilia, or inability of the blood to clot, and absence of two center incisor teeth are known to be the effects of recessive genes located on the X chromosome, and so may be transmitted by a mother, in whom their effects are not apparent, to half her sons. Theoretically, she might also hand these characters down to some of her daughters but actually this is rarely, if ever, the case, for it could only happen if she married a man also with the recessive gene, the probability for which is slight in large and mixed human populations. Red-green color blindness is, for example, found in about 8 per cent of the male population, but only in about 0.64 per cent of the female.

### The balance theory of sex inheritance

Certain deviations from the ordinary pattern of chromosome distribution, that have been cytologically demonstrated and correlated with abnormalities in the development of sex characters, have led to the theory that sex is the expression of a balance of tendencies for maleness and femaleness both of which are present in the fertilized egg, and the expression of genes located on the autosomes as well as on the heterosomes.

Sometimes chromosomes fail to disjoin from each other at anaphase, and so are unequally distributed to the daughter cells. If such failure, or non-disjunction, occurs in a mitotic division of cells destined to become germ cells, or in the meiotic divisions of

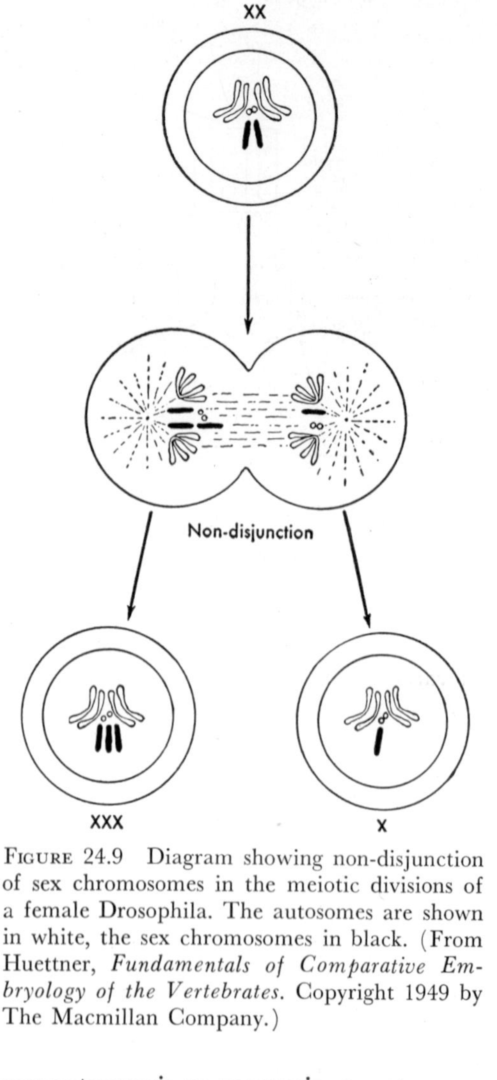

FIGURE 24.9 Diagram showing non-disjunction of sex chromosomes in the meiotic divisions of a female Drosophila. The autosomes are shown in white, the sex chromosomes in black. (From Huettner, *Fundamentals of Comparative Embryology of the Vertebrates.* Copyright 1949 by The Macmillan Company.)

spermatogenesis or oogenesis, gametes may be produced with more, or less, than the haploid number of chromosomes. The entire set may be involved and if such total non-disjunction occurs in oogenesis, the egg nucleus may be left with both sets of chromosomes, as a diploid gamete; when fertilized by an ordinary, haploid sperm, the zygote has a triple set of chromosomes and may, if this combination is viable, develop into a triploid (3n) individual. Or only one or two chromosomes may fail to separate; again, if their non-disjunction occurs during oogenesis, the chromosomes involved may be eliminated in a polar body or retained in the egg and the gamete resulting may have less than the haploid number of chromosomes, or more than the haploid number, expressed as $2n-1$ or $2n-2$, or $2n+1$ or $2n+2$ (Fig. 24.9).

*The effects of non-disjunction in Drosophila:* Both diploid eggs and eggs with and without an extra chromosome are known to originate in this way in Drosophila; those that have an extra IV chromosome, the smallest in the set, and those that lack one, as well as those with an extra X chromosome and without any are known to develop, on fertilization, into individuals whose structural characteristics and breeding behavior are not like those of ordinary diploid flies. Fertilization of diploid eggs by X-carrying sperm results in triploid females, externally very similar to diploid ones. But although they are fertile and lay large numbers of eggs, comparatively few of their offspring survive and those that do show a good deal of variation and some of them, marked abnormalities. This breeding behavior is the consequence of irregularities in the segregation of the three sets of chromosomes, certain combinations giving rise to zygotes that cannot survive and others to those that develop into flies with different relative numbers of autosomes and heterosomes. Table XV shows the chromosomal constitution of the eggs and of the individuals that are known, from cytological examination, to develop from them after fertilization by sperm from an ordinary diploid male.

The intersexes look alike, with some of the secondary sex characters of males and some of those of females, either rudimentary gonads or one ovary and one testis, and the other sex organs mixtures of male and female ones, or predominantly those of one or the other sex. The supersexes look like males or females and have either testes or ovaries, but they are feeble, and if they live long enough to reach maturity, are sterile.

Normal expression of the characters of maleness and femaleness thus depends upon a balance between genes on the X chromosome and those on the autosomes; when the scales are tipped in one direction or the other by the addition of an extra X chromosome or of a set of autosomes, the imbalance is apparent in developmental abnormalities, affecting the sex organs particularly. This conception of genic balance in the definition of the sex of an individual is confirmed by breeding experiments on other animals.

TABLE XV

| Eggs from triploid females | Sperm from diploid male | |
|---|---|---|
| | 1A + 1X | 1A + 1Y |
| 2A + 2X | 3A + 3X triploid ♀ | 3A + 2X + 1Y intersex |
| 1A + 1X | 2A + 2X diploid ♀ | 2A + 1X + 1Y diploid ♂ |
| 1A + 2X | 2A + 3X super ♀ | 2A + 2X + 1Y diploid ♀ |
| 2A + 1X | 3A + 2X intersex | 3A + 1X + 1Y super ♂ |

*The influence of the Y-chromosome in Drosophila:* In Drosophila few genes are located on the Y chromosome, and its presence or absence does not affect the development of the sex organs, although it does affect the fertility of the males. Flies with the genetic constitution 2AA+XXY, the result of fertilization by a Y-carrying sperm of an egg with two X chromosomes,* are fertile females, but those with the genetic constitution 2A+XO, the result of fertilization by an X-carrying sperm of an egg with no X chromosome, develop as males and are sterile. In some other species, however, the Y chromosome plays a greater role both as a bearer of genes for bodily characters and of those for sex, and its elimination from a gamete or a zygote has fatal, or lethal, effects.

* Such eggs are the result of non-disjunction of the X chromosomes, which has been found to occur naturally during oogenesis about once in every 25,000 eggs formed.

### Sex genes in Zea mays

Intersexes of triploid constitution, like those in Drosophila, have also been found in dioecious plants, where the mechanism of sex determination is also similar. And genes that may properly be called sex genes, since they influence the development of sex organs, have been found in some monoecious plants in which, however, there is no such precise mechanism of sex determination, for a single individual bears both carpellate and staminate flowers and so produces both female and male germ cells. In maize, for example, there are several genes, located on different chromosomes, any pair of which, in the homozygous condition, cause the development of carpellate flowers in the usual position of staminate ones, converting tassels to ears and hence called tassel-seed genes. Another gene, called silkless, results in defective development of the ovules; plants homozygous for it are actually males, since only their staminate flowers develop functional germ cells. Plants homozygous for these genes thus virtually become dioecious, since each individual can produce only one type of gamete, and in inbred stocks the chromosomes on which they are located act as sex chromosomes in determining its sex.

## *Mutations*

### Genic change

The entire science of genetics has been built up from the study of the characteristics of the progeny of two parents differing from each other in one or more visible characters, and is based upon the segregation of different alleles, their possible combinations in gametes and recombinations in zygotes. Presumably these differences must have arisen through changes in the inheritable material, or mutations (Latin, mutare = to change), which have, indeed, been observed to occur spontaneously in laboratory cultures of Drosophila and in some plants while under cultivation. In the strict meaning of the word, mutation is a change in the composition of a gene so that its effect upon the organism is altered, but it is frequently used to include other changes that produce a difference in characteristics and that may be inherited.

*Frequency of gene mutation:* Statistical studies of gene mutations show that their occurrence is usually a rare one, taking place, in the organisms studied, at an average rate such that the probability of mutation of any given gene in any one generation is about one chance in 100,000 or 1,000,000. But they can be experimentally induced, a fact which was first generally recognized in 1927, when an American scientist, H. J. Muller (1890–), reported that in experiments he and others had been carrying on for some ten years it had been possible to increase the rate of spontaneous mutation in Drosophila several hundred per cent by exposing the flies to X-rays. It has since been found that, in addition to X-rays, ultraviolet radiation or indeed any high-energy radiation, as well as the chemical compounds known as mustard gases or nitrogen mustards, developed in great numbers during the recent war, are also effective mutagens, or mutation-producers, for many other organisms. Most mutated genes are recessive ones and, in general, ones that are disadvantageous to the organism in its effort for survival. A fly with vestigial wings, for example, incapable of flight, competes less successfully in many environments for food and mates than one with long wings; a human being with hemophilia can only survive if there is no damage to his tissues resulting in blood loss. The genes of most natural, or wild, populations are dominant ones, and are therefore spoken of as "normal" genes and designated by a capital initial of the character with which they are associated, or by a plus sign, while their recessive alleles are indicated by a small letter.

*Multiple alleles:* Some genes appear to be more stable and less subject to mutation than others, and there is also evidence that mutation may have occurred more than once at the same locus, giving rise to a series of alleles, only two of which are ordinarily present in a diploid cell. For example, in Drosophila one of the genes affecting eye color is known to have 13 alleles; in snapdragons (Antirrhinum), there is a series of 9 at the same locus, each influencing the color of the flowers in a different way; in rabbits, 4 affecting coat color; and in ducks, at least 3 controlling plumage color. Inheritance of sex in the parasitic wasp, Habrobracon, is directed by multiple alleles, and so, too, is the inheritance of certain properties of the blood in mammals.

THE INHERITANCE OF COAT COLOR IN MAMMALS: In some cases, such multiple alleles show a gradation of dominance; in mammals, for example, a dominant gene, indicated by C or +, controls the production of pigment and, when this gene is present, animals like rabbits and mice have coats of a uniform color. But at some point in the evolutionary history of mammals, this gene must have undergone mutation to at least three alleles recessive to it, $c^{ch}$ or chinchilla, producing less intense but still uniform coloration, $c^H$ or Himalayan, restricting the pigment to the tips of the ears, feet, tail and nose and c, or albino (Latin, albus = white), preventing the development of any pigment. Breeding experiments show that chinchilla is recessive to full color but dominant to Himalayan and albino, and Himalayan dominant to albino but recessive to chinchilla.

THE INHERITANCE OF BLOOD GROUPS IN MAN: In human heredity, multiple alleles are concerned in the determination of the different blood groups into which human beings fall. The most familiar of these are the so-called A, B, AB and O blood types, whose inheritance is based upon the distribution of at least three alleles involved in the production of antigens (agglutinogens) in the blood corpuscles and of antibodies (agglutinins) in the plasma. Blood corpuscles of individuals of the A group contain the agglutinogen A, and their blood serum the agglutinin $\beta$; those of the B group contain the agglutinogen B and their serum the agglutinin $a$; those of the AB group, the agglutinogens A and B, but no agglutinins; and those of the O group no agglutinogens and their serum both $a$ and $\beta$ agglutinins.

When blood from an individual with one type of agglutinogen is mixed with that of another with the corresponding agglutinin, the two react together, bringing about a clumping of the corpuscles. Blood of an A individual will therefore agglutinate the blood of a B or an O individual, but not that of an A or an AB, and blood from a B individual will agglutinate that of an A or an O, but not that of a B or an AB; AB blood, with both agglutinogens, agglutinates all blood but that of AB individuals, and O blood, with neither, does not cause the agglutination of blood of any of these four types. A, B and O are all alleles, which may be present in any of the following combinations:

AA, AO, BB, BO, AB, OO.

Individuals heterozygous for A and O and for B and O belong to the A and B blood groups respectively, but those heterozygous for A and B constitute a new group with both A and B agglutinogens.

Since the original discovery of these blood groups and the analysis of their inheritance, various sub-groups, and so more alleles, have been detected within them. These discoveries have been of great practical value both to medicine and to law, for they have enabled doctors to determine what persons can be safely used for direct blood transfusions, without danger of blood agglutination and so of disastrous effects from blockage of the smaller vessels, and lawyers to obtain evidence, in disputed paternity cases, of impossible inheritance. Other antigens in human blood, and so other blood groups, have also been found, whose inheritance depends also upon multiple alleles at loci other than those of the A, B, O series. Again, the most familiar of these are the Rhesus blood groups, so called because they were first detected, in 1940, in rhesus monkeys. An agglutinogen, designated as Rh, is present in the blood of these monkeys, and of man, with the dominant gene R, which stimulates the production of an antibody in those without it; there are several other alleles of R, all of which are dominant to the recessive r. The effect of these genes is evident particularly in the development of

[ 548 ]   THE OPERATION OF BIOLOGICAL SYSTEMS

the embryo, for both the antigen and its antibody are able to pass across the placenta from one circulatory system to the other. The agglutinogen in the blood of an Rh positive embryo, with genes of the R series derived from its paternal ancestry dominant to those of its mother, may therefore enter the maternal blood stream and provoke the production of an agglutinin there, which in the same fashion can enter the embryonic circulation and, in sufficient concentration, cause the agglutination of its blood, with disastrous, and sometimes fatal, results to its normal development.

### Genic rearrangement

Changes other than those in the composition of its genes are known to occur in chromosomes as a result of irradiation, and also to take place spontaneously, which likewise produce inheritable differences in the characters of individuals, and are therefore also often considered mutations. These are caused by breaks in the chromosomes, in

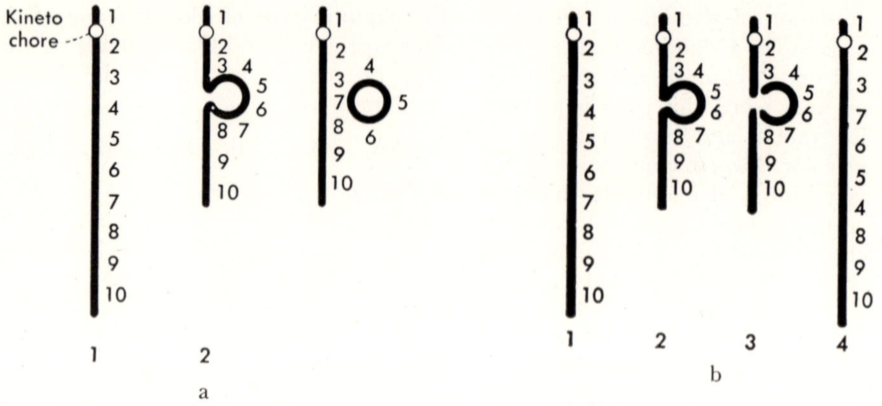

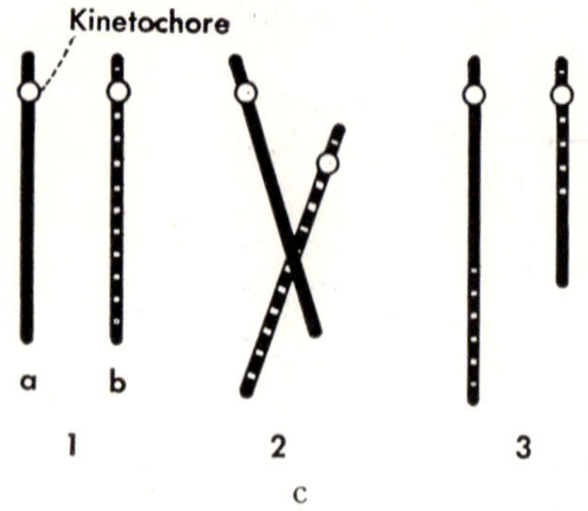

FIGURE 24.10 Diagrams showing how changes in the distribution of genes on the chromosomes may come about. The chromosome is shown as a solid black rod, with an open circle that marks the position of the kinetochore; the numbers along the rod indicate the loci of different genes.

a. Deletion. In 1, an intact chromosome is shown. In 2, the chromosome is shown as if looped between locus 3 and locus 8. If the chromosome breaks near these points, and fusion of the broken ends occurs, genes at loci 4, 5, 6 and 7 will be lost from the fragment of the chromosome with the kinetochore, and the genes at locus 3 and 8 are brought into a new relationship. The fragment containing loci 4, 5, 6 and 7 will be lost from the nucleus in the course of division, since it lacks a kinetochore and is therefore incapable of autonomous movement.

b. Inversion. In 1, an intact chromosome is shown; in 2, a chromosome with a loop as in a 2; in 3, breaks in the chromosome near loci 3 and 8 are represented; in 4, the chromosome is shown after re-fusion of its broken ends, with the segment containing loci 4, 5, 6 and 7 in inverted order. The chromosome shown in 4 contains all the genes represented in 1, but their linear arrangement is now different.

c. Reciprocal translocation. In 1, two non-homologous chromosomes are shown, one represented by a solid black rod, the other by an interrupted one. In 2, they are represented lying close to each other. If both break, their ends may re-fuse in such a way that a piece of chromosome a becomes attached to chromosome b, and one of chromosome b attached to chromosome a. By such means, an exchange of genic material may occur between any two or more chromosomes in the nuclear complement.

consequence of which genes may be lost from them, or, if the broken ends fuse, brought together in new arrangements. Such rearrangements fall into three general categories—deletions, inversions and translocations (Fig. 24.10). In the first case, that part of the broken chromosome that lacks a kinetochore may be carried along passively with the others for two or three divisions after the break has occurred but ultimately, having lost the capacity for autonomous movement with the loss of the kinetochore, is lost from the telophase nucleus. How drastic an effect the loss of part of one chromosome has upon the organism as a whole depends upon the length of the part and the number and kind of genes represented in it. In the case of inversions, while no genes are lost, certain ones are brought into new associations with others; and the differences evident in individuals with chromosomes with inverted segments make it clear that the final effect of the gene is different when it operates from a new locus and in immediate association with different genes than before. The effect of genes B and C, for example, is different when they occupy the linear order A, B, C, D upon the chromosome than when, as a result of inversion, they are placed in the series A, C, B, D. This "position effect" is manifested not only in the characters of individuals having one or more chromosomes with inverted segments, but also in those in which for other reasons the position of one or more genes has shifted.

Translocations, or the attachment of one chromosome fragment to another, represents a transference of genic material within the nucleus quite different from that of crossing-over, in that it may take place between any two chromosomes and may involve different segments and ones of unequal length, while crossing-over takes place between similar segments of homologous chromatids. Through its attachment to a chromosome with a kinetochore, the translocated fragment is not lost from the nucleus but carried along through successive cell generations. The fact of translocation has been demonstrated cytologically in Drosophila and in maize, where definitely identified pieces of certain chromosomes have been recognized as missing from them and attached to others in the set.

### Changes in chromosome number

Inheritable differences that are the result of duplication of the entire chromosomal set, or of one, two or even in some cases, three, of the elements in it are sometimes included in the general category of mutations. Organisms resulting from such changes as these are said to be polyploid (Greek, polys = many + -ploos = fold) and show characteristic differences both in breeding behavior and in bodily attributes from the diploid stock from which they have originated. There are many such polyploid species among plants, with chromosome numbers that represent multiples higher than 2 of the basic chromosome set. In wheat (Triticum), for example, one wild species has a diploid number of 14, another of 28, while in the cultivated wheats the diploid number is 42; if 7 is the haploid (n) number of the species from which the present-day wheats have originated, those with 28 chromosomes represent a tetraploid (4n) stock, and those with 42 chromosomes a hexaploid (6n) stock. Different kinds of roses, too, appear to have originated through the addition of whole chromosome sets to the basic diploid number of 14, for chromosome counts of 28, 35, 42 and 56 have been established for certain of the species existing to-day. Polyploidy is relatively rare in animals, for which a possible explanation lies in the mechanism of their sex inheritance, although there are tetraploid species of the brine shrimp, Artemia, the sowbug, Trichoniscus, and the bag-worm moth, Solenobia, and the chromosome numbers of some annelids and mollusks suggest that polyploidy has played a part in the development of these species. Haploidy, in which but one set of chromosomes is represented in the cells of the individual, is common among the thallophytes and regularly characterizes one of the alternate generations of mosses and the vascular plants, but is also relatively rare among animals. But the males of some insects—the bees, some wasps, aphids and scale insects, for example—are haploid, developing parthenogenetically from unfertilized eggs.

It was first shown for the jimson weed, Datura stramonium, that the addition of a single chromosome to the diploid complement resulted in the production of new types. The diploid number in Datura is 24, and twelve new mutants were found, each showing structural characteristics unlike those of the parent stock, or those of other mutants. These differences were associated with the presence of an extra chromosome, which could be recognized on cytological examination of the cells of the mutants and identified in each case as a different one of the haploid set. With a chromosome number of 25, or 2n+1, these plants are called trisomic, since in each new type one chromosome is present in triplicate rather than in duplicate as in the ordinary diploid species. Tetrasomic varieties, 2n+2, of Datura have also been identified, in which there are four chromosomes of one kind, two of the others, in all the cells. Monosomic individuals, or those in which one chromosome of the diploid set is missing and whose chromosome complement may therefore be represented as 2n−1 are also theoretically possible—and in tobacco (Nicotiana), whose diploid number is 48, 20 of the 24 possible monosomic types are already known. In Drosophila, the small IV chromosome may be omitted, or repeated, without disastrous effects; and haplo-IV, with only one IV chromosome, and triplo-IV, with three IV chromosomes, stocks have been maintained. But as a rule in animals the loss or addition of a chromosome upsets the genic balance with resulting abnormalities or fatal effects. And in nearly all polyploids there is some reduction of fertility, as well as deviations from the numbers and types of offspring expected in Mendelian inheritance, because of derangement of the ordinary course of meiosis.

## The effects of genes

### Genotype and phenotype

The results of hybridization experiments have made it clear that two individuals, superficially resembling each other, may be quite different in the developmental potentialities they pass on to their offspring. Two stocks of fruit flies, for example, may have wings of apparently equal length, yet one, on inbreeding, may produce only long-winged offspring and the other long-winged and short-winged in the Mendelian ratio of three to one. A distinction can thus be made between the phenotype (Greek, phanein = to show), or the external characteristics of an individual, and the genotype (Greek, genos = race), its genic constitution, or the total of its inherited and transmissible units. Whether two individuals phenotypically similar are also genotypically alike, or are genotypically different, can be determined only by breeding experiments and observation of the types of offspring that they produce. Individuals of the same genotype produce the same kinds of offspring; individuals of different genotype produce offspring of different kinds and individuals of like genotype, homozygous for all their genes, produce offspring both phenotypically and genotypically like themselves and so constitute a pure line, or strain.

### Dominance

The phenotypic characteristics of an individual are the result of the combined operations of all its genes, and of the environmental conditions in which they operate, which may greatly influence their expression. While it is customary, for convenience, to refer to particular genes by the name of the character whose development they appear to control, it is recognized that no one characteristic is the expression of the effect of a single gene, or that any one gene operates only in the production of a single character. In Drosophila, for example, the so-called gene for red eyes influences the development of pigment in other regions of the body, although the expression of its presence in the genotype is most evident in the ommatidia of the eye. And while the terms dominant and recessive of the early hybridizers are still used to express the comparative effects of different alleles, it is recognized that one member of a pair does not operate to the exclusion of the other, but that both have some influence in the production of the final character. For example, the first generation of offspring of a mating between a fruit fly of wild stock, with long wings, and one of vestigial stock, with rudimentary wings, with the genotype $+$ vg are phenotypically long-winged, but measurements show that their heredity, in the production of AB type blood, for in individuals with the genotype AB, each allele influences the production of its own agglutinogen, with a resulting new blood group. And in plants, crosses between red-flowered varieties and ivory-flowered

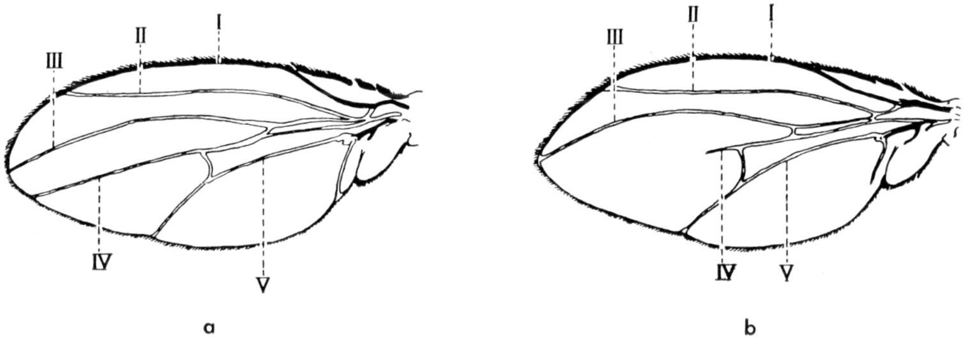

FIGURE 24.11 The effect of the gene cubitus interruptus (ci) on the venation of the wing in Drosophila. (After Tiniakow and Terentieva.)

The principal wing veins are numbered I (costa); II (subcosta); III (radius); IV (cubitus); V (anal).
 a. Wild-type wing $(++)$.
 b. Cubitus interruptus wing (cici).

wings are actually shorter than those of their wild-type parent, indicating that the vestigial gene has not been without effect. Analysis of the effect of another mutant gene, called cubitus interruptus (ci), on the IV chromosome of Drosophila, indicates that a recessive gene may be doing the same kind of thing as its normal allele, but doing it less effectively. The effect of the ci gene is to shorten one of the veins of the wing, so that it is incomplete, or interrupted (Fig. 24.11). Breeding experiments with flies of the ci stock, in which the number of ci genes, and so the gene dosage, can be varied from one to three, show that there is a positive correlation between the number of ci genes in the nucleus and the length of the vein—the more genes, the longer the vein. Such direct quantitative relationships are, however, not true for all genes.

Sometimes, too, the effect of different alleles is apparently equal so that an individual heterozygous for them may not be phenotypically like either parent, but different from them. This is the case, in human

ones often result in pink-flowered offspring, for the color in the petals is determined by the pigment in the chromoplasts, and when genes that lead to the production of red anthocyanins are brought together in a hybrid with those that cannot effect the formation of anthocyanin, some of its chromoplasts are red and some colorless, so that the color of its flowers is neither so deep as that of its red parent, nor so pale as that of its white one.

### The effects of multiple genes

There are instances, too, in which the effect of two non-allelic genes is directly evident in the production of a single character. One of the first of these to be analyzed on the chromosome theory was that of the inheritance, in fowls, of the type of comb known as walnut. Most of the common breeds of chickens have the high spiked comb known as "single," but there are certain breeds, notably the Indian game and Brahma fowls, which have a lower and broader comb, called "pea" and others, like

Dorkings, with "rose" combs, a triangular mass of small spikes. Breeding experiments have shown that both rose and pea are dominant to single comb, for the first generation of a cross between a rose- and a single-combed fowl, or between a pea-combed one and a single-, are either rose- or pea-combed; the descendants of hens and cocks of this generation show typical Mendelian segregation of the dominant and recessive characters. But if a pea-combed fowl is mated to a rose-combed one, the hybrid offspring have a type of comb quite different from that of either parent; it is broad and fleshy, with a corrugated surface that makes it resemble a walnut. Walnut-combed fowls, when mated with each other, or inbred, produce offspring in which walnut, pea, rose and single combs are represented in the ratio of 9 walnut : 3 rose : 3 pea : 1 single, the Mendelian ratio resulting from the segregation of two pairs of inheritable units. The production of the walnut character is therefore the expression of the interaction of at least two different pairs of alleles, whose combinations are shown in Table XVI.

TABLE XVI

| | |
|---|---|
| Genotype of rose-combed fowls | RRpp |
| Genotype of pea-combed fowls | rrPP |
| Genotype of single-combed fowls | rrpp |
| Genotype of walnut-combed hybrid of cross between RRpp and rrPP | RrPp |
| Gametes of hybrids | RP, rP, Rp, rp. |

| | Sperm | | | |
|---|---|---|---|---|
| Eggs | RP | rP | Rp | rp |
| RP | RRPP walnut | RrPP walnut | RRPp walnut | RrPp walnut |
| rP | rRPP walnut | rrPP pea | rRPp walnut | rrPp pea |
| Rp | RRpP walnut | RrpP walnut | RRpp rose | Rrpp rose |
| rp | rRpP walnut | rrpP pea | rRpp rose | rrpp single |
| Ratio: | walnut 9 | rose 3 | pea 3 | single 1 |

Numerous other instances of the cooperative effect of two or more genes in the final production of a bodily character have also been found. In some cases, the effect of one gene is evident only in the presence of another; this is the case in the production of hair color in mammals, in which the kind and amount of pigment that is formed depends upon the combined activity of genes at several different loci, but the production of pigment at all upon the presence of a gene of the C series dominant to the recessive c. Some genes modify the effects of others, and in their presence the final character may be different than it is when they are absent, and some genes inhibit the expression of others. A rabbit or a mouse, for example, may have all the genes necessary for the formation of black pigment in its hairs, but if it also has a modifying, or "diluting" gene that controls the amount of pigment, its final coat color is not black, but the smoky color called "blue." The whiteness of white Leghorn fowls is not due to the absence of a color gene, as is whiteness in mammals, but to the presence of an inhibitor gene, which prevents the expression of any potentialities the fowls may have of developing black, brown or barred plumage. That they have such potentialities is shown by their progeny, some of which may have colored feathers through loss of the inhibitor gene from their genotype in the segregation of their chromosomes. Some genes may have a destructive or lethal effect; there are some in plants that singly prevent the formation of the pollen or the ovule, as gamete lethals, and others in both plants and animals that destroy the zygote when they are brought together in homozygous combination in it, or sooner or later in the course of its development and growth into an embryo.

### The effect of the environment upon the expression of the gene

The final effect of any pair of genes, and of the entire genotype, is influenced by the environment of the organism as a whole, as well as the more immediate environment of the cell and the cytoplasm in which they operate. External conditions of temperature and humidity, as well as those of oxygen supply and nutrition, condition genic action. Indeed, experiments with animals have shown that temperature changes at critical periods of development may bring about such radical phenotypic alterations in an individual that it may in all major respects resemble one of quite different genotype, or become a "phenocopy" of it. Plants, grown in soils or other media deficient in minerals necessary for the synthesis of chlorophyll, for example, cannot make it no matter how well endowed they may be genetically, and the small, stunted specimens grown in poor soil, with small leaves and tiny flowers, often bear little resemblance to those of the same stock, with luxuriant foliage and large, bright blossoms, grown in rich soil. The influence of hormones upon the expression of the genotype is recognized also in plants and animals in growth differences, and in animals in which hormones are concerned in the differentiation of sex characters, in the development of these characters. This was recognized early in the development of genetics in the analysis of the conditions causing the production of "free-martins" by cattle. Twinning is relatively rare in cattle, and when it does occur both members of the pair are normal only when they are of the same sex. More frequently, one calf is a bull and the other an intersex, or free-martin. This is explained by the fact that genotypically one is a male and the other a female, and that the sex organs in the male embryo develop before those in the female, and so its sex hormones become effective earlier. The peculiar condition in cattle is that there is continuity between the circulatory systems of the two embryos, although they are the result of the fertilization of two different eggs, so that the male sex hormones are carried into the blood stream of the female at a time when its sex organs are at a critical stage of development, and so turn the course of their differentiation in a male direction, making the potentially female calf into a free-martin. This effect is not apparent in other mammals, where there are no anastomoses between the blood vessels of the two or more embryos that may develop simultaneously from separately fertilized eggs, but the direct effect of the embryo's own hormones upon the expression of the sex genotype has been demonstrated in them and in a number of other animal species.

## The nature of the gene

### Physical and chemical characteristics

Like the atom and the electron, the gene is not yet directly visible and the properties attributed to it are those that follow logically from analysis of the effects it is known to produce. Calculations of the possible dimensions of genes indicate that they are molecules of large size, or aggregates of molecules, and studies of nuclear and chromosomal chemistry have revealed that they are most likely nucleoprotein. Recent electron micrographs, photographs taken with an electron microscope at a magnification of some 120,000 diameters, have shown the presence of discrete particles in positions on the large chromosomes of the salivary glands of Drosophila larvae that correspond to the location of the chromomeres visible with the ordinary microscope, suggesting that the chromomeres are collections of genes. The size and density of these particles are comparable to those of virus particles under similar conditions of observation. Viruses are also self-perpetuating units within cells, and it seems likely, from present evidence, that they and genes are similar in their chemical nature, and in the order of magnitude of their dimensions.

### The relation of genes to biochemical reactions

During the past twenty years there has been a gradual accumulation of evidence that genes exert their morphological effects through control of biochemical reactions. This has been most clearly shown in the direct relationships that have been demonstrated between the presence of certain genes in the genotype and the capacity of organisms to make pigments of one kind or another and to synthesize vitamins. In plants, the synthesis of chlorophyll and of the carotenoids, flavones and anthocyanins has been shown to be directly under genic control. The most complete analysis of a direct relationship between the genotype of a flowering plant and the chemical reactions that lead to the production of different anthocyanins has been made by a group of English scientists in crosses between blue and red species of the Cape primrose, Streptocarpus. Seven different shades of flower color are represented in the hybrids of this cross, through the distribution of four pairs of alleles, whose dominant members control the production of different anthocyanins from different precursors. The anthocyanins range in color from salmon to blue, and are chemically different from each other in the number of hydroxyl (OH) or methoxyl ($CH_3O$) groups in the molecule; the greater the number of such groups, the bluer the color. The four genes concerned in their production are directly related to the addition of these groups, or of hexose radicals, to the anthocyanin molecule, and their distribution and that of their recessive alleles result in genotypes in which their combined activity is expressed by seven different phenotypes, plants with ivory, salmon, pink, rose, magenta, mauve or blue flowers.

Pigmentation in animals has also been shown to be the result of chemical changes directly related to the presence of certain genes. The pigment melanin is derived from tyrosine, an amino acid that may, in animal metabolism, be directly incorporated into the body proteins or be converted to other substances, acting, in the case of melanin production, as a chromogen or pigment precursor. Failure on the part of an organism to produce melanin might be due to the absence of the chromogen, or to its incapacity to bring about the conversion of the chromogen to the pigment. The latter condition has been found to be true in rabbits, for chemical analysis of the tissues of albinos, whose white fur and pink eyes reveal the absence of any dark pigment, shows that they contain tyrosine but lack certain enzymes which are found in animals with dark fur and eyes. In man, who can convert one of the essential amino acids, phenylalanine, to tyrosine, there is also an inheritable incapacity to bring about its further conversion to melanin, also related to a recessive gene which in homozygous condition results in albinism. Moreover, a direct relationship has been established between his inherited genetic constitution and his capacity to carry on the series of metabolic reactions through which tyrosine and another derivative of phenylalaline, phenylpyruvic acid, are finally converted to carbon dioxide and water, through a series of intermediate compounds. One of these intermediates is alcapton, and a few individuals have been found who are incapable of carrying the series beyond this stage. Alcapton therefore accumulates in their blood and is excreted in their urine; the breakdown in the metabolic sequence is indicated by the pathological condition known medically as "alcaptonuria," which, like albinism, is the expression of a recessive gene for which such individuals are homozygous.

Even more exact evidence of correspondence between specific genes and specific biochemical reactions is accumulating from genetic and biochemical studies on the ascomycete, Neurospora, an organism that is particularly favorable for experimental work. The mold can be grown on nutrient media of known composition; wild strains thrive on a comparatively simple one consisting of sucrose, as a source of carbon and of energy, a nitrate or an ammonium salt as a source of nitrogen, inorganic salts, and the single vitamin, biotin. From these compounds it derives all that it needs for growth and synthesis of the complex substances that are obtained from chemical analysis of full-grown mycelia—some twenty amino acids, at least nine other vitamins, carotinoid pigments and a number of other compounds. The mycelia, and the conidia through which they reproduce asexually, are haploid in chromosomal constitution, and of two different sex types, which can be mated; after each such mating, a diploid cell is formed from which, after meiosis, eight haploid ascospores are produced, arranged in linear order within the fruiting body (Fig. 24.12). By very delicate manipulative technique, each individual ascospore can be isolated and grown separately, and its genetic constitution, and so the segregation of any different alleles that may have been brought together in the zygote nucleus, tested by the characteristics of the mycelium germinated from it, and equally by those of the mycelia developed from any of its conidia.

It has been found that by irradiation of

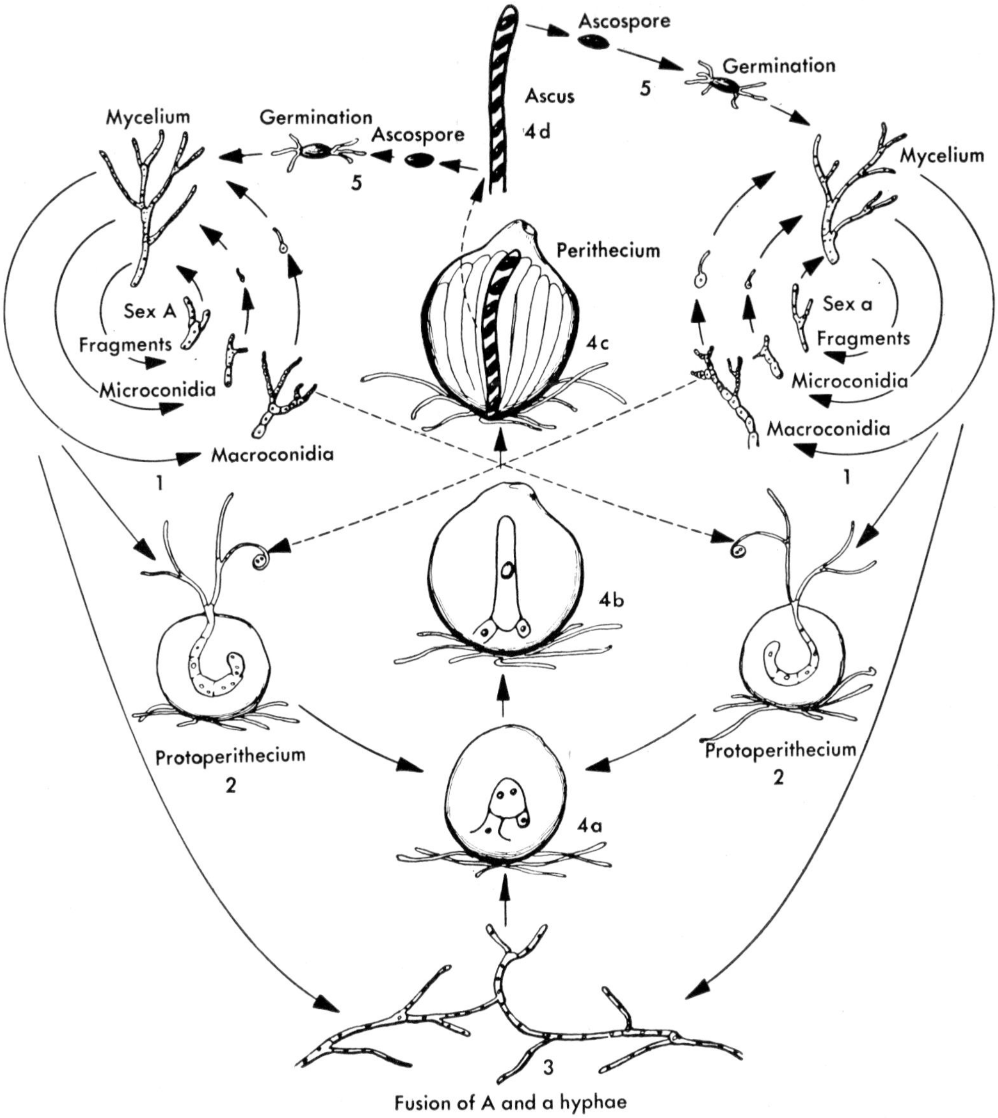

FIGURE 24.12 Diagram showing the life cycle of the mold Neurospora. (After Beadle.)

1. Individual mycelia of two different strains, as A and a, reproduce by fragmentation, and by the germination of micro- and macroconidia cut off from the tips of aerial hyphae.

2. Under certain conditions of growth, spherical masses of hyphae called protoperithecia are produced from a mycelium. These do not bear spores, but if brought into contact with conidia and hyphae of opposite strain develop as perithecia, or fruiting bodies. (4a, 4b, 4c and 4d).

3. The hyphae of two different strains (as A and a) may meet and fuse to form a perithecium.

    4. a. Nuclei of the two opposite strains fuse.

       b. Meiotic division of the diploid (2n) nuclei takes place. Each resulting cell divides, forming 8 spores in all.

       c. The perithecium, or fruiting body, develops as a number of slender, finger-like spore sacs, or asci, each containing 8 haploid spores, and all enclosed within an outer wall.

5. Each haploid spore within an ascus may germinate into a new mycelium.

the conidia mutations directly affecting certain of the fundamental synthetic reactions of the mold are produced, and it has been possible to develop and maintain a number of strains in which some one biochemical process has been so modified. This is shown by the ability or inability of the strain to grow upon the simple medium that is adequate for the wild stocks, or upon that medium supplemented with the amino acids or the vitamins that the mold is known to synthesize. In testing for the particular process that has been modified, conidia from a mycelium grown from an ascospore resulting from the mating of an irradiated and a wild strain are "planted" individually in culture tubes containing the basic nutrient medium supplemented by all the amino acids or all the vitamins that the mold is known to synthesize. Failure to grow in the tubes supplemented by amino acids, for example, but not by vitamins, indicates that the modification has been in a vitamin synthesis; which particular synthesis is involved can then be determined by planting other conidia from the same mycelium, or the same strain, in tubes, each of which contains the basic nutrient medium supplemented by one of the vitamins that the wild strain can make. The mutated strain can grow effectively only in the medium that supplies the vitamin it can no longer synthesize, and there will be no growth, or very much reduced growth, in the tubes from which this vitamin is absent.

Through experiments such as these it has been possible to develop strains incapable of conducting some one synthesis characteristic of the wild strains and by breeding experiments to establish a direct correlation between the modification of a single gene and the modification of a single biochemical process. Such correspondence has been shown for all the modified strains that have been analyzed genetically, and it has been possible also to assign loci to a number of the genes concerned on each of the seven chromosomes of the species of Neurospora in which this kind of inheritance has been studied. It has also become apparent that a mutation at more than one locus may affect the synthesis of the same end product. For example, four separate genes have been identified which are directly concerned with the synthesis of niacin, apparently, according to present biochemical evidence, in a different way, or at a different stage in the series of reactions that end in the formation of the vitamin.

Although these experiments with Neurospora have demonstrated the connection between a single inheritable unit and a single biochemical process, essential to the life of the organism, it is not yet clear how close the reaction identified with an individual gene is to its primary effect, nor how that gene actually contributes to the biochemical mechanism. Since most biological reactions are enzymatic ones, it is reasonable to suppose that the genes may themselves be enzymes and, as self-perpetuating entities of the chromosomes, act as models, or patterns, for similar self-perpetuating entities within the nucleus and cytoplasm. The results of investigations which are now in progress in various laboratories on the relationship of individual genes to enzyme systems and to particular enzymes in unicellular fungi support this hypothesis, which has not, however, as yet been conclusively proved.

### Cytoplasmic inheritance

While the development of genetics has led primarily to the establishment of the chromosomal theory of inheritance, and the theory of the chromosomal gene, biologists have always recognized the influence of the cytoplasm in inheritance, not only as the medium in which the nuclear genes must operate, but also as a possible vehicle for the transmission of inheritable material. Indeed, experiments on animal hybridization carried out early in this century made it clear that the pattern of very early embryonic development is determined by the nature of the egg cytoplasm, and that the contribution of the paternal chromosomes is manifested at some later stage. This is perhaps to be expected, since except for the few isogamous species among simply constructed biological systems, the egg contributes much more cytoplasm to the zygote than does the sperm, if indeed the male gamete contributes any.

## Influence of the egg cytoplasm upon early development

The most extreme case of delayed paternal influence has been found among the gastropods, where the direction of coiling of the visceral hump, and so of the shell, is determined by the genotype of the individual that produces the egg and the effect of the paternal genes delayed for one generation. In most species, the direction of coiling is to the right, or dextral, but some individuals may be found among them, and there are some species, in which it is to the left, or sinistral; breeding experiments have shown that dextral coiling is dominant to sinistral. But if a cross is effected between dextrally coiled and sinistrally coiled individuals, the first generation of offspring of a sinistrally coiled mother are also sinistrally coiled, in spite of the fact that their genetic constitution is $+$s, where s stands for sinistral coiling. Phenotypically they resemble the recessive parent, although genotypically they are heterozygous for the dominant and the recessive gene. Embryological studies of snails have shown that the final direction of coiling can be detected as early in the course of development as the second division of the zygote, in which the spindle rotates through approximately 45°, and so lies at an angle to the long axis of the cell. If this rotation is to the left, the direction of coiling is sinistral; if it is to the right, the direction of coiling is dextral. While, therefore, the eggs of a sinistral mother will all develop into sinistral adults, these adults, if their genotype is $+$s, will, when inbred, produce only phenotypically dextral offspring, although genotypically they fall into three classes, $++$, $+$s, and ss. But the $++$ individuals will continue to produce only dextral broods, and the ss, only sinistral, unless they mate with one of the opposite type, or one heterozygous for the gene s, while the $+$s individuals show the same breeding behavior as their parents. Direction of coiling, like other characteristics, thus follows the pattern of Mendelian inheritance, although the effect of the sperm, in this particular character, becomes evident in the second filial generation, and not the first.

## The inheritance of plastids in plants

There is, however, evidence that certain characteristics are transmitted from generation to generation through formed elements in the cytoplasm, best illustrated by the inheritance of plastids in plants. In the seed plants, the plastids develop from chondriosome-like bodies in the egg cytoplasm, which are self-perpetuating units and, distributed to the cells of the embryo sporophyte, multiply and develop characteristic pigments there. In a number of genera, including geraniums, four-o'clocks, corn and barley, there are variegated species with leaves that are green and white; the white areas, often making a definite pattern of bands or isolated patches, are the result of chlorophyll deficiency. Sometimes these plants have branches that are uniformly green, others that are variegated and a few that are uniformly white, their tissues maintained through the photosynthetic activities of the green parts of the plant. When a flower formed on a green branch is pollinated with pollen from one on a green, a variegated or a white one, all the seeds resulting germinate into seedlings that are uniformly green; when a flower on a white branch is so pollinated, its seeds germinate as colorless seedlings that cannot maintain themselves and die as soon as the reserves within the seed are exhausted; and when those on a variegated branch are so pollinated, their seeds germinate as green, variegated or white seedlings, depending on the combination of plastids that has been included in the megaspore and so in the cells of the embryo sac. The genotype of the embryos thus has no effect upon the color characteristics of the plastids in their leaves which, as self-reproducing units in the cytoplasm of the egg cell, are expressions of its genotype and convey the characters so determined through successive generations.

## Inheritance of "Kappa" in Paramoecium

A somewhat analogous condition of cytoplasmic inheritance has been discovered in a species of Paramoecium within the past decade. Within this species there are some races known as killers, for, when they are put into the same environment with others, those that are sensitive to them within a few hours show abnormalities in their behavior and in the appearance of their cytoplasm; they stop feeding and begin to spin rapidly on their long axes without moving forward,

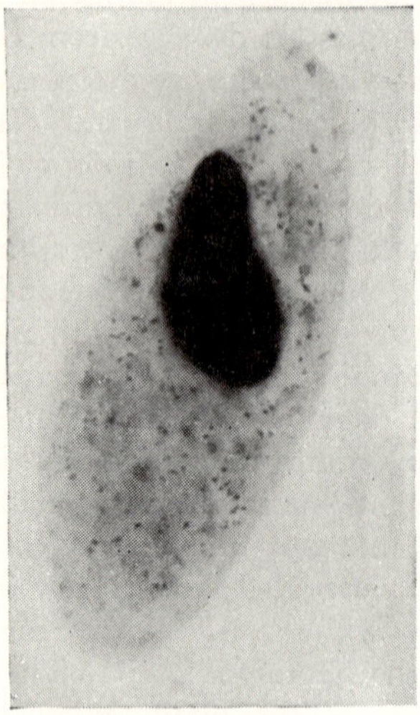

FIGURE 24.13 Paramoecium aurelia stained to show kappa particles in the cytoplasm. (From Preer, Genetics 35, 1950.)

and their cytoplasm shows an accumulation of vacuoles and of crystals. If sensitive animals remain long enough in the neighborhood of killers, they die. This biological conditioning of an environment is the result of the diffusion of a substance, called paramecin, from the bodies of the killers. But conjugation between sensitives and killers is possible, for if the pairs come together and separate before the killer effect is evident, the sensitive conjugant, removed to a non-conditioned environment, will continue to divide and give rise to a clone whose characteristics can be studied. From such a mating between a killer and a sensitive individual, two different clones are produced, one killer, from the killer conjugant, and one non-killer, and sensitive, from the sensitive conjugant, although genetic analysis shows that both have the same genotype and are heterozygous for the dominant killer gene K, and its recessive allele k. In spite of the presence of K, the sensitive strain never develops the killer substance, and the killer strain maintains it as long as its nucleus retains the K gene. But in such a heterozygote, the reassortment of chromosomes that takes place during autogamy (see page 529) may lead to the production of individuals homozygous for the recessive k, in which the killer effect disappears, in the clone from the killer strain, after a number of fissions. This effect seems to be due to a component of the cytoplasm called kappa, that must be present for the killer gene to manifest itself, since Kk clones derived from a sensitive individual do not become killers, and that can only be maintained in the continued presence of K, since later generations of kk clones derived from a killer are not killers. The nature of kappa is still undetermined, but in the cytoplasm of killer animals are microscopically visible particles that are not evident in sensitive ones (Fig. 24.13). These particles give the same staining reaction as the genetically active regions of the chromosomes, complexes of protein and a nucleic acid, and there is a direct relationship between their numbers and the intensity of the killer effect. Also, in recent experiments, it has been shown that kappa can be inactivated by a chemical mutagen, one of the nitrogen mustards, for killer animals exposed to it show reduction, and even total loss, of their killer effect, with which there is a parallel decrease of cytoplasmic particles.

## Possible mechanisms of inheritance

All the information about the mechanisms of inheritance that has been gathered in the past fifty years by experimental biologists working in many countries suggests that there may be three systems, or levels, for the transference of inheritable material. The first of these is the nuclear and genic system, which is best established and about which most is known. The second is a corpuscular or plastid system, through which microscopically identifiable elements in the cytoplasm are conveyed, through its division at mitosis, from one cell generation to the next, imparting certain distinctive characters to them. The third is one at the molecular level, consisting of as yet invisible entities in the cytoplasm, for which the names "plasmagene" or "cytogene" have been proposed. In sexually reproducing organisms, both parents contribute nuclear genes, and the characteristics of the zygote determined by them represent a balance between them, but those characteristics that are determined by either of the other two systems are of the maternal type alone.

But whatever may be the mechanism for the determination of individual characteristics, in their final form they are the results of nuclear-cytoplasmic reactions within cells, whose nature is determined by the combinations brought together in the union of the gametes, but which are always influenced by the conditions of the environment within the organism itself and in that part of the physical world in which it lives. The development of the individual is thus the expression of its nuclear genes, inherited in unbroken sequence from its ancestry directly through its parents, and of the nature of the cytoplasm in which these genes operate, which may, on its part, contribute some determiners of the individual's attributes. And while the expression of the genes, or cytoplasmic determiners, may be modified during the course of development, or during the life span of the individual, by conditions of their environment, they themselves are not modified by those conditions, and are passed on unchanged, except by mutation, to its descendants.

# CHAPTER 25

# THE DEVELOPMENT OF THE INDIVIDUAL

## Definition and province of embryology

The development of organisms is a biological phenomenon that has puzzled and fascinated man since classical times at least. The first recorded observations of animal development are those of Aristotle on the hen's egg, where all but the earliest developmental stages can be traced in incubated eggs from the time of laying to that of hatching, twenty-one days later. In the succeeding centuries, the developing chick has furnished much of the embryologist's information about the succession of changes through which a single cell, a zygote, becomes transformed to an organized mass of cells, a functioning organism. The eggs of aquatic animals that are shed into the water and fertilized there have also furnished much of the embryologist's material, for in them the entire developmental process, from the union of the egg and sperm to the completion of the organism, can be watched. The transparent eggs of echinoderms have been widely studied, particularly for information about the fertilization process and the early divisions of the egg; so also have those of amphibia, which have provided especially favorable material for the experimental embryologist because of their size and because they can be obtained * at all seasons of the year and raised successfully at least to the larval stage in the laboratory. And in spite of the many obstacles to the study of mammalian development, which is naturally of particular interest to man, it has been followed in great detail in a number of species.

\* Ovulation can be induced outside the ordinary breeding season by injection of the pituitary gland into the body cavity, and eggs so shed can be fertilized by sperm taken from the males at any time of the year.

The problems of the embryologist concern the course and interpretation of events that take place from the time of union of the gametes until the parts of the organism are established in their final form as functional units within it. They are problems not only of the anatomical relationships of the tissues and the organs derived from them, but also of the functional relationships between these tissues and between parts of the organism as they successively appear. These problems are raised equally by development in plants and animals, but man, as an animal himself, has given greater time and attention to analysis of the processes of embryological organization and differentiation in animals. The fact that in the higher plants the fertilization and the embryological development of the zygote take place within the tissues of the pistil, and the impossibility of removing the egg or the zygote from the embryo sac for study in the living condition, or for the kind of experimentation that has been most useful in the interpretation of relationships in animal development, are obvious reasons for the greater concentration on animal development, and the virtual restriction, through common use, of the word "embryology" to it. But techniques developed in recent years of removing the embryo sporophyte from its seed coats and culturing it in artificial media, as well as those of culturing isolated pieces of plant tissue, may well provide, for plant embryology, the same kind of information that direct observation and experimental methods have provided for animals.

## Descriptive embryology of animals

Embryological development, in any sexually reproducing organism, begins with the

[ 560 ]

fertilization of the egg and proceeds through its division into an indefinite number of cells to the organization of those cells into the tissues and organs of the embryo, and finally those of the adult (Fig. 25.1). It is, in most animals, a continuous process, a series of changes that under ordinary conditions follow each other in unbroken sequence. Exceptions to this are found among the rotifers, crustaceans, and Lepidoptera, whose eggs, after fertilization, may remain dormant while temperature and humidity are unfavorable for their development, but begin to divide and differentiate as soon as they become favorable. In some insects, such as the silkworm and some grasshoppers, such an arrest, or diapause (Greek, dia = through + pausis = stopping) occurs spontaneously at some point in the developmental sequence; this is independent of external conditions and is determined by those within the embryo itself. And in the higher plants, while some seeds may, and others must, germinate as soon as they are mature, the embryo sporophyte often remains in a condition of arrested development for months and even years (see p. 517).

## Stages in the development of the individual

For purposes of convenience in describing Metazoan development, to certain phases of which this chapter is confined, the sequence of embryological changes may be grouped under the headings of fertilization, cleavage, gastrulation, embryogenesis, and organogenesis, although this does not imply, any more than the division of the mitotic sequence into a number of phases implies it, that the transition from one stage to another is an abrupt one, or that a definite line of demarcation can be drawn between any two of them.

***Fertilization:*** Fertilization, whether it takes place within the body of the female or outside it, involves the union of egg and sperm, a union that can take place only during a limited period in the lives of most gametes. It depends therefore not only upon the proximity of the males and females of a species and the various devices that have evolved for insuring it, but upon the condition of the gametes themselves. Eggs are fertilizable for a comparatively short time, which varies in different species in relation to the events of meiosis. The male gamete, on the other hand, invariably completes its meiosis and metamorphosis to a motile sperm before it is capable of fertilization. Its life, as an independent cell, is usually a short span of hours, or at most of days, and its capacity for fertilization, under ordinary conditions, even shorter. Motile spermatozoa have, however, been found in the oviducts of hens two weeks after copulation; the queen bee is known to receive at a single mating all the sperm for her entire crop of offspring, and in the recent practice of artificial insemination of sheep and cattle, mammalian sperm, kept at about 40°C, have remained functional for as long as seven days.

Eggs of different species vary greatly in size and in appearance, the differences in size depending upon the amount of reserve material synthesized during the growth period rather than upon any significant differences in the amount of cytoplasm, and those in appearance upon the kind and distribution of pigment granules, and other visible inclusions in them, and of accessory membranes, external to the cell proper, that it may have acquired in its passage along the oviduct (Figs. 25.2, 25.4a). Polarity of the egg cell is indicated externally by the position of the polar bodies and, in heavily-yolked eggs, by the greatest concentration of the yolk mass. The site of the polar bodies marks the "animal pole"; the opposite pole, where the yolk is usually concentrated, is the "vegetal pole."

Although sperm are produced and shed in enormous numbers and, actively swimming, may swarm around an egg, ordinarily but a single one is successful in entering it. But polyspermy, or the entrance of several, is a natural occurrence in birds, and can be experimentally induced in species ordinarily monospermic. It has been established for sea urchins, and may be true for other animals as well, that both egg and sperm produce hormones, called gamones, that influence the fertilization process. One produced by the sea urchin egg is known to stimulate the

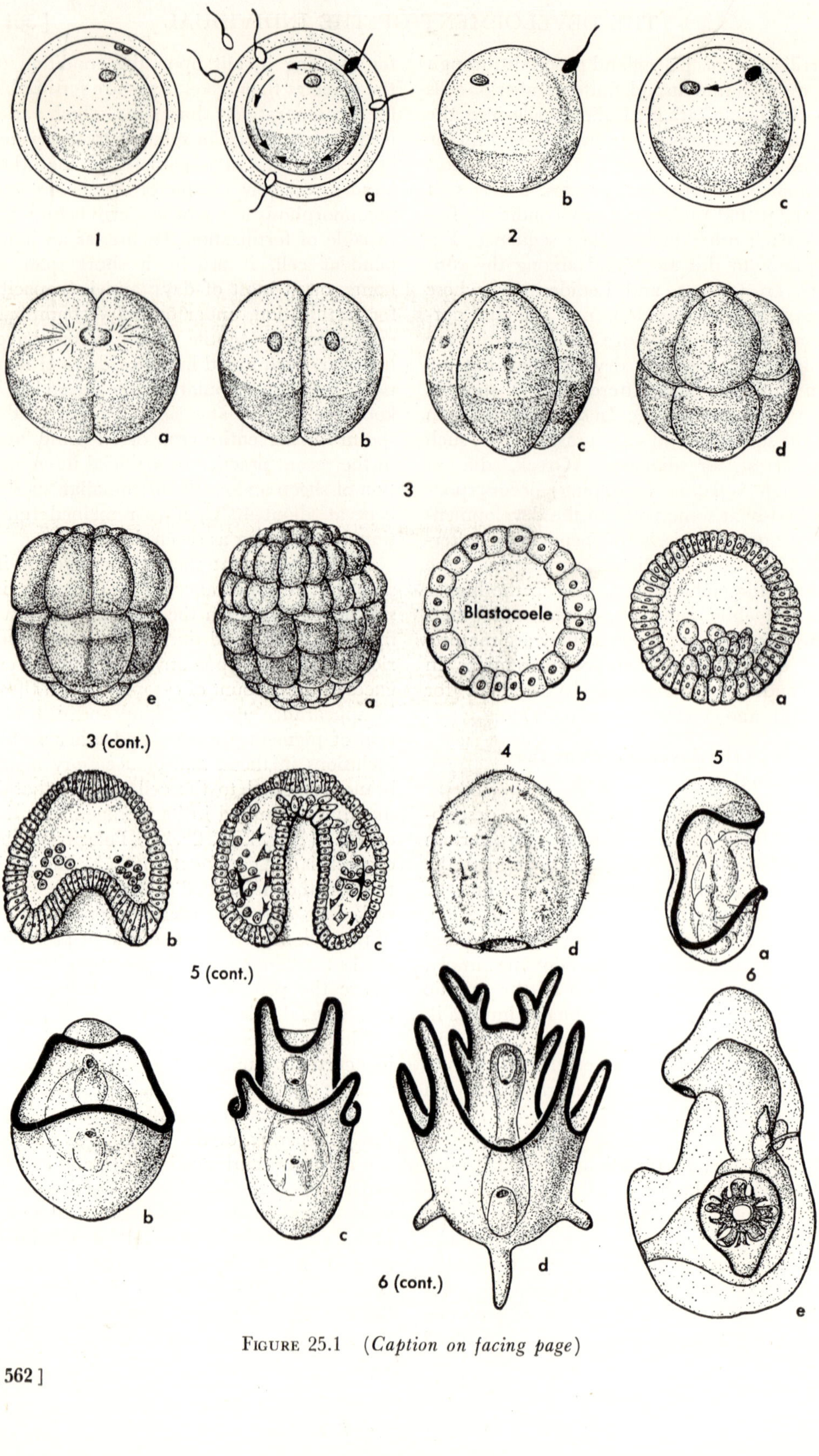

FIGURE 25.1  (*Caption on facing page*)

[ 562 ]

FIGURE 25.1 Stages in the development of the sea urchin, based upon that of Strongylocentrotus lividus. (1–6 after Korschelt; 6e after Grassi.)

1. The ripe egg, ready for fertilization, enclosed in its jelly membrane. The pronucleus can be seen in the clear cytoplasm of the upper hemisphere; the two polocytes (polar bodies) formed during meiosis lie just outside the cell membrane but inside the jelly layer, and the pigment granules are collected in a band in the lower hemisphere.

2. Stages in the process of fertilization.
   a. Penetration of spermatozoa through the jelly layer. The sperm first to make contact with the cell surface is here shown in solid black, the others in outline. From the point of contact, a wave of negativity, indicated by arrows, spreads over the surface of the egg.
   b. At the point of contact, the surface of the egg is raised as a "fertilization cone," and the sperm is drawn into the egg cytoplasm. (In this and subsequent drawings, the jelly membrane is omitted.)
   c. Elevation of the fertilization membrane and progression of the sperm nucleus toward the egg nucleus. The fluid-filled space between the egg surface and the fertilization membrane is the perivitelline space.

3. Cleavage Stages.
   a. The fertilized egg in the course of its first division. (The fertilization membrane is omitted.)
   b. First cleavage of nucleus and cytoplasm completed.
   c. Second cleavage completed.
   d. Third cleavage completed. The pigment is now localized in the cells of the lower hemisphere.
   e. Fourth cleavage complete in the cells of the upper hemisphere, in progress in those of the lower hemisphere.

4. Blastula.
   a. Exterior of a young blastula, showing the pigment granules located in cells between the equator and the lower pole of the cellular mass.
   b. Section through a young blastula, showing the central cavity, the blastocoele or primary body cavity. (The pigmented cells are indicated by heavy black borders.)

5. Gastrulation.
   a. Section through an early gastrula, showing the first migration of cells (primary mesenchyme) from the lower pole into the blastocoele.
   b. Section through a later gastrula, showing invagination of the pigmented cells at the blastopore, and the first indication of the archenteron. Certain of the cells at the upper pole have become differentiated as an apical plate.
   c. Section through a still older gastrula, showing the archenteron extending almost to the upper pole and open to the outside only through the blastopore, the secondary mesenchyme being formed by the migration of cells from the tip of the archenteron; and the formation of skeletal rods by the primary mesenchyme.
   d. Exterior view of a gastrula at a stage comparable to c, showing the single opening of the archenteron at the lower pole, and the uniform distribution of cilia over the surface.

6. Larval Stages.
   a. Young larva seen from the right side. Between this stage and that shown in 5d, the archenteron has acquired a second opening to the exterior and growth has been more rapid on one side of the body than the other, bringing the two openings of the archenteron together on one surface of the larva, and so distinguishing its ventral from its dorsal surface. The archenteron has further become differentiated into oesophagus, opening to the outside through the aperture secondarily acquired (mouth), stomach and intestine, opening to the outside through the old blastopore (anus). The left coelomic cavity (secondary body cavity) is evident through the transparent body wall, and is shown as differentiated into anterior and posterior coelomes, and a middle coelome, the hydrocoele. The strongly ciliated cells are shown as a dark band extending down the sides of the larva, and crossing from one side to the other on the ventral surface.
   b. A slightly older larva seen from the ventral surface.
   c. An older larva, showing the rapid growth of the ciliated band and the development of the larval arms.
   d. A pluteus, with well-developed larval arms. (In b, c and d internal structures other than the enteron are not shown.)
   e. A larva in the course of metamorphosis, seen from the left side, showing the "echinoderm rudiment" containing those larval structures that are included and developed in the adult. The others are discarded when metamorphosis is complete.

[ 564 ]   THE OPERATION OF BIOLOGICAL SYSTEMS

sperm to more active swimming movements, and another to cause their agglutination so that they are clumped together when in the immediate vicinity of the egg; one produced by the sperm is antagonistic to the activating hormone of the egg, for it slows down their movements and so delays the exhaustion of these minute, active cells with small energy reserve to draw upon, and another acts as a lysin and dissolves the jelly with which the egg is surrounded, allowing the sperm to come into direct contact with its surface. This point of contact is marked in the echinoderm egg, and in those of other species in which the actual course of fertilization can be followed, by the elevation of a small mass of cytoplasm, called the fertilization cone, which later sinks below the surface of the egg, apparently drawing the sperm in with it (Fig. 25.1 2b).

The entrance of the sperm into the egg is evidenced, in the echinoderm and amphibian egg at least, by certain visible changes and others that can be detected by physical and chemical means. Among the visible changes are the appearance of a membrane, the fertilization membrane, that seems to be lifted off the surface of the egg, separated from it by a fluid-filled space, the perivitelline space (Greek, peri = around + Latin, vitellus = egg yolk) and a shift in position of some of the visible components of the cytoplasm (Figs. 25.1, 25.2b). In the frog's egg, for example, the dark pigment granules flow along with the cytoplasm toward the point of entrance of the sperm, so that a

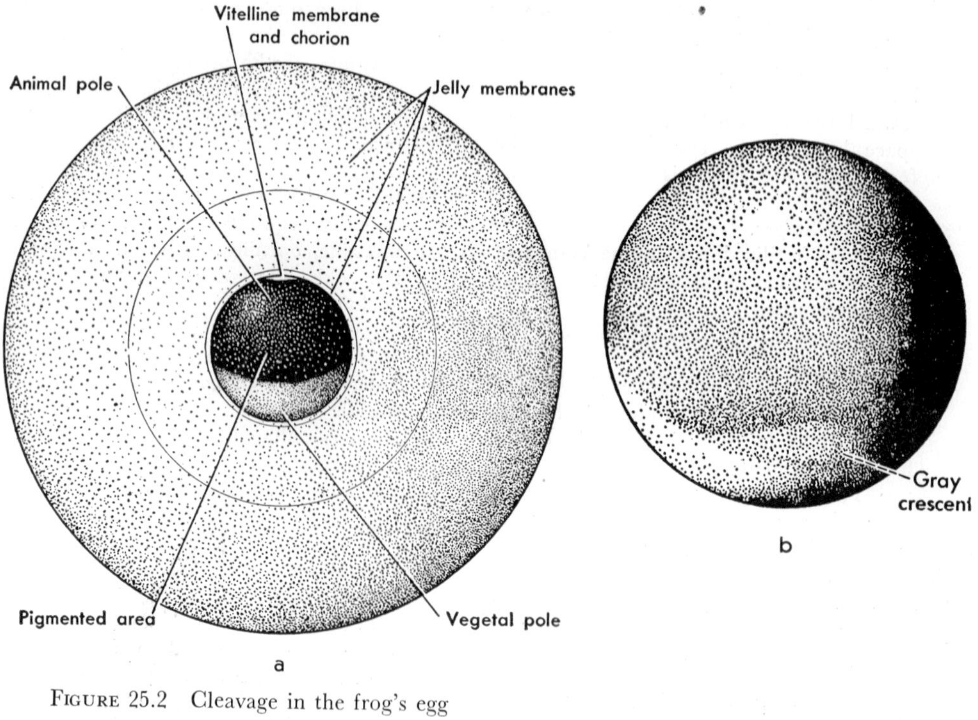

FIGURE 25.2  Cleavage in the frog's egg

a. Unfertilized egg with its membranes.

b. The egg after penetration of the sperm, showing the "gray crescent" resulting from pigment migration.

c–f. First, second, third and fourth cleavages. (The interval between b and f is approximately 4 hours for the egg of Rana sylvatica at 18°C.) (a, redrawn from Schultz, from Huettner, *Fundamentals of Comparative Embryology of the Vertebrates.* Copyright 1949 by The Macmillan Company. b–f, after Pollister and Moore. The egg is drawn with membranes omitted, and to a larger scale than in a.)

region of the egg's surface becomes lighter in color; this region, the gray crescent, lies opposite the point of entrance of the sperm. Physical measurements have shown that from this point a wave of electrical negativity spreads over the surface of the egg, a condition that is believed to be the factor effective in preventing the entrance of other sperm; that the surface membrane becomes more permeable, so that substances may enter and leave the egg more readily; and that its heat production is increased. Chemical measurements show that the respiratory rate of the cell is likewise increased, and that the end products of protein metabolism, ammonia in the sea urchin and urea in the frog, are excreted in greater quantity. The increased heat production, respiratory rate and excretion all indicate an increased metabolism of the fertilized egg over that of the unfertilized, and point to the conversion of the potential energy stored in the reserve material, or yolk, to kinetic energy.

After penetration, the sperm nucleus moves toward the egg nucleus, waiting, in eggs naturally fertilized while still in meiosis, until this is completed, and fuses with it; the paternal set of chromosomes is thus added to the maternal set, and the zygote endowed with the capacity to develop attributes of its paternal as well as its maternal line.

## Cleavage

Cleavage, or the segmentation of the egg by a rapid series of mitotic divisions into a number of cells, or blastomeres (Greek, blastos = sprout + meros = part), begins shortly after nuclear fusion. Its character is greatly influenced by the amount and distribution of yolk, which impedes the passage of the cleavage furrows. Cleavage in such eggs as the echinoderm's, the mammal's (exclusive of the monotremes), and the amphibian's is total or holoblastic, each division resulting in two complete blastomeres, although in the amphibian egg, cytoplasmic division progresses more slowly in the vegetal hemisphere than in the animal. Cleavage in such eggs as the hen's is said to be partial or meroblastic, since the great mass of the yolk is not segmented at all, and division is limited to the blastodisc, the small pool of cytoplasm surrounding the nucleus (Figs. 25.1, 25.2c–e, 25.4a).

Cleavage results in the conversion of a single cell, the zygote, into a mass of cells of indefinite number, called a blastula. In species with total cleavage, like echinoderms and amphibia, the blastula is a hollow ball, for the inner margins of the blastomeres, conforming to the physical law of minimal surfaces, round off as they are formed, leaving a space, the segmentation cavity or blas-

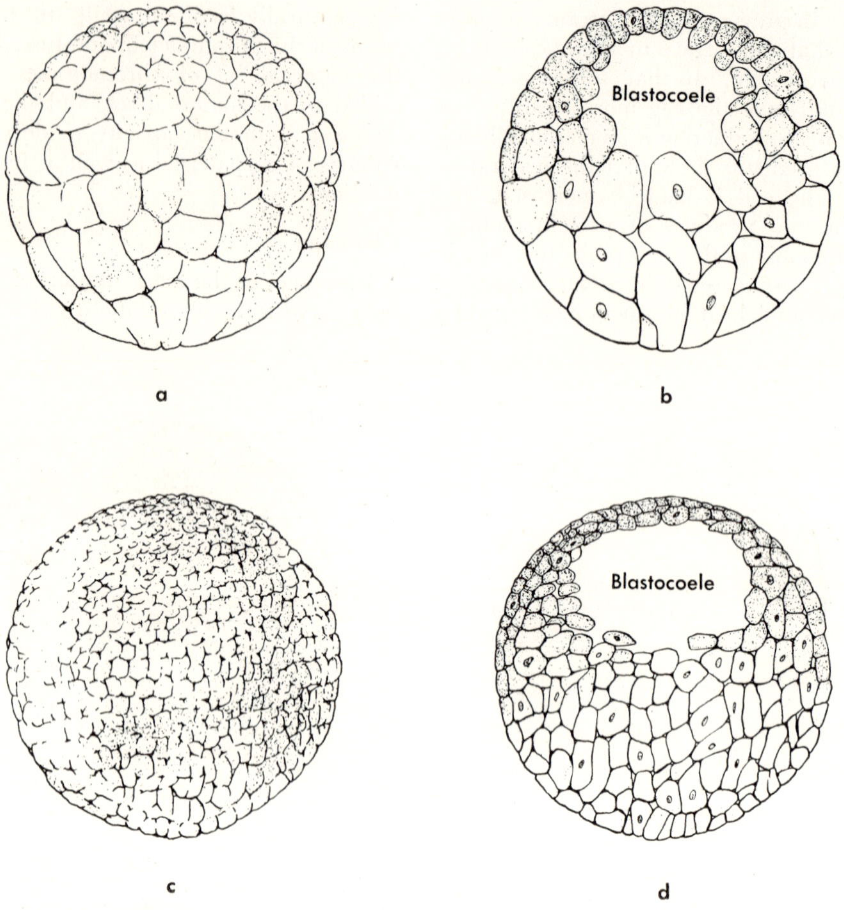

FIGURE 25.3   The blastula of the frog. (From various sources.)

a. Exterior of an early blastula.
b. Section through an early blastula.
c. Exterior of a late blastula.
d. Section through a late blastula.

tocoele, that becomes filled with fluid. The wall of the echinoderm blastula is but one cell in thickness; these cells are ciliated, and the blastula revolves slowly through the water. The wall of the amphibian blastula consists of several layers of small cells at the animal pole and many more, of large ones, at the vegetal (Figs. 25.1, 25.3).

In an egg with much yolk, like that of the hen's, the blastula is represented by a disc, or plaque, of cells spread over a small area of the yolk. As one looks at this plaque, the blastoderm, in a living egg, the central part appears light and translucent, while the periphery is opaque. These two areas were distinguished by the early observers of chick embryology as the area pellucida and the area opaca, respectively. The area pellucida is that region of the blastoderm where the cells are complete, with inner as well as outer and lateral walls, and separated from the underlying yolk by the blastocoele; in the area opaca, the cells have no inner walls and are actually continuous with the yolk (Fig. 25.4b–c).

Cleavage in the mammalian egg has been followed in a number of species, including the rabbit, bat, pig and some of the primates, but has not yet been observed in man, except in one case of an artificially fertilized and cultured ovum, carried only to the three-cell stage. It results in the formation

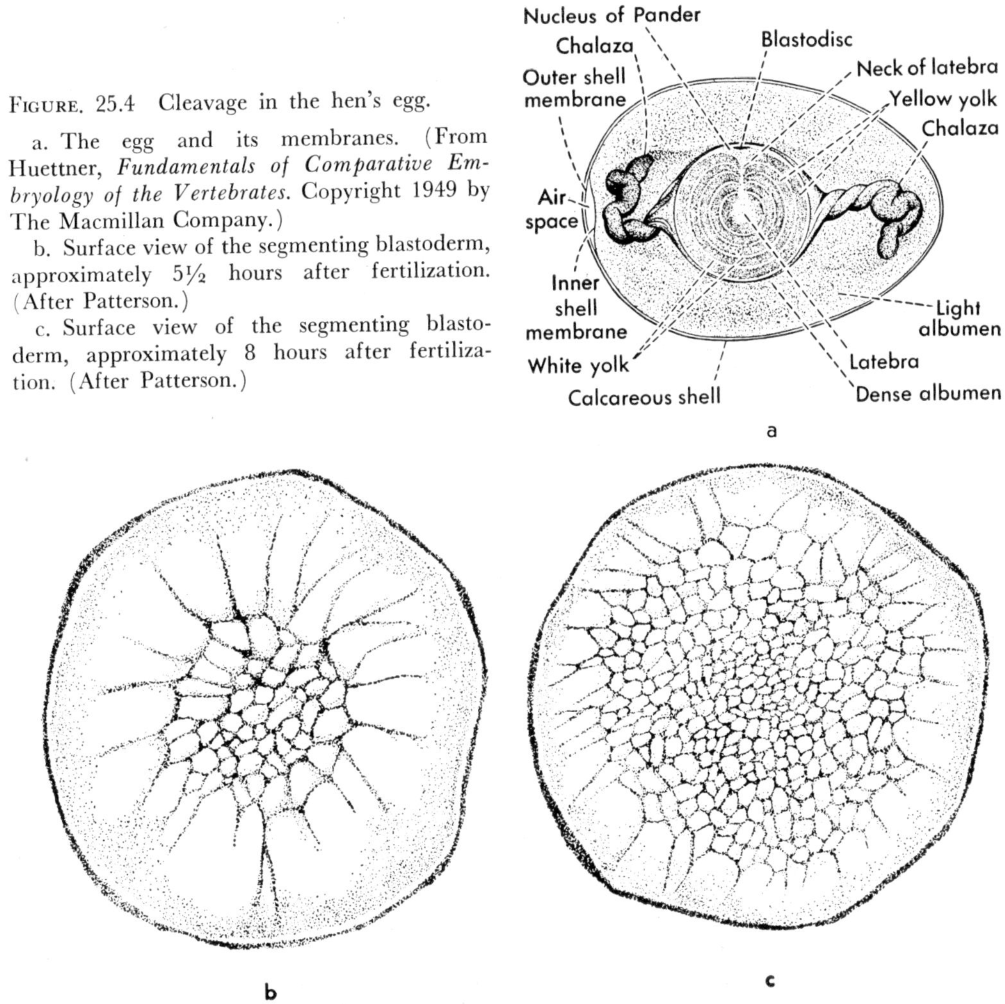

FIGURE. 25.4 Cleavage in the hen's egg.

a. The egg and its membranes. (From Huettner, *Fundamentals of Comparative Embryology of the Vertebrates.* Copyright 1949 by The Macmillan Company.)

b. Surface view of the segmenting blastoderm, approximately 5½ hours after fertilization. (After Patterson.)

c. Surface view of the segmenting blastoderm, approximately 8 hours after fertilization. (After Patterson.)

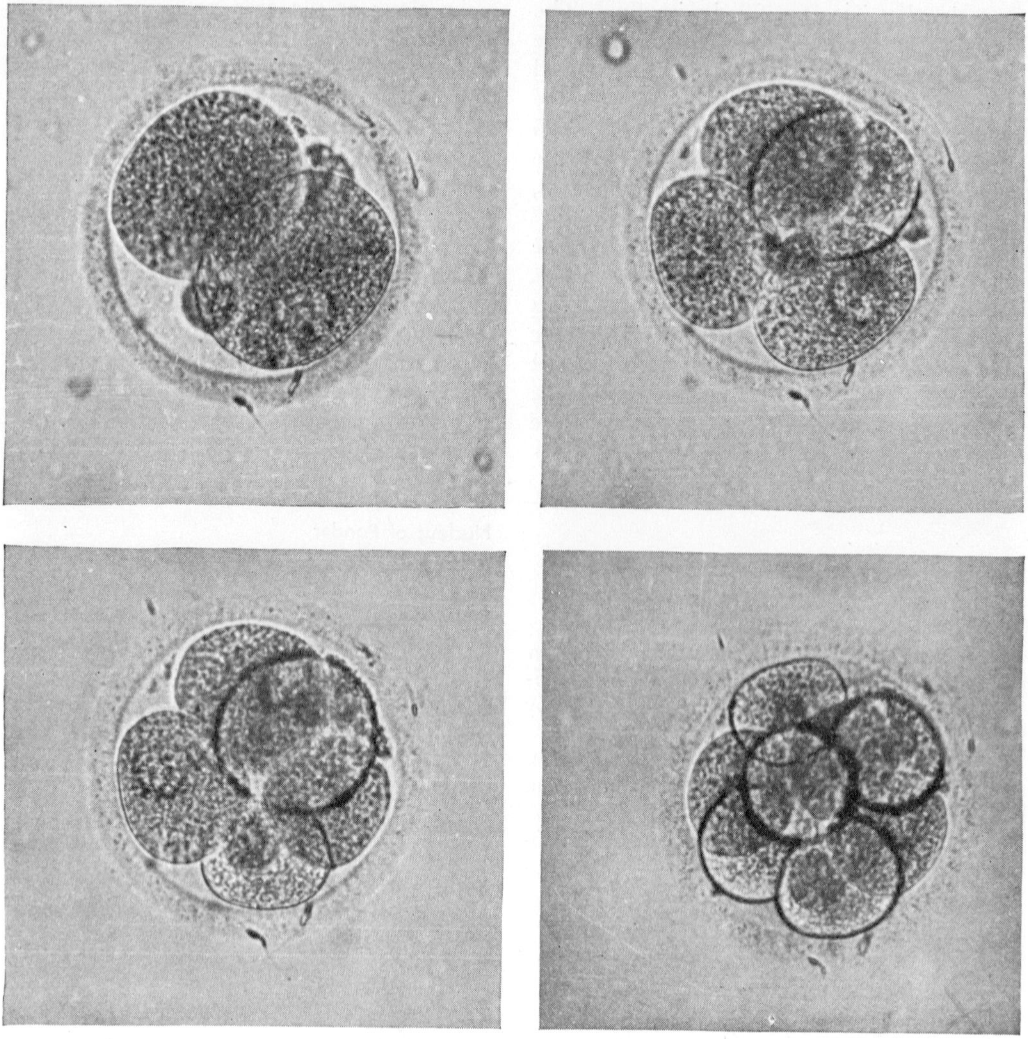

FIGURE 25.5 Cleavage in the monkey's egg. Accessory sperm can be seen in the zona pellucida, an albuminous envelope that surrounds the egg. (From Lewis and Hartman, by courtesy of the Carnegie Institution of Washington.)

of a blastocyst, corresponding to the blastula stage of other embryos. The blastocyst consists of a cluster of cells, the inner cell mass, at one pole, and a fluid-filled cavity, the blastocyst cavity, surrounded by a wall, the trophoblast (Figs. 25.5, 25.6).

**Gastrulation:** Gastrulation is essentially a rearrangement of the cells of the blastula, and the movement of certain of them into the blastocoele. Through it the primary tissues of the organism—ectoderm, endoderm and mesoderm—are brought into the position and relations to each other suitable or advantageous for their differentiation into the tissues and organs of the embryo, and ultimately those of the adult. The process of gastrulation is, like cleavage, influenced by the amount of yolk stored up in the egg, which presents a mechanical impediment to the free movement of all the cells.

GASTRULATION IN ECHINODERM EGGS: The conditions of gastrulation are simplest in eggs like those of the echinoderms. In one species of sea urchin, Strongylocentrotus lividus, it can be followed especially well, for a band of reddish cells surrounds the blastula just below its equator, whose origin can be traced back to a band of pigment granules in a similar location in the fertilized egg (Fig. 25.1). At the beginning of gastrulation, the non-pigmented cells at the vegetal pole of the blastula migrate into the blastocoele; then the pigmented cells fold into it, or invaginate (Latin, in = in + vagina = sheath) forming a blind pocket within it. This is the archenteron (Greek, arch = first + enteron = digestive tract); the pigmented cells of its walls differentiate as endoderm and become the lining of the oesophagus, stomach and intestine of the larva. The non-pigmented cells become mesenchyme and, migrating through the blastocoele, are active in the formation of the skeletal rods that support the larval arms. The cells of the animal hemisphere, surrounding the blastocoele and archenteron as ectoderm, continue to divide and the spherical, single-layered blastula becomes as elongated, gastrula (dim. of Greek, gaster = stomach) with an outer layer of ectoderm enclosing a cavity, containing mesenchyme cells, into which there projects a hollow tube of endoderm communicating with the outside by an opening, the blastopore, which marks the position where the infolding of endoderm cells first began. From cells at the inner end of this tube there are formed two hollow pouches, the coelomic sacs, from which the coelomic system of the adult is derived. These cells are mesoderm cells and by the end of gastrulation the three primary tissues of the organism are established.

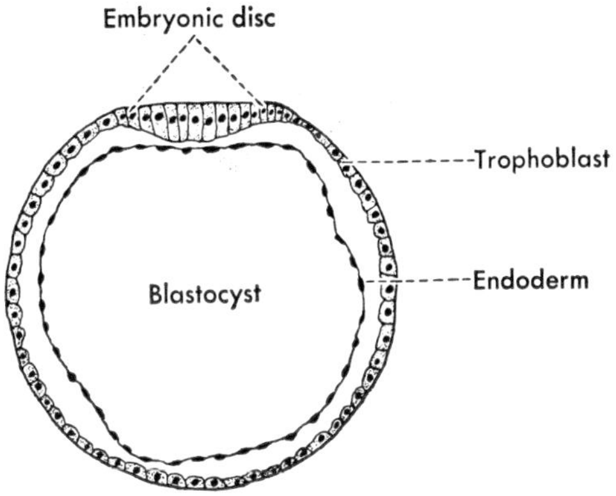

GASTRULATION IN AMPHIBIAN EGGS: Active invagination is not mechanically possible in blastulae like those of the amphibia, where the cells of the vegetal pole are large and heavy with yolk; gastrulation in such eggs is a combination of four factors: the movement of certain groups of cells toward one region of the blastula's surface, their involution (Latin, involvere = to roll around), or turning inward there, the downward movement of the remaining cells of the animal hemisphere over the yolk-filled cells, or epiboly (Greek, epibole = a throwing upon) and the consequent invagination of these cells as walls of the archenteron (Figs. 25.7, 25.8).

*The mapping of areas of presumptive tissues:* The amphibian egg has no natural markers like the pigment band of the egg of Strongylocentrotus, but by staining small areas of it and of the blastula with non-toxic dyes of contrasting colors, it has been possible to trace the fate of definite areas, the direction of movement of the cells during gastrulation and their location at the end of it. In practice this is done by saturating small strips of agar with dyes such as Nile Blue Sulphate and Neutral Red, and holding them against the desired surface of the egg or blastula until the dye has diffused from the agar into the cells. The movements of the stained areas can be watched in the living egg, and if they are ones that involute, their location within the gastrula, at different times in the gastrulation process, can be ascertained by fixing and sectioning it. By this technique it has been possible to determine with great accuracy the regions of the blastula from which the tissues, and ultimately the organs, of the embryo arise under ordinary conditions of development, and very complete maps of the potential, or presumptive, potencies of groups of blastula cells have been made for a number of amphibian species, both caudate and acaudate.

FIGURE 25.6 Blastocyst of a mammalian (pig) embryo after 8 days gestation. (After Arey.)

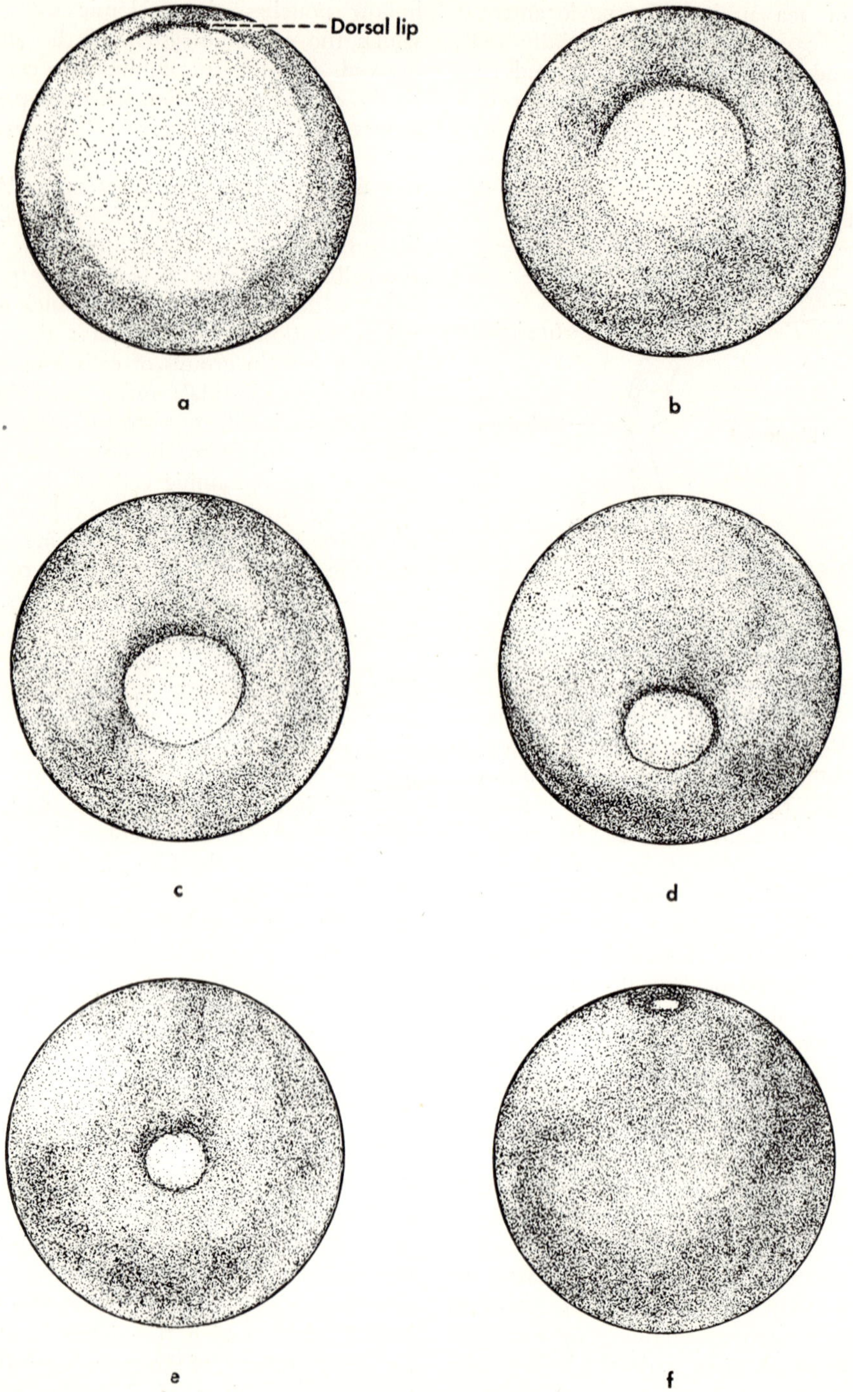

FIGURE 25.7 Gastrulation in the frog. (After Jenkinson.) Changes in the external appearance of the developing frog's egg in the course of gastrulation. The events between a and f occupy some 9 hours in the egg of Rana sylvatica at 18°C. Rotation of the egg within its membranes, which brings the blastopore uppermost, has begun in e, and is complete in f.

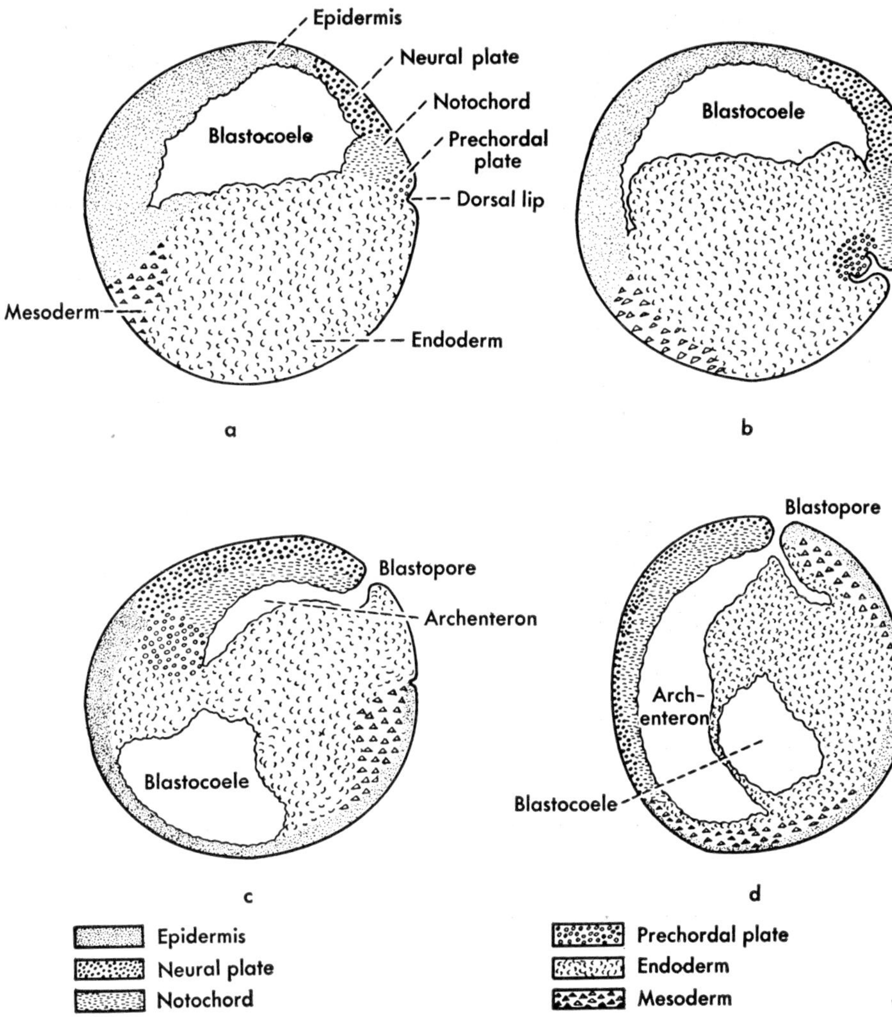

FIGURE 25.8 Gastrulation in the frog. (After Shumway.) Changes in the internal anatomy of the developing frog's egg corresponding to the external changes shown in Fig. 25.7. The areas of presumptive tissues are labeled in a, and indicated conventionally in the subsequent figures.

Figure 25.9 represents a generalized map of this kind.

By such staining methods, it has been established that the involution of cells first begins in the region of the gray crescent; the site of this initial involution is the dorsal lip of the blastopore, and is evident in the living blastula as a small curved slit upon its surface. As cells from the surface of the blastula lateral to this slit move toward it, and also turn into the blastocoele, lateral lips are formed, and the slit becomes first crescentic, then horse-shoe shaped, the ends of the horse-shoe finally meeting at the ventral lip. The blastopore thus becomes a circular opening, its margins elevated slightly above the other superficial cells as low ridges, the lips. While involution is in progress, the cells of the animal hemisphere not involved in the process move down over the yolk cells, and as they do so, the lips of the blastopore are brought closer and closer together. The yolk cells, at first filling the circular area between them as the yolk plug, are gradually covered over and the yolk plug becomes smaller and smaller as gastrulation proceeds. The blastopore is finally closed by the apposition of its lateral lips, and its former position marked only by a small, elongated ridge of cells, the primitive streak, with a slight groove along its length.

chenteron, forming temporarily the greater part of its roof. As the presumptive notochordal material moves in, the presumptive neural tissue, an elliptical sector of the blastula's surface, is brought nearer the blastopore, and drawn out in a plane transverse to its long axis, so that it first becomes pear-

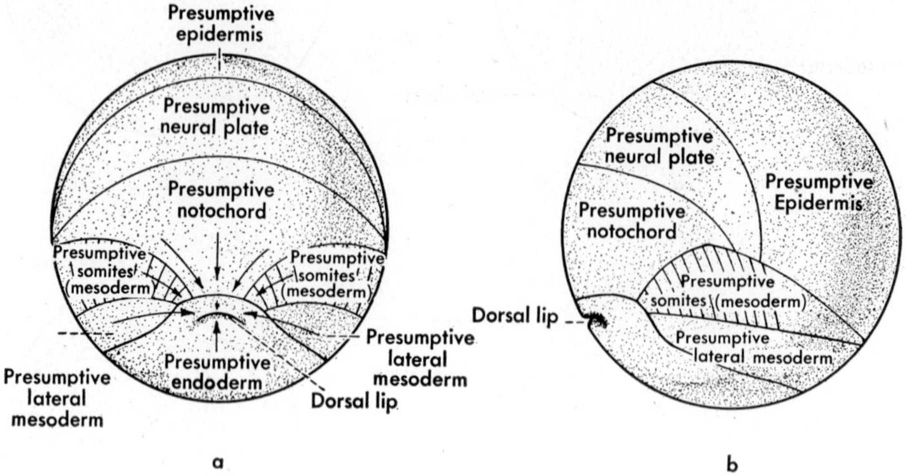

FIGURE 25.9 Map of the presumptive areas of the blastula of the frog. (After Barth.)

a. The blastula is so oriented that the dorsal lip of the blastopore is directed toward the observer.

b. The blastula is so oriented that the dorsal lip of the blastopore is at the observer's left.

At the end of gastrulation, the anterior-posterior and dorsal-ventral axes of the embryo are established, and the materials for the formation of the notochord, the alimentary canal and its derivatives, the mesoderm and its derivatives, the nervous tissue and the epidermis have been brought into place. The first cells that slip in under the dorsal lip of the blastopore have been traced to endoderm of the head, those that follow to the notochord and mesoderm, while the invaginated yolk cells become the endoderm of the archenteron. Reference to Figure 25.9 will show that at the beginning of gastrulation the presumptive notochord cells are spread out in a fan shape over the spherical blastula, but as they move toward the dorsal lip, and into the archenteron through it, they are drawn together in a linear mass that, as their inward migration continues, extends almost the entire length of the ar-

shaped, but later narrowed to a linear mass expanded at the end distal to the blastopore. When the presumptive notochordal material has all moved into the blastocoele the presumptive neural material overlies it as the neural plate, and both extend along the anterior-posterior axis of the future embryo, the enlarged part of the neural plate marking the region of the future head (Fig. 25.8). The remaining cells of the blastula, that have not undergone involution or transformation to the neural plate, stretch out over the gastrula as a complete investing ectodermal layer. The archenteron is thus an enclosed space within the gastrula, with a floor and sides of invaginated endoderm cells, but its roof arched over by involuted chorda-mesoderm cells.

GASTRULATION IN THE HEN'S EGG: Gastrulation in the developing hen's egg begins while the egg is still passing along the oviduct; for this reason, and because of the nature of the egg itself, it has not yet been possible to follow the events of the process with the completeness and precision with which they have been traced in the amphibian egg. Fundamentally, however, they appear to be very similar, although the great mass of unsegmented yolk in the hen's egg, which takes no part in the gastrulation process, imposes even greater mechanical difficulties to movements of the cells. Certain cells of the blastoderm, however, move into the blastocoele, as endoderm cells (Fig. 25.10). While this ingression is going on, other cells move toward its midline; their convergence there forms the primitive streak, visible in the living embryo as a narrow band on the surface of the blastoderm (Figs. 25.11a, 25.12). At one end of the primitive streak is a small cluster of cells, called the primitive knot or Hensen's node. Sections show that cells migrate from the sides of the primitive streak, between the ectoderm and the internal sheet of endoderm; some of these may be included in the endoderm, but they become, for the most part, mesoderm. There is also a migration of cells from Hensen's node, forming what earlier embryologists called the head process, like the primitive streak visible externally as a dark strip in the blastoderm. Staining experiments have shown that these cells are presumptive notochord; their location distinguishes the anterior end of the gastrula from the posterior. They, and Hensen's node, lie anteriorly, below the ectoderm cells that later become the neural plate, and above the first of the endoderm cells to have moved into the blastocoele. The primitive streak of the avian egg is thus homologous with that of the amphibian, although there is no actual blastopore, for both mark the site of the entrance of chorda-mesoderm into the blastocoele.

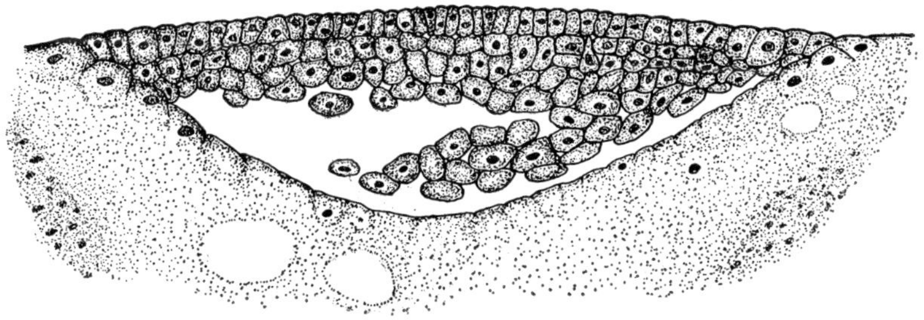

At the end of gastrulation, conditions in the chick are essentially like those in the amphibian; if the gastrula of a frog, for example, were cut open and stretched out over the surface of a ball with a diameter considerably larger than its own, the relations of the primordial tissues would be very much the same. While in the intact frog gastrula, these tissues conform to the shape of a sphere, and curve around its periphery from the dorsal to the ventral regions of the embryo, and the archenteron is a complete, closed tube, with floor, roof and sides, in the chick these tissues must conform to the shape of a flat plate, spread out over part of the surface of an inert, spherical yolk mass. The endoderm as yet forms only the roof of the archenteron; its floor is yolk, and it has no sides, although the material for their construction is already assembled. While these changes in the central part of the blastoderm are in progress, the cells at its periphery continue to divide and to grow down over the yolk, steadily increasing the extent of the area opaca.

FIGURE 25.10 Gastrulation in the hen's egg. (From various sources.) Transverse section of the cellular mass at the beginning of gastrulation. The roof of the archenteron (future endoderm, notochord and mesoderm) is derived from cells that have migrated inward from the blastoderm; its floor is unsegmented yolk.

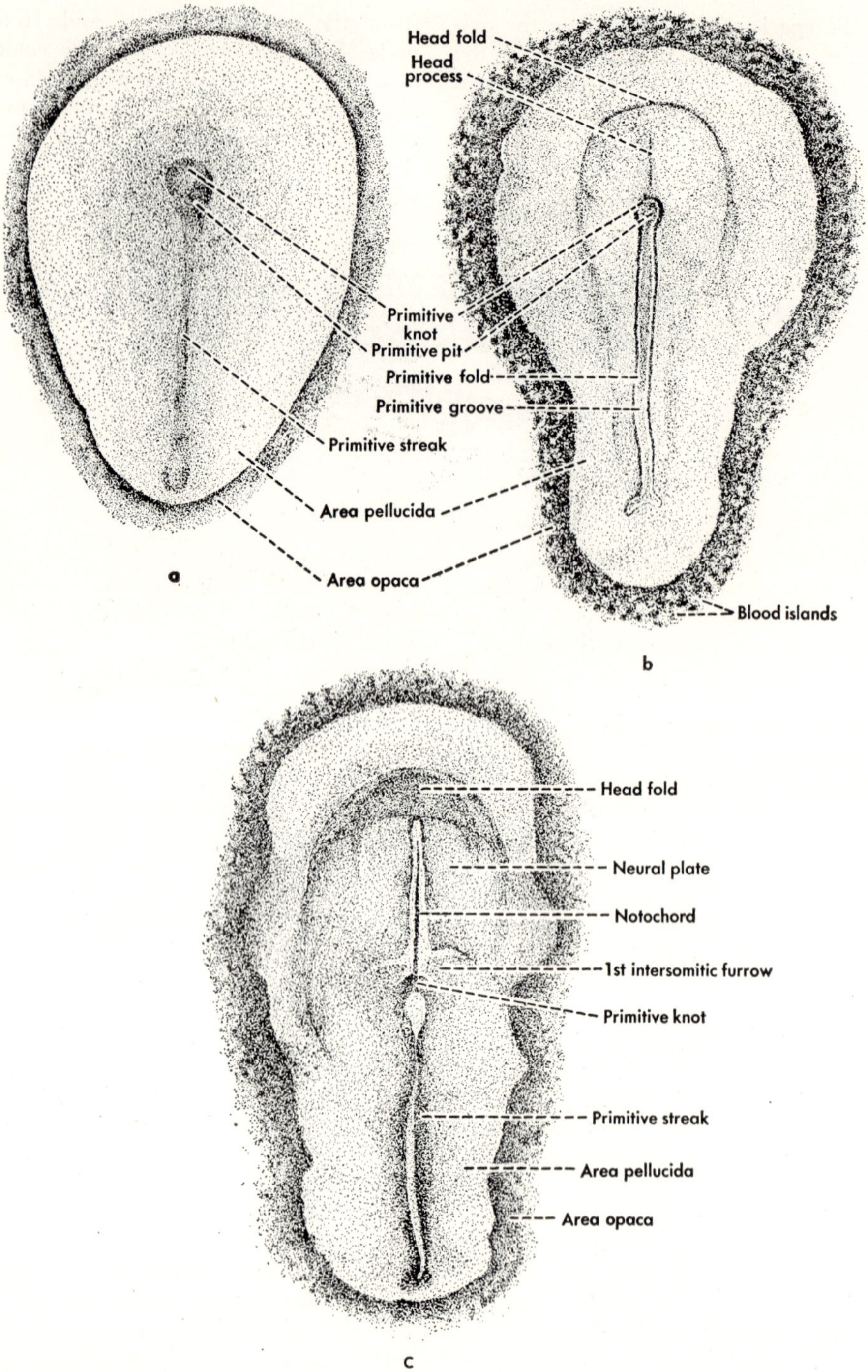

FIGURE 25.11 Surface views of the blastoderm and developing embryo of the chick. (After Arey.)
  a. After 16 hours incubation.
  b. After 19 hours incubation.
  c. After 21 hours incubation.

[574]

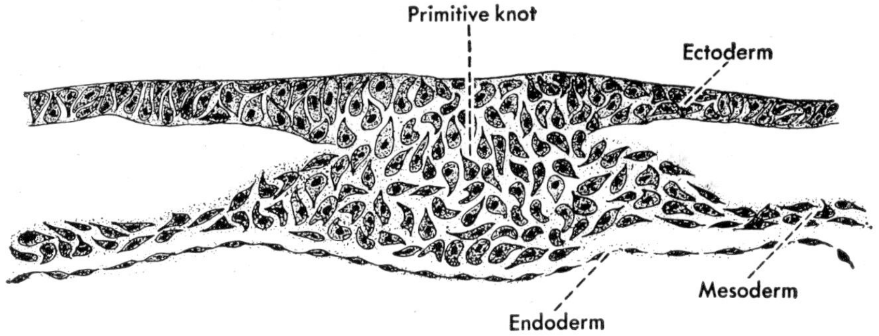

FIGURE 25.12 Sections through the blastoderm of the chick at the primitive streak stage.

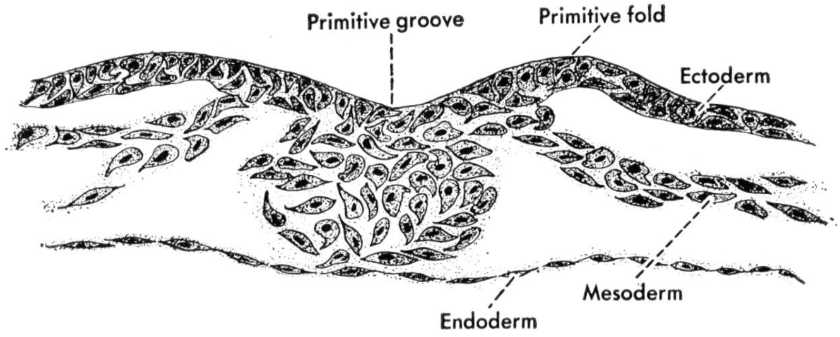

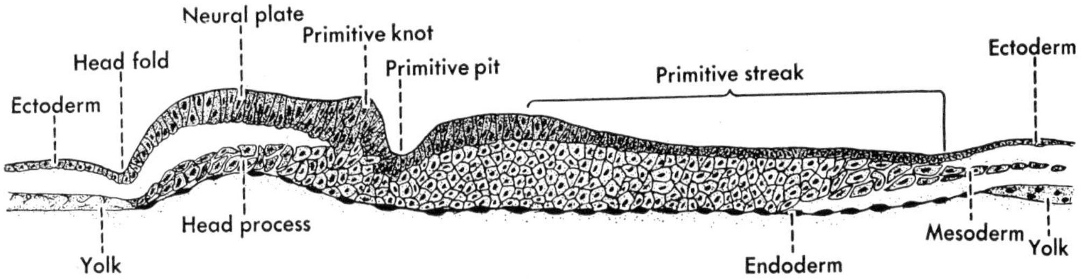

   a. Transverse section through the primitive knot (approximately 16-hour embryo).
   b. Transverse section through the primitive streak (approximately 24-hour embryo).
   c. Longitudinal section through the primitive streak (approximately 16-hour embryo).

GASTRULATION IN THE EGG OF PLACENTAL MAMMALS: The conditions of gastrulation in placental mammals definitely reflect their evolutionary descent from ancestors whose eggs contained much yolk. With the exception of the monotremes, the eggs of none of them contain a sufficient amount of yolk to act as an impediment to direct invagination, yet the mechanism of their gastrulation closely approximates that of heavily yolked eggs. It takes place while the blastocyst is in the uterus, or sinking into its endometrium, and involves a rearrangement of cells of the inner cell mass. Some of these cells, as endoderm, separate from the inner cell mass and become distributed in a sheet below it and above the blastocyst cavity (Fig. 25.6). In most mammals studied, the endoderm eventually lines this cavity completely, but only those directly below the inner cell mass are included in the embryo. These cells and the others of the inner cell mass, the future ectoderm and mesoderm of the embryo, constitute the blastoderm, or germ disc.

A primitive streak and a primitive knot appear on the mammalian blastoderm as they do on that of the chick; mesoderm likewise moves out from the primitive streak and the notochordal material is segregated anterior to the primitive knot in a similar fashion. The spread of the mesoderm is very rapid in most mammals; it quickly extends beyond the embryonic area and moves in between the trophoblast and the endoderm lining the blastocyst cavity.

*Embryogenesis.* PRIMARY DIFFERENCES BETWEEN ANAMNIOTES AND AMNIOTES; BETWEEN PLACENTAL AND APLACENTAL MAMMALS: Echinoderms and most amphibia pass through a larval stage in the course of their embryology in which they are free living individuals, capable of moving about from place to place, obtaining their own food and exchanging materials directly with the external environment. Differentiation of the primary tissues of the gastrula, in these animals, then results in the formation of larval organs and systems, some of which foreshadow those of the adult and may be directly transformed into them. The entire embryonic life of a bird or a mammal, on the other hand, is spent within the outer membranes of the egg or in the body of the mother, and though the young of different species are hatched or born at different levels of maturity, they have in general the organization of an adult when they do emerge. But, shut off during their entire embryonic life from direct contact with the external environment, they must obtain their food and effect their metabolic exchanges with it indirectly. This they accomplish through embryonic or fetal membranes, actually external to the embryo proper but intimately associated with it and essential to its development. Embryogenesis in these animals involves not only the differentiation and organization of the primary tissues into the rudiments of the adult organs, but also the development of auxiliary structures—the yolk sac, amnion, chorion and allantois in birds, and in mammals, except monotremes and marsupials, also the placenta. It is the presence of these embryonic structures that distinguishes the amniote chordates from the anamniote, and the placental from the aplacental mammals.

POSTGASTRULATION CHANGES IN ECHINODERMS: Postgastrulation changes in the echinoderms involve growth of the body as a whole, connection of the blind end of the archenteron with the ectoderm and the formation of a mouth at this point, differentiation of the archenteron into oesophagus, stomach and intestine, the development of the system of coelomes from the paired coelomic pouches, the limitation of the external cilia to thickened ridges of cells that form bands around the body of the larva, and in the sea urchins, the extension of parts of these bands and the cells adjacent to them into the arms of the pluteus, supported by skeletal rods made and deposited by the mesenchyme cells (Fig. 25.1). Externally the larva is bilaterally symmetrical, although internally it is asymmetrical, for on the left side there is a development of the coelomic system, the hydrocoele, to become the water-vascular system of the adult, that does not take place on the right.

The young sea urchin spends some days of its life as a pluteus; as a member of the plankton, it feeds upon minute organisms swept into its mouth by the cilia of the oral band, and is in turn preyed upon by other animals. If it survives, it ultimately settles down, attaching itself to some object in the water by a mucous secretion exuded from cells near its mouth and begins its metamorphosis. This involves the growth of organs on the left side of its body, in the neighborhood of the hydrocoele, to form the echinoderm rudiment, in which are included only parts of the larval ectoderm, digestive tract and coleomic spaces. When the organs of the adult sea urchin are organized, and established, within this rudiment, it breaks free from the rest of the larval body and continues to feed and to develop adult proportions and characters.

POSTGASTRULATION CHANGES IN VERTEBRATES. *Amphibia:* Postgastrulation changes in the vertebrate embryo are considerably more complicated, involving the separation of the involuted cells into their tissue components, the distribution of these components to the regions of the body appropriate for their structural and functional differentiation into more elaborate organs and systems, the formation of a tubular nervous system, and its peripheral nerves, and of specialized sense organs from the material of the neural plate and the completion of the archenteron as a tube with anterior and posterior openings and a number of accessory structures. These changes have been followed in detail in a great many different kinds of vertebrates, in all of which the fundamental ones have been found to follow the same general pattern. The amphibia may be taken as illustrative of this pattern, and have been here chosen for description of it because information about the causal relationships of events within that pattern are at present most complete for them.

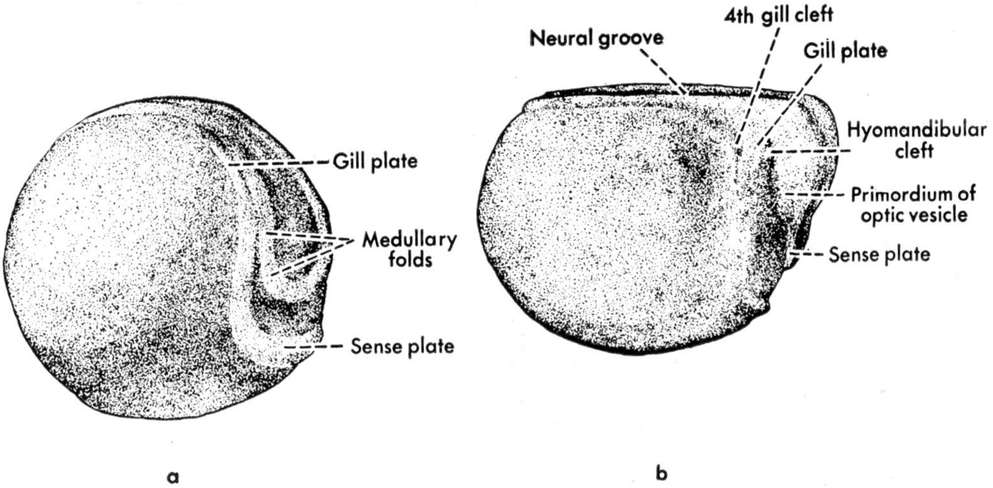

During gastrulation, when the multiplication as well as the movement of cells is actively in progress, the amphibian embryo elongates along its anterior-posterior axis, and the neural plate, the notochord and the enteron become correspondingly extended. The external appearance of the embryo changes by this growth, and by the appearance of ridges along the margins of the neural plate, whose sides begin to fold upward (Fig. 25.13). This folding continues, and the folds, turning toward the midline, gradually

FIGURE 25.13 The neurula stage of the frog. (After McEwan.)

a. Antero-lateral view of embryo of Rana pipiens (approximately 40-hour development).

b. Right lateral view of a 2.2 mm. embryo of Rana pipiens (approximately 50-hour development).

meet and fuse there. Their fusion begins in the central region of the embryo and continues both anteriorly and posteriorly, completed last of all at the posterior end where they finally meet over the primitive streak. In this way a hollow neural tube with a bulbous enlargement at the anterior end is formed; as the neural folds converge and meet, the presumptive epidermis at the sides of the neural plate is brought together in the midline of the embryo and covers over the tube, which gradually sinks into the underlying tissues. The cells between its roof and the overlying ectoderm form the neural crests, derived from the lateral portions of the folds (Fig. 25.15b). During the period of formation and fusion of the neural folds, the embryo is known as a neurula.

Before the fusion of the neural folds is complete, there is a marked thickening of the ectoderm along their antero-lateral borders, which results in the formation of plate-like areas visible anterior to and along the sides of the neural tube. The more anterior of these is the sense plate; the more posterior, lying on either side of the tube where its expanded anterior region tapers off, is the gill plate. The other ectoderm cells develop cilia, which by their beating, cause the embryo to rotate within its jelly membranes.

While these changes are going on externally, internal ones are also in progress that lead to the completion of the archenteron as an endodermal tube. This is brought about by the separation of the involuted cells into notochord and mesoderm and the convergence, beneath the notochord, of endoderm cells that have migrated dorsally from the floor and sides of the archenteron. The presumptive notochord material detaches itself from the rest of the involuted cell mass and becomes a separate cylindrical cord of cells lying between the neural plate and the archenteron; these differentiate as notochordal tissue and form an axial rod in the embryo. With the upward movement of the endoderm, there is also a downward movement of the mesoderm; the result of these movements is the formation of a complete endodermal sac, surrounded by mesoderm. The roof of this sac is comparatively thin, and its cells small; the floor and sides are thicker, and made of large yolk-filled cells. As embryogenesis continues, the yolk in these cells is digested and used for the metabolic needs of the embryo, until it has attained its larval condition and feeds for itself.

In the anterior region, the continuous solid sheets of mesoderm on either side of the notochord break up into separate blocks, the mesodermal somites. This segmentation continues posteriorly so that somites continue to arise as the embryo grows in length and its tissues differentiate. The solid sheets of mesoderm that extend around the archenteron separate into a thin outer, or somatic layer, in contact with the ectoderm, and a thicker inner, or splanchnic layer, in contact with the endoderm. The space between these two layers becomes the coelome.

With growth in length, the embryo acquires a definite head and tail region. In the head, two crescentic swellings arise on the ventral surface, which later become the mucous glands peculiar to amphibian embryos through whose secretion they temporarily attach themselves, after hatching, to some object in the water. Between these two swellings is a depression which marks the position of the stomodaeum, the ectodermal invagination that, as the mouth, ultimately makes connection with the anterior end of the enteron (Fig. 25.14). Two depressions, the olfactory pits, appear in the sense plate, one on each side of the stomodaeum, and the optic vesicles, later indented as optic cups, are evident as two lateral enlargements of the anterior part of the neural tube. Over these enlargements, the ectoderm differentiates as the future lens of the eye. The visceral clefts first become evident as grooves curving over the two gill plates, and the otocysts as thickenings of the neural ectoderm, or placodes (Greek, plax = flat plate), on either side of the neural tube where the bulb tapers off into the cylindrical cord; these later become depressed as pits and then, as vesicles, sink beneath the epidermis. Posteriorly, the tail bud first appears as an outgrowth of the tissues dorsal and posterior to the notochord, and ventral to this, below the old primitive streak, is the proctodaeum, an ectodermal invagination whose connection with the posterior end of the archenteron is established as the cloaca even before the appearance of the tail bud.

Internally the bulbous enlargement of the neural tube becomes divided by shallow grooves, first into the three primary cavities modaeal invagination. Lateral expansions of the pharynx later meet the grooves evident on the gill plate and become the visceral clefts. Large, yolk-filled cells still form the wall of the mid- and the hind-gut; from the posterior end of the fore-gut a finger-like di-

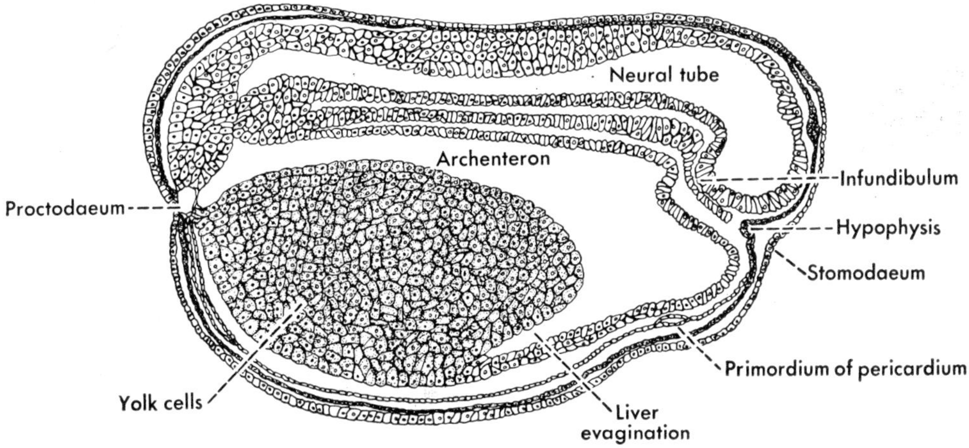

FIGURE 25.14 Saggital section through a frog embryo approximately 3 mm. in length. (After McEwan.)

of the brain, prosencephalon, mesencephalon and rhombencephalon and later into the five characteristic of the adult brain. The prosencephalon, which expands more rapidly than other parts of the embryo, is bent ventrally over the anterior end of the notochord; the rudiments of the epiphysis and of the infundibulum appear as outgrowths of its dorsal and ventral walls respectively.

Cranial nerves become differentiated, some earlier than others, from neural crest cells. The dorsal roots of the spinal nerves and their ganglia likewise become organized and differentiated from neural crest material which, like the dorsal mesoderm, has broken up into segmental blocks, on either side of the cylindrical cord. Later, ventral roots grow out from the cord into the developing muscles.

The enteron becomes marked off into regions of fore-gut, mid-gut and hind-gut. The fore-gut, or pharynx, is an expanded region ventral to the prosencephalon; its thin wall is almost in contact with the prosencephalon, and does make contact with the sto- verticulum extends posteriorly into them; this is the anlage of the liver. The hind-gut is continuous with the cloaca, which opens to the outside at the anus.

The compact blocks of mesoderm that constitute the somites become detached from the sheets that surround the gut, definitely distinguishing the dorsal from the lateral mesoderm (Fig. 25.15b). Cells migrate into the head region from the somites as mesenchyme, forming a loose cellular mass with much intercellular substance. Just prior to the separation of the dorsal from the lateral mesoderm in the trunk, cells in the dorsal region of the somatic layer of the lateral mesoderm divide rapidly and move away from the region of their origin as nephrotomes, from which is formed the mass of tissue along the sides of the embryo in which the pronephric, and later the mesonephric, tubules develop. A cavity appears in each mesodermal somite, separating its cells into a thin outer layer, the dermatome (Greek, derma = skin + tome = section), and a much thicker inner

[ 580 ] THE OPERATION OF BIOLOGICAL SYSTEMS

layer, the myotome (Greek, mus = muscle + tome). The dermatome gives rise to the connective tissue and the under layers of the integument; the myotome to the musculature of the body. Both layers grow down around the sheets of lateral mesoderm, inserting themselves between its somatic layer and the ectoderm. The somatic layer is thus pushed inward, and differentiates as the slender cells of the coelomic epithelium.

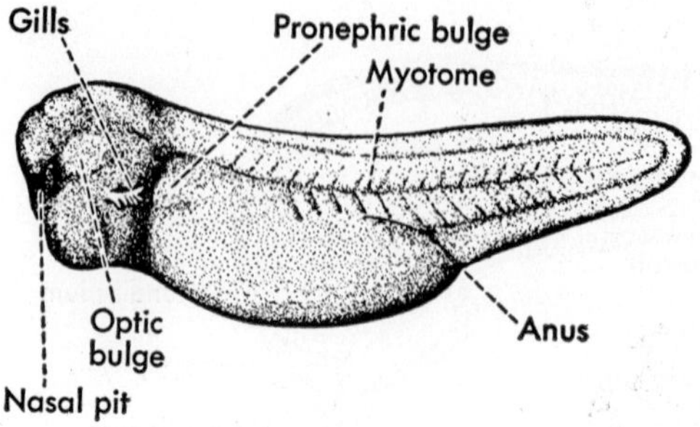

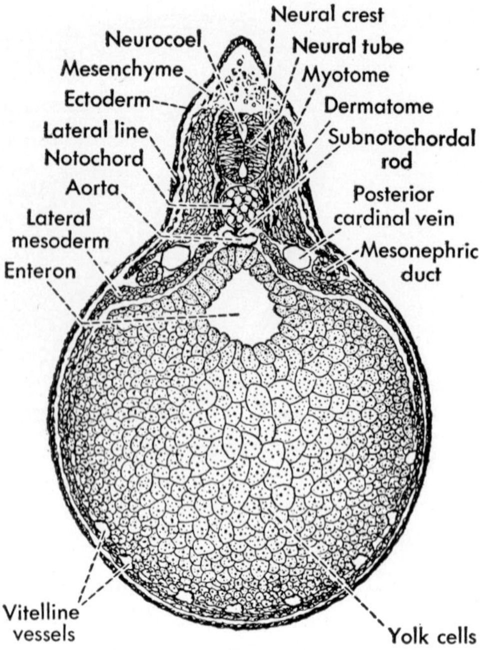

Other cells migrating from the myotomes, and so initially segmental in their distribution, come to surround the notochord and the neural tube as a mesenchymal sheath, the sclerotome, from which, after hatching, cartilage is differentiated, later replaced by bone, as the axial skeleton of the larva and the adult.

The blood and blood vessels also are differentiated from mesenchyme. At the time when the neural folds are closing, the splanchnic mesoderm and the endoderm just below the pharynx separate, leaving a space which becomes invaded with mesenchyme derived from the splanchnic mesoderm. These mesenchyme cells become organized as a tube, surrounded by splanchnic mesoderm, from which the heart develops, the mesenchyme cells becoming its lining and the splanchnic mesoderm its muscular wall. These muscles begin to contract rhythmically soon after their differentiation and before any nerves have reached them. The tube continues anteriorly into the head mesenchyme, where the differentiation of blood and blood vessels continues, and posteriorly, separating into two vessels around the liver. Blood islands, patches of cells which differentiate as endothelium lining the blood vessels and as blood, develop throughout the splanchnic mesoderm. Originally discrete clumps of tissue, the numerous blood islands ultimately meet and join together, forming a continuous network of fine vessels on both sides of the body, some of which become defined as the main blood channels of the larva.

The destinies of the areas of presumptive tissues of the blastula, shown in Figure 25.9, as they are fulfilled in the course of normal development, may then be tabulated as follows:

FIGURE 25.15 The larva of a frog at the time of hatching. (From Huettner, *Fundamentals of Comparative Embryology of the Vertebrates.* Copyright 1949 by The Macmillan Company.)

a. Exterior of the larva.
b. Transverse section through the midregion. The sclerotome is not labeled.

## TABLE XVII

| | | |
|---|---|---|
| Presumptive Epidermis | becomes | Outer layers of integument<br>Lens of eye<br>Cornea of eye |
| Presumptive Neural Plate | becomes | Brain and cord<br>Nerves<br>Organs of special sense |
| Presumptive Notochord | becomes | Notochord |
| Presumptive Somite Mesoderm | becomes | Somites<br>  Head Mesenchyme<br>  Dermatome<br>    connective tissue and inner layers of integument<br>  Myotome<br>    body musculature mesenchyme<br>  Sclerotome<br>    cartilage and bone |
| Presumptive Lateral Mesoderm | becomes | Nephrotome<br>  pro- and mesonephroi<br>Somatic mesoderm<br>  coelomic epithelium<br>Splanchnic mesoderm<br>  blood islands<br>    blood vessels and blood<br>  mesenchyme<br>    blood vessels and blood |
| Endoderm | becomes | Mucosa of digestive tract<br>Digestive glands |

At about this stage of its development, while still rotating within the jelly, the embryo begins to bend from side to side at intervals, giving evidence that anatomical and functional connection has been established between the ventral nerve roots and the appropriate muscles. As the embryo grows, these movements become more vigorous, and the frog embryo, when about 6 mm. in length, is able to make its way out of the jelly capsule, which has become softer than it was around the egg or gastrula. After a few spasmodic swimming movements, the embryo attaches itself by means of its suckers; during its period of attachment, changes go on which convert it to a free-living larva, capable of locomotion and of feeding, and with all the organs for an independent existence. Anatomically, these changes include the connection of the fore-gut with the stomodaeum and the formation of a mouth with rasping teeth for the maceration of the algae upon which the larvae feed, the connection of the visceral clefts with the pharyngeal pouches and the establishment of the gills as the main respiratory surface, and of the gill circulation in connection with them, the completion of the development of the eyes and other sense organs and of the mesonephros as a functional excretory organ.

Metamorphosis from larva to adult includes both structural changes and those in habits of life. The herbivorous frog larva becomes a carnivorous adult, with a respiratory mechanism that enables it to live on land. In addition to the development of lungs and a shift in blood flow from the gills to them and the skin, metamorphosis involves the loss of the larval tail and the growth of fore and hind limbs, with their bones, muscles and blood vessels. The period of metamorphosis is a critical one in the history of the individual, and one in which there is a high rate of mortality in amphibian populations.

*Amniotes:* In the Amniotes embryogenesis involves the definition of embryonic and extra-embryonic areas and concurrent changes in both of them. In the developing chick, the limitation of the embryonic area in the area pellucida is first indicated by the appearance of a fold in front of the anterior margin of the neural plate that pushes in beneath it and its underlying tissues (Fig. 25.11b). As this fold deepens, a similar one arises posteriorly, and the embryo thus acquires a ventral wall, except in the region of the mid-gut, where neither embryo nor archenteron has a floor, but are open directly to the yolk. The tissues peripheral to these folds, continuous with those in the embryo, extend out over the yolk and continue their growth down and around it. These extra-embryonic tissues include a superficial sheet of ectoderm, and an inner one of endoderm between which is mesoderm which, as growth within the embryo progresses, becomes organized as somatic and splanchnic layers, enclosing the extra-embryonic coelome. It is these tissues that form the fetal membranes, whose development takes place while changes are going on within the embryo of a general nature like those outlined for the amphibian.

blood vessels, arise in the mesoderm of the yolk sac and join the intra-embryonic vessel through the yolk stalk, as the two vitelline veins, whose branches spread out over the yolk and which internally are continuous with those arising from the posterior end of

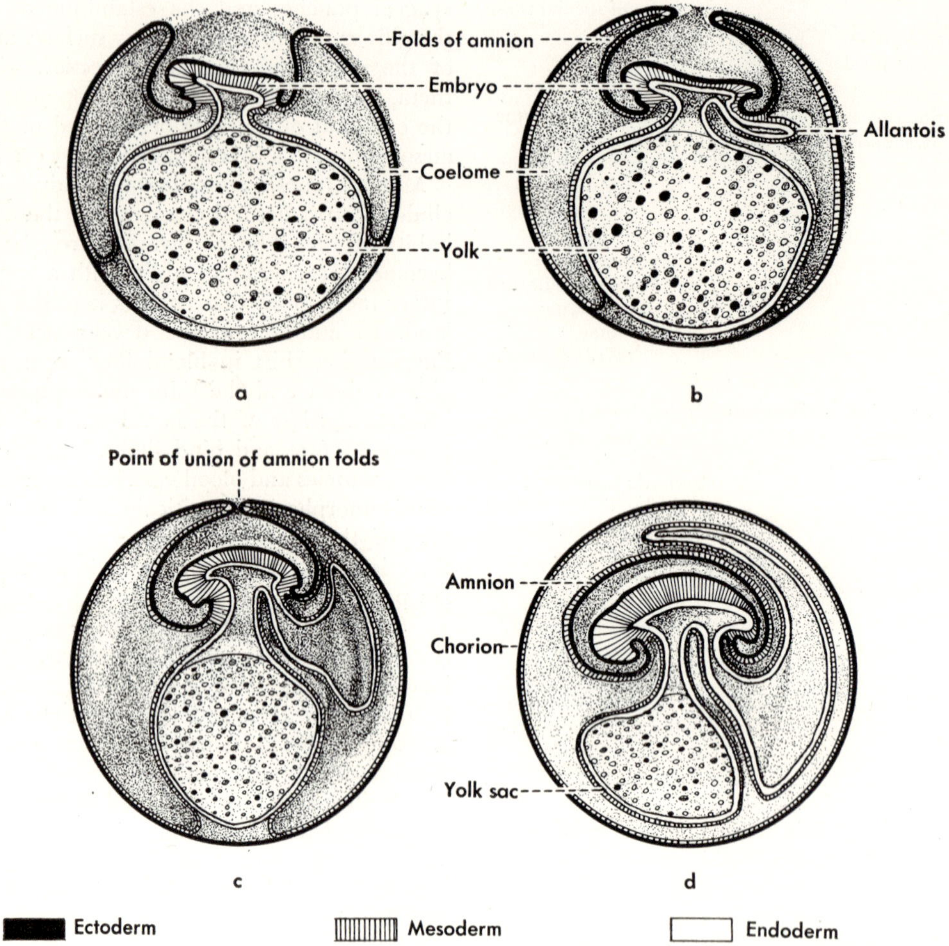

FIGURE 25.16 Diagrams showing the origin of the embryonic membranes in the chick. (After Arey.)

*The origins and functions of the fetal membranes and auxiliary organs in the chick. Yolk Sac:* The splanchnic mesoderm and the endoderm together form the yolk sac that grows around the yolk, finally completely enclosing it. The endoderm thus comes to form a continuous lining of the enteron, the yolk sac and short yolk stalk connecting the two. Blood islands, and later the tubular heart. The yolk is progressively digested by the endoderm cells, and the end products of its digestion carried into the embryo through these veins, and used in its metabolism. As the yolk is consumed, the yolk sac becomes smaller and smaller, and finally, just before hatching when the floor of the mid-gut closes over, what remnant remains is drawn into the enteron.

*Amnion:* The amnion is formed from the ectoderm and somatic mesoderm that constitute the outer wall of the extra-embryonic coelome (Fig. 25.16). Two crescentic ridges, or folds, arise in this sheet of tissue, one at the anterior end of the embryo and one at the posterior, which, increasing in depth, curve over it, and enclose it as two hoods, pulled up at opposite ends, might do. The margins of these hoods finally meet over the dorsal surface of the embryo as the amnion, a membrane, whose outer surface is somatic mesoderm and whose inner surface is ectoderm, separated from the body of the embryo by a space, the amniotic cavity. This space becomes filled with a fluid that filters in from the surrounding tissues, and the whole organ, enveloping the embryo except in the immediate vicinity of the yolk stalk, serves to buoy it up, to prevent its dehydration, to cushion it against mechanical jars, and also, being soft and compressible, allows it room to grow and to move. Muscle cells differentiate in its mesodermal layer, which by contraction rock the embryo in its fluid and thus serve a purpose similar to the ciliary movements of the amphibian embryo in preventing any adhesions that might mechanically retard the development of the growing body.

*Chorion:* The rest of the sheet of ectoderm and somatic mesoderm forms the chorion, a membrane that lies just beneath the egg-shell, and encloses all extra-embryonic as well as embryonic structures. As the folds of the amnion grow up over the embryo, their margins remain continuous with the rest of the outer wall of the extra-embryonic coelome, but when they meet they become detached, bringing the ectoderm and the mesoderm of this wall together. These then fuse, forming a continuous membrane over the amnion, in which somatic mesoderm forms the internal layer, ectoderm the external. These two layers have also continued their growth downward around the yolk, the somatic mesoderm of the developing chorion being continuous with the splanchnic mesoderm of the yolk sac at the limits of the extra-embryonic coelome. When both these membranes have progressed all around the yolk and met at the vegetal pole, the homologous tissues unite and the yolk sac becomes a complete and separate membrane around the yolk and the chorion a complete and separate one around all the others.

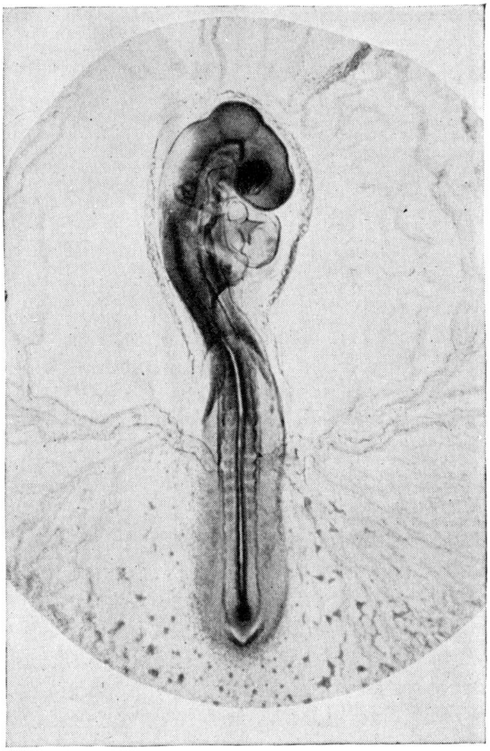

FIGURE 25.17 The embryo of a chick after 48 hours of incubation. (Photograph by courtesy of the General Biological Supply House, Inc., Chicago.)

*Allantois:* The allantois originates as an outgrowth of the hind-gut, and so consists of endoderm and its investing splanchnic mesoderm. Its growth is rapid, and it pushes out into the extra-embryonic coelome, expanding there into a large sac connected to the hind-gut by a slender stalk. In its growth, its outer wall becomes pressed against the chorion and so forms a common chorio-allantoic membrane in contact with the shell. This serves as the main respiratory surface for the embryo, the gaseous interchange being effected through the porous shell, the chorion, and the blood vessels that develop in its mesoderm, continuous with those of the embryo proper. (This region provides an aseptic and neutral environment and is frequently used in experiments for the culture of viruses and tissues of other warm-blooded animals, which are inserted into the allantoic cavity through a hole cut in the shell and its underlying membranes, and later sealed over, often with a piece of glass, so that the implanted material can be kept under observation.) The allantois also functions in the absorption of the albumen, and its cavity as a reservoir for urea, the waste product of protein metabolism first formed in the embryo, and later for uric acid. Like the yolk sac, the allantois becomes smaller as development of the embryo progresses and at hatching is drawn up into the enteron, having become detached from the chorion, which like the amnion, the embryo breaks through at the time of hatching, and leaves behind with the discarded shell.

The umbilical cord is derived from the yolk stalk, the stalk of the allantois and the region of the amnion adjacent to them. As the folds of the amnion come closer to each other on the ventral surface of the embryo, they surround the yolk stalk, where the body of the embryo is open to the yolk, and the allantoic stalk, where it is open to the cavity of the allantois, forming a short, cylindrical structure through which pass the blood vessels carrying blood to and from the embryo proper and the extra-embryonic areas (Fig. 25.17).

*The placenta of mammals:* In addition to these auxiliary embryonic structures, which are developed in varying degrees in the different orders, the embryos of all mammals, with the exception of the egg-laying montotremes, acquire also a placenta. The placenta is the embryonic structure peculiar to mammals that has enabled them to combine the advantages of an egg with little yolk with a protected embryonic life long enough for the development of all the major adult structures. In its construction both maternal and fetal tissues are associated with varying degrees of intimacy, and in its highest development, as it is found in rodents such as rats and guinea pigs and in primates, it combines the nutritive functions of the avian yolk sac, and the respiratory and excretory ones of the chorion and allantois, and possesses also others peculiar to itself.

Although there is no yolk mass present, a yolk sac, in many species with a well-developed vitelline circulation, appears in the course of embryology of all placental mammals, further evidence of their common ancestry with birds. But the degree of development of the amnion in all species equals that of the birds; in some, it originates in a similar way, by folding of the extra-embryonic tissues, but in others, including man, it arises directly from the inner cell mass by a rearrangement of the cells remaining after the migration of the endoderm. The allantois arises as a growth of the hind-gut, when that is established; in some mammals, like the carnivores and the ungulates, its development is similar to that in the chick, and it becomes applied in a similar fashion to the chorion, but in others, including the primates, it remains vestigial during embryonic life, although at all times connection is maintained between the embryo and its chorion by a bridge of somatic mesoderm, the body stalk, ultimately included in the umbilical cord connecting the embryo with the placenta.

The final stages of gastrulation, and the initial ones of embryogenesis and development of the fetal membranes, take place when the embryo is free in the uterus of its mother and while it is sinking into the endometrium, which under the influence of the hormone progesterone, has become more glandular and more vascular. As the tissues of the germ disc become organized as those of the embryo, in much the same fashion that they do in the chick, extra-embryonic somatic mesoderm becomes applied to the inner surface of the trophoblast, forming the chorion (Fig. 25.18). During the period of implantation, the chorion sends out finger-like processes, the villi, which fit into corresponding depressions in the vascular wall of the uterus. The chorion and its villi and that part of the uterine wall with which it is most intimately associated together become the placenta. The number and distribution of villi in the fully developed placenta vary in different species, as does the relation of the blood vessels that develop in them, as parts of the embryonic circulatory system, to the vessels of the uterus, parts of the maternal circulatory system. In man, the walls of the maternal blood vessels in the endometrium between the villi are destroyed, and the villi, branched vascular gen and nutritive substances, ingested and digested by the mother, pass into the embryonic blood stream, while from it carbon dioxide and the embryo's other metabolic wastes pass into the maternal circulation. There is apparently free diffusion, along the

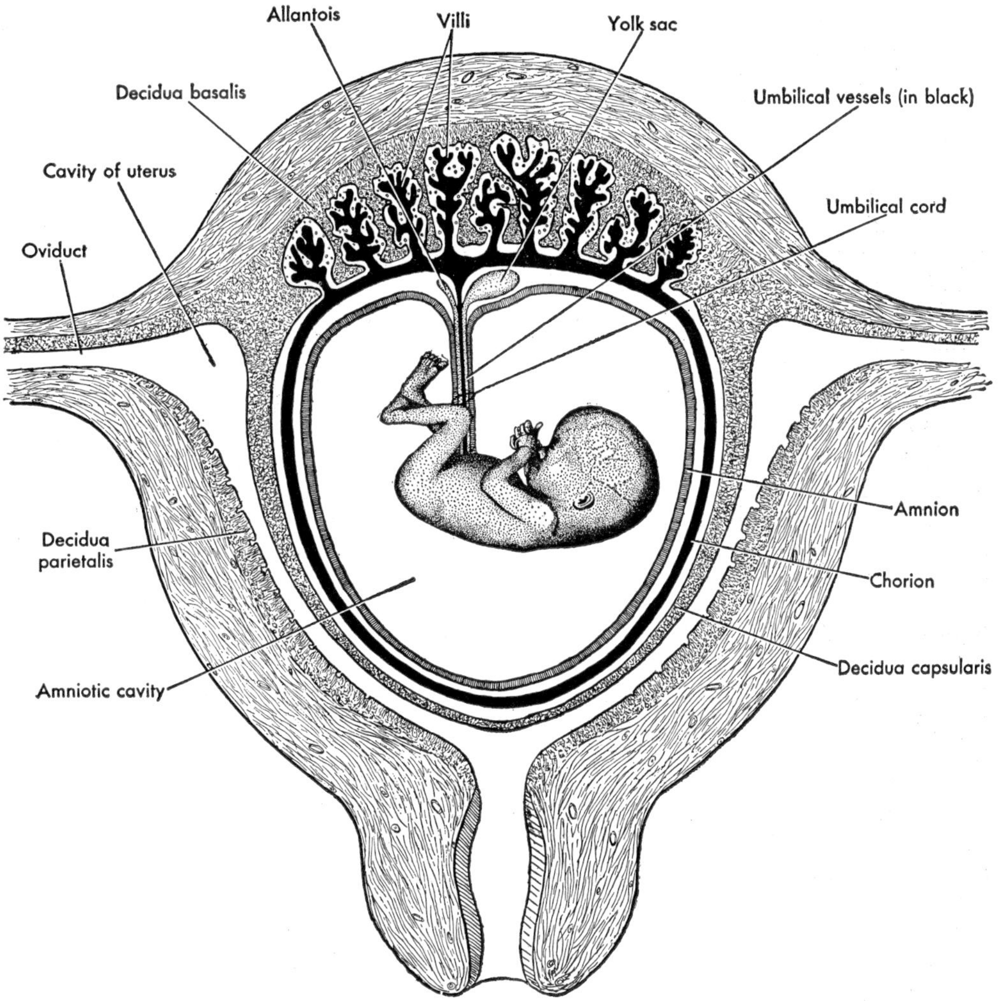

FIGURE 25.18 Sectional diagram of a human uterus, showing the placenta, embryo and fetal membranes. (From Huettner, *Fundamentals of Comparative Embryology of the Vertebrates.* Copyright 1949 by The Macmillan Company.)

tufts localized, when the placenta has reached full development, on one surface of the chorion, extend into these blood spaces. Thus the only barrier to free diffusion between the maternal and embryonic blood streams is the chorion and the endothelium of its blood vessels. Across this barrier, oxy- concentration gradient, of molecules of small dimensions between the maternal and embryonic blood. Some of the larger molecules, such as fats, and the products of protein digestion above the level of amino acids do not cross from the maternal circulation to the embryonic, nor is there an exchange of plasma protein between them, yet viral particles, and antibodies, such as diphtheria antitoxin and Rh agglutinins, are known to pass across it. There is also evidence that the cells of the placenta carry on the degradation of compounds, by means of enzymes and enzyme systems within them, and that they concentrate and synthesize materials as well. The concentration of amino acids in embryonic blood, for example, is higher than it is in the maternal, indicating an active participation of the placental tissues in their absorption, and the expenditure of energy by them in doing this work of concentration; also, glucose is made into glycogen and stored there. The placenta also functions as an endocrine gland, developing hormones that in their action parallel certain of those of the anterior pituitary and the ovary. One of these, whose formation begins in the trophoblast of the embryo even before its incorporation into the placenta, is a gonadotropin which, like the luteinizing hormone of the pituitary, stimulates the development of the corpus luteum in the ovary. The placenta also produces an estrogen and progesterone. It thus virtually takes over the functions of the anterior pituitary and the ovary in maintaining conditions in the body of the mother such as to allow an extended period of gestation, during which the embryo is retained in the uterus and the events of the ordinary reproductive cycle arrested until its birth and the restoration of the uterine tissues. These hormones diffuse into the blood of the mother and can be recovered from her urine; the hormone of the embryonic trophoblast is present in the urine of the human mother very early in her pregnancy, and if injected into the body of a rabbit, a rat, or a guinea pig has a gonadotropic effect there that can readily be detected. The human pregnancy tests in current use are based upon these conditions of hormone production by the auxiliary tissues of the human embryo, transference of the hormone to the body fluids of the mother, its recovery from them and its stimulating effects upon the reproductive tissues of another mammal of different species.

The umbilical cord develops into a cylindrical structure connecting the embryo with the placenta. It is considerably longer in mammals than in birds, in humans reaching as great a length as the full-grown fetus. It includes the body stalk, and the remnants of the yolk sac and allantois, and through it run the continuations of the embryonic arteries and veins that carry blood between the embryo and the placenta.

At birth, when the fetus is expelled from the uterus by contractions of its muscular walls, whose action has been inhibited during the period of embryonic growth through the influence of progesterone, the flow of blood in these vessels lessens, and the cord is severed. The placenta and other fetal membranes are also expelled, after which there follows a period of reconstruction of the uterine wall and a return to the regular series of events in the ordinary reproductive cycle.

ORGANOGENESIS: The period of embryonic life in which the organs acquire their definitive forms and functions, and their functional relationships to each other, is known as organogenesis. Knowledge of organogenesis is of such importance to the understanding of adult anatomy that a consideration of the development of the principal organ systems of vertebrates has been included with the descriptions of their anatomy.

## Experimental embryology

The developmental histories of organisms raise many fundamental biological problems, such as those concerning the organization of the egg; the factors that initiate its development and, equally, those that prevent it; the contribution of the sperm in the initiation of development; and the extent to which these processes, as well as those of development itself, are controlled or influenced by factors external or internal to the system. It is such questions as these that the experimental embryologist is seeking to answer, using various procedures and techniques through which he can alter the natural conditions of development and so determine the factors involved in them. He may alter these conditions by physical agents, such as temperature, pressure, centrifugal force, electrical currents, or radiations; by chemical agents, adding to the environment of the egg or embryo chemical compounds of various kinds; or by physicochemical agents, such as alterations in pH or osmotic relations. He may also subject the egg or the embryo to various operative procedures, removing parts, adding parts or transplanting parts from one region to another, or from one embryo to another. Obviously, for such experiments the eggs and embryos of oviparous species offer more favorable material than those of viviparous, and for this reason echinoderms, certain marine worms, fish, and amphibia have been most widely experimented upon.

### Organization in the egg

One of the oldest of embryological questions, raised by those who first saw the progress of development of the individual from egg to functioning organism, is that of the extent to which the parts of that organism are predestined, or preformed, in the single cell from which it grows. There were those who, as late as the eighteenth century, believed that they were all preformed in the egg, and that embryology was but a gradual unfolding and enlargement of them. Carried to its logical conclusion, this doctrine of preformationism implied that not only the parts of the individual of any one generation, but also those of all succeeding generations, must be contained within the egg; the manifest absurdity of this conception, as well as observation of the progressive development of the organs in the embryo, finally led to its rejection.

There is, however, evidence that the cytoplasm of the unfertilized egg is organized in such a way that localized regions of it possess particular capacities for differentiation along certain lines, and that the removal or destruction of these regions results in more or less far-reaching disturbances of development. It is evident, for example, that in the ordinary development of the sea urchin, Strongylocentrotus, the cytoplasm marked by the pigment band has the capacity for differentiation as endoderm, while that at the vegetal pole has the capacity for differentiation as mesoderm. If the unfertilized egg is cut into two parts, so that one portion contains most of the material of the animal hemisphere and the other that of the vegetal, the two fragments round up and each is capable of fertilization. The developmental capacities of the two parts are, however, quite different, though neither ever becomes a pluteus. Both cleave in the ordinary fashion, but development of the animal half never progresses beyond the blastula stage; the vegetal half undergoes gastrulation, but beyond that its development is blocked. If, on the other hand, the egg is cut from animal to vegetal pole into two, or even four, parts, each part, on fertilization, develops into a small but complete pluteus. Such experiments show that in this egg the material necessary for gastrulation and the formation of endoderm and mesoderm is localized below the equator, and that for the formation of the ectoderm above it, but that these localizations are not fixed and rigid, but capable of rearrangement if their ordinary relations are disturbed. That this material is not directly related to any of the visible and easily shifted components of the egg has been proved by centrifugation experiments. When the egg is centrifuged, the pigment granules are thrown to the centrifugal pole, and the lipids and other lighter inclusions to the centripetal. The centrifuged egg, when fertilized, develops into a pluteus normal in every way except for the displacement of the pigment, which instead of being localized in the endoderm, is variously scattered through all the cells of the body. The distinctions between presumptive ectoderm, endoderm and mesoderm material thus are shown to be expressions of the nature and organization of submicroscopic components of the egg cytoplasm, possibly those localized in its cortex.

Experiments with chemical agents have shown that these materials are not fixed and rigid in their nature, any more than in their position, for if potassium sulfocyanide is added to the sea water in which intact, fertilized eggs are developing, they behave as do the isolated animal halves, cleaving and forming blastulae but never progressing beyond this stage, and if lithium chloride is added to the water in which isolated animal halves are allowed to develop, they gastrulate and form endoderm as they would otherwise have failed to do.

Amphibian eggs have also provided evidence that the egg is an organized system of locally differentiated cytoplasm. Staining experiments have shown that the dorsal lip of the blastopore forms always in some part of the gray crescent, and that it is gray crescent material that first enters the blastocoele. The first cleavage plane of the dividing egg may or may not pass through the gray crescent; if it does, so that the first two blastomeres contain approximately half of it, each will, if experimentally separated from the other, develop in the ordinary way into a complete larva, but if the cleavage furrow does not pass through the gray crescent, only the blastomere containing it becomes a larva, and the other, though continuing to divide, remains an undifferentiated mass of cells.

Experiments of this kind show that the egg is a protoplasmic system in which there is some differentiation of potential organ-forming substances and a localization of these substances along its principal axis, externally indicated by its polar differentiation. But it is a labile, not a rigid, system and one capable, within limits, of adjusting to unusual conditions and of compensating for displacement or loss of its parts. In some animals, such as annelids and mollusks, the period when such readjustment is possible is much shorter than in echinoderms and amphibia, and the organ-forming materials segregated from each other in early cleavage. In these eggs removal or destruction of certain blastomeres results in irreparable loss.

### Initiation of development

That the sperm is not essential to the initiation of development is shown by the parthenogenetic development of eggs that occurs naturally in some species and that can be induced in others through mechanical or chemical means. Even in those species in which fertilization normally precedes development, penetration of the sperm alone, without the union of egg and sperm nuclei that naturally follows, may start the egg on its course of development into an embryo. For eggs whose nuclei have been inactivated by irradiation can be fertilized and will develop in a normal fashion, and sperm whose nuclei have been similarly inactivated can penetrate the egg and stimulate its division and development. In either case the resulting individuals are normal in every respect, except in having an exclusively maternal or paternal genotype.

According to current theory, the egg is a system in which all mechanisms for development are in a static condition; its level of metabolism is low and it is incapable of change without stimulation of some sort, usually, but not necessarily, provided by the entrance of the sperm. Upon such stimulation the static condition of the egg is changed to a dynamic one, through the unmasking or unblocking of enzymes or enzyme systems in some way. The activation of these enzymes makes possible the series of chemical reactions that underlie cleavage and embryonic development.

The sperm has thus been shown to have at least a dual role in embryology, each part of which can be independent of the other. The first of these roles is activation, or stimulation to development, and the second is the contribution of a set of chromosomes which confers upon the zygote capacities for certain modifications of the pattern of its development and for the transmission, through its germ cells, of those capacities to its progeny.

*Factors in development:* External factors, such as the availability of oxygen and of nutrients, opportunity for the removal of metabolic wastes and freedom from mechanical constraints for the growing parts all influence the course of embryological development and the realization of the potentialities of the activated egg. But the concern of the biologist is even more with factors within the system itself and conditions and relationships existing there that may influence the differentiation of tissues and the organization of parts.

These problems have been attacked by experimental embryologists principally by

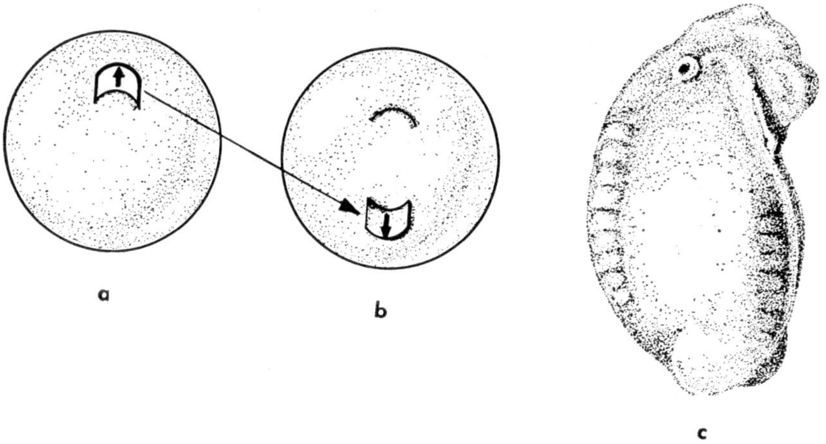

FIGURE 25.19  Induction of a secondary embryo by an extra primary organizer. (After Arey.)

   a. The early gastrula of a newt showing the area removed for transplantation.
   b. Transplantation of the extirpated dorsal lip to the presumptive ventral surface of another gastrula.
   c. Development of the embryo with two organizers; the primary embryo is on the left with the somites and neural tube of the secondary embryo evident along its ventral surface.

operative techniques, in experiments that may be classified as:

1. Defect experiments, or the removal of parts, to determine the extent to which the egg or embryo at various stages of its development can compensate for such loss.
2. Isolation experiments, or the culture of removed parts in suitable nutrient media, to test their capacities for differentiation outside of their natural environments.
3. Transplantation experiments, or the transference of parts from one region of the embryo to another, or from one embryo to another, to test their capacities for differentiation in a different, or foreign, position in the body. In the amphibia, tissues taken from one species, as donor, will grow when implanted in those of another, the host; if the two species used differ, for example in their pigmentation, it is possible to distinguish structures derived directly from donor or host materials, or from a combination of both.

The results of experiments of this kind have led to the modern concept of induction in development, or the directing influence of one part upon the development of another. The part exerting the influence is called the inductor, or organizer; its influence is only upon cells with which it is in contact and only during the period in which they are receptive to it, or competent.

That the dorsal lip of the blastopore is the primary organizer has been shown by experiments on amphibia and the chick. If, for example, the group of cells identified by staining experiments as those of the dorsal lip of the blastopore are removed from an amphibian blastula, gastrulation does not take place, nor is there any differentiation of neural plate from general ectoderm. Moreover, if the dorsal lip is removed from an early gastrula and grafted beneath the presumptive ectoderm of another, it develops there as a notochord and mesoderm, and the overlying ectoderm of the host is transformed into a neural plate. An archenteron and other mesodermal structures may develop from the host's tissues and the gastrula with the implanted dorsal lip becomes a neurula with two neural tubes and two notochords and their associated tissues (Fig. 25.19). But by the end of gastrulation the chorda-mesoderm has lost some of its capacity as a master organizer for all parts of the

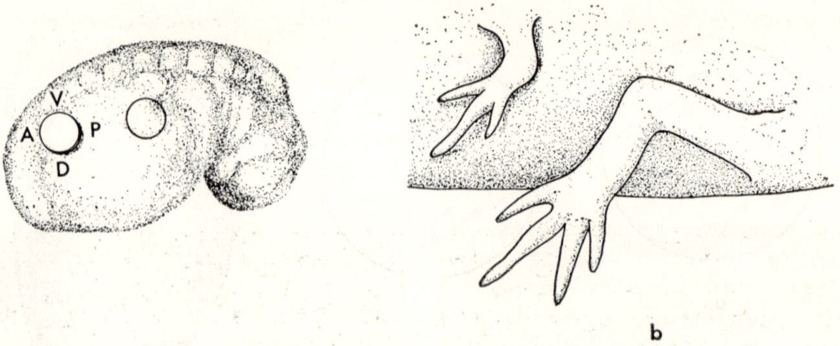

FIGURE 25.20 Diagram showing the results of transplantation of a limb bud rotated through 180°. (After Detwiler.)

a. The operated embryo, showing its anterior limb anlage (stippled) in its normal position, and anterior limb mesoderm (unstippled) transplanted to it after rotation through 180°. A anterior; P posterior; V ventral; D dorsal.

b. Part of the larva 42 days after the operation. A supernumerary, reversed and smaller limb has developed from the implanted tissue.

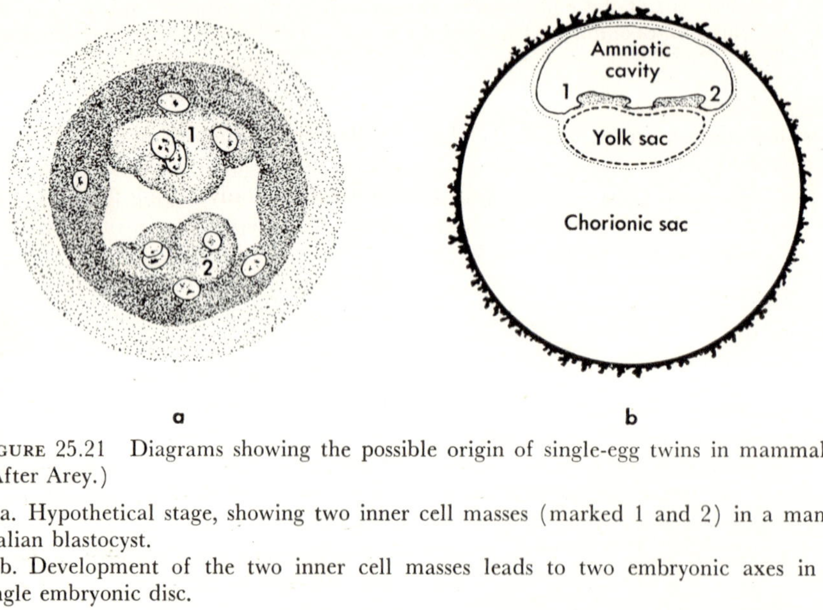

FIGURE 25.21 Diagrams showing the possible origin of single-egg twins in mammals. (After Arey.)

a. Hypothetical stage, showing two inner cell masses (marked 1 and 2) in a mammalian blastocyst.

b. Development of the two inner cell masses leads to two embryonic axes in a single embryonic disc.

embryo, for if a piece from the anterior end of the roof of the archenteron is grafted beneath the presumptive epidermis of an early gastrula, only a head develops there, and only a tail when a piece from the posterior part is similarly grafted.

Other parts of the embryo, as they appear in the course of development, likewise become organizers. Optic vesicles, for example, removed from the forebrain and implanted beneath the ectoderm in another part of the body of the same or a different embryo, continue to grow there and induce the transformation of the ectoderm with which they are in contact into lens tissue, which, when it has sunk below the surface as the lens vesicle, in turn induces the transformation of the cells above it into cornea, forming an eye in a region where there naturally would not have been one. Such transformations do not take place in presumptive lens ectoderm when the optic vesicle beneath it is removed, but they do, when it is allowed to remain in place, in

development of particular parts are limited to certain areas or fields within it, and the future of each such field fixed or determined by its own organizers and not influenced by those outside it. For example, a disc of ectoderm and mesoderm taken from

FIGURE 25.22 Reproduction in the armadillo (Dasypus).

a. Four male fetuses, showing 4 umbilical cords and a single chorion. (Collected in Texas. Photograph by E. R. Kalmbach, by courtesy of the U.S. Fish and Wildlife Service.)

b. Adult armadillo. (Photograph by W. P. Taylor, by courtesy of the U.S. Fish and Wildlife Service.)

ectoderm transplanted from any region of the body to the position of the presumptive lens.

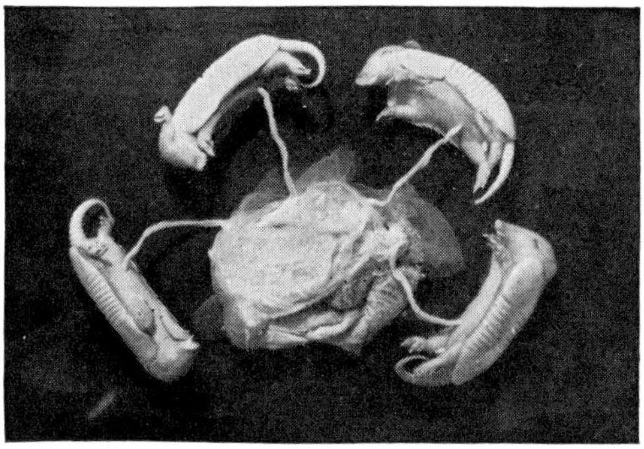

Transplantation and defect experiments of this kind with other tissues and organs of early embryos have shown that other parts of the body, as organizers of the first, second or third class, dominate the differentiation of tissue with which they are in contact and so direct their potentialities of development, which in the early embryo may be generalized, along specific paths appropriate to their location in the body and to the construction of the organ of which they are destined to be a part. And as development progresses, the potentialities of the embryonic parts, under the influence of these organizers, become more and more limited and their possible paths of differentiation more restricted. While, for example, the amphibian at the gastrula stage is a labile system, whose tissues can be induced to differentiate in different ways under the influence of different organizers, at the neurula stage it is one in which the possibilities of

the side of a salamander neurula, from the region where the fore limb appears in the ordinary course of development, becomes a fore limb wherever it may be transplanted in the body of the same or another embryo; the differentiation of its muscles, and bones from the mesoderm and of its epidermis from the ectoderm is not influenced by the tissues with which it is brought into contact. Yet within itself, this self-differentiating field is to some extent labile, and able to adjust to unnatural conditions. For if a limb bud is removed from a slightly older embryo and rotated through 180° before transplantation into another, so that its ventral surface is uppermost and its anterior surface directed posteriorly, it will continue its development into a complete limb, directed anteriorly instead of posteriorly as it normally is, but with normal dorsal-ventral distinctions. At this stage, therefore, the limb bud cannot adjust to a change in its anterior-posterior orientations, but it can to its dorsal-ventral ones (Fig. 25.20).

Experimental studies such as these have

shown that development is an orderly progression of events directed by organizers, groups of cells or tissues that directly or indirectly dominate others in their vicinity. Various anomalies in development may arise if the organizing system is upset, such as failure in development of a part, or its duplication. Duplication may occur through the origin of two organization centers in the same region, or the subdivision of a single one, and may lead to the formation of two or more complete embryos, or of double parts within a single embryo. Identical twins in mammals, known through the presence of a single placenta to be derived from a single fertilized egg, are believed to originate in this way, either by subdivision of the inner cell mass into two blastoderms, or by the origin of two primary organization centers on a single blastoderm or by the division of the primary center into two (Fig. 25.21). In the Texas armadillo, two such centers regularly arise on the blastoderm, each of which then divides and acts as a primary organizer for a complete and separate embryo, so that four identical offspring are produced at each birth (Fig. 25.22). Incomplete separation of two organizing centers may result in attached embryos, such as the Siamese twins occasionally produced by man and others among the higher mammals.

Investigation of the nature of the organizing effect has shown that it is the result of the diffusion of material from the organizer to the cells whose destiny it directs. Induction takes place only when the organizer is in contact with these cells, and extracts from dead organizer tissue produce the same effects as the organizer itself. Moreover, some chemical compounds, such as nucleoproteins and sterols, injected into the blastocoele of an amphibian blastula, have been found to induce the formation of a neural plate, without, however, as the natural organizer does, that of other embryonic structures. Since all the cells of an embryo, and an adult, have nuclei with essentially the same chromosomal composition, the effect of the organizing substance must be primarily upon their cytoplasm, in some way altering its composition or the character of its reactions so that certain groups of cells become distinct, or differentiated from others, both morphologically and functionally.

### Chemical embryology

Conditions of other kinds arising in the embryo also influence its development. Among these may be mentioned such influences as those of the myotomes in determining the paths of growing nerve fibres, the relationships between blood flow and the more actively metabolizing tissues, and the development of enzymes and hormones within localized groups of cells that enable them to carry on particular functions. Investigation of the chemical functioning of the embryo, its biochemistry and its integration into a harmoniously operating individual is another aspect of experimental embryology, called chemical embryology, like that of the factors controlling the morphological development of its parts, under vigorous investigation today.

# SECTION FOUR

## THE EVOLUTION OF BIOLOGICAL SYSTEMS

# CHAPTER 26
# THE DOCTRINE OF ORGANIC EVOLUTION

## The meaning of organic evolution

To the biological scientist organic evolution (Latin, evolutio = unrolling) means the gradual unfolding or development of life forms and life processes as opposed to their special creation as fixed and permanent types and mechanisms. It implies unity in these forms and processes, and so relationships between all biological systems existing today, or at any other time, upon the earth, and it implies also their mutability, or capacity to change and transmit these changes to their descendants.

The Doctrine of Evolution, probably biology's greatest contribution to human thought and one of deep moral, religious, sociological as well as scientific significance, has itself evolved slowly with man's greater and greater understanding of the world that he inhabits and of the other living things that inhabit it with him. It has progressed as biology as a science has progressed. Its beginnings are to be found in man's first inquiries into the conditions of his surroundings, in his speculations on the origin of matter and the development of the cosmos as an orderly and organized system from disordered Chaos. Throughout its development it has been closely linked with his concepts of the origin of the earth and the solar system and of the forces through which they were formed and which control and direct them, and thus it has always been closely associated with his religious beliefs. As a biological principle, it has developed along with his increasing knowledge of the anatomy and distribution of animals and plants, for with increasing awareness of the similarities and differences between life forms, both existing and extinct, has come increasing understanding of the relationships and divergences between them (Fig. 26.1). It is upon this understanding that systems of classification have been built, so that taxonomy, with its grouping of species into the larger categories of genera, orders, classes, phyla and finally kingdoms, has contributed more than any one branch of biology to the evolution of the doctrine of evolution in the organic world.

## Historical development
### The classical period

Greek mythology represents the attempts of the earliest Greeks of whose thoughts we have record to explain that part of the universe with which they were acquainted, and the natural phenomena, both ordinary and extraordinary, that took place in their lives. Their gods personified the elements and forces of nature and, in control of the rising and the setting of the sun, the waxing and waning of the moon, the seasons and the harvest, as well as of life and death, might manifest their pleasure or displeasure, and sometimes their wantonness or caprice, by all kinds of natural events. According to one system, all things emerged from Chaos, the personification of infinite, empty space, who first produced Erebus and Nyx (Night), and they, in turn, produced Aether, the upper air, and Hemera (Day). According to another, Chronos, the personification of time, produced Aether and Chaos. Zeus, the god of all the elements, is also represented as the son of Chronos and the chief of all the Olympian gods, among whom was delegated responsibility for the conduct of various aspects of nature and all events in it (Fig. 26.2). Interest in the natural events, but a less imaginative and more realistic attitude toward them, was manifest throughout the period when Greek culture was dominant in the civilized world, and it was the Greeks, with their intellectual liberty and emphasis upon the rights of the individual, who were the founders of natural science both in fact and in method. They had no means of pre-

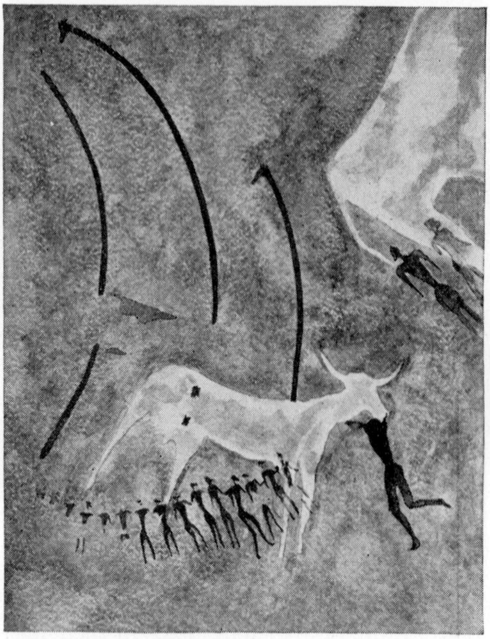

FIGURE 26.1 Cliff painting from the Libyan Desert, west of the Nile. (Probably before 5000 B.C.) (Photograph by courtesy of the Academy of Natural Sciences of Philadelphia.) It is in such paintings as these, found on the rocks of North Africa and in caves in the south of Europe, that man has left the first records of his observations of objects in the living world.

serving specimens but they made living collections and, though their own domestic animals were the starting point for their zoological observations, as their conquests and their trade increased they were made familiar with the domestic animals of the other peoples inhabiting the shores of the Mediterranean and with the wild animals of their own and neighboring countries. They had perhaps a greater background of botanical than of zoological knowledge, for the search for therapeutic plants that would alleviate or cure the ills of the human body led to the accumulation of a good deal of information about the effects of plants and to some extent about their habits and their types. It was Aristotle (384–322 B.C.) who collected and organized the current zoological facts, and since his own botanical writings are lost, it is to his pupil Theophrastus (?–287 B.C.) that we are indebted for a similar assembling of botanical knowledge. Both these men were far more than mere compilers of inherited information; both were independent investigators and both contributed original observations and penetrating generalizations to the body of facts presented in their writings. Of the voluminous writings attributed to Aristotle, three books contain the main biological contributions—the *History of Animals*, the *Parts of Animals* and the *Generation of Animals*. In these are described the natural history of animals native to Greece and its surrounding waters; the anatomy, presumably from first-hand dissections, of a number of mammals, birds, fish and mollusks and some few reptiles, amphibia, arthropods and echinoderms. That order reigns in nature is a dominant idea in the Aristotelian writings and throughout them one finds an attempt to define this order. In the body the upper part is superior to the lower, the front to the back, the right side to the left; in the entire animal world, the animals with blood (Enaima) are superior to those without blood (Anaima). Although he makes no formal outline of classification, references to animals throughout the books show that subdivisions of animal types falling within each of these two main categories had been made. Though apparently incidental to Aristotle's main interest in the bodily form of animals of different kinds, this is the first serious attempt, of which a record remains, at their classification, itself a preliminary to the development of comparative anatomy as one aspect of biology and to the doctrine of evolution.

Aristotle himself must have been familiar with plants, for there was a large botanical garden in connection with the Lyceum, the Academy at Athens where he and his students worked and talked, yet no botanical work of his has survived. Of the 227 treatises attributed to his pupil Theophrastus, on the other hand, there are two botanical works—the *History of Plants* and the *Causes of Plants*—in which the separation of plants into different groups is made. Plants are divided into the flowering and the flowerless, with a further subdivision of the flowering into those which bear "covered" and those which bear "naked" seeds, categories equivalent to the modern Angiosperma and Gymnosperma. Specific definitions are also given to certain parts of plants and so a technical terminology was begun. Plants such as the banyan, the tamarind and the thorny mimosa are described, indicating that Theophrastus was familiar with plants not native to Greece.

With the conquest of Greece by Alexander, the cosmopolitan city of Alexandria became the center of Mediterranean culture. It was the leading market for drugs imported from the East, so that new and strange plants were constantly added to the numbers of those already known and their medicinal properties, if not their other characteristics, determined. In the medical school anatomical studies progressed by dissection of animals and even of humans, and some experimentation was carried on. When, in 80 B.C., Alexandria was given over to Roman jurisdiction, though the medical school went on, the emphasis in scholarship changed from natural science to theology and the study of Christianity. Roman interest in science was largely in its practical aspects, for the Romans were concerned less with speculation about living things and their possible relationships than with the ways they could be put to use for domestic and agricultural purposes. Yet they recorded the new and strange beasts they met with—elephants, first seen in 286 B.C. by the Roman soldiers in Pyrrhus' army—the hippopotamus, first brought to Rome in 58 B.C., and zebras, later also brought there.

The Romans added little that was new to biology as a science, although they made some compilations of existing information, some of them discriminating and accurate,

FIGURE 26.2 Decoration on an Attic Krater (about the middle of the fifth century B.C.) represents the rising of the sun and the setting of the moon as natural events directed by the gods. On the right Helios, the sun, comes out of the sea in his chariot to begin his drive across the sky; on his appearance, the stars dive into the sea. On the left, Selene, the moon, rides away on her mule, while Eos, the dawn, pursues a youth, Kephalos. The figure in the center, over the handle of the vase, is probably to be identified as Endymion. (Photograph by courtesy of Dr. M. H. Swindler.)

others vague and full of misinformation, but significant none the less as repositories of contemporary knowledge and belief. The best known of these are the great botanical compendium of Dioscorides (first century A.D.), an Asiatic Greek who was a surgeon in Nero's army and hence familiar with the medicinal plants, and the *Natural History* of Pliny (23–79), in whose thirty-seven books is gathered all of the natural science known at that time, some of it extracts from earlier writings, some of it the superstitions of the country people and some of it travellers' tales and sailors' narratives.

## The Middle Ages

The death of Galen (see page 102) marks the end of the development of Greek natural science. After it, biology stagnated until the Middle Ages, when the Greek and Arabic scientific works were translated into Latin and again made available to scholars, who recognized in them not only a treasure house of information but also a system and method of scientific inquiry. During this period, some compilations and compendia were made, but their purpose was not primarily scientific and if any biological information is included, it is incidental. For example, the Amarakosa, the work of the oldest Indian lexicographer, Amarisimha, who lived about the middle of the sixth century, contains an index of animals with some attempt to classify them as domestic animals (the cow, the sheep, the goat and the donkey), animals of war (the elephant and the horse), animals of the chase (the dog), animals of luxury (the monkey and the parakeet) and wild animals (the pig, the yak, the cat, the lion, the tiger, the panther and the hyena).

*Travels and explorations:* In the thirteenth century, European travellers, at first missionaries or representatives of religious societies and later merchants interested in commerce with foreign lands, penetrated more and more frequently into central Asia, Africa and Abyssinia and brought back tales of the strange beasts and exotic plants that were found there. Many of their descriptions, probably inaccurate to start with, were undoubtedly embellished in successive repetitions so that fantastic and fabulous creatures were believed to exist and to have equally fabulous relations with each other. Actually some strange foreign animals and plants did find their way into Europe. In 550 two monks brought silkworm eggs from China and the Emperor Justinian kept their culture a secret, realizing the value to the country which controlled their products; Haroun-al-Raschid sent an elephant to Charlemagne and Frederick II imported a giraffe. Seeing and hearing of the existence at their own courts of animals as odd as these, it is perhaps not surprising that the Europeans believed also in the existence of the phoenix, the unicorn and dragons of all kinds. Dates, balsams and flax were imported from Egypt, sugar cane was brought and planted on the Mediterranean islands and cotton in southern Europe. The introduction of these foreign plants had scientific as well as economic importance, for it gave those interested in the living world an opportunity to learn at first hand about some of the plants of which they had hitherto only heard.

Although fossils must have been as abundant in the surface of the earth at all times of man's history as they are today, even throughout the Middle Ages no connection was made between those that were found and any existing species. They were regarded as "formed" or "figured" stones, freaks of nature like the patterns made by frost and ice. Perhaps the first to recognize their true nature was Leonardo da Vinci who, seeing the resemblances between those that he studied and the animal forms with which he was familiar, maintained that they, too, were once living creatures, and, moreover, that the land where they were found was once covered by the sea. Yet half a century later, Fallopio, expert anatomist though he was, believed them inorganic concretions and denied that they had ever had life.

*Influence of Christianity upon the development of natural science:* Political strife and religious domination of education retarded the development of science during these centuries. Much emphasis was laid upon the identification of the animals mentioned in the Bible with those known or believed to inhabit the world, and upon the superiority of man among all living things; man indeed was held to be the epitome of the universe, and everything in the natural world relative and subordinate to him. The great work of this period was the *Physiologus*, a low-grade natural history, probably a product of Alexandria in the third or fourth century but widely circulated in the Middle Ages. It had many variant forms and in the course of a number of changes became restricted to animals only; from it were derived the Bestiaries which represent the zoological encyclopedias of this age but which belong rather more to the history of folklore and literature than to that of biology.

***Scholasticism:*** With the thirteenth century came the first stirrings of awakened intellectual interest in Europe. This was the period when the universities, the great centers of learning, were founded; the old texts were revived, copies made and commentaries added to them. The transcriptions were often inaccurate and many of these early records are therefore legendary; much of this legend persisted through later centuries when fact and fable were confused in a heterogeneous mass of lore about living things, some of which still exists to-day in popular belief. There was still the reliance upon authority for the word of the masters, especially Galen, who was accepted uncritically. This reliance cramped free investigation and perpetuated the mistakes instead of correcting them or adding new facts, for the prestige of the men who made them influenced the judgment of many of their successors in the field of natural science.

The result of this scholastic movement was a vast system of organized knowledge bound up with a system of theology about which there could be no skepticism; inquiry into the natural world was dominated by the Christian idea of God and his relation to it, held so by the belief in special creation. The impulse to independent and original thinking seems to have come from Italy, where the revival of learning was tied up with the new commercial age, and the creative spirit manifested itself in art, architecture, education and to a certain extent in science. But it was not until the sixteenth and early seventeenth centuries that this revived intellectual curiosity began really to shake itself free from the traditions of the "knowledge books," the encyclopedias of information of all kinds that were the products of the age of scholasticism.

### Sixteenth century

***Travels and explorations:*** Not only were men's intellectual horizons widened but their geographical ones as well. Voyages of exploration were more frequent and took men further afield. The New World was opened up, its wonders described and some of them introduced into Europe. Columbus brought back some skins of American animals and Queen Isabella is said to have commissioned him to collect birds especially, but it was to the doctors and missionaries rather than to the explorers that the European world was indebted for descriptions and specimens of Indian, African and American species of plants and animals. These were collected more for their practical use than for their scientific interest, and plants because of their medicinal value are represented in far greater numbers than animals. The explorations were directed largely toward the discovery of a western passage to India and in the journals and records of the explorers and the men who followed them into these new regions the animals of the two hemispheres are often confused with each other, as are the American Indians with those of Asia. There was a lively popular interest in the New World and in the less well-known parts of the Old World. Both the English and the Dutch made a serious effort to investigate the extreme North and the Germans, looking for a passage to China and southeast Asia, explored Russia. With the discovery of printing in 1450, the writing not only of travellers returned to Europe but also of the natives of foreign lands could be shared by scholars and the educated public; the addition of illustrations, first by woodcuts, and later by copperplates, and often hand-colored, made the books more attractive to the general public and provided more accurate records for the scholars than had been achieved by the earlier written descriptions, often flowery and confusing fact with fancy.

However, much of the confusion between fact and fiction still remained. A natural history of Sweden, for instance, written in the sixteenth century by Olaus Magnus, a Swede living in Rome, describes among other recognizable animals a monster of the sea which could grasp ships in its arms and drag them to its depths, and a whale so large that mariners landed and encamped on it, thinking it an island. José d'Acosta (1539–1588), who went as a Jesuit missionary to Peru, wrote in his *Natural and Moral History of the Indians* of the discovery of huge bones that must have been those of giants; in this same book he raises the question of how the animals from the Ark could have got to America and how it could have come about that the American species are different from those of the Old World, a problem that was to vex natural historians who tried to reconcile the Biblical narrative with the facts of natural history, until, little less than 100 years ago, Charles Darwin offered an explanation in his theory of the origin of species by means of natural selection.

*The "Historia Animalium" of Conrad Gesner:* The great zoological treatise of this period was the *Historia Animalium* of a Swiss physician, Conrad Gesner (1516–1565), four volumes of which were published in 1551 and the fifth and a fragment of the sixth after his death. This was the standard work on zoology until the time of Linnaeus; in it are included Gesner's personal observations on animals as well as those made by his friends and widely scattered correspondents. Gesner emphasizes the need for verification of facts before their dissemination, yet he includes descriptions of mermaids, sea-serpents and other creatures of whose unreality he undoubtedly was aware; possibly this was a concession to public interest on the part of a keen and meticulous observer and a man of great learning. Each volume of the *Historia* deals with animals of different kinds—the first with mammals, the second with "oviparous quadrupeds," the third with birds, the fourth with fish and aquatic animals, the fifth with serpents and the unfinished sixth with insects—and each is divided into chapters, which present the names of animals in different ancient and modern languages, their habitats and descriptions, their customs and instincts, their general utility as well as their uses for food and for therapy, and their less-used and poetic names and variants of them, fables about them and their symbolism. The only attempt at a systematic classification is, because of "doubt and uncertainty about the relationship of animals," an alphabetical one in which he lists them according to their Latin names, recognizing that it was neither a natural nor a scientific grouping. The written descriptions are accompanied by excellent illustrations, which, together with the list of names by which the same animal was known in different languages and different localities, were of tremendous service to his contemporaries and successors, for the vague and inaccurate descriptions and the inconsistencies in terminology added even more confusion to what must have seemed a sufficiently confusing and disorderly natural world.

*The Herbals:* There were a number of treatises similar to Gesner's in some of which attempts were made to classify the animals described while in others personal observations alone were presented. The Herbals did for botany what books of this kind did for zoology (Fig. 26.3). Herbals were compendia of information primarily about plants but in a considerable number of them animals, minerals and other natural objects and phenomena were included. In 1530, Otto Brunfels identifies his plants, mostly collected around Strasbourg, with those described by Dioscorides; since Dioscorides' collections were chiefly from the Mediterranean countries, some confusion in identification naturally arose. Brunfels' *Herbarium* deals mainly with the medicinal properties of plants, but he did attempt some orderly arrangement of them on the basis of their similarities in these properties and, more significantly, upon the nature of their roots, stems, leaves and seeds.

In 1542, Leonard Fuchs (1501–1566), a German botanist in whose honor the ornamental plant fuchsia is named, published his *Historia Stirpium* in which, in Latin, he lists alphabetically the various medicinal plants, giving an account of the form, habitat, season in which the collection should be made, "temperament" and powers of each plant, and adds to his descriptions over 500 beautiful and accurate woodcuts of specimens. Two years later, Pietro Andrea Matthioli (1500–1577), physician at the court of Siena, published his commentaries on Dioscorides, which, after passing through his hands, became the standard botanical text of the period, profusely illustrated with original pictures. Besides such descriptive listings as these of continental plants, a catalogue of over a thousand English ones grown in the London garden of John Gerard was published in 1596. A year later Gerard's more complete *Herball* was published and widely circulated; this included not only the English plants of the original catalogue but descriptions of many European ones taken from other treatises.

***The revival of independent inquiry in science:*** At the same time that these great compilations of botanical and zoological information were being made, new and revolutionary methods were being introduced into the study of anatomy and new and more exact information about the construction and operation of living systems was being acquired by doctors and anatomists in the great universities. Leader in this revival of fresh and free inquiry was Vesalius (see page 102), and the close of the sixteenth century showed tremendous gains in scientific methods, scientific knowledge and scientific thought. In addition to the great works of Vesalius and Copernicus, Galileo's treatise on the acceleration of falling bodies was published and William Gilbert's on magnetism. The English natural philosopher and statesman, Francis Bacon (1561–1626), in his *Novum Organum* decried man's tendency to interpret natural phenomena according to his own preconceptions, and to ascribe to nature the orderliness and regularity that he admired and found useful. In the new system of thought that Bacon developed, knowledge of nature was to be achieved only by observation of things as

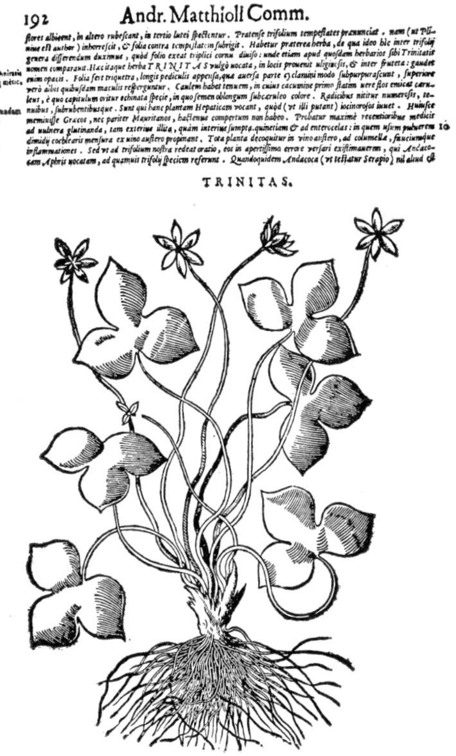

192 Andr. Matthioli Comm.

flores albicent, in altero rubescant, in tertio lutei spectentur. Pratense trifolium tempestates praenunciat. nam (ut Plinius est author) inhorrescit, & folia contra tempestatem subrigit. Habetur praeterea herba, de qua ideo hic inter trifolij genera disserendum duximus, quòd folio exeat triplici cornu diuiso: unde etiam apud quosdam herbarios sibi Trinitatis nomen comparant. Haec itaque herba TRINITAS vulgò uocata, in locis prouenit uliginosis, & inter fruteta: gaudet enim opacis. Folia fert triquetra, longis pediculis appensa, quae auersa parte cyclamini modo subpurpurascunt, superiore verò albis quibusdam maculis resperguntur. Caulem habet tenuem, in cuius cacumine primo statim uere flos emicat caeruleus, è quo capitulum oritur echinata specie, in quo semen oblongum subcaeruleo colore. Radicibus nititur numerosis, tenuibus, subrubentibusque. Sunt qui hanc plantam Hepaticam vocant, quòd (vt illi putant) iocinorosos iuuet. Huiusce meminisse Graecos, nec pariter Mauritanos, hactenus compertum non habeo. Probatur maximè recentioribus medicis ad uulnera glutinanda, tam exterius illita, quàm interius sumpta. quinetiam & ad enterocelas: in quem usum puluerem 10 dimidij cochlearis mensura ex uino austero propinant. Tota planta decoquitur in vino austero, ad columellae, fauciumque inflammationes. Sed vt ad trifolium nostra redeat oratio, eos in apertissimo errore versari existimauerim, qui Andacocam Aphris uocatam, ad quamuis trifolij speciem referunt. Quandoquidem Andacoca (vt testatur Serapio) nil aliud est

TRINITAS.

FIGURE 26.3 Drawing and part of the description of the hepatica from Mattioli's Commentaries on Dioscorides. (Page 192, Pietro Andrea Mattioli, *Commentarij in VI libros Pedacij Dioscorides Anazarbei de matica materia . . . Venetijs,* apud Felicem Valgrisium MDLXXXIII.)

they are and by experiment to change them; if an experiment asks a "fair question," nature will give an answer from which man, by inductive reasoning, may arrive at the knowledge that he seeks. And by classification of the knowledge so acquired, he may derive general laws governing natural events. In this system, Bacon defined "the scientific method," a phrase so frequently used to-day and often so little understood.

About the same time a French philosopher and mathematician, René Descartes (1596–1650), in speculating upon the natural world had the temerity to suggest that all things in it operated wholly in accordance with physical principles, and that all events taking place in the natural world do so out of mathematical necessity. This mechanistic point of view, applied to biological systems, denied their special creation and also excluded any external supernatural force to guide their courses and direct their destinies, and Descartes' expression of it, guarded though his statements were, marks the first clear distinction between mechanistic and vitalistic interpretations of life. Subsequent biological and philosophical thought has been divided between these two interpretations, for the biologist, as he seeks to discover more and more about the operations of biological systems, is always confronted by their complexity, their individuality and their lability, and the philosopher finds it hard to conceive of "life" and "living" and to contemplate the delicacy and precision with which living things achieve their ends without some vital force or guiding principle to direct them.

### Seventeenth century

*The popularization of natural science:* The next century brought the beginning of the development of the microscope and introduction to micro-organisms and to the minutiae of the larger ones already known in their gross aspects. The work of the great microscopists of this period has been summarized on pages 54–56. The popular and scientific interest in natural history, in the kinds of living things inhabiting all parts of the globe, their habits and their uses was as great as, if not greater than, in preceding years. Huge tomes on natural history were published which listed animals and plants in various ways, but usually alphabetically and often with the same species occurring several times under different local names. Shorter epitomes were also put out, intended to summarize the principal points of science and to bring them within the reach of everyone. Travellers continued to bring back tales, sketches and specimens of animals and plants from distant countries; exotic foreign plants were cultivated in gardens and cabinets of specimens of minerals, plants and animals were made. Some natural historians still tried to reconcile the strange foreign animals with those of the Bible, developing a kind of religious zoology that taught that animals existed for other purposes than to provide food and pleasure for man; they were here to exemplify and teach the principles of Christianity.

*Steno and the beginning of paleontology:* One of the great original contributions of this century was made by a Danish natural historian, Nils Steenson (1638–1686), commonly known as Steno, who in addition to anatomical studies on existing species, proved by detailed comparisons that the "stone tongues" found in great numbers in the vicinity of Florence, must have been the teeth of sharks. This establishment of the position of fossils in the world of organic life was the beginning of the science of paleontology (Greek, palaios = ancient + onto = existing things + logos = discourse), which has provided the critical evidence for the doctrine of organic evolution. Steno also made a study of the strata of the earth's crust, and outlined a theory of their origin by the deposition of successive layers of sediment from water, an idea which he applied also to living things, believing them to be continually precipitated from fluids and to grow, as a crystal grows, by the accumulation of material from the parent solution. False as this biological notion was, his conception of sedimentation as a geological process is an accurate one, and one fundamental to the concept of geologic time, for in the successive layers of sedimentary rocks is the sequence of events in the earth's history (Fig. 26.4).

*The organization of scientific societies:* During this century, too, scientific societies were organized, providing opportunity for the exchange of ideas and the presentation and discussion of new discoveries and so promoting scientific achievement and scientific thought. The oldest of these were the Academy for the Secrets of Nature, founded in Naples in 1560, and the Academy of the

Lynx-Eyed Associates, organized in 1603 in Rome, and so called because of the sharpness of vision attributed to the lynx. Both of these had to operate under cover, for exploration into the secrets of nature was frowned upon by the powerful Church of

1657, and the Académie des Sciences in Paris in 1665. This, like the Royal Society of England, is still an organization active in the recognition of scientific work and the dissemination of scientific knowledge and both have their counterparts in the United

FIGURE 26.4  The Calvert cliffs, near Plum Point, on the western Maryland shore of Chesapeake Bay, showing strata of sedimentary rocks. The lowest stratum represents rocks of the Miocene Epoch, in which fossils, especially those of bivalve mollusks, are abundant. (Photograph by courtesy of Dr. Horace Richards.)

Rome. Twice disbanded and twice revived, the Academy of the Lynx carried on the first systematic study of biological systems by means of the newly acquired microscopical technique. In 1645, the Invisible College was founded in England, which later became the Royal Society, the society to which Leeuwenhoek, among many others in all branches of science, communicated his findings. The Philosophical Transactions of this Society, covering all phases of scientific discovery and thought, were first published in 1665 and their unbroken publication has continued ever since. The Academy of Experiments was organized in Florence in States in the American Philosophical Society founded a century later, in 1743, by Benjamin Franklin.

*The beginnings of taxonomy:* Several of the attempts to bring living things into some kind of an orderly arrangement on the basis of natural rather than artificial distinctions between them were made during these years. Caspar Bauhin (1560–1642), a Swiss and a pupil of Fabricius and also influenced by the work of Fuchs, made tours throughout Italy and extensive botanical studies of its flora; he initiated the comparative method in botany by arranging his collections according to the form of their leaves, and he also found synonyms for their different names and worked out his own system of identification, using a double name for each type of plant and so in a way foreshadowing Linnaeus' binomial nomenclature. Joachim Jung (1587–1657), a little known German botanist, used a system of naming plants that approaches even more closely the binomial system of to-day. None of his work was made public during his life, probably because he lived constantly under the suspicion of heresy, but in 1678 a number of his students collected his notes and published them. Here the emphasis is on the morphology of plants, and their parts are given names, many of which are still in use such as perianth, stamen and style. He also made the important distinction between the different aspects of botanical study, distinguishing between the morphological, the physiological the ecological and the systematic.

The work of both Bauhin and Jung was known to John Ray (1627–1705), an English natural historian who with a fellow student, Francis Willughby (1635–1672), travelled through England and widely on the continent, observing and collecting plants and learning all they could of their natural history and that of animals. Together they embarked upon an ambitious project of making a systematic organization of the entire organic world but Willughby, who was to have done the animals, died before much more than the preliminaries were completed. Ray, however, edited and published his friend's notes; these books, together with his own, represent the beginnings of modern systematics and are the basis and background of Linnaeus' system. In Ray's *Historia generalis plantarum,* published in three volumes in London between the years 1686 and 1704, over 18,000 plants are carefully and accurately described and catalogued according to the character of their fruits, the shape of their leaves and the type of their flowers. This is a more natural grouping on the basis of constant and well-defined characters and not as completely an artificial one as an alphabetical listing or the division into trees, herbs and shrubs of some of the earlier botanists. Ray gave more space to insects than to the other "bloodless" animals, for he knew more about them, and among those with blood he devoted himself more to quadrupeds than to birds and fishes.

***The idea of constancy of species:*** Ray was the first man to attempt to define a species precisely and to make a distinction between the inherent and constant differences of organisms and those that were incidental or accidental, such as the curling of leaves, color and taste variations and the range of sizes of flowers, fruits and leaves of plants from the same stock. In doing this, he provided the germ for the doctrine of the constancy of species, a doctrine that guided biological thought for many succeeding decades. And in bringing some kind of order into the chaotic assemblages of real and fictitious plants and animals, Ray laid foundations upon which Linnaeus could build. But actually the classes and orders of plants in the Linnaean system are very similar to those, and in some cases the same, which were established by a Frenchman contemporary with Ray, Joseph Pitton Tournefort (1656–1708), a professor at the Jardin des Plantes in Paris, the botanical garden founded in 1626 by Cardinal Richelieu and for many years a center for biological research. Tournefort laid great stress on generic differences and drew up a code of rules based on the parts of the flower by which genera should be distinguished and described. A certain definition had therefore been given both to the genus and the species before Linnaeus began his survey of biological systems and his systematic organization of them (see page 98 ff.).

### Eighteenth century

***The ideas and influence of Georges Buffon:*** The practical aspects of Linnaeus' work were disregarded and his artificial and unnatural distinctions vigorously attacked by a contemporary Frenchman, Georges Louis Leclerc de Buffon (1707–1788). He criticized the Linnaean system on many counts, pointing out the impossibility, in his sexual method, of distinguishing between the orders and classes of plants when they were not in flower, or if they did not flower, and hence its general impracticality, and also the weaknesses of his classification of animals, especially that of the Insecta and Vermes, where he claimed with ample justification that or animate particles were scattered around in space from which living creatures have been assembled. Only with reservations could he accept species distinctions as natural ones, for he was puzzled by the fine gradations between some of them and he

FIGURE 26.5 The "ill-equipped and miserable" two-toed sloth (Choloepus hoymanni), a perissodactyl native to Central America. (Photograph by courtesy of the Zoological Society of Philadelphia.)

there should be many more classes. The whole system was to him too artificial to be valid or even useful; a natural classification would distinguish first between animals, plants and minerals, then in the case of animals, between those of different habitats and modes of life, those that are wild and those that are tame, and finally between those that have structural differences. He clearly expressed the idea that there is no definite boundary between the animal and the vegetable world; life is a physical characteristic of matter and just as the inorganic world is made up of particles collected together in configurations of different kinds, so to his mind was the organic world. Living utterly denied their divine creation; indeed, he even criticized nature on several scores, especially for turning out any creature so ill-equipped and so wretched as the sloth, a mammal indigenous to tropical America and one of the many strange animals brought to Europe by travellers (Fig. 26.5). His approach to the problems of biology was entirely different from that of the philosopher, religionist and natural historian, Linnaeus. Buffon had begun his scientific studies as a physicist and his first contributions to scientific literature were translations of Newton's *Fluxions* and Hales' *Vegetable Staticks*. After his appointment to the Jardin des Plantes, his interests broad=

ened to include all natural science and he determined to write singlehanded a great natural history in which all existing information would be collected. Only the biological part of his *Histoire naturelle* was finished, although the greater part of his life was devoted to it. He emphasized the need for experimentation coupled with observation in the study of the natural world and defined the goal of the natural scientist as the derivation and deduction of general laws equally applicable to all natural phenomena. The experiments of John Mayow and of Robert Boyle in the previous century, and those that were currently being conducted by Joseph Priestley and Antoine-Laurent Lavoisier, supported his conception of the unity in nature and in science that is the accepted principle in scientific thought today, and supported also his belief that all natural phenomena could be reduced to those explicable by established physical laws.

***The ideas and influence of Charles Bonnet:*** A still different approach to the problem of the relationships of organisms was taken by a Swiss natural philosopher, Charles Bonnet (1720–1793), who began his life's work as a lawyer but early in it became interested in natural history. He studied propagation in the aphids minutely, and established the fact that they reproduce by parthenogenesis, and he experimented with plants, observing their tropisms and growth movements. It was primarily his studies on aphid parthenogenesis, insect metamorphosis and the development of flowers and seeds that led him to the "emboîtement" theory that confused both embryological and evolutionary thought for a number of years. Seeing in the body of the female aphid, newly hatched from a parthenogenetic egg, the rudiments of the next generation to which she would give rise, in the body of the insect pupa, the outlines of the imago that will emerge from it and, enfolded in the bud, all parts of the forthcoming flower and in the seed, the cotyledons and the germ of the plant that will grow from it, he came to think that every existing organism held within itself, in miniature, the bodies of all its descendants and conceived of the development of the individual as an unfolding and enlargement of parts already formed. This idea, carried further than Bonnet himself did, developed into the Preformation Theory which, pushed to its logical limits, asserted that in the germ cells of individuals of each generation were contained, in successive order, the rudiments of all their posterity. This idea was entirely contrary to that of change, and implied a fixity of type in every line of descent that denied the possibility of variation upon which evolution depends.

Later in Bonnet's life, an eye disease prevented him from close observation and experimentation, but he read widely in scientific literature and speculated about the meaning of what he had learned. His writings cover a wide range of biological subjects; from the point of view of evolution, his crystallization of the slowly growing idea of "une échelle des êtres naturelles" is significant in its direction of thought toward a progressive relationship between living things. He could not accept the idea that there were sharp differences between species; in his ladder of nature, minerals occupy the lower rungs, and then in ascending order, plants from the simple through transitional types to the complex, then animals in the same way and finally man on the topmost rung. In his later works, there is some indication that he suspected that this series was not wholly a linear or connective one, and that some types of animals at least might be collateral with each other, reaching the same degree of complexity by different routes, and not, as his early scheme implied, by using the type immediately preceding it in the scale as a stepping stone. Accepting Buffon's radical idea that the earth had existed far longer than the six thousand years of the Biblical narrative, he developed the theory that it had undergone a series of catastrophes in each of which its living population had been completely wiped out, although the animate particles were preserved as germs from which new types could arise. The last great catastrophe had taken place before the six days of Creation, after which existing types had appeared, but no one could have recognized their prototypes in previous intercatastrophic periods. A deeply religious man, he believed in a continual ascent of the ladder of nature and in the ultimate attainment, after a succession of catastrophes, of organic status by minerals, mentality by plants, speech by animals and something at least approximating divinity by man.

**Speculative philosophy and biological experimentation:** There was much speculative philosophy of this kind during the latter part of the seventeenth and the early part of the eighteenth centuries. Bonnet was but one of many who surveyed nature on a grand scale, and conjectured about its origins, its causes, directional forces and possible meanings, as well as about the relationships between its existing forms. In the writings of the great philosophers of this period are expressed ideas both of the fixity and of the mutability of animal species, of continuity between them and of their origin from a common ancestor and their gradual development from this prototype, according to the purpose and design of nature. But a great deal of experimentation and close and critical observation was also going on, steadily bringing to light new facts about the natural world and clearing up the confusion about the operation of living things and their interrelationships with each other. Malpighi's and Swammerdam's work had given impetus and inspiration to the study of insects and in this period a number of treatises on insects were published, each embodying the idea of critical investigation and observation. Among such studies were those of René de Réaumur (1683–1757), a Frenchman, whose six-volume history of insects included also reptiles and amphibians and covered also aspects of animal physiology as well as anatomy and natural history. Besides his experiments on digestion (see page 397), Réaumur studied the effect of heat on the development of insects, the formation of pearls in mollusks, the regeneration of missing parts in crayfish, the electricity and phosphorescence produced by certain fishes and a host of other general and special activities. Abraham Trembley (1700–1784), a Swiss, made detailed investigations of fresh water polyps, producing conclusive evidence that they were animals and not plants and carrying out experiments especially on Hydra (see page 156), an organism of which Leeuwenhoek had supplied the first printed sketch. Pierre Lyonet (1707–1789), born in Holland of French parents and a man of unusual patience and manual dexterity, made detailed studies of the sheep tick and of the goat moth which feeds on willow trees, tracing its life history and its metamorphosis from caterpillar to moth. His *Traité de la chenille qui ronge le bois de Saule* is equal in its anatomical detail and the exactness and beauty of its illustrations to Malpighi's treatise on the silkworm. And the experimental studies of the Italian priest, Lazzaro Spallanzani (1729–1799), extended knowledge of regeneration, fertilization and embryology. He followed by dissection and microscopic study the course of the re-formation of parts removed from the bodies of salamanders and other amphibians, and studied the effects of environmental conditions, such as cold and heat and nutrition, upon the course of regeneration; by filtering the sperm of certain animals, he proved that the presence of spermatozoa, the minute cells that Leeuwenhoek had also been the first to see and to describe, were essential to the development of their eggs in which he believed, accepting Bonnet's "emboîtement" theory, that all parts of the adult and of succeeding generations were contained. He also performed experiments to show that new organisms could only rise from pre-existing ones, combating the idea that they were constantly being created by the spontaneous assemblage of animate particles into the proper configuration; this controversy was to crop up again and again in succeeding years and nearly a century later to end in the beautiful experiments of Louis Pasteur (1822–1895) and his dramatic proof of the failure of life to originate in media from which all living things were excluded (see p. 132).

More general anatomical studies were also making progress. In London, the Scotch doctor John Hunter (1728–1793) was going far beyond human surgery and dissection and studying every kind of animal that he could lay his hands on under as many different conditions of their lives as he could obtain them. His effect upon biology is perhaps more in method and in direction than in actual findings, although the collection of specimens of both living and fossil forms that he made was a treasure house of information for the comparative anatomist until its destruction in the bombings of London during World War II. But it was in developing the comparative method that Hunter gave a new emphasis to biological science, opening a road which many were to follow in the next century with results most fruitful to biology in factual information and to all scientific and philosophical thought in the theoretical implications of these facts. A contemporary Frenchman, Felix Vicq d'Azyr (1748–1794), like Hunter a practicing physician, also made dissections of animals of different species, particularly of mammals, and studied especially their limbs and their muscles; he also made comparative studies of the teeth of the vertebrate animals, distinguishing between those which were set in sockets and those carried on the jawbone, pointing out the dental similarities in those with similar feeding habits, and further than that, the correlation between the type of dentition and other organs of the body. This principle of correlation, carried further by Cuvier, is applied to-day in the reconstruction of extinct forms, for from one part the others can be deduced in at least very closely approximate types and proportions.

In addition to anatomical and physiological studies such as these, travellers and explorers were observing and collecting specimens from little known parts of the world and fitting them into the system and scale of living things. Chief among these, from the point of view of systematics and evolutionary theory, was a German, Peter Simon Pallas (1741–1811), who studied in Holland and travelled in England before he was sent by Catherine the Great on a series of expeditions into Asiatic Russia. Besides straightening out some of the tangles in the classification of mollusks and certain of the Vermes, Pallas improved upon Buffon's ladder of life by conceiving of specific relationships as a branching tree, not a linear series. Believing that some types may have had a common starting point, he pointed out that they could have developed along divergent lines and so have the same relationship to each other as the collateral branches of a family tree instead of the direct line of succession that Bonnet had originally suggested.

*The ideas and influence of Jean Baptiste Lamarck and Georges Cuvier:* Contemporary with Pallas were two Frenchmen whose influence upon almost all aspects of biology was tremendous during their lives and is still felt in biological method and theory. These were Jean Baptiste de Monet Lamarck (1744–1829) and Georges Cuvier (1769–1832). Lamarck was trained as a priest, served as a soldier in the Seven Years' War and then settled down in Paris to become a writer. During his apprenticeship as a literary hack the interest that he had always had in natural history became his dominant one and the rest of his life was devoted to speculation, teaching and writing about the animate world. Indeed, it was he who first introduced the term "Biology" for the science of living things, for he saw in them a unity and a continuity that made the separate sciences of botany and zoology undesirable distinctions in a common field of knowledge. Among his numerous writings three in particular express his theories of the relationships between organisms—*Récherches sur l'organisation des corps vivants* published in 1802, *Philosophie zoologique* (1809) and *Histoire naturelle des animaux sans vertèbres* (1815–1822). Like Buffon, he surveyed the whole organic world and saw in it a common principle of life. Like Buffon, too, Lamarck rejected the current systems of classification, believing that their categories existed only in human thought and had no natural basis. Nor could he accept the idea of the constancy or fixity of species, since species was in his mind but another artificial distinction; real differences existed only between individuals. He recognized that individuals with structural and other similarities could be grouped together and that such groups could also be united into larger ones with certain common characters, and he saw in the organic world a progressive series of types, like Bonnet's ladder, with mammals at the top and polyps at the bottom. He believed, too, in the constant creation of living forms from material particles under the influence of the physical forces of heat, light and electricity and he apparently had no doubt, in spite of Spallanzani's experiments, that the most simply organized animals and plants were spontaneously generated whenever the conditions were favorable. He even stated that it was highly probable that fresh water polyps died off in toto each year when cold weather came and were spontaneously recreated in the spring. While recognizing that the animals at the top of his scale were the most complex in their structure and their habits, he preferred—or he thought it more instructive—to consider the interrelationships between organisms from a retrogressive rather than a progressive point of view, that is, from the loss of parts rather than the acquisition of new ones. Starting from the mammals, whose young are born alive, which have milk glands, breathe by means of lungs and are warm-blooded, one then finds that the birds are next simplest in the scale, for while they are lung-breathers and warm-blooded, their young are hatched from eggs laid by the females; the reptiles are next, for they are cold-blooded, they lay eggs and in the lowest orders the two pairs of limbs possessed by animals higher in the scale disappear, and so on down the whole series. He put considerable emphasis upon the transitional forms between classes and orders, pointing out that the tortoises, sharing certain characteristics with reptiles and with birds, represent transitional stages between those two classes, while the duck-billed platypus of Australia bridges the gap between birds and mammals.

Although he believed that the great classes of animals presented an unbroken series of type forms, he did recognize that the orders and genera within them might branch off on independent lines of development, so that, while the rungs of his ladder were represented by the general types, from each there were divergent branches made up of individuals which had departed from the type form in one or more particulars. These digressions were, he thought, the result of pressure put upon organisms by the conditions of their environment. He argues this point exhaustively, and carries it over to the development of type forms, saying that long-necked animals have become so by stretching their necks in search of food, that ducks and other swimming birds have webbed feet because generations of their ancestors stretched their toes swimming through the water, and that modern moles are blind because their ancestors burrowed in the ground and so their eyes atrophied through disuse. This idea of the "inheritance of acquired characters" has become so firmly attached to Lamarck's name that it is often unfairly thought of as his principal contribution to biological theory and the doctrine of evolution in particular. Although he carried his arguments in support of it to the point of absurdity, his thinking along other lines was so brilliant and so profound and his expertness in the detection of formal relationships so great that this part of his natural philosophy should not be allowed to obscure his great service to the development of biology as a whole.

Born in the same year as Napoleon and the Duke of Wellington, Cuvier, however, managed to live a wholly unmilitary life, most of which he spent as a professor in the University of Paris and inspector general of education in the French Government. He is, above all, the man who developed the comparative method in biology, conducting his investigations on animals of all kinds and extending them to fossil remains of all those he could obtain. Although he drew theoretical conclusions from his observations, he was no speculative biologist; he did not concern himself with the origins or the principles of life and he studied animals as he found them and never defended a point to which he could not bring the evidence of his own eyes or that of reliable witnesses. His approach to systematics and to other biological matters was therefore wholly different from that of Linnaeus, Buffon, Bonnet and his contemporary Lamarck. From his early training it was also different from the earlier comparative anatomists, John Hunter and Vicq d'Azyr, both of whom were physicians with a primary interest in man. Cuvier had spent some time after completing school as tutor to a family living on the coast of Normandy and he began his dissection and the study of animal structure on marine animals that he collected from the shores and deeper waters of the English Channel—fish and mollusks and starfish and worms—all of which he dissected with great care and drew with equal meticulousness and precision. After he went to Paris, his interest turned to the vertebrates, especially mammals, and to the study of fossil forms which were most abundant in the soft rocks of Paris and its surroundings. Much of the stone quarried for the city buildings was rich in fossils and Cuvier organized a series of excavating parties to dig them out of the foundations of buildings as well as from the quarries and fields and other open spaces around Paris. He thus enlarged the world of living things to be studied, compared and classified to include extinct as well as existing species. His emphasis in the study of animals was primarily on their form, rather than on the purpose to which the various parts were put, for in his opinion organs of so many different kinds served the same function that they cannot be used as a basis of comparison between animal types. Yet within the same animal, and within groups of closely related animals, the presence of an organ of a certain type presupposes, even demands, the presence of other organs of correlative types. An animal, for example, which has long teeth suited to seizing and tearing prey will also have claws for holding that prey, powerful and quickly moving muscles, a form of body that can be moved rapidly by these muscles, and eyes and nose that are keenly sensitive to see and scent the prey. He carried the idea of the correlation of parts, which Vicq d'Azyr had outlined, through all his comparative studies and it became the cornerstone of his own system of classification. He disagreed with Lamarck about the changeability of species, for he believed that these were fixed and established configurations of matter of different forms manifesting the phenomena of life, and he accepted the Linnaean idea that the individuals of a species arose from a common parentage. But he did not concern himself especially with the original creation of these species, although he developed further the theory of catastrophes, believing with Bonnet that there had been a series of disasters during the earth's history in which most of its existing population had been destroyed. He avoided the necessity for the special or spontaneous creation of new species after each catastrophe by assuming that there was always a small residue of its inhabitants left somewhere on the earth from which the new species of the next cycle had descended.

His ideas and his findings are expressed in a number of books, chief among which are *Leçons sur l'anatomie comparée* published in 1812, and *La règne animale, distribué après son organisation,* published in 1817. In the latter he presents his system for the classification of animals. From his comparative studies of the organization of the animal body, he came to the conclusion that it was impossible and inexcusable to arrange animals in a progressive series or to place one type above or below the other in the scale of living things. The fish is as perfect in its way as the bird is in its way, and who shall say that the lowest order of birds is more perfect than the highest order of fishes or the lowest mammal a better thing than the highest bird? He saw in the animal kingdom certain basic type forms which have become modified in various ways into the various existing species. Consequently he divided animals on the basis of these type forms into four great groups—Vertebrata, Mollusca, Articulata and Radiata—so fundamentally different in their body plans that comparison between them was virtually impossible. Within these main divisions he placed animals basically similar, yet different in particular characters, constituting the orders, genera and species within the principal group. Perhaps Cuvier, in his classificatory system, was less enlightened than Linnaeus in placing man in a separate category and not including him among mammals of the highest order, yet his work and his ideas gave greater impetus to evolutionary thought, if only by stimulating the study of comparative anatomy. His principle of classification gave new direction, too, to biological speculation, for it directed attention toward ancestral forms or archetypes that might fill the gaps in the entire system and so provide a complete evolutionary sequence; where such archetypes could not be found, they were postulated and hypothetical forms sketched in by the speculative biologists.

### Nineteenth century

The years following the publication of *La règne animale* saw great extensions of anatomical studies and further applications of Cuvier's method of comparison and correlation of parts. Some of these studies were concentrated on fossils of extinct species, others on developmental stages of existing ones, for the science of paleontology made great strides and comparative embryology became recognized as a special method of biological investigation. Knowledge of new species was acquired through scientific expeditions, some of which went out solely for the purpose of studying organisms in their native habitats, while those that went for cartographical or other reasons almost invariably took along a naturalist to make notes and collect specimens. The flora and fauna of the United States were studied mainly by their own inhabitants and, as new territories were opened up, new types from them were sent back to England and Europe by men commissioned to collect for natural historians there, or by those individually interested in the exchange of specimens and ideas.

The acquisition of these new specimens provided the systematists with new material to fit into their classificatory schemes, and the comparative anatomists with new forms to study and dissect. The breadth of knowledge of the biologist became correspondingly extended and he became increasingly aware of structural features shared by members of related groups and of the modification of these common features in individuals and in groups of closely related individuals.

### The development of embryology

Comparative embryologists contributed to the concept of evolution by drawing attention to the parallelism between developmental stages in individuals and the degree of specialization attained by different species and genera in the same class of animals. The Preformation Theory was discarded and embryologists returned to the older notion of epigenesis (Latin, epi = upon + genesis = development) or progressive development through a series of steps, each depending upon the one preceding it. This idea had been expressed by Aristotle, from his observations on the course of development in the hen's egg, reaffirmed by William Harvey and established by the German naturalist, Caspar Friedrich Wolff (1738–1794). In thus regarding individual development as a gradual progression from the simple to the complex, as they could watch it take place, embryologists were providing evolutionists with an analogy for species development, which they could not see but could only suppose. Indeed, some embryologists, like Johann Friedrich Meckel (1781–1833), a student of Cuvier's, went so far as to say that animals, at each level of the evolutionary scale pass in the course of their development through the same forms that those lower in the evolutionary scale attain as adults. This idea was modified by another German, Karl Ernst von Baer (1792–1876), who summarized in his book *über Entwicklungsgeschichte der Thiere* the existing embryological knowledge and added to it many new facts from his own studies. While recognizing that the law of development is the law of the entire universe, von Baer was clear that embryonic stages of "higher" animals do not have counterparts in existing "lower" ones, rather, that the embryos of both lower and higher types resemble each other more closely than do the fully developed adults, and the more closely related they are, the more complete this resemblance is. Applying this to the idea of organic evolution, von Baer saw that the further apart two animals are in their positions in the evolutionary scale, the further back in the embryological history of each will one have to go to find the stage where they have most in common. This led him to rely upon Cuvier's theory of archetypes; among animals, the egg is the embryonic stage common to all, and all eggs have certain features in common, however different the adults that develop from them may be, and so in the development of life forms one might expect to find ancestral types that were much alike, however divergent the modern forms may be. He pointed out, too, that a series of animals may be progressive in respect to the development of one organ, retrogressive in respect to another and that some animals low in the evolutionary scale may attain a degree of differentiation and complexity greater than some of those in higher groups. He thus conceived of evolution as a process of parallel development, not one of uniform ascent from lower to higher, substituting for Bonnet's ladder of life, Pallas' analogy of a branching tree.

### Development of geology

The influence of another science, geology, which reached an independent status among the natural sciences in the nineteenth century, was also deeply reflected in the doctrine of organic evolution. The development of geology as an exact science is due largely to an Englishman, Sir Charles Lyell (1797–1875), and his insistence upon the principle that one must proceed from the known to the unknown, and only attempt to explain the past in terms of present, known phenomena. In his *Principles of Geology. An Attempt to Explain the Former Changes of the Earth's Surface by Reference to Causes now in Operation*, first published in 1830, he explains the formation of the earth's crust as a slow process of development, through the operation of the same physical processes that can now be observed at work upon it. Here, as the astronomers before him had done in their theories of the emergence of the solar system from a gaseous state, he emphasized the cumulative effect of physical forces in shaping the earth to its present form. He did not include biological evolution in his theory of geological evolution, but concerned himself rather with the distribution of species in the different geological epochs and with their increase or extinction as conditions changed (Fig. 26.6). In opposition to Lamarck, Lyell believed firmly in the constancy of species, admitting only the possibility of slight variation among the individuals composing them, and in the special creation of each species in a locality especially suited to it. He pointed out, too, that if conditions in a locality changed, it was no longer favorable to those particular inhabitants, who either perished or were crowded out by other forms, already existing and ready to move in.

### Charles Darwin and the theory of natural selection

The name of Charles Darwin (1809–1882) is so intimately associated with the doctrine of organic evolution that to many people he alone is identified with it. But such identification does justice neither to the natural scientists before him and contemporary with him who had conceived of a general movement of spontaneous progress in all nature, nor to Darwin himself, who contributed to geological and biological science much exact observation and accurate interpretation in addition to the great generalization with which his name is universally linked. What Darwin did for the doctrine of organic evolution was, by seeing in the greatness of his genius how the operation of a natural process could bring about the gradual development of new types, to provide a natural mechanism for its operation and so to remove it from the sphere of speculation and conjecture and establish it, as an inevitable consequence of natural events, among other natural laws.

*The life of Charles Darwin:* Charles Darwin was born with a heritage, on both maternal and paternal sides, of the highest intellectual and cultural traditions, and into a family life of security, comfort and prosperity. His mother was Susannah Wedgwood, the daughter of Josiah Wedgwood, the founder of the great ceramic industry in Staffordshire, and his father, Robert Darwin, was a doctor and the son of Erasmus Darwin, one of the great speculative philosophers of the eighteenth century. Charles Darwin received his early education in the schools of Shrewsbury, the town in the west of England, on the banks of the Severn, where he was born. This was, according to

FIGURE 26.6 Reconstruction of a Jurassic scene, showing the cycads that were dominant plants; Archaeornis, an extinct, reptile-like bird; and, in the background, the dinosaurs that were dominant land animals. (Photograph by courtesy of the Academy of Natural Sciences of Philadelphia.)

the traditions of education in nineteenth century England, entirely a classical one, including nothing but instruction in the Greek and Latin languages, the reading of Greek and Latin authors and a little ancient history and geography. But his interest in natural history asserted itself early in his life, and he spent many hours learning the names of plants, collecting minerals (which, however, he did not take the trouble to identify or classify), shells and birds' eggs. He writes of himself as a naughty and rather simple little boy, easily trickled by others and considered by his masters and his father a very ordinary one "rather below the common standard in intellect."

He left school at an earlier age than was customary, not because of any brilliant showing on his part but because he was "doing no good" there and followed his elder brother, Erasmus, to Edinburgh where, like him, he undertook the study of medicine. This he found intolerably dull and, knowing that his family fortunes were such that he would not have to work to support himself, gave his lecturers little attention. Perhaps if there had been less emphasis on instruction through lectures and more upon learning through dissection and experiment, Darwin's interest might have been aroused, yet what he saw of the clinical side of medicine both distressed and disgusted him and he was not able to stay through the two operations, performed without benefit of anaesthetic, that he tried to attend. But during his two years in Edinburgh, he became one of a group of young men interested in natural history, and often went with his friends on geological and biological expeditions in the surrounding country. Two of them were particularly interested in marine zoology, and Darwin went with them to the tide pools along the coast and with them collected and dissected animals they found there, reporting at least one of his findings at a meeting of the Plinian Society, a student society for the exchange and discussion of scientific news. He reports, too, the enthusiasm which one of these friends felt for Lamarck's views on evolution, and his own admiration for his grandfather's *Zoonomia,* an attempt to define the laws of organic life on the basis of epigenesis, in which, however, he was disappointed in a later reading, finding the amount of speculation in it disproportionately large in relation to the facts given.

After two years at Edinburgh, it became evident to Dr. Darwin that medicine was not the career for his son Charles, and after due consideration and thought, it was decided that he should be a clergyman and go to Cambridge University for his preparation. This was not immediately accomplished, for while his powers of concentration and memory had made it possible for him to meet the standards of his school, he had retained practically nothing of what he had learned there, and he had to be tutored in Greek and Latin before he could enter the University, which he finally did early in 1828. The three years he spent there were, according to his own statement, as completely wasted, as far as academic studies were concerned, as his time at school and at Edinburgh. He felt, indeed, that much of the time at Cambridge was worse than wasted, for there he indulged to the full his tastes for hunting, shooting and hard riding and fell in with a circle of friends whose influence upon him he felt, in his more mature years, to have been bad. But he also made friends whose interests were intellectual ones, and developed his musical and artistic knowledge and appreciation. The strongest influence in his intellectual life was his friendship with John Stevens Henslow (1796–1861), professor of botany in the University and a man with wide interests in all branches of science, as well as in the Cambridge undergraduates. He voluntarily attended Henslow's lectures on botany, in spite of the repugnance for lectures the years in Edinburgh had engendered in him, and he joined in the expeditions organized for the students to study plants and animals in their natural environments. He himself collected beetles with eagerness, finally assembling a large collection which included many rare species and later, at Henslow's suggestion, took up the study of geology.

In his last year in the University, Darwin read the *Personal Narrative* of the German scientist and South American explorer, Alexander von Humboldt (1769–1859), and the *Introduction to the Study of Natural Philosophy* of the astronomer and philosopher, Sir John Herschel (1792–1871). Both these books influenced him enormously, for they roused in him an urgent desire to make some contribution to natural science, and Humboldt's especially, to see something of the glories of Teneriffe, the largest of the Canary Islands, described so vividly in the *Personal Narrative.*

He spent the summer after passing the examinations for the B.A. degree and completing his studies at Cambridge accompanying, at Henslow's suggestion, the geologist Adam Sedgwick (1785–1873) on an expedition in North Wales. On his return home, he found a letter from Henslow saying that Captain Fitz-Roy, master of the 235-ton brig *Beagle,* would take along as naturalist any young man who would volunteer to go on the voyage he was about to undertake for the Admiralty "to complete the survey of Patagonia and Tierra del Fuego, commenced under Captain King in 1826–1830; to survey the shores of Chile and Peru and some islands in the Pacific; and to carry a chain of chronometrical measurements around the world." It was finally settled that Darwin should go, although his father objected strongly at first, believing such a journey a poor beginning for the clerical life for which his son had been educated and upon which he hoped he would soon be ready to start. It was indeed the end of it, but the beginning of his life as a natural historian, and the critical point in the evolution of the greatest of evolutionists.

THE VOYAGE OF THE "BEAGLE": Darwin started the voyage in many ways ill equipped for it. For one thing, he was a very bad sailor and suffered horribly from seasickness even before the *Beagle* left Plymouth Harbor, where they rocked and tossed at anchor during all the autumn of 1831, waiting for a succession of storms to subside. These attacks of seasickness and those he had during the five-year voyage (1831–1836) were believed to have been the cause of his poor health during the rest of his life. For another, he had little biological knowledge and though he collected animals of all kinds in the course of the voyage, could neither draw nor dissect them with any precision, so that many of the records he kept of them, and of plants as well, were of little or no real value. One exception to this were his observations upon barnacles, and one of his greatest contributions to zoology as such was his *Cirrepedia*, a work in several volumes, which covered the natural history, anatomy and evolutionary development of these crustaceans. But his knowledge of geology stood him in good stead; while at sea he read the first volume of Lyell's *Principles* that he had taken along with him, and wrote that the book "was of the highest service to me in many ways." Its influence upon him, as that of the author's himself, was great, for in Lyell's representation of the earth in its history passing through successive stages of climatic change, upheaval and subsidence of land, and procession and recession of waters before reaching its present state is the obvious suggestion that living things may also have shared in this developmental process.

Of the many new things that he saw and by which he may well have been astonished, the one that seems to have impressed and puzzled Darwin most was the diversity of species found in limited geographical areas. For example, in the month that he spent in the Galapagos Archipelago, a group of volcanic islands well off the west coast of South America, he studied birds particularly and found that, while they clearly belonged to South American genera, they were not the same species as those on the mainland and, moreover, that each of the little islands, though not far apart, had its own particular species. These facts seemed to him irreconcilable with the idea of special creation, which he had hitherto accepted without question. For what reason could there be behind the creation of an individual species of the same genus for each individual small island? But if they were not specially created, how had these many different species arisen, if not through some process of modification of the general features that they all showed?

*Return to England and the development of the theory of the origin of species through natural selection:* This was the germ of the idea that he took back with him to England where, in 1839, he married his cousin Hannah Wedgwood and settled down to the quiet life of a private scholar, working with all the diligence and intensity his health permitted, free from the necessity of earning a living and carefully guarded by a devoted family from interruptions that might interfere with his thought or sap his strength. Only a few months after he disembarked from the *Beagle* he started on the systematic organization of the notes he had made during the expedition. He was convinced that by following Lyell's example and collecting all the facts in any way related to variation among animals and plants, he might in some way arrive at the solution of the problem that puzzled him. He did not confine himself to the facts he himself had ascertained, but read widely in both scientific journals and records of plant and animal breeders, deliberately adopting the Baconian method of assembling as many facts as possible before attempting to postulate a theory. While he was collecting these data he read, for amusement and relaxation, *The Principle of Population* written by Thomas Henry Malthus (1766–1834), an English clergyman, who, in addition to his clerical duties, devoted himself to a study of the national economy. In this book, which was widely circulated and widely read, Malthus expressed the view that the evils of a society that allowed some individuals to be very rich and others very poor could not be cured by a redistribution of wealth, as many have proposed, but rather by an education that would teach man not to raise a family without guaranteed means of subsistence. Malthus believed that among all living things reproduction of individuals exceeds the production of materials necessary to maintain them and that there is, therefore, active competition among them for the available necessities. Applying this principle to human populations, he attempted to show by statistical methods that they never grow as rapidly as theoretically they might because of this competition, since the poorest in any society are not able to obtain what they actually need, so that poverty and want, with its attendant vice and crime, tend to thin them out.

As Darwin read the book, he appreciated at once that this competition, which he had seen for himself in operation among plants and animals, might be the means by which favorable variations in a population were preserved and unfavorable ones destroyed, and so species established. This gave him a reasonable hypothesis upon which to work, and he began to test it out by applying it to known situations in the biological world, and to write out his exposition of it, a task that was not completed until twenty years later.

*Alfred Russel Wallace and the origin of species:* In the course of his writing, he consulted many times with Lyell, and with others of his scientific friends, all of whom encouraged him to make his theory public, but none of whom agreed with him, convinced as they were of the permanency and constancy of species. As his task was nearing completion, he received a manuscript from Alfred Russel Wallace (1823–1913) entitled *On the Tendency of Varieties to Depart Indefinitely from the Original Type*, with the request that he read it critically and, if he thought well of it, to send it on to Lyell for his consideration. Wallace was an English engineer and schoolmaster, with a great interest in the collection of plants and insects. He had visited Brazil, and was in the East Indies at the time he wrote the paper and sent it to Darwin. Struck with the same things that Darwin had been when he visited the same places, Wallace had drawn the same conclusions and arrived at the same theory.

Two courses seemed open to Darwin, either to abandon his work and make Wallace's alone public, which was questionable, or to suppress Wallace's and publish only his own, which was unthinkable. Finally he arrived at a compromise, at the advice of his fellow-scientists and with Wallace's consent, to publish Wallace's paper and an abstract of his own manuscript simultaneously in the Journal of the Linnean Society. This was done, but neither excited much comment, beyond the criticism of an Irish scientist that neither would be worthy of notice were it not that they had been presented under the aegis of Lyell and of the botanist J. D. Hooker, for if the speculation "means what it says, it is a truism; if it means anything more, it is contrary to fact." This showed, said Darwin, how necessary it is to expound any new view at considerable length in order to arouse attention.

*"The Origin of Species by Means of Natural Selection":* His longer exposition of the theory came out the next year, in November, 1859, under the title of *The Origin of Species by Means of Natural Selection, or the Preservation of Favored Races in the Struggle for Life*. The argument set forth in it is a simple one, and it is the wealth of examples supporting it and to which it is made to conform that make up the bulk of the book. These examples are drawn from his own voluminous field notes and from his extensive reading. The main argument rests upon two premises:

1. that no two members of a species are exactly alike, and that this variability extends even to individuals of the same parentage, and
2. that some of these variations are advantageous, in that they give the organism a better chance of surviving in its particular

environment, or of exploiting new ones, and of procreating, while some are disadvantageous in that they diminish its chances of survival and procreation.

Then, by applying the sociological principle of Malthus, Darwin concludes that individuals with favorable variations are successful in their competition for the necessities of life, while those with unfavorable variations are destroyed and ultimately eliminated. Nature therefore does essentially what the human animal and plant breeder does in consciously selecting the types he wishes to establish and perpetuate, for by eliminating those that are unfit, it selects the types best able to meet the conditions of life on the earth. This is the principle of natural selection, which Darwin believed to have been "the most important, but not the exclusive means of modification." In the recognition of this principle, Darwin provided a natural cause for evolution among living things, and so removed organic evolution, as a natural event, from the supernatural and established its position among natural laws.

While Darwin was by no means clear about the causes of variability among living things, he never considered natural selection a factor inducing it, but only as one preserving the favorable variants, just as, in human selection, man cannot create new varieties of the domestic animals and plants that he breeds, but can only preserve and accumulate those that naturally occur. He pointed out that certain variations might be neither useful nor injurious, and so would not be affected by natural selection; these would remain as fluctuating elements, or would become fixed.

He attributed variability to changes in the conditions of life acting either directly upon the organization of the individual or indirectly by affecting its reproductive system and so its progeny, and he believed that the greatest effect might be the consequences of the relative use and disuse of parts, those that were most frequently used tending toward increase in development from generation to generation, and those that were little used tending toward decrease in size and degree of differentiation.

Mendel's experiments on the hybridization of peas and the laws he derived from them (see page 534 ff.) and reported in 1865, seventeen years before the sixth and final edition of *The Origin of Species by Means of Natural Selection*, would have provided an explanation for the variability that was the keystone of Darwin's theory, yet no mention is made of them in any of Darwin's works, and no notice of them was ever found in any of the notes he so assiduously collected. Indeed, he developed his own theory of inheritance on purely theoretical grounds in "the provisional hypothesis of pangenesis" expounded in *Animals and Plants Under Domestication* (1868). Had he been aware of Mendel's experiments and their results, their significance to his theory could hardly have escaped him, and the doctrine of organic evolution would have immediately rested upon a more secure foundation.

Nor was Darwin entirely sure of the nature of the checks to overpopulation, and of the conditions bringing about the destruction of individuals less well fitted to survive. He demonstrated to his own satisfaction that the predatory habits of animals and plants account of the elimination of many individuals, for he measured off a small plot of ground in his garden, and marked all the seedlings of native weeds as they came up. Of the 357 that began their existence in this little rectangle, 295 were destroyed chiefly by insects and slugs, and the feebler plants that escaped this end were crowded out by more vigorous growers. The amount of food available was another factor in the elimination process, and climatic changes, with periodic seasons of extreme cold or drought, he believed to be probably the most effective of all checks. The degree of dependence of one species upon another seemed to him also a causal factor in determining their survival. He used as illustration of this the often-quoted example of the ecological relationship between bumble bees and red clover, whose flowers have corollas too long for honey bees to reach the nectaries at the base and which is dependent upon transference of pollen from one flower to another for its fertilization. Elimination of the one species from any area might well result in the elimination of the other. But, he also points out, it might be advantageous for honey bees to develop mouth parts capable of obtaining the nectar, for in regions where red clover is abundant, an enormous potential supply of food is denied them, and similarly it might be advantageous to the clover to have blossoms with shorter corollas so that they might be visited and cross-pollinated by honey, as well as bumble, bees. "Thus I can understand," he writes, "how a flower and a bee might slowly become, either simultaneously or one after the other, modified and adapted to each other in the most perfect manner, by the continued preservation of all the individuals which presented slight deviations of structure mutually favorable to each other." * His recognition that the structure of every organism is related to that of all the other organisms with which it coexists and with which it comes into competition for food, or residence, from which it has to escape or upon which it preys, led him to believe that adaptations to these conditions of existence account for the divergence between organisms descended from the same common stock. He assumed, moreover, that all existing animals are descended from not more than four or five original ancestors, and plants from no more, and probably less, than this number.

*The reception of the theory:* The book was immediately a "best-seller," and excited both violent criticism and enthusiastic approval from readers in every walk of life. Although Darwin did not actually define man's position in the evolutionary scheme until he wrote *The Descent of Man,* published in 1871, it was implied in *The Origin of Species,* and the most vigorous attacks upon the theory came from theologians who could not consider the origin of man by any other means than divine creation, whatever they might be willing to concede for lower forms. Politicians then in power and complacent citizens attacked it, because in its concept of progression they saw threats to the preservation of the way of life to which they were accustomed and which they cherished, while social reformers hailed it because that very concept encouraged them to think that, if man had reached his present biological heights by a process of evolution, the social system he had built for himself might also advance to better things. It was a doctrine of free enterprise and equal opportunity for all and one of hope for men of liberal minds and social conscience.

Three leading scientists attacked it—Sir Richard Owen (1804–1892), a great comparative anatomist, at that time director of the Hunterian Museum in London, Louis Agassiz (1807–1873), a native Swiss who came to the United States in 1846 and as a professor at Harvard University is identified with the development of zoology and geology in this country, and Rudolf Kölliker (1817–1905), also a Swiss zoologist, whose principal interest was anatomy and embryology. Their criticisms centered mainly on the lack of exact evidence for the hypothesis, the weakness of the proofs and the fact that it did not recognize other factors possibly equally as influential in species formation as natural selection, which could not be entirely excluded although there was not adequate proof for them either. Agassiz, who had made the fishes, both fossil and modern, his especial study, pointed out particularly the inadequacy of the geological record and the absence of any transitional forms that would definitely establish affinities between existing species; these, he argued, must certainly be found if species had really arisen as Darwin supposed they had. The critics also raised the question of whether or not the evolutionary process had come to an end, and if it had not, why could it not be seen in operation?

Other contemporary scientists upheld the theory and some even went further than Darwin in their exposition of it and in contributing new material to support and amplify it. Among these were Lyell, finally convinced, by Darwin's evidence and argument, of the mutability of species, and Wallace, returned to England, who developed the idea of survival value in the protective coloration and mimicry among animals (Fig.

---

* Darwin, Charles, *The Origin of Species by Means of Natural Selection,* 6th edition, Chapter IV.

FIGURE 26.7 Protective coloration and mimicry in animals.

a. The Monarch butterfly (Anosia plexippus Linn.), which migrates from the Gulf States northward during the summer, has bright reddish wings with black veins and borders that are black except for two rows of light spots. The Viceroy butterfly (Basilarchia archippus Goodart), with the same range, is smaller than the Monarch, but as an adult is a faithful copy of its color and pattern, and quite unlike any others of its genus. Its larvae, feeding on willows and poplars, presumably are protected because of the resemblance of the adults to the Monarch, whose larvae, feeding on milkweed, are shunned by birds and other predators because of their acrid taste. (Photographs by courtesy of the American Museum of Natural History, New York, N.Y.)

b. Polar bears are hardly distinguishable from their natural background of ice and snow. (Photograph by courtesy of the Zoological Society of Philadelphia.)

26.7). Darwin had not given much attention to this, but Wallace attached great importance to it as evidence of natural selection, citing as illustrations the close resemblance often found between an animal and the environmental background in which it habitually lives, like that of insects like "walking sticks" that are barely distinguishable from the twigs on which they crawl, and polar animals whose white coats fit their background of ice and snow; the resemblance that certain harmless snakes have to poisonous ones; and the fact that animals with conspicuous coloration often have particular means of protection, like the hard shells of brightly colored turtles, the deadly venom of the coral snake, and the unpleasant and irritating smells emitted by brilliantly colored insects. Wallace attributed survival value to these conditions, for through them the animal may either escape the notice of others, and so be more successful in preying upon them or in escaping from them, or may warn others away or destroy those who come too near it; it therefore lives to propagate its kind while others less advantageously endowed perish.

The most zealous of Darwin's protagonists was Thomas Henry Huxley (1825–1895), an English physician and gifted zoologist and anatomist, with unusual ability to interpret science in a popular way. Although Huxley, like Darwin himself, had early in his scientific life fully accepted the idea of the fixity of species, he was, like Lyell, immediately convinced by Darwin's argument, and defended it in lectures, public debates and many published articles. He made an important addition to its first premise, that of the variability of individuals, by pointing out that the variations upon which natural selection operates may not always be small and continuous ones, as Darwin had implied, but might be large or small changes occurring at considerable intervals. He offered as one illustration of this the sudden and inexplicable appearance of a male lamb with extremely short and rather bent legs borne by one of the ewes in the flock of a Massachusetts farmer, from which the strain of Ancon, or "otter," sheep was bred, particularly valued by pioneer American farmers because of their inability to jump fences or to run away. This raised the question not only of the extent of the variations that might arise spontaneously, but also of their random, non-purposive nature, for such a change as this could hardly be considered a small and progressive one, directed toward the improvement of sheep, or contributing to their survival under natural conditions.

Another ardent supporter of Darwinism was Herbert Spencer (1820–1903), a natural philosopher who built his entire system of philosophy upon the concept of evolution, apparent to him in all nature. He accepted whole-heartedly natural selection as the force behind biological evolution, and indeed was responsible for the phrase "survival of the fittest" in which the Darwinian theory has often been summarized, and which Darwin himself adopted as suitably expressing his idea and used in later editions of *The Origin of Species*. In Germany, the zoologist Ernst Haeckel (1834–1919) became an active promotor of the doctrine. Familiar with the anatomy and life histories of many different kinds of animals, Haeckel had a broad and comprehensive view of the problems of nature and was convinced that real understanding of the organism could only come through an understanding of its relation to the environment, and it was he who introduced the term "ecology" into biological language. He believed that competition was not limited to that between an organism and others in the same locality but that within the organism itself there is also competition between the different parts; modification of an individual is the result of cooperation between its heredity and its environment. His own contribution to the doctrine of evolution was the "gastraea theory" which he developed particularly from his knowledge of the embryological history of sponges and coelenterates, and from his acceptance of the theory of recapitulation then current. This theory, known also as the "biogenetic law," was an expansion of Meckel's idea that in its individual development, each organism passes through successive stages in which it has essentially the form achieved by adults lower in the evolutionary scale; support of this idea had been provided by embryological studies of certain isolated groups of animals, notably the Crustacea, where the larval stages of some species strikingly resemble the adults of others, and the notion that "the history of the individual is the history of the race" had been advanced especially by the German biologist Fritz Müller (1821–1897). Haeckel saw in this principle a bulwark for the theory of descent, and especially for human descent. Man, like all other living things, originates from a single cell, the egg, which through division becomes first a ball of undifferentiated cells, comparable to a protozoan colony and then a two-layered system, or gastrula, comparable to the simplest kinds of animals, like coelenterates, with a localized region for digestion. Therefore, Haeckel reasoned, all animals must have a common ancestry in some unicellular animal, and all multicellular animals must have passed, in the course of their evolution, through a stage when they were essentially colonial aggregates, and then through one in which they were simple two-layered systems. This two-layered "gastraea" Haeckel postulated as the ancestral form common to all higher animals, including man; the third primary germ layer, the mesoderm, split off from the walls of the gastrula and became the muscles and other internal organs, exclusive of the digestive tract, characteristic of these higher animals. The "gastraea theory" was entirely a speculative one, with little embryological evidence to support it and a good deal, even when it was formulated, to controvert it, but it had tremendous influence, and for at least fifty years the thinking of biologists and the interpretation of embryological data were markedly affected by it, and much biological investigation was directed toward confirmation of the parallelism between individual and species development which it and the recapitulation theory implied.

Strong support of Darwin's theory came also from the American botanist Asa Gray (1810–1888), who recognized with Agassiz, his colleague on the Harvard faculty, the weaknesses of the proofs presented yet maintained that the theory made it more possible for the scientist to believe in evolution. This was the attitude very generally of biologists at the beginning of the present century, who, accepting the idea of evolution, were not satisfied with natural selection as the sole explanation of it, if indeed it offered any explanation at all.

### Twentieth century

During the past fifty years much evidence has been accumulated to establish the fact of evolution in the biological world, and to offer more adequate explanation of evolutionary processes. Paleontologists, although they have not yet been able to uncover all the fossils needed to piece together the sequence of events in the entire evolutionary picture, have provided ample evidence of evolutionary change in particular groups of plants and animals, as exhibits in all the great natural history museums testify (Fig. 26.8). Since the beginning of the century, when the attention of biologists was directed toward the laws of inheritance derived by Mendel and the chromosome theory of inheritance formulated and proved, it has been evident that the rapidly growing body of facts supplied by geneticists gives evidence of the mechanisms by which inheritable variations in individuals may be brought about. In the sorting out of genes in meiosis and the recombinations of them effected by random matings within a population, and in the mutations, including both changes in the gene itself and those in its relations to others in the genic complex through such established phenomena as translocation, inversion, duplication, etc., there rests the possibility of almost infinite variability in organisms arising through gametic union (Fig. 26.9). The ways in which such spontaneous changes in the genes and in the chromosomes take place remain a matter of conjecture, since the nature of the gene and the composition of the chromosome are still unknown, but it is clear that through the different characters developed in consequence of alterations in the genic complex, individuals may become better, or less well, adapted to the conditions of any given environment. For the Darwinian idea of small, continuous and progressive variations, influenced by the environment and directed toward the advancement of the species, modern biology substitutes, as a basis for the evolutionary process, the idea of discontinuous, random and entirely fortuitous variations, which may be advantageous or disadvantageous, or neither. The same modification, moreover, may be advantageous in one set of environmental conditions, disadvantageous in another. Short wings, with accompanying limitation in flight, may be, for example, disadvantageous to a terrestrial insect inhabiting an inland area and needing to cover considerable distance in its search for food and mates, but advantageous to another inhabiting an island where flights of the same extent might carry it so far out over the ocean that it could not return to land. In the one case, the long-winged flies have the best chance for survival and reproduction, in the other, the short-winged.

***Mutation as a basis for variability:*** Mutations, however they may have arisen, have resulted in the structural changes for which paleontology offers direct evidence, and some must also have resulted in functional changes, for which the evidence, though no less convincing, is indirect, since it is usually only the hard parts of living things or the general configuration of their bodies that are so faithfully preserved in the fossil record—the bones and teeth of vertebrates, the shells of invertebrates and the mechanical tissues of plants, or the imprint of their bodies made in the soft mud that finally hardened into rock. Mutations have, presumably, led to the acquisition of new enzymes or enzyme systems that have allowed living things to adopt new nutritive mechanisms and to exploit new materials as sources of food, and they must have resulted, as the study of those experimentally induced in Neurospora has shown, in the loss of enzyme systems and restriction of the sources from which adequate nutrition can be obtained, and consequent functional and structural specialization in nutritional mechanisms. Some of them have led, too, to mechanisms for the regulation of the internal environment, the condition, as Claude Bernard pointed out, of an independent life. For example, two species of sandhoppers, Gammarus locusta and Gammarus pulex, inhabiting salt and fresh water respectively, have glands in the basal segments of their an-

FIGURE 26.8 Restoration of marine forms common in the Jurassic Period. (Photograph obtained from the American Museum of Natural History, New York, N.Y.) At the left is the coiled shell and protruding body of an extinct mollusk, an ammonite, from which modern cephalopods have evolved. To the right is a group of stalked echinoderms, like modern sea lilies, or crinoids; in the center is a squid and a horseshoe crab (compare figure 14.28 b), to the right of which is an extinct crustacean (compare Figure 14.1).

tennae which act as water regulatory and excretory organs. In the marine species, Gammarus locusta, whose body fluids are in osmotic equilibrium with the medium in which it lives, the organ consists of a bladder and a short tubule across whose walls

Comparative studies of the excretory mechanisms of fishes, the first vertebrates to appear on earth, have shown that adaptations of a similar kind have arisen in them (see page 322 ff.). The evidence from these studies, confirmed by the paleontological

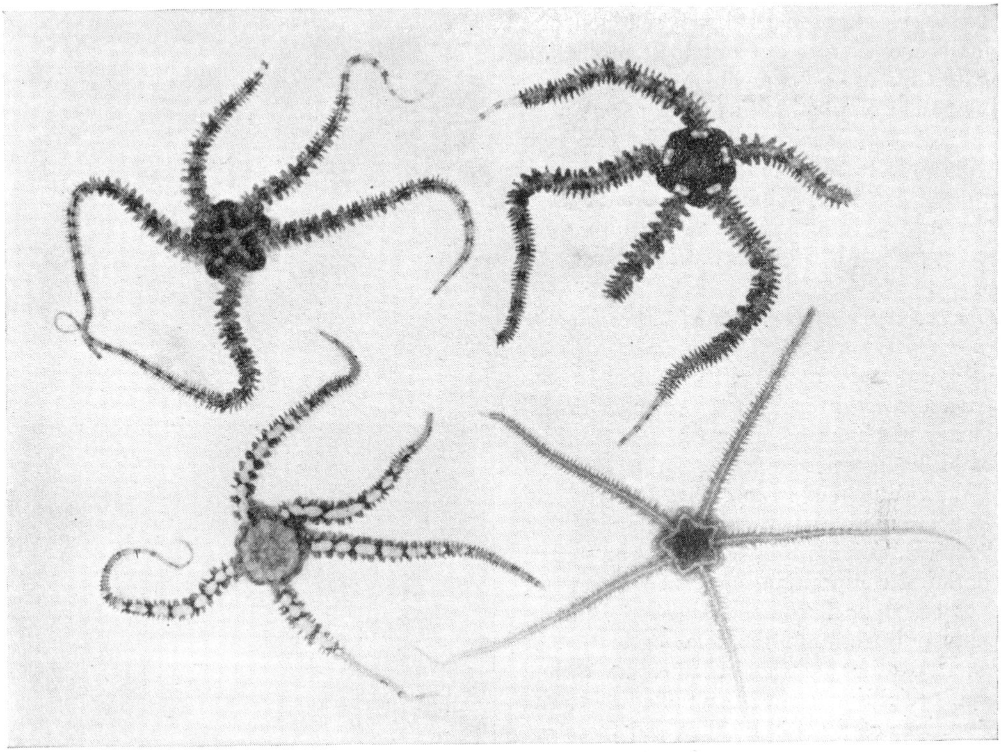

FIGURE 26.9 Variation among closely related animals. Variation in color and pattern among brittle stars of the same species (Ophiopholis aculeata). (From Moment, *General Biology for Colleges.* Copyright 1942 by D. Appleton-Century Company, Inc.)

the diffusible contents of its blood, including salts as well as water, is filtered. In Gammarus pulex, a fresh water form, to which such loss of salts would be fatal since it cannot readily replace them from the water around it, the tubular part of the organ is longer and includes a region in which the salts are reabsorbed from the blood filtrate. This particular adaptation to a fresh water environment, or some other that would produce the same results, was thus a necessary condition in the emancipation of crustaceans from an exclusively marine environment, allowing them to extend the area which they might populate to streams and rivers, ponds and lakes.

record, indicates that their common ancestor, which presumably they also share with all the vertebrates, was a dweller in fresh water, or in the much diluted sea water of estuaries, to whose survival the elimination of the excess water passing in through its exposed semi-permeable membranes but the retention of valuable salts, was a prime necessity. Possibly these conditions might have been met in a number of ways, but actually they were met by the development of an effective filtration device, the glomerulus, and of various mechanisms for reabsorbing from the filtrate the materials desirable for the animal to retain. The presence of a glomerular kidney in all fresh water fishes, and the anatomical evidence that in marine teleosts, which are in osmotic equilibrium with sea water and therefore have not the problem of excess water to handle, the the glomeruli are reduced both in number and in size or, in some, even absent, is indicative of their fresh water ancestry. The marine elasmobranchs have retained the glomerular kidney but obtained protection against water loss by mechanisms for the reabsorption of urea from the glomerular filtrate so that their body fluids are kept hypertonic to the external medium and an osmotic gradient maintained conducive to the constant entrance of water into their bodies across their exposed membranes.

***The influence of the rate of reproduction upon the establishment of species:*** Modern biologists, too, attach little value to the struggle for existence as the primary evolutionary mechanism and no longer consider established species evidence of their survival as the fittest in the sense that Darwin and Spencer used the words "struggle" and "survival." Living things are not engaged in continual competition with each other, nor does one type become established in a locality only through the total extinction of others. Rather, a type becomes established as a species because it is well adapted to the conditions of a given locality and therefore survives in greater numbers to reproduce its kind and so to increase its population and spread throughout the area in greater numbers than other types less well adapted. It is those that have won in the reproductive race rather than in the "struggle for existence" that are represented in existing species. And species have become extinct because they could not adapt to the extreme climatic and other changes through which the earth passed in the course of its evolution, or escape from them. Those that have been most successful in the reproductive race are those that have achieved, through mutation, along with their other modifications, modifications of various kinds to favor gametic union and preserve and protect the young during their embryonic development and early life, for it is not the number of gametes produced that count, but the number of young that successfully reach maturity and themselves reproduce their kind.

Examples of such modifications are seen in the evolution of the Spermatophyta and the development of the pollen grain as a

a

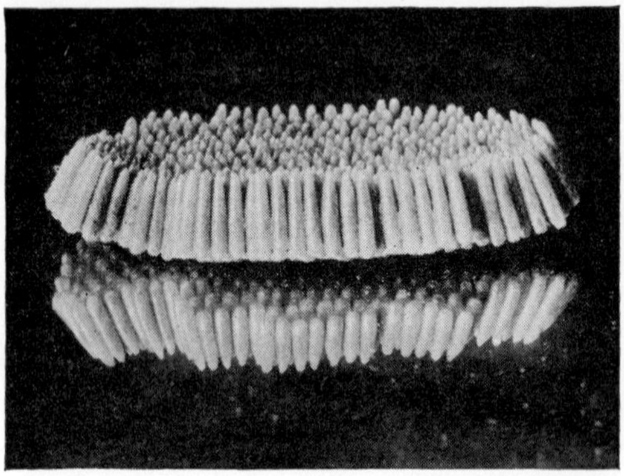

b

FIGURE 26.10 Egg cases of insects. (Photographs by courtesy of the U.S. Department of Agriculture, Bureau of Entomology and Plant Quarantine.)

a. Egg case of the praying mantis (Tenodera sinensis), containing hundreds of fertile eggs.

b. Egg raft of the mosquito (Culex pipiens). Each cylindrical egg, in its protective coat, is cemented to its neighbors and the whole mass is deposited on the surface of the water.

fertilizing agent, and of the ovule and ovary that become the flesh and coats of the seed, protecting and nourishing the embryo within until it becomes independent and capable of providing for itself, and in the various devices for seed dispersal; in the development of internal fertilization among animals, and the various means for guarding the fertilized egg from damage during its period of incubation and for shielding the young from harm. Most animals, for example, have attained in the course of evolution mechanisms for secreting a tough membrane or a shell around the delicate egg cell and of supplying it with nourishment, and in strictly terrestrial animals, with some source of water sufficient to carry it through its embryonic life (Fig. 26.10). Many insects, for example, lay their eggs on the bark of trees whose leaves provide the proper diet for the larvae, and their reproductive cycle is so timed that the larvae emerge when the plant is in foliage; the mud dauber, a wasp that builds a tube of clay around its eggs, seals into each chamber where an egg has been laid a spider that will serve as food for the newly hatched grub; most of the vertebrates, except mammals, provide the egg with considerable amounts of yolk which is consumed by the embryo during its growth and development. Terrestrial vertebrates had also to meet the problem of water supply for their embryos, if they were to free themselves of the necessity of returning to water to lay their eggs. Mammals have met this, and also the problem of food supply and suitable temperature for their developing young, by adjustments that keep the fertilized egg within the body of the mother during its period of incubation and allow the embryo to draw upon her for all that it needs from an external source. Reptiles and birds have met it by surrounding the egg cell with an adequate supply of nourishment and water before enclosing all within a shell more or less impermeable to water. With the habit of producing such cleidoic eggs (Greek, kleidoun = to enclose) is associated a biochemical modification, in that the end product of nitrogenous metabolism during all but the very earliest part of their embryonic lives of these vertebrates is uric acid and not urea. This is undoubtedly an adaptive modification, for uric acid is less soluble in water than urea and precipitates out before its concentration reaches a level sufficient to alter the osmotic relations within the system, or prove otherwise toxic to the developing embryo; deposited in solid form within the shell, or in birds, in the allantoic sac, it is without effect.

*The modern concept of species:* Advances in biological knowledge in the past fifty years have also brought changes both in the scientist's concept of a species and of the ways that species have become established as natural divisions among living things. By a species, the modern biologist means any interbreeding population of animals or plants, whose typical characters he defines as the mean around which the individuals composing that population vary. He has thus abandoned the idea of a type form, convenient as that may be to the morphologist, and thinks of a species as an aggregate of variant types, all with the same general characters, to be sure, and all capable of mating freely with each other and of producing fertile offspring, but reproductively isolated from other such groups. Within a species, there may be sub-species or varieties, geographically separated and with certain distinctive characters, but the members of such polytypic species remain potentially interbreeding unless they become in some way reproductively isolated from each other. Reproductive isolation may be effected in a number of ways, and it is by such isolating mechanisms that species have become established.

*Reproductive isolation as a factor in the establishment of species; isolating mechanisms:* The barriers set up to free interbreeding between members of a potentially interbreeding population may be geographical, ecological or biological ones. Geographical barriers are set up by changes in the contours of the land, separating one group within a population from another by land or water masses that they cannot cross; so separated, they may remain essentially unchanged and so persist as a polytypic species, or they may each evolve in different ways and so become distinct though closely related species. Ecological barriers are set up by the preferences groups may show for one kind of environment over another, and by changes that occur in the character of any given locality. Preference for one kind of climatic condition rather than another, of one range of temperature over another, or for different intensities and duration of light are all factors that may bring about the separation of one group of individuals from another, and so diminish their chances of interbreeding. Draining of swamps, diversion of rivers, deforestation and forestation and other changes in the vegetation, which may occur naturally or be deliberately brought about by man, all tend to alter the character of any given region and so, by favoring the spread of certain populations, bring about the segregation of others. Biological barriers are set up by conditions in the individuals themselves, so that even though they may coexist within the same local area, they are effectively prevented from mating. Such barriers are apparent in differences in breeding habits, in breeding seasons and in anatomical differences in reproductive structures. For example, the chances of interbreeding between individuals that are active by day and those that are active by night are less good than they are between those of the same diurnal or nocturnal habits, and similarly there is more likelihood of mating between two individuals that climb than there is between one of climbing and one of creeping habit. Differences in the structure of the reproductive organs may make fertilization impossible, and so effect a reproductive barrier. But even if fertilization is possible, there are certain genetic combinations that are incompatible and result in the death of the embryo or, if it grows to maturity, reduction in its fertility or its complete sterility. Immunological studies have shown, too, that antigen-antibody reactions may effectively prevent interbreeding; such reactions may be the cause of the failure of the pollen tubes of certain spermatophytes to grow in the styles of flowers of others closely related to them, and are known to affect the successful development of the human embryo. Any condition that reduces or prevents reproduction between individuals becomes thus an isolating mechanism and one that tends to segregate one group of individuals in a population from another.

*Hybridization and mutation in species formation:* Geographical and ecological factors may also operate to bring about the variability upon which the evolution of species depends, for they may bring together individuals that would otherwise be separated and so give them a chance to interbreed, if biological factors do not prevent them. The development of land bridges, connecting previously isolated land masses, and of straits, connecting previously distinct bodies of water, have provided means for the mixing of populations and so have increased the chances of their hybridization. When fertile individuals result from such matings, new types may develop. Such hybridization seems to have been an important factor in the evolution both of plants and animals, and in plants particularly, hybridization followed by an increase in chromosome number, or polyploidy, may have been responsible for the origin of many existing species. In both plants and animals, cytogenetic evidence has shown that structural changes in the chromosomes brought about by inversions, deletions, translocations and similar mechanisms distinguish certain existing species. But recombinations of genes through hybridization and redistribution of them in the genetic complex through such structural alterations as these are of less significance, as far as the fundamental fact of evolution goes, than changes in the genes themselves, or genic mutation, without which diversity among living things could never have begun, whatever factors may have been involved in its continuation.

*The rate of evolution:* Nor does the modern biologist or paleontologist accept evolution as a continuous process proceeding at a uniform rate for all species or, within a species, at a uniform rate for all its distinguishing characters. The rate at which evolution has taken place in any one group of organisms can only be determined through their fossil record, by which it can be estimated in terms of the diversity of types derived in any given period from a common ancestor, or by the extent of structural change that took place within any given group in a given period. From such evidence it appears that at certain times in the earth's history evolution has been rapid in some groups, slow or even at a standstill in others. But by "rapid" one means, in terms of the human life span, a period of years of almost incredible length. For example, the evolution of the cephalopods is considered to have been more rapid during the Triassic than at other times in their history, yet estimates of its rate, based upon fossil ammonites of the Permian and Triassic rocks, indicate that some 20,000 years elapsed before the combined effects of chromosomal alterations and selection had brought about evolutionary changes sufficient to distinguish a new genus.

In the evolution of the modern horse, which has left an almost complete record of its ancestry in the rocks of Europe and North America, is evidence of the different rates at which different structures have evolved (Fig. 26.11). The ancestor of the horse was a little tetrapod about the size of a fox terrier that browsed in the Eocene forests. This animal, called Eohippus (Greek, eos = dawn + hippus = horse) was also the ancestor of other Perissodactyls (Greek, perissos = odd + daktylos = finger), an order of mammals that includes the modern rhinoceros, tapir and sloth as well as the horse, in which the third digit on both the fore and the hind limbs is considerably larger than the others. The skull of Eohippus was not more than 6 inches long, with the orbits midway between the occiput and the snout; its teeth were comparatively simple; it had relatively long legs, with four toes on the forefeet and three on the hind, and in walking it used all its toes, which had hoof-like thickenings on the terminal phalanges. In the direct line of equine descent, Eohippus was succeeded in the later Eocene by Orohippus (Greek, oros = mountain, referring to the Rocky Mountain region where its fossils have been found), and Epihippus (Greek, epi = above), both of which were slightly larger animals with heads longer than that of Eohippus and with the last two premolar teeth modified as molars. Epihippus was succeeded by Mesohippus (Greek, mesos = middle), which appeared in the early Oligocene, a three-toed tetrapod about the size of a collie, and by Miohippus (Greek, meion = smaller), appearing somewhat later. Parahippus (Greek, para = alongside of) appeared in the Miocene; its face was considerably longer than that of any of its ancestors with orbits nearer the occiput than the snout, its teeth were longer and all but the middle digit on each foot was reduced in size, so that while all three may have touched the ground in walking, only one was probably effective when the animal was running. In the late Miocene, Parahippus was succeeded by Merychippus (Greek, meryx = ruminant), with teeth essentially like those of modern horses and longer, thicker and stronger bones in the third digit of each foot, and heavier hoofs covering the terminal phalanx of this digit than its predecessors had. Merychippus was far better adapted to life on the wide meadowlands that had begun to appear in the Oligocene than any of the browsing types from which it was descended. Merychippus gave rise to several closely related types, among them Hipparion, a pony-sized creature that spread over Eurasia, Protohippus (Greek, protos = first), that migrated from North to South America, and Pliohippus (Greek, pleion = more) and Plesippus (Greek, plesios = near) that remained in North America. Both Pliohippus and Plesippus were slightly larger than Hipparion; Plesippus had broad molars with folded surfaces like those of modern horses, and seems to have been the immediate ancestor of the present genus, Equus.

This fossil record shows that Eohippus did not evolve into Equus by a continuous and uniform modification of all its parts; it was the brain and skull that seem to have changed most radically during the Eocene, with little alteration of the teeth and feet; later, the evolution of the feet proceeded most rapidly, in terms of evolutionary rapidity, while the teeth underwent their greatest change still later, in the Miocene Period, when the herbaceous angiosperms were beginning their great spread over the dried-up swamps and the newly formed meadow-lands. And if one recognizes in these successive stages of equine evolution types that may be considered genera in the

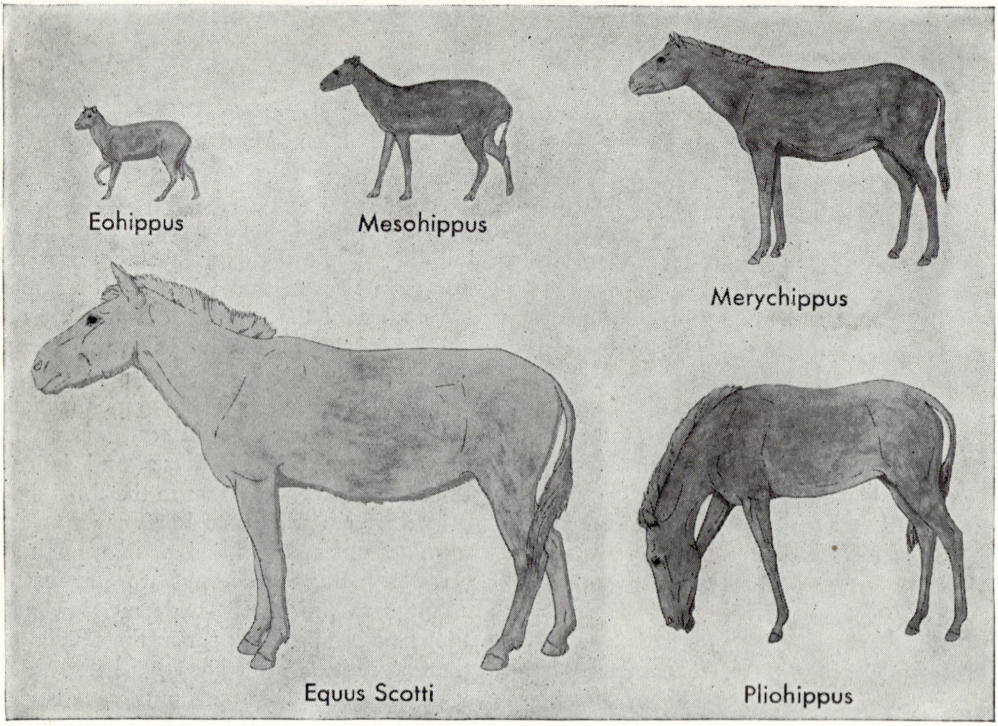

a

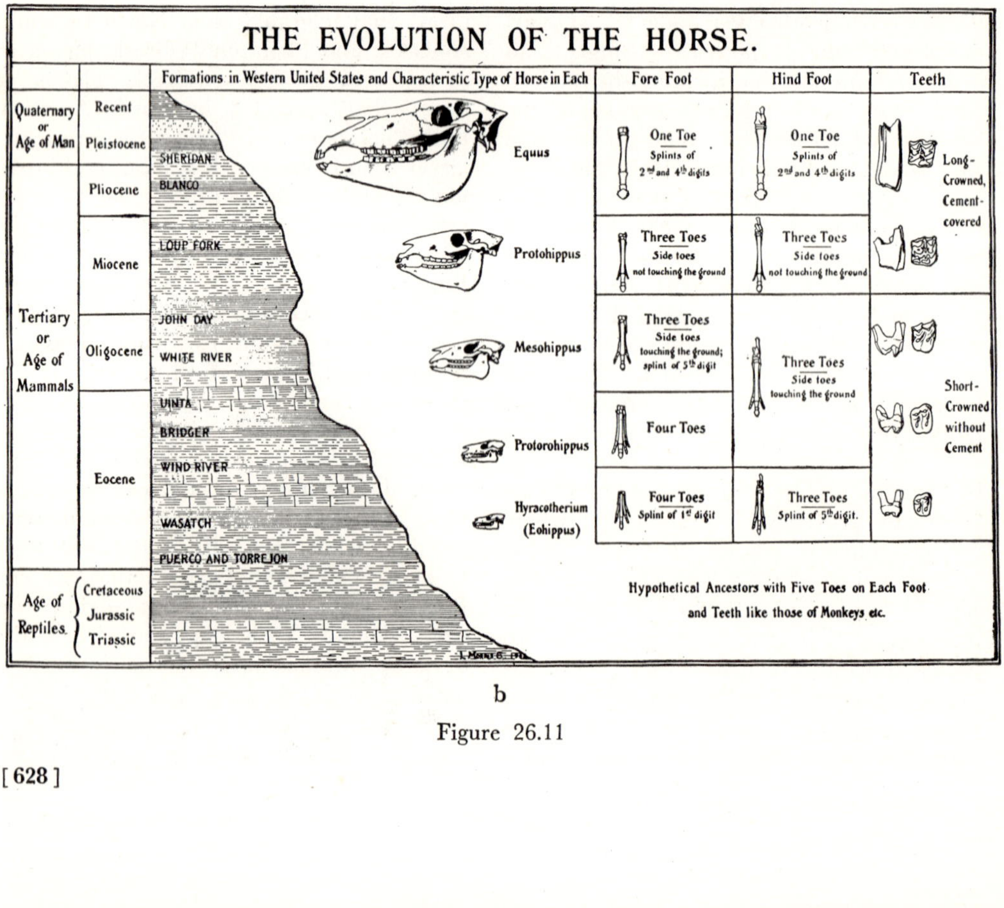

Eohippus

Mesohippus

Merychippus

Equus Scotti

Pliohippus

## THE EVOLUTION OF THE HORSE.

| | | Formations in Western United States and Characteristic Type of Horse in Each | | Fore Foot | Hind Foot | Teeth | |
|---|---|---|---|---|---|---|---|
| Quaternary or Age of Man | Recent | | Equus | One Toe Splints of 2nd and 4th digits | One Toe Splints of 2nd and 4th digits | | Long-Crowned, Cement-covered |
| | Pleistocene | SHERIDAN | | | | | |
| | Pliocene | BLANCO | | | | | |
| Tertiary or Age of Mammals | Miocene | LOUP FORK | Protohippus | Three Toes Side toes not touching the ground | Three Toes Side toes not touching the ground | | |
| | Oligocene | JOHN DAY / WHITE RIVER | Mesohippus | Three Toes Side toes touching the ground; splint of 5th digit | Three Toes Side toes touching the ground | | Short-Crowned without Cement |
| | Eocene | UINTA / BRIDGER | | Four Toes | | | |
| | | WIND RIVER / WASATCH / PUERCO AND TORREJON | Protorohippus / Hyracotherium (Eohippus) | Four Toes Splint of 1st digit | Three Toes Splint of 5th digit | | |
| Age of Reptiles | Cretaceous / Jurassic / Triassic | | Hypothetical Ancestors with Five Toes on Each Foot and Teeth like those of Monkeys etc. | | | | |

b

Figure 26.11

mammalian order Perissodactyla, then the rate of evolution of this order as a whole, in terms of its most highly evolved representatives, the horses, with each genus enduring about seven and a half million years, may be considered a rapid one, at least in comparison to that of the cephalopods between the Permian and the Triassic Periods or to that of other animal types whose evolutionary rate has been estimated.

*The evolutionary stream:* Bonnet thought of a ladder of life, Pallas and von Baer of a tree of life. An analogy that better fits the modern concept of evolutionary processes, however inconsistent it may be with the facts of physical geography, is that of a stream, in whose main current there is a constant gene flow, but from which new channels have arisen into which some of this gene flow has been diverted. And as these channels have cut their way through new areas, and carved out new courses for themselves, the genes in their main current have been modified and changed so that the gene flow in the smaller branches may be of a nature quite unlike that of the parent stream from which they originated. The course of some of these branches may run parallel to that of the main stream, while others run in wholly different directions, and they in turn may branch and start smaller streams upon their courses. The farther away the course of any minor or major stream carries it from the parent stream, the greater is their divergence and the less the likelihood of their reconvergence and a reunion of their gene flow. And like the real streams that cut their way across the surface of the earth, the evolutionary stream may at times flow rapidly, or, entering a pond or a lake, be temporarily checked, only to resume its flow again, with a slow or swift current, when it leaves the quiet waters. Sometimes, too, the evolutionary stream seems to have entered a back-

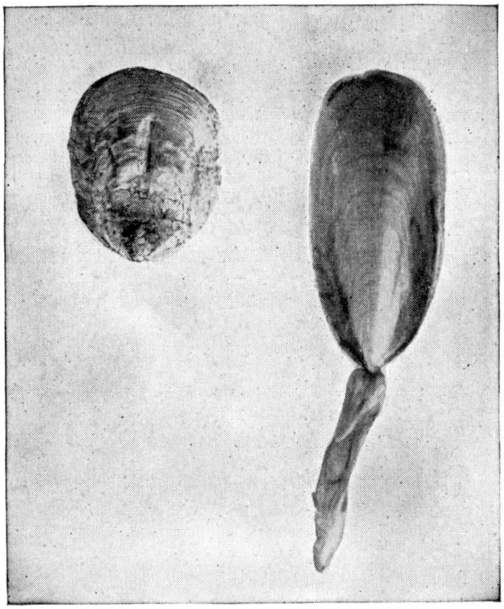

FIGURE 26.12 Modern and fossil brachiopods. (Photograph by courtesy of Dr. H. G. Richards.)

Left: Lingula cincinnatiensis Hall and Whitfield, from the Ordovician beds, Cincinnati, Ohio.

Right: Lingula unguis Linné, a recent brachiopod from Australia.

water and become stagnant, with neither progress nor change, or to have turned back upon itself, following a course that leads toward its beginnings. Such backwaters are represented by groups of animals like some of the brachiopods that seem to have under-

◄─────────────────────

FIGURE 26.11 The evolution of the horse. (Photographs by courtesy of the American Museum of Natural History, New York, N. Y.)

a. Restorations (Louise Germann A.M.N.H.) showing the external appearance of some of the ancestors of the modern horse. The genus Equus appeared in North America in the Pleistocene Age, and spread to every continent (except Australia), giving rise in the Old World to zebras (Equus zebra) and asses (Equus asinus) as well as to true horses (Equus caballus), which have been domesticated by man and subjected to intensive selective breeding, producing a number of different varieties. By the end of the Pleistocene, the genus Equus had become extinct in the New World, but horses were reintroduced by Europeans in their colonization of North and South America.

b. Diagrams showing the changes in the skull, the feet and the teeth in the course of evolution of the genus Eohippus into the genus Equus, from fossils found in western U.S.A.

gone little change since their first appearance in the Paleozoic seas, and some echinoderms which after retracing their evolutionary course from a bilaterally symmetrical animal and adopting the more primitive pattern of radial symmetry, have remained, presumably in complete adjustment with their environment, without any fundamental change in character since Carboniferous times (Fig. 26.12).

Plasticity is essential to evolutionary change, and by the smaller streams and rivulets of the evolutionary stream are represented those groups of animals and plants which approach or have already arrived at the limit of specialization and differentiation beyond which they cannot advance. But in the main streams the current still flows on, and who can say what channels these streams may cut, or where their courses may lead? The doctrine of organic evolution is the doctrine of progress in the world of life, a progress that there is no reason to believe has stopped, and every reason to believe is going on and on, with no less hope than it offered one hundred years ago for man's improvement in his understanding of the world in which he lives and of his relations to the other living things that coexist in it with him.

# BIBLIOGRAPHY

*(List of titles most frequently used for reference)*

Amberson, W. R., and Smith, D. C., *Outlines of Physiology,* 2nd edition. New York, Appleton-Century-Crofts, 1948.

Arey, L. B., *Developmental Anatomy.* Philadelphia, Saunders, 1946.

Ariëns Kappers, C. U., *The Evolution of the Nervous System in Invertebrates, Vertebrates and Man.* Haarlem, Bohn, 1929.

Barth, L. G., *Embryology.* New York, Dryden Press, 1949.

Bainbridge, F. A., and Menzies, J. A., *Essentials of Physiology,* 6th edition. London, Longmans, Green, 1929.

Baldwin, E., *Dynamic Aspects of Biochemistry.* New York, Macmillan, 1947.

Bayliss, Sir W. M., *Principles of General Physiology.* London, Longmans, Green, 1924.

Bourne, G., *Cytology and Cell Physiology.* Oxford, England, Oxford University Press, 1942.

Bremer, J. L., and Weatherford, H. L., *Textbook of Histology.* Philadelphia, Blakiston, 1944.

*Cambridge Natural History.* London, Macmillan, 1895–1910.

Carus, J. V., *Geschichte der Zoologie.* Leipzig, Hagenmuller and Schneider, 1880.

Cheronis, N. D., Parsons, J. B., and Ronneberg, C. E., *The Study of the Physical World.* New York, Houghton, Mifflin, 1942.

Cowdry, E. V., *Textbook of Histology.* Philadelphia, Lea and Febiger, 1938.

Dampier, Sir W., *A History of Science.* New York, Macmillan, 1932.

Downey, H., *Handbook of Hematology.* New York, Hoeber, 1938.

Eames, A. J., and MacDaniels, L. H. *Introduction to Plant Anatomy.* New York, McGraw Hill, 1925.

Fulton, J. F., *Selected Readings in the History of Physiology.* Baltimore, Thomas, 1930.

Goodrich, E. S., *Studies on the Structure and Development of Vertebrates.* London, Macmillan, 1930.

Harrow, B., *Textbook of Biochemistry.* Philadelphia, Saunders, 1943.

Heilbrunn, L. V., *An Outline of General Physiology.* Philadelphia, Saunders, 1943.

Hyman, L., *The Invertebrates.* New York, McGraw Hill, 1940.

Kingsley, J. S., *Outlines of Comparative Anatomy of Vertebrates.* Philadelphia, Blakiston, 1917.

Krauskopf, K., *Fundamentals of Physical Science.* New York, McGraw Hill, 1941.

Krogh, A., *Osmotic Regulation in Aquatic Animals.* Cambridge, England, The University Press, 1939.

Kudo, R., *Protozoology,* 3rd edition. Springfield, Illinois, Thomas, 1946.

Maximow, A. A., and Bloom, W., *Textbook of Histology.* Philadelphia, Saunders, 1948.

Mitchell, P., *Textbook of Biochemistry.* New York, McGraw Hill, 1946.

Needham, J., and Pagel, W. ed., *Background to Modern Science.* Cambridge, England, The University Press, 1938.

Noble, G. K., *Biology of the Amphibia.* New York, McGraw Hill, 1931.

Nordenskiold, E., *History of Biology.* New York, Knopf, 1928.

Parker, G. H., *Smell, Taste and Allied Senses in the Vertebrates.* Philadelphia, Lippincott, 1922.

Romer, A. S., *Man and the Vertebrates.* Chicago, University of Chicago Press, 1937.

Romer, A. S., *The Vertebrate Body.* Philadelphia, Saunders, 1949.

Simpson, G. G., *The Meaning of Evolution.* New Haven, Yale University Press, 1949.

Singer, C., *The Story of Living Things.* New York, Harper, 1931.

# INDEX

References in **bold face** are to pages containing illustrations.

Abdominal vein, of vertebrates, 346
Abiogenesis, 131–132
 (*see also* Spontaneous generation)
Abscission layer, 195
Absorption,
 in intestine of vertebrates, 434–435
 in kidney of vertebrates, 322–325
 in lymphatics of vertebrates, 351–352
 of solar energy by chlorophyll, 408–409
 of solar energy by melanin, 289
Académie des Sciences, 603
Academy of Experiments, 603
Academy of the Lynx-Eyed Associates, 602–603
Academy for the Secrets of Nature, 602
Accommodation in the vertebrate eye, **376**, 377
Acellular systems, 117–134
 (*see also* Protozoa and Protophyta)
Acetabulum, 277
Acetone bodies, 457
Acetylcholine, 390
Acicula, 212
Acidosis, 439
Acids, 48–51
Acoelous (Acoelomate) animals, **158**, **160**, 205–206
d'Acosta, José, 600
Acrania (Cephalochordata), 258, **259**
Acrodont vertebrates, 300
Acromegaly, 471, **473**
Actinotrichia, 275
Action current, *of nerve,* 388
Activation,
 energy of, 29
 of enzymes, 402
Addison, Thomas (1763–1860), 470
Addison's disease, 470
Adenosinediphosphate (ADP), 281

Adenosinetriphosphate (ATP), 281
Adrenal bodies, 469–471
Adrenalin, 390, 470
Adventitious roots, 173, 180, **186**
Aeolosoma, 211
Aerobes, 90
Aerobic oxidation (respiration), 90, 414
Afferent branchial vessels, in vertebrates, 343
Afferent (sensory) neuron, 356
Agametic (asexual) reproduction, 487–489
Agar-agar, 133, 417
Agassiz, Louis, 618, 621
Agglutination,
 of blood cells, 547–548
 of foreign bodies in blood, 329
 of Paramoecium, 331, 530
 of sperm, 564
Agglutinins, 329
 in human blood groups, 547–548
Agglutinogens, 329
 in human blood groups, 547
Agranulocytes, 327
Air (swim) bladder, of fishes, 264
Air, composition of, 77
Air sacs,
 in birds, 309, **310**
 in insects, 239
Albinism, 547, 554
Albumen, 41
 in blood of vertebrates, 326
 in milk of vertebrates, 303
 synthesis of, by plants, 419
Alcaptonuria, 554
Aleurone, **417**, 419
Alexandria, as center of mediaeval culture, 597
Algae, 117, 125–126
 blue-green, 125
 brown, 137–138, 408
 colonial, 135–137
  reproduction in, **496**, 497
 coralline, 137
 gametic meiosis in, 497, 520
 green, 125, **137**, **140**

pigments of, 137, 408
 red, 137–138, 408
 reproduction of, **496**, 497–498
 zygotic meiosis in, 497
Alkaline solutions, 49–50
Alkaloids, 203, 420
Allantois, 576, 583–584
Allele, 533
Allergy, 331
Alternation of generations (metagenesis), 498
 in algae, 520, **521**
 in bryophytes, 498–499
 haploidy and diploidy in, 520, 549
 in pteridophytes, 499–501, **502**
 in spermatophytes, 501–520
Altmann, Richard (1852–1902), 61
Alveoli, of mammalian lung, **308**, 309
Ameloblast, 300
American Philosophical Society, foundation of, 603
Amino acids, 38–39
 indispensable to animal nutrition, 437
 synthesis by plants, 411–412
Amitosis, 483
Ammonia,
 as end product of protein metabolism, 317, 457
 excretion of,
  by ammonotelic organisms, 458
  by echinoderm egg, 565
 oxidation of, by bacteria, 129
Ammonites, 627
Ammonotelic organisms, 458
Amnion, 262, 576, 583
Amniota, 262, 576
 brain, development of, 357–359
 cerebral cortex, 361
 cranial nerves, 367
 embryogenesis, 581–586
 eyelids, 305
 hypophysis, 365
Amoeba, **71**, **118**, 119
 feeding methods of, **426**, 427

[ 633 ]

# INDEX

Amoeba—*continued*
  localization of enzymes in, **403**
Amoebocyte, 147, 317, 327
Amphibia, **260**
  (*see also* Frog)
  accommodation of eye, 377
  aortic arches, 341, **342**, 343
  blastula, 566, 567
  blood vessels, **334**, 341–343
  cleavage, 566–567
  coelome, 305
  corpora bigemina, 365
  egg-laying habits, 525
  eggs, as embryological material, 560, 569–572, 588
  excretory organs, 318
  excretory products, 458
  gastrulation, 569–572
  heart, 336–338
  induction of ovulation in, 560
  integument, **290**
    pigment cells, 290
    respiration through, 264, 302
    scales, 291
  intestine, 315
  larva, 576, **580**, 581
  limbs, 277
  lungs, 306
  lymphatic system 349, 350–351
  maps, of egg, 569–572
  meninges, 355
  mesonephros, 318, 320
    experiments on, 322–325
  nervous system, 357, **361**, 364, 380, 383
  photophores, 304
  post-gastrulation changes, in embryo, 577–581
  respiration, 264, 302, 306–308, **309**
  skeleton, 269–270
  teeth, 300
  transplantation experiments, on embryos, 588, 589–591
  urinogenital system, **319**, 523–524
Amphimixis, 491, 529
  (*see also* Fertilization)
  in molds, **530**, 531, 532, **555**
  in Paramoecium, **528**, 530–532
Amphioxus, 259
Amygdalin, 419
Amylopsin, 432
Amylum (starch),
  synthesis, 417
Anabolism, 393, 394, 458–459
  in plants, 415–421

Anaerobe, 90, 128
Anaerobic oxidation (respiration), 90, 414
  (*see also* Fermentation)
  in bacteria, 127–128
  in vascular plants, 90, 203
  in yeasts, 133
Analogous parts, 95
Anamniota, 262, 576
  cranial nerves, 367
  eyelids, 305
  lateral line organs, 383
Anatomy, 101, 102–104, 607–608
Ancon (otter) sheep, 620
Androgens, 467
Androsterone, 467
Anemia, and iron deficiency, 454
Angiospermae, 168, 170, **171**
  (*see also* Vascular plants)
Angler fish, 304
Ångstrom units, 39
Animals,
  acoelous, **158**, **160**, 205–206
  body plans of, 204–211
  coelomate, 206–219
  distinctions from plants, 96–97, 116
  pseudocoelous, 205–206
Anion, 21
Anisogametes, 490
Annelida, 211–219
  fission in, 488
  gametic reproduction in, 522–523
  polyploidy in, 549
Annual rings, in plants, 196
Anomalies in development, 592
Anteater (Tachyglossus), 526
Antennae,
  of Crustacea, 222
  of insects, 229, **231**
Antennules, of Crustacea, 222
Anterior cardinal vein (precardinal), of vertebrates, 345
Anterior commissure, of vertebrate brain, 363
Anterior mesenteric artery, of vertebrates, 344
Anther, 511, **512**
Antheridia, 498
Anthocyanins, 70, 409, 419
  and genes, 553–554
Anthophysis, 134, **136**
Antibiotics, 139
Antibodies, 329–331, 352, 402
  in human blood groups, 547–548
Anticoagulants, of vertebrate blood, 329
Antigens, 329–331, 402

  in human blood groups, 547–548
Antipodal cells, 515
Antivitamins, 452
Ants,
  autotomy, 256
  chemoreception, 248
  life cycle and polymorphism, **255**
  sound reception, 247
Aorta, 335, 340, **341**
Aortic arches, in vertebrates, 341–344
Aplacental mammals, 576
Aponeuroses, 279
Appendages,
  of Crustacea, 220–223, **224**
  of insects, 229, 237
  of vertebrates, 275–279
Appendicular skeleton, of vertebrates, 265, 275–279
Apposition image, of arthropod eye, **246**, 247
Aqueduct of Sylvius, 358
Arachnids, 251–254
Arachnoid membrane, of vertebrate nerve cord, 355
Arcella, **118**, 119
Archegonia, 498
Archenteron, 569, 572, 573, 578
Archetypes, 611
Archimedes (287–212 B.C.), 286
Area opaca, of hen's egg, 567, 573
Area pellucida, of hen's egg, 567
Arenicola, 219
Arginase, 458
Aristotle (384–322 B.C.), 98, 102, 131, 560, 596, 611
Armadillo, **591**, 592
Arteries of vertebrate circulatory system, 335, 343–344
Arthropoda, 220–256
  chemical regulation in, 461–465
  polyploidy in, 549
Ascaris
  enzyme inhibitors in, 402
  reproduction in, 525
Ascomycetes, 133, 138
  amphimixis in, **531**, 532, **555**
Ascorbic acid (Vitamin C), 445, 449
  oxidation of, 453
  resorption of, by mammalian kidney, 323
Aselli, Gasparo (1581–1626) (Asellio), 352
Asexual reproduction (*see* Agametic reproduction)
Aster, of mitotic figure, 480

# INDEX [635]

Asymmetry, in Crustacea, **224**, 225
Atlas, of vertebral column, 270
Atmosphere, 77
  aerial, 77
  relation to life, 90–92
  soil, 83
Atmospheric pressure, 77
Atomic combinations, 18–22, **23, 24**
Atomic numbers, 13
Atomic unions, 17, 22
Atoms, 8, 9–12
ATP (adenosinetriphosphate), 281
Atrium, of vertebrate heart, 335, **336, 337**
Audioreceptors (*see* Otic organs)
Audition, evolutionary significance of, 379
Autolysis, 57
Autonomic nervous system
  of Crustacea, 229
  of insects, 243
  of vertebrates, 356, 367, 370–372
Auto-oxidation, 28
Autosome, 541
Autotomy, 255
Autotrophic nutrition, 408–423
Autotrophs, 92–93, 396
  biological importance of, 422
  carbon fixation by, 31–32
  chemosynthesis by, 408, 413
  metabolism of, 413–421
  photosynthesis by, 408–411
Auxins, 460–461
Avidin, 452
Avitaminosis, 445
  of A group, 445–446
  of B group, 446–448, 449
  of C group, 449
  of D group, 450
Axial skeleton, of vertebrates, 265, 268–272
Axis, of vertebral column, **270**
Axon (axis cylinder), of vertebrate neuron, 353
Azygous vein, of vertebrates, 346

Bacon, Francis (1561–1626), 334, 601
Bacteria, 32, 90, 126–134
  as antigens, 330
  carbon fixation by, 31–32
  chemosynthesis by, 408, 413
  and disease, 132
  general characters of, 126–127
  in intestinal tract of vertebrates, 435, 436
  pigments, 408
  relation to iron, 130
  relation to nitrogen, 128–130
  relation to oxygen, 127
  relation to sulphur, 130
  and sulfa drugs, 406
  synthesis of polysaccharides by, 417
  and thiamine synthesis, 448
Bacteriophage, 41
von Baer, Karl Ernst (1792–1876), 611
Balance Theory of sex inheritance, 544–545
Baleen, 297
Banting, Frederick G. (1891–) 467
Barnacles, 426, 615
Barriers to reproduction, 625–626
Basal metabolism, 438–439, 468
Bases, 49–51
Basic seven foods of human diet, 454
Basidiomycetes, 138
Bast fibres, 178
Bauhin, Caspar (1560–1642), 603–604
"Beagle," 614, 615
Beaks, of birds, 272, 297
Beaumont, William (1785–1853), 398, 428–429
Bees
  as agents of pollination, 514
  chemoreception in, 248
  haploidy in, 549–550
  modifications of appendages, 230
"Bends," 91
Benedict, F. G. (1870–), 438
Bensley, R. R. (1867–), 61
Benzene ring, 34
Beri-beri, 441, 442–443
Bernard, Claude (1813–1878), 89, 465, 622
Berthold, Arnold A. (1803–1861), 465
Berzelius, Jans Jakob (1770–1848), 398, 429
Bestiaries, 599
Bicuspid (mitral) valve, of vertebrate heart, 339
Bilateral symmetry, 151
Bile, 316, 432
Bile duct, 316
Bile salts, 432, 435
Bilirubin, 432
Biliverdin, 432
Binomial nomenclature, 99
Biocatalysts (*see* Enzymes)
Biochemistry, 105, 398, 457
  and genes, 553–556
Bioelectricity, 72, 287, 305
Biogenetic Law (Recapitulation Theory), 346, 620
Biological assay, of vitamin requirements, 452
Biological conditioning of environment, 83, 90, 455–456, 558
Biology
  development of, 3–7, 595–630
  introduction of term by Lamarck, 608
  subdivisions of, 101–105
  terminology of, 104–105
Biosynthesis
  (*see also* Anabolism, Chemosynthesis, Photosynthesis)
  of carbon compounds, 31–42
  by Euglena, 123–124
  of protein, 42
Biotin (Vitamin H), 445, 452
Birds
  accommodation of eye in, 377
  air sacs, 309
  aortic arches, **342**, 343–344
  beaks, 272, 297
  cerebellum, 366, 386
  claws, 292
  cloaca, 316, 320
  crop, 314
  excretory organs, 318
  feathers, 292–293, **295**
  heart, 336, 338–339
  integumental glands, 302
  lungs, 308–309
  lymphoid tissue, 350
  meninges, 355
  nervous coordination in brain, **387**
  neurotendinal spindles, 384
  nictitating membrane, 305
  optic tectum, 387
  perching mechanism, 287
  pneumatic bones, 271, 309
  scales, 291
  skeleton, 270–271, **272**, 277
  stomach, 314
  syrinx, 275
  veins, 345–346
Black, Joseph (1729–1799), 5
Black tongue, 448
Bladder
  air (swim) of fishes, 264
  urinary, of tetrapods, 321
Blastema, 486
Blastocoele (primary body cavity), 205, **562**, 566–567
Blastocyst, 568, **569**
Blastomeres, 566
Blastopore, 569, 571–572
Blastostyle, 155
Blastula, 566
Blind sac plan of Metazoan organization, 204

# INDEX

Blind spot, of vertebrate eye, 375
Blood, 141
  (*see also* Vascular system)
  cells
    of Crustacea, 227
    of vertebrates, 327–328
  change in composition of, in course of flow, 348
  coagulation of,
    in Crustacea, 227
    in vertebrates, 328–329
  conditions determining flow, 347
  destruction and formation in vertebrates, 328
  development of, in vertebrate embryo, 580
  protective properties of, in vertebrates, 328–331
  sites of formation, in vertebrates, 328, 349–350
Blood groups (types), of man, 331
  inheritance of, 547–548, 551
Blood sinuses
  in Crustacea, 225
  in elasmobranchs, 345
Blow-fly (*see* Calliphora)
Blum, F., 57
Body plans of Metazoa, 204–211
Bone, 141, **142**, 265–268
  pneumatic, of birds, 271, 309
Bones (*see also* Skeleton),
  of middle ear of vertebrates, 381
  movement of, 284–286
Bonnet, Charles (1720-1793), 606–607, 609, 610
Botallus, L., 343
Botany, 101, 102
  in classical period, 596–597
  in seventeenth century, 603–604
  in sixteenth century, 600–601
Bowman, Sir William (1816–1892), 318
Bowman's capsule, 318
Boyle, Robert (1627–1691), 5, 606
Boysen-Jensen, Peter (1883–), 459
Brachiopods, evolution of, 629–630
Bracts, 511
Bradycardia, 446
Brain, of vertebrates, 357–366
  (*see also* Nervous system)
Brain case (skull), of vertebrates, 271–275
Branch (secondary stem), 189
Branchia (gills),
  of annelids, 219

of arthropods, 223, 242
of vertebrates, 264, **265**
Branchial vessels, of vertebrates, 343
Bronchus, 308, 311
Brown, Robert (1773–1858), 15
Brownian movement, 15, 44, 61, 72, 352
Brunfels, Otto (1488?–1534), 600
Brunner, J. C. (1653–1737), 316
Brunner's glands, 316
Bryophyllum, 173
Bryophyta, 161–165
  reproduction in, 498–499
Buchner, Eduard (1860–1917), 399
Budding, 488
Buds, 181
  accessory, 189
  adventitious, 189
  leaf, 189
Buffers, 51, 326
Buffon, Georges Louis Leclerc (1707–1788), 604–606, 608, 609
Bulbs, 187
Bundle, fibro-vascular, 178
  distribution of, 182–185
  distribution of, in leaves, 191, 194–195
  types of, 182
Bundle of His, 340
Bush sickness, 454

Caecum,
  hepatic, of Crustacea, 226
  intestinal, of vertebrates, 316
Calcium,
  and coagulation of vertebrate blood, 328
  concentration in blood, controlled by parathyroid, 461
  concentration of, by sponges, 147
  in coralline algae, 137
  and digestion of milk, 431
  entrance into roots, 197
  as essential element in nutrition, 411, 431
  oxalate, in plant tissues, 419
  in rickets, 450
  salts, in bone, 266
    in milk, 303
    in shells of rhizopods, 121
    in skeletons of coelenterates, 156
    in statoliths, 155
Calliphora, 238, 427–428
Callus, 185, 485
Calorie, 13

Calorimetry, 6, 394–395, 438
Cambium, 178, 193, 484
  cork, 178, 184, 485
Cancellous bone, 267
Cancer, 352, 485
Cane sugar (*see* Sucrose)
Cape primrose (Streptocarpus), inheritance of flower color in, 553–554
Capillary, of vascular system, 331, 344
Capillary water, 83
Carapace, of crustacean skeleton, 220
Carbohydrates,
  energy equivalent of, 35–36
  heat of combustion of, 440
  metabolism of, 395
    and adrenal glands, 470
    and cortin, 470
    and riboflavin, 449
    and thiamine, 447
    and thyroxin, 468
  oxidation of, 413–414
  synthesis of, 31–32, 408–411, 415–418, 421–423
  value in animal diet, 439
Carbon, 33
  assimilation by plants, 422
  fixation, 31–32, 421–423
Carbon compounds, 33–42
  biosynthesis of, 31–42
  chain configurations of, 33
  metabolism of, 457–458
  ring configuration of, 33–34
    as active group in A vitamins, 451
Carbon dioxide, 26, 31, **35**, 47, 90, 96
  (*see also* Photosynthesis and Respiration)
  as chemical regulator, 455
  elimination in plants, 203
Carbonic acid, 31, 47, 48, 78
Carboxyl radical, 36, **37**
Carboxypeptidase, 432
Carcinogens, 485
Carnivores, **91**, 301, 427
Carotene, 375, 408, 446
Carotid artery, of vertebrates, 104, 343
Carpel, of flower, 511
Cartier, Jacques, 441
Cartilage, 141, **142**, 265–266
Casein, 303, 315, 437, 444
Caseinogen, 431
Casparian strip, 184
Catabolism, 393, 394, 457–458
Catalase, 407
Catalysts, 26, 30–31, 398
  (*see also* Enzymes)
Catastrophes, Theory of, 606, 610

# INDEX [637]

Cation, 21
Cauda equina, of vertebrate nerve cord, 357
Caudal vein, 345
Caudal vertebrae, 269, 270, 271
Cell, 16, 54–72
 (see also Histology)
 differentiation, 141–145
 surface-volume relationship, 476
Cell aggregates, 134
Cell division
 amitotic, 483
 mitotic, 476–482, 483–484
 in unicellular systems, 487–488
Cell plate, 482
Cell sap, 70
Cell surface, 62
Cell Theory, 56
Cell wall, in plants, 69, 144
Cellulase, 404, 427
Cellulose, 69, **143**, 144, 184, 404, 427
Centipedes, 245, 251
Central nervous system, of vertebrates, 356–366
Centrifugation, 58, **403**
Centriole, 480
Centromere (Kinetochore), 481
Centrum, of vertebra, 268
Cephalization, 225, 368
Cephalochordata (Acrania), 258, **259**
Cephalopods, rate of evolution of, 627
Cerebellum, 366, 386–387
Cerebral hemispheres, 359, 361, 387–388
Cerebral peduncles, 365
Cerebrospinal fluid, 355
Cerebrum (see Cerebral hemispheres)
Cervical vertebrae, 268, 269, 270
Cestum Veneris, 157
Chelicerae, 252
Chemical embryology, 592
Chemical equations, 17
Chemical equilibrium, 31
Chemical reactions, 22–31, 397–407
Chemical regulation, of metabolic reactions, 455–475
Chemoautotrophic nutrition, 413
Chemoreceptors, 248, 382–383
Chemosynthesis, 32, 408, 413
Chiasma,
 chromosomal, 495
 optic, 363
Chironomus, 239

Chitin, 70, 127, 138, 156, 220, 249
Chitinase, 427
Chlamydomonas, 124
Chloragogue cells, 218
Chlorella, 125
Chlorenchyma, 143
 in aerial roots of spermatophytes, 180
 in bryophytes, 162–163, 499
 in leaves, 191, 194
Chlorine, 20, 21, **24**, 197
Chlorocruorin, 219
Chloromycetin, 140
Chlorophyll, 32, 70, 123, 408–409
Chloroplasts, **70**, 143, 182, 408
Choanocyte, 146
Choanoflagellata, 134
Cholecystokinin, 466
Cholesterol, 418, 467, 474
Choline, 445, 451
Cholinesterase, 390
Chorda-mesoderm, 572, 573, 589–590
Chordae tendinae, 338, **339**
Chordata, 257–262
Chorio-allantoic membrane, 583–584
Chorion, 576, 583, 584
Choroid coat, of vertebrate eye, 373
Choroid plexus, 358, **360**, 364
Christianity, influence on development of natural science, 598–599, 602
Chromatid, 481
Chromatin, 60
Chromatophores,
 chemical regulation of, 461–463, 471, 473
 of Crustacea, 225, **461**
 of vertebrate eye, 373
 of vertebrate integument, 290
Chromogen, 554
Chromomeres, 479
Chromonema, 479
Chromoplasts, 70, 123
Chromosome numbers, 479, 494, 495, 549–550
Chromosome Theory of Inheritance, 533, 621
Chromosomes, 60, 478–480
 breaks in, 548–549
 homologous, 494
 maps, 539
 in meiosis, 494–497
 in mitosis, 476–482
 as physical basis of inheritance, 533, 537
Chyle, 352
Chylomicrons, 351

Chyme, 432
Chymotrypsin, 432
Chymotrypsinogen, 432
Cilia, 121
Ciliary body, of vertebrate eye, 377
Ciliary muscles, of vertebrate eye, 370
Ciliata, **120**, 121–123
Ciliated pits, in flatworms, 159
Circulatory system (see Vascular system)
Cirrus, 212
Citrin (Vitamin P), 420, 445
Cladophyll, **188**, 189
Classical period, of biology, 595–598
Classification of biological systems, 105–115
 in Amarakosa, 598
 Aristotle's, 596
 Bonnet's, 606
 Buffon's, 605
 Cuvier's, 610–611
 Gesner's, 600
 Lamarck's, 609
 Linnaeus', 98
 modern, 99–100
 Ray and Willughby's, 604
Clavicle, 275
Claws, 292, **294**
Clearance, in vertebrate kidney, 324
Cleavage, of egg, 565–568
Cleavage furrow, 482
Cleidoic eggs, 625
Cleithra, 275
Cloaca, 316, 320–321, 579
Clone, 488
Clot, blood, 328
Clothes moth (see Tineola)
Cnidoblast, 153
Coagulation of blood, 227, 328–329
Coal, 422
Coat color, in mammals, 293
 inheritance of, 547, 552
Cobalt, and bush sickness, 454
Coccyx, 271
Cochlea, of vertebrate ear, 380
Codosiga, 134, **136**
Coelenterata, 149–157
 diffusion in, 210
 gametic reproduction in, 521
Coelenteron, 152
Coeliac artery, of vertebrates, 344
Coelomate animals, 206–209
Coelome (secondary body cavity), 204–211
 in amphibian embryo, 578
 in annelids, 213, 217
 in arachnids, 253

[ 638 ]    INDEX

Coelome (secondary body cavity)—*continued*
  in Crustacea, 227
  in echinoderm embryo, 569
  in vertebrates, 305–306
Coelomoduct, **208**, 209
Co-enzymes, 401
Coiter, Volcher (1543–1576), 104
Coleoptile, 459
Coleps, **120**, 121, 123
Collagen, 266
Collateral nerve fibres, 354
Collenchyma, 143
Colloidal solutions, 52
Colloids, 53
Colon, 315, 435
Colonial algae, 135–137
  reproduction, **496**, 497
Colonial coelenterates, 155
Color,
    (*see also* Pigment)
  changes in Crustacea, 461–463
  changes in vertebrates, 290, **292**
  of coat, in mammals, 293, 547, 552
  of plumage, in fowls, 293, 552
  protective, 618–620
  of spectrum, 77
  structural, 234, 249, 290, 293
Color-blindness, inheritance in man, 544
Combs, fowl, inheritance of, 551–552
Commensal, **93**, 158
Commissures, of cerebral hemispheres, 363
Common cardinal vein, of vertebrates, 345
Companion cell, 176
Complement, 330
Complete proteins, 437
Composition of earth's crust, 79–83
Compound eyes, 245–247
Compounds, chemical, 17
Conditioned reflex, 429–430
Conduction of nervous impulse, 388–390
Cones, of vertebrate eye, 375
Conjugation, 497
  in Paramoecium, 529–532
  in Phycomycetes, **530**
  in Spirogyra, **496**, 497
Connective tissue, 141, **142**
Conservation of Energy, Law of, 5, 27
Conservation of Matter, Law of, 5
Constancy of species, concept of, 98–99, 604, 608, 610, 612
Continuity of the germ plasm, Doctrine of, 491–494
Contractile tissues, 141, 279–284
Contractile vacuole, 119, 122, 123, 146
Conus arteriosus, 335, **336**, **337**
Cook, Captain, 330, 442
Copernicus, 601
Coracoid bone, 275
Coralline algae, 137
Corium, 289
Cork, 185
Cork cambium, 178, 184, 485
Corm, 187
Corn (*see* Zea mays),
Corn smut (Ustilago zeae), 139
Cornea, of vertebrate eye, 305
Corolla, 170, 511
Coronary arteries, 343
Coronary veins, 346
Corpora allata, 464
Corpora bigemina, 365
Corpora quadrigemina, 365
Corpus callosum, 363
Corpus luteum, 527
Corpus striatum, 360
Correlation of parts, Doctrine of, 608, 610
Cortex
  of cerebellum, 366
  of cerebrum, 361–362
  of plant root, 174, **175**
Corti, A. (1822–1876), 380
Cortin, 470
Corticotropin, 472
Cothurnia, 134, **135**
Cotyledon, 170, 505, 517
Coulomb, 9
Covalent compounds (non-ionic compounds), 22, 45
Coxal glands, 253
Co-zymase, 401
Crago, color regulation in, 462
Cranial nerves, 367–370, 579
Craniata (Vertebrata), 259–390
  reproduction of, 565–568, 569–576, 577–587
Cranium, 271–275
Creatine, 321
Creatinine, 321
Cretinism, 468, **469**
Crop,
  of birds, 314
  of earthworms, 217
Cross-fertilization, in plants, 514, 534–537
Crossing-over, 538–539
Crossopterygii, 264
Crura cerebri, 365
Crustacea, 220–229
  color changes in, 461–463
  Darwin's studies of, 615
  embryology, as evidence for Biogenetic Law, 620
Crypts of Lieberkühn, 315
Crystalline solutions, 51
Crystals, 44, **45**, 62, 203
Ctenoid scales, 297
Ctenophora, 149, 157
Cubitus interruptus (ci gene), 551
Cutaneous sensation, in vertebrates, 383
Cuticle,
  of insects, 249–251
  of Nereis, 213
Cutin, 70, 182, 193, 249
Cuvier, Georges (1769–1832), 335, 608, 609–611
Cyanogenic glucosides, 419
Cycads, 168, **169**, 170
  reproduction in, 501–508
Cycloid scales, 297
Cyclosis, 72
Cytochrome, 280
Cytogene, 559
Cytology, 56, 105
Cytolysis, 67
Cytopharynx, 121, 123
Cytoplasm, 61
  division of, 482
  influence on early development of egg, 557
  inheritance through, 533, 556–558
  volume of, as limiting factor in cell size, 68
Cytoplasmic inheritance, 556–558
Cytosome, 121
Cytostome, 121

Dalton, John (1766–1844), 8, 56
Dam, Henrik, 329
Darwin, Charles (1809–1882), 600, 612–621, 624
  and fertilization of clover by bees, 514
  and regulation of plant growth, 459
Darwin, Erasmus, 612
Datura (jimson weed), mutants of, 550
Devaine, Casimir Joseph (1812–1882), 133
DDT (dichlor-diphenyl-trichlorethane), 251
Deamination, 317
Deficiency diseases, 17, 411, 441–443, 453–454
de Graaf, Regner (1641–1673), 397, 526

Deletions, of genes on chromosomes, **548**, 549
Dendrite, **353**, 354
Dental formulae, of mammals, 301
Dentine, 298
Dermal bone, 265, 275, 297–298
Dermal muscles, 283
Dermatome, 579, 580
Dermis, 289–290, **291**, 297–298
Descartes, René (1596–1650), 602
Desmids, 126
Determination of sex, 542–544
Detritus feeders, 425
Deuterium, 12
Dialysis, 401
Diapause, 561
Diaphragm, 306
Diarthrosis, 284
Diastole, 340
Diatoms, 125, 126
  gametic meiosis in, 520
  pigments in, 408
Dicotyledonae, 170
Didinium, **120**, 121
Diencephalon, 357, **358**, **359**, 363–365
Diet,
  recommended composition of, for man, 440–441
  synthetic, 436, 443–444
Difflugia, **118**, 123
Diffusion, 14–15
  between air and water, 77
  across capillary endothelium, 331–332
  in coelomate and acoelous animals, 210
  as feeding mechanism, 428
  of "inducing substances," 592
  in insect tracheae, 240
  as limiting factor to cell size, 476
  across placenta, 585–586
  in vascular plants, 197, 203
Digestion, 393
  (*see also* Digestive tract)
  Beaumont's experiments on, 428–429
  chart of human, 431, 433
  early experiments on, 397
  extracellular, 393
  intracellular, 152, 393, 413
  in man, 428–435
  in plants, 413
  in vertebrates, 435
Digestive tract,
  in annelids, 213, 217
  in arthropods, 226, 237–239
  in man, **431**
  in vertebrates, 313–318
Digitigrade mammals, 279

Dileptus, 122
Diluting gene, 552
Dinosaurs, 357
Dioecious species, 490, 513–514
Dioscorides (1st Century A.D.), 102, 598, 600, 601
Dipnoi, 346
Disaccharides, 36
  synthesis of, in plants, 415
Disease,
  deficiency, 17, 411, 441–443, 453–454
  germ theory of, 132–133
Division of cells, 476–484
Doctrine (*see also* Theory),
  of Constancy of Species, 98, 604, 612
  of Continuity of the Germ Plasm, 491–494
  of Correlation of Parts, 608, 610
  of Organic Evolution, 94, 595–630
  of Preformation, 587
  of Signatures, 162
Dodder, 180
Dominance,
  of genes, 547, 550–551
  of man, in the biological world, 261–262, 279
  physiological, 487
Dominant characters, in inheritance, 535, 546, 550–551
Dorsal ciliated organ, **212**, 216
Dorsal column (fibre tract), of vertebrate nerve cord, 356
Dorsal lip, of blastopore, 571
  as primary organizer, 589–590
Dorsal vertebrae, 268, 269, 271
Double decomposition (partner exchange), 24, 50
Drosophila,
  changes in chromosome number, 550
  chromosome maps, 539
  cubitus interruptus (ci gene), 551
  induction of mutation in, 546
  inheritance of sex, 543–544
  linkage and crossing-over in, 538–539
  multiple alleles, 547
  non-disjunction, 545
  red pigmentation in, 550
  salivary gland chromosomes, 539, **540**, 553
  spontaneous mutation in, 546
  translocation of chromosomes in, 549
  Y-chromosome inheritance in, 545

DuBois, Jacques (Sylvius), (1478–1555), 358
Duchesne, E., 139
Duct,
  bile, 316
  of Botallus (ductus arteriosus), 343
  of Cuvier, 335, 336, **337**, 345
  endolymphatic, 378
  excretory, 209
  lactiferous, 185
  Mullerian, **319**
  pancreatic, 317
  reproductive (gonoduct), 209, 523
  resin, 185
  thoracic, 349
  Wolffian, 318, **319**
Ductus arteriosus (Duct of Botallus), 343
Duodenum, 315
Duplicity Theory, of vertebrate eye, 375
Dura spinalis, 355
Dyne, 13

Ear, 378–382
Earth,
  as environment for living things, 75–93
  history of, 75, 80–81
Earthworm (*see* Lumbricus)
Ecdysis (moulting), in insects, 249–251
  chemical regulation of, 463–465
Echinoderms,
  blastula, **562**, 566
  egg,
    as embryological material, 560
    organization of, 587–588
    pigment, 569
  gastrulation, **562**, 568–569
  larva, **562**, 576–577
  metamorphosis, 577
  postgastrulation changes in, 576–577
Ecology, 105, 620
Ectoderm, 151, 205, 568, 581
Ectoplasm, 62, 121
Edema, 349
Efferent branchial vessels, of vertebrates, 343
Efferent (motor) neurons, of vertebrates, 356
Egestion, in vertebrates, 435
Egg (ovum), 62, 68, 490, 588
  cleidoic, 625
  cytoplasm of, influence on early development, 557
  evolutionary significance of protection of, 624–625

Egg (ovum)—*continued*
  growth of, in animals, 520
  polarity of, 561
  variations in size of, 68, 561
Egg-laying habits, of animals, 523, 525–526
Egg-white injury, 452
Eighteenth Century,
  development of biology in, 604–611
Eijkman, Christian (1858–1930), 442
Elasmobranchs, **259**
  accommodation of eye, 377
  blood sinuses, 345
  blood vessels, **333**
  brain and cranial nerves, **368**
  electric organs, 289
  gills, **265**
  integument, 297
  nictitating membrane, 305
  olfactory pits, 306, **381**
  placoid scales, 298, **299**
  skeleton, 265, 271, 275
  veins, 345
  water balance, 323
Electric catfish (Malapterurus), 305
Electric eel, 288
Electric organs, in vertebrates, 287, **288**, 305
Electric ray, 288
Electrolytes, 48–51
Electromagnetic spectrum, 77, 79
Electron, 8, 9
Elementary substance, 16
Elements, chemical, 8
  distribution, on earth, 77–79
  as essential nutrients, 17
    to animals, 437–438, 453–454
    to plants, 409, 411–413
  sources of, 393
  inert gases, 18
  metals, 19
  non-metals, 20
  Periodic Table of, 10–11
  in protoplasm, 16–17
  radioactive, 19
  stability and reactivity of, 18
  "trace," 393
Elephantiasis, 349, **350**
Elvehjem, C.A. (1901–), 448
"Emboîtement Theory," 606, 607
Embryo (*see also* Embryology)
  of angiosperms, 517
  of man, and Rh factor, 547–548
  of pine, 510
  of Zamia, 510
Embryo sac, 514–516

Embryogenesis, 576–586
Embryology, 105, 490, 560
  of amphibia, 560–587
  chemical, 592
  development of, in 19th Century, 611–612
  experimental, 586–592
Empusa musca, 139
Enamel, 300
Endochondral bone, 267
Endocrine organs, 318, 465–474
Endoderm, 151, 205, 568, 581
Endodermis, 175, 184
Endolymph, 379
Endolymphatic ducts, 378
Endometrium, 527, 585
Endomixis, in Paramoecium, 529, 532
Endoparasite, 425
Endoplasm, 62, 121
Endopodite, of crustacean appendage, 223
Endoskeleton,
  of chordates, 257–279
  of coelenterates, 155
  of Crustacea, 225
  of sponges, 147–148
Endosperm, 505, 517
Endosperm cell, 516
Endospore, of bacteria, 127
Endothelium, 331
Endothermic reactions, 28
Energy, 13
  activation, 29, 404
  chemical, 28, 32, 72
  Conservation of, Law of, 5, 27
  electrical, of cells, 72, 287, 305
  equivalents of food, 394, 440
  expenditure,
    by kidney, 325
    in mitosis, 484
    by placenta, 586
    by sponge, in formation of skeleton, 147
  manifestations of, 13, 83
  of molecules and atoms, 14–15
  of molecule of glucose, 32
  of molecule of water, 14, 28, 43–44
  as physical factor in determining conditions of life, 76
  radiant, 76–77, 79
  relations,
    in leaves, 200–202
    in muscular contraction, 281–282
  release,
    in aerobic oxidation of carbohydrate, 414

    in anaerobic oxidation of carbohydrate, 414
    in luminescence, 249
    in muscular contraction, 281
  requirements,
    of animals, 438–440
    of plants, 203, 413
  solar, 76–77, 79
    absorption of, by chlorophyll, 409
    absorption of, by melanin, 289
  sources of,
    in animals, 394, 439–440
    in plants, 203, 413
Enteroceptors, 373
Enterogastrone, 466
Enterokinase, 402, 432
Enteron, 204, 579
Environment,
  aquatic, **84**, **85**, 86
  biological conditioning of, 83, 90, 455–456, 558
  effects of, upon genes, 552–553
  effects of, upon organisms, 609
  internal, 89
  regulation of, 465, 622–624
  terrestrial, 89–90
  types of, on earth, 83–86
Enzymes (biocatalysts), 30, 60, 152, 397, 399–407
  in gastric juice, 315, 430–432
  in intestinal juice, 432–434
  localization of, in Amoeba, **403**
  and mutations, 622
  in pancreatic juice, 432
  in placenta, 586
  in saliva, 430
Ependyma cells, 355
Epiboly, 569
Epicotyl, 505
Epidermis
  of Nereis, 213
  of vascular plants, 143, 174, **175**, 193–194
  of vertebrates, 289–291
Epididymis, 524
Epigenesis, 611
Epiglottis, 311
Epinephrin, 470
Epiphysis, 364, 579
Epiphyte, 171
Epistylis, 134, **135**
Epithalamus, 364
Epithelium, 141, **142**
  coelomic, origin of, in vertebrates, 580
  (*see also* Peritoneum)
  neuro-, 155

# INDEX

[641]

Equilibration,
 in arthropods, 247
 in coelenterates, 155
 in vertebrates, 378–379, 386
Equilibrium,
 chemical, 31
 osmotic, 67
  regulation of, in vertebrates, 470
Equisetum, 166, **167**
Erector pili muscles, of mammals, 370
Erg, 13
Ergosterol, 418, 450
Erythrocruorin, 219
Erythrocytes, 327
Erythrophores, 290
Erythroplastids, 327
Essential oils, 203, 418
Estradiol, 467
Estriol, 467
Estrogens, 467
 of placenta, 526–529, 586
Estrone, 467
Estrus, 527
Eudorina, 136
Euglena, 123–124
Euplanaria, 159
Eustachi, Bartolommeo (1520–1574), 104, 380
Eustachian tubes, 312, 380
Evolution (*see also* Organic evolution)
 rate of, 626
 retrogressive, 96
Excretion
 in annelids, 215
 in arthropods, 227, 242–243, 622–623
 in fertilized eggs, 565
 in flatworms, 159–161
 in plants, 203, 420
 in vertebrates, 302, 321–325, 623, 624
Excretory organs
 in annelids, 215, 218
 in arthropods, 227, 242–243, 253
 in coelomates, 209–210
 in vertebrates, 318–321
Exocrine glands, 318, 465
Exopodite, of crustacean appendage, 223
Exoskeleton
 of coelenterates, 155, 156
 of Crustacea, 220
 of insects, 249, 251
 of Protozoa, 121, 123
 of vertebrates, 297–298
Exothermic reactions, 27
Experiment, biological, 101, 589
External meatus, of vertebrate ear, 381

Exteroceptors (*see* Organs of special sense)
Extracellular digestion, 393
Eyes (*see also* Photoreceptors)
 of annelids, 211, **212**, 216, 217
 of arthropods, 244–247
 of flatworms, 159
 of vertebrates, 373–378
Eyestalk hormone, of Crustacea, 462

Fabrizzi, Hieronymo (Fabricius of Aquapendente) (1537–1619) 104, 333, 603
Fabroni, G.V.M. (1752–1822), 398
Fallopio, Gabriele (1523–1562), 104, 598
Fangs, 300–301
Faraday, Michael (1791–1867), 21
Fat body, of insects, 242
Fats, 36–37
 absorption of, by lymphatics in vertebrates, 352, 435
 catabolism of, in animals, 439
 energy equivalent of, 440
 as solvent, 46, 47, 445
 synthesis by plants, 418
Fatty acids, 36
 essential to animal nutrition, 439–440
 synthesis of, by animals, 439
 synthesis of, by plants, 412
Feathers, 292–293, **295**
Feeding mechanisms of heterotrophs, 424–425
Femoral artery, 344
Fenestra ovalis, of vertebrate ear, 380
Fenestra rotundum, of vertebrate ear, 380
Fermentation (*see also* Anaerobic respiration)
 alcoholic, 414
 butyric acid, 414
 early studies on, 398
 of glucose, 399, **400**
 lactic acid, 414
 by molds, 139
 by yeast, 133–134
"Ferments," 398
Ferns (*see* Pteridophyta)
Fertilization, 491, 561–565
 in animals
  external, 523
  internal, 523–524
 and Mendelian inheritance, 537
 in plants, 499, 503–505, 508, 516
 Spallanzani's experiments, 607

Fertilization cone, 562, 564
Fertilization membrane, **562**, 564
Fetal membranes, 582–584
Fibrinogen, 326
Fibroin, 39
Fibrous proteins, 39–40
Fibrous roots, 179
Fibro-vascular bundles, 178, 182, **183**, 195
 distribution of, 182–185, 191
Ficin, 402
Filaria bancrofti, 349
Filum terminale, of vertebrate nerve cord, 357
Fins, 262–264, **276**
First Law of Thermodynamics, 5, 27
Fishes, **259**, 262, 264, **304**
 (*see also* Elasmobranchs)
 accommodation of eyes, **376**, 377
 aortic arches, **342**, 343
 branchial circulation, 341–343
 cartilage, 265
 cerebellum, 386
 coelome, 305–306
 corpora bigemina, 365
 ear, 378, 380
 electric organs, 287, **288**, 305
 excretory mechanisms, as evidence of organic evolution, 623–624
 excretory organs, 318, 320
 fins, 262–264
 gill slits, 274
 gills, 264
 heart, 335
 hypothalamus, 364
 integument, 297
 integumental glands, 302
 intestine, 315
 islet cells, 317–318
 jaws, 273
 lateral line, 373, 383
 luminescence, 304
 lymphoid tissue, 349
 meninges, 355
 photophores, 304
 pigment cells, 290
 respiratory areas, 264
 ribs, 269
 scales, 297
 skeleton, 268, 272
 stomach, 314
 swim bladder, 264
 taste buds, 383
 teeth, 300
 water balance, 322–323
Fission
 in multicellular systems, 488

# INDEX

Fission—*continued*
   in unicellular systems, 487–488
Fistula, 429
Flagella, 123, 152
Flagellata (Mastigophora), 123–124
Flame cells, **160**, 209
Flatworms (*see* Platyhelminthes)
Flavines, 449
Flavones, 70, 419
Fleming, Sir Alexander, 139
Flemming, Walter (1843–1913), 476
Fleshy roots, 179, 180
Flexures, of vertebrate brain, 358, **359**
Flight, in insects, 234–237
Flocculus, of cerebellum, 366
Flower, 168, 511–513
   inheritance of color in, 553–554
Fluid feeders, 252, 425
Fluorescence, of chlorophyll, 408
Food, 393
   (*see also* Nutrition)
   digestion of, by man, 429–434
   energy values of, 394
   ingestion of, by heterotrophs, 424–427
   loss of vitamin content from, 453
   utilization of, 455–459
Foramen magnum, of vertebrate skull, 271
Foraminifera, **119**, 121
Formaldehyde, as preserving agent, 57
Fossils, **77**, **78**, 121, 156, 259, 598, 602, 610, 621, 622
Fovea centralis, of vertebrate eye, 375
Fowls
   inheritance of color in, 552
   inheritance of combs in, 551–552
Fragmentation, 488
Franklin, Benjamin (1706–1790), 603
Free-martins, 553
Frequency of gene mutation, 546
Frog, **260**
   axial skeleton of, 269
   blastula, 566
   cleavage, **564**, **565**
   ear, 381
   experiments on conduction of the nervous impulse in, 389–390
   experiments on excretion in, 322–325
   gastrulation, **570**, **571**
   larva, **580**
   length of intestine, 315
   maps of egg, **572**
   movement of pigment in egg, 564
   neurula, **577**
   respiratory movements in, 309
Frölich, T., 443
Fructose, 34, 410
Fruits, 518–519
Fuchs, Leonard (1501–1566), 601, 603
Fucoxanthin, 137, 408
Fundamental tissues of plants, 143
Fungi, 117, 126–134, 138–140
   amphimixis in, **530**, **531**, **532**, **555**
Funk, Casimir (1884– ), 444
Fusel oil, 414

Galactose, 415, 417
Galen (1st Century A.D.), 102, 104, 214, 314, 598, 599
Galileo (1562–1642), 8, 334, 534, 601
Galls, 420, 485
Galvani, Luigi (1737–1798), 288
Gametangia, 490, 511
Gametes, 116, 490, **491**, 521–525
Gametic meiosis, 520–529
Gametic reproduction, 490–532
Gametogenesis, 494, 520–521
Gametophyte
   of angiosperms, 515–516
   of cycads, 503
   of ferns, 499–500
   of mosses, 498
Gammarus, water regulation in, 622–623
Gamones, 561
Ganglion
   of afferent neurons of vertebrate nervous system, 367
   of annelid nervous system, 216
   of arthropod nervous system, 227–229, 243, 244, 253–254
   of autonomic nervous system of vertebrates, 370
   of flatworm nervous system, 159
Ganoid scales, 297
Gaseous interchange (*see also* Respiratory areas)
   in acoelous and coelomate animals, 210
   in plants, 203, 413
Gastraea Theory, 620–621

Gastric juice, 315, 429, 430–432
Gastric vacuoles, 119
Gastrin, 430, 466
Gastropods
   inheritance of direction of coiling in, 557
Gastrulation, 568–576
Gel, 52
Gemmation, 488
Generative cell, of pollen, 503, 504
Genes, 41, 479, 533, 553
   and biochemical reactions, 553–556
   diluting, 552
   dominant, 550–551
   effects of, 550–553
   inhibitor, 552
   lethal, 552
   linear order of, 539
   mutation of, 546–547
   position effect of, 549
   rearrangements of, 548–549
   recessive, 550–551
   sex, 541, 546
   Theory of, 533
   on Y-chromosome, 545
Genetics, 105, 490, 533
Genic balance, 545
Genic change
   through mutation, 546–547
   through rearrangements, 548–549
Genotype, 550
Geological time scale, 75, 80–81
Geology, development of in 19th Century, 612
Geotropism, 459
Gerard, John, 601
Germ cells, 141
   (*see also* Gametes)
Germ-plasm, continuity of, 491–494
Germ theory of disease, 132
Germination of seed, in Zamia, 505, 506
Gessner, Conrad (1516–1565), 600
Gilbert, William, 601
Gill books, 252
Gill plate, 578
Gill slits, 274
Gills (branchia),
   in annelids, 219
   in arthropods, 223, 242
   in vertebrates, 264, **265**
Gizzard
   of bird, 314
   of earthworm, 217
Glands
   adrenal, 469–471
   Brunner's, 316

cement, 523
coxal, 253
crop, 314
digestive, in Crustacea, 226
electric, in vertebrates, 305
endocrine, 318, 465–474
epidermal
  of annelids, 213–214
  of leaves, 194
  of vertebrates, **290, 291,** 302–305
exocrine, 318, 465
gastric, 315, 430–432
integumental, 302–305
intestinal, **313,** 315–316, 432–434
mammary (milk), 302–304
mucous, 302, 578
oral, 312–313
pancreatic
  endocrine, 466–467
  exocrine, 317–318, 432
parathyroid, 468–469
parotid, 312, 429–430
pineal, 364
pituitary, 364–365, 471–473
poison, 313
salivary
  in insects, 237, 539, **540,** 553
  in vertebrates, 312, 429–430
sebaceous, **291,** 302
shell, 523
sinus, 462
spinning, in spiders, 254
sublingual, 312
submaxillary, 312, 372
sweat, **291,** 302, 387
thymus, 350, **468**
thyroid, 467–468
uropygial, 302
yolk, 523
Glenoid fossa, 275
Gley, E., 469
Glia cells, 355
Gliadin, 419
Glisson, Francis (1597–1677), 441
Globulin
  in blood of vertebrates, 326
  immune, 330
  specificity of, 331
  synthesis by plants, 419
Glomerulus, 318, 623
Glossina, digestion in, 238, 427–428
Glottis, 306, **311**
Glucose, 32, 34, **35**
  aerobic oxidation of, 414
  anaerobic oxidation of, 414
  fermentation of, 399, **400**
  in insulin deficiency, 466

as product of photosynthesis, 410
regulation of metabolism of, in vertebrates, 456
Glucoseamine, 156
Glucosides, 419
Glumes, 511
Glutelin, 419
Glycerol, 36
Glycogen, 139, 417
  in muscular contraction, 282
  synthesis of, in vertebrate liver, 317
Glycosides, 419
Glycosuria, 324, 466
Goldberger, Joseph (1874–1929), 448
Golgi, Camillo (1844–1926), 61
Golgi substance, 61, 449
Gonads, 209, 490, 523–524
  as endocrine organs, 467, 526–529
Gonium, 136
Gonoducts (reproductive ducts), 209, 523
Graafian follicle, 526, **527**
Gram atom, 18
Gram molecule, 18
Granulocytes, 327
Grasshoppers
  chemical regulation of adult differentiation, 464
  mouth parts, **231**
Gravity, 86
  (see also Equilibration)
Gray, Asa (1810–1888), 621
Gray crescent, **564,** 565, 588
Gray matter, of vertebrate nerve cord, 356
Greek science, 3, 595–597
Grew, Nehemiah (1641–1712), 56
Growth, 476
  atypical, 484–485
  in multicellular systems, 484
  of leaves, 189, 193
  of roots, 173–178
  of seed, 505–508
  of stems, 181–182
  in plants, 195–196, 415, **416**
  and regeneration, 486
  regulation of
    in animals, 471
    in plants, 459–461
  typical, 484, 485
Guanine, 290
Guard cells, 182, 193, 194, **201**
Gum, 417
Guttation, 203
Gymnospermae, 168, **169**
  reproduction in, 501–510

Habrobracon, multiple alleles in sex inheritance of, 547
Haeckel, Ernst (1834–1919), 117, 347, 620
Haemolysis, 313
Hairs
  leaf, 194
  mammalian, 293–296
    genetic control of color in, 547, 552
Hales, Stephen (1677–1761), 4, 68, 198, 334, 605
Halteres, 233, **234**
Haploidy, 495, 549
Harden, Arthur (1865–1940), 401
Harrison, Ross (1870–), 57
Harvey, William (1578–1657), 332, 534, 611
Haustoria, 180
Havers, Clopton, 268
Haversian system, **267,** 268
Heart
  in coelomate animals, 211
  in Crustacea, 226
  in vertebrates, 332, 335–340
    development of, in amphibia, 580
    initiation of beat, 340
    regulation of beat, 372
Heart, lymph, 349
Heartwood, 196
Heat
  of combustion of foods, 6, 394
  conservation in bodies of homoiothermic animals, 438
  as energy, 5, 6, 13, 29–30, 83
  loss by animals, 5, 6, 438
  loss by plants, 415
  production, in body, 5, 6, 395, 438
  production, by fertilized egg, 565
  production, by nerve, 388
  relation to life, 87–89
  unit of measure of, 13
Helium, 12
Helix, digestive enzymes of, 427
van Helmont, Jan Baptist, (1577–1644), 4, 32
Hematochrome, 123
Hematococcus, 123, 124
Hemiazygous vein, 346
Hemichordata, 257, **258**
Hemocoele, 206, 220, 225, 239, 253
Hemocyanin, 226, 239
Hemoglobin, 215, 218, 219, 239, 327
Hemophilia, 544

## INDEX

Henle's loop, of vertebrate kidney, 321
Hensen's node (primitive knot), 573
Henslow, John Stevens (1796–1861), 614
Heparin, 329
Hepatic caeca, in Crustacea, 226
Hepatic portal system, 345
Hepatic sinus, 345
Hepaticae (liverworts), 161, 162–163
  reproduction by gemmation, 488
Heptoses, 415
Herbals, 102, 600–601
Herbivores, **91**, 301, 427
Herbs, 186
Herschel, Sir John (1792–1871), 614
Hertwig, Richard (1850–1937), 134
Heteroauxin, 460
Heterochromosome (heterosome), 540
Heteromorphosis, 486
Heterosome (heterochromosome), 541
Heterospory, 500, 502
Heterotrophic nutrition, 424–435
Heterotrophs, **91**, 92, 96, 396
  dependence of, on autotrophs, 424
  feeding mechanisms, 424–427
  nutritional requirements, 424, 436–454
Heterozygosity, 534
Hexapoda, 229
  (*see* Insecta)
Hexose (monosaccharide), 35, 36, 415
Hippocampus, 363
Hirudin, 329
His, William (1831–1904), 57, 340
Histamine, 390, 430, 466
Histology, 105
  of animals, 141–142
    Crustacea, 225–226
    Hydra, 151–153
    flatworms, 157–161
    Nereis, 213, 214
    sponges, 147–148
    vertebrates
      alimentary canal, 313
      bone, 265–268
      blood, 327–328
      blood vessels, 331–33.
      brain, 357–366
      cartilage, 265–266
      ear, 378–382

eye, 373–375
joints, 285
kidney, 318–321
lungs, 309–310
lymphatic system, 348–349
muscle, 279–281
nervous system, 353–355
of plants, 143–144, 196
  bryophytes, 162–163
  vascular plants
    leaves, 191–195
    roots, 173–179
    stems, 181–186
Holoblastic cleavage, 566
Holst, A., 443
Homoiothermism, 88, 438
Homologous chromosomes, 494
Homologous parts, 95
Homomorphosis, 486
Homospory, 500
Homozygosity, 534
Hoofs, 292, **294**
Hooke, Robert (1635–1703), 54, 185
Hooker, J. D., 616
Hopkins, Sir Frederick Gowland (1861–1947), 444
Hormones, 407, 455–457
  (*see also* Chemical regulation of metabolic reactions)
  and expression of genes, 553
  in fertilization, 561
  in growth, 459–461, 471
  in invertebrates, 461–465
  reproduction of mammals, 526–529, 586
  synthesis of, by plants, 420
  in vertebrates, 465–474
  and vitamins, 474–475
Horns, 296
Horse, evolution of, 627–628
von Humbolt, Alexander (1769–1859), 614
Hunter, John (1728–1793), 607–608, 609
Huxley, Thomas Henry (1825–1895), 16, 620
Hybridization
  Mendel's experiments on, 534–537
  in species formation, 626
Hybrids, 534
Hydra, 150–153
  reproduction, 488, **491**, 521
  viridis, symbiosis in, 126
Hydranth, 155
Hydration movements, 97
Hydrochloric acid, 22, 49, 50, 315
Hydrocoele, of echinoderm larva, 576

Hydrogen, 8, 9, **12**
  heavy (deuterium), 12
  ion (hydrion), 48–51
  molecule, 22, **23**
Hydrogen peroxide, decomposition of (auto-oxidation), 28, 407
Hydrolysis, 24
Hydrophyte, 202
Hydroxyl ion, 21, 48–51
Hygroscopic water, 83
Hyoid arch, 274, 343
Hyomandibular bone (bar), 274
Hyperglycemia, 466
Hyperthyroidism, 468
Hypervitaminosis, 452
Hypocotyl, 505
Hypophysis, 364, **365**, 471–473
Hypostome, 150
Hypothalamus, 364, 387

Ileum, 315
Iliac artery, 344
Ilium, 277
Imago, 251
Immunity, in vertebrates, 329–331
Immunopolysaccharides, 417–418
Implantation, of mammalian embryo, 527
Incus, 381
Indicators, 49
  plant pigments as, 420
Induction
  of gene mutation, 546
  in morphogenesis, 485, 589–592
  of ovulation in frog, 560
Inert gases, 18
Infundibulum, 364, 579
Ingestion, 427, 429
  (*see also* Feeding mechanisms)
Inheritance
  of acquired characters, 609
  blood groups in man, 547–548, 551
  chromosome theory of, 533
  of coat color in mammals, 547, 552
  of color in flowers, 553–554
  of combs in fowls, 551–552
  cytoplasmic, 556–558
  of direction of coiling in gastropods, 557
  of kappa in Paramoecium, 557–558
  of plastids in plants, 557
  possible mechanisms of, 558–559
  of sex, 540–545, 547

sex-linked, in Drosophila, 543–544
  in man, 544
Inhibition
  of enzyme activity, 402
  of growth, 460–461
  of moulting, 463–465
  nervous
    in annelids, 216
    in insects, 244
    in vertebrates, 372
  of vitamin activity, 452
Inhibitor gene, 552
Inner cell mass, 568
Innominate vein, 346
Insecta, 229–251
  as agents of pollination, 514
  chemical regulation in, 463–465
  egg-laying habits, 525
  reproductive organs, **524**
  treatises on, in 18th Century, 607
Instar, 251
Insulin, 318, 466, 467
Integument
  of ovule, 503, 515
  of vertebrates, 289–305
Intermedin, 473
Internal environment, 89
  regulation of, 465, 622–624
Interphase, of mitosis, 483–484
Inter-renal bodies, 470
Intersegmental artery, of vertebrates, 344
Intersex
  in cattle, 553
  in Drosophila, 545
Intestinal juice, 316, 432–434
Intestinal mucosa, as endocrine organ, 465–467
Intestine, of vertebrates, 315–316
  movements of, 432
  secretions of, 432–434
Intracellular digestion, 152, 393, 413
Inulin, 324, 417
Invagination, 569
Inversions, of genes on chromosomes, **548**, 549
Invisible College, 603
Involution, 569, **570**
Iodine, as essential element in nutrition, 438
Iodothyroglobulin, 468
Ionic compounds, 22
  solution of, in water, 45
Ions, 19, 20–21
  and enzymatic reactions, 402
  diffusion into roots, 197
  hydrated, 45
Iridiocytes, 290

Iron
  bacteria in relation to, 130
  in desmid shells, 126
  as essential element in nutrition, 409, 438
"Iron enzymes," 406, 407, 438
Ischium, 277
Islet cells, of vertebrates, 317–318, **466**
Islets of Langerhans, 466
Isogametes, 490
Isolating mechanisms, in evolution, 625–626
Isomers, 34
Isotopes, 12
  as "tracers," 267, 412, 459

Jardin des Plantes, 604, 605
Jaws
  of Crustacea, **222**
  of vertebrates, 273–274, **298**
Jejunum, 315
Jenner, Edward (1749–1823), 330
Joints, 284–287
Jugular vein, of vertebrates, 346
Jung, Joachim (1587–1657), 604
Juvenile hormone, in insects, 464

Kappa, inheritance of in Paramoecium, 557–558
Kelp, 137
Kelvin, Lord (1824–1907), 14, 29
Keratin, 39, **40**, 289
  digestion of, by Tineola, 428
Keratinase, 428
Kerona, 153
Ketone bodies, 457, 467
Kidney, 318–321
  absorption in, 322
  aglomerular, 324
  clearance values of, 324
  comparative anatomy of fish, as evidence of organic evolution, 623–624
  filtration in, 322
  regulation of phosphate excretion in, 469
  secretion in, 325
  work of, 325
Killer strains of Paramoecium, 455–456, 557–558
Kinetic energy, 14
Kinetochore (centromere), 481
Koch, Robert (1843–1910), 131, 132, 417
Kölliker, Rudolf (1817–1905), 618
Kühne, Willy (1837–1900), 399

Kupffer, K. W. (1829–1902), 317
Kupffer cells, 317, 353

Labium, 229, **231**
Labrum, 229
Labyrinths, of vertebrate ear, 379
Lacteals
  in fat absorption, 351
  of intestinal villus, **313**, 315
Lactic acid
  as end product of fermentation, 414
  in muscular contraction, 282
  structural formula, 424
Lactiferous ducts, 185
Ladder of nature, 606, 608, 609, 612
Lagena, of vertebrate ear, 379
Lamarck, Jean Baptiste de Monet (1744–1829), 608–609, 610, 612, 614
Lamina terminalis, of vertebrate brain, 359
Laminaria, 137, 176, 520
Langerhans, Paul (1847–1888), 466
Larva
  amphibian, **580**, 581
    branchial circulation in, 341–343
    epidermal teeth, 296, 297
    excretion of ammonia, 458
    feeding habits, 297
  echinoderm, **562**, 576–577
  insect, **241**, 251
Larynx, 275
Lateral line organs, 383
Latex, 186
Lavoisier, Antoine (1743–1794), 4, 5, 606
Law
  Biogenetic, 346, 620
  of Conservation of Energy (First Law of Thermodynamics), 5, 27
  of Conservation of Matter, 5
  of Constant Proportions, 18
  of Independent (Random) Assortment, of inheritable factors, 537
    modifications of, 537–538
  Periodic, 9
  of Segregation, 537
Leaves, 189–195
Lecithin, 37
  synthesis by plant, 418
Leeches, 219
Leeuwenhoek, Antony van (1632–1723), 55, 117, 126, 130, 206, 529, 603, 607
Lemna, **84**, 202

Lenticel, 181, **184**, 185
Lepisma, 233
Lethal genes, 552
Leucocytes, **71**, 327
Leucoplasts, 70
Lever, 286
Leverage, in vertebrate body, 286–287
Lichens, 140
Lieberkühn, J. N. (1711–1756), 315
Light
  and carbohydrate synthesis 31–32
  (*see also* Photosynthesis)
  and chlorophyll synthesis, 409
  as energy, 13, 83
  production
    in insects, 248–249
    in vertebrates, 304–305
  relation to living things, 86–87
  responses to (*see* Photoreceptors)
  spectrum, 77
Lignin, 70, 96, 177, 184, 186
Limbs, of tetrapods, 262–264, **278**
Limulus, 245, **253**
Lind, Captain, and scurvy, 441
Linkage, 538
Linnaeus, Karl (1707–1778), 98–99, 511, 600, 604, 605, 609, 610
Lipase of gastric juice, 401, 431
Lipids, 36–37
  heat of combustion, 395
  synthesis by plants, 418
Liquid crystals, 45
Lister, Joseph (1827–1912), 131, 139
Lithocyte, 155
Litmus, 49, 140
Liver, 265, 316–317, 579
Liverworts (*see* Hepaticae)
Lock and key theory of enzyme action, 404–406
Loewi, Otto, 389
Luciferinase, 249, 304
Luciferin, 248, 304
Lumbricus (earthworm), 216–219
Lung books, 252–253
Lungs, 264–265, 306–312
Luteinizing hormone, 527
Lycopodium, 15, **167**, 183
Lyell, Sir Charles (1797–1875), 612, 615, 616, 618, 620
Lygaeus
  chromosomes of, 540, **542**
Lymantria, regulation of moulting in, 463

Lymph, 141, 349–352
Lymph hearts, 349
Lymph nodes, 350, **351**
  as filters, 352
Lymph valve, **351**
Lymphatic system, of vertebrates, 348–352
Lymphocytes, **327**, 349
Lymphoid tissue, 349
Lyonet, Pierre (1707–1789), 607
Lysis
  of bacteria, 330
  of erythrocytes by snake venom, 313
  of jelly membrane of echinoderm eggs, 564

McCollum, E. V. (1879–), 444
Macleod, J. R. (1876–1935), 467
Macronucleus, in cell division, 123, 487
Macrophages, 353
Macrophagous feeders, 427
Magnesium, 19, **20**
  as essential element in plant nutrition, 411
Malapterurus (electric catfish), 305
Malleus, 381
Malpighi, Marcello (1628–1694), 55, 242, 320, 607
Malpighian corpuscle
  of vertebrate kidney, 320
Malpighian layer of vertebrate integument, 289, **291**
Malpighian tubules, 242, **238**
Maltase
  in pancreatic juice, 432
  in saliva, 430
Malthus, Thomas Henry (1766–1834), 615–616
Maltose, synthesis in plants, 415
Mammals (*see also* Placental mammals), **263**
  accommodation of eye, 377
  aortic arches, **342**, 343–344
  blood vessels, 335
  cerebellum, 366, 386
  cerebral cortex, 361–363, 387
  claws, 292
  cloaca, 316, 320
  corpora quadrigemina, 365
  cutaneous sensation, 383
  digitigrade, 278, **279**
  ear, 381–382
  excretory organs, 318
  eyelids, 305
  hair, 293–296
  heart, 336, 338–339
  hoofs, 292

  horns, 296
  hypothalamus, 364
  inheritance of coat color, 547
  integumental glands, 302–304
  intestine, 315–316
  lungs, 309–312, **308**
  lymphatic system, 349–352
  meninges, 355
  nails, 292
  nervous coordination in brain, **388**
  neurotendinal spindles, 384
  placenta, 526
  plantigrade, 278, **279**
  scales, 291
  skeleton, 271, 272, 273, 277–279
  stomach, 314–315
  taste buds, 383
  unguligrade, 278, **279**
  veins, 345–346
Mammary (milk) glands, 302
Man
  dominance in biological world, 261, 279
  inheritance of blood groups, 547–548, 551
  inheritance of color blindness, 544
  inheritance of hemophilia, 544
  kidney, 321
  relative composition of blood and urine, 321
Mandibles (jaws)
  of Crustacea, 222
  of insects, 229
Mandibular arch, in vertebrate circulation, 343
Mannitol, 324
Maps
  chromosome, 539
  areas of presumptive tissues in amphibian eggs, 569–572
Marey, Etienne Jules (1830–1904), 236
Marrow cavity, of bones, 268
Marsupials, 525, 526
Marsupium, 525
Mastigophora (Flagellata), 123–124
Mating types in Paramoecium, 530
Matter
  concept of, 8
  Conservation of, Law of, 5
  elementary particles of, 12
Matthioli, Pietro Andrea (1500–1577), 601
Maturation
  of germ cells (*see* Oogenesis and Spermatogenesis)

# INDEX [647]

of plant tissues, 196
zone of plant root, 174
Maxillae
  of Crustacea, **222**
  of insects, 229
Mayow, John (1640–1679), 3, 606
Mechanistic philosophy, 602
Meckel, Johann Friedrich (1781–1833), 611, 620
Medulla oblongata, 366
Medullary sheath, of vertebrate neuron, 353
Medusae, **149**, 150, 153
Megagametophyte
  of angiosperms, 516
  of Selaginella, 501
  of Zamia, 503
Megaspores, 501
Megasporogenesis
  in angiosperms, 515
  in Zamia, 503
Meiosis, 494–497
  and evolution, 621
  and Mendelian inheritance, 537
Meissner's corpuscles, **382**, 383
Melanin, 289, 373, 554
Melanophores, 290
Membrane
  arachnoid, 355
  cell, 63
  chorio-allantoic, 583
  egg, 561
  embryonic (fetal), 576, 582–584
  fertilization, **562**, 564
  nictitating, 305
  plasma, 63–68, 197–198
  semi-permeable, 63, 197
  synovial, 285
Membrane bone, 267
Mendel, Johann (1822–1884), 534–537, 617, 621
  Laws of inheritance, 537, 621
Mendel, L. B. (1872–), 445
Mendeleef, Dimitro (1834–1907)
  and the Periodic Table of the Elements, 8, 27
Meninges, 355
Meninx primitiva, 355
Menstruation, 527
von Mering, Joseph (1848–1908), 465
Meristem, 143, 173, 484
Merkel's corpuscles, **382**, 383
Meroblastic cleavage, 566
Mesencephalon, 357, **358**, **359**, 365, 579
Mesenchyme, 141, **142**, 147, 205, 569, 579, 580
Mesenteron, of Crustacea, 226

Mesoderm, 141, 157–148, 159, 204, 205, 206, 568, 572
  derivatives of, in vertebrate embryogenesis, 581
  dorsal, 579
  lateral, 579
  somatic, 578
  splanchnic, 578
Mesogloea, 147, 151
  composition of, 155
Mesonephros, 318, **319**
Mesophyll, 194
Mesophyte, 202, 203
Mesopterygium, 275
Mesostoma, 153
Mesothelium, 206
Metabolism, 16, 203, 393–394, 413–421, 455–475
  anabolic, 415–421, 458–459
  basal, 438–439, 468
  of carbohydrate, 447, 449, 468, 470
  catabolic, 413–414, 457–458
  chemical regulation of, 455–475
  of fertilized egg, 565
Metabolites, 393
  (*see also* Excretion)
Metagenesis, 498
  (*see also* Alternation of Generations)
Metals, 19
Metamerism (segmentation), 97
  in annelids, 219
  in arthropods, 220, 229
  in chordates, 257, 367, 578
Metamorphosis, 249–251, 577, 581
Metanephros, 318
  (*see also* Kidney)
Metanephridium, **208**, **209**, 210
  in earthworm, 218
  in Nereis, 215
Metaphyta (*see also* Bryophyta, Pteridophyta, Spermatophyta)
  reproduction in, 498–520
Metapterygium, 275
Metastasis, 352
Metazoa, 144
  body plans of, 204–211
  embryology of, 561–592
Metencephalon,
  divisions of, 357, **359**, 366
Meyer, Julius Lothar (1830–1895), 8
Micelles, 39
Microchemistry, 57, 58
Microgametophyte,
  of angiosperms, 514, 516
  of pine, 508
  of Selaginella, 501
  of Zamia, 503, 504

Microincineration, 58
Micromanipulator, 58
Micronucleus, in cell division, 123, 487
Microphagous feeders, 425
Micropyle of ovule, 503
Microscope, 54
  early use of, 55–56
Microscopy, 58–59
Microspores, 501
Microsporogenesis,
  in angiosperms, 511
  in pine, 508
  in Zamia, 503
Microtome, 57
Middle Ages, development of biology in, 598–599
Midrib, of leaves, 191
Milk (mammary) glands, composition of, 302, 304
Millepedes, 245, 251
Milne-Edwards, Henri (1800–1885), 141
Mimicry in animals, 618–620
Minerals, 79, 83
  essential to animal nutrition, 437–438, 453–454
  essential to plant nutrition, 409, 411
  and expression of genes, 553
  in shells of coelenterates, 156
  in shells of desmids and diatoms, 126
  in shells of foraminifera, 121
  in shells of sponges, 147
Minkowski, Oscar (1858–1931), 465
Mistletoe, 180
Mitochondria, 61, 70
  and ascorbic acid, 449
  and enzymes, 404
Mitosis, 476–482, 483–484
  and Mendelian inheritance, 537
Mitral (bicuspid) valve, of vertebrate heart, 339
Mixonephridium, 209, 218
Molds, 138, 139–140
  reproduction, 488–489, 532, **555**
  slime, 71, **92**, 134
"Mole," 18
Molecules, 18
Monocotyledonae, 170
Monoecious species, 490, 513–514
Monosaccharide (hexose), 35, 36, 415
Monosiga, 134
Monosomic varieties, in tobacco, 550
Morgan, T. H., (1866–1945), 533

# INDEX

Morphogenesis, organizers in, 485
Mosses (*see* Bryophyta)
Motor end plate, 373
Motor neuron (*see* Efferent neuron)
Moulting (ecdysis), 249–251
  chemical regulation of, 463–465
Moulting hormone, in insects, 464
Mouth parts,
  of Crustacea, 220–222
  of insects, 229, **231**, **232**
Movement,
  of biological systems, 96–97
  of leucocytes, 327–328
  of protoplasm, 71–72
  of protozoa, 119, 121, 123
  of vertebrates
    mechanical efficiency of, 286–287
    types of, at joints, 285–286
  of water in plants, 197–202
Mucilage, 70, 417
Mucus (*see also* Glands, mucous), 141
Müller, Fritz (1821–1897), 620
Muller, H. J. (1890– ), 546
Multinucleate organisms, 134
Multiple alleles, 546–548
Multiple genes, 551–552
Musci (mosses), 161
  (*see also* Bryophyta)
Muscle, 96, 141, **142**, 280–281
  chemical events in contraction, 281–283
  dermal, of vertebrates, 283
  development of, in vertebrates, 580
  skeletal, of vertebrates, 283–284
  specialization of, 287–289
Muscle spindle, 384
Mustard gases,
  as mutagens, 546
  and kappa, 558
Mutagens, 546
Mutation, 546–550
  and evolution, 621–626
Mycelium, 138
Myelencephalon, 357, **359**
  development of, 366
Myelin, 353
Myocomma, 257, **259**
Myofibril, 280
Myoneme, 121
Myosin, 280
Myotome, 257, **259**, 580
Mythology, 595–596

Nägeli, Karl (1817–1891), 537
Nails, 292, **294**

Nares, 306, **307**
Natural Selection, Theory of, 612–621
Neanthes (*see* Nereis)
Needham, John, 131
Nematocyst, 153, **154**
Nematodes, 206
  limited growth in, 484
Neon, 20
Neoplasm, 484
Nephridiopore, **208**, 210
Nephridium, **208**, 209
Nephrocytes, 242
Nephron, in human kidney, 321
Nephrostome, **209**, 210
Nephrotome, 579
Nereis (Neanthes), 211–216
  gametic reproduction, 522
Nerve cells, 96, **142**
  (*see also* Neuron)
  conduction and transmission by, 388–390
Nerve endings, in vertebrates,
  afferent, 373–385
  efferent, 372–373
Nervous system,
  of annelids, **213**, 216, 217
  of arachnids, 253
  of coelenterates, 152, 154
  conduction and transmission in, 388–390
  coordination in, 385–388
  of Crustaceans, 227–229
  development of, 574–579
  of insects, 243–248
  vertebrates, 353–390
Neural crest, 354, 355
  in amphibian embryo, 578
Neural plate,
  in amphibian embryo, 572
  in chick, 573, **574**
Neural tube, 354, 355
  in amphibian embryo, 578
Neurilemma, 353
Neuro-epithelium, 155, 355
Neuromast, 383
Neuromuscular spindle, **384**
Neuron (nerve cell), 353–354
  afferent (sensory), 356
  efferent (motor), 356
Neurospora, 404, 532, 554–556, 622
Neurotendinal spindle, 384
Neurala stage in amphibian development, **577**, 578
Neutralization of acids, 50–51
Newlands, John Alexander (1838–1898), 8
Newton, Isaac (1642–1727), 5, 76, 605
Niacin (*see* Nicotinic acid)
Nicotiana, monosomic varieties of, 550

Nicotinic Acid (niacin), 448–449
  synthesis by Neurospora, 556
Nictitating membrane, 305
Night blindness, 445
Nineteenth Century, development of biology in, 611–621
Nitella, 197
Nitrifying bacteria, 129
  as chemoautotrophs, 413
Nitrogen,
  in atmosphere, 77, 90–91
  in autotrophic nutrition, 411
  bacteria in relation to, 128–130
  cycle, **129**, 130
  as essential element in nutrition, 411
  fixation, 129
  in protein, 38
  solubility in body fluids, 90–91
  solubility in water, 77
Non-disjunction, of chromosomes, 544–545
Non-electrolytes, 48
Non-ionic compounds, 22
  (*see also* Co-valent compounds)
Non-metals, 20
Non-polar compounds, solubility of, in $H_2O$, 46
Nostoc, 137
Notochord, 257
  in amphibian development, 572, 578
  in chick development, 573
Nucellus, 503
  development of, in angiosperms, 514–515
Nuchal flexure, of vertebrate brain, 358, **359**
Nuchal organs, 211, 216
Nucleic acid, 60
Nucleolus, 60
Nucleoprotein, 40, 60
  and genes, 553
  and induction, 592
Nucleus,
  atomic, 9
  cell, 59
  division of, 476–482
Nutrients, 92, 393
  required by autotrophs, 411–413
  required by heterotrophs, 424
  required by Neurospora, 554
Nutrition, 393–407
  autotrophic, 408–423
  heterotrophic, 424–435
  human, 454

"Obstetrical toad" (Alytes), 525

# INDEX

Ocellus,
  of arthropods, 245
  of coelenterates, 155
Odontoblast, 300
Oedigonium, 137
Oenocytes, 242
Oesophagus, of vertebrates, 313–314
Oils, 36, 37, 418
  essential, 203, 418
  as products of photosynthesis by diatoms, 126
  solubility of, 46
  as solvents, 47
Olaus Magnus, 600
Oleomargarine, 418, 453
Olfactory bulbs, 360
Olfactory organs,
  of insects, 248
  of vertebrates, 306, 382–383, 578
Ommatidium, **245**
Omnivores, 427
Ontogeny, 485
Oogenesis, 520, **522**
Oogonia, 520
Opsonins (tropins), 330
Optic chiasma, 363
Optic cup,
  in amphibian development, 578
  of vertebrate eye, 373, **374**
Optic lobes, 365
Optic tectum, 387
Optic vesicles, 373
  in amphibian development, 578
  as organizers, 590–591
Ora serrata, 375
Oral glands, in vertebrates, 312–313
Organ of Corti, 380
Organic evolution, doctrine of, 94, 595–630
Organization,
  in egg, 587–588
  in protoplasm, 54
Organizers,
  in development, 485, 589–592
Organogenesis, in vertebrate embryo, 586
Organs of special sense, 153
  in annelids, 211–212, 216, 217
  in arthropods, 244–248
  in flatworms, 159
  in vertebrates, 373–385
*Origin of Species by Means of Natural Selection, The*, 616–621
Ornithine cycle, 458, 459
Osborne, T. B. (1859–1929), 445
Oscillatoria, 137

Osculum, 147
Osmosis, 63–68
Osmotic equilibrium, regulation of, in vertebrate body, 65, 470
Osteoblast, 266
Otic organs (audioreceptors),
  of insects, 247–248
  of vertebrates, 378–382
  development of, 578
Otic vesicles, of vertebrates, 378, 578
Otocysts, 578
Otoliths, 247
Ovaries, 467
  of angiosperms, 513
  of animals, 523
  hormones of, in mammalian reproduction, 527–529
Oviduct (Mullerian duct), **319**, 523
Oviparous species, 525
Ovoviviparous species, 525
Ovulation, 526
  induction of, in amphibia, 560
Ovule,
  of angiosperms, 511, 513
  of Zamia, 503
Ovum (*see* Egg)
Owen, Sir Richard (1804–1892), 618
Oxidation, 5
  aerobic, 90, 414
  anaerobic, 90, 127–128, 133, 203, 414
Oxidation-reduction reactions, 25
  and nicotinic acid, 448
  and nitrates, 129–130, 411
Oxygen (*see also* Gaseous interchange), 4, 20, **21**, **22**, **23**, 26
  in atmosphere, 77
  bacteria, in relation to, 127
  combination with hemoglobin, 215
  plants, in relation to, 413–414
  solubility in water, 47
Oxyhemoglobin, 348
Oxytocin (pitocin), 473

Pacinian corpuscle, 384
Paedogenesis, 265
Palaemonetes, chemical regulation of color changes in, 461–462
Paleontology, beginnings of, 602
Pallas, Peter Simon (1741–1811), 608
Pallial commissure, of vertebrate brain, 363
Pallium, 360

Palm, A. T., 442
Pancreas, 265, 317–318
  digestive enzymes, 432
  as endocrine organ, 465, 466–467
Pancreatic juice, 317
  composition of, 432
Pancreozymin, 466
Pandorina, 136
Pangenesis, provisional hypothesis of, 617
Papain, 403
Paraamino benzoic acid, **406**, 445, 452
Paracelsus (1493–1541), 3, 162
Paramecin, 558
Paramoecium, 121, 122
  agglutinating reaction, 331
  amphimixis, **528**, 530–532
  endomixis, **529**, 532
  food currents in, **425**
  inheritance of kappa in, 557–558
  "killer" strains of, 455–456, 557–558
  mating reaction, 530
  symbiosis in Paramoecium bursaria, 92, 125
Paraphysis, 364
Parapodium, 212
Parasite, 92, 93, 130
  enzyme inhibition by, 402
Parasitism,
  in flatworms, 158
  in molds, 139
  in spermatophytes, 180
Parasympathetic nervous system, 371
Parathyroid glands, 468–469
Parenchyma,
  in flatworms, 159
  in phloem, 176
  in plant tissues, 143
Parietal organ, 364
Parotid glands, 312
Parthenogenesis, 488, 489
  in aphids, 606
  in bees, 549–550
  in rotifers, 489
  in Volvox, 497
Pasteur, Louis (1822–1895), 130, 398, 402, 414, 443, 607
Pavlov, Ivan (1849–1936), 429–430
Peas, Mendel's experiments on, 534–537
Peat, 163
Pectin, 144, 174
Pectoral girdle, 275, **276**
Pedipalps, 252
Pellagra, **448**
Pelvic girdle, 275, **276**, **277**

[ 649 ]

# INDEX

Penicillin, 6, 140
Penicillium, **138**, 139
   Penicillium notatum, 140
Pentadactyl limb, of tetrapods, 277–279
Pentoses, 415
Pepsin, 315, 398, 431
Pepsinogen, 407
Peptides, 433
Peptidase, 433
Perching mechanism in birds, **287**
Pericardium, 226
Pericycle, 175, 184
Periderm, 179
Perilymph, 379
Periodic Law, 9
Periodic Table, 8, **10–11**, 12, 18, 27
Periosteum, 267
Peripatus, 220, 251, **253**
Perisarc, 156
Perissodactyl, 627
Peristalsis, 214
Peristome, 121
Peritoneum, 206, 213, 306
  parietal (somatic), 214
  splanchnic, 214
Perivitelline space, 564
Permeability,
  of capillary endothelium, 331–332, 351
  of kidney tubules, 322–325
  of Malpighian corpuscle, 322
  of plasma membrane, 63–68
  of root hairs, 197–198
Petals, 511
Petiole, 191, 193, 195
Peyer, J. K. (1653–1712), 316
Peyer's patches, 316, 350
pH, 49–50, 70, 90, 215, 402, 420, 467
Phagocytosis, 327
Phenocopy, 553
Phenotype, 550
Phenylalanine,
  as essential amino acid, 437
  conversion to tyrosine, 554
Phloem, 144, 175, 176
  differentiation of elements of, 176
Phloridzin, 324, 419
Phosphocreatine, 281
Phosphorus, as essential element, 437, 450
Photoautotrophic nutrition, 408–411
Photon, 13
Photoperiodism, 87
Photophores,
  in insects, 248–249
  in vertebrates, 304
Photoreceptors, 87

  in annelids, 211, **212**, 217
  in arthropods, 244–247
  in coelenterates, 155
  in flatworms, 159
  in Protozoa, 123
  in vertebrates, 373–378
Photosynthesis, 32, 86, 408–411, 421, 422
Phototropism, 87, 459
Phycoerythrin, 408
Phycomycetes, 138
  amphimixis, **530**, 532
Phyllotaxy, 189, **190**
Physalia (Portuguese Man-of-War), 155
Physiology, 101, 105
Phytopthora infestans, 139
Pia mater, 355
Pigment cells (*see* Chromotophores)
Pigmentation,
  inheritance of, in animals, 552, 554
  in flowers, 551, 553–554
  red, in Drosophila, 550
  of vertebrate skin, 289
Pigments,
  in animal eggs, 564, 569
  in bacteria, 408
  in bile, 432
  in brown algae, 137, 408
  in cells, 62, 70, 569
  in chloroplasts, 408
  in Crustacea, 225
  in diatoms, 408
  in feathers, 293
  in flagellates, 123
  in flowers, 511
  in hairs, 293
  as indicators, 49
  in insects, 234
  in leaves, 194
  in plants, 70, 419–420
  in plastids, inheritance of, 557
  in spores of molds, 489
  in red algae, 137, 408
  respiratory, 215
    in annelids, 215, 219
    in arthropods, 226, 239
    in chordates, 258, 290, 327
Pine, **169**
  reproduction in, 508–510
Pineal body, 364
Pisces (*see* Fishes)
Pistil, 511, **513**
Pith, 175, **176**, 184
Pitressin, 473
Pituitary body, 364, **365**
  influence of, in mammalian reproduction, 526, 527–529
  secretions, 471–473
Placenta, 526, 527–529, 548, 576, 584–586

Placental mammals,
  embryology,
    cleavage, 567–568
    extra embryonic membranes, 584–586
    gastrulation, 576
    reproduction, 526–529
Placode (neural), 355, 578
  olfactory, 382
  otic, 378
Placoid scales, 298, **299**
Plankton, 126, 577
Plantigrade mammals, 278, **279**
Plants,
  cell, 69, 116
  cell aggregates, 134–139
  chromosome numbers in, 549
  distinctions from animals, 96–97, 116
  histology, 143–144, 162, 163, 173–179, 181–186, 191–195, 196
  inheritance of plastid pigments, 557
  life span, 195–196
  nutrition, 408–423
  reproduction, 497–520
  unicellular, 125–134
  vascular, 166–202
Plasma, of vertebrate blood, 326
Plasma membrane, 63–68, 197–198
Plasmagene, 559
Plastids, 70
  inheritance of, 557
Platelets, of vertebrate blood, **327**, 329
Platyhelminthes (flatworms), 149, 157–161
  reproduction by fission, 488
Platypus (Ornithorhynchus), 526, 609
Pleodorina, 136
Pleurococcus, 125
Pleurodont vertebrates, 300
Plexus (nerve), 367
Pliny (23–79), 598
Plumule, 181
Pluteus, **562**, 576
Poikilothermism, 88
Polar body (polocyte), 520, **523**
Polar compounds, 43, **44**
  solubility of in $H_2O$, 46
Polarity,
  in coelenterates, 156–157
  in egg cell, 561
  in flatworms, 161
  in vertebrate nerve, 389
Pollen,
  in angiosperms, 514
  in pine, 508
  in Zamia, 503
Pollen chamber, in Zamia, 504

# INDEX [651]

Pollen tube,
  of angiosperms, 516
  of Zamia, 504
Pollination,
  in angiosperms, 513–514
  in pine, 508
  in Zamia, 503–504
Polymerization, 43
Polymorphism,
  in ants, **255**
  in coelenterates, 155
Polyneuritis (avian beri-beri), 442
Polyploidy, 549–550
Polyps, 150
Polysaccharides, 36
  condensation of, in plants, 411, 415
Polyspermy, 561
Polytrichum, **164**
  reproduction, 498
Pons Varolii, 366
Pontine flexure, of vertebrate brain, 358
Porifera, 145–149
  diffusion in, 210
  reproduction of,
    gametic, 521
    gemmation, 488
Porocyte, 145
Portal system, 345
Portuguese Man-of-War (Physalia), 155
"Position effect," 549
Post cardinal vein, 345
Postcava (vena cava inferior), 346
Posterior commissure, of vertebrate brain, 365
Posterior mesenteric artery, 344
Potassium, 19
Potential energy, 14
Pouchet, Félix Archimède (1800–1872), 132
Preformation Theory, 587, 611
Pregnancy tests, 586
Pressure,
  atmospheric, 77
  osmotic, 64
  partial, of gases, 77
  root, 198
Priestly, Joseph (1733–1804), 606
Primary body cavity (blastocoele), 205, **562**, 566–567
Primary divisions of vertebrate brain, 357
Primary flexure, of vertebrate brain, 358
Primary tissues,
  of animals, 205, 568
  derivatives, 581
  of plants, 177

Primitive knot (Hensen's node),
  of chick, 573, **574**, **575**
  of mammalian embryo, 576
Primitive streak,
  of amphibian embryo, 572
  of chick, 573, **574**
  of mammalian embryo, 576
Printing, discovery of, 599
Proboscis, in Nereis, 213, **214**
Proctodaeum, 204, 226, 578
Proembryo, of Zamia, 505
Proenzyme, 402
Progesterone, 527, 584
  of placenta, 586
Prolactin, 472–473
Pronephros, 318, **319**
Pronuba yucasella (yucca moth), 514
Proprioceptors, in vertebrates, 373, 384
Propterygium, 275
Prosencephalon, 357, **358**
  of amphibian embryo, 579
Prosthetic group,
  of enzyme molecule, 406
  of thiamine, 447
Protection of eggs and young, in animals, 525–526
Protective coloration, 618–620
Protective properties of vertebrate blood, 328–331
Protein, 37–42, 60
  energy in, 440
  digestion of, 434
  heat of combustion of, 395
  nature of enzymes, 403–404
  requirement of vertebrates, 436–437, 440
  synthesis by plants, 419
Protenor,
  chromosomes, **541**
  sex chromosomes, 540
Proterospongia, 134, **136**
Prothallial cell, 503, 508
Prothrombin, 328
Protista, 117
Proton, 9
Protonema, 163
Protonephridium, **208**, 210
Protophyta, 117
  reproduction in, 487
Protoplasm, 16–17, 50, 52–53, 54, 71–72
Protoplast, 125
Protopodite, of crustacean appendage, 222
Protozoa, 117–124
  division in, 487
  sexuality, 529–532
Prout, William (1785–1850), 398, 429
"Provisional hypothesis of pangenesis," 617

Provitamin, 446, 450
Pseudocoelous (pseudocoelomate) animals, 205–206
Pseudopodium, 119, 152
Pteridophyta, 166, **167**, **168**
  reproduction, 499–501
Pteris, reproduction in, 499
Ptyalin, 312, 430
Pubis, 277
Puccinia graminis (wheat rust), 139
Pupation hormone, in insects, 464
Pygostyle, 271
Pylorus, 314
Pyruvic acid, 447

Radial symmetry, 151
Radiations,
  as mutagens, 546
  solar, 76–77, **79**
Radical, 25, 173
  amino, 38, 317, 412
  bicarbonate, 48
  carboxyl, 36
  hydroxyl, 21
  nitrate, 25, 129
  nitrite, 129
Radicle, 173
Radioactive elements, 18
Radium, disintegration of, 19
Raffinose, synthesis in plants, 415
Ramus communicans, of vertebrate nervous system, 370
Ray, John (1627–1705), 604
de Réaumur, René (1683–1757), 255
  experiments, 397
  treatise on insects, 607
Recapitulation theory (Biogenetic law), 620
  comparative anatomy of vertebrate blood system as evidence for, 346
Recessive characters, in inheritance, 535, 546, 550–551
Reciprocal innervation of antagonistic muscles in vertebrates, 372
Rectal gills, 242, 244
Rectum, in vertebrates, 316
Redi, Francesco (1626–1698), 131
Reduction, in chromosome number, 495
Reflex arc,
  conditioned, 429
  as functional unit in vertebrate nervous system, 384–385
Refractory period, of nerve, 389

[ 652 ]                                                      INDEX

Regeneration, 486–487
  in arthropods, 254–256
  coelenterates, 156
  experiments on, 156, 607
  in flatworms, 161
  in plants, 116, 164
  in vertebrate liver, 317
Regulation,
  of heart beat in vertebrates, 372
  of metabolic reactions, 455–475
  of vision, in vertebrates, **376**, 377
  of water content (*see* Water balance)
Renal artery, 344
Renal portal system, 345
Rennin, 315, 431
Reproduction,
  agametic (asexual), 487–489
  gametic, 490–532
    in angiosperms, 510–520
    in bryophytes, 498–499
    in colonial algae, 497–498
    in pine, 508–510
    in pteridophytes, 499–501
    in spermatophytes, 501–520
    in Zamia, 501–508
  rate of, in establishment of species, 624–625
Reproductive cycles, in mammals, 527
Reproductive isolation, in establishment of species, 625–626
Reproductive organs,
  in animals, 523–524
  as endocrine organs, 467, 526–529
Reproductive tissues, 141
Reptiles, **261**
  accommodation of eye, 377
  aortic arches, **342**, 343–344
  cerebellum, 366
  cerebral cortex, 361
  claws, 292
  cloaca, 316, 320
  coelome, 305–306
  corpora bigemina, 365
  corpora quadrigemina, 365
  dermal skeleton, 298
  ear, 378
  excretory organs, 318
  heart, 336, 338
  lungs, 308
  meninges, 355
  nervous coordination in brain, **386**
  nictitating membrane, 305
  optic tectum, 387
  parietal organ, 364
  pigment cells, 290

poison glands, 313
scales, 291
skeleton, 270, **271**
teeth, 300–301
veins, 345–346
venom, 331
Resin, 186, 418
Resin ducts, 185
Respiration, 90, 133, 203, 210, 311, 413
Respiratory areas,
  in annelids, 215, 218–219
  in arthropods, 227, 239–242, 252
  in vertebrates, 264–265, 306–312
Respiratory pigments,
  in annelids, 215, 219
  in arthropods, 226, 239
  in chordates, 258, 327
Respiratory quotient (R. Q.), 394–395, 457, 473
Reticulo-endothelial system, 352–353
Retina, of vertebrate eye, 373–376
Retinene, 375
Retinula, 244
Rh factor, in blood, 547–548
Rhabdome, 245
Rhabdite, 159
Rhizoids, 162
Rhizome, 173, 187
Rhizopoda, 119–121
Rhizopus, 138
  amphimixis in, **530**, 532
Rhodnius, chemical regulation of moulting in, 463–464
Rhodopsin (visual purple), 375
Rhombencephalon, 357, **358**, 579
Rhopalium, 155
Riboflavin, 449
Ribs, 268, 269, 270, 271
Riccia, 162
Richards, Alfred N. (1876–), 322
Rickets, 441, 442, 443, 450
Rock, 78
Rods, in vertebrate eye, 375
Roman science, 597–598
Root cap, 173
Root hairs, **68**, 174, 202
Root pressure, 198
Roots, 96, 170, **172**, **174**, **175**
  aerial, 173, **186**
  adventitious, 173, 180, **186**
  branch, **175**
  climbing, 173
  differentiation of tissues in, 173–179
  fibrous, 179
  fleshy, 179, 180

primary, 173, 179
prop, 172, **173**
secondary, 179
tap, 179
Rotifers, 205, 206
  limited growth, 484
  reproduction by gametes, 522
  reproduction by parthenogenesis, 489
Royal Society, 603
Rubner, Max, 5, 438, 440
Ruminant stomach, 314
Sacculus, 378
Sacral vertebrae, 269, 270, 271
St. Martin, Alexis, 398, 428–429
Saliva
  composition of, 312, 429, 430
  secretion, as conditioned reflex, 429–430
  secretion, influenced by autonomic system, 372
Salivary glands,
  chromosomes in, 539, **540**, 553
  in insects, 237
  in vertebrates, 312, 429
Salts, 49, 51
Saprolegnia, 139
Saprophyte, **92**, 93, 130
Sapwood, 196
Sarcoplasm, 280
Scala media, of vertebrate ear, 380
Scala tympani, of vertebrate ear, 380
Scala vestibuli, of vertebrate ear, 380
Scales,
  bony, 297
  of grasses, 511
  horny, 291, **293**
  of pine cone, 508
  placoid, 298, **299**
Scapula, 275
Schleiden, M. J., 56
Scholasticism, 599
Schultz, Max, 375
Schwann, Theodor, 56, 132, 398
Scientific expeditions of the 19th Century, 611
Scientific method, 334, 601
Scientific societies, rise of, 602–603
Sclerenchyma, 144, 173, 175, 181, 182
Sclerotic coat, of vertebrate eye, 373
Sclerotome, 580
Scorpions,
  eyes, 245
  respiration, 252

# INDEX

Scurvy, 229, 230, 441–442, 449
    effect upon mitochondria, 61
Scute, 298
Sea urchin,
    embryology of, **562–563**
    fertilization hormones, 561, 564
    gastrulation, 568–569
    larva, 562–563
    organization in eggs of, 587–588
Sebaceous glands, 302
Secondary body cavity (coelome), 204–211
    (*see also* Coelome)
Secondary sex characters, 467
Secretin, 455, 465–466
Secretion, 325
Sedgwick, Adam (1785–1873), 614
Sedimentation, geological, 602
Seed, 168, **172**
    of angiosperms, 516–518
    dispersal, 519–520
    of pine, 510
    as storage area, 417, 418, 419
    of Zamia, 505–506
Segment, definition of, 219
Segmentation, 97
    in annelids, 219
    in arthropods, 220, 229
    in chordates, 257, 367, 578
Segmentation cavity (blastocoele), **562**, 566–567
Selaginella, reproduction in, 501
Self-duplication,
    of chromosomes, 60
    of genes, 479
    of protein molecules, 41–42
Self-fertilization, in angiosperms, 514
Semicircular canals, 378, **379**
Semilunar valves, **338**
Semi-permeable membrane, 63, 197
Sense plate, in amphibian development, 578
Sepals, 511
Serum, blood, 328
Seventeenth century, development of biology in, 602–604
Sex, 544
Sex chromosomes, 541–542
Sex genes, 546
Sex inheritance, 540, 542–546
Sex types,
    in Neurospora, 554, **555**
    in Paramoecium, 530
Sheath of Schwann, 353
Shrubs, 186
Sieve plate, 176
Sieve tube, 176
    in translocation, 197

Silicon,
    concentration by sponges, 147
    in diatom shells, 126
Silkworm,
    introduction into Europe, 598
    Malpighi's monograph on, 55
Simple sac plan of metazoan organization, 149
Sino-auricular node, 340
Sinus, blood,
    in Crustacea, 225
    in elasmobranchs, 345
Sinus gland, in Crustacea, 462
Sinus venosus, 335, **336, 337**
Sinusoids, hepatic, 345
Sitosterol, 418
Sixteenth century, development of biology in, 599–602
Skeletal muscle, classification of, 283
Skeleton,
    of arthropods, 220, 249–251
    of coelenterates, 155–156
    of Protozoa, 121, 123
    of sponges, 147
    of vertebrates,
        appendicular, 275–279
        axial, 265, 268–272
        dermal, 297–298
        visceral, 272–275
Skull (brain case), vertebrate, 271–275
Slime molds, 71, **92**, 134
Sloth, 295, 605, 627
Smallpox, 330–331
Smell, sense of, 248, 382–383
Smooth (visceral) muscle, 279
Snakes,
    fangs, 300–301
    skeleton, 270
    venom, 313, 331
Soaps, 46
Sodium, 20, 21, **24**
Sodium chloride, 17, **24**, 44, **45**
    dissociation of, **45**
    solubility of, 45–46
Soil, 79–83
    atmosphere, 83
    solution, 83, 171
Sol, 52
Solar energy, 76–77, **79**
    absorption by chlorophyll, 409
    absorption by melanin, 289
    conversion to potential, 31–32, 421–422
    and rickets, 442
Solids,
    dissolution of, in water, 45
    properties of, 44
Solubility,
    of gases in body fluids, 91–92
    of gases in water, 47, 77–78

    of polar and non-polar compounds, 46–47
    of solids in water, 45–46
Solution,
    acid, 49–50
    alkaline, 49–50
    colloidal, 52
    crystalline, 51
    hypertonic, 66
    hypotonic, 66
    isotonic, 66
    in oil, 46
    soil, 83, 171
Somatic (striated) muscle, 279, **280**
Somatoplasm, 494
Somite, 578
    (*see* Segment)
Sørensen, Søren Peter Lauritz, 49
Sorus, 499
Sound-producing organs,
    in insects, 248
    in vertebrates, 275
Spallanzani, Lazzaro (1729–1799), 607
    experiments on digestion, 397, 429
    experiments on spontaneous generation, 131, 609
Special sense, organs of (*see* Organs of special sense)
Specialization, 95
Species,
    concept of constancy in, 98–99, 604, 608, 610, 612, 625
    dioecious, 490, 513–514
    factors in establishment of, 622–629
    Linnean, 99
    monoecious, 490, 513–514
    oviparous, 525
    ovoviviparous, 525
    polytypic, 625
    viviparous, 525
Specific dynamic action of food stuffs, 440
Specificity,
    of enzyme action, 404
    of plant products, 418
    of pollination in yucca, 514
    of protein synthesis in plants, 419
    of proteins as basis for taxonomic distinctions, 331, 419
Spectrum,
    absorption, of chlorophyll, **409**
    electromagnetic, **79**
    of visible light, 77
Speculative biology, 607–610

# INDEX

Spemann, Hans (1869–1941), 485
Spencer, Herbert (1820–1903), 620, 624
Sperm, 490, **491**
  duration of motility, 561
  of Polytrichum, 498
  of Pteris, 499
  role in development, 588, 607
  of Volvox, 497
  of Zamia, 504, **507**
Spermatogenesis, 520, **522**
Spermatophyta, 166–170
  reproduction, 488, 501–520
    evolutionary significance of, 624, 625
Sphenodon, 364
Spiders, **252**, **254**
  behavior patterns, 254
  feeding habits, 425
  ocelli, 245
  respiration, 252
Spinal cord, 356–357
  coordination in, 386
Spinal nerves, 367, 579
Spindle, 480
Spiracle,
  in fishes, 274, 380
  in insects, 239
Spirogyra, 136, **137**
  conjugation, **496**, 497
  meiosis in, **496**, 497
  reproduction by fragmentation, 488
Spirostomum, 122
Spleen, 349
Sponges, 145–149
  diffusion in, 210
  reproduction,
    gametic, 521
    by gemmation, 488
Spongin, 147
Spontaneous generation (abiogenesis), 131–132, 607, 609
Sporangia,
  of ferns, 499
  of molds, 488
  of mosses, 499
Spore mother cell, 499
Spores,
  of angiosperms, 511, 514–515
  of bacteria, 127
  of ferns, 499
  of molds, **138**, 139, 488
  of mosses, 499
  of Selaginella, 501
  of Zamia, 502–503
Sporic meiosis, 498–520
Sporophyll, 168
  of angiosperms, 511
  of fern, 499, 500–501
  of Zamia, 502
Sporophyte, 498

Stachyose, 415
Stamen, 511
Standard human dietary, 454
Stanley, W. M. (1904–), 42
Stapes, 381
Starch, 36
  (see also Amylum and Glycogen)
Statocyst,
  in arthropods, 247
  in coelenterates, 155
Statolith, 155, 378
Statoreceptors (see Equilibration)
"Steady state" 67
Steapsin, 432
Steenson, Nils (Steno) (1638–1686), 602
Stele, 174, 175, 184
Stems, 180–188, 189
Steno (1638–1686), 602
Stentor, 122
Sternum,
  of Crustacean skeleton, 220
  of vertebrate skeleton, 276
Steroid configuration, **451**
Sterols,
  as androgens, 467
  and induction, 592
  synthesis by plants, 418
  and Vitamin D, 450
Stigmasterol, 418
Stinking smut (Tilletia), 139
Stipule, 191
Stomach, of vertebrates, 314–315
  digestion in, 430–432
Stomata, 181, 182, 193, **201**
  opening and closing of, 200
Stomodaeum, 204, 226, 578
Stone cells, 144, 505
Storage
  of glycogen, in vertebrate liver, 317
  in plants, 415
Strasburger, Eduard (1844–1912), 476
Streptocarpus (Cape primrose), color inheritance in, 553–554
Striated (somatic) muscle, 279, **280**
Strobilus, 168
  of pine, **509**
  of Selaginella, 501
  of Zamia, 502
Strongylocentrotus lividus,
  embryology, 562–563
  gastrulation, 569
  organization of egg, 587–588
Structural coloration,
  of birds, 293
  of fishes, 290
  of hairs, 293

  of insects, 234, 249
Structural formulae, of chemical compounds, 34
Structure proteins, of cytoplasm, 61
Subcardinal vein, of vertebrates, 346
Subclavian artery, of vertebrates, 344
Subclavian vein, of vertebrates, 346
Subdivisions of biological science, 105
Suberin, 70, 178
Sublingual glands, 312
Submaxillary glands, 312
  secretion, influenced by autonomic system, 372
Subspecies, 625
Substrate, of enzymes, 401
Succus entericus, 316
Sucrose (cane sugar), **35**, 36
  hydrolysis of, 24
  synthesis, in plant, 36, 411, 415
Sugars, 35–36, 415–417
Sulfanilimide, **406**, 452
Sulphur,
  bacteria in relation to, 130
  as essential element, 411, 437
  in protein, 38
Sumner, James (1887–), 403
Superior commissure, of vertebrate cerebrum, 364
Superposition image, of arthropod eye, **246**, 247
Supersexes, in Drosophila, 545
Suprarenal bodies (see Adrenal bodies)
"Survival of the fittest," 620, 624
Swammerdam, Jan (1637–1680), 56, 607
Sweat glands, **291**, 302
  regulation of, by hypothalamus, 387
Swim (air) bladder, of fishes, 264
Symbiosis, 92, 93, 125–126
Symmetry, in animals, 151
Sympathetic nervous system, 371
Sympathin, 390, 470
Synapse, 384, 389
Synapsis, of homologous chromosomes, 494
Synarthrosis, 284
Syncytial organisms, 134
Synergids, 515
Synkaryon, 531
Synovia (synovial fluid), 285
Synsacrum, 270
Synthetic diets, 436, 443–444
Syrinx, 275

# INDEX

Systematics, 98
  (*see also* Classification)
Systemic arch, of vertebrate circulatory system, 343
Systole, 340

Tactoreceptors,
  in arthropods, 247
  in vertebrates, 383
Takaki, Baron, 442
Tannins, 70, 420
Taste organs,
  in insects, 248
  in vertebrates, **382**, 383
Taxonomy, 98, 105, 331, 603
  (*see also* Classification)
Tectin, 122
Teeth, of vertebrates, 298–302
  epidermal, of tadpoles, 297
Telencephalon, 357, **358, 359**
  development of, 359–363
Temperature, 29–30
  (*see also* Heat)
  and enzymatic reactions, 403
  and expression of genes, 552–553
  scales, **30**
Tendon, 279
Tendril, 187, 191
Tergum, of crustacean skeleton, 220
Testes (testicles), 467, 523
Testosterone, 467
Tetrapoda, 95, 262
  aortic arches, 343
  ear, 380–381
  heart, 335, 336
  jaws, 273–275
  oral glands, 312–313
  pentadactyl limb, 277, 278
  ribs, 269
  skeleton, 268, 272, 275–276
  urinary bladder, 321
  veins, 345
Tetrasaccharides, 411, 415
Tetrasomic varieties, in Datura, 550
Thalamencephalon, 363
Thalamus, 364
  as coordinating center, 387
Thallophyta, 117, 125–140
  (*see also* Algae and Fungi)
  haploidy in, 549
Thallus, 117
Thecodont vertebrates, 300
Theophrastus (?–287 B.C.), 102, 104, 596–597
Theory (*see* Doctrine)
  of Archetypes, 611
  of Catastrophes, 606, 610
  Cell, 56
  Chromosome, of Inheritance, 533

of Emboîtement, 606, 607
  Gastraea, 620–621
  of Gene, 533
  of Natural Selection, 612–621
  of Preformation, 587, 611
  of Recapitulation, 346, 620
Thermodynamics,
  First Law of, 5, 27
  Second Law of, 14
Thiaminase, 452
Thiamine, 446–447
  destruction of, 452, 453
Thigmocytes, 227
Thomson, Sir J. J. (1856–1940), 9
Thoracic duct, 349
Thoracic vertebrae, 269, 270, 271
Thorns, 187
Thrombocytes, 327
Thrombogen, 328
Thromboplastin, 329
Thymus gland, 350, **468**
Thyroid gland, **38**, 467–468
  and pituitary gland, 472
Thyrotropin, 472
Thyroxin, 38, 468
Tilletia (stinking smut), 139
Tineola, digestion of keratin, 428
Tintinnidae, 123
Tissue culture, 57, **58**, 59
Tissues, 141–144
  (*see also* Histology)
  conducting, in plants, 178
  connective, in animals, 141, **142**
  contractile, in animals, 279–284
  extra-embryonic, in vertebrates, 581–582
  fundamental, in plants, 143
  integrating, in vertebrates, 326–390
  integumental, in vertebrates, 289–305
  lymphoid, in vertebrates, 349–350
  maturation and ageing of, in plants, 196
  muscular, in animals, 280–281
  nervous, in animals, 354–355, 572
  presumptive, in amphibian egg, 569–572, 581
  primary, in animals, 205, 568, 581
  primary, in plants, 177
  supporting, in plants, 181, 186, 196
  supporting, in vertebrates, 265–268

Tongue, 275
Tonoplast, 69
Tonsils, 350, **468**
Torpedo, electric organs of, **288**, 289
Tournefort, Joseph Pitton (1656–1708), 604
"Trace elements," 393
Trachea,
  respiratory, in arachnids, 252
  in insects, 239
  in tetrapods, **275**, 306, **311**
  (xylem vessel), in plants, 176, 177, 183
Tracheal gills, 242
Tracheid (xylem vessel), 176, 177, 183
Tracheoles, 239, **240**
Tracts (fibre), in vertebrate spinal cord, 356–357
Translocation
  of genes on chromosomes, 549
  of solutes in plants, 196–197
Transpiration, 198–202
Travels and explorations, effect of, on development of natural science, 598, 599–600, 608
Tree, 186, **416**
Trembley, Abraham (1700–1784), 156, 607
Trichocyst, 122
Tricuspid valve, of vertebrate heart, 339
Trisaccharides, 411, 415
Trisomic varieties, in Datura, 550
Tritocerebral commissure, in arthropods, 462
Trophoblast, 568, **569**, 576
Tropins (opsonins), 330
Trypsin, 399, 402, 432
Trypsinogen, 402, 432
Tryptophane, 460
Tsetse fly (*see* Glossina)
Tube cell, of pollen, 503, 504
Tube-within-a-tube plan of Metazoan organization, 204
Tuber, 180, 187, 417
Tumor, 485
Tunicin, 257
Turgor, 67, 196
Turgor movements, 97
Tusks, 302
Twentieth Century, development of Doctrine of Organic Evolution in, 621–630
Twinning, in mammals, 553, 592
Tympanum, of vertebrate ear, 380
Tyndall, John (1820–1893), 15
Tyndall phenomenon, 15

# INDEX

Typhlosole, 217, **218**
Tyrosine, 470, 554

Ulva, 137
Umbilical cord, 584, 586
Unguligrade mammals, 278, **279**
Unicellular systems, 117–134
  (*see also* Protophyta and Protozoa)
Union and disunion, chemical combination by, 22, 35
United Nations Food Conference (1943), 454
Urea
  in allantois, 584
  as end product of protein metabolism, 317, 458
  excretion of, by vertebrate kidney, 321–325
  excretion of, by plants, 412
  production of, by fertilized frog's egg, 565
  resorption of, by vertebrate kidney, 322–323
  structural formula of, 317
  in sweat, 302
  synthesis of, in vitro, 6, 458
  in tissues of elasmobranchs, 323
Urease, 403
Ureotelic organisms, 458
Ureter, 320
Uric acid
  in allantois, 584
  as end product of protein metabolism, 317, 458
  excretion of, in insects, 242
  production of, in cleidoic eggs, 625
  structural formula of, 317
Uricotelic organisms, 458
Urinary bladder, 320
Urine, 318, 321
Urinogenital system, of vertebrates, 318–321
Urochordata, 257, **258**
Uropygial gland, 302
Urostyle, 269
Ustilago zeae (corn smut), 139
Uterus, 523
  preparation of, for implantation of embryo, 527–529
Utriculus, 378

Vaccination, 330–331
Vacuoles,
  in cells, 62, 69
  contractile, 119, 122, 123, 146
  gastric, 119
Valence, 18, 20
Valence electrons, 19
Valonia, 134

Valves,
  bicuspid, 339
  lymph, 349, **351**
  semilunar, 338
  tricuspid, 339
  of veins, 345
Vanadium, 258
Variegation, inheritance of, in plants, 557
Varieties, 625
Varoli (1543?–1575), 366
Vas deferens, 523
Vascular plants, 166–203
Vascular system
  in annelids, 215, 218
  in arthropods, 226–227, 239
  in coelomate animals, 210
  in vertebrates, 326–348
Vascular tissues of plants, 143, 171, **176**, **177**, 178
Veins,
  of circulatory system of vertebrates, 345–346
  of leaves, 191
Velamen, 180
Velocity,
  of chemical reactions, 29, 30–31
  of enzymatic reactions, 403, 407
  of flight, in insects, 236
Vena cava inferior (post cava), of vertebrates, 346
Venom, of snakes, 313, 331
Ventral column (fibre tract), of vertebrate nerve cord, 356
Ventricles,
  of brain, of vertebrates, 358, 359, 366
  of heart, of vertebrates, 335, 336, 337
Venule, 345
Vermis, of cerebellum, 366
Vertebra, 268
Vertebral column, 268–271
Vertebrata, 259–390
  (*see also* Amphibia, Birds, Fishes, Reptiles, Mammals)
  reproduction of, 565–568, 569–576, 577–587
Vesalius, Andreas (1514–1564), 102–104, 270, 471, 601
Vibrissae, 295
Vicq d'Azyr, Felix (1748–1794), 608, 610
Villi,
  in absorption of fat, 351
  of intestine of vertebrates, **313**, 315
  of placenta, 584
da Vinci, Leonardo (1452–1519), 8, 102, 196, 598

Vine, 186
Viruses, 40, 352, 553
Visceral clefts (gill slits), 274, 578, 579
Visceral (smooth) muscle, 279
Visceral skeleton, 265, 272–275
Vision
  in arthropods, 244–247
  in vertebrates, 375–376
Visual purple (rhodopsin), 375
Vitalistic philosophy, 602
Vitamin A, 375, 420, 445–446
Vitamin B, 446–449
Vitamin C, 449
  (*see also* Ascorbic acid)
Vitamin D, 37, 418, 450
Vitamin H (biotin), 445, 452
Vitamin K, 329
Vitamin P (citrin), 445, 420
Vitamine hypothesis, 444
Vitamins, 47, 441–454
  and genes, 552
  and hormones, 474–475
  as prosthetic group in enzymes, 406
  required by man, 445–453
  sources of, 126, 453
  storage of, in seeds, 517
  synthesis of, by plants, 420
Vitelline veins, in vertebrate embryo, 582
Viviparous species, 525
Volvox, 136, **137**
  reproduction, 497
Vorticella, **120**, 121, 123

Waldeyer, Otto (1863–1921), 60
Wallace, Alfred Russel (1823–1913), 616, 618
Water, 22, **23**, 43–48
  biological properties of, 43
  capillary, 83
  content, of atmosphere, 77
  content, of bone, 267
  content, of protoplasm, 43, 52–53
  content, of soil, 83
  dissociation of, 49
  electrolysis of, 28
  energy in molecule of, 14, 28, 42–43
  as environment for living things, 84, **85**, 86
  hygroscopic, 83
  and plasma membrane, 63–68
  relation to life, 89–90
  relation to plants, 96, 196–203
  (*see also* Photosynthesis)
  entrance into roots, 179
  in fertilization of mosses and ferns, 499

# INDEX

translocation of, 196–197
transpiration of, 198–202
soil, 83
as solvent, 45–48
Water balance (regulation),
  in annelids, 219
  in Crustacea, 227
    Gammarus, 622–623
  evolutionary significance of, 89–90
  in flatworms, 159
  in plants, 202–203
  in Protozoa, 119–120, 122
  in vertebrates, 318, 322–323, 326, 387, 470, 623–624
"Water cells," of camels, 315
Waxes, 36, 418
W-chromosome, 542
Web spinning by spiders, 254
Weismann, August (1834–1914), 491–494
Wheat (Triticum),
  chromosome numbers in, 549
  specific protein of, 419
Wheat rust (Puccinia graminis), 139

White matter, of vertebrate spinal cord, 356
Williams, R. R. (1886–), 447
Willughby, Francis (1635–1672), 604
Wings, of insects, 233–237
Wöhler, Friedrich, 6, 458
Wolff, Caspar Friedrich (1738–1794), 318, 611
Wolffian bodies, 318, **319**
Wolffian ducts, 318, **319**
"Wound gum," 417

Xanthones, 70, 419
Xanthophores, 290
Xanthophyll, 408
X-chromosome, 541–542
Xerophthalmia, **446**
Xerophyte, 202
Xylem, 144, 175, 176–177
Xylem vessels, 176, 177, 183

Y-chromosome, 541–542, 545
Yeasts, 133–134, 399

Yolk plug, 571
Yolk sac, 576, 582
Young, Sydney (1857–1937), 401
Yucca moth (Pronuba yucasella), 514

Zamia, reproduction of, 501–508
Z-chromosome, 542
Zea mays (corn), **170**
  chromosome maps of, 539
  crossing-over in, 539
  efficiency of photosynthesis in, 421–422
  prop roots of, **172**, 173
  sex genes of, 546
  specific protein of, 419
  translocation of genes in, 549
Zone of maturation, in plant root, 174
Zoology, 101–105, 595–612
Zoothamnium, 134, **135**
Zygote, 490
Zygotic meiosis, 497–498
Zymase, 399